Eukaryotic DNA
Replication

CANCER CELLS

 COLD SPRING HARBOR LABORATORY
1988

6
Eukaryotic DNA Replication

Edited by
Thomas Kelly
Johns Hopkins University School of Medicine

Bruce Stillman
Cold Spring Harbor Laboratory

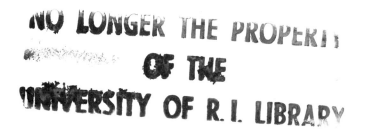

CANCER CELLS
1 / The Transformed Phenotype
2 / Oncogenes and Viral Genes
3 / Growth Factors and Transformation
4 / DNA Tumor Viruses:
    Control of Gene Expression and Replication
5 / Papillomaviruses
6 / Eukaryotic DNA Replication

Eukaryotic DNA Replication
© 1988 by Cold Spring Harbor Laboratory
Printed in the United States of America
Cover design by Emily Harste

Library of Congress Cataloging-in-Publication Data

Eukaryotic DNA replication / edited by Thomas Kelly,
    Bruce Stillman.   p. cm.—(Cancer cells ; 6)
    Includes index.
    ISBN 0-87969-308-8
    1. DNA—Synthesis.   2. Viruses, DNA—Replication.
3. Eukaryotic cells.   I. Kelly, Thomas J., 1941–   .
II. Stillman, Bruce.   III. Series.
QP624.E94   1988
574.87′3282—dc19   88-2558
                                                          CIP

Conference Participants

Allshire, Robin, MRC Clinical and Population Cytogenetics, Western General Hospital, Edinburgh, Scotland

Almouzni, Genevieve, Institut Jacques Monod, Paris, France

Anachkova, Boyka, Department of Biochemistry, University of Virginia, Charlottesville

Andrulis, Irene, Mt. Sinai Hospital Research Institute, Toronto, Ontario, Canada

Ascenzioni, Fiorentina, Department of Biologia Cellulare e Dello, Universita La Sapienza di Roma, Italy

Baker, Tania, Department of Biochemistry, Stanford University Medical Center, California

Baldacci, Giuseppe, Department of Molecular Biology and Genetics, IRSC, Villejuif, France

Baril, Earl, Worcester Foundation for Experimental Biology Shrewsbury, Massachusetts

Bartholomew, James, University of California, Berkeley

Beach, David, Cold Spring Harbor Laboratory, New York

Bennett, Ellen, Department of Microbiology and Immunology, McGill University, Montreal, Quebec, Canada

Berezney, Ronald, Department of Biological Sciences, State University New York, Buffalo

Berko-Flint, Yehudith, Department of Microbiology, Tel Aviv University, Israel

Berns, Kenneth, Department of Microbiology, Cornell University, New York, New York

Biamonti, Giuseppe, Instituto di Genetica Biochimica e Evoluzionistica, Pavia, Italy

Blackburn, Elizabeth, Department of Molecular Biology, University of California, Berkeley

Blow, Julian, Department of Zoology, CRC Molecular Embryology Group, Cambridge, England

Bohensky, Roy, Department of Microbiology, Cornell University Medical College, New York, New York

Bondesson, Kare, Biomedical Center, University of Uppsala, Sweden

Bonne-Andrea, Catherine, Department of Biochemistry and Biophysics, University of California, San Francisco

Bonner, William, NCI, National Institutes of Health, Bethesda, Maryland

Bordet, Sylvie, Department of Microbiology and Immunology, McGill University, Montreal, Quebec, Canada

Borowiec, James, Department of Molecular Biology, Memorial Sloan-Kettering Cancer Center, New York, New York

Botchan, Michael, Department of Molecular Biology, University of California, Berkeley

Bradley, Margaret, Dana-Farber Cancer Institute, Boston Massachusetts

Bravo, Rodrigo, European Molecular Biology Laboratory, Heidelberg, Federal Republic of Germany

Brewer, Bonita, Department of Genetics, University of Washington, Seattle

Brizuela, Leonardo, Cold Spring Harbor Laboratory, New York

Broach, James, Department of Molecular Biology, Princeton University, New Jersey

Brooke, Glenn, Department of Biochemistry, Cell and Molecular Biology, Northwestern University Evanston, Illinois

Brooks, Mindy, Department of Biochemistry, Cell and Molecular Biology, Northwestern University, Evanston, Illinois

Brown, Neal, Department of Pharmacology, University of Massachusetts Medical School, Worcester

Bullock, Peter, Department of Molecular Biology, Memorial Sloan-Kettering Cancer Center, New York, New York

Burhans, Bill, Roche Institute of Molecular Biology, Nutley, New Jersey

Burrow, Christopher, Department of Medicine, John Hopkins University, Baltimore, Maryland

Caddle, Mark, Department of Pathology, University of Vermont College of Medicine, Burlington

Campbell, Judith, Department of Chemistry, California Institute of Technology, Pasadena

Carbon, John, Department of Biological Sciences, University of California, Santa Barbara

Carroll, Susan, The Salk Institute, La Jolla, California

Carty, Michael, NICHHD, National Institutes of Health, Bethesda, Maryland

Celis, Julio, Department of Medical Biochemistry, Aarhus University, Denmark

Cha, Tai-An, Department of Biochemistry and Biophysics, University of California, San Francisco

Challberg, Mark, NIAID. National Institutes of Health, Bethesda, Maryland

Chang, Lucy, Department of Biochemistry, Uniformed Services University of Health Sciences, Bethesda, Maryland

Cheng, Linzhao, Department of Molecular Biology and Genetics, Johns Hopkins Medical School, Baltimore, Maryland

Chinault, A. Craig, Baylor College of Medicine, Houston, Texas

Ciarrocchi, Giovanni, Instituto di Genetica Biochimica Evoluziionistica del CNR, Pavia, Italy

Clark, Louise, Department of Biological Sciences, University of California, Santa Barbara

Clayton, David, Department of Pathology, Stanford University Medical School, California

Coen, Donald, Department of Biological Chemistry and Molecular Pharmacology, Harvard Medical School, Boston, Massachusetts

Cooney, Craig, Department of Biochemistry, University of California, School of Medicine, Davis

Cordeiro-Stone, Marila, Department of Pathology, University of North Carolina, Chapel Hill

Creacy, Steven, Department of Biochemistry, University of Virginia, Charlottesville

Crute, James, Department of Biochemistry, Stanford University Medical Center, California

D'Anna, Joseph, Genetics Group, Los Alamos National Laboratory, New Mexico

Davey, Scott, Cancer Research Laboratory and Department of Biochemistry, University of Western Ontario, London, Canada

Kops, Ann DeBruyn, Department of Microbiology, Harvard Medical School, Boston, Massachusetts

DePamphilis, Melvin, Department of Cell Biology, Roche Institute of Molecular Biology, Nutley, New Jersey

DeRosa, Lauren, Department of Biological Sciences, Stanford University, California

Dean, Frank, Department of Molecular Biology, Memorial Sloan-Kettering Cancer Center, New York, New York

Delidakis, Christos, Biological Laboratories, Harvard University, Cambridge, Massachusetts

Dermody, James, Department of Biological Sciences, Hunter College, New York, New York

Diffley, John, Cold Spring Harbor Laboratory, New York

Dodson, Mark, Department of Molecular Biology, Memorial Sloan-Kettering Cancer Center, New York, New York

Dove, William, McArdle Laboratory for Cancer Research, University of Wisconsin, Madison

Downey, Kathleen, Department of Medicine and Biochemistry, University of Miami, Florida

Draetta, Giulio, Cold Spring Harbor Laboratory, New York

Dresler, Steven, Department of Pathology, Washington University Medical School, St. Louis, Missouri

Du, Hong, Department of Biological Sciences, Hunter College, New York, New York

Dufort, Daniel, Department of Microbiology and Immunology, McGill University, Montreal, Quebec, Canada

Dumas, Lawrence, Department of Biochemistry, Molecular and Cell Biology, Northwestern University, Evanston, Illinois

Earnshaw, William, Department of Cell Biology and Anatomy, Johns Hopkins School of Medicine, Baltimore, Maryland

El Shami, Said, Department of Research and Development, Diagnostic Products Corporation, Los Angeles, California

Engler, Jeffrey, Department of Biochemistry, University of Alabama, Birmingham

Evans, Elizabeth, Department of Cell Biology and Anatomy, Cornell University Medical College, New York, New York

Fangman, Walt, Department of Genetics, University of Washington, Seattle, Washington

Fanning, Ellen, Institute for Biochemistry, University of Munich, Federal Republic of Germany

Faust, Emanuel, Department of Biochemistry, Cancer Research Laboratory, University of Western Ontario, London, Canada

Fisher, Paul, Department of Pharmacological Sciences, State University of New York, Stony Brook

Foreman, Pamela, Department of Biochemistry, University of Virginia, Charlottesville

Frappier, Lori, Cancer Centre, McGill University, Montreal, Quebec, Canada

Frattini, Mark, Department of Pathology, Washington University Medical School, St. Louis, Missouri

Fung, Yuen-Kai, Department of Hematology and Oncology, Childrens Hospital of Los Angeles, California

Gahn, Toni, Department of Cell Biology, Albert Einstein College of Medicine, Bronx, New York

Ganguly, Subinay, Department of Human Genetics, Yale University School of Medicine, New Haven, Connecticut

Geis, Amy, Department of Pathology, Stanford University School of Medicine, California

Gilbert, David, Department of Genetics, Stanford University Medical Center, California

Givens, Robert, Department of Molecular and Cell Biology, Roswell Park Memorial Institute, Buffalo, New York

Gluzman, Yakov, Cold Spring Harbor Laboratory, New York

Goetz, George, Department of Developmental Biology and Cancer, Albert Einstein College of Medicine, New York, New York

Gough, Gerald, Molecular Immunochemistry Laboratory, Imperial Cancer Research Fund, South Mimms, England

Goulian, Micky, Department of Medicine, University of California, San Diego

Greenberg, Adam, Department of Cell Biology and Anatomy, Cornell University Medical College, New York, New York

Grosse, Frank, Department of Chemistry, Max-Planck Institute for Experimental Medicine, Gottingen, Federal Republic of Germany

Grummt, Friedrich, Institute of Biochemistry, University of Wurzburg, Federal Republic of Germany

Guo, Zong Sheng, Roche Institute of Molecular Biology, Nutley, New Jersey

Gutierrez, Crisanto, Department of Cell Biology, Roche Institute of Molecular Biology, Nutley, New Jersey

Hasse, Steve, Department of Genetics, Stanford University School of Medicine, California

Hamlin, Joyce, Department of Biochemistry, University of Virginia, Charlottesville

Hartl, Markus, Institute for Biochemistry, University of Munich, Federal Republic of Germany

Hassell, John, Department of Microbiology and Immunology, McGill University, Montreal, Quebec, Canada

Hay, Ronald, Department of Biochemistry and Microbiology, University of St. Andrews, Scotland

Heck, Margarete, Department of Cell Biology and Anatomy, Johns Hopkins University, Baltimore, Maryland

Heine, Uwe, Roche Institute of Molecular Biology, Nutley, New Jersey

Heintz, Nathaniel, Laboratory of Molecular Biology, Rockefeller University, New York, New York

Heintz, Nicholas, Department of Pathology, University of Vermont College of Medicine, Burlington

Hickey, Robert, Department of Cell Biology, Worcester Foundation for Experimental Biology, Shrewsbury, Massachusetts

Heiter, Philip, Department of Molecular Biology and Genetics, Johns Hopkins University Medical School, Baltimore, Maryland

Holmes, Andrew, Department of Biochemistry, Uniformed Services University of Health Sciences, Bethesda, Maryland

Holst, Andreas, Institute fur Biochemie, University of Wurzburg, Federal Republic of Germany

Horwitz, Marshall, Department of Microbiology and Immunology, Albert Einstein College of Medicine, Bronx, New York

Hu, Chin-Hwa, Department of Biochemistry and Biophysics, Oregon State University, Corvallis

Huber, Hans, Department of Biological Chemistry, Harvard Medical School, Boston, Massachusetts

Huberman, Joel, Department of Molecular and Cellular Biology, Roswell Park Memorial Institute, Buffalo, New York

Hübscher, Ulrich, Department of Pharmacology and Biochemistry, University of Zurich-Irchel, Switzerland

Hupp, Ted, Department of Biochemistry, Michigan State University, East Lansing

Hurwitz, Jerard, Memorial Sloan-Kettering Cancer Institute, New York, New York

Hwang, Deog Su, Department of Biochemistry, Michigan State University, East Lansing

Ishimi, Yokio, Department of Molecular Biology, Memorial Sloan-Kettering Cancer Center, New York, New York

Jackson, Dean, Sir William Dunn University of Oxford, School of Pathology, England

Jessee, C. Bret, Department of Biological Chemistry, Johns Hopkins Medical School, Baltimore, Maryland

Johnson, Edward, Brookdale Center for Molecular Biology, Mt. Sinai School of Medicine, New York, New York

Jonak, Zdenka, Smith Kline and French, Swedeland, Pennsylvania

Jones, C. Hal, Department of Microbiology and Immunology, Emory University School of Medicine, Atlanta, Georgia

Kaguni, Jon, Department of Biochemistry, Michigan State University, East Lansing

Kaguni, Laurie, Department of Biochemistry, Michigan State University, East Lansing

Kajiji, Shama, Department of Neurosciences and Cancer, Pfizer Central Research, Groton, Connecticut

Kalvonjian, Susan, Department of Microbiology, Michigan State University, East Lansing

Kauffman, Michael, Department of Molecular Biology and Genetics, Johns Hopkins University School of Medicine, Baltimore, Maryland

Kearsey, Stephen, Department of Zoology, University of Oxford, England

Kelly, Thomas, Department of Molecular Biology and Genetics, Johns Hopkins University School of Medicine, Baltimore, Maryland

Kenny, Mark, Department of Molecular Biology, Memorial Sloan-Kettering Cancer Center, New York, New York

Kenter, A., Department of Microbiology and Immunology, University of Illinois, Chicago

Khan, Saleem, Department of Microbiology, University of Pittsburgh School of Medicine, Pennsylvania

Knipe, David, Department of Microbiology, Harvard Medical School, Boston, Massachusetts

Knippers, Rolf, Facultat fur Biologie, Universitat Konstanz, Federal Republic of Germany

Krauss, Sharon, Department of Biochemistry, University of California, Berkeley

Kunzi, Myriam, Department of Anatomy and Cell Biology, Cornell University Medical College, New York, New York

Lambert, Paul, Laboratory of Tumor Virus Biology, National Cancer Institute, Bethesda, Maryland

Lane, David, Clare Hall Laboratories, Imperial Cancer Research Fund, Potters Bar, England

Laskey, Ronald, Department of Zoology, University of Cambridge, England

Lavi, Sara, Department of Microbiology, Tel Aviv University, Israel

Lawlor, Kenneth, Department of Biological Sciences, Hunter College, New York, New York

Leffak, Michael, Department of Biochemistry, Wright State University, Dayton, Ohio

Lehman, I. Robert, Department of Biochemistry, Stanford University School of Medicine, California

Leu, Tzeng-Horng, Department of Biochemistry, University of Virginia, Charlottesville

Li, Congjun, Worcester Foundation, Shrewsbury, Massachusetts

Li, Joachim, Department of Molecular Biology and Genetics, Johns Hopkins University School of Medicine, Baltimore, Maryland

Lin, Patrick, Department of Pathology, Stanford University School of Medicine, California

Linder, Patrick, Department of Microbiology, Biozentrum, Basel, Switzerland

Linskens, Maarten, Department of Molecular and Cellular Biology, Roswell Park Memorial Institute, Buffalo, New York

Lipps, Hans, Institut fur Biologie, University of Tubingen, Federal Republic of Germany

Lockshon, Daniel, Fred Hutchinson Cancer Research Center, Seattle, Washington

Lupton, Steve, Immunex Corporation, Seattle, Washington

Lusky, Monika, University of Heidelberg, Federal Republic of Germany

Ma, Doreen, Department of Chemistry and Biology, California Institute of Technology, Pasadena

Malkas, Linda, Cell Biology Group, Worcester Foundation for Experimental Biology, Shrewsbury, Massachusetts

Mann, Kristine, Department of Biology, University of Alaska, Anchorage

Marraccino, Robert, Department of Biochemistry, University of Rochester, New York

Martin, Robert, Department of Molecular Biology, National Institutes of Health, NIADDK, Bethesda, Maryland

Martinez-Salas, Encarnita, Department of Cell Biology, Roche Institute of Molecular Biology, Nutley, New Jersey

Masai, Hisao, Department of Molecular Biology, DNAX Research Institute, Palo Alto, California

Maulbecker, Catharina, Lawrence Berkeley Laboratory, University of California, Berkeley

Maundrell, Kinsey, Sclavo Research Centre, Siena, Italy

McDonald, William, Department of Microbiology, Cornell University Medical College, New York, New York

McFadden, Grant, Department of Biochemistry, University of Alberta, Edmonton, Canada

McHenry, Charles, Department of Biochemistry, Biophysics and Genetics, University of Colorado, Denver

McMacken, Roger, Department of Biochemistry, Johns Hopkins Hospital, Baltimore, Maryland

Meinkoth, Judy, The Salk Institute, San Diego, California

Meisterernst, Michael, Institut fur Biochemie, University of Munich, Federal Republic of Germany

Melendy, Thomas, Molecular Biology Institute, University of California, Los Angeles

Merchlinsky, Michael, Department of Viral Diseases, National Institutes of Health, Bethesda, Maryland

Micheli, Gioacchino, Department of Genetics and Molecular Biology, Centro Acidi Nucleici, Rome, Italy

Mignotte, Bernard, Universite de Paris-Sud, Orsay, France

Mohr, Ian, Cold Spring Harbor Laboratory, New York

Muller, Friedemann, Department of Biochemistry, University of Wurzburg, Federal Republic of Germany

Murakami, Yasufumi, Tsukuba Life Science Center Riken Institute, Japan

Newlon, Carol, Department of Microbiology and Molecular Genetics, UMDNJ-New Jersey Medical School, Newark

Nishida, Craig, Department of Biochemistry, University of California, Berkeley

Nurse, Paul, Imperial Cancer Research Fund, London, England

O'Neill, Edward, Department of Molecular Biology and Genetics, Johns Hopkins Medical School, Baltimore, Maryland

Ohmori, Haruo, Institute for Virus Research, Kyoto University, Japan

Olivo, Paul, Laboratory of Viral Disease, National Institutes, Bethesda, Maryland

Opgenorth, Andrea, University of Alberta, Edmonton, Canada

Orr-Weaver, Terry, The Whitehead Institute, Cambridge, Massachusetts

Osheroff, Neil, Department of Biochemistry, Vanderbilt University School of Medicine, Nashville, Tennessee

Ozer, Harvey, Department of Biology, Hunter College, New York, New York

Padmanabham, R., Department of Biochemistry, University of Kansas Medical Center, Kansas City

Palzkill, Timothy, Department of Microbiology and Molecular Genetics, New Jersey Medical School, Newark

Pearson, George, Department of Biochemistry and Biophysics, Oregon State University, Corvallis

Plevani, Paolo, Genetica e di Biologia dei Microrganismi, Universita degli Studi di Milano, Italy

Prelich, Gregory, Cold Spring Harbor Laboratory, New York

Prives, Carol, Department of Biological Sciences, Columbia University, New York, New York

Prussak, Charles, University of California, San Diego, La Jolla

Que, Benito, Department of Biochemistry, University of Washington, Seattle

Rabkin, Samuel, Memorial Sloan-Kettering Cancer Center, New York, New York

Rao B. Sridhara, NIADDK, National Institutes of Health, NIADDK, Bethesda, Maryland

Raveh, Dina, Department of Biology, Ben Gurion University of the Negev, Beer Sheva, Israel

Rawlins, Dan, Department of Microbiology and Immunology, Emory University School of Medicine, Atlanta, Georgia

Ray, Dan, Molecular Biology Institute, University of California, Los Angeles

Reed, Steven, Department of Molecular Biology, Scripps Clinic and Research Foundation, La Jolla, California

Richardson, Charles, Department of Biological Chemistry, Harvard Medical School, Boston, Massachusetts

Rine, Jasper, Department of Biochemistry, University of California, Berkeley

Roberts, Jim, Fred Hutchinson Cancer Center, Seattle, Washington

Roberts, John, Laboratory of Genetics, National Institute of Environmental Health Sciences, Research Triangle Park, North Carolina

Rolfe, Mark, Molecular Biology Laboratory, Imperial Cancer Research Fund, London, England

Romanczuk, Helen, Brandeis University, Waltham, Massachusetts

Rossignol, Jean-Michel, Department of Molecular Biology and Genetics, IRSC, Villejuif, France

Ruyechan, William, Department of Biochemistry, Uniformed Services University of Health Sciences, Bethesda, Maryland

Ryan, Kathleen, Department of Biological Chemistry, Johns Hopkins School of Medicine, Baltimore, Maryland

Ryder, Kevin, Department of Molecular Biology and Genetics, Johns Hopkins University, Baltimore, Maryland

Salvino, Ralph, Department of Biochemistry, Cancer Research Laboratory, University of Western Ontario, London, Canada

Sarkar, Nilima, Department of Metabolic Regulation, Boston Biomedical Research Institute, Massachusetts

Sauer, Helmut, Department of Biology, Texas A&M University, College Station

Schildkraut, Carl, Department of Cell Biology, Albert Einstein College of Medicine, Bronx, New York

Schimke, Robert, Department of Biological Sciences, Stanford University, California

Schvartzman, Jorge, Department of Cell Biology, Albert Einstein College of Medicine, Bronx, New York

Shaw, Barbara, P.M. Gross Chemical Laboratory, Duke University, Durham, North Carolina

Sheehan, Moira, Department of Zoology, University of Cambridge, England

Sheline, Christian, Department of Biology, University of California, Los Angeles

Sherley, James, Department of Molecular Biology and Genetics, Johns Hopkins Medical School, Baltimore, Maryland

Snapka, Robert, Department of Radiology, Ohio State University, Columbus

So, Antero, Department of Medicine and Biochemistry, University of Miami, Florida

Spencer, Forrest, Department of Molecular Biology and Genetics, Johns Hopkins University School of Medicine, Baltimore, Maryland

Spradling, Allan, Department of Embryology, Carnegie Institution of Washington, Baltimore, Maryland

Stillman, Bruce, Cold Spring Harbor Laboratory, New York

Strauss, Phyllis, Department of Biology, Northeastern University, Boston, Massachusetts

Stuart, David, Department of Biochemistry, University of Alberta, Edmonton, Canada

Studwell, Pat Sue, Department of Microbiology, Cornell University Medical College, New York, New York

Stürzbecher, Horst, Marie Curie Research Institute, Oxted, England

Subramanian, Kiranur, Department of Microbiology and Immunology, University of Illinois, Chicago

Sunstrom, Noelle-Ann, Department of Microbiology and Immunology, McGill University, Montreal, Canada

Swimmer, Candace, The Biological Laboratories, Harvard University, Cambridge, Massachusetts

Sykes, Robert, Department of Biochemistry, Baylor College of Medicine, Houston, Texas

Taddie, John, Department of Cell Biology and Anatomy, Cornell University Medical College, New York, New York

Tegtmeyer, Peter, Department of Microbiology, State University of New York, Stony Brook

Tlsty, Thea, Lineberger Cancer Research Center, University of North Carolina Chapel Hill

Traktman, Paula, Department of Cell Biology and Anatomy, Cornell University Medical College, New York, New York

Tseng, Ben, University of California, San Diego, La Jolla

Umek, Robert, Department of Molecular and Cellular Biology, Roswell Park Memorial Institute, Buffalo, New York

Upton, Chris, Department of Biochemistry, University of Alberta, Edmonton, Canada

Van Houten, Virginia, Department of Microbiology and Molecular Genetics, New Jersey Medical School, Newark

van der Vliet, Peter, Laboratory for Physiological Chemistry, State University of Utrecht, The Netherlands

Vaughn, James, Department of Biochemistry, University of Virginia, Charlottesville

Vessey, Adele, Eastman Pharmaceuticals, Great Valley, Pennsylvania

Virshup, David, Department of Pediatrics, Johns Hopkins University School of Medicine, Baltimore, Maryland

Vishwanatha, J., Department of Biochemistry, University of Nebraska Medical Center, Omaha

Vos, Jean-Michel, Department of Biological Sciences, Stanford University, California

Wahl, Alan, Department of Pathology, Stanford University School of Medicine, California

Wahl, Geoff, The Salk Institute, La Jolla, California

Walter, Gernot, Department of Pathology, University of California, San Diego, La Jolla

Wang, Edith, Department of Biological Sciences, Columbia University, New York, New York

Wang, Quingping, Department of Biochemistry, Michigan State University, East Lansing

Wang, Teresa, Department of Pathology, Stanford University School of Medicine, California

Weinberg, David, Department of Molecular Biology and Genetics, Johns Hopkins Medical School, Baltimore, Maryland

Weiner, Beth, Dana Farber Cancer Institute, Boston, Massachusetts

Weller, Sandra, Department of Microbiology, University of Connecticut Health Center, Farmington

Wernette, Catherine, Department of Biochemistry, Michigan State University, East Lansing

Wold, Marc, Department of Molecular Biology and Genetics, Johns Hopkins University School of Medicine, Baltimore, Maryland

Wong, Scott, Department of Pathology, Stanford University School of Medicine, California

Wood, Richard, Mutagenesis Laboratory, Imperial Cancer Research Fund, Potters Bar, England

Wu, Carol, NIAID, National Institutes of Health, Bethesda, Maryland

Wu, Duu-Gong, Department of Molecular Biology and Genetics, Johns Hopkins University School of Medicine, Baltimore, Maryland

Xu, Fu-Yun, Department of Biochemistry and Biophysics, Oregon State University, Corvallis

Yamaguchi, Masamitsu, Laboratory of Cell Biology, Aichi Cancer Center Research Institute, Nagoya, Japan

Yan, Hong, Department of Biochemistry, Cornell University, Ithaca, New York

Yates, John, Department of Human Genetics, Roswell Park Memorial Institute, Buffalo, New York

Zannis-Hadjopoulos, Marie, McGill University, Montreal, Quebec, Canada

Zhao, Lingjun, Department of Biochemistry, University of Kansas Medical Center, Kansas City

Zmudzka, Barbara, Department of Biochemistry, NCI, National Institutes of Health, Bethesda, Maryland

First row: M. Luskey; K. Berns, C. Prives, R. Martin, C. Schildkraut; A. Spradling
Second row: W. Earnshaw; A. Wahl, I.R. Lehman, C.C. Richardson, D. Clayton; P. Nurse
Third row: M. DePamphilis, D. Knipe, M. Horwitz; J. Kaguni, J. Rossignol, L. Kaguni; M. Challberg
Fourth row: J. Hamlin, M. Fairman; H. Huber, R. McMacken; J. Broach

Preface

The double helical structure of DNA, with its complementary base pairs that specify our genotype, immediately suggests how the genome can be replicated and passed from one generation to the next. However, understanding of the mechanism and regulation of eukaryotic chromosome replication remains a major area of modern biological research. The main reason for this is that DNA is not self-replicating. The replication process is complex, and it will be necessary to understand the mechanism of DNA replication and how it is controlled prior to obtaining a complete insight into cellular growth control throughout development and how these controls are reversed during tumorigenesis.

The replication of DNA in eukaryotes provides some unique problems that cannot be addressed by studying prokaryotic replication systems. For example, and most obviously, eukaryotic chromsomes are complex, containing multiple origins of replication per DNA molecule and special structures such as telomeres and centromeres that aid in chromosome replication, segregation, and stability. Additionally, eukaryotic chromosomes are organized into complicated structures containing DNA and proteins, both of which must be duplicated, thereby maintaining chromosome structures that may influence gene expression.

During cell proliferation, the rate of cell division must be controlled, and in multicellular organisms, this must be coordinated with other replicating cells. Thus, the initiation of the DNA replication cycle, S phase, must be precise. Although control of DNA replication is by no means unique to eukaryotes, the mechanisms of regulation must be responsive to a large number of influences, including hormonal, developmental, environmental, and physiological stimuli. Furthermore, within a single cell, the replication of multiple chromosomes and the initiation at many origins on one chromosome must be accurately coordinated. This is perhaps the most distinguishing feature of eukaryotic chromosome replication.

In eukaryotes, specific gene amplification plays an important role in developmental gene expression and in the resistance of cells to many commonly used drugs. The mechanism by which specific regions of the chromosome amplify in response to developmental regulation or to the treatment of cells with drugs is not understood, although progress is being made in this area.

With these thoughts in mind, it became obvious that there was a need for an open, international meeting devoted to the important subject of eukaryotic DNA replication. It was also evident that this topic would be a valuable addition to the annual Cold Spring Harbor autumn symposium series on Cancer Cells, which focuses attention on areas of basic biology that relate to cancer research. As organizers, we sought to include the many varied biological systems that have contributed important information about DNA replication in eukaryotic cells, but we also attempted to focus attention on rapidly developing topics such as replication control. These studies will provide valuable links to other areas of research aimed at understanding how cells proliferate. The meeting was graced with exciting science and stimulating discussions, even though, because of the pressure of time and attempting to include everything into the program, the "free" time for discussion was somewhat limited. It was also clear that many independent lines of investigation were beginning to converge, particularly the relationship between replication proteins and transcription factors and the value of virus systems as models for understanding chromosomal DNA replication. However, it was also clear that much needs to be done. The papers in this volume are representative of the exciting accomplishments that were reported at the meeting.

We wish to thank Jim Watson for his encouragement and support of this meeting on DNA replication. A special session that summarized some of the best work on DNA replication in prokaryotes was included so that comparisons could be drawn, and we thank the speakers in this session for their stimulating examples. We are especially grateful to the staff of the meetings office at Cold Spring Harbor Laboratory, under the direction of Barbara Ward, and in particular to Maureen Berejka, for help with the organization of the meeting and in coordinating the registration of participants. Their efficiency was marvelous. Herb Parsons and the audiovisual department certainly ensured that the sessions would run smoothly, for which we are grateful. This meeting and expenses of some of our colleagues were supported by grants from the Institute of General Medical Sciences and the Institute on Aging within the National Institutes of Health, the National Science Foundation, and by the Cold Spring Harbor Corporate Sponsors Program.

The Publications Department at Cold Spring Harbor, under the direction of Nancy Ford, saw that the abstract book and this volume were completed without delay. This volume was coordinated through the efforts of Joan Ebert, Liz Ritcey, and Patricia Barker, whom we thank for their cheerful approach to a difficult task.

The Editors

Contents

REPLICATION OF VIRAL DNA

REPLICATION AND AMPLIFICATION OF CHROMOSOMAL DNA

REPLICATION PROTEINS

In Vitro Studies of the T4 Bacteriophage DNA Replication System

T.-A. Cha and B.M. Alberts
Department of Biochemistry and Biophysics, University of California,
San Francisco, California 94143

Seven bacteriophage T4-encoded proteins reconstitute an in vitro DNA replication system that catalyzes coupled leading and lagging strand DNA synthesis at a replication fork. The proteins involved are the T4 DNA polymerase holoenzyme (the products of T4 genes 43, 44/62, and 45), a helix-destabilizing (SSB) protein (gene 32 protein), and the T4 primosome, which is composed of a DNA helicase (gene 41 protein) and an RNA primase (gene 61 protein). The 61 protein alone is shown to catalyze a single-stranded DNA template-dependent oligoribonucleotide synthesis with the dimers pppApC and pppGpC as the major products and longer oligomers of various lengths as minor ones. However, the physiologically relevant pentaribonucleotides that are responsible for priming de novo DNA chain starts on the lagging strand are produced only in the presence of both 41 and 61 proteins (the complete primosome).

We show here that the presence of 41 protein alone on the lagging strand of the fork enables the polymerase holoenzyme to catalyze leading strand DNA synthesis at maximum rate and high processivity even without the gene 32 protein. When the 61 protein is added to complete the primosome, Okazaki fragment synthesis on the lagging strand accompanies leading strand synthesis, irrespective of the presence of 32 protein. On a double-stranded DNA template, the main effect of 32 protein is to increase the lagging strand polymerization rate and stabilize the complete fork assembly. These effects are likely to be mediated through its cooperative binding to the single-stranded regions of the DNA template and by direct protein-protein interactions with selected components of the polymerase holoenzyme and primosome.

Bacteriophage T4 has provided a favorable model system for studying the basic mechanisms of DNA replication. T4 encodes the proteins for its own replication with a relatively small number of genes, and a combined genetic and biochemical approach has allowed the proteins essential for T4 DNA replication fork movement to be identified, purified, and studied in vitro. Combining seven purified proteins (the products of T4 genes 32, 43, 45, 44/62, 41, and 61) with a nicked-duplex DNA as the template generates an efficient in vitro DNA replication system (Alberts et al. 1983). This seven-protein system produces replication forks that closely resemble those formed by the T4 replication apparatus in vivo, with a similar speed, geometry, and fidelity of DNA synthesis (Hibner and Alberts 1980; Sinha et al. 1980).

To unravel the detailed mechanisms by which this multiprotein system functions, the individual activities of the T4 replication proteins have been examined in the presence of specially designed DNA molecules. Some important properties of the proteins are outlined in Table 1. Gene 43 codes for T4 DNA polymerase. It possesses both 5'–3' polymerase and 3'–5' exonuclease activities. By itself, the 43 protein is capable of elongating pre-existing primers, either DNA or RNA, on single-stranded templates with a low degree of processivity (Goulian et al. 1968). The products of genes 44/62 and 45 are known as the polymerase accessory proteins. When these three proteins are added to the polymerase, they increase its rate and processivity in an ATP-depen-

dent fashion (Huang et al. 1981; Mace and Alberts 1984b). The complex of the accessory proteins with the DNA polymerase is referred to as the DNA polymerase holoenzyme. Some of the hairpin helical regions in a single-stranded DNA template act as kinetic blocks for the polymerase (Huang et al. 1981). The accessory proteins help the polymerase pass these blocks by clamping it down onto the primer-template junction, thereby preventing its dissociation from the template. However, an extensive region of helical structure, such as that found in natural duplex DNA, acts as a permanent block for the polymerase holoenzyme (Liu et al. 1979).

The helix-destabilizing protein (32 protein) stimulates DNA synthesis catalyzed by either the polymerase or the polymerase holoenzyme on a single-stranded template by melting out the hairpin helices in the DNA (Huberman et al. 1971; Huang et al. 1981). In addition, at high concentrations, 32 protein permits strand displacement synthesis by the polymerase holoenzyme on a double-stranded DNA template (Liu et al. 1979; Nossal and Peterlin 1979). Further addition of the gene 41 protein to such a system enhances the rate and processivity of the DNA synthesis by unwinding the double helix just ahead of the polymerase holoenzyme (Alberts et al. 1980; Venkatesan et al. 1982). The 41 protein is an enzyme that moves rapidly and processively along a single-stranded DNA molecule in a 5' to 3' direction driven by the energy of GTP hydrolysis (Liu and Alberts 1981). It is able to displace short DNA fragments paired

1

Table 1 Seven-protein Set of T4 Replication Proteins

Type of protein	T4 gene	Activities
DNA Polymerase holoenzyme	43 (DNA polymerase)	5′ → 3′ polymerase 3′ → 5′ exonuclease
	44/62;45 (polymerase accessory proteins)	DNA-terminal-dependent ATPase primer-template junction recognition
Primosome	41 (DNA helicase)	ssDNA-dependent GTPase processive DNA unwinding
	61 (RNA primase)	template-dependent oligoribonucleotide synthesis
Helix-destabilizing protein	32 (SSB protein)	cooperative binding to ssDNA

to the strand along which it is moving, thus serving as a DNA helicase (Venkatesan et al. 1982).

At a DNA replication fork, the leading strand is synthesized continuously, and the lagging strand is synthesized discontinuously. To observe lagging strand DNA synthesis, the above in vitro system requires addition of the gene 61 protein. The 61 protein is an RNA primase, but it must be mixed with the 41 protein to produce the pentaribonucleotides that prime each Okazaki fragment (Liu and Alberts 1980; Nossal 1980; Cha and Alberts 1986). Together, the 41 and 61 proteins constitute the primosome component of the T4 replication apparatus.

A DNA replication process that is carried out by a large number of sequential reactions of randomly colliding individual proteins is avoided by assembling a large multienzyme complex of replication proteins at the replication fork. As the fork advances, the multiple tasks involved in the DNA replication process are carried out by a "protein machine" that results from the coherent activities of all the individual protein parts, which move relative to each other without disassembling (Alberts et al. 1983; Alberts 1984). For example, frequent synthesis of RNA primers by the primosome is needed on the lagging strand to initiate successive Okazaki fragments at the observed rate of about one every 3 seconds. In addition, the lagging strand DNA polymerase must be able to utilize these primers efficiently. A high concentration of free DNA polymerase would be needed to supply the polymerase molecule for the synthesis of each Okazaki fragment by random collision. Instead, the replication fork is thought to be folded in a way that brings the start site for each succeeding Okazaki fragment in close juxtaposition to the place where the previous Okazaki fragment will end. Figure 1 shows a schematic of the proposed protein complex at such a folded DNA replication fork.

The recycling of the lagging strand DNA polymerase was demonstrated by dilution experiments. If the initiation of the synthesis of each Okazaki fragment requires free polymerase molecules, it should be possible to reduce the concentration of polymerase to levels that produce abnormally long Okazaki fragments. However,

the average length of Okazaki fragments is observed to be insensitive to dilutions of the polymerase molecules, and we have concluded that both leading and lagging strand DNA polymerase molecules remain bound to the fork at all times (Alberts et al. 1983).

The assembly of a multiprotein complex at the replication fork presumably requires multiple protein–protein and protein–nucleic acid interactions. Protein affinity chromatography has been employed to determine the protein–protein interactions. Figure 2 summarizes the results from these experiments (Alberts et al. 1983; Formosa et al. 1983), showing that the T4 replication proteins form a highly interactive protein network.

In this report, we present the results of some recent in vitro studies of the T4 DNA replication apparatus that emphasize the key role of the DNA helicase component of the primosome at the fork.

Results

A tailed-duplex DNA template facilitates the assembly of the helicase at the fork

On a nicked-duplex DNA template, the presence of 32 protein is absolutely required to observe strand displacement DNA synthesis catalyzed by the T4 DNA polymerase holoenzyme (Liu et al. 1979; Nossal and Peterlin 1979). Upon further addition of the 41 helicase, two populations of replication forks are formed, one moving faster than the other (Alberts et al. 1980; Venkatesan et al. 1982). The fast-moving forks contain the 41 protein. Although the 32 protein is required to obtain the fast-moving forks on this DNA template, it could merely be needed to allow assembly of the 41 protein onto a fork that starts at a nick. To address this point, we carried out the reactions illustrated in Figure 3. A chemically synthesized DNA oligonucleotide of 45 nucleotides was used to prime DNA synthesis on a single-stranded closed-circular M13mp8 DNA template. Because only the 3′ end of this primer is complementary to the template, the polymerase holoenzyme produces a complete duplex DNA circle with a 24-nucleotide single-stranded 5′-end tail in an initial reaction (T. Cha, unpubl.). Be-

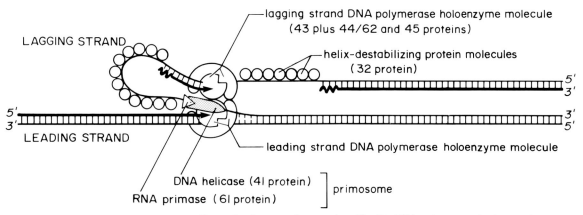

Figure 1 Schematic representation of the T4 replication protein complex. The T4 DNA polymerase is the product of gene 43. Together with the gene 44/62 and 45 proteins, it forms the DNA polymerase holoenzyme. The gene 41 protein is both a DNA helicase and a protein that is required, along with the gene 61 RNA primase, for RNA primer synthesis on the lagging strand. Together the 41 and 61 proteins form the primosome. The gene 32 protein binds to all of the single-stranded DNA at the fork. As indicated, a large multiprotein complex composed of a dimeric DNA polymerase holoenzyme linked by the primosome is thought to catalyze concerted leading and lagging strand DNA synthesis at the replication fork. In this complex, the lagging strand DNA is folded in a way that brings the start site for the next Okazaki fragment in close juxtaposition to the site where the previous Okazaki fragment will end.

T4 Replication Protein Network

Protein Affinity Column   **Protein from Lysate**

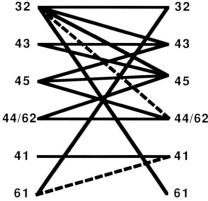

Figure 2 Schematic representation of the protein network formed by the T4 replication proteins. Purified T4 replication proteins have been coupled to an Affi-Gel matrix (Bio-Rad) and used to construct the protein affinity columns listed on the left side of the figure. A cleared lysate of T4-infected *E. coli* cells was applied to these columns. The T4 replication proteins from the lysate that bound to each column were those indicated by solid lines. (The binding of 61 protein to the 32 protein column was not detected initially owing to the minute amount of 61 protein present in the T4-infected *E. coli* cell lysate [Alberts et al. 1983; Formosa et al. 1983]; however, strong binding to the 32 protein column by the 61 protein was detected using purified 61 protein [T. Cha, unpubl.].) The dashed lines indicate two special cases in which the protein affinity columns (32 and 61 protein columns) were constructed by binding the proteins to a single-stranded DNA cellulose matrix; specific binding was then detected by passing purified 44/62 and 41 proteins over these columns (Mace and Alberts 1984a; P. Pryciak, unpubl.).

cause the 41 protein moves in a 5′ to 3′ direction along a single-stranded DNA chain, this tail provides an entry site for loading the 41 protein onto a fork without requiring the prior opening of the helix by the replication proteins (unlike a nicked-duplex DNA template). The tailed template therefore allows the effect of 41 protein on fork movement to be assessed in the absence of the 32 protein. For comparison, the effects of 32 protein alone and of a combination of the 32 and 41 proteins were also examined. Moreover, leading strand DNA synthesis alone was compared with coupled leading and lagging strand DNA synthesis by omitting or including the 61 primase in the reaction.

In the experiments to be described, radioactive deoxyribonucleotides are added after completing the initial synthesis of the tailed-duplex DNA molecules, and the DNA products are identified by the radioactivity they contain. Reactions are usually analyzed by alkaline agarose gel electrophoresis followed by autoradiography. It is easy to distinguish the products made on the leading and lagging strands, because the Okazaki fragments move much faster than the leading strand products in a denaturing gel system, due to their relatively small size.

The 41 helicase induces a maximum rate of leading strand DNA synthesis

Figure 4 displays a gel analysis of the products produced by leading strand DNA synthesis on the tailed-duplex DNA template. DNA synthesis by the polymerase holoenzyme is shown in the presence of the 41 protein (lanes 1–7), the 32 protein (lanes 8–14), and both the 41 and 32 proteins (lanes 15–21). A synthesis rate of about 250 nucleotides/second is obtained when only the 41 protein is added to the polymerase holoenzyme, and this rate is not further increased by the presence of

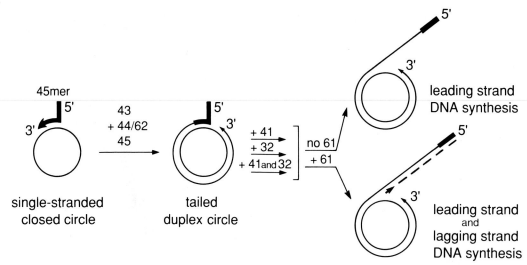

Figure 3 Production and use of a tailed-duplex DNA template that facilitates the assembly of the 41 protein DNA helicase at the fork. The single-stranded closed circular template employed was bacteriophage M13mp8 DNA. The 45-nucleotide-long DNA primer was synthesized chemically. The replication proteins used at each stage of various reactions are represented by their gene numbers. To perform these reactions the 45 mer (5 μg/ml) was annealed to the M13mp8 single-stranded closed-circular DNA (12 μg/ml) at 37°C for 30 min in 40 μl of replication buffer (33 mM Tris-acetate [pH 7.8], 66 mM potassium acetate, 10 mM magnesium acetate, 0.5 mM dithiothreitol). Nucleoside triphosphates (1 mM each of ATP and GTP, and 150 μM each of the four deoxyribonucleoside triphosphates) were also present. The T4 DNA polymerase holoenzyme (mixture of 5.8 μg/ml 43 protein, 70 μg/ml 45 protein, and 45 μg/ml 44/62 protein) was then added and the reaction mixture was incubated at 37°C for 5 min. The synthesis of a tailed-duplex circular molecule was completed at this stage. To induce strand displacement synthesis, the 41 protein (65 μg/ml) and/or 32 protein (170 μg/ml) were then added and $[\alpha\text{-}^{32}P]dCTP$ (2.2 Ci/mmol) was included to label the DNA made during the subsequent incubation at 37°C. When examining the synthesis of Okazaki fragments on the lagging strand, the 61 protein (2.1 μg/ml) and 200 μM each of CTP and UTP were also included. Small aliquots of the reaction mixture were sampled at various time intervals and quenched with alkaline stop buffer (30 mM NaOH, 20 mM Na_3EDTA, 10% sucrose, and 0.04% bromocresol green) for subsequent analysis by agarose gel electrophoresis.

32 protein. Moreover, the polymerase catalyzes highly processive leading strand DNA synthesis in the presence of 41 protein alone, as judged by the absence of DNA products of intermediate lengths between the size of the starting DNA strand and the growing leading strand DNA. On the other hand, 32 protein alone induces strand displacement synthesis by the polymerase holoenzyme with a much slower rate and less processivity, and many discrete bands representing pause sites appear. These results indicate that the presence of the 41 helicase on the fork ensures a high rate and processivity of DNA synthesis and that the 32 protein is not required. However, the 32 protein affects other aspects of the DNA replication process, as will be discussed later.

When the 61 primase and all four ribonucleoside triphosphates are included in the above reaction, Okazaki fragment synthesis accompanies the leading strand DNA synthesis, as shown in Figure 5 (the electrophoresis time in Fig. 5 is half of that in Fig. 4). The bands with sizes below 7 kb contain the heterogeneous population of Okazaki fragments produced in this system. The rate of leading strand synthesis is unaffected by these additions (data not shown). No lagging strand DNA synthesis is observed in the absence of the 41 protein, even with the 61 primase present (T. Cha, unpubl.).

An RNA primase and a DNA helicase constitute an active primosome

Although no priming activity can be detected for the individual primosome proteins at their physiological concentrations, we have demonstrated that some RNA-primed DNA synthesis occurs at an elevated 61 protein concentration (Cha and Alberts 1986). We have further characterized the primase activity of 61 protein by using a previously described procedure (Hillenbrand et al. 1979) to detect the synthesis of RNA primers directly. For these experiments, RNA primers are radioactively labeled by the incorporation of a labeled nucleotide from $[\alpha\text{-}^{32}P]CTP$ during their synthesis. After treatment with alkaline phosphatase to remove the 5′-terminal-triphosphate group on the RNA primers, the primers are loaded directly onto a urea-containing polyacrylamide gel with Tris-borate-EDTA as the running buffer for electrophoresis. The phosphatase treatment causes the primers to move slowly enough in this gel system to separate them from the unincorporated radioactive ribonucleotides and their contaminants, so that no laborious primer purification steps are needed.

The RNA primer synthesis catalyzed by the 61 protein can thereby be analyzed readily. Figure 6 shows an autoradiogram from one of these experiments. Without the 41 protein, the 61 protein produces a dinucleotide as the major product. Upon longer exposure of the

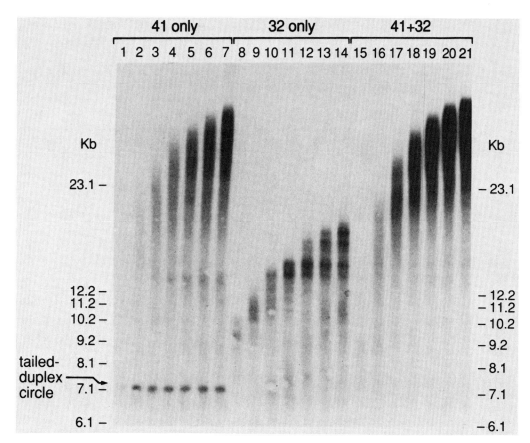

Figure 4 Analysis by alkaline agarose gel electrophoresis of DNA synthesis using the tailed-duplex DNA as the template. DNA synthesis by the polymerase holoenzyme is monitored in the presence of the 41 protein (lanes *1–7*), the 32 protein (lanes *8–14*), and both the 41 and 32 proteins (lanes *15–21*). The DNA products were sampled at 30-second intervals after the addition of the 41 and / or 32 proteins, which begins the DNA synthesis.

autoradiograph, minor species of oligoribonucleotides with various lengths up to at least 50 nucleotides can be seen to be produced as well under these conditions (T. Cha, unpubl.). The 41 protein alone does not make detectable RNA primers even at very high protein concentrations (Hinton et al. 1987; T. Cha, unpubl.). Significantly, however, the synthesis of long oligomers by the 61 protein ceases when the 41 protein is added; instead, pentaribonucleotides become the major products (Fig. 6). As demonstrated previously, both in vivo (Kurosawa and Okazaki 1979) and in vitro (Liu and Alberts 1980; Nossal 1980; Cha and Alberts 1986), these pentaribonucleotides are the physiologically active species responsible for priming de novo DNA chain starts. Thus, the primase is essentially inactive by itself, requiring an interaction with a DNA helicase to form an active primosome.

The trinucleotide sequence 5′-GTT-3′ on the DNA template specifies the site for RNA primer synthesis

The specific template sequences that serve as the RNA primer start sites have been mapped on single-stranded M13 DNA (Cha and Alberts 1986). We find that the trinucleotide sequences 5′-GTT-3′ and 5′-GCT-3′ are both necessary and sufficient to specify the efficient synthesis of RNA primers by the primosome complex, whereas the 61 protein alone only primes DNA chain starts at the GCT sequence. The primers begin by binding of a complementary nucleotide to the center nucleotide in these trinucleotide sequences, and thus start with either pppApC or pppGpC.

By omitting either ATP or GTP from the reaction, we have determined the relative usage of GTT or GCT sites for primer synthesis in the Figure 6 type of assay. We find that both the 61 primase and the primosome complex can recognize both GCT and GTT sites; however, the 61 protein has a higher affinity for the GCT sites, whereas the primosome complex has a higher affinity for the GTT sites (T. Cha, unpubl.). However, hydroxymethylation of all of the cytosine residues occurs naturally in native T4 DNA, which completely abolishes the recognition of GCT sites by both the 61 protein and the primosome complex; thus, ATP is absolutely required for primer synthesis on single-stranded natural T4 DNA templates (Liu and Alberts 1980; T. Cha, unpubl.). Inside the cell, therefore, only the GTT sites will be used by the primosome.

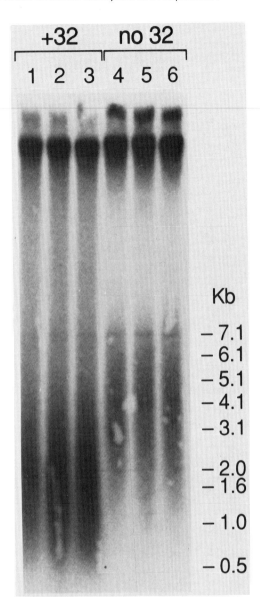

Figure 5 The detection of Okazaki fragment synthesis. DNA synthesis was carried out as in Fig. 4, except that the 61 protein and all four ribonucleoside triphosphates were included, and the electrophoresis time was half of that in Fig. 4 so that small DNA molecules could be detected. The 32 protein was present in lanes *1–3*, and it was omitted in lanes *4–6*. The reactions were stopped at 5 min (lanes *1* and *4*), 10 min (lanes *2* and *5*), and 15 min (lanes *3* and *6*).

Considering the frequency of occurrence of GTT sequences in T4 DNA, which is about one per 55 nucleotides, and the average size of an Okazaki fragment, which is about 1200 nucleotides, the probability that the replication apparatus will use any particular GTT sequence encountered on the lagging strand must be low. An interesting question that can be asked is whether a primer is made but not utilized at most sites, as opposed to being made only when it is needed for priming an Okazaki fragment. To answer this question, we have conducted an experiment similar to that de-

scribed in Figure 5 except that we labeled the RNA with [α-^{32}P]CTP instead of labeling the DNA. During the time course of DNA synthesis, the amount of free primer was determined by a direct gel analysis procedure similar to that used in Figure 6 and compared to the amount of primers attached to Okazaki fragments. (The free primers correspond to the fraction of primers made by the primosome that are not used to prime the Okazaki fragment synthesis.) The results indicate that only a small amount of free primer is produced in the complete reaction, whereas about a 40-fold excess of free primer is produced in identical reactions in which 32 protein is omitted (T. Cha, unpubl.). Thus, the presence of 32 protein on the lagging strand seems to block wasteful primer synthesis by the primosome complex, ensuring that a primer is only produced when it is needed for priming an Okazaki fragment.

A timing mechanism governs the initiation of Okazaki fragment synthesis

The findings above do not explain how the replication apparatus skips over more than 20 GTT sites on the lagging strand (plus an equal number of GCT sites on a C-containing DNA) before each initiation of Okazaki fragment synthesis. The DNA synthesis rate of about 600 nucleotides/second on a single-stranded DNA template (Mace and Alberts 1984b) is much faster than the rate of the leading strand (about 250 nucleotides/second in Fig. 4). Therefore, a timing mechanism has been proposed to govern the initiation of Okazaki fragment synthesis (Selick et al. 1987), as schematically illustrated in Figure 7. In this view, the dimeric DNA polymerase holoenzyme and the primosome complex advance along the fork as a single unit of a multiprotein machine, catalyzing DNA synthesis on both leading and lagging strands. Once the lagging strand DNA polymerase reaches the 5'-end of a previously synthesized Okazaki fragment, it pauses before releasing its DNA template (note that the polymerase holoenzyme cannot penetrate the double-stranded DNA). During this pause, the leading strand polymerase continues its translocation, displacing an additional amount of single-stranded template for the next round of lagging strand synthesis. Finally, the release of the DNA by the lagging strand polymerase signals the associated primosome to synthesize an RNA primer at the next available primer site, and a refolding of the lagging strand DNA hands off this primer to the lagging strand DNA polymerase molecule, beginning the next cycle of Okazaki fragment synthesis. In the absence of 32 protein (a situation not occurring in vivo), primers can be made at every GTT (and GCT) site. However, those primers made before the release of DNA by the lagging strand DNA polymerase molecule are wasted.

Based on this mechanism, the length of each Okazaki fragment is equivalent to the distance that the leading strand DNA polymerase molecule travels during the time required to complete the recycling of the lagging strand DNA polymerase molecule. This time is the sum of the

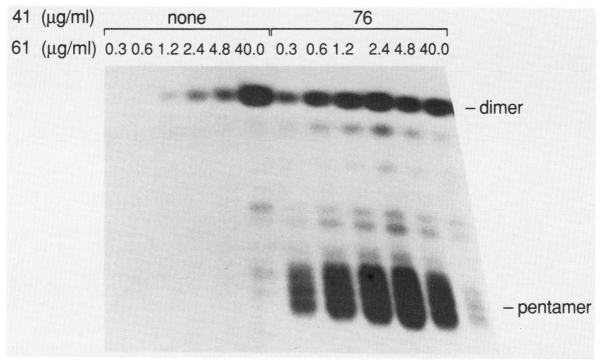

Figure 6 Analysis of the oligoribonucleotide primers made by the T4 61 protein, either alone or in the presence of the 41 protein. The primers were produced using a single-stranded closed-circular M13 viral DNA as the template, and the primers were subsequently treated with alkaline phosphatase before analyzing them by polyacrylamide gel electrophoresis. The protein concentrations employed during the synthesis reaction are indicated; the positions corresponding to a dimer and a pentamer are also marked.

travel time and the pause time for the lagging strand DNA polymerase molecule. When expressed algebraically (Selick et al. 1987), it can be shown that the size of successively synthesized Okazaki fragments quickly converges to an average length that is independent of the length of the initial fragment. This idea has been tested and confirmed by experiments in which abnormally long Okazaki fragment lengths are initially established by limiting the concentration of ribonucleoside triphosphates; the normal size of Okazaki fragments is restored very rapidly after raising rNTP concentrations (Selick et al. 1987).

If we assume that the leading strand synthesis rate and the pause time on the lagging strand are fixed quantities, reducing the lagging strand synthesis rate should cause longer Okazaki fragments to be made (see Fig. 7). This prediction is confirmed in Figure 5, where slowing the lagging strand DNA synthesis rate by omitting the 32 protein results in an increase of Okazaki fragment size by a factor of 2.5 (note that 32 protein has no effect on the leading strand synthesis rate, see Fig. 4).

Discussion

The role of the 41 protein at a replication fork

Recent studies of the origin-dependent initiation of DNA replication in the *Escherichia coli* (Kornberg et al. 1987)

and λ bacteriophage (McMacken et al. 1987) systems indicate that loading the primosome onto the fork is the key step that follows the recognition of origin DNA by the initiator proteins, with the dnaB DNA helicase being added before the dnaG primase. In the T4 system, the enzymology of initiating DNA replication from a replication origin has not yet been defined. However, since the presence of the 41 protein at the fork is both necessary and sufficient to establish the in vivo DNA synthesis rate and processivity, it should be loaded onto the fork from the onset of DNA replication. Thus, loading of the primosome at the fork should also be the central event in the origin-dependent initiation of T4 DNA replication.

The 41 protein also plays the key role in coupling leading and lagging strand DNA syntheses. Inside a cell, single-stranded DNA regions can be created through recombination and repair processes as well as by replication. If new replication forks formed at any single-stranded DNA region, the replication of chromosomal DNA would become hopelessly complex. Presumably, therefore, a special DNA helicase has evolved that can be put onto DNA only at a DNA replication origin inside the cell, and this helicase is likely to remain with the same fork until DNA synthesis is complete, due to its highly processive character. In this way, the T4 41 protein will serve as marker for a T4 replication fork, and the requirement of the RNA primase for this protein guarantees that Okazaki fragments will start only at a fork. From this perspective, the analogies among pro-

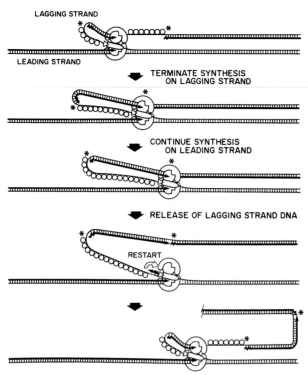

Figure 7 A model for DNA synthesis at a replication fork that allows the same DNA polymerase molecule to be repeatedly recycled to synthesize all of the Okazaki fragments on the lagging strand. For the different symbols used to represent the T4 replication proteins, see Fig. 1. (∗) marks the position of one RNA primer. The postulated timing mechanism that governs the initiation of Okazaki fragment synthesis is described in the text.

karyotic DNA replication systems are striking. In the *E. coli* DNA replication system (Kornberg 1980, 1982; LeBowitz and McMacken 1986), the 41 protein is replaced by the dnaB protein, and the dnaG protein apparently is the counterpart of the 61 protein. In the T7 bacteriophage system (Richardson et al. 1987), a single polypeptide chain, the gene 4 protein, possesses both helicase and primase activities. However, a truncated form of the gene 4 protein has recently been purified, which is a helicase but defective in primer synthesis (Huber et al., this volume).

The T4 dda protein is a second DNA helicase with a separate role
There are several DNA helicases present inside the T4-infected cell, but they do not have equivalent functions. For instance, the product of the T4 dda gene, like the 41 protein, is a DNA helicase that can utilize the energy of nucleotide hydrolysis to unwind the helix in front of the growing fork (Krell et al. 1979; Jongeneel et al. 1984b). Unlike the 41 protein, however, the dda protein functions in a nonprocessive manner, and it is unable to interact with the 61 protein to form a primosome. When an experiment similar to that described in Figure 4 is performed, the dda protein stimulates fork rates increasingly as the dda protein concentration is

raised or as the 32 protein concentration is lowered (T. Cha, unpubl.). However, no stimulation is seen in the presence of the 41 protein. These results are consistent with the earlier findings that the 41 protein and dda protein do not cooperate in vitro, either for DNA unwinding or for the stimulation of strand displacement DNA synthesis (Jongeneel et al. 1984a,b). In addition, the average size of Okazaki fragments is not altered by the presence of the dda protein (T. Cha, unpubl.); this result is consistent with the previous observation that the dda protein does not stimulate the rate of DNA synthesis by the polymerase on a single-stranded DNA template (Jongeneel et al. 1984a).

A feature unique to the dda protein is its ability to push the fork past protein molecules that are bound tightly to the DNA ahead of the replication complex. Thus, an advancing replication fork stops or stalls when it encounters a promoter-bound or a transcribing RNA polymerase molecule or an operator-bound repressor protein. This block can be released by the dda protein but not by the 41 protein (Bedinger et al. 1983; J. Barry, unpubl.). Genetic evidence suggests that there are other proteins that can substitute for the dda protein in vivo, since dda⁻ mutants do not prevent normal T4 DNA replication (Gauss et al. 1983). The dda protein seems not to be an integral part of the replication protein complex; it moves in the same direction as the 41 protein, and it presumably enters and leaves the DNA just ahead of the 41 protein on the lagging strand, where it can push other template-bound protein molecules out of the way as the fork advances.

Control of the rate of dissociation of the DNA polymerase holoenzyme from DNA
The asymmetric mode of DNA synthesis at a replication fork seems to demand that a functionally asymmetric polymerase reside on each of the two strands of the fork. The polymerase on the leading strand must be stably bound for processive DNA synthesis, whereas much less tight binding of the polymerase is required on the lagging strand if it is to be capable of recycling to initiate successive Okazaki fragments. This functional asymmetry may have a structural basis in many replication systems. Although not proven, the two different DNA polymerases α and δ in mammalian cells may coexist in one replication fork in higher eukaryotes (Downey et al., this volume). In *E. coli*, evidence for a functional asymmetry between the two halves of a dimeric polymerase holoenzyme has been provided by detecting allosteric interactions between the two halves (McHenry et al. 1987). In the T4 system, however, there is no evidence for structural asymmetry: The two halves of the dimeric polymerase holoenzyme appear to be composed of the same 43, 44/62, and 45 polypeptides.

Previous kinetic studies show that the polymerase accessory proteins tie down the DNA polymerase molecule on a DNA strand, when the polymerase is moving either in the 5′ to 3′ direction (polymerase activity) (Piperno and Alberts 1978) or the 3′ to 5′ direction (exonuclease activity) (Bedinger and Alberts 1983).

However, we have suggested that the lagging strand DNA polymerase shifts from a tight binding to a loosely binding enzyme when the polymerase encounters the 5′-end of a previously synthesized Okazaki fragment and stalls, leading to the rapid dissociation of the holoenzyme complex from the DNA molecule as pictured in Figure 7. A decay process is postulated to begin in the accessory protein complex when the polymerase pauses, which thereby represents a "clock" that measures the time of polymerase stalling (Munn 1986; Selick et al. 1987). Such a timing mechanism is biologically useful because it allows the lagging strand polymerase to dissociate rapidly after it finishes its synthesis; at the same time, it prevents the unnecessary dissociation of a moving DNA polymerase molecule that has only transiently paused, thereby allowing the leading strand DNA polymerase molecule to move processively for a long period of time.

A theoretical basis for such a timing mechanism can be derived from a kinetic proofreading scheme formulated by Hopfield (Hopfield 1974). Any biological clock mechanism requires an input of energy, because it is the unidirectional nature of energetically favorable reactions that is capable of measuring time. Hopfield has further pointed out that an energy relay mediated by multiple conformational changes can occur in addition to the simpler kinetic proofreading formalism (Hopfield 1980). Thus, the energy required by a clock mechanism could come from the ATP hydrolysis catalyzed by the polymerase accessory proteins, but it might alternatively be provided by a coupling to the polymerase cycle driven by the unidirectional translocation of the whole complex along the DNA strand.

DNA footprinting techniques have been utilized to probe the protein–DNA interactions in a stalled replication complex. We have obtained footprints that represent the assembly of a complete accessory protein complex at either a primer–template junction (Munn 1986) or a replication fork (T. Cha, unpubl.). The binding of the T4 DNA polymerase alone to the primer–template junction is weak, but it is detectable at a high concentration of polymerase (Munn 1986). Attempts to observe the entire stalled holoenzyme complex at the primer–template junction, however, have failed. We suggest that the maximum pause time before decay of the holoenzyme complex is shorter than the time required to perform standard DNA footprinting experiments.

The role of the gene 32 protein at a replication fork

The effects of the 32 protein on an advancing replication fork warrant special mention. Previously, the true role of the 32 protein has been masked by an absolute requirement for this protein for DNA synthesis by the polymerase holoenzyme on a nicked double-stranded DNA template. In this paper, however, we find that the 32 protein has no effect on the leading strand synthesis rate and processivity once the 41 helicase has been loaded onto the lagging strand of the fork. However, as discussed

previously, there are at least two effects of the 32 protein on synthesis on the lagging strand of the DNA replication fork. Through its cooperative binding to the single-stranded regions of the lagging strand DNA template, the 32 protein stimulates the rate of movement of the lagging strand DNA polymerase holoenzyme and thereby decreases the size of Okazaki fragments (Fig. 5). Furthermore, the presence of an excess of 32 protein prevents the synthesis of large numbers of unused RNA primers on the lagging strand.

A further effect of 32 protein on the fork has not yet been mentioned. As seen in Figure 4, the amount of radioactive DNA product (and thus the number of replication forks generated) is higher in the presence of 32 protein (lanes 15–21) than in its absence (lanes 1–7). Thus, the 32 protein stimulates the formation of the replication forks that start on our tailed DNA template. When we perform experiments like that described in Figure 4 at different 32 protein concentrations, we find that the 32 protein stimulation of fork assembly requires a high concentration of 32 protein similar to that found inside the cell; in fact, the number of replication forks generated at very low concentrations of 32 protein is less than that produced without the 32 protein present (T. Cha, unpubl.). It seems that low concentrations of 32 protein compete with 41 protein for binding to the single-stranded tail on the DNA template in Figure 3, whereas higher concentrations help. The assembly of the multiprotein replication complex must be dictated by a variety of specific protein–protein interactions and by a complicated set of stoichiometric relationships among the replication proteins. Affinity chromatography experiments reveal that 32 protein interacts with all but one (the 41 protein) of the seven T4 replication proteins (see Fig. 2), and we suggest that the 32 protein can facilitate fork formation through its direct interaction with selected components of the polymerase holoenzyme and primosome.

The 32 protein, and possibly also the polymerase accessory proteins on the lagging strand, may dissociate and reassociate from the replication complex as it moves. Further experiments are required to decide this issue.

Acknowledgments

This work was supported by a National Institutes of Health postdoctoral fellowship to T.A.C. and by grant GM-24020 from the National Institutes of Health to B.M.A. T.A.C. would like to thank Dr. Jon Minden for numerous stimulating discussions.

References

Alberts, B.M. 1984. The DNA enzymology of protein machines. *Cold Spring Harbor Symp. Quant. Biol.* **49:** 1.
Alberts, B.M., J. Barry, P. Bedinger, T. Formosa, C.V. Jongeneel, and K.N. Kreuzer. 1983. Studies on DNA replication in the T4 bacteriophage in vitro system. *Cold Spring Harbor Symp. Quant. Biol.* **47:** 655.

Alberts, B.M., J. Barry, P. Bedinger, R.L. Burke, U. Hibner, C.-C. Liu, and R. Sheridan. 1980. Studies of replication mechanisms with the T4 bacteriophage in vitro system. *ICN-UCLA Symp. Mol. Cell. Biol.* **19**: 449.

Bedinger, P. and B.M. Alberts. 1983. The 3′-5′ proofreading exonuclease of bacteriophage T4 DNA polymerase is stimulated by other T4 DNA replication proteins. *J. Biol. Chem.* **258**: 9649.

Bedinger, P., M. Hochstrasser, C.V. Jongeneel, and B.M. Alberts. 1983. Properties of the T4 bacteriophage DNA replication apparatus: The T4 dda DNA helicase is required to pass a bound RNA polymerase molecule. *Cell* **34**: 115.

Cha, T.-A. and B.M. Alberts. 1986. Studies on the DNA helicase-RNA primase unit from bacteriophage T4. *J. Biol. Chem.* **261**: 7001.

Formosa, T., R.L. Burke, and B.M. Alberts. 1983. Affinity purification of T4 bacteriophage proteins essential for DNA replication and genetic recombination. *Proc. Natl. Acad. Sci.* **80**: 2442.

Gauss, P., D.H. Doherty, and L. Gold. 1983. Bacterial and phage mutations that reveal helix-unwinding activities required for bacteriophage T4 DNA replication. *Proc. Natl. Acad. Sci.* **80**: 1669.

Goulian, M., Z.J. Lucas, and A. Kornberg. 1968. Enzymatic synthesis of deoxyribonucleic acid. XXV. Purification and properties of deoxyribonucleic acid polymerase induced by infection with phage T4. *J. Biol. Chem.* **243**: 627.

Hibner, U. and B.M. Alberts. 1980. The fidelity of DNA replication catalyzed in vitro on a natural DNA template by the T4 bacteriophage multienzyme complex. *Nature* **285**: 300.

Hillenbrand, G., G. Morelli, E. Lanka, and E. Scherzinger. 1979. Bacteriophage T7 DNA primase: A multifunctional enzyme involved in DNA replication. *Cold Spring Harbor Symp. Quant. Biol.* **43**: 449.

Hinton, D.M., R.W. Richardson, and N.G. Nossal. 1987. Bacteriophage T4 DNA replication: Role of the T4 41 and 61 protein primase-helicase and the T4 uvsX recombination protein. *UCLA Symp. Mol. Cell. Biol.* **47**: 173.

Hopfield, J.J. 1974. Kinetic proofreading: A new mechanism for reducing errors in biosynthetic processes requiring high specificity. *Proc. Natl. Acad. Sci.* **71**: 4135.

———. 1980. The energy relay: A proofreading scheme based on dynamic cooperativity and lacking all characteristic symptoms of kinetic proofreading in DNA replication and protein synthesis. *Proc. Natl. Acad. Sci.* **77**: 5248.

Huang, C.-C., J.E. Hearst, and B.M. Alberts. 1981. Two types of replication proteins increase the rate at which T4 DNA polymerase traverses the helical regions in a single-stranded DNA template. *J. Biol. Chem.* **256**: 4087.

Huberman, J.A., A. Kornberg, and B.M. Alberts. 1971. Stimulation of T4 bacteriophage DNA polymerase by the protein product of T4 gene 32. *J. Mol. Biol.* **62**: 39.

Jongeneel, C.V., P. Bedinger, and B.M. Alberts. 1984a. Effects of the bacteriophage T4 dda protein on DNA synthesis catalyzed by purified T4 replication proteins. *J. Biol. Chem.* **259**: 12933.

Jongeneel, C.V., T. Formosa, and B.M. Alberts. 1984b. Purification and characterization of the bacteriophage T4 dda protein, a DNA helicase that associates with the viral helix destabilizing protein. *J. Biol. Chem.* **259**: 12925.

Kornberg, A. 1980. *DNA replication.* W.H. Freeman, San Francisco.

———. 1982. *Supplement to DNA replication.* W.H. Freeman, San Francisco.

Kornberg, A., T.A. Baker, L.L. Bertsch, D. Bramhill, B.E. Funnell, R.S. Lasken, H. Maki, S. Maki, K. Sekimizu, and E. Wahle. 1987. Enzymatic studies of replication of oriC plasmids. *UCLA Symp. Mol. Cell. Biol.* **47**: 137.

Krell, H., H. Durwald, and H. Hoffman-Berling. 1979. A DNA-unwinding enzyme induced in bacteriophage-T4-infected *Escherichia coli* cells. *Eur. J. Biochem.* **93**: 387.

Kurosawa, Y. and T. Okazaki. 1979. Structure of the RNA portion of the RNA-linked DNA pieces in bacteriophage T4-infected *E. coli* cells. *J. Mol. Biol.* **135**: 841.

LeBowitz, J.H. and R. McMacken. 1986. The *Escherichia coli* dnaB replication protein is a DNA helicase. *J. Biol. Chem.* **261**: 4738.

Liu, C.-C. and B.M. Alberts. 1980. Pentaribonucleotides of mixed sequence are synthesized and efficiently prime de novo DNA chain starts in the T4 bacteriophage DNA replication system. *Proc. Natl. Acad. Sci.* **77**: 5698.

———. 1981. Characterization of the DNA-dependent GTPase activity of T4 gene 41 protein, an essential component of the T4 bacteriophage DNA replication apparatus. *J. Biol. Chem.* **256**: 2813.

Liu, C.-C., R.L. Burke, U. Hibner, J. Barry, and B.M. Alberts. 1979. Probing DNA replication mechanisms with the T4 bacteriophage in vitro system. *Cold Spring Harbor Symp. Quant. Biol.* **43**: 469.

Mace, D.C. and B.M. Alberts. 1984a. The complex of T4 bacteriophage gene 44 and 62 replication proteins forms an ATPase that is stimulated by DNA and by T4 gene 45 protein. *J. Mol. Biol.* **177**: 279.

———. 1984b. Characterization of the stimulatory effect of T4 gene 45 protein and the gene 44/62 protein complex on DNA synthesis by T4 DNA polymerase. *J. Mol. Biol.* **177**: 313.

McHenry, C.S., R. Oberfelder, K. Johanson, H. Tomasiewicz, and M.A. Franden. 1987. Structure and mechanism of the DNA polymerase III holoenzyme. *UCLA Symp. Mol. Cell. Biol.* **47**: 47.

McMacken, R., C. Alfano, B. Gomes, J.H. LeBowitz, K. Mensa-Wilmot, J.D. Roberts, and M. Wold. 1987. Biochemical mechanisms in the initiation of bacteriophage lambda DNA replication. *UCLA Symp. Mol. Cell. Biol.* **47**: 227.

Munn, M. 1986. "Analysis of the bacteriophage T4 DNA replication complex." Ph.D. thesis, University of California, San Francisco.

Nossal, N.G. 1980. RNA priming of DNA replication by bacteriophage T4 proteins. *J. Biol. Chem.* **255**: 2176.

Nossal, N.G. and B.M. Peterlin. 1979. DNA replication by bacteriophage T4 proteins: The T4 43, 32, 44/62, and 45 proteins are required for strand displacement synthesis at nicks in duplex DNA. *J. Biol. Chem.* **254**: 6032.

Piperno, J.R. and B.M. Alberts. 1978. An ATP stimulation of T4 DNA polymerase mediated via T4 gene 44/62 and 45 proteins: The requirement for ATP hydrolysis. *J. Biol. Chem.* **253**: 5174.

Richardson, C.C., B.B. Beauchamp, H.E. Huber, R.A. Ikeda, J.A. Myers, H. Nakai, S.D. Rabkin, S. Tabor, and J. White. 1987. Bacteriophage T7 DNA replication. *UCLA Symp. Mol. Cell. Biol.* **47**: 151.

Selick, H.E., J. Barry, T.-A. Cha, M. Munn, M. Nakanishi, M.-L. Wong, and B.M. Alberts. 1987. Studies on the T4 bacteriophage DNA replication system. *UCLA Symp. Mol. Cell. Biol.* **47**: 183.

Sinha, N.K., C.F. Morris, and B.M. Alberts. 1980. Efficient in vitro replication of double-stranded DNA templates by a purified T4 bacteriophage replication system. *J. Biol. Chem.* **255**: 4290.

Venkatesan, M., L.L. Silver, and N.G. Nossal. 1982. Bacteriophage T4 gene 41 protein, required for the synthesis of RNA primers, is also a DNA helicase. *J. Biol. Chem.* **257**: 12426.

Interactions of DNA Replication Proteins of Bacteriophage T7

H.E. Huber, J. Bernstein, H. Nakai, S. Tabor, and C.C. Richardson
Department of Biological Chemistry, Harvard Medical School, Boston, Massachusetts 02115

The genome of bacteriophage T7 consists of a 40-kb linear duplex DNA molecule with a terminal redundancy. Replication is initiated by the T7 RNA polymerase at two T7 promoters within the primary origin. DNA synthesis then proceeds bidirectionally. In the later stages of infection, most of the newly synthesized DNA is found in the form of concatemers. Four proteins account for the major reactions at the replication fork: the products of T7 genes 5, 4, and 2.5, and *Escherichia coli* thioredoxin. Gene 5 protein is a distributive DNA polymerase. Thioredoxin serves as an accessory protein. It binds tightly to the gene 5 protein, turning it into a highly processive polymerase. Gene 4 protein is both a helicase and a primase. As a helicase it interacts with the complex of DNA polymerase and thioredoxin at the replication fork to promote highly processive leading strand synthesis. On the lagging strand, gene 4 protein recognizes pentameric sequences at which it synthesizes tetraribonucleotide primers. The primers are extended by T7 DNA polymerase in a specific interaction with gene 4 protein. Discrete molecules of gene 4 protein act as either helicase or primase. In contrast to the helicase, the primase does not operate processively. Gene 2.5 protein, a single-stranded DNA-binding protein, stimulates lagging strand synthesis by facilitating priming of Okazaki fragments.

Bacteriophage T7 provides a model system for studying the replication of a linear duplex DNA molecule (Richardson 1983). The 40-kb genome (Dunn and Studier 1983) is replicated more than 100 times within a 12-minute period after infection of *E. coli*. This high efficiency of replication is accomplished in part through the use of phage-encoded replication proteins, thus bypassing the more complex host replication machinery. Replication is initiated in vivo at a specific site on the T7 chromosome, the primary origin, located 15% of the distance from the genetic left end of the molecule (Saito et al. 1980; Sugimoto et al. 1987). DNA synthesis leads to a replication bubble whose center is shifted to 17% (Dressler et al. 1972; Tamanoi et al. 1980). The primary origin contains two T7 RNA polymerase promoters and an AT-rich sequence. Initiation from this origin in vitro requires the phage RNA and DNA polymerases (Romano et al. 1981; Fuller and Richardson 1985a,b). If the primary origin is deleted, secondary sites can serve as initiation sites in vivo (Tamanoi et al. 1980). All secondary origins contain a T7 promoter; however, not all T7 promoters can function as secondary origins (S. Rabkin and C. C. Richardson, in prep.).

After initiation, DNA synthesis proceeds bidirectionally. Four proteins are known to be involved at the T7 DNA replication fork (see Fig. 1). The phage gene 5 protein (the DNA polymerase), *E. coli* thioredoxin (an accessory protein to the DNA polymerase), T7 gene 4 protein (a helicase and primase), and the T7 gene 2.5 protein (a single-stranded DNA-binding protein). The gene 5 protein, in addition to being a distributive DNA polymerase (Huber et al. 1987; Tabor et al. 1987), has an exonuclease activity that is several hundred-fold more active

on single-stranded than on double-stranded DNA (Adler and Modrich 1979; Hori et al. 1979a,b). The host protein thioredoxin binds tightly to gene 5 protein in a 1 to 1 stoichiometry (Modrich and Richardson 1975). In the presence of thioredoxin the activity on double-stranded DNA is increased approximately 200-fold, whereas that on single-stranded DNA remains unchanged. The gene 5 protein-thioredoxin complex is a highly processive polymerase on a single-stranded DNA template (Tabor et al. 1987), but it cannot synthesize through double-stranded regions without the help of gene 4 protein (Lechner and Richardson 1983). Gene 4 protein binds to single-stranded DNA in the presence of NTPs, preferentially dTTP, and translocates 5′ to 3′ along the DNA using the energy of hydrolysis of NTPs (Kolodner et al. 1978; Tabor and Richardson 1981). Upon encountering duplex DNA, gene 4 protein will unwind the helix processively (Matson et al. 1983). As a primase, gene 4 recognizes predominantly 3′-CTGGG/T-5′ primase sites and synthesizes pppACCC/A RNA primers (Scherzinger et al. 1977a,b; Romano and Richardson 1979a,b; Tabor and Richardson 1981). In a specific interaction with gene 4 protein, T7 DNA polymerase extends these primers to form Okazaki fragments (Scherzinger et al. 1977a), which are finally processed to create a continuous lagging strand. The ends of the linear T7 molecule are replicated via concatemer formation. In vivo and in vitro evidence suggests that concatemers are formed through the annealing of the terminally redundant tails of the T7 molecules (Serwer et al. 1982; White and Richardson 1987), yielding concatemers many phage genomes in length. Upon packaging, concatemeric DNA is cleaved and processed to yield

11

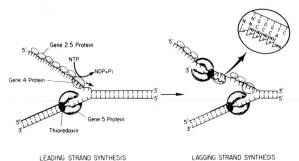

LEADING STRAND SYNTHESIS   LAGGING STRAND SYNTHESIS

Figure 1 Model of the T7 DNA replication fork.

unit length T7 DNA with terminal repeats. Processing can be reconstituted in vitro (White and Richardson 1987) and is strictly coupled to packaging.

Many aspects of the T7 replication have been reviewed previously (Richardson 1983; Richardson et al. 1987). In this paper we will concentrate on recent advances in our understanding of protein-protein and protein-DNA interactions at the replication fork of phage T7.

Experimental Procedures

Materials

Enzymes
E.coli thioredoxin was overproduced (Tabor et al. 1986) and purified by the procedure of Modrich and Richardson (1975). The purification of the T7 gene 5 protein is described in Tabor et al. (1987). The T7 gene 4 protein was purfied by the procedure of Fisher and Hinkle (1980) as modified by Nakai and Richardson (1986a). The purification of the small form of gene 4 protein will be described elsewhere (J. Bernstein and C.C. Richardson, in prep.). The T7 2.5 protein was from the preparation described in Fuller and Richardson (1985a). *E. coli* single-stranded DNA-binding protein was a gift from Dr. J. Chase (Albert Einstein College of Medicine).

DNA
Single-stranded M13 and f1 DNA were prepared as described (Nakai and Richardson 1986a). The preparation of double-stranded M13 DNA with a single-stranded tail (preformed fork, originally designed by Lechner and Richardson 1983) will be described (H. Nakai and C. C. Richardson, in prep.). Homopolymers and oligonucleotide primers were obtained from Pharmacia P.L.

Methods

DNA polymerase assay
Polymerase assays using primed single-stranded M13 DNA and poly(dA) · oligo(dT)$_{20}$ are described in Tabor et al. (1987) and Huber et al. (1987). The reconstitution of polymerase activity with gene 5 protein and thioredoxin has been described in Huber et al. (1986).

Processivity
The processivity of DNA polymerase synthesis was determined using the conditions described in Tabor et al. (1987). Reactions were run at 37°C in the absence of NaCl and single-stranded DNA-binding protein. The products were analyzed on 10% polyacrylamide gels in the presence of 8 M urea or on 0.7% agarose gels in the presence of 0.5 μg/ml ethidium bromide.

Results and Discussion

T7 DNA polymerase
The phage gene 5 and the *E. coli* thioredoxin gene, *trxA*, have been cloned individually and their gene products purified from overproducing strains (Tabor et al. 1987). The purified proteins have allowed us to determine the characteristics of DNA synthesis by gene 5 protein in the presence and absence of thioredoxin. Thioredoxin, by binding to gene 5 protein, stimulates the activities of the enzyme on double-stranded DNA, i.e., the polymerase and double-stranded DNA exonuclease activities (Adler and Modrich 1979; Hori et al. 1979a,b). In past experiments we found that the stimulation varied from 10- to more than 1000-fold depending on the DNA template used. A systematic study with different primer-template DNAs shows that the stimulation observed is a direct function of the available template length (Fig. 2). Although with very long templates the stimulation is several thousand-fold, thioredoxin can even become inhibitory with very short templates.

What is the basis of this stimulation and its template length dependence? Products synthesized by gene 5 protein in the presence and absence of thioredoxin have been analyzed on polyacrylamide and agarose gels. Figure 3 shows the extension of an oligonucleotide primer annealed to a single-stranded M13 molecule. The incorporation of 1–12 nucleotides per cycle in the ab-

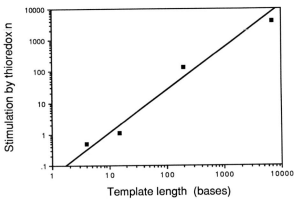

Figure 2 Stimulation of T7 DNA polymerase by thioredoxin on templates of increasing length. Templates used were poly(dA)$_n$ · oligo(dT)$_{20}$ and singly primed single-stranded M13 DNA. Polymerase assays were performed as described (Huber et al. 1987). The ratio of polymerase activity in the presence and absence of thioredoxin is plotted against the average template length.

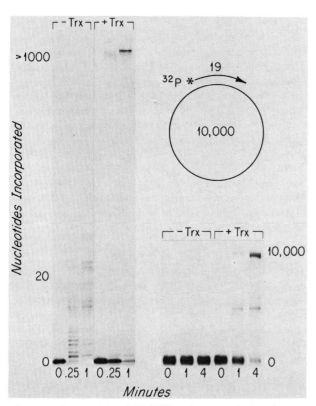

Figure 3 Processivity of T7 DNA polymerase in the absence and presence of its accessory protein thioredoxin (Trx). Single-stranded M13 DNA approximately 10 kb in length primed with a 5′-labeled oligonucleotide was incubated with limiting amounts of gene 5 protein as described (Tabor et al. 1987). Thioredoxin in tenfold molar excess over gene 5 protein was added where indicated. The reactions were stopped at the indicated times and the products were run on a denaturing polyacrylamide gel (*left panel*) or on an agarose gel in the presence of ethidium bromide (*right panel*). The band labeled "0" corresponds to the unextended primer (*left panel*) and to the primed single-stranded DNA (*right panel*), respectively.

sence of thioredoxin increases to greater than 1000 nucleotides in its presence. Clearly, thioredoxin makes DNA synthesis catalyzed by gene 5 protein highly processive. Agarose gel electrophoresis of the products shows that some primers are extended all the way around the M13 molecule and others are not used. The processivity of the gene 5 protein-thioredoxin complex is thus greater than 10,000 nucleotides. The rate of incorporation on the single-stranded template varies greatly with conditions and reaches a maximum of 750 nucleotides per second at 37°C in the presence of *E. coli* single-stranded DNA-binding protein (Tabor et al. 1987). As we will show below, a second effect of thioredoxin is to slow the recycling of gene 5 protein, which results in the observed inhibition of synthesis on very short templates.

Accessory protein thioredoxin
E. coli thioredoxin, like all thioredoxins, has an active-site disulfide that can undergo an oxidation-reduction

cycle. In *E. coli*, thioredoxin serves a variety of metabolic functions, all involving the active-site disulfide (see Holmgren 1985). The only known essential functions of thioredoxin, however, are as an accessory protein to the T7 DNA polymerase and in the morphogenesis of filamentous phage f1 (Mark and Richardson 1976; Russel and Model 1985). Curiously, in both these cases the redox potential of thioredoxin is not required (Huber et al. 1986; Russel and Model 1986). In a study on the mechanism of action of thioredoxin in phage replication, mutant thioredoxins with amino acid substitutions in and around the active site have been tested for their ability to stimulate gene 5 protein. All mutants showed a lowered affinity for gene 5 protein (down 3- to 600-fold), but all, including those with one or both cysteines replaced, were able to stimulate gene 5 protein to similar maximal levels of polymerase activity as wild-type thioredoxin. In wild-type thioredoxin, the cysteines have to be reduced to allow interaction with gene 5 protein (Adler and Modrich 1983), but they clearly play no catalytic role. A comparison of wild-type thioredoxin with the mutant TrxA7, which has both cysteines replaced by serine, is shown in Figure 4. Even though the affinity of the mutant for gene 5 protein is reduced almost 100-fold, it is still able to support highly processive synthesis when present at a high enough concentration.

It appears that accessory proteins normally have to form a stable complex with the core polymerase to confer processive DNA synthesis. This is achieved in phage T7 through a very high affinity of wild-type thioredoxin for gene 5 protein with a K_d of less than 5 nM (Huber et al. 1986). For *E. coli* DNA polymerase III and phage T4 DNA polymerase, formation of stable polymerase-accessory protein complexes requires ATP (see Nossal 1983). The use of ATP for complex stabilization may be advantageous where reversible binding is required, and it is not clear how phage T7 could dispense with this requirement. Alternatively, stable complex formation can be bypassed with a large excess of accessory protein, such as is the case with the thioredoxin mutant TrxA7. Similarly, with *E. coli* DNA polymerase III, a large excess of the β subunit (the major contributor to processivity) can bypass the need for an ATP-stabilized initiation complex (Crute et al. 1983; LaDuca et al. 1986).

Modified T7 DNA polymerase
When the gene 5 protein-thioredoxin complex is purified from phage-infected cells, it can be isolated in one of two forms, depending on the conditions of purification (Fisher and Hinkle 1980; Engler et al. 1983). When the complex is purified in the presence of EDTA, the enzyme has high single- and double-stranded DNA exonuclease activity. Consequently, the enzyme will not catalyze strand displacement synthesis at a nick (Lechner et al. 1983). In the absence of a resulting 5′ single-stranded tail, the T7 helicase (gene 4 protein) has no route by which it can enter the reaction (Lechner and Richardson 1983; Matson et al. 1983). Hence, the T7 helicase will

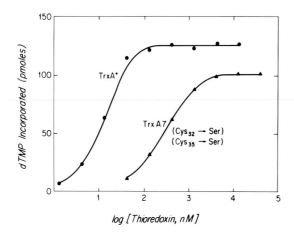

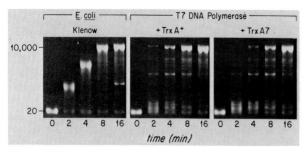

Figure 4 Effect of mutant thioredoxin on T7 DNA polymerase. (*Top*) Stimulation of polymerase activity by increasing concentrations of wild-type thioredoxin (TrxA$^+$) and of a mutant thioredoxin with both active-site cysteines replaced by serine (TrxA7). Assay conditions were as described in Huber et al. (1986). (*Bottom*) Processivity of polymerase reaction on a singly primed M13 molecule. (*Left*) Control for distributive synthesis with limiting concentrations of the Klenow fragment of *E. coli* DNA polymerase I (*Middle* and *right*) Processive synthesis by limiting concentrations of the T7 DNA polymerase complexed with wild-type or mutant thioredoxin. Thioredoxin was present in a molar excess over gene 5 protein of 5-fold for TrxA$^+$ and 50-fold for TrxA7. Reaction conditions were as described (Tabor et al. 1987). Products were separated on a 0.7% agarose gel.

not stimulate this form of T7 DNA polymerase on nicked DNA templates. The other form is obtained when the purification is carried out in the absence of EDTA or when EDTA is removed from the purified enzyme. The polymerase obtained under these conditions has relatively low levels of exonuclease activity, can initiate strand displacement synthesis at nicks, and, as a consequence, can be stimulated by the T7 helicase on nicked DNA (Lechner et al. 1983).

The native polymerase can be converted into the modified form by exposure to molecular oxygen, iron, and a reducing agent, in a reaction involving hydroxyl radicals (Tabor and Richardson 1987b). The specific inactivation of the exonuclease activity is probably due to a metal-binding site that can bind iron and locally generate reactive oxygen species. A metal-binding site is present in the exonuclease domain of the large fragment of the *E. coli* DNA polymerase I (Ollis et al. 1985b).

The homology to the T7 DNA polymerase (Ollis et al. 1985a) suggests the presence of a metal-binding site on the phage enzyme as well. Due to the lack of exonuclease activity, the modified T7 DNA polymerase has the ability to synthesize processively through secondary structures on a single-stranded DNA template and to incorporate nucleotides at very low concentration as well as nucleotide analogs. These features make the modified form uniquely suited for DNA sequencing by the dideoxy method (Tabor and Richardson 1987a). Possible in vivo functions for the modified DNA polymerase have been suggested (Lechner et al. 1983). However, no evidence exists for modification of T7 DNA polymerase in vivo, at least in the reducing environment of the *E. coli* cell.

DNA polymerase–DNA interaction

The DNA-binding constants of the DNA polymerase have been determined in the presence and absence of its accessory protein thioredoxin (Huber et al. 1987). Gene 5 protein alone has a high affinity for single-stranded DNA with K_d of 500 nM (per nucleotide of theoretical binding site) but hardly binds double-stranded DNA (K_d greater than 250 μM). The strongest binding is found with primer-template structures (K_d = 20–70 nM). Thioredoxin increases specifically the affinity for primer-template junctions by a factor of 20–80, depending on the ionic strength. The binding to single-stranded DNA, on the other hand, is not significantly affected. However, due to the large number of binding sites, single-stranded DNA can still act as a sink for DNA polymerase. For example, on a singly primed single-stranded M13 molecule only approximately one out of ten DNA-bound polymerase molecules will be bound to the primer, even in the presence of thioredoxin. This strong binding makes single-stranded DNA an ideal competitor DNA for probing the stability and processivity of replication complexes (Nakai and Richardson 1986a,b; Huber et al. 1987).

The complex formed between gene 5 protein and a primed template in the absence of Mg^{++} and nucleotides is very short-lived. Incorporation of thioredoxin into the complex increases its half-life at least 80-fold. Interestingly, the dissociation of the complex is accelerated by the single-stranded challenger DNA. Kinetic analysis suggests that the gene 5 protein-thioredoxin complex can transfer directly from one primer-template to another by a mechanism that involves a second DNA-binding site (see Berg et al. 1981; Huber et al. 1987). The transfer might involve the exonuclease site of the polymerase as a second DNA-binding site. Intriguingly, the reverse transcriptase from HIV 1, which lacks an exonuclease activity, shows no such challenger dependence. In the presence of thioredoxin, the dissociation of the T7 DNA polymerase–DNA complex is the rate-limiting step in vitro under many conditions of synthesis. In vivo the slow dissociation may impair reactions where frequent cycling of the polymerase is required, such as during synthesis of Okazaki fragments. The release of the accessory protein thioredoxin, which would allow for rapid dissociation of gene 5 protein, is highly unlikely due to the low K_d of less than 5 nM (Huber et al. 1986). Therefore, DNA-mediated direct transfer might provide an efficent means of recycling the T7 polymerase–accessory protein complex. In *E. coli* the dissociation of DNA polymerase III from DNA is ATP-dependent (Burgers and Kornberg 1983). Dissociation is probably required during lagging strand synthesis since DNA polymerase III cannot diffuse upstream along single-stranded DNA to locate the next primer (O'Donnell and Kornberg 1985). For the phage T4 DNA polymerase, release of the accessory proteins, controlled by an ATP-dependent clock mechanism, has been proposed (Selick et al. 1987).

T7 primase/helicase

DNA synthesis at the T7 replication fork is dependent on the activities of the phage gene 4 protein. Gene 4 protein is both a helicase and a primase. As a helicase it unwinds the duplex region in front of the leading strand DNA polymerase–thioredoxin complex; as a primase it synthesizes RNA primers for lagging strand synthesis (Fig. 1). Gene 4 protein is synthesized in two molecular weight forms as a result of a second in-frame ATG and a ribosome-binding site within the structural gene (Dunn and Studier 1983). The smaller form lacks 63 amino acids from its amino terminus, including a Zn-finger, a putative DNA-binding domain (see Berg 1986). We have subcloned the gene for the small form and over-produced the protein. It shows a low level of aberrant template-independent primer synthesis but is devoid of template-dependent primer synthesis; its DNA-dependent dTTPase activity is increased. As a consequence, it is unable to initiate lagging strand synthesis, but its helicase activity stimulates gene 5 protein to the same maximal incorporation at a replication fork (J. Bernstein and C.C. Richardson, in prep.).

Gene 4 protein binds to single-stranded DNA in the presence of dNTPs (Matson and Richardson 1985). In the presence of dTTP or a nonhydrolyzable analog, gene 4 protein forms a stable complex with single-stranded M13 DNA, a complex that can be isolated by gel filtration (Nakai and Richardson 1986a). A complex of DNA polymerase and single-stranded M13 DNA can be isolated similarly, without a requirement for nucleotides. Gene 4 protein and DNA polymerase form complexes as well. This protein-protein interaction in the absence of DNA is the weakest of the three interactions, as judged by their sensitivity toward ionic strength (Nakai and Richardson 1986a). In fact, the protein-DNA interactions play the dominant role in the formation of replication complexes. For example: An excess of single-stranded DNA template inhibits RNA-primed DNA synthesis due to dilution of the protein and reduction in the frequency of protein-protein encounters. If, on the other hand, the ternary complex is allowed to form in the presence of dTTP, but before addition of excess single-stranded DNA, RNA-primed DNA synthesis proceeds most efficiently. Protein-protein interaction is important, however, for the stability of ternary complexes. Gene 4 protein–RNA

primer-template complexes are stabilized several-fold by the interaction with DNA polymerase (Nakai and Richardson 1986b). Furthermore, protein–protein interaction is critical for the specificity of the replication proteins: Gene 4 protein will not interact productively either as a helicase or a primase with DNA polymerases other than that from T7 (Scherzinger et al. 1977a,b; Kolodner et al. 1978; Lechner and Richardson 1983).

Leading strand synthesis

Experiments addressing the multiple interactions at the replication fork have been carried out using the preformed fork shown schematically in Figure 5. It consists of a fully duplex circular M13 molecule with a 5′-single-stranded tail. The single-stranded tail is required for the initial binding of gene 4 protein. Without the helicase activity of gene 4 protein the DNA polymerase cannot initiate leading strand synthesis. In the presence of gene 4 protein, leading strand synthesis leads to a rolling circle type replication. The products of synthesis have been resolved on a denaturing agarose gel (Fig. 5). Products of greater than 40 kb in length accumulate, corresponding to at least six cycles of synthesis around the M13 molecule.

As shown above, the DNA polymerase has the potential for virtually unlimited processive synthesis on a single-stranded template. An interesting question then is whether the helicase would act processively as well and would thus allow processive leading strand synthesis at a replication fork. Experiments using template-challenging and dilution show that this is the case (H. Nakai and C. C. Richardson, in prep.). In the presence of dTTP, the DNA polymerase and gene 4 protein form a stable complex at a preformed fork. When the reaction is started by the addition of all four dNTPs and excess challenger DNA (single-stranded f1 DNA), leading strand synthesis again proceeds uninterruptedly for at least six revolutions around the M13 circle. The gene 4

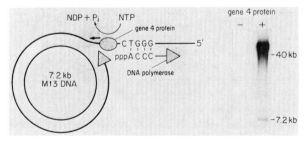

Figure 5 DNA synthesis at a preformed replication fork. (*Left*) Model of the preformed fork consisting of a 7.2-kb, fully duplex circular M13 molecule with a 5′ single-stranded tail. Leading strand synthesis by gene 4 protein and the gene 5 protein-thioredoxin complex results in rolling circle replication. Priming by gene 4 protein on the lagging strand template initiates Okazaki fragment synthesis. (*Right*) Products of leading strand synthesis by gene 5 protein-thioredoxin in the absence or presence of gene 4 protein, resolved on a denaturing agarose gel.

protein acting as helicase does so in a highly processive manner and the leading strand replication complex, once actively synthesizing, is not susceptible to challenge.

The rate of leading strand synthesis by the gene 4 protein–polymerase–thioredoxin complex at the replication fork is 300 nucleotides per second at 30°C (Lechner and Richardson 1983). For comparison, on a single-stranded DNA template the incorporation rate by the polymerase–thioredoxin complex, in the presence of *E.coli* single-stranded DNA-binding protein, reaches 750 nucleotides per second at 37°C (Tabor et al. 1987).

Lagging strand synthesis

As discussed above (see Figs. 1 and 5), gene 4 protein is not only a helicase but also a primase. Since the gene 4 protein acts as a helicase on the lagging strand template, it will encounter primase sites and might thus serve simultaneously as a primase. However, template-challenge experiments analogous to the one described for leading strand synthesis indicate that distinct gene 4 molecules act as helicase and primase (H. Nakai and C.C. Richardson, in prep.). Leading strand synthesis continues uninterrupted after addition of single-stranded challenger DNA. However, synthesis of Okazaki fragments on the lagging strand is inhibited completely. The same result is obtained in experiments where the replication complexes are challenged by dilution. These results also imply that the gene 4 protein molecules acting as primases, and possibly the lagging strand polymerase, dissociate from and reassociate with the DNA between priming events.

The fourth protein known to be involved in T7 replication is the phage-encoded single-stranded DNA-binding protein, the product of gene 2.5. Recent genetic evidence indicates that gene 2.5 protein is essential for T7 replication and cannot be replaced by *E. coli* single-stranded DNA binding (F.W. Studier, pers. comm.). In vitro experiments show that the gene 2.5 protein cannot be substituted with *E. coli* single-stranded DNA-binding protein at a replication fork. Gene 2.5 protein increases the initiation rate of Okazaki fragment synthesis on the lagging strand several-fold, but the *E. coli* protein does not. The stimulation is both on the level of primer synthesis by gene 4 protein and primer utilization (H. Nakai and C.C. Richardson, in prep.).

Even in the presence of gene 2.5 protein the T7 primase at a replication fork is susceptible to DNA challenge and dilution. In contrast to gene 4 protein acting as helicase and the leading strand DNA polymerase, the primase does not operate processively. Whether the lagging strand DNA polymerase gets recycled for multiple rounds of Okazaki fragment synthesis is not yet clear. Evidence for recycling of the lagging strand DNA polymerase does exist for *E. coli* and phage T4 DNA replication (see McHenry et al. 1987; Selick et al. 1987). Whether and how leading and lagging strand synthesis might be coordinated (Sinha et al. 1980) during T7 DNA replication is a problem currently under investigation.

References

Adler, S. and P. Modrich. 1979. T7-induced DNA polymerase: Characterization of associated exonuclease activities and resolution into biologically active subunits. *J. Biol. Chem.* **254:** 11605.

———. 1983. T7-induced DNA polymerase: Requirement for thioredoxin sulfhydryl groups. *J. Biol. Chem.* **258:** 6956.

Berg, J.M. 1986. Potential metal-binding domains in nucleic acid binding proteins. *Science* **232:** 485.

Berg, O.G., R.B. Winter, and R.H. von Hippel. 1981. Diffusion-driven mechanisms of protein translocation on nucleic acids. I. Models and theory. *Biochemistry* **20:** 6929.

Burgers, P.M.J. and A. Kornberg. 1983. The cycling of *Escherichia coli* DNA polymerase III holoenzyme in replication. *J. Biol. Chem.* **258:** 7669.

Crute, J.J., R.J. LaDuca, K.O. Johanson, C.S. McHenry, and R.A. Bambara. 1983. Excess β subunit can bypass the ATP requirement for highly processive synthesis by the *Escherichia coli* DNA polymerase III holoenzyme. *J. Biol. Chem.* **258:** 11344.

Dressler, D., J. Wolfson, and M. Magazin. 1972. Initiation and reinitiation of DNA synthesis during replication of bacteriophage T7. *Proc. Natl. Acad. Sci.* **69:** 998.

Dunn, J.J. and F.W. Studier. 1983. Complete nucleotide sequence of bacteriophage T7 DNA and the locations of T7 genetic elements. *J. Mol. Biol.* **166:** 477.

Engler, M.J., R.L. Lechner, and C.C. Richardson. 1983. Two forms of the DNA polymerase of bacteriophage T7. *J. Biol. Chem.* **258:** 11165.

Fisher, J. and D.C. Hinkle. 1980. Bacteriophage T7 DNA replication in vitro. Stimulation of DNA synthesis by T7 RNA polymerase. *J. Biol. Chem.* **255:** 7956.

Fuller, C.W. and C.C. Richardson. 1985a. Initiation of DNA replication at the primary origin of bacteriophage T7 by purified proteins. Site and direction of initial DNA synthesis. *J. Biol. Chem.* **260:** 3185.

———. 1985b. Initiation of DNA replication at the primary origin of bacteriophage T7 by purified proteins. Initiation of bidirectional synthesis. *J. Biol. Chem.* **260:** 3197.

Holmgren, A. 1985. Thioredoxin. *Annu. Rev. Biochem.* **54:** 237.

Hori, K., D.F. Mark, and C.C. Richardson. 1979a. Deoxyribonucleic acid polymerase of bacteriophage T7: Purification and properties of the phage-encoded subunit, the gene 5 protein. *J. Biol. Chem.* **254:** 11591.

———. 1979b. Deoxyribonucleic acid polymerase of bacteriophage T7: Characterization of the exonuclease activities of the gene protein and the reconstituted polymerase. *J. Biol. Chem.* **254:** 11598.

Huber, H.E., S. Tabor, and C.C. Richardson. 1987. *Escherichia coli* thioredoxin stabilizes complexes of bacteriophage T7 DNA polymerase and primed templates. *J. Biol. Chem.* **262:** 16224.

Huber, H.E., M. Russel, P. Model, and C.C. Richardson. 1986. Interaction of mutant thioredoxins of *Escherichia coli* with the gene 5 protein of phage T7. *J. Biol. Chem.* **261:** 15006.

Kolodner, R., Y. Masamune, J.E. LeClerc, and C.C. Richardson. 1978. Gene 4 protein of bacteriophage T7. Purification, physical properties, and stimulation of T7 DNA polymerase during the elongation of polynucleotide chains. *J. Biol. Chem.* **253:** 566.

LaDuca, R.J., J.J. Crute, C.S. McHenry, and R.A. Bambara. 1986. The β subunit of the *Escherichia coli* DNA polymerase III holoenzyme interacts functionally with the catalytic core in the absence of other subunits. *J. Biol. Chem.* **261:** 7550.

Lechner, R.L. and C.C. Richardson. 1983. A preformed, topologically stable replication fork. *J. Biol. Chem.* **258:** 11185.

Lechner, R.L., M.J. Engler, and C.C. Richardson. 1983. Characterization of strand displacement synthesis catalyzed by bacteriophage T7 DNA polymerase. *J. Biol. Chem.* **258:** 11174.

Mark, D.F. and C.C. Richardson. 1976. *Escherichia coli* thioredoxin: A subunit of bacteriophage T7 DNA polymerase. *Proc. Natl. Acad. Sci.* **73**: 780.

Matson, S.W. and C.C. Richardson. 1983. DNA-dependent nucleoside 5′-triphosphatase activity of the gene 4 protein of bacteriophage T7. *J. Biol. Chem.* **258**: 14009.

———. 1985. Nucleotide-dependent binding of the gene 4 protein of bacteriophage T7 to single-stranded DNA. *J. Biol. Chem.* **260**: 2281.

Matson, S.W., S. Tabor, and C.C. Richardson. 1983. The gene 4 protein of bacteriophage T7: Characterization of helicase activity. *J. Biol. Chem.* **258**: 14017.

McHenry, C.S., R. Oberfelder, K. Johanson, H. Tomasiewicz, and M.A. Franden. 1987. Structure and mechanism of the DNA polymerase III holoenzyme. *UCLA Symp. Mol. Cell. Biol. New Ser.* **47**: 47.

Modrich, P. and C.C. Richardson. 1975. Bacteriophage T7 deoxyribonucleic acid replication *in vitro*. *J. Biol. Chem.* **250**: 5515.

Nakai, H. and C.C. Richardson. 1986a. Interactions of the DNA polymerase and gene 4 protein of bacteriophage T7. *J. Biol. Chem.* **261**: 15208.

———. 1986b. Dissection of RNA-primed DNA synthesis catalyzed by gene 4 protein and DNA polymerase of bacteriophage T7. *J. Biol. Chem.* **261**: 15217.

Nossal, N.G. 1983. Prokaryotic DNA replication systems. *Annu. Rev. Biochem.* **52**: 581.

O'Donnell, M.E. and A. Kornberg. 1985. Dynamics of DNA polymerase III holoenzyme of *Escherichia coli* in replication of a multiprimed template. *J. Biol. Chem.* **260**: 12875.

Ollis, D.L., C. Kline, and T.A. Steitz. 1985a. Domain of *Escherichia coli* DNA polymerase I showing sequence homology to T7 DNA polymerase. *Nature* **313**: 818.

Ollis, D.L., P. Brick, R. Hamlin, N.G. Xuong, and T.A. Steitz. 1985b. Structure of large fragment of *Escherichia coli* DNA polymerase I complexed with dTMP. *Nature* **313**: 762.

Richardson, C.C. 1983. Bacteriophage T7: Minimal requirements for the replication of a duplex DNA molecule. *Cell* **33**: 315.

Richardson, C.C., B.B. Beauchamp, H.E. Huber, R.A. Ikeda, J.A. Meyers, H. Nakai, S.D. Rabkin, S. Tabor, and J. White. 1987. Bacteriophage T7 DNA replication. *UCLA Symp. Mol. Cell. Biol. New Ser.* **47**: 151.

Romano, L.J. and C.C. Richardson. 1979a. Requirements for synthesis of ribonucleic acid primers during lagging strand synthesis by the DNA polymerase and gene 4 protein of bacteriophage T7. *J. Biol. Chem.* **254**: 10476.

———. 1979b. Characterization of the ribonucleic acid primers and the deoxyribonucleic acid product synthesized by the DNA polymerase and gene 4 protein of bacteriophage T7. *J. Biol. Chem.* **254**: 10483.

Romano, L.J., F. Tamanoi, and C.C. Richardson. 1981. Initiation of DNA replication at the primary origin of bacteriophage T7 by purified proteins: Requirement of T7 RNA polymerase. *Proc. Natl. Acad. Sci.* **78**: 4107.

Russel, M. and P. Model. 1985. Thioredoxin is required for filamentous phage assembly. *Proc. Natl. Acad. Sci.* **82**: 29.

———. 1986. The role of thioredoxin in filamentous phage assembly. *J. Biol. Chem.* **261**: 14997.

Saito, H., S. Tabor, F. Tamanoi, and C.C. Richardson. 1980. Nucleotide sequence of the primary origin of bacteriophage T7 DNA replication: Relationship to adjacent genes and regulatory elements. *Proc. Natl. Acad. Sci.* **77**: 3917.

Scherzinger, E., E. Lanka, and G. Hillenbrand. 1977a. Role of bacteriophage T7 DNA primase in the initiation of DNA strand synthesis. *Nucleic Acids Res.* **4**: 4151.

Scherzinger, E., E. Lanka, G. Morelli, D. Seiffert, and A. Yuki. 1977b. Bacteriophage T7 induced DNA-priming protein. A novel enzyme involved in DNA replication. *Eur. J. Biochem.* **72**: 543.

Selick, H.E., J. Barry, T. Cha, M. Munn, M. Nakanishi, M.L. Wong, and B.M. Alberts. 1987. Studies on the T4 bacteriophage DNA replication system. *UCLA Symp. Mol. Cell. Biol. New Ser.* **47**: 183.

Serwer, P., G.A. Greenhaw, and J.L. Allen. 1982. Concatemers in a rapidly sedimenting, replicating bacteriophage T7 DNA. *Virology* **123**: 474.

Sinha, N.K., C.F. Morris, and B.M. Alberts. 1980. Efficient *in vitro* replication of double-stranded DNA templates by a purified T4 bacteriophage replication system. *J. Biol. Chem.* **255**: 4290.

Sugimoto, K., Y. Kohara, and T. Okazaki. 1987. Relative roles of T7 RNA polymerase and gene 4 primase for the initiation of T7 phage DNA replication *in vitro*. *Proc. Natl. Acad. Sci.* **84**: 3977.

Tabor, S. and C.C. Richardson. 1981. Template recognition sequence for RNA primer synthesis by gene 4 protein of bacteriophage T7. *Proc. Natl. Acad. Sci.* **78**: 205.

———. 1987a. DNA sequence analysis with a modified bacteriophage T7 DNA polymerase. *Proc. Natl. Acad. Sci.* **84**: 4767.

———. 1987b. Selective oxidation of the exonuclease domain of bacteriophage T7 DNA polymerase. *J. Biol. Chem.* **262**: 15330.

Tabor, S., H.E. Huber, and C.C. Richardson. 1986. *Escherichia coli* thioredoxin: An accessory protein for bacteriophage T7 DNA polymerase. In *Thioredoxin and glutaredoxin systems: Structure and function* (ed. A. Holmgren et al.), p. 285. Raven Press, New York.

———. 1987. *Escherichia coli* thioredoxin confers processivity on the DNA polymerase activity of the gene 5 protein of bacteriophage T7. *J. Biol. Chem.* **262**: 16212.

Tamanoi, F., H. Saito, and C.C. Richardson. 1980. Physical mapping of primary and secondary origins of bacteriophage T7 DNA replication. *Proc. Natl. Acad. Sci.* **77**: 2656.

White, J.H. and C.C. Richardson. 1987. Processing of concatemers of bacteriophage T7 DNA *in vitro*. *J. Biol. Chem.* **262**: 8851.

Enzymatic Mechanism of Initiation of Replication from the Origin of the *Escherichia coli* Chromosome

T.A. Baker, L.L. Bertsch, D. Bramhill, K. Sekimizu, E. Wahle, B. Yung, and A. Kornberg
Department of Biochemistry, Stanford University, Stanford, California 94305

An in vitro system that faithfully replicates plasmids from the *E. coli* chromosomal origin (*oriC*) depends on twelve purified enzymes, acting in a sequence of six or more stages. In initiation (prepriming) stages, replication forks are assembled at *oriC* as a prerequisite for priming and DNA synthesis. The stages include (1) binding of the dnaA (initiator) protein to its four 9-mer recognition sequences in *oriC*; (2) catalysis by the dnaA protein of a specific, ATP-dependent, duplex opening of a sequence at one end of *oriC*; (3) direction by dnaA protein of dnaB helicase into this open duplex of the *oriC* complex, in a reaction requiring dnaC protein; (4) unwinding of the duplex in both directions by dnaB protein to create a single-stranded bubble of about 400 residues. These reactions are sufficient to make the template competent for priming and DNA synthesis. Upon addition of primase, pol III holoenzyme, and gyrase, priming and DNA synthesis start at *oriC* and proceed bidirectionally around the template. This initiation pathway is blocked specifically at the duplex opening stage by factors that stabilize the helix. Transcription by RNA polymerase overcomes this inhibition by laying down an RNA-DNA hybrid that activates the origin for replication.

Regulation of cell growth and proliferation is a major issue in biology today. Understanding the various motifs used by biological switches is the first step to understanding regulation. The switches that function to regulate individual genes and groups of genes are revealing recurring themes as to how proteins and nucleic acids can respond to environmental stimuli to change gene expression. However, an understanding of the molecular mechanism of a switch that regulates the firing of an origin of replication is not yet in hand. This is due partially to the lack of knowledge of the essential steps that must occur at origins, for it is these very steps that will be the targets of regulation.

Toward this end, we have been studying the enzymology of replication from *oriC*. *oriC* has been defined as a 245-bp sequence that is necessary and sufficient to impart autonomous replication to plasmids lacking another functional origin. It must therefore contain all the information required for the assembly of functional replication forks. Furthermore, since replication in *E. coli* is regulated at the point of initiation, and the timing of replication of *oriC* plasmids within the cell cycle is like that of the chromosome, the target of this timing mechanism must also be within *oriC*. (For reviews on replication and its regulation, see McMacken et al. 1987; von Meyenberg and Hansen 1987).

Comparison of the nucleotide sequence of *oriC* from *E. coli* and related bacteria revealed several important features (Zyskind et al. 1983). It is composed of two types of sequences: highly conserved portions that contain very few changes and intervening regions in which the nucleotide sequence is randomized, but the number

of nucleotides has been maintained. Inasmuch as deletions and insertions are not tolerated within these regions, they are regarded as "spacers" between the conserved portions. The conserved regions contain two classes of elements whose function we are beginning to understand at the molecular level: (1) There are four repeats of the 9-mer recognition sequence for the tight binding of the essential initiator dnaA protein, and (2) three tandem repeats of a 13-mer sequence that is also recognized by dnaA protein and is the first region of the duplex to be opened for the insertion of the replication enzymes between the strands. Finally, the sequence GATC, which occurs 11 times (three of them introducing each of the three 13-mers), should occur statistically only once; GATC is the recognition sequence of the DNA adenine methylase. Methylation of these sequences seems to affect origin function in vivo and in vitro, but the basis of this effect is not yet understood.

How the *oriC* sequence is recognized and used by a dozen replication proteins has been the object of our recent studies.

Materials and Methods

Reagents
Rifampicin was from Sigma; P1 from PL Biochemicals; RNase A was a gift from the R. Baldwin group (this department). Other sources were as described previously (Sekimizu et al. 1987). Replication proteins were purified as described previously (Kaguni and Kornberg 1984). The template pCM959, a gift from M. Meijer (University of Amsterdam), is a minichromosome (4012

19

bp) consisting of only *E. coli* DNA surrounding *oriC*. Construction of templates for deletion of the 13 mers and analysis of the effect of heterologous RNA polymerases will be described in detail elsewhere (D. Bramhill and A. Kornberg; T.A. Baker and A. Kornberg; both in prep.).

Assay for open and prepriming complexes by P1 sensitivity

For open complexes, the standard reaction (50 μl) contained 40 mM HEPES-KOH (pH 7.6), 8 mM magnesium acetate, 30% (v/v) glycerol, 320 μg/ml BSA, 150 fmol supercoiled plasmid DNA, 67 ng HU protein, 240 ng dnaA protein, and 5 mM ATP. Following incubation at 38°C for 2 minutes, 1.2 units of P1 nuclease were added in 3 μl of 30 mM potassium acetate (pH 4.8). P1 cleavage was stopped after 5 seconds by adding 40 μl of 25 mM EDTA, 1% SDS. For prepriming complexes, reactions were similar to the open complex reactions except that magnesium was 0.3 mM (not 8 mM) and dnaB (120 ng) and dnaC (40 ng) were included. Incubation at 38°C was for 30 minutes, after which reactions were chilled to 16°C and P1 nuclease (1.2 units) added. After 5 or 10 seconds, digestion was stopped by EDTA/SDS as for open complexes. For quantitation of the fraction of linear molecules, a portion of the reaction was electrophoresed through a 0.7% agarose gel in TBE buffer at 6 V/cm, stained with ethidium bromide, and photographed using Polaroid film. Densitometric scanning of the negative was used to determine the proportion of linear molecules.

Assays for replication

Replication reactions were done essentially as described previously for the RNA polymerase + primase system (Ogawa et al. 1985). Rifampicin was used at 20 μg/ml, RNase A at 4 μg/ml, and RNase H at 0.05 μg/ml.

Results and Discussion

A cycle of replication in vitro

By purifying the factors from the crude soluble enzyme system capable of specifically replicating plasmids containing *oriC*, we have identified 12 proteins that are intimately involved in *oriC*-directed replication (Kaguni and Kornberg 1984). The actions of these purified proteins and the overall replication reaction have been divided into six major stages (Fig. 1).

Initiation requires that *oriC* be part of the supercoiled template. (1) The first identified stage is binding of dnaA protein to its 9-mer recognition sites within *oriC*; 20–40 monomers bind cooperatively to form a big complex encompassing about 200 bp of DNA (Fuller et al. 1984). DNase I footprinting established that the 9-mers (dnaA boxes) are especially recognized. The 10-bp periodicity of protection and electron microscopy (EM) analysis of the complex suggest that the DNA is wrapped around the complex as in a nucleosome. Although binding studies show that ATP is not required for 9-mer binding, formation of an open complex required that dnaA contain a tightly bound ATP (see Fig. 2 for more detailed description of the early stages). The histone-like protein

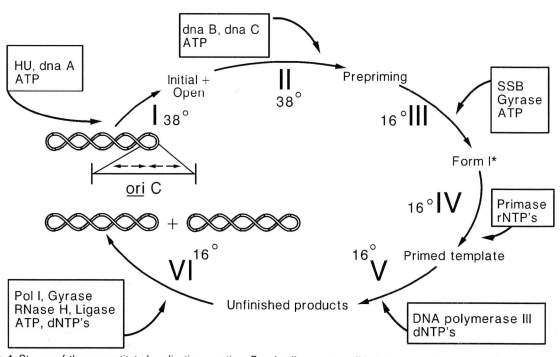

Figure 1 Stages of the reconstituted replication reaction. For details, see text. (Modified from Kornberg et al. 1987.)

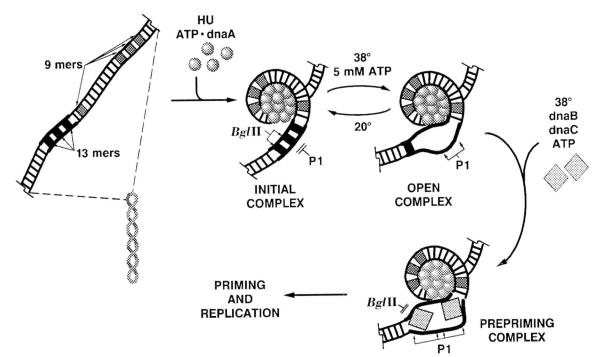

Figure 2 Model of dnaA protein recognition and opening of *oriC* for formation of the prepriming complex. For details, see text. (Figure from D. Bramhill and A. Kornberg, in prep.)

HU stimulates early initiation stages, and so is normally present at the outset. Stability of this dnaA-*oriC* complex requires isolation to be at a high temperature (38°C).

(2) Once bound to *oriC*, dnaA allows the entry of the dnaB helicase into the complex in a reaction that requires dnaC protein (Funnell et al. 1987). This stage depends on ATP and involves an opening of the DNA duplex, which will be discussed in detail below (Sekimizu et al. 1987). The resulting prepriming complex is now stable to lower reaction temperatures (16°C). Upon incubation of the complex with ATP and single-strand-specific DNA-binding protein (SSB), dnaB helicase can leave the origin, unwinding the template in both directions (Baker et al. 1987).

(3) In the presence of gyrase to relieve the topological strains associated with unzipping the double helix, unwinding the dnaB protein can proceed unchecked almost entirely around the circle. When this unwinding is allowed to proceed in the absence of replication, a highly single-stranded DNA is the product (FI*) (Baker et al. 1986).

(4) Once unwinding by dnaB is initiated (and long before it is as extensive as in FI*), the template becomes competent for priming by primase (Baker et al. 1987). These first primers are restricted to the origin region if primase is present at the start of dnaB unwinding. If unwinding is extensive, then primers are distributed all over the template.

(5) The primers are then elongated by the multisubunit DNA polymerase III holoenzyme (Baker et al. 1986, 1987; Funnell et al. 1986).

(6) Finally, primers are excised by DNA polymerase I (pol I) with the help of RNase H. The gaps are then filled by pol I or pol III holoenzyme and the nicks sealed by ligase. Gyrase decatenates and supercoils the daughter molecules, generating two plasmids identical to the starting template (Funnell et al. 1986).

dnaA protein opens the origin for dnaB helicase

Electron microscopic studies of the prepriming complex and early unwinding bubbles indicated that dnaB protein enters the *oriC*-dnaA protein complex at the far left portion of the origin not previously bound by dnaA protein (Funnell et al. 1987). Examination of this region revealed that it contained three repeats of the 13-bp sequence: GATCTNTTNTTTT (10/11, 10/11, and 9/11 matches with two unspecified bases) (D. Bramhill and A. Kornberg, in prep.). Using this consensus sequence, similar repeats were found near the dnaA boxes in the origin of pSC101 and the promoter regions of the genes for dnaA protein and the 16-kD protein (the gene immediately to the right of *oriC*). Attempts to observe binding of dnaB or dnaC proteins to this sequence in the absence of dnaA-dependent prepriming complex formation were unsuccessful (D. Bramhill, unpubl.). Interactions between dnaA protein and this region were examined in more detail.

Under the conditions of the replication reaction, dnaA protein can open the duplex at the 13-mer sequences. This opening can be observed by incubating dnaA protein, a supercoiled template, and ATP (under appropriate buffer conditions) followed by a brief digestion with the single-strand-specific nuclease P1. P1 is similar to S1 nuclease in its specificity but is active under the neutral pH conditions required for the replication reaction. About 40% of the template is linearized by this treatment. (Low levels of HU protein are included to reduce dnaA-independent cleavage by P1; the dnaA- or ATP-independent cleavage is determined separately as a background value and subtracted.) Like replication, this duplex-opening reaction required that dnaA be in the ATP-bound form; in a typical experiment, ATP · dnaA gave 46% linearization, whereas the ADP · dnaA form gave only 6%, the background level. Mapping of the location of the cleavages showed that they are clustered within the 13-mers (D. Bramhill and A. Kornberg, in prep.). The observation that the predominant products after P1 digestion are linears suggests that the structure created by dnaA protein is a single-stranded bubble, unprotected by protein on either strand. We call it the *open complex* (Fig. 2). (The first stage of dnaA interacting with *oriC* has been divided into two stages in this figure, including both the initial complex and open complex.)

This duplex opening by dnaA protein allows the entrance of dnaB protein into the 13-mer region to form the *prepriming complex*. In addition to the EM evidence described above, localization of dnaB to the 13-mers can be shown in two ways. One way is by P1-sensitivity. After addition of dnaB and dnaC proteins, the P1-sensitivity of the 13-mers can be observed at low temperature (i.e., 16°C), whereas with dnaA protein alone, P1-sensitivity can be observed only above 25°C. The pattern of cleavages is also slightly changed. The other way is by restriction at the two *Bgl*II sites within the 13-mers. These sequences become resistant to digestion after addition of dnaB and dnaC proteins, indicating that the protein is stably bound between the strands.

Deletion analysis further established the interaction between dnaA and the 13-mers and suggests the detailed functions of these three tandem repeats, all of which are essential for replication in vivo. The three 13-mers (L-left, M-middle, R-right) were sequentially deleted from left to right and the resulting constructions were assayed for their capacities to form an open complex (P1^s at 38°C), a prepriming complex (P1^s at 16°C), and for replication (Table 1). A dramatic difference was seen between the behaviors of these deletions in the three different assays. Deletions lacking the left, or left

and middle, repeats show a level of duplex opening near that of the wild type. Only upon deleting the final 13-mer does the reaction fall to the level of the vector lacking *oriC*. Thus, one 13-mer is sufficient for duplex opening by dnaA protein. When assaying for prepriming complex formation or replication, however, all three 13-mers are needed. Deletion of the left 13-mer reduces the level of prepriming complex fivefold, and replication more than tenfold. Deletion of the left and middle 13-mers reduces the activity of the plasmids to levels indistinguishable from that of the vector lacking *oriC*. Although one 13-mer can be opened by dnaA protein, indicating that a 13-mer is the unit of recognition, three 13-mers in a row are necessary for introduction of dnaB protein. A similar conclusion was drawn from the fact that a higher transition temperature (by 3–4 degrees) is required for forming the prepriming complex than for the open complex. Thus, melting of the entire 13-mer region, about 40 bp, is required to start the assembly of replication forks at *oriC*.

Transcription activates *oriC* for duplex opening

The studies outlining the pathway for initiation were generally made in the absence of RNA polymerase, which is not absolutely required for initiation in vitro. However, in vivo, the rifampicin sensitivity of initiation after a period when protein synthesis is no longer required implies the existence of a transcript essential to initiation. *rpoB* mutants, encoding altered β subunits of RNA polymerase, suppress *ts* mutants in the *dnaA* gene, again implying RNA polymerase action in initiation (see von Meyenburg and Hansen 1987).

In the crude in vitro system for replication of *oriC* plasmids, rifampicin-sensitivity of the reaction also implied a requirement for RNA polymerase. Initial attempts at staging the reaction indicated its activity was required very early. However, upon purification and reconstitution of the replication system, RNA polymerase was not always essential; its contribution depended on the levels of the other proteins and the reaction conditions (Ogawa et al. 1985). Three of the factors that modulate the dependence on RNA polymerase are the level of the histone-like protein HU, the reaction temperature, and the superhelix density (the balance between topoisomerase I and gyrase). HU, at levels sufficient to coat more than one-third of the template, reaction temperatures of less than 25°C, and superhelix densities more relaxed than −0.03, blocks the replication reaction in the absence of RNA polymerase transcription. Replication in the presence of HU coating or at 20°C is completely dependent on transcription.

All three of these factors specifically inhibit the dnaA-dependent duplex opening reaction in parallel to their inhibition of replication (T. Baker and A. Kornberg, unpubl.). Since they appeared not to inhibit the proceeding reaction stage (i.e., dnaA protein binding to the template), we conclude that they inhibit replication by inhibiting duplex opening. This places the role of RNA

Table 1 Effect of 13 mer Deletions on Origin Function

13 mers present in *oriC*	Open complex (%)[a]	Prepriming complex (%)[a]	Replication (pmol)
L M R	100	100	178
M R	97	19	16
R	92	9	4
None	16	5	4
Vector	15	4	4

[a]Percentages expressed as percent of maximal signal; at 100% approximately half the template is linearized.

polymerase transcription at the point of assisting duplex opening under conditions when dnaA protein, acting alone, is insufficient. Apparently, the large region of the duplex (about 40 bp) that must be melted by dnaA protein for the entrance of dnaB helicase is energetically very costly and highly sensitive to agents that stabilize the helix (e.g., low temperature, relaxation, and HU protein binding).

How does RNA polymerase counteract the inhibition by these "freezing" agents? Activation absolutely requires transcription. Titration of RNA polymerase for activation (most commonly replication on a template inhibited by high levels of HU) revealed that about five polymerase molecules per template was optimal. Furthermore, the holoenzyme form was required (Table 2). When amounts of holoenzyme and core polymerase that gave equal RNA synthesis on activated calf thymus DNA (a template that does not require the σ subunit for initiation) were compared for the ability to activate replication, the core form was nearly tenfold less active than the holoenzyme. Apparently, the interaction of RNA polymerase with promoters is required. All four rNTPs were also required, as were time and temperature (T. Baker and A. Kornberg, unpubl.). The phage RNA polymerases of T3 and T7 substituted readily for *E. coli* RNA polymerase on plasmids containing promoters for these polymerases. Thus, what is required for activation is transcription rather than a special interaction between RNA polymerase and dnaA protein or some structure (i.e., promoter or terminator) within the origin.

RNA polymerase can act first, before addition of any replication proteins. Transcription and replication stages were separated by the use of rifampicin. When transcription was allowed for a time period (less than a minute) before addition of rifampicin (added just before the replication proteins), there was no inhibition. However, when rifampicin was added at the outset of the transcription phase, the reaction was completely inhibited. Thus transcription acts first and the template retains some "memory" of the transcription event.

This memory of transcription strongly suggested that the product RNA was involved in the activation reaction. However, other experiments showed that activation worked only in *cis*, and that attempts to use free RNA as a substitute for transcription were not successful. It seemed likely that an RNA-DNA hybrid was responsible for activation. The behavior of the activated templates after treatment with RNases confirmed this conclusion

Table 2 Stimulation of an HU Inhibited Template by RNA Polymerase

RNA polymerase	DNA synthesis (pmol)	RNA synthesis (pmol)
None	17	23
Holoenzyme	188	232
Core	20	264

DNA synthesis was on the *oriC* plasmid pCM959 in the presence of inhibitory levels of HU. RNA synthesis was on activated calf thymus DNA.

Table 3 Effect of RNase Treatment on the Activated Template

Treatment	Replication activity (pmol)	RNA remaining (pmol)
No addition	120	648
RNase A	83	69
RNase H	9	53

Replication activity and RNA remaining were determined 2 min after addition of RNase. Reaction containing RNase H also contained RNase A.

(Table 3). Transcription was allowed to proceed in the absence of replication proteins for 5 minutes. RNase A, or RNase A together with RNase H, was added and samples were removed after 2 minutes to determine the amount of activation and RNA remaining. Treatment of the activated template with RNase A reduced replication activity less than twofold, while removing more than 90% of the RNA. Gel electrophoresis of the RNA confirmed that it was converted into short pieces by this treatment, leaving only the small amount hybridized to the template. Incubation with RNase H (specific for RNA in RNA-DNA hybrids), in addition to RNase A, completely inactivated the template. Gel analysis confirmed that the hybrids were destroyed at the same time, showing that an RNA-DNA hybrid is necessary for activation by RNA polymerase. The hybrid, isolated away from the small RNA pieces and from RNA polymerase by gel filtration, retained activity, thus confirming that it is sufficient.

The molecular mechanism by which an RNA-DNA hybrid counteracts the inhibition of duplex opening is still unclear. Further experiments are needed to establish the length and location of the hybrid required. It seems likely that alterations of the template structure by the hybrid must be involved. The results should be of broad interest, considering that transcriptional activation is appearing as a recurring theme in prokaryotic (λ, ColE1) and eukaryotic initiation of replication (adenovirus, SV40) as well as in recombination.

Summary

DnaA protein locates *oriC* and directs the assembly of replication forks. To achieve this it first binds in a sequence-dependent manner to the four "dnaA boxes" located there. Then, in a step highly sensitive to configuration of the duplex, it separates the strands to allow the entry of dnaB helicase. Entry of dnaB helicase can be thought of as the "committed step" to replication; priming and replication follow easily once dnaB is established. In this scheme, dnaA protein appears to play a role similar to that of the σ subunit in RNA polymerase. dnaA directs the "sequence-blind" elongation enzymes to the "replication promoter" or origin as σ does for the RNA polymerase core. Plasmids and phage of *E. coli* encode their own initiator proteins, specific to their own origins as "alternate σ factors" to redirect the replication machinery away from *oriC*.

References

Baker, T.A., B.E. Funnell, and A. Kornberg. 1987. Helicase action of dnaB protein during replication from the *Escherichia coli* chromosomal origin *in vitro. J. Biol. Chem.* **262:** 6877.

Baker, T.A., K. Sekimizu, B.E. Funnell, and A. Kornberg. 1986. Extensive unwinding of the plasmid template during staged enzymatic initiation of DNA replication from the origin of the *E. coli* chromosomes. *Cell* **45:** 53.

Fuller, R.S., B.E. Funnell, and A. Kornberg. 1984. The dnaA protein complex with the *E. coli* chromosomal replication origin (*oriC*) and other DNA sites. *Cell* **38:** 889.

Funnell, B.E., T.A. Baker, and A. Kornberg. 1986. Complete enzymatic replication of plasmids containing the origin of the *Escherichia coli* chromosome. *J. Biol. Chem.* **261:** 5616.

———. 1987. *In vitro* assembly of a prepriming complex at the origin of the *Escherichia coli* chromosome. *J. Biol. Chem.* **262:** 10327.

Kaguni, J.M. and A. Kornberg. 1984. Replication initiated at the origin (*oriC*) of the *E. coli* chromosome reconstituted with purified enzymes. *Cell* **38:** 183.

Kornberg, A., T.A. Baker, L.L. Bertsch, D. Bramhill, B.E. Funnell, R.S. Laskin, H. Maki, S. Maki, K. Sekimizu, and E. Wahle. 1987. Enzymatic studies of replication of *oriC* plasmids. *UCLA Symp. Mol. Cell. Biol. New Ser.* **47:** 137.

McMacken, R., L. Silver, and C. Georgopoulos. 1987. DNA replication. In Escherichia coli *and* Salmonella typhimurium *cellular and molecular biology* (ed. F.C. Neidhardt et al.), vol. 1, p. 564. American Society for Microbiology, Washington, D.C.

Ogawa, T., T.A. Baker, A. van der Ende, and A. Kornberg. 1985. Initiation of enzymatic replication at the origin of the *Escherichia coli* chromosome: Contributions of RNA polymerase and primase. *Proc. Natl. Acad. Sci.* **82:** 3562.

Sekimizu, K., D. Bramhill, and A. Kornberg. 1987. ATP activates dnaA protein in initiating replication of plasmids bearing the origin of the *E. coli* chromosome. *Cell* **50:** 259.

von Meyenburg, K. and F.G. Hansen. 1987. Regulation of chromosome replication. In Escherichia coli *and* Salmonella typhimurium *cellular and molecular biology* (ed. F.C. Neidhardt et al.), vol. 2, p. 1555. American Society for Microbiology, Washington, D.C.

Zyskind, J.W., J.M. Cleary, W.S. Brusilow, N.E. Harding, and D.W. Smith. 1983. Chromosomal replication origin from the marine bacterium *Vibrio harveyi* functions in *Escherichia coli*: *oriC* consensus sequence. *Proc. Natl. Acad. Sci.* **80:** 1164.

Reconstitution of Purified Protein Systems for the Initiation and Regulation of Bacteriophage λ DNA Replication

R. McMacken, K. Mensa-Wilmot, C. Alfano, R. Seaby,
K. Carroll, B. Gomes, and K. Stephens
Department of Biochemistry, The Johns Hopkins University,
School of Hygiene and Public Health, Baltimore, Maryland 21205

We have established an in vitro system, composed of nine highly purified bacteriophage λ and *Escherichia coli* proteins, that specifically replicates supercoiled plasmid templates bearing the λ replication origin (*ori*λ). The complete system is composed of three groups of proteins: the viral-encoded initiator proteins (the λ O and P proteins), the *E. coli* replication fork propagation machinery (single-stranded DNA binding protein, dnaB helicase, dnaG primase, DNA polymerase III holoenzyme, and DNA gyrase), and two bacterial heat shock proteins (dnaJ and dnaK proteins). DNA replication in this system is initiated at or near *ori*λ and proceeds unidirectionally rightward through θ-structure intermediates, ultimately yielding a pair of intertwined daughter circles as the final product. Studies of the early steps in the initiation process revealed that a series of nucleoprotein structures are formed at *ori*λ prior to RNA priming and DNA synthesis. In striking contrast to the situation in vivo, initiation of λ DNA replication in vitro does not require "transcriptional activation" of the origin region by *E. coli* RNA polymerase. We have found that the dependence of λ DNA replication in vitro on transcription can be restored by supplementation of the purified protein replication system with the histonelike HU protein of *E. coli*.

Following more than two decades of genetic and biochemical studies, many of the fundamental features of the replication of bacteriophage λ chromosomes have been revealed (for review, see Furth and Wickner 1983). The known characteristics of λ DNA replication suggest that enzymological studies of this process will provide useful mechanistic models for the initiation of DNA replication at eukaryotic chromosomal replication origins. For example, replication of the SV40 genome shares several of the characteristics of the early circle-to-circle phase of λ DNA replication. Replication of both viral genomes is initiated at a unique origin sequence that is recognized by a viral-encoded initiator protein, and in each case replication proceeds in a bidirectional fashion through θ-structure intermediates, generating multiply-intertwined daughter molecules that are resolved into unit length circles by the action of DNA topoisomerases. Additionally, both λ and SV40 have evolved mechanisms for recruiting cellular replication proteins that perform the RNA priming and DNA elongation steps during the replication of infecting viral genomes. Another common property of λ and SV40 DNA replication is the linkage that exists in vivo between transcription and viral DNA replication. In the case of λ, initiation of DNA replication depends on the action of cellular transcription machinery at or near *ori*λ (Dove et al. 1969, 1971). Likewise, optimal initiation of SV40 DNA replication apparently depends on the presence of proteins that interact with the SV40 early promoter or with transcription enhancer sequences located near the viral origin (for review, see DePamphilis et al. 1987).

To study the molecular events that occur in the initiation and regulation of bacteriophage λ DNA replication, we and others have developed crude soluble systems that can support the specific replication of supercoiled plasmid templates (*ori*λ plasmids) that contain a cloned λ replication origin (Anderl and Klein 1982; Tsurimoto and Matsubara 1982; Wold et al. 1982). The properties of DNA synthesis in this crude enzyme system indicate that both the initiation and regulation of λ DNA replication occur in a physiological manner. Initiation of λ DNA replication depends on the addition of the two λ replication proteins, the products of the phage *O* and *P* genes, and on the presence of a partially purified *E. coli* protein fraction. Replication of *ori*λ plasmid DNA is initiated in a bidirectional fashion at or near the cloned λ replication origin (Tsurimoto and Matsubara 1982; M. Wold and R. McMacken, unpubl.). Initiation of λ DNA replication in the crude system, as in vivo, requires transcription. Furthermore, addition of purified λ cl repressor to the soluble system blocks DNA replication directly, apparently by inhibiting transcription required for activating the initiation process (McMacken et al. 1983).

The crude λ DNA replication system also supports the conversion of single-stranded circular DNA templates to a duplex form (LeBowitz and McMacken 1984). Although DNA chain initiation in this reaction occurs nonspecifically, it does depend on the λ O and P initiators and on several *E. coli* proteins that are known to participate in λ DNA replication in vivo (LeBowitz and McMacken 1984; LeBowitz et al. 1985). The required host proteins include proteins that act in the propagation of

25

E. coli replication forks (dnaB protein, dnaG primase, single-stranded DNA binding protein [SSB], and DNA polymerase III holoenzyme) and proteins that function in the cellular heat shock response (dnaJ and dnaK proteins).

More recently, we have established a reconstituted enzyme system, composed of these eight phage and bacterial proteins, that supports the replication of single-stranded DNA templates (LeBowitz et al. 1985). An analysis of DNA chain initiation in this process, which we have named the λ SS replication reaction, indicated that the overall rate-limiting step involves the assembly of an activated form of the *E. coli* dnaB protein on SSB-coated DNA. Formation of this nucleoprotein structure depends on the presence of the λ O and P initiator proteins and the dnaJ and dnaK heat shock proteins. Once assembled on the template strand, the dnaB protein apparently migrates in a processive fashion along the SSB-coated DNA chain, serving as locus for the synthesis by primase of one or more RNA primers (LeBowitz et al. 1985). The properties of dnaB protein function in this reaction and in the replication of φX174 viral DNA (McMacken et al. 1977) led to the discovery that the dnaB protein is a DNA helicase (LeBowitz and McMacken 1986). Since the dnaB protein was long known to function in the propagation of *E. coli* replication forks (Kornberg 1980), this finding suggests that the dnaB protein serves as the primary replicative DNA helicase during the replication of the *E. coli* and λ chromosomes.

Guided by the properties of the λ SS replication reaction, we have recently reconstituted a purified protein system that will specifically replicate supercoiled DNA templates that contain a λ replication origin. In this report, we will summarize our initial studies of the biochemical properties of this system.

Materials and Methods

Plasmids

The template utilized for initiation of λ DNA replication was the *ori*λ plasmid pRLM4. Plasmid pRLM5 is nearly identical to plasmid pRLM4, except that it contains the replication origin of lambdoid phage 82 instead of *ori*λ. The construction and maps of plasmids pRLM4 and pRLM5 have been described previously (Wold et al. 1982). The duplex replicative form (RF) of phage M13*oriC*26 contains the replication origin of *E. coli* (Fuller et al. 1981).

Replication proteins

Purification and specific activities of the λ O and P proteins and the *E. coli* dnaB, dnaJ, primase (dnaG protein), SSB, and DNA polymerase III holoenzyme proteins have been described previously (LeBowitz et al. 1985). *E. coli* RNA polymerase (Fr. VI, 170 units/mg) was purified from bacterial strain Q13 (*rna, pnp*-13) by the method of Burgess and Jendrisak (1975), as modified by Lowe et al. (1979).

E. coli DNA gyrase subunits A (Fr. V, 7×10^6 units/mg) and B (Fr. VI, 6×10^5 units/mg) were purified from bacterial strains RW1053/pMK90 and RW1053/pMK47, respectively, by modifications of the procedures of Mizuuchi et al. (1984). gyrA subunit was purified through the Polymin P fractionation step as described (Mizuuchi et al. 1984), concentrated by $(NH_4)_2SO_4$ precipitation, and then applied to a linear 15–35% (v/v) glycerol gradient prepared in 50 mM Tris-HCl, 0.2 M KCl, 1 mM EDTA, and 5 mM dithiothreitol (DTT). Following centrifugation at 4°C for 38 hours at 38,000 rpm in a Beckman SW41 rotor, 0.3-ml fractions were collected from the bottom. Fractions containing gyrA subunit at a concentration of at least 50% of the concentration of gyrA in the peak fraction (as assayed in the reconstituted *ori*λ plasmid replication assay) were frozen in liquid N_2 and stored at −70°C.

gyrB subunit was purified as described (Mizuuchi et al. 1984) through the hydroxylapatite chromatography step, except that the order of the DEAE-Sephacel and the heparin-agarose chromatography steps were reversed. gyrB in the peak fractions from the hydroxylapatite column was concentrated by $(NH_4)_2SO_4$ precipitation and further purified by sedimentation in a glycerol gradient as described above for the gyrA subunit.

The *E. coli* dnaK protein (Fr. V, 8.2×10^3 units/mg) was purified to homogeneity from strain B178/pMOB45*dnaK*⁺ by modifications of a published protocol (Zylicz and Georgopoulos 1984).

Purified HU protein, the generous gift of C. Gualerzi (Losso et al. 1986), was supplied as individual preparations of homogeneous α and β subunits (proteins NS-2 and NS-1, respectively). Unless stated otherwise, native HU protein was reconstituted for each experiment by mixing equimolar amounts of the α and β polypeptide chains together.

Assay of *ori*λ plasmid DNA replication in vitro

The standard reaction mixture (30 μl) was modified from that used in the crude soluble in vitro replication system (Wold et al. 1982) and contained the following components: HEPES/KOH (pH 7.6) 40 mM; magnesium acetate, 11 mM; ATP, 4 mM; dATP, dCTP, and dGTP, each 180 μM; dTTP, 80 μM, with [*methyl*-³H]dTTP at 100–150 cpm per pmol of total deoxynucleotide; bovine serum albumin (BSA), 50 μg per ml; negatively supercoiled DNA (pRLM4 DNA), 215 ng; λ O protein, 195 ng; λ P protein, 100 ng; dnaB protein, 175 ng; SSB, 540 ng; dnaJ protein, 50 ng; dnaK protein, 3 μg; primase, 100 ng; DNA polymerase III holoenzyme, 80 ng; DNA gyrase A subunit, 230 ng; DNA gyrase B subunit, 240 ng. Reaction mixtures were assembled at 0°C and incubated for 30 minutes at 30°C, unless stated otherwise. DNA synthesis was measured by determining the level of incorporation of labeled deoxynucleotide into acid insoluble material, which was collected on glass fiber filters (Whatman 934-AH) and counted in a liquid scintillation spectrometer.

Electron microscopy

Reactions to be analyzed by electron microscopy were terminated by the addition of sodium dodecyl sulfate to 0.3% and subsequently filtered through a 0.7-ml Bio-Gel A-15m agarose column equilibrated in 0.01 M Tris-HCl (pH 8.0). Fractions (30 μl) containing void volume material were pooled and 20-μl portions were supplemented with 0.1 volume of 10 × core buffer (0.5 M Tris-HCl, 0.1 M MgCl$_2$, 10 mM DTT, 1 mg/ml BSA) containing an appropriate level of NaCl, and digested with *Hin*dIII or *Bam*HI restriction endonucleases for 60 minutes at 37°C. DNA molecules were spread for electron microscopy by a drop method (Delain and Brack 1974) according to a protocol suggested by Dr. J. Griffith of the University of North Carolina. A 100 μl drop containing DNA, cytochrome *c*, and formamide was prepared on a parafilm sheet and touched to a parlodion-coated grid after an appropriate interval. Grids were stained with uranyl acetate, rotary shadowed with platinum/paladium on a Denton (DV-502) high vacuum evaporator and examined with a Jeol Jem-100s electron microscope.

Results and Discussion

A multienzyme system for the initiation of λ DNA replication

We have extensively purified nine λ and *E. coli* replication proteins that, based on published genetic studies, should be essential for the replication of *ori*λ plasmid DNA. These proteins include the two phage initiators, the λ O and P replication proteins, as well as seven proteins from the bacterial host, namely, SSB, the dnaB, dnaJ, and dnaK proteins, primase, DNA polymerase III holoenzyme, and DNA gyrase. Each purified protein is judged to be at least 70% pure, and in most instances greater than 90% pure, as evidenced by electrophoretic analysis of the individual proteins in a SDS-polyacrylamide gel (Fig. 1).

Extensive DNA synthesis was obtained when a mixture of these purified proteins was incubated with *ori*λ plasmid DNA (pRLM4) in the presence of ATP and dNTPs (Table 1). With the exception of DNA gyrase, each of the purified proteins is required for initiation of DNA replication on the *ori*λ template. Omission of any of these proteins from the reaction mixture results in at least tenfold reduction in the level of DNA synthesis. Limited DNA synthesis is obtained on negatively supercoiled templates in the absence of DNA gyrase (Table 1). Such DNA synthesis is confined to regions surrounding the λ replication origin (R. Seaby and R. McMacken, unpubl.). DNA synthesis in this reconstituted λ DNA replication system requires the presence of ATP, but does not depend on either polyvinyl alcohol or an ATP-regenerating system, two components that are essential for *ori*λ DNA replication in the crude in vitro system (Wold et al. 1982). Finally, linearized pRLM4 plasmid DNA is not an effective template in this multienzyme

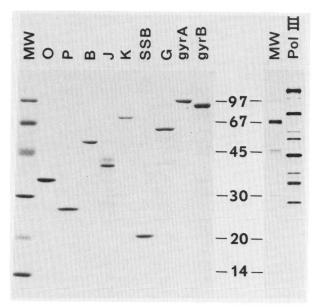

Figure 1 Analysis of purified λ and *E. coli* replication proteins by polyacrylamide gel electrophoresis. (*Left*) A sample (5–12 μg) of each protein required for the initiation of λ DNA replication in vitro was electrophoresed through a 10–20% polyacrylamide gradient gel in the presence of sodium dodecyl sulfate. Polypeptide bands were visualized by staining with Coomassie blue. (*Right*) DNA polymerase III holoenzyme (560 ng) was electrophoresed through a polyacrylamide gradient gel and the separated polypeptide bands were visualized by silver staining.

system (Table 1). This latter finding suggests that initiation of λ DNA replication depends on the presence of negative superhelicity in the template DNA.

Table 1 Requirements for the Reconstitution of *ori*λ Plasmid DNA Replication with Purified Proteins

Component omitted or added	DNA synthesis (pmol)
None	311
−λ O protein	8
−λ P protein	13
−dnaB protein	6
−dnaJ protein	30
−dnaK protein	7
−SSB	10
−dnaG primase	19
−DNA polymerase III holoenzyme	18
−DNA gyrase[a]	50
−ATP	16
+Polyvinyl alcohol (7% wt/vol)	320
+Creatine phosphate and kinase[b]	305
None[c]	16

The standard *ori*λ plasmid replication reaction was carried out as described in Materials and Methods, except that the individual components were omitted or added as indicated.

[a]Coumermycin was present at 50 μM.

[b]Creatine phosphate and creatine kinase were added at 43.2 mM and 100 μg/ml, respectively.

[c]The *ori*λ plasmid template had been linearized by digestion with *Hin*dIII at a site located 1.4 kb from *ori*λ.

Template specificity of the multienzyme replication system

The template specificity of the reconstituted enzyme system was determined. Supercoiled plasmid templates containing the replication origins of λ, lambdoid phage 82, phage M13 (replicative form origin), and *E. coli* (*oriC*) were individually incubated in the standard reaction mixture. Replication of the template containing *ori*λ was extensive, yet no measurable DNA synthesis was observed on any of the other DNA templates (Table 2). The absence of *E. coli* RNA polymerase from the standard multienzyme system contributed to the nearly complete specificity observed here. When the reconstituted system was supplemented with RNA polymerase and rNTPs, the specificity for DNA templates containing *ori*λ was significantly reduced (Table 2).

Products and directionality of *ori*λ plasmid DNA replication

As visualized by electron microscopy, the first replication intermediates detected after the initiation of DNA synthesis on *ori*λ plasmids were "early Cairns forms" (θ structures) that contain a single small replication bubble ranging in size from 5–20% of the length of the template (Fig. 2A). Branched circular intermediates of this type appear to be rapidly converted to larger θ structures (Fig. 2B) and "late Cairns forms," a figure-eight replication intermediate containing 100–700 bp of unreplicated parental DNA (Fig. 2C). Replication of the final region of parental DNA apparently occurs in the absence of significant topoisomerase action. This results in the production of catenated dimer daughter molecules that are multiply-intertwined (Fig. 2D). As analyzed by agarose gel electrophoresis and electron microscopy (data not shown), 70% of the final products of the in vitro system were catenated dimers, each composed of a pair of nicked circular plasmid monomers that were joined by one or two intertwinings (complete decatenation can be achieved by incubation of this product with DNA gyrase under conditions that are more optimal for DNA gyrase function [data not shown]). The majority of the remaining product molecules synthesized in the purified protein system were late Cairns forms.

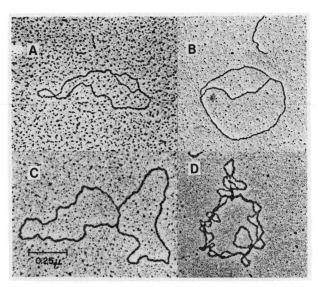

Figure 2 Electron micrographs of *ori*λ plasmid replication intermediates formed in the replication system reconstituted with purified proteins. (*A*) An early θ structure; (*B*) an intermediate θ structure; (*C*) a typical late Cairns intermediate; and (*D*) a multiply-intertwined catenated dimer.

Addition of appropriate levels of the chain terminating nucleotide dideoxythymidine triphosphate to the standard reaction mixture results in the accumulation of early replication intermediates (θ structures). Following linearization of these circular intermediates at a unique restriction site, the positions of the replication forks were mapped by electron microscopy. Digestion of the *ori*λ plasmid θ structures with *Hind*III yielded linear molecules containing a replication bubble (Fig. 3). The genetically defined λ replication origin is located asymmetrically at 0.26 genome length from one end of these molecules. After alignment, the left branch point on slightly more than half of the molecules mapped, within experimental error, at the *ori*λ sequence present on the plasmid template (Fig. 3). In the remaining molecules the left branch point mapped 200–900 bp to the right of *ori*λ. This pattern is most consistent with a mechanism in which DNA synthesis is initiated at or near *ori*λ and proceeds unidirectionally rightward. The frequent rightward displacement from *ori*λ of the initial site of DNA

Table 2 Template Specificity of the Reconstituted λ Replication System in the Presence and Absence of Transcription

Template DNA	Origin type	DNA synthesis (pmol)	
		−RNA polymerase	+RNA polymerase
pRLM4	λ	480	306
pRLM5	phage 82	2	92
M13*oriC*26	*E. coli*	0	20
M13mp8 RF	M13 RF	0	74

Reactions were carried out as described in Materials and Methods for the reconstitution assay for *ori*λ plasmid DNA replication, except that the added template DNA (215 ng) was varied as indicated. Where specified, the minimal enzyme system for λ DNA replication was supplemented with RNA polymerase (1.6 μg) and with CTP, GTP, and UTP (each at 500 μM).

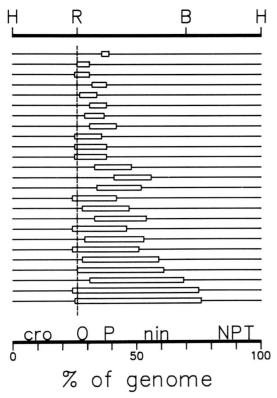

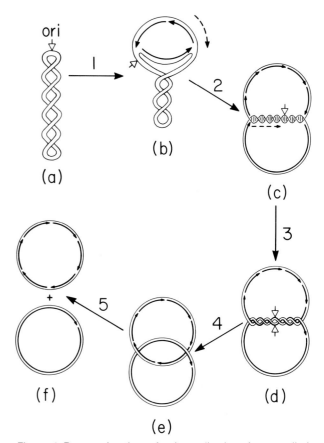

Figure 3 Replication initiates near *ori*λ and proceeds unidirectionally rightward. DNA replication was initiated at *ori*λ in the purified protein system for λ DNA replication (Materials and Methods) except that the system contained 6–25 μM 2',3'-dideoxythymidine 5'-triphosphate. Plasmid DNA molecules were isolated and converted into linear forms by digestion with *Hind*III restriction endonuclease. The linearized molecules were examined by electron microscopy and the branched molecules were photographed and measured. The branched molecules are aligned with the shortest unreplicated segment to the left. Replication bubbles are represented by open boxes. A partial restriction map of the 6.15-kb pRLM4 *ori*λ plasmid template is shown at the top (H, *Hind*III; R, *Eco*RI; B, *Bam*HI). A partial genetic map of this plasmid is shown at the bottom (NPT, the gene coding for neomycin phosphotransferase II; *nin*, a portion of the λ genome situated between phage genes *P* and *Q*). The genetically defined λ replication origin is located 15–160 bp to the left of the vertical dashed line.

Figure 4 Proposed pathway for the replication of supercoiled *ori*λ plasmids in the system reconstituted with purified proteins. See text for details.

synthesis may reflect the capacity of the prepriming replication machinery to migrate unidirectionally rightward after it is assembled at *ori*λ (see below).

A scheme for the replication of *ori*λ plasmids in the nine-protein system is depicted in Figure 4. Replication is initiated at or near the *ori*λ sequence present on the negatively supercoiled plasmid template (a) and proceeds (step 1) unidirectionally rightward through θ structure intermediates (b). Replication fork propagation continues (step 2), generating a late Cairns form (c) in which several hundred bp of parental DNA remain unreplicated. Replication of the last stretch of parental DNA (step 3) produces a multiply-intertwined, catenated dimer (d). DNA gyrase acts (steps 4 and 5) to decatenate the intertwined daughter molecules, yielding a pair of monomeric daughter circles (f).

Isolation and characterization of nucleoprotein prepriming complexes formed at *ori*λ

In collaboration with Mark Dodson and Harrison Echols, we have used electron microscopy to examine the molecular events that occur during the initiation of λ DNA replication in the purified protein system (Dodson et al. 1985, 1986). These studies have identified three separate nucleoprotein structures that are assembled in succession at *ori*λ during this process. First the λ O initiator specifically binds to a quartet of repeating sequences present at *ori*λ and forms a nucleosome-like structure, termed an O-some, in which the origin DNA appears to be wrapped in a specific manner (Dodson et al. 1985). This nucleoprotein structure serves as the foundation for the assembly of an even larger complex (Dodson et al. 1985), one that also contains the λ P replication protein and the *E. coli* dnaB helicase (McMacken et al. 1987; C. Alfano et al., unpubl.). The helicase activity of the dnaB protein is not expressed at this stage of the initiation reaction, presumably because the dnaB protein is firmly tethered by protein interactions to the origin complex.

Addition of ATP, SSB, and the dnaJ and dnaK heat shock proteins to the *ori*λ-O-P-dnaB structure, however, results in the localized unwinding of the DNA in the region immediately to the right of the λ replication origin present on the supercoiled plasmid substrate (Dodson et al. 1986). Binding of SSB to displaced single-stranded DNA chains, apparently created by the helicase activity of dnaB protein, stabilizes the unwound structure. In the absence of DNA topoisomerases, this unwinding is limited to approximately 800–1300 bp. We presume that, in the complete λ replication system, primase and DNA polymerase III are targeted to act on a partially unwound nucleoprotein structure. Although DNA gyrase function is not required for initiation of λ DNA replication on a negatively supercoiled template, its action is required for the extensive unwinding that accompanies complete replication of the plasmid template.

We have examined which of the various nucleoprotein complexes formed at *ori*λ prior to priming are physiological intermediates in the initiation of λ DNA replication. To address this problem, we first separated, using agarose gel filtration chromatography, each of the nucleoprotein structures from the unbound proteins used in the assembly reactions. Each isolated nucleoprotein structure was then incubated under replication conditions with a mixture of all those proteins required for λ DNA replication that had not been present during the assembly of that particular structure. If the plasmid DNA in a nucleoprotein assembly was efficiently replicated under these conditions, then we presumed that the nucleoprotein structure is a bona fide intermediate in the initiation of λ DNA replication in vitro. Using this guideline, we have previously demonstrated that the λ O-some and the *ori*λ-O-P-dnaB structures are physiological replication intermediates (McMacken et al. 1987).

More recently, we have found that the dnaJ protein specifically binds to the *ori*λ–O-P-dnaB structure and that the assembly containing the dnaJ protein is physiologically active (C. Alfano and R. McMacken, unpubl.). In contrast, to date, we have not been able to isolate functional nucleoprotein structures that contain the *dnaK* protein, nor have we succeeded in isolating a partially unwound DNA molecule in an active form. The latter structures, which apparently are formed by dnaB helicase-mediated unwinding in the absence of DNA topoisomerase action, are believed to be highly positively supercoiled. Increasing positive superhelicity of the template DNA impedes further unwinding by the dnaB helicase and, concomitantly, may stimulate the release of helicase molecules from the unwound structures. Such behavior may account for our inability to isolate the unwound structures in a functional state.

The availability of antibodies specifically directed against each of the proteins required for λ DNA replication permitted us to utilize a sensitive immunoblotting technique to identify the protein components of isolated nucleoprotein prepriming complexes formed at *ori*λ. Replication proteins were incubated with supercoiled *ori*λ plasmid DNA and then cross-linked with glutaraldehyde. Portions of the treated incubation mixtures were electrophoresed in each of multiple neutral agarose gels.

One gel was stained with ethidium bromide and visualized under ultraviolet illumination to identify the positions of plasmid DNA bands and of protein–DNA complexes. With the remaining gels, the proteins present in the nucleoprotein structures were transferred by electroelution to nitrocellulose sheets and identified by standard Western blotting analysis. Using this protocol, we have demonstrated that the larger, asymmetric structure (Dodson et al. 1986) formed at *ori*λ in the presence of the λ O and P proteins and the *E. coli* dnaB helicase is composed of each of these three proteins (McMacken et al. 1987).

We have initiated similar experiments aimed at identifying the protein components of the unwound structures formed at *ori*λ that were first observed by electron microscopy (Dodson et al. 1986). Since the observed unwinding appears to be initiated in response to the action of the dnaK heat shock protein on an *ori*λ-O-P-dnaB-dnaJ structure, we have examined how dnaK protein function affects the nature of prepriming nucleoprotein structures. In the experiment depicted in Figure 5, *ori*λ plasmid DNA was mixed with the λ O and P initiators and the *E. coli* SSB, dnaB, and dnaJ proteins. This mixture was divided into two portions, and dnaK protein was added to one of the portions. Following incubation of the proteins and DNA at 30°C to allow

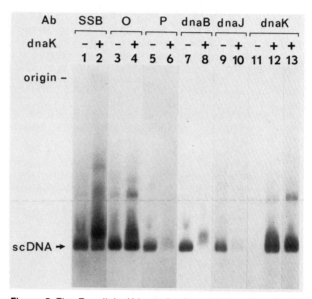

Figure 5 The *E. coli* dnaK heat shock protein functions in the rearrangement of prepriming nucleoprotein structures formed at *ori*λ. Plasmid pRLM4 DNA (*ori*λ) was incubated in the presence of ATP with SSB, O, P, dnaB, and dnaJ proteins (lanes *1, 3, 5, 7, 9,* and *11*) or with the same set of proteins and dnaK protein (lanes *2, 4, 6, 8, 10,* and *12*). The *ori*λ plasmid DNA applied to lane *13* was incubated with SSB, O, P, dnaB, and dnaK proteins. Nucleoprotein complexes were fixed with glutaraldehyde and resolved by electrophoresis in agarose. The proteins present in each nucleoprotein structure were identified using antibodies specifically directed against each required replication protein, as described in the text. The band position of protein-free, negatively supercoiled template DNA (scDNA) is indicated. (Reprinted, with permission, from McMacken et al. 1987.)

assembly of prepriming nucleoprotein structures, the structures were fixed with glutaraldehyde and analyzed by the immunodetection approach described above.

In the absence of one of the required heat shock proteins, a nucleoprotein structure is assembled on the oriλ plasmid template. This complex migrates just behind protein-free oriλ plasmid supercoils during electrophoresis in agarose (Fig. 5). The protein components of this complex, as detected by specific antibodies, are the bacteriophage λ O and P initiators and the E. coli dnaB, dnaJ, dnaK, and SSB proteins (Fig. 5, lanes 3, 5, 7, 9, 13, and 1, respectively). Formation of a nucleoprotein complex containing these proteins is highly specific. In the absence of O protein, neither the λ P protein nor the bacterial dnaB, dnaJ, and dnaK proteins bind to oriλ plasmid DNA (data not shown). SSB, in contrast, binds nonspecifically to a variety of negatively supercoiled DNA templates.

When both the dnaJ and dnaK heat shock proteins were included in the prepriming incubation mixture, at least two new types of nucleoprotein structures were formed. One of these structures, which appeared to contain 20–30% of the input template DNA (C. Alfano and R. McMacken, unpubl.), migrated more slowly during electrophoresis than the oriλ-O-P-dnaB complex. Immunological analysis of this complex (Fig. 5) indicated that it contained large quantities of SSB. We presume, therefore, that this slowly migrating species is similar or identical to the partially unwound structures observed by electron microscopy (Dodson et al. 1986). Detectable quantities of the λ O protein and the E. coli dnaB helicase were also associated with the putative unwound structure (Fig. 5). Although this species may have contained some dnaK protein, little, if any, λ P protein or E. coli dnaJ protein was associated with this structure.

The second new nucleoprotein species formed on oriλ DNA in the presence of the complete prepriming system migrated at the same rate during electrophoresis as the starting oriλ-O-P-dnaB-dnaJ complex. This species contained more than 50% of the template DNA (C. Alfano and R. McMacken, unpubl.), yet had little or no associated λ P protein, E. coli dnaB helicase, or dnaJ heat shock protein (Fig. 5). Except for the presence of dnaK protein, this new nucleoprotein structure appears to be similar to the O-some.

Taken together, the available data suggest the following scheme for the prepriming steps during the initiation of DNA replication at oriλ. The λ O protein binds to the repeating sequences at oriλ to form an O-some. The second viral initiator, the λ P protein, initiates the recruitment of the host elongation machinery by binding tightly to the bacterial dnaB helicase to form a protein complex. This complex associates with the O-some, and a nucleoprotein structure containing the O, P, and dnaB proteins is subsequently assembled at oriλ. The dnaB helicase, however, is apparently maintained in an inert form in this prepriming intermediate. Activation of the suppressed dnaB helicase activity, which permits localized unwinding of the plasmid DNA adjacent to oriλ, is

one consequence of the action of the host dnaJ and dnaK heat shock proteins on the O-P-dnaB structure. Binding of the dnaJ protein to this nucleoprotein structure may initiate this process, perhaps by creating an appropriate substrate for the action of the dnaK heat shock protein. A partial disassembly of the protein complex at oriλ, accompanied by the removal of a significant portion of the λ P and E. coli dnaJ proteins, stimulates the latent helicase activity of the dnaB protein and results in unwinding of the duplex DNA near oriλ on a portion of the template DNA molecules. We presume that early during the unwinding reaction on a bacteriophage λ chromosome in vivo the bacterial dnaG primase interacts with the moving dnaB helicase to synthesize the first primer for initiating λ DNA replication.

It is interesting that the action of the dnaK heat shock proteins on the oriλ-O-P-dnaB-dnaJ prepriming structure apparently results, in the majority of the events, in the release of most of the bound P, dnaB, and dnaJ polypeptides. Thus, besides activating the forward pathway toward DNA unwinding, priming, and replication, the heat shock proteins also promote a partial reversal of the multistep assembly reaction that has taken place at oriλ. This disassembly process is clearly not permanent, however, since nearly all of the oriλ template molecules added to the in vitro protein system are ultimately replicated. It is apparent that following disassembly of the prepriming complex, the replication proteins function once again to reassemble precursor nucleoprotein structures, a portion of which, as described earlier, are converted into unwound structures by the action of the dnaJ and dnaK heat shock proteins.

Transcriptional activation of bacteriophage λ DNA replication

One of the most thoroughly documented features of λ DNA replication in vivo is the strong dependence of the initiation process on transcription of the viral origin region by the host RNA polymerase (Dove et al. 1969, 1971). This requirement is also seen in vitro in crude soluble systems that support the replication of oriλ plasmids (Tsurimoto and Matsubara 1982; Wold et al. 1982; McMacken et al. 1983; Yamamoto et al. 1987). Surprisingly, however, RNA polymerase is not required for the initiation of λ DNA replication in the in vitro system we reconstituted with nine purified proteins (Table 1). It is unlikely that significant levels of RNA polymerase contaminate the purified protein system. Addition of rifampicin, a specific inhibitor of E. coli RNA polymerase, to the system had no effect on the rate or level of λ DNA replication (McMacken et al. 1987). Moreover, supplementation of the minimal λ replication system with RNA polymerase did not stimulate λ replication and, in fact, reduced the origin specificity of the reaction (Table 2).

We presume, from the results presented above, that the nine-protein system without added RNA polymerase initiates λ DNA replication in a relatively physiological manner. One possibility to account for the discrepancy between the in vivo results and those presented here, in regard to the requirement for RNA polymerase action to observe λ DNA replication, is that RNA polymerase does not act directly in the initiation of λ DNA replication in vivo. For example, it is possible that RNA polymerase acts to counteract the effect of some bacterial factor that acts directly to block the initiation of λ DNA replication. Such an inhibitor undoubtedly would not be present in the more recently developed λ replication system that is reconstituted with highly purified proteins.

Our initial exploration of this possibility confirmed that partially purified protein fractions from *E. coli* contained an inhibitor that hindered replication of *ori*λ plasmid DNA in the nine-protein system. Additionally, we found that the inhibitory effect of this factor could largely be obviated by supplementation of the purified protein system with RNA polymerase and rNTPs (K. Mensa-Wilmot, unpubl.). The inhibitory protein was purified to near homogeneity and characterized. By several criteria, including size and antibody cross-reactivity, the purified inhibitor appears to be identical to *E. coli* protein HU. HU protein, a small, basic histonelike protein that forms nucleosomal structures on duplex DNA, has been identified as one of the major components of the bacterial nucleoid.

The identification of the purified λ replication inhibitor as HU protein is strengthened by the demonstration that a preparation of homogeneous HU protein also was a potent inhibitor of the initiation of DNA replication at *ori*λ in the reconstituted multiprotein system (Fig. 6). When the reconstituted system for *ori*λ plasmid replication contained inhibitory levels of HU protein, the capacity of the system to initiate λ DNA replication could be restored by further supplementation of the system with *E. coli* RNA polymerase and rNTPs (Table 3). It is reassuring that in the presence of both HU protein and RNA polymerase, *ori*λ plasmid DNA replication (1) still depended on the presence of both of the λ O and P

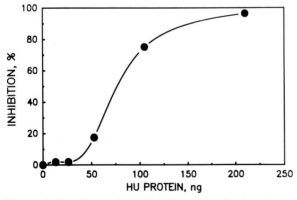

Figure 6 *E. coli* protein HU inhibits the replication of *ori*λ plasmids in the replication system reconstituted with purified proteins. Purified HU protein was added, as indicated, to 215 ng of *ori*λ plasmid DNA and incubated for 10 min at 30°C. The mixture was then supplemented with each of the nine proteins required for λ DNA replication in vitro (see Materials and Methods), incubated for an additional 30 min at 30°C, and analyzed for the production of acid-insoluble radioactivity.

Table 3 RNA Polymerase Transcription Counteracts the Inhibitory Effect of HU Protein on *ori*λ DNA Replication

Component omitted or added	DNA synthesis (pmol)
None	340
−λ O protein	3
−λ P protein	0
−RNA polymerase	41
+Rifampicin	50
−HU protein	310

The standard *ori*λ replication assay mixture (Materials and Methods) was supplemented with HU protein (100 ng), RNA polymerase (1.6 μg), and CTP, GTP, and UTP (each at 500 μM). Rifampicin, where indicated, was present at 20 μg/ml.

initiators and (2) was still sensitive to the inhibitory effect of rifampicin on transcription. Thus, an eleven-protein system, reconstituted with HU protein and RNA polymerase plus nine viral and bacterial replication proteins, is capable of supporting the transcriptional activation and initiation of λ DNA replication in an apparently physiological manner.

The precise molecular mechanism by which HU protein blocks the initiation of λ DNA replication has not been determined. In our initial attempts to study this problem, we have found that once the dnaB helicase has been assembled into an O-P-dnaB structure at *ori*λ, subsequent steps in the initiation pathway are relatively resistant to a challenge with HU protein (K. Mensa-Wilmot and R. McMacken, unpubl.). Thus, once λ DNA replication is initiated, HU protein does not impede replication fork propagation. Instead, HU protein exerts its inhibitory effect by interfering with the initiation of λ DNA replication, possibly by blocking the conversion of an O-some into a functional *ori*λ-O-P-dnaB prepriming complex.

The initiation of DNA replication at the *E. coli* chromosomal origin in vivo and in crude in vitro systems also appears to depend on transcriptional events in the *oriC* region (Lark 1972; Fuller et al. 1981). As with λ DNA replication, initiation of DNA synthesis at *oriC* does not require RNA polymerase action when the system is reconstituted with purified proteins (Ogawa et al. 1985; Funnell et al. 1986). The similarity between the λ and *oriC* systems extends further. HU protein at high concentrations blocks *oriC* DNA replication, except when actively transcribing RNA polymerase is present (Ogawa et al. 1985). But, at lower concentrations, in contrast to its behavior in the λ system, HU protein actually stimulates in vitro *oriC* DNA replication several fold (Dixon and Kornberg 1984). The molecular mechanisms responsible for these HU-mediated effects on the initiation of *oriC* DNA replication remain to be resolved.

The possible involvement of a histonelike protein and transcription in the regulation of the initiation of both λ and *E. coli* DNA replication could be relevant to the mechanisms involved in the regulation of DNA replication in higher eukaryotes. An analysis of the sequence requirements for the replication of several DNA tumor viruses, including SV40, polyomavirus, Epstein-Barr virus, and bovine papillomavirus, have led to the identification of promoter and / or transcriptional enhancer elements, located near each respective viral origin, that play important roles in the replication process in vivo (de Villiers et al. 1984; Reisman and Sugden 1985; DeLucia et al. 1986; Hertz and Mertz 1986; Lee-Chen and Woodworth-Gutai 1986; Li et al. 1986; Lusky and Botchan 1986; DePamphilis et al. 1987). Cell-free systems capable of supporting the initiation of SV40 and polyomavirus DNA replication have been established (Li and Kelly 1984; Murakami et al. 1986). Unfortunately, however, the absence of any requirement for transcription or for viral promoter or enhancer sequences to obtain optimal DNA replication in vitro precludes a molecular analysis of the roles of transcription or transcription factors in such replication systems. Until these eukaryotic viral replication systems are reconstituted with a set of purified proteins, it may be difficult to determine if the required transcription factors act directly in the replication process. But considering the close analogy with the results reported here for bacteriophage λ DNA replication, we conjecture that transcription factors and enhancer binding proteins may act in eukaryotic replication in an indirect fashion, perhaps by neutralizing the inhibitory effect of chromatin structure on the formation or activity of nucleoprotein structures required for the initiation of viral DNA replication.

References

Anderl, A. and A. Klein. 1982. Replication of lambda *dv* DNA *in vitro. Nucleic Acids Res.* **10**: 1733.

Burgess, R.R. and J.J. Jendrisak. 1975. A procedure for the rapid, large-scale purification of *Escherichia coli* DNA-dependent RNA polymerase involving Polymin P precipitation and DNA-cellulose chromatography. *Biochemistry* **14**: 4634.

Delain, E. and C. Brack. 1974. Visualization des molecules d'acides nucleiques. II. Microversion de la technique de diffusion. *J. Microsc.* **21**: 217.

DeLucia, A.I., S. Deb, K. Partin, and P. Tegtmeyer. 1986. Functional interactions of the simian virus 40 core origin of replication with flanking regulatory sequences. *J. Virol.* **57**: 138.

DePamphilis, M.L., R.S. Decker, M. Yamaguchi, R. Possenti, D.O. Wirak, R. Perona, and J.A. Hassell. 1987. Transcriptional elements and their role in activation of simian virus 40 and polyoma virus origins of replication. *UCLA Symp. Mol. Cell. Biol. New Ser.* **47**: 367.

de Villiers, J., W. Schaffner, C. Tyndall, S. Lupton, and R. Kamen. 1984. Polyoma virus DNA replication requires an enhancer. *Nature* **312**: 242.

Dixon, N.E. and A. Kornberg. 1984. Protein HU in the enzymatic replication of the chromosomal origin of *Escherichia coli. Proc. Natl. Acad. Sci.* **81**: 424.

Dodson, M., J. Roberts, R. McMacken, and H. Echols. 1985. Specialized nucleoprotein structures at the origin of replication of bacteriophage λ: Complexes with λ O protein and with λ O, λ P, and *Escherichia coli dnaB* proteins. *Proc. Natl. Acad. Sci.* **82**: 4678.

Dodson, M., H. Echols, S. Wickner, C. Alfano, K. Mensa-Wilmot, B. Gomes, J. LeBowitz, J.D. Roberts, and R. McMacken. 1986. Specialized nucleoprotein structures at

the origin of replication of bacteriophage λ: Localized unwinding of duplex DNA by a six-protein reaction. *Proc. Natl. Acad. Sci.* **83**: 7638.

Dove, W.F., H. Inokuchi, and W.F. Stevens. 1971. Replication control in phage lambda. In *The bacteriophage lambda* (ed. A.D. Hershey), p. 747. Cold Spring Harbor Laboratory, Cold Spring Harbor, New York.

Dove, W.F., E. Hargrove, M. Ohashi, F. Haugli, and A. Guha. 1969. Replicator activation in lambda. *Jpn. J. Genet.* (suppl.) **44**: 11.

Fuller, R.S., J.M. Kaguni, and A. Kornberg. 1981. Enzymatic replication of the origin of the *Escherichia coli* chromosome. *Proc. Natl. Acad. Sci.* **78**: 7370.

Funnell, B.E., T.A. Baker, and A. Kornberg. 1986. Complete enzymatic replication of plasmids containing the origin of the *Escherichia coli* chromosome. *J. Biol. Chem.* **261**: 5616.

Furth, M.E. and S.H. Wickner. 1983. Lambda DNA replication. In *Lambda II* (ed. R.W. Hendrix et al.), p. 145. Cold Spring Harbor Laboratory, Cold Spring Harbor, New York.

Hertz, G.Z. and J.E. Mertz. 1986. Bidirectional promoter elements of simian virus 40 are required for efficient replication of the viral DNA. *Mol. Cell. Biol.* **6**: 3513.

Kornberg, A. 1980. *DNA replication*. W.H. Freeman, San Francisco.

Lark, K.G. 1972. Evidence for the direct involvement of RNA in the initiation of DNA replication in *Escherichia coli* 15T. *J. Mol. Biol.* **64**: 47.

LeBowitz, J.H. and R. McMacken. 1984. The bacteriophage λ O and P protein initiators promote the replication of single-stranded DNA. *Nucleic Acids Res.* **12**: 3069.

———. 1986. The *Escherichia coli dnaB* replication protein is a DNA helicase. *J. Biol. Chem.* **261**: 4738.

LeBowitz, J.H., M. Zylicz, C. Georgopoulos, and R. McMacken. 1985. Initiation of DNA replication on single-stranded DNA templates catalyzed by purified replication proteins of bacteriophage λ and *Escherichia coli. Proc. Natl. Acad. Sci.* **82**: 3988.

Lee-Chen, G.-J. and M. Woodworth-Gutai. 1986. Simian virus 40 DNA replication: Functional organization of regulatory elements. *Mol. Cell. Biol.* **6**: 3086.

Li, J.J. and T.J. Kelly. 1984. Simian virus 40 DNA replication *in vitro. Proc. Natl. Acad. Sci.* **81**: 6973.

Li, J.J., K.W.C. Peden, R.A.F. Dixon, and T. Kelly. 1986. Functional organization of the simian virus 40 origin of DNA replication. *Mol. Cell. Biol.* **6**: 1117.

Losso, M.A., R.T. Pawlik, M.A. Canonaco, and C.O. Gualerzi. 1986. Proteins from the prokaryotic nucleoid. A protein-protein cross-linking study on the quaternary structure of *Escherichia coli* DNA-binding protein NS (HU). *Eur. J. Biochem.* **155**: 27.

Lowe, P.A., D.A. Hager, and R.R. Burgess. 1979. Purification and properties of the sigma subunit of *Escherichia coli* DNA-dependent RNA polymerase. *Biochemistry* **18**: 1344.

Lusky, M. and M.R. Botchan. 1986. Transient replication of bovine papilloma virus type 1 plasmids: *cis* and *trans* requirements. *Proc. Natl. Acad. Sci.* **83**: 3609.

McMacken, R., K. Ueda, and A. Kornberg. 1977. Migration of *Escherichia coli dnaB* protein on the template DNA strand as a mechanism in initiating DNA replication. *Proc. Natl. Acad. Sci.* **74**: 4190.

McMacken, R., C. Alfano, B. Gomes, J.H. LeBowitz, K. Mensa-Wilmot, J.D. Roberts, and M. Wold. 1987. Biochemical mechanisms in the initiation of bacteriophage λ DNA replication. *UCLA Symp. Mol. Cell. Biol. New Ser.* **47**: 227.

McMacken, R., M.S. Wold, J.H. LeBowitz, J.D. Roberts, J.B. Mallory, J.A.K. Wilkinson, and C. Loehrlein. 1983. Initiation of DNA replication *in vitro* promoted by the bacteriophage λ O and P replication proteins. *UCLA Symp. Mol. Cell. Biol. New Ser.* **10**: 819.

Mizuuchi, K., M. Mizuuchi, M.H. O'Dea, and M. Gellert. 1984. Cloning and simplified purification of *Escherichia coli* DNA gyrase A and B proteins. *J. Biol. Chem.* **259**: 9199.

Murakami, T., T. Eki, M. Yamada, C. Prives, and J. Hurwitz.

1986. Species-specific *in vitro* synthesis of DNA containing the polyoma virus origin of replication. *Proc. Natl. Acad. Sci.* **83**: 6347.

Ogawa, T., T.A. Baker, A. van der Ende, and A. Kornberg. 1985. Initiation of enzymatic replication at the origin of the *Escherichia coli* chromosome: Contributions of RNA polymerase and primase. *Proc. Natl. Acad. Sci.* **82**: 3562.

Reisman, D. and B. Sugden. 1985. A putative origin of replication of plasmids derived from Epstein-Barr virus is composed of two *cis*-acting components. *Mol. Cell Biol.* **6**: 3838.

Tsurimoto, T. and K. Matsubara. 1982. Replication of λ *dv* plasmid *in vitro* promoted by purified λ O and P proteins. *Proc. Natl. Acad. Sci.* **79**: 7639.

Wold, M.S., J.B. Mallory, J.D. Roberts, J.H. LeBowitz, and R. McMacken. 1982. Initiation of bacteriophage λ DNA replication *in vitro* with purified λ replication proteins. *Proc. Natl. Acad. Sci.* **79**: 6176.

Yamamoto, T., J. McIntyre, S.M. Sell, C. Georgopoulos, D. Skowyra, and M. Zylicz. 1987. Enzymology of the pre-priming steps in λ*dv* DNA replication *in vitro*. *J. Biol. Chem.* **262**: 7996.

Zylicz, M. and C. Georgopoulos. 1984. Purification and properties of the *Escherichia coli dnaK* replication protein. *J. Biol. Chem.* **259**: 8820.

Coordination of Leading with Lagging Strand Synthesis by the Asymmetric Dimeric DNA Polymerase III Holoenzyme of *Escherichia coli*

C.S. McHenry, A.M. Flower, and J.R. Hawker, Jr.

Department of Biochemistry, Biophysics, and Genetics, University of Colorado
Health Sciences Center, Denver, Colorado 80262

The DNA polymerase III holoenzyme is the complex multisubunit enzyme responsible for the majority of replicative synthesis in *E. coli*. It contains two polymerase subunits and at least two copies of most of the auxiliary subunits. We have suggested previously that the two halves of this dimeric replicative complex interact to permit coordination of leading with lagging strand replication. The ability of the holoenzyme halves to communicate is derived from its being an allosteric enzyme. The holoenzyme also appears to function asymmetrically, consistent with the asymmetric functional requirements of leading strand versus lagging strand replication. Both the γ and the τ subunits of the holoenzyme are products of the *dna*ZX gene. The carboxy-terminal domain of τ contains a very basic region that is lacking from γ. Using specific monoclonal antibodies directed against only the τ subunit, we have demonstrated that τ and γ reside within the same holoenzyme assemblies. The existence of these two related proteins in the same dimeric complex may give rise to the proposed asymmetry.

The DNA polymerase III holoenzyme is the complex multisubunit DNA polymerase that is responsible for the synthesis of the majority of the *E. coli* chromosome. It contains at least seven different subunits, α, τ, γ, β, δ, ε, and θ, ranging from 130,000 to 10,000 daltons (for review, see McHenry 1985, 1988). This enzyme contains a catalytic core, termed DNA polymerase III, that is capable of efficiently filling gaps in activated DNA (Kornberg and Gefter 1972; Livingston et al. 1975) The core is composed of the catalytic α subunit (*dna*E gene product), ε, which contains the proofreading exonuclease (*mut*D gene product), and θ, a subunit without an identified structural gene or function (McHenry and Crow 1979; Spanos et al. 1981; Scheuermann and Echols 1984).

The polymerase III core is inert, without the remaining auxiliary subunits, on natural chromosomal templates such as that provided by the bacteriophage G4 (Godson 1974; Bouché et al. 1975). Much attention has been paid to these auxiliary subunits, since they confer on the core polymerase those special properties that distinguish true replicative complexes from simpler DNA polymerases. The auxiliary subunits that have been established to date include β (*dna*N), τ and γ (both products of the *dna*ZX gene), and δ (Wickner and Hurwitz 1976; McHenry and Kornberg 1977; Hübscher and Kornberg 1980; Burgers et al. 1981; McHenry 1982; Kodaira et al. 1983; Mullin et al. 1983).

The addition of τ to DNA polymerase III forms DNA polymerase III′, causes the polymerase to dimerize, and increases its processivity sixfold (McHenry 1982; Fay et al. 1982). DNA polymerase III*, which also contains the γ and δ subunits plus additional components that are either subunits or tightly associated proteins, exhibits a processivity at least 20-fold greater than the core polymerase and gains the ability to interact with the *E. coli* single-stranded DNA-binding protein (Fay et al. 1982).

The most striking difference between the DNA polymerase III holoenzyme and simpler DNA polymerases is its ability to form a stable initiation complex with primed single-stranded DNA at the expense of ATP hydrolysis (Hurwitz and Wickner 1974; Wickner and Kornberg 1974; Johanson and McHenry 1980; Burgers and Kornberg 1982). These complexes show remarkable stability in comparison to the labile DNA polymerase III holoenzyme. Upon formation of initiation complexes, the β subunit becomes immersed such that elongation becomes resistant to the inhibitory action of anti-β IgG (Johanson and McHenry 1982). Upon addition of the required deoxynucleoside triphosphates, the complex can processively replicate an entire 5000-nucleotide G4 circle without ever dissociating (Fay et al. 1981). The stability of these complexes in vitro creates kinetic barriers with respect to the expected rate for cycling between Okazaki fragments during synthesis on the lagging strand of the *E. coli* replication fork. In this paper we report recent findings that influence our understanding of how the holoenzyme overcomes these difficulties at natural replication forks and how it may coordinate leading with lagging strand synthesis.

Experimental Procedures

Specificity of anti-τ IgG binding to holoenzyme subunits

DNA polymerase III holoenzyme was subjected to SDS polyacrylamide gel electrophoresis and detected by the

35

immunoblot method. Electrophoretic transfer of the resolved proteins from the gel to a nitrocellulose sheet
was conducted as described (Johanson and McHenry
1982), except that the urea treatment was omitted and
the transfer was conducted in 20% methanol. After
transfer, individual lanes were cut out for processing.
Lanes to be treated with antibody were blocked (1 hr,
43°C) with BSA-saline. Strips were then treated with
antibody (5 ml each, 1.5 hr, 23°C) and then washed in
0.05% Tween 20 in Tris-saline (3 times in 30 min).
Strips were then treated with peroxidase-conjugated
goat antimouse IgG in BSA-saline (1.5 hr, 23°C). The
strips were washed in Tris-saline (3 times—10 min/
wash) and visualized by incubation with *o*-dianisidine as
described (Johanson and McHenry 1982). β and α were
detected with specific antibodies as described previously (Johanson and McHenry 1982; Wu et al. 1984).
Holoenzyme (10 μg) was stained to provide markers for
subunit positions. For detection of τ, holoenzyme (7 μg)
was treated with anti-τ IgG$_{123\text{-}28}$. The antibody solutions
were used at concentrations of ∼ 1000 units/ml.

Protein homology searches

The protein homology analysis was performed using the
Intelligenetics "IFind" program to select proteins with
regions of similarity to the *dna*ZX protein products. The
search was performed using a 20-amino-acid window
and a gap penalty of 2. Selected proteins with the
highest scores were examined using the "Align" program of Intelligenetics. This program allows two proteins to be aligned in regions of maximum homology.
Alteration of the parameters in this analysis (window,
gap penalty) allowed the alignments to be made either
looking for regions of high homology or for longer regions of less homology. The adenovirus E1B 55-kD and
9-kD proteins had the highest score of 10 from the IFind
search (completely random proteins usually score 2–4).
The alignment showed an 18-amino-acid stretch with
61% homology or a 25-amino-acid stretch with 64%.
The histone H1 from sea urchin had the second highest
IFind score (9) and had a 20-amino-acid stretch of 55%
homology. The area of homology could be lengthened to
123 amino acids, but the homology dropped to 28%.
The gene B protein from bacteriophage mu had an IFind
score of 8, and had an alignment of 25 amino acids with
48% homology. The ribosomal proteins all scored a 7
with IFind, and the alignment ranged from 7 amino acids
with 100% homology (50S L7/L12) to 120 amino acids
with 23% homology (30S S1). The three polymerases
also scored 7 on IFind, and they range from 11-amino-
acid stretches with 73% homology (simian AIDS virus)
to 54 amino acids with 30% homology (also simian
AIDS). The HBV polymerase and *E. coli* RNA polymerase were intermediate to these two values. The ATPase
and the 32-kD protease from cowpea mosaic virus also
both scored 7. The 32-kD protease was 67% homologous over a 12-amino-acid stretch or 38% over 40
amino acids, whereas the ATPase was 80% homologous over 10 amino acids or 36% over 36 amino acids.

Immunoprecipitation of τ and associated proteins

^{125}I-holoenzyme (4.7 × 10^5 cpm, 1.7 μg in 20 μl) was
added to 20 μl *E. coli* cell lysate (20 mg/ml protein)
diluted to 100 μl total volume by the addition of immunoprecipitation buffer before the addition of anti-τ$_{123\text{-}28}$
IgG (10 μg, 1 hr, 4°C). The solutions were then treated
with goat antimouse affinity gel (20 μl of 50% suspension, gentle vortexing, 1 hr, 4°C), then centrifuged (10
sec), and the pellets washed (4 times with Tris-saline;
the first 3 washes contained 0.05% NP-40). Pellets
were resuspended in SDS gel buffer, boiled (10 min),
clarified by centrifugation, and subjected to SDS polyacrylamide gel electrophoresis. Bands were detected by
autoradiography. Holoenzyme was radioactively labeled
by the Iodo-bead method (Markwell 1982) with modifications. The enzyme was dialyzed to remove dithiothreitol
(DTT), which interferes with the iodination reaction.
Iodination was only permitted to proceed for 6 minutes
and DTT was added back immediately to preserve
holoenzyme structure. The labeled enzyme was purified
by gel filtration.

ATPγS experiments with holoenzyme

The support and dissociation of complexes with ATPγS
was as described (Johanson and McHenry 1984).
ATPγS binding was measured by nitrocellulose filtration
as described (Oberfelder and McHenry 1987).

Results and Discussion

Kinetic barrier for holoenzyme recycling

Starting from a preformed initiation complex, the DNA
polymerase III holoenzyme can replicate an entire 5000-
nucleotide G4 molecule in under 15 seconds without
dissociating; yet it remains stably bound for over 40
minutes to the completed RFII product (Johanson and
McHenry 1982). The stability of these complexes varies
somewhat with reaction conditions, the presence of
excess exogenous subunits, and the enzyme preparation
used, but it remains a severe problem relative to the
cellular requirements for polymerase cycling during
Okazaki fragment synthesis. One Okazaki fragment
must be synthesized approximately every second at the
E. coli replication fork. Our in vitro elongation rate
approximates the required elongation velocity, but the
slow recycling from a completed strand to the next
primed template presents a severe kinetic barrier.

Taking a lead from the proposal of Bruce Alberts and
colleagues that originated from the T4 replication system (Sinha et al. 1980), it occurred to us that modification of their theory could provide a solution to the
recycling problem of the DNA polymerase III holoenzyme. We had demonstrated previously that the more
complex forms of DNA polymerase III were dimeric
(McHenry 1982). We reasoned that perhaps the release
of the lagging strand polymerase upon completion of the
synthesis of an Okazaki fragment might be facilitated by
the leading strand polymerase being in a productive
elongation conformation. Such information could be

communicated by allosteric interactions between polymerase halves. Support for this model came from an investigation of the effect of an ATP analog on initiation complex formation.

DNA polymerase III holoenzyme functions as an asymmetric dimer

We have gained further insight into the functioning of the dimeric holoenzyme by the use of ATPγS (Johanson and McHenry 1984). This analog substitutes for ATP in the formation of initiation complexes between the DNA polymerase III holoenzyme and primed DNA. It is hydrolyzed, like ATP, to ADP during and subsequent to initiation complex formation. Initiation complexes formed in the presence of ATPγS are indistinguishable from those formed with ATP, both by their resistance to antibody directed against the β subunit of the DNA polymerase III holoenzyme and by the ability of the complex to elongate without any further nucleotide-mediated activation.

However, the most striking result to come from these studies was the twofold difference in the maximal extent to which ATP and ATPγS can support initiation complex formation. ATPγS will only support one-half as much complex formation as ATP (Fig. 1). This effect is also seen upon reversal of the reaction. If maximal initiation complex is formed in the presence of ATP and isolated free of nucleotide by gel filtration, the resulting complex can be 50% dissociated by ATPγS (Fig. 2). ATP causes no more dissociation than the addition of a buffer control. The extent of dissociation does not vary with ATPγS concentration once sufficient ATPγS has been added to saturate its binding site on holoenzyme (1 μM). Thus, this is not an equilibrium effect that can be pushed to complete dissociation by ATPγS. This argues for two distinct populations of holoenzyme in solution: one that can form initiation complexes in the presence of ATPγS

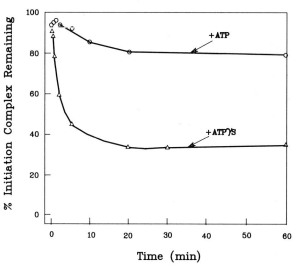

Figure 2 ATPγS induces the dissociation of one-half of the initiation complexes formed in the presence of ATP.

and one that only forms complexes via ATP and is dissociated by ATPγS.

Keeping in mind our notions concerning the role of a dimeric holoenzyme in the natural replicative reaction, we proposed that these data were not indicative of two distinct holoenzyme populations in solution, but of a difference between the two halves of a dimeric holoenzyme (Johanson and McHenry 1984; McHenry 1985). This asymmetry could have a structural basis. One-half of the holoenzyme could contain a different subunit composition or a covalent modification. Alternatively, this asymmetry could be induced by allosteric interactions between the two halves of the enzyme when bound to the replication fork. In any case, this asymmetry could be used to solve the problems imposed by the asymmetry in functional requirements of polymerases at the replication fork. The leading strand polymerase, once bound to its template, need not dissociate until the chromosome is completely replicated, a process that takes 40 minutes in *E. coli*. The lagging strand polymerase, however, must synthesize an Okazaki fragment each second and recycle to the next primer synthesized at the replication fork. An asymmetric dimeric DNA polymerase might have a higher affinity for the template in the leading strand half and a diminished affinity that would permit efficient recycling in the lagging half. We are also aware that this geometry might permit the dimeric holoenzyme to associate with the priming apparatus, the helicases, and other enzymes and cellular structures associated with the replication fork in one large replicative complex.

Cooperative interactions between the two holoenzyme halves

The asymmetric dimer model makes several testable predictions. One is that the two halves are not merely stuck to one another but that they are functionally interacting. This was tested by examination of the binding of

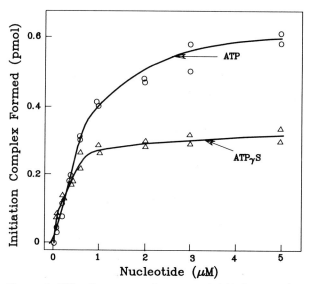

Figure 1 ATP will support twice as much initiation complex formation between the DNA polymerase III holoenzyme and primed DNA as ATPγS.

ATP and ATPγS, the two nucleotides that will support initiation complex formation. Both bind with strong positive cooperativity. Instead of the straight line obtained for a Scatchard plot in a noncooperative system, the plot exhibits a maximum, a feature diagnostic of positive cooperativity (Fig. 3). From the position of the maximum or from the slope of a Hill plot, we calculate a Hill coefficient of approximately 1.5, indicating strong positive cooperative interactions between the ATP-binding sites of this cooperative enzyme.

That the two halves of the holoenzyme are communicating has implications not only for the mechanism of cycling on the lagging strand, but for the coordination of leading with lagging strand synthesis. Perhaps this communication is useful in causing the opposing polymerase to stall if a polymerase encounters a barrier such as a chemically damaged region or an annealed oligonucleotide or a tightly associated protein. Causing the opposing polymerase to pause for a few seconds until a barrier is removed would prevent it from extending thousands of nucleotides beyond the blocked polymerase. Extensive single-stranded structures created by noncoordinated polymerases should be disadvantageous to the cell for multiple reasons. They would create packaging problems for the cell, they would exceed the cell's capacity to provide adequate single-stranded DNA-binding protein, and they would be exposed to cellular nucleases. A scission in a single-stranded region would present serious repair problems, since the ends would not be held near one another as in double-stranded DNA. A coordinated dimeric polymerase could bypass most of these difficulties. In addition to the allosteric basis for holoenzyme asymmetry, recent data suggest a structural basis as well.

Relationship between τ and γ

The *dna*ZX gene encodes two proteins of approximately 75,000 and 52,000 daltons. Both of these proteins contain common sequences, since identical peptides are generated by partial proteolysis. The smaller protein was known from previous work to be the γ subunit of the DNA polymerase III holoenzyme (Wickner and Hurwitz 1976; Hübscher and Kornberg 1980). It is encoded by the amino-terminal portion of the *dna*ZX gene. The larger protein was proposed to be τ, based on its electrophoretic mobility (Kodaira et al. 1983). We confirmed this conclusion by using a τ-specific monoclonal antibody to demonstrate that τ is overproduced by strains carrying the *dna*ZX gene on a plasmid and to specifically immunoprecipitate the 75,000-dalton product of *dna*ZX. The specificity of the anti-τ monoclonal is demonstrated in Figure 4. Despite the majority of the γ sequence being contained within τ, this antibody reacts exclusively with τ. The antibody must be directed toward

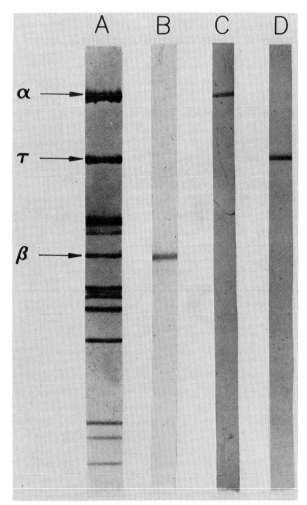

Figure 4 Specificity of monoclonal antibody directed against τ. All four lanes contain the resolved holoenzyme subunits. (Lane *A*) Stained holoenzyme permitting visualization of all bands. (Lanes *B*, *C*, *D*) Immunostaining of the β, α, and τ subunits, respectively, with specific antibodies.

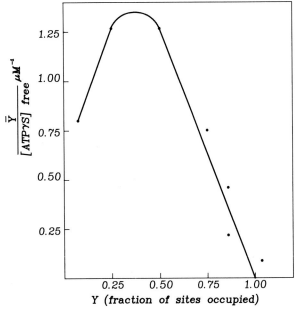

Figure 3 The dimeric DNA polymerase III holoenzyme is an allosteric enzyme. Cooperative binding of ATPγS.

a sequence within the unique carboxy-terminal domain of τ that is lacking from γ.

Sequencing of the *dna*ZX gene has indicated that it contains one continuous open reading frame encoding a protein of approximately 71,000 daltons (Flower and McHenry 1986; Yin et al. 1986). The mechanism by which γ arises from τ is uncertain. Proteolysis of τ to yield γ has been proposed (Kodaira et al. 1983; Mullin et al. 1983) If so, this cleavage must be tightly controlled to yield adequate γ for cellular needs without excessively diminishing the essential τ protein. Alternatively, the generation of γ could be translationally regulated through a frameshifting mechanism (McHenry 1988; A.M. Flower and C.S. McHenry, unpubl.).

From the sequence of τ, several homologies of potential significance with other proteins has been determined. Previously, a homology between τ and a conserved ATPase sequence was found (Yin et al. 1986). We have found more extensive homology in adjacent regions of the amino-terminal segment of τ with the major membrane ATPase of *E. coli* underscoring the relationship between these proteins (Fig. 5). The holoenzyme contains an ATPase that is essential for tightly clamping the holoenzyme on the template in processive form. Recently, a τ-β-galactosidase fusion protein has been shown to have feeble ATPase activity (Lee and Walker 1987). The putative ATPase site of τ overlaps with a region of homology with the bacteriophage mu gene B protein (Maxwell et al. 1987; Surette et al. 1987). The gene B protein, like γ, is involved in the ATP-dependent formation of a multiprotein complex with DNA (Surette et al. 1987). Additional homologies have also been found. Toward a more central segment, homology with the 32,000-dalton cowpea mosaic virus protease has been detected. This raises the possibility of an autoproteolytic mechanism being involved in the generation of γ from τ. Perhaps a τ-τ pair forms and one τ cleaves the other and inactivates its proteolytic activity guaranteeing a 1:1 ratio of the two proteins. The strongest homology was observed between τ and the adenovirus E1B 55-kD and 9-kD sequences. The region of homology falls within a variable region that has been postulated to be of importance for transformation by some strains of adenovirus (Dijkema et al. 1982). Toward the carboxy-terminal end that is unique to τ, we observe homology with a number of proteins that interact with nucleic acids. These include ribosomal proteins, RNA polymerases, and reverse transcriptases. The strongest homology in this zone is with histone H1 from sea urchin. This homology arises primarily from the content of lysines and alanines for the two proteins, but may suggest a tight DNA-binding domain within τ that is lacking in γ. This could have functional significance.

Both τ and γ are contained within the same holoenzyme assemblies

Treatment of DNA polymerase III holoenzyme with anti-τ IgG and secondary precipitating reagents permits it to be quantitatively removed from solution. Thus, we know that all active holoenzyme molecules contain τ. Examination of the immunoprecipitated subunits from radiolabeled holoenzyme indicated that roughly equivalent amounts of both γ and τ were precipitated (Fig. 6). Thus, γ and τ reside in the same holoenzyme assemblies. If proteolysis had been artifactual, one would

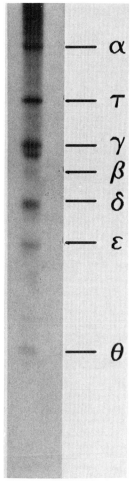

Figure 6 Immunoprecipitation of τ and associated proteins by monoclonal anti-τ IgG.

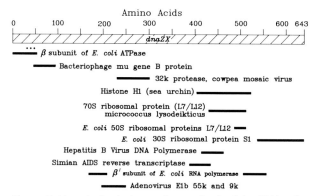

Figure 5 Homologies between the τ subunit of the DNA polymerase III holoenzyme and other proteins.

expect some subassemblies to contain only γ and others only τ.

The existence of the two related proteins within the same holoenzyme assembly may provide a basis for a structural difference between the two halves of the holoenzyme, in addition to the allosteric interactions we have observed, and may predetermine which half is the leading strand polymerase and which is the lagging strand half. The leading strand half may use the basic domain of τ to form a tight clamp on the DNA, and the lagging strand half might contain the analogous γ protein bound by similar molecular interactions with the other holoenzyme components. Perhaps the γ-driven complex is capable of more efficient cycling mediated in part by looser interactions with the DNA.

Since the purpose for coverage of this prokaryotic topic in a eukaryotic replication publication is to provide a basis for comparison, I should mention that in addition to the prokaryotic T4 system, suggestions pertaining to dimeric replicative complexes have been made in mammalian systems. Fisher and Korn (1979; Fisher et al. 1981) in their kinetic description of the human α polymerase reaction provided evidence for multiple DNA-binding sites, and Ottiger and Hübscher (1984) have made a proposal regarding distinguishable leading and lagging strand polymerases. Thus, the basic principles now being defined in prokaryotic systems may have broad applicability to all life forms.

Acknowledgments

This work was supported by grant MV-348 from the American Cancer Society and grant GM-36255 from the National Institutes of Health.

References

Bouché, J.P., K. Zechel, and A. Kornberg. 1975. *dna*G gene product: A rifampicin-resistant RNA polymerase initiates the conversion of a single-stranded coliphage DNA to its duplex replicative form. *J. Biol. Chem.* **250:** 5995.

Burgers, P.M.J. and A. Kornberg. 1982. ATP activation of DNA polymerase III holoenzyme of *Escherichia coli*: ATP dependent formation of an initiation complex with a primed template. *J. Biol. Chem.* **257:** 11468.

Burgers, P.M.J., A. Kornberg, and Y. Sakakibara. 1981. The *dna*N gene codes for the β subunit of DNA polymerase III holoenzyme of *Escherichia coli*. *Proc. Natl. Acad. Sci.* **78:** 5391.

Dijkema, R., B.M.H. Dekker, and H. van Ormondt. 1982. Gene organization of the transforming region of adenovirus type 7 DNA. *Gene* **18:** 143.

Fay, P.J., K.O. Johanson, and C.S. McHenry. 1981. Size classes of products synthesized processively by DNA polymerase III and DNA polymerase III holoenzyme of *Escherichia coli*. *J. Biol. Chem.* **256:** 976.

Fay, P.J., K.O. Johanson, C.S. McHenry, and R. Bambara. 1982. Size classes of products synthesized processively by 2 subassemblies of *Escherichia coli* DNA polymerase III holoenzyme. *J. Biol. Chem.* **257:** 5692.

Fisher, P.A. and D Korn. 1979. Enzymological characterization of KB cell DNA polymerase α. II. Specificity of the protein nucleic acid interaction. *J. Biol. Chem.* **254:** 11033.

Fisher, P.A., J.T. Chen, and D. Korn. 1981. Enzymological characterization of KB cell DNA polymerase α. Regulation of

template binding by nucleic acid base composition. *J. Biol. Chem.* **256:** 133.

Flower, A.M. and C. S. McHenry. 1986. The adjacent *dna*Z and *dna*X genes of *Escherichia coli* are contained within one continuous open reading frame. *Nucleic Acids Res.* **14:** 8091.

Godson, G.N. 1974. Evolution of φx174 isolation of four new φx-like phages and comparison with φx174. *Virology* **58:** 272.

Hübscher, U. and A. Kornberg. 1980. The *dna*Z protein, the γ subunit of DNA polymerase III holoenzyme of *Escherichia coli*. *J. Biol. Chem.* **255:** 11698.

Hurwitz, J. and S. Wickner. 1974. Involvement of 2 protein factors and ATP in in-vitro DNA synthesis catalyzed by DNA polymerase III of *Escherichia coli*. *Proc. Natl. Acad. Sci.* **71:** 6.

Johanson, K.O. and C.S. McHenry. 1980. Purification and characterization of the β subunit of the DNA polymerase III holoenzyme of *Escherichia coli*. *J. Biol. Chem.* **255:** 10984.

———. 1982. The β subunit of the DNA polymerase III holoenzyme becomes inaccessible to antibody after formation of an initiation complex with primed DNA. *J. Biol. Chem.* **257:** 12310.

———. 1984. Adenosine 5′-O-3-thio-triphosphate can support the formation of an initiation complex between the DNA polymerase III holoenzyme and primed DNA. *J. Biol. Chem.* **259:** 4589.

Kodaira, M., S.B. Biswas, and A. Kornberg. 1983. The *dna*X gene encodes the DNA polymerase III holoenzyme τ subunit precursor of the γ subunit the *dna*Z gene product. *Mol. Gen. Genet.* **192:** 80.

Kornberg, T. and M.L. Gefter. 1972. Deoxyribonucleic acid synthesis in cell-free extracts. *J. Biol. Chem.* **247:** 5369.

Lee, S.-H. and J.R. Walker. 1987. *Escherichia coli* dnaX product, the τ subunit of DNA polymerase III, is a multifunctional protein with single-stranded DNA-dependent ATPase activity. *Proc. Natl. Acad. Sci.* **84:** 2713.

Livingston, D.M., D.C. Hinkle, and C.C. Richardson. 1975. DNA Polymerase III of *Escherichia coli*: Purification and properties. *J. Biol. Chem.* **250:** 461.

Markwell, M. 1982. A new solid-state reagent to iodinate proteins. *Anal. Biochem.* **125:** 427.

Maxwell, A., R. Craigie, and K. Mizuuchi. 1987. B protein of bacteriophage Mu is an ATPase that preferentially stimulates intermolecular DNA strand transfer. *Proc. Natl. Acad. Sci.* **84:** 699.

McHenry, C. S. 1982. Purification and characterization of DNA polymerase III′: Identification of τ as a subunit of the DNA polymerase III holoenzyme. *J. Biol. Chem.* **257:** 2657.

———. 1985. DNA polymerase III holoenzyme of *Escherichia coli*: Components and function of a true replicative complex. *Mol. Cell. Biochem.* **66:** 71.

———. 1988. DNA polymerase III holoenzyme of *Escherichia coli*. *Annu. Rev. Biochem.* **57:** (in press).

McHenry, C.S. and W. Crow. 1979. DNA polymerase III of *Escherichia coli*: Purification and identification of subunits. *J. Biol. Chem.* **254:** 1748.

McHenry, C.S. and A. Kornberg. 1977. DNA polymerase III holoenzyme of *Escherichia coli*: Purification and resolution into subunits. *J. Biol. Chem.* **252:** 6478.

Mullin, D.A., C.L. Woldringh, J.M. Henson, and J. Walker. 1983. Cloning of the *Escherichia coli* dnaZX region and identification of its products. *Mol. Gen. Genet.* **192:** 73.

Oberfelder, R. and C.S. McHenry. 1987. Characterization of 2′,3′-trinitrophenyl-ATP as an inhibitor of ATP-dependent initiation complex formation between the DNA polymerase III holoenzyme and primed DNA. *J. Biol. Chem.* **262:** 4190.

Ottiger, H. and U. Hübscher. 1984. Mammalian DNA polymerase α holoenzyme with possible functions at the leading and lagging strand of the replication fork. *Proc. Natl. Acad. Sci.* **81:** 3993.

Scheuermann, R.H. and H. Echols. 1984. A separate editing exonuclease for DNA replication the ε subunit of *Escherichia* coli DNA polymerase III holoenzyme. *Proc. Natl. Acad. Sci.* **81:** 7747.

Sinha, N.K., C.F. Morris, and B.M. Alberts. 1980. Efficient in vitro replication of double-stranded DNA templates by a purified T4 bacteriophage replication system. *J. Biol. Chem.* **255:** 4290.

Spanos, A., S. Sedgwick, G.T. Yarranton, U. Hübscher, and G.R. Banks. 1981. Detection of the catalytic activities of DNA polymerases and their associated exonucleases following SDS-polyacrylamide gel electrophoresis. *Nucleic Acids Res.* **9:** 1825.

Surette, M.G., S.J. Buch, and G. Chaconas. 1987. Transpososomes: Stable protein-DNA complexes involved in the in vitro transposition of bacteriophage mu DNA. *Cell* **49:** 253.

Wickner, S. and J. Hurwitz. 1976. Involvement of *Escherichia coli dna*Z gene product in DNA elongation in vitro. *Proc. Natl. Acad. Sci.* **73:** 1053.

Wickner, W. and A. Kornberg. 1974. A holoenzyme form of DNA polymerase. III. Isolation and properties. *J. Biol. Chem.* **249:** 6244.

Wu, Y.H., M.A. Franden, J.R. Hawker, and C.S. McHenry. 1984. Monoclonal antibodies specific for the α subunit of the *Escherichia coli* DNA polymerase III holoenzyme. *J. Biol. Chem.* **259:** 12117.

Yin, K.-C., A. Blinkowa, and J.R. Walker. 1986. Nucleotide sequence of the *Escherichia coli* replication gene *dna*ZX. *Nucleic Acids Res.* **14:** 6541.

Herpes Simplex Virus DNA Replication: Identification of the Essential Genes and Their Products

P.D. Olivo and M.D. Challberg

Laboratory of Viral Diseases, National Institute of Allergy and Infectious Diseases,
National Institutes of Health, Bethesda, Maryland 20892

The herpes simplex virus (HSV) genome contains both *cis*- and *trans*-acting elements that are important in viral DNA replication. The *cis*-acting elements consist of three origins of replication: two copies of ori_S and one copy of ori_L. A method was previously developed (Challberg 1986) to identify all the essential *trans*-acting elements and has subsequently been used to identify seven HSV genes that are necessary for transient replication of plasmids containing ori_S or ori_L (Wu et al. 1988). The identification of these genes depended in part on the sequence data and analysis of McGeoch et al. (1988). Our extensive subcloning and deletion analyses are in total agreement with the sequence interpretation. In addition, antisera directed against peptides and fusion proteins, corresponding to the predicted gene products of several of these genes, recognize proteins of the predicted size in HSV-infected VERO cells. Two of these genes encode the viral DNA polymerase and single-stranded DNA-binding protein, which are known from conventional genetic evidence to be essential for viral DNA replication and likely to be directly involved in HSV DNA synthesis. We propose that the other five gene products are also directly involved in DNA replication.

Herpes simplex virus (HSV) shows increasing promise as a model system for studying eukaryotic DNA replication. This potential is related to several features of the HSV genome and life cycle, as well as to a number of recent developments in the field. HSV has a linear double-stranded DNA genome of approximately 150 kb, which has recently been entirely sequenced (McGeoch et al. 1988). It is an α herpesvirus that replicates rapidly during its lytic cycle, and it is thus easily propagated in tissue culture (Roizman and Batterson 1985). Little is known of the details of HSV DNA replication, but a number of salient features have emerged. HSV DNA replication occurs in the nucleus, where it is detectable within a few hours of infection and continues for up to 12 hours (for review, see Roizman and Batterson 1985). Replicative intermediates have been shown to lack termini, and thus consist of either circles or head-to-tail concatemers (Jacob and Roizman 1977; Jacob et al. 1979; Jongeneel and Bachenheimer 1981). On the basis of this, a rolling-circle mechanism of replication, similar to bacteriophage λ, has been proposed. Unit length genomes are subsequently generated by events closely linked to the packaging of DNA into virions.

As originally shown by structural studies of defective viral genomes, HSV contains *cis*-acting elements necessary for DNA replication (Spaete and Frenkel 1982; Vlasny and Frenkel 1982; Stow and McMonagle 1983). These consist of two related sequences: ori_L, found in the long unique region, and ori_S, occurring twice, one in each of the two inverted repeat regions flanking the short unique region. The finding that plasmids contain-ing either ori_L or ori_S are amplified when transfected into HSV-infected cells supports the view that these are origins of replication (Spaete and Frenkel 1982; Stow 1982; Stow and McMonagle 1983; Weller et al. 1985). However, there is as yet no proof that they are in fact sites of initiation of replication.

Genetic and biochemical studies have shown that the HSV genome also contains *trans*-acting elements in-volved in DNA replication. In fact, the available evidence suggests that the HSV genome probably codes for many enzymes with a role in DNA synthesis. For example, a variety of virus mutants have been isolated with lesions affecting viral DNA replication. Such mutants include members that fall into at least ten complementation groups (Hay et al. 1971; Chartrand et al. 1979; Chu et al. 1979; Preston 1979; Dixon and Schaffer 1980; Matz et al. 1983; Coen et al. 1984; Stow and Stow 1986; Sacks and Schaffer 1987). Biochemical studies also support the view that the HSV genome encodes many replication proteins. A number of DNA metabolism and synthesis enzymes unique to HSV-infected cells have been identified. These include a nuclease (Morrison and Keir 1968; Hay et al. 1971), a thymidine kinase (Kit and Dubbs 1963), a ribonucleotide reductase (Cohen 1972), a single strand-specific DNA-binding protein (DBP) (Bayliss et al. 1975), a DNA polymerase (pol) (Hay et al. 1971; Powell and Purifoy 1977), and recently an origin-specific DNA-binding protein (Elias et al. 1986). In several instances the genetic and biochemical approaches have been complementary; mutants with lesions that affect DNA replication have been identified

43

that map to the locations of the genes that code for known replication enzymes (Bayliss et al. 1975; Hay and Subak-Sharpe 1976; Chartrand et al. 1979; Conley et al. 1981; Weller et al. 1983; Coen et al. 1984; Preston et al. 1984; Gibbs et al. 1985; Quinn and McGeoch 1985; Moss 1986; S.K. Weller, pers. comm.).

Aware of the inherent limitations of biochemical and genetic studies, our laboratory took a different approach to the study of HSV DNA replication. Our approach is derived from the observation of others that plasmids containing ori_L or ori_S are replicated when transfected into HSV-infected cells. In addition, we have taken advantage of the infectious nature of HSV DNA, whereby the normal sequence of gene expression is set in motion in cells transfected with HSV DNA. Finally, this approach was made possible by the relatively simple organization of the HSV genome (e.g., intronless genes). These observations formed the basis of a transient replication assay in which we tested segments of HSV DNA for their ability to support replication of cotransfected origin-containing plasmid DNA. This enabled us to develop a simple complementation assay for identifying *trans*-acting genes required for HSV DNA replication (Challberg 1986) and ultimately to systematically locate all the HSV genes necessary for DNA replication (Wu et al. 1988).

Materials and Methods

Cells and virus
VERO cells were propagated in Eagle's minimal essential medium containing 10% fetal calf serum. The KOS strain of HSV-1 was used, and virus stocks were grown and assayed in VERO cells.

DNA isolation
HSV-1 DNA and plasmid DNA were isolated by standard methods as described previously (Challberg 1986).

Construction of recombinant plasmids
The fragment of viral DNA used to construct all recombinant plasmids used in this work was derived from the KOS strain of HSV-1. The restriction maps and arrangement of genes were deduced from sequence analyses of HSV-1 strain 17. Strain KOS and strain 17 are closely similar and every restriction site used was shown to be present in the cloned KOS DNA. Construction of plasmids containing HSV *Xba*I fragments was described previously, as was construction of pMC110, which contains ori_S (Challberg 1986). Subcloning was done by standard methods (Maniatis et al. 1982) using fragments derived from the *Xba*I clones and inserting them into the multiple cloning site of "Bluescribe," a 3.2-kb vector obtained from Vector Cloning Systems, San Diego, CA.

Unidirectional deletions of the *Bam*HI L fragment were constructed using *Exo*III and S1 nuclease according to the procedure of Henikoff (1984).

Assay for plasmid DNA replication
Plasmid DNA replication was assayed as described previously (Peden et al. 1980; Challberg 1986). Briefly, combinations of plasmid DNAs (0.5 μg each) were mixed and used to transfect monolayers of VERO cells by the calcium phosphate coprecipitation technique (Graham and van der Eb 1973). At 14–16 hours following transfection, the cells were lysed and total cellular DNA was isolated. The purified DNA was digested with *Eco*RI, *Hin*dIII, and *Dpn*I, and fractionated by agarose gel electrophoresis. The DNA in the gel was transferred to a nylon membrane and probed with ^{32}P-labeled pUC19 DNA.

Our standard assay for HSV origin-dependent DNA replication contained the following plasmids: pK1-2, encoding the immediate early protein, IE175; pMC122 (*Xba*I F), which contains *dbp*, *pol*, and ori_L; pSG25, which contains two copies of ori_S but no essential *trans*-acting genes; and pMC121 (*Xba*I C), pMC123 (*Xba*I E), and pMC124 (*Xba*I D), each of which contains at least one unidentified *trans*-acting gene. DNA replication was assayed by transfecting VERO cells with a mixture of these six plasmids and following the procedure described above. Under these conditions, ori_L-dependent replication gives rise to a *Dpn*I-resistant fragment of 2.7 kb derived from *Xba*I F, and ori_S-dependent replication gives rise to a *Dpn*I-resistant fragment of 4.6 kb derived from pSG25 (Challberg 1986).

Fusion proteins
Portions of the reading frame of the HSV replication genes were fused in frame to the *LacZ* reading frame in an expression vector containing the *lac* operon (pMLB series, kindly provided by M. Berman, Bionetics, Inc., Gaithersburg, MD). The fusion proteins were purified by affinity chromatography using a monoclonal antibody against β-galactosidase (Promega Biotec, Madison, WI).

Peptides
Carboxy or amino decapeptides were made commercially by Biosearch, San Rafael, CA. Following purification by gel filtration chromatography, the peptides were coupled to keyhole limpet hemocyanin (KLH) by standard techniques.

Antisera
New Zealand rabbits were immunized by a standard protocol with 20–50 μg fusion protein or with 0.5–1.0 mg of KLH-coupled peptide and boosted at least twice at biweekly intervals.

Immunoblotting
Extracts from VERO cells infected with HSV at 10–20 plaque forming units per cell were made at various times after infection using a standard triple detergent buffer. Extracts from the equivalent of 5×10^5 cells were elec-

trophoresed in 10% SDS-polyacrylamide gels and transferred electrophoretically to a nylon membrane (Gene Screen, Dupont, Wilmington, DE). After blocking nonspecific sites with 10% nonfat dry milk, the blots were incubated with antisera at various dilutions in phosphate-buffered saline (PBS), 0.3% Tween 20 for 1 hour at room temperature, washed with PBS, 0.3% Tween 20 and incubated with ^{125}I-labeled protein A (Amersham Corp., Arlington Heights, IL), washed, and the blot exposed to X-ray film.

Results

As a first step in locating essential replication genes, HSV-1 DNA was digested with various restriction enzymes to test whether the resulting fragments could supply the *trans*-acting functions required for HSV origin-specific replication of transfected plasmids. VERO cell monolayers were transfected with a mixture of the plasmid pMC110, containing ori_S, and HSV-1 DNA that had been digested to completion with a given enzyme. Among the several restriction enzymes tested, one enzyme, *Xba*I, was found that apparently does not cleave within an essential DNA replication gene. When HSV DNA was digested to completion with *Xba*I, the digestion products were found to be equivalent to intact HSV DNA at all concentrations tested in their ability to provide the *trans*-acting functions necessary to replicate pMC110, an ori_S-containing plasmid (Challberg 1986). Neither intact DNA nor *Xba*I-cleaved DNA supported the replication of a control plasmid lacking ori_S and ori_L.

The *Xba*I restriction fragments C, D, E, and F were then cloned into the plasmid vector pUC19. The locations of these fragments on the standard map of the HSV genome are shown in Figure 4 below. Two additional plasmids (pSG25 and pSG1) (Preston et al. 1984) provided the remainder of sequences not present in the four *Xba*I clones. A mixture of the six plasmids and pMC110, containing ori_S, was used to transfect VERO cells, and plasmid replication was assayed using the restriction enzyme *Dpn*I (Peden et al. 1980). It was found that these six plasmids can supply all of the functions needed for HSV origin-dependent replication (see Challberg 1986 and Fig. 1).

To determine which of the plasmids contain functions essential for DNA replication in this system, replication was assayed using mixtures in which individual plasmids were omitted. As shown in Figure 1, omission of the plasmids containing any of the four *Xba*I fragments (lanes 2, 3, 4, and 5) or *Eco*RI JK fragment (lane 6) completely eliminated plasmid DNA replication. Omission of pSG25 (lane 7) eliminated the 4.7-kb *Eco*RI/*Hind*III digestion product as expected, since this fragment is derived from replicated pSG25, which contains two copies of ori_S. Omission of pSG25 did not, however, decrease the amount of the 2.7-kb *Eco*RI/*Hind*III fragment derived from replicated pMC110, containing ori_S, and pMC122, containing ori_L. Therefore, each of

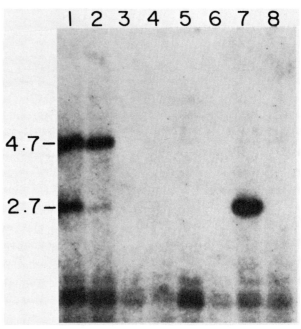

Figure 1 Identification of individual plasmids necessary for origin-dependent replication. VERO cells were transfected with pMC121 (*Xba*I C), pMC122 (*Xba*I F), pMC123 (*Xba*I E), pMC124 (*Xba*I D), pSG25 (*Eco*RI H), pSG1 (*Eco*RI JK), and pMC110 (ori_s) (lane 1) or with mixtures in which one of those plasmids was omitted. The plasmid omitted in each of the lanes is as follows: lane 2, pMC110; lane 3, pMC121; lane 4, pMC122; lane 5, pMC123; lane 6, pMC124; lane 7, pSG1; lane 8, pSG25. DNA from the transfected cells was digested with *Dpn*I, *Eco*RI, and *Hind*III and analyzed. The numbers at the left indicate the position and size (in kb) of markers run on the same gel. (Reprinted, with permission, from Challberg 1986.)

the six plasmids, except pSG25, contains at least one essential *trans*-acting replication function.

To locate the genes required for plasmid DNA replication in our assay, we used the following general strategy. *Xba*I C, *Xba*I D, *Xba*I E, or *Xba*I F was digested with one of a number of different restriction enzymes, and the resultant fragments were tested for their ability to substitute for the intact plasmid. Once we found a restriction enzyme that did not inactivate a plasmid, we cloned each of the fragments produced by that enzyme and tested the subclones, alone and in combinations, for their ability to supply the required function(s). This process was repeated until we obtained an active subclone containing a limited number of genes as deduced from DNA sequence analysis. Finally, plasmids containing single intact genes were constructed and tested in a similar fashion.

Our approach was facilitated by the simple organization of the HSV genome (i.e., intronless genes) and by the sequence data of McGeoch et al. (1988). The sequence analysis revealed intact HSV genes within each subclone that we found to be necessary for origin-dependent plasmid replication. As is always the case, however, the reliability of the sequence interpretation

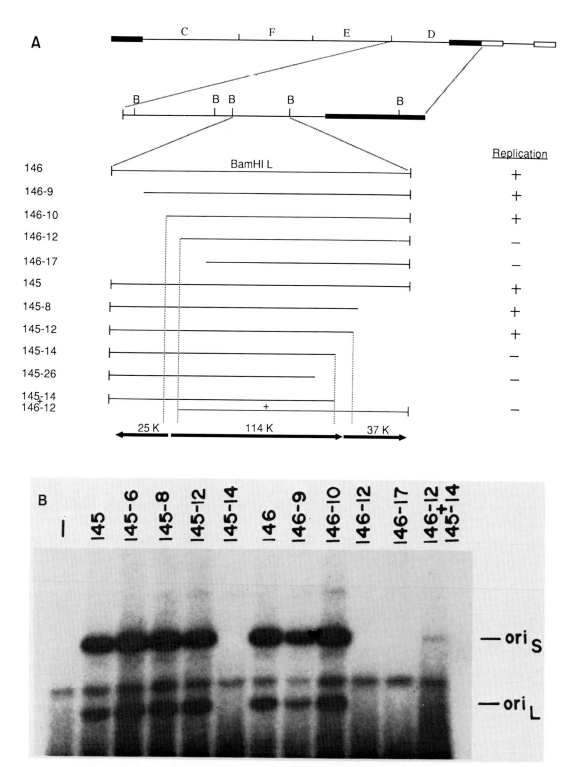

Figure 2 Deletion analysis of *Bam*HI L. (*A*) Diagrammatic representation of plasmids used to determine the location of the essential replication function in *Bam*HI L. The horizontal lines represent the HSV sequences contained in the indicated plasmid. The column headed "Replication" summarizes the results shown in *B*. The locations and sizes of the open reading frames predicted by the sequence of McGeoch et al. (1988) are shown at the bottom of the figure. (*B*) Replication assays of plasmids containing deletions in *Bam*HI L. VERO cells were transfected with 0.5 μg each of pMC121 (*Xba*I C), pMC122 (*Xba*I F), pMC123 (*Xba*I E), pK1-2 (IE175), pSG25, pSG1 (*Eco*RI JK), pKB-B (*Bam*HI B), and the plasmid(s) indicated at the top of each lane. The structure of each of the indicated plasmids is diagramed in *A*. *ori_S* and *ori_L* refer to the positions of *Eco*RI/*Hin*dIII-digested pSG25 and pMC122, respectively, which were run as markers on the same gel.

ultimately rests on corroboration with functional data. To our satisfaction, in all cases, our subcloning data were consistent with the sequence data; restriction enzymes that inactivated subclones were shown to interrupt genes identified independently by large scale DNA sequencing.

Our analysis of an essential subfragment of *Xba*I D illustrates how closely our subcloning data, involving careful deletion analysis, correlated with the DNA sequence data of McGeoch et al. (1988). Preliminary experiments showed that digestion of *Xba*I D with *Bam*HI did not reduce its ability to support origin-dependent DNA replication. We therefore cloned the fragments produced by *Bam*HI and tested them for their ability to substitute for *Xba*I D in a standard replication assay. These experiments revealed that there must be at least one essential replication gene within the subfragment of *Xba*I D named *Bam*HI L (see Fig. 2). To locate this gene(s), we constructed a series of nested deletions removing sequences from the left or right end of *Bam*HI L. Each of these deletions was tested for its ability to substitute for *Bam*HI L in the standard plasmid replication assay. The results of these experiments are shown in Figure 2B and summarized in Figure 2A. The plasmids 145-12 and 145-14 define a boundary of an essential replication function on the right side of *Bam*HI L to within about 300 bp. Similarly, the plasmids 146-10 and 146-12 define a boundary of an essential *trans*-acting element on the left side of *Bam*HI L. A combination of 146-12 and 145-14 did not reconstitute full activity (a weak signal can be seen that probably results from recombination between the two overlapping fragments; see Fig. 2A). We conclude that there is a single essential gene within *Bam*HI L, the boundaries of which lie within the pairs of dashed vertical lines in Figure 2A. The DNA sequence analysis of McGeoch et al. (1988) revealed three intact genes within *Bam*HI L. One of these genes (UL52), encoding a 114-kD protein, falls precisely within the boundaries of the essential replication function as determined by the deletion analysis. We believe that these data are strong evidence that the product of the UL52 gene is essential for origin-dependent plasmid replication.

Using the general approach outlined above, and shown in detail for *Bam*HI L, we have found that seven HSV-1 genes are each necessary for origin-dependent DNA replication. Included among these genes are two genes, *pol* and *dbp*, which genetic and biochemical data have shown to be essential for viral DNA replication. Moreover, these seven genes, together with three immediate early genes, are sufficient to support replication of origin-containing plasmids. Figure 3 shows the results of an experiment in which a mixture of ten plasmids, each containing one of the seven essential genes or one of the immediate genes, was cotransfected into VERO cells together with pKB-X, which contains ori_S but no intact HSV gene. This combination of plasmids supports the replication of pKB-X at a level only slightly lower than that seen with a mixture of the four cloned *Xba*I fragments and pK1-2. We conclude that the HSV genome

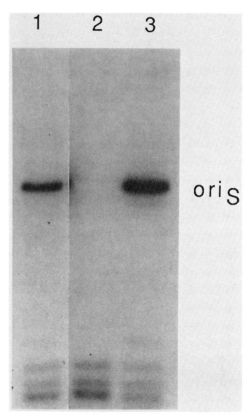

Figure 3 DNA replication supported by a combination of the seven essential replication genes and three immediate early genes. (Lane *1*) VERO cells were transfected with each of the following plasmids: pCW21 (UL5), pMC160-1 (UL9), pMC160-2 (UL8), pNN1 (*dbp*), pNN3 (*pol*), pNN4 (UL42), pNN5 (UL52), pK1-2 (IE175), pMC150 (IE63), pMC151 (IE110), and pKB-X. The gene contained within each plasmid is indicated in parentheses; for a complete description see Wu et al. (1988). (Lane *2*) Identical to lane *1* except lacking pNN3 as a negative control. (Lane *3*) Standard replication assay with *Xba*I clones (Challberg 1986). (Reprinted, with permission, from Wu et al. 1988.)

contains no other genes that are essential for origin-dependent plasmid replication. Figure 4 shows the location of the essential genes and the predicted sizes of the proteins encoded by them.

As a first step toward identifying the products of the essential replication genes, antibodies were made against each of the seven gene products. Armed with the nucleotide sequence of all of these genes, we fused a portion of the open reading frame of each to the β-galactosidase gene in an *Escherichia coli* expression vector that contained the *lac* operon. Rabbits were then immunized with the immunoaffinity-purified fusion proteins. We also immunized rabbits with decapeptides identical to the predicted carboxyl or amino terminus of several of these gene products. The resultant antisera were then used in immunoblot analysis of HSV-infected cell proteins.

Figure 5 combines the results of immunoblots obtained using antisera against five of the proteins. The antisera raised against the polymerase-β-galactosidase fusion protein recognizes a band in a crude extract from

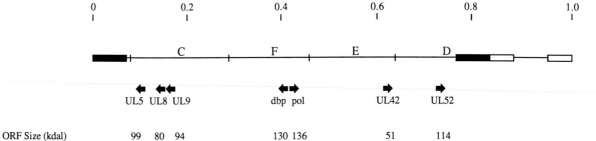

ORF Size (kdal)   99   80   94   130 136   51   114

Figure 4 Summary of essential HSV replication genes. The locations of essential replication genes of HSV are indicated by arrows. The predicted open reading frame (ORF) size and nomenclature for the genes other than *dbp* and *pol* are derived from the DNA sequence analysis of U$_L$ (McGeoch et al. 1988). The locations are shown with respect to the standard "P" arrangement of HSV-1 DNA (Goldin et al. 1981). The narrow line indicates unique sequences; the closed boxes indicate the long inverted repeat; and the open boxes indicate the short inverted repeat. Also shown are the locations of the *Xba*I restriction fragments, C, D, E, and F.

infected cells 6 hours after infection that comigrates with purified HSV polymerase. Immunoreactivity using this antisera copurifies with polymerase activity during the purification process (data not shown). Our antisera against a DBP-β-galactosidase fusion protein also recognizes a single band of the predicted size in infected cells as early as 2 hours after infection.

Antisera raised against the carboxyl and amino termini of the UL42 gene product (predicted molecular weight: 51,000) both recognize a band on SDS polyacrylamide gels that migrates at about 62 kD. This protein appears

as early as 2 hours after infection and becomes very abundant by 8 hours.

The UL5 gene product (predicted molecular weight: 99,000) migrates as an approximately 100-kD protein on SDS-PAGE. It can be seen on immunoblots, using antisera raised against a fusion protein, at 6 hours after infection, but it is clearly not an abundant protein.

The UL9 gene product (predicted molecular weight: 94,000) has been identified in infected cells as a protein migrating on SDS-PAGE at about 90 kD, and it is detectable 6 hours after infection.

Antisera raised against peptides and fusion proteins of both the UL8 (predicted molecular weight: 80,000) and UL52 (predicted molecular weight: 114,000) gene products have yet to identify HSV-infected cell-specific proteins. Rabbit antisera against the UL52 predicted carboxyl terminus does recognize a protein of about 120 kD in extracts of *E. coli* that express the UL52 gene; likewise antisera against the UL8 predicted carboxyl terminus recognizes an *E. coli*-expressed UL8 gene product of about 75 kD (data not shown).

Discussion

We have taken an approach to the study of HSV DNA replication that has enabled us to identify all of the HSV genes that are essential for HSV origin-dependent plasmid replication. Using a transient complementation assay, we have shown that seven HSV genes are both necessary and sufficient to support the replication of plasmids containing an HSV origin. Two of these genes are known replication genes, *pol* and *dbp*, which have been shown by genetic and biochemical studies to be essential for viral DNA replication, and whose products are likely to be directly involved in DNA replication. We propose that the other five genes found to be essential for HSV origin-containing plasmid replication are also directly involved in DNA replication.

The fact that we have found seven genes that are essential for origin-dependent plasmid replication in no way rules out the possibility that there are other viral genes whose products are essential for viral DNA replication, but not plasmid replication. Such proteins might perform functions related to recombination or packag-

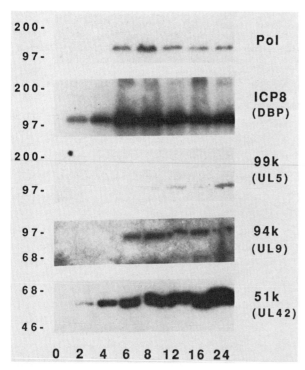

Figure 5 Composite of five immunoblots obtained using antisera made against the five replication proteins identified at the right. The numbers on the bottom indicate the time (in hours) after infection that extracts were made from HSV-infected VERO cells (see text for details). The numbers to the left indicate molecular weight markers (× 10^{-3}).

ing, or to other events closely linked to, but not directly involved with, the replication process. In addition, there may be cellular proteins that directly participate in both viral and plasmid replication. Despite these possibilities, we believe that the products of these seven HSV genes will eventually be shown to represent a complete, or nearly complete, set of replication proteins that are capable of replicating plasmids that contain an HSV origin of replication.

The identification of these genes relies partly on the sequence analysis of McGeoch et al. (1988). Several criteria for authentic HSV genes were used in the interpretation of their sequence data (for a full discussion, see McGeoch et al. 1988). The high G-C content of the HSV sequence results in a characteristic codon usage, which was used to test the likelihood that any open reading frame is a true HSV coding region. In addition, the locations of potential transcription polyadenylation signals (AATAAA and ATTAAA) helped to correlate open reading frames with possible transcript organization. Finally, comparison of the HSV sequence with the published sequence of another α herpesvirus, varicella-zoster virus (VZV) (Davison and Scott 1986), revealed VZV counterparts for each of the identified HSV genes. Our data provide a functional corroboration of the sequence interpretation. Extensive subcloning and deletion analyses are in complete agreement with the sequence interpretation. Moreover, antisera directed against peptides and fusion proteins, made using the sequence data, detect previously unidentified proteins in HSV-infected cells.

Little or nothing is known about the function of these seven gene products with the exception of the polymerase. The HSV DNA polymerase (pol) has been purified and partly characterized from HSV-infected cells (Hay et al. 1971; Powell and Purifoy 1977; O'Donnell et al. 1987a). It consists of a single polypeptide of about 140 kD which has 5′–3′ polymerase activity and 3′–5′ exonuclease activity. It is highly processive on primed, SSB-coated ssDNA templates, but inactive on duplex molecules (O'Donnell et al. 1987a).

The other six proteins are likely to perform replication functions analogous to those found in better-characterized systems such as the T4, λ, and E. coli replication complexes. Predictable activities might include an origin-binding protein to direct the polymerase and other proteins to the site of initiation, polymerase accessory proteins to increase the processivity and efficiency of the polymerase, a primase to prime lagging strand synthesis, a helicase for fork movement, etc.

The major DBP of HSV is clearly directly involved in DNA replication, but its role remains unclear. It has a molecular weight of approximately 130,000, is very abundant in HSV-infected nuclei, and binds cooperatively to ssDNA at a stoichiometry of about one molecule per 12 nucleotides (O'Donnell et al. 1987b). Under certain conditions it aggregates in a manner superficially resembling rec A protein, forming cord-like structures when viewed in the electron microscope (Ruyechan 1983; O'Donnell et al. 1987b). Limited biochemical analysis

has shown that under conditions that allow E. coli SSB to stimulate HSV polymerase activity, DBP is inhibitory (O'Donnell et al. 1987b). A stimulatory effect was found, however, with duplex DNA in the presence of an infected cell extract (O'Donnell et al. 1987b). It remains to be seen whether the major DBP of HSV is an analog of ssDNA binding proteins that act as helix destabilizing proteins, such as the T4 gene 32 product or E. coli SSB protein.

The UL42 gene product (predicted molecular weight: 51,000) represents a previously identified infected cell protein (Bayliss et al. 1975; Purifoy and Powell 1976), but its association with DNA replication was vague, and there are no mutants whose lesions map to its gene location. The abundance of this protein may provide a clue to its role in the replication process, but at present its function remains obscure. Earlier work revealed a 54-kD protein that was found to persist in preparations of purified polymerase (Powell and Purifoy 1977), and one laboratory has preliminary evidence of an association between the UL42 gene product and the polymerase (D.S. Parris, pers. comm.). In our laboratory, the bulk of the polymerase and the UL42 gene product separate from each other when HSV-infected cell extracts are eluted off a phosphocellulose column (C. Wu, pers. comm.). It is possible that the 62-kD protein that we see on our immunoblots of column fractions is an inactive form, and that the active form does in fact associate with the polymerase. Using antisera against both the carboxyl and amino termini has enabled us to rule out proteolytic degradation. It is clear, however, that the polymerase does not depend on stoichiometric amounts of the 62-kD protein for polymerase activity as measured by the standard activated calf thymus DNA assay. The 62-kD protein may be shown to be important in polymerase assays using other templates. This issue is currently under investigation.

Analysis of the predicted amino acid sequence of the UL5 gene reveals a canonical ATPase site similar to that found on known ATPase enzymes and nucleotide binding proteins, including the HSV polymerase and thymidine kinase (Walker et al. 1982). This of course, prompts speculation that the UL5 gene product may have helicase or primase activity. Biochemical analyses are ongoing.

There are no particular clues as to the role of the UL8, UL9, or UL52 gene products in the replication process at present. We feel that our inability to use our antisera to detect the products of the UL8 and UL52 genes in HSV-infected cells reflects the low abundance or instability of these proteins. Data from other laboratories are also consistent with low abundance of the UL8 gene product. This, of course, would not be an unprecedented property of a replication protein. Characterization and biochemical analysis of these proteins will be assisted, and may even depend on, their overexpression in either prokaryotic or eukaryotic systems.

In conclusion, we have identified seven HSV genes that are essential for replication of plasmids containing an HSV origin of replication. We propose that the products of all seven of these genes are directly involved in viral DNA synthesis. We have raised antisera against each of these proteins and have begun their biochemical characterization.

References

Bayliss, G.J., H.S. Marsden, and J. Hay. 1975. Herpes simplex virus proteins: DNA-binding proteins in infected cells and in the virus structure. *Virology* **68**: 124.

Challberg, M.D. 1986. A method for identifying the viral genes required for herpesvirus DNA replication. *Proc. Natl. Acad. Sci.* **83**: 9094.

Chartrand, P., N.D. Stow, M.C. Timbury, and N.M. Wilkie. 1979. Physical mapping of *paa'* mutations of herpes simplex virus type 1 and type 2 by intertypic marker rescue. *J. Virol.* **31**: 265.

Chu, C.-T., D.S. Parris, R.A.F. Dixon, F.E. Farber, and P.A. Schaffer. 1979. Hydroxylamine mutagenesis of HSV DNA and DNA fragments: Introduction of mutations into selected regions of the viral genome. *Virology* **98**: 169.

Clements, J.B., J. McLaughlin, and D.J. McGeoch. 1979. Orientation of herpes simplex type 1 immediate early mRNAs. *Nucleic Acids Res.* **7**: 73.

Coen, D.M., D.P. Aschman, P.T. Gelep, M.J. Retondo, S.K. Weller, and P.A. Schaffer. 1984. Fine mapping and molecular cloning of mutations in the herpes simplex virus DNA polymerase locus. *J. Virol.* **49**: 236.

Cohen, G.H. 1972. Ribonucleotide reductase activity of synchronized KB cells infected with herpes simplex virus. *J. Virol.* **9**: 408.

Conley, A.J., D.M. Knipe, P.C. Jones, and B. Roizman. 1981. Molecular genetics of herpes simplex virus. VII: Characterization of a temperature-sensitive mutant produced by *in vitro* mutagenesis and defective in DNA synthesis and accumulation of polypeptides. *J. Virol.* **37**: 191.

Davison, A.J. and J.E. Scott. 1986. The complete DNA sequence of varicella-zoster virus. *J. Gen. Virol.* **67**: 1759.

Dixon, R.A.F. and P.A. Schaffer. 1980. Fine-structure mapping and functional analysis of temperature-sensitive mutants in the gene encoding the herpes simplex virus type 1 immediate early protein VP175. *J. Virol.* **36**: 189.

Elias, P., M.E. O'Donnell, E. Mocarski, and I.R. Lehman. 1986. A DNA binding protein specific for an origin of replication of herpes simplex virus type 1. *Proc. Natl. Acad. Sci.* **83**: 6322.

Gibbs, J.S., H.C. Chiou, J.D. Hall, D.W. Mount, M.J. Retondo, S.K. Weller, and D.M. Coen. 1985. Sequence and mapping analysis of the herpes simplex virus DNA polymerase gene predict a C-terminal substrate binding domain. *Proc. Natl. Acad. Sci.* **82**: 7969.

Goldin, A.L., R.M. Sandri-Goldin, M. Levine, and J.C. Glorioso. 1981. Cloning of herpes simplex virus type 1 sequences representing the whole genome. *J. Virol.* **38**: 50.

Graham, F.L. and A.J. van der Eb. 1973. A new technique for the assay of infectivity of human adenovirus 5 DNA. *Virology* **52**: 456.

Hay, J. and J.H. Subak-Sharpe. 1976. Mutants of herpes simplex virus types 1 and 2 that are resistant to phosphonoacetic acid induce altered DNA polymerase activities in infected cells. *J. Gen. Virol.* **31**: 145.

Hay, J., H. Moss, and I.W. Halliburton. 1971. Induction of deoxyribonucleic acid polymerase and deoxyribonuclease activities in cells infected with herpes simplex virus type II. *Biochem. J.* **124**: 64.

Henikoff, S. 1984. Unidirectional digestion with exonuclease III created targeted breakpoints for DNA sequencing. *Gene* **28**: 351.

Jacob, R.J. and B. Roizman. 1977. Anatomy of herpes simplex virus DNA. VIII. Properties of the replicating DNA. *J. Virol.* **23**: 394.

Jacob, R.J., L.S. Morse, and B. Roizman. 1979. Anatomy of herpes simplex virus DNA. XII. Accumulation of head-to-tail concatemers in nuclei of infected cells and their role in the generation of the four isomeric arrangements of viral DNA. *J. Virol.* **29**: 448.

Jongeneel, C.V. and S.L. Bachenheimer. 1981. Structure of replicating herpes simplex virus DNA. *J. Virol.* **39**: 656.

Kit, S. and D. Dubbs. 1963. Acquisition of thymidine kinase activity by herpes simplex virus-infected mouse fibroblast cells. *Biochem. Biophys. Res. Commun.* **11**: 55.

Maniatis, T., E.F. Fritsch, and J. Sambrook. 1982. *Molecular cloning: A laboratory manual.* Cold Spring Harbor Laboratory, Cold Spring Harbor, New York.

Matz, B., J.H. Subak-Sharpe, and V.G. Preston. 1983. Physical mapping of temperature-sensitive mutations of herpes simplex virus type 1 using cloned restriction endonuclease fragments. *J. Gen. Virol.* **64**: 2261.

McGeoch, D.J., M.A. Dalrymple, A. Dolan, D. McNab, L.J. Perry, P. Taylor, and M.D. Challberg. 1988. Structures of the herpes simplex virus type 1 genes required for replication of virus DNA. *J. Virol.* (in press).

Morrison, J.M. and H.M. Keir. 1968. A new DNA-exonuclease in cells infected with herpes virus: Partial purification and properties of the enzyme. *J. Gen. Virol.* **3**: 337.

Moss, H. 1986. The herpes simplex virus type 2 alkaline DNase activity is essential for replication and growth. *J. Gen. Virol.* **67**: 1173.

O'Donnell, M.E., P. Elias, and I.R. Lehman. 1987a. Processive replication of single-stranded DNA templates by the herpes simplex virus-induced DNA polymerase. *J. Biol. Chem.* **262**: 4252.

O'Donnell, M.E., P. Elias, B.E. Funnell, and I.R. Lehman. 1987b. Interaction between the DNA polymerase and single-stranded DNA binding protein (infected cell protein 8) of herpes simplex virus 1. *J. Biol. Chem.* **262**: 4260.

Peden, K.W., J.M. Pipas, S. Pearson-White, and D. Nathans. 1980. Isolation of mutants of an animal virus in bacteria. *Science* **209**: 1392.

Powell, K.L. and D.J.M. Purifoy. 1977. Nonstructural proteins of herpes simplex virus. I. Purification of the induced DNA polymerase. *J. Virol.* **24**: 618.

Purifoy, D.J.M. and K.L. Powell. 1976. DNA binding proteins induced by herpes simplex virus type 2 in HEp-2 cells. *J. Virol.* **19**: 717.

Preston, C.M. 1979. Control of herpes simplex virus type 1 mRNA synthesis in cells infected with wild-type virus or the temperature-sensitive mutant tsK. *J. Virol.* **29**: 275.

Preston, V.G., J.W. Palfreymand, and B.M. Dutia. 1984. Identification of a herpes simplex virus type 1 polypeptide which is a component of the virus-induced ribonucleotide reductase. *J. Gen. Virol.* **65**: 1457.

Quinn, J.P. and D.J. McGeoch. 1985. DNA sequence of the region in the genome of herpes simplex virus type 1 containing genes for DNA polymerase and the major DNA binding protein. *Nucleic Acids Res.* **13**: 8143.

Roizman, B. and W. Batterson. 1985. Herpesviruses and their replication. In *Virology* (ed. B.N. Fields et al.), p. 497. Raven Press, New York.

Ruyechan, W.T. 1983. The major herpes simplex virus DNA-binding protein holds single-stranded DNA in an extended configuration. *J. Virol.* **46**: 661.

Sacks, W.R. and P.A. Schaffer. 1987. Deletion mutants in the gene encoding the herpes simplex virus type 1 immediate early protein ICP0 exhibit impaired growth in cell culture. *J. Virol.* **61**: 829.

Schaffer, P.A., G.M. Arn, N. Biswal, and M. Benyesh-Melnick. 1973. Temperature-sensitive mutants of herpes simplex virus type 1: Isolation, complementation, and partial characterization. *Virology* **52**: 57.

Spaete, R.R. and N. Frenkel. 1982. The herpes simplex virus amplicon: A new eucaryotic defective-virus cloning-amplifying vector. *Cell* **30**: 295.

Stow, N.D. 1982. Localization of an origin of DNA replication within the TR$_s$/IR$_s$ repeated region of the herpes simplex virus type 1 genome. *EMBO J.* **1**: 863.

Stow, N.D. and E.C. McMonagle. 1983. Characterization of the IR$_s$/IR$_s$ origin of DNA replication of herpes simplex virus type 1. *Virology* **130**: 427.

Stow, N.D. and E.C. Stow. 1986. Isolation and characterization of herpes simplex virus type 1 mutant containing a deletion within the gene encoding the immediate early polypeptide Vmw110. *J.Gen. Virol.* **67**: 2571.

Vlasny, D.A. and N. Frenkel. 1982. Replication of herpes simplex virus DNA: Localization of replication recognition signals within defective virus genomes. *Proc. Natl. Acad. Sci.* **78**: 742.

Walker, J.E., M. Saraste, M.J. Runswick, and N.J. Gay. 1982. Distantly related sequences in the A and B subunits of ATP synthase, myosin, kinases, and other ATP-requiring enzymes and a common nucleotide fold. *EMBO J.* **1**: 945.

Weller, S.K., K.J. Lee, D.J. Sabourin, and P.A. Schaffer. 1983. Genetic analysis of temperature-sensitive mutants which define the gene for the major herpes simplex virus type 1 DNA-binding protein. *J. Virol.* **45**: 354.

Weller, S.K., A. Spadaro, J.E. Schaffer, A.W. Murray, A.M. Maxam, and P.A. Schaffer. 1985. Cloning, sequencing, and functional analysis of *ori$_L$*, a herpes simplex virus type 1 origin of DNA synthesis. *Mol. Cell. Biol.* **5**: 930.

Wu, C.A., N.J. Nelson, D.J. McGeoch, and M.D. Challberg. 1988. Identification of the herpes simplex virus type 1 genes required for origin dependent DNA synthesis. *J. Virol.* (in press).

Use of Host Range Mutants to Identify Genes Involved in DNA Replication of Herpes Simplex Virus

S.K. Weller, E.P. Carmichael, D.J. Goldstein, and L. Zhu
Department of Microbiology, University of Connecticut Health Center,
Farmington, Connecticut 06032

We review here the isolation and characterization of mutants in five herpes simplex virus type 1 (HSV-1) genes believed to play a role in viral DNA synthesis, including the viral ribonucleotide reductase (RR) and four genes of unknown function. Two null mutants in the gene for the large subunit of the viral RR have been isolated and found to be viable in cells in culture. Thus, viral RR is not essential for viral growth and DNA synthesis in exponentially growing cells in culture; however, these null mutants are compromised when propagated in serum-starved cells, suggesting that HSV-1 RR mutants are dependent on the status of cellular nucleotide metabolism. Analysis of certain DNA negative host range and temperature-sensitive mutants has identified four genes whose products are essential for viral DNA synthesis in infected cells. The four genes identified in this study all map to the unique long arm of the HSV-1 genome (U_L) and correspond to open reading frames designated UL5, UL8, UL9, and UL52 in the DNA sequence of HSV-1 (D. McGeoch, pers. comm.).

The genome of HSV is large (152 kb) and structurally complex: It is composed of a long (U_L) and a short (U_S) region of unique DNA, each of which is bounded by inverted repeat sequences (Fig. 1A) (Sheldrick and Berthelot 1975). The mode of replication of HSV DNA is not completely understood, but recent studies have revealed important features of this system. Three cis-acting elements are believed to act as origins of DNA synthesis: Two copies of ori_S are located within the inverted repeat sequences flanking U_S (Vlazny and Frenkel 1981; Stow 1982), and ori_L is located in the middle of U_L (Spaete and Frenkel 1982; Weller et al. 1985). Four different HSV origins have now been identified and sequenced (ori_L and ori_S of HSV-1 and HSV-2) and are very similar (see Fig. 1B). All four contain palindromes whose centers of symmetry are composed predominantly of A and T residues; ori_L of HSV-1 contains the largest palindrome (144-bp perfect inverted repeat) (Weller et al. 1985), whereas ori_S of HSV-1 contains a much smaller, almost perfect 45-bp palindrome (Stow 1982). The similarities between all four origins are found predominantly to the left of the center of symmetry (see Fig. 1B).

In addition to structural elements required for the initiation of DNA synthesis, the HSV genome encodes many proteins involved in nucleotide metabolism and DNA synthesis. These include RR (Dutia 1983), thymidine kinase (tk) (Dubbs and Kit 1964), dUTPase (Preston and Fisher 1984), alkaline nuclease (Preston and Cordingley 1982), a single-stranded DNA-binding protein (infected cell protein 8 or ICP8) (Conley et al. 1981; Lee and Knipe 1983; Weller et al. 1983), and DNA polymerase (Purifoy et al. 1977).

The most direct approach to the identification of gene products essential for viral DNA replication is to isolate mutants that exhibit alterations in DNA synthesis. Of the known functions listed above, only ICP8 (Conley et al. 1981; Weller et al. 1983) and the HSV DNA polymerase (Purifoy et al. 1977; Purifoy and Powell 1981) have been shown by the analysis of temperature-sensitive (ts) and other mutants to be absolutely essential for viral DNA replication in infected cells. Studies with a ts mutant of HSV-2 suggest that alkaline nuclease may also be essential (Moss 1986). Some enzymes involved in nucleotide metabolism, such as tk and dUTPase, are dispensable in actively dividing cells, although tk appears to be required for optimal growth in growth-arrested cells (see Jamieson et al. 1974; Fisher and Preston 1986).

A second complementary approach to the identification of gene products required for DNA synthesis has been the isolation of DNA-negative mutants in genes whose functions are currently unknown. Null mutations (insertions and deletions) are especially powerful because they are not leaky (i.e., no residual activity can be expressed under nonpermissive growth conditions) and mutations can easily be targeted to specific genes. To isolate and propagate null mutants in essential viral genes, cell lines were isolated that can express the wild-type version of the gene to be altered. VERO cells were cotransfected with plasmids containing HSV DNA and a selectable marker. Null mutants that fail to grow on VERO cells but which can be propagated on complementing cell lines are called host range (hr) mutants. hr and nonleaky ts mutants representing five distinct HSV-1 genes will be described here.

53

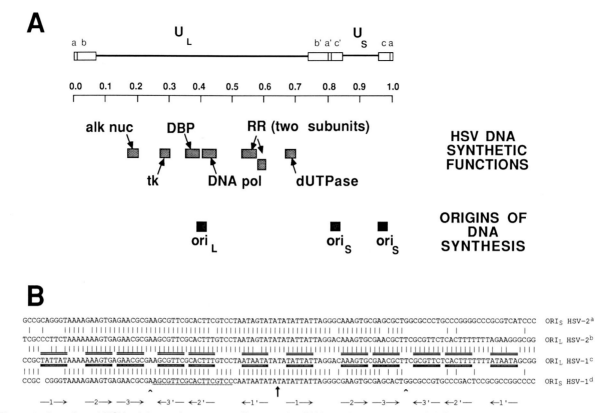

Figure 1. Location of HSV origins and genes encoding putative DNA synthetic functions. (*A*) Sequence arrangement and physical map coordinates of the HSV-1 genome. The map locations of genes that encode functions involved in nucleotide metabolism or DNA synthesis are shown, as well as those of origins of DNA synthesis. Genes and origins are not drawn to scale. (*B*) Nucleotide sequence of 114 bp flanking the centers of symmetry of four origins of replication. The centers of symmetry of the palindromes are marked with an arrow. Double underlines mark the locations of tandem short direct repeats (arrows 1, 2, 3, 1′, 2′, and 3′) reported first for *ori*$_L$ of HSV-1 (Weller et al. 1985). Sequences in repeats 1, 2, and 3 are complementary to sequences in repeats 1′, 2′, and 3′, respectively, and are drawn to reflect a dyad symmetry within each half of the larger palindrome, marked with a ∧. The 18-bp sequence in *ori*$_S$ of HSV-1 that was protected in a DNase protection experiment is indicated with a wavy underline (Elias et al. 1986). References: [a] Whitton and Clements (1984); [b] Lockshon and Galloway (1986); [c] Weller et al. (1985); [d] Stow (1982), and modified for *ori*$_S$ HSV-1 strain KOS by M.R. Seghatoleslami and S.K. Weller (unpubl.).

Methods

Cells and viruses

African green monkey kidney cells (VERO, ATCC) and viruses were grown as described previously (Weller et al. 1983). The KOS strain of HSV-1 was used as wild type in this study. Temperature-sensitive mutants *ts* K13 and *ts* M19 were originally described by Schaffer et al. (1973).

Recombinant DNA plasmids containing HSV-1 DNA

Plasmids containing the coding sequences for β-galactosidase (the *Escherichia coli lacZ* gene) were generously provided by D. Panicali (Applied Biosystems, Cambridge, MA; Panicali et al. 1986). Plasmids containing an ICP6::*lacZ* fusion containing the *lacZ* gene under the control of the ICP6 regulatory region will be described (D. Goldstein and S. Weller, in prep.).

Mutant isolation and characterization

Host cell lines for the propagation of null mutants were isolated as described previously (Carmichael et al.

1988; Goldstein and Weller 1988). For mutant isolation, permissive cells were cotransfected with wild-type DNA and a recombinant clone containing the desired mutation (Goldstein and Weller 1988). Since β-galactosidase activity can be easily detected in the presence of the chromogenic substrate X-gal (5-bromo-4-chloro-3-indoyl-βD-galactoside), recombinants that express the *lacZ* gene were readily detected. Mutants were characterized with respect to map location, complementation group, and ability to induce viral DNA and protein synthesis as described previously (Weller et al. 1987; Carmichael et al. 1988; Goldstein and Weller 1988).

Results

Permissive host cell lines capable of expressing various HSV-1 genes suspected to be involved in DNA synthesis were isolated for the propagation of mutants carrying potentially lethal defects (i.e., *hr* mutations). Since it is likely that *hr* mutants such as insertions and deletions would be incapable of synthesizing any active protein under nonpermissive growth conditions, an accurate assessment of the requirement of each gene product in DNA synthesis can be obtained. Cell lines containing specific HSV genes were constructed by cotransfection of VERO cells with HSV DNA-containing plasmids and pSV2neo (Table 1).

Ribonucleotide reductase
The viral RR consists of two subunits encoded by coterminal transcripts mapping between 0.56 and 0.60 on the HSV-1 genome (see Fig. 3). The viral RR has been reported to be essential for viral growth and DNA synthesis based on the characterization of a *ts* mutant (*ts* 1207) in the gene for the large subunit (Dutia 1983; Preston et al. 1984). To explore this issue further, two null mutants in the ICP6 gene were constructed: an in-frame insertion of the *lacZ* gene into ICP6 coding sequences (hrR3) and a 2.9-kb ICP6 deletion (ICP6Δ) (Goldstein and Weller 1988 and in prep.) (Fig. 3). Both hrR3 and ICP6Δ encode no detectable viral RR activity (Goldstein and Weller 1988 and in prep.). The growth properties of both hrR3 and ICP6Δ indicate that the HSV-1 RR activity is dispensable for virus growth and DNA replication in exponentially growing cells in culture (Table 2). However, we have shown that viral RR is required for optimal growth and viral DNA synthesis in growth-restricted cells (Goldstein and Weller 1988, and in prep.).

Mutations in four gene products of unknown function
Host range or nonleaky *ts* DNA negative mutants that fall into four distinct complementation groups have been isolated and characterized. The map locations of these

Table 1 Host Cell Lines

Cell line	Coordinates[a]	HSV Genes expressed[b]	Viruses supported
D14	0.527–0.608	large subunit RR small subunit RR	hrR3, ICP6Δ
S22	0.086–0.194	UL8 UL9	tsS38, hr80 hr27
E22	0.072–0.108	UL5	tsK13, tsM19
BL1	0.708–0.715	UL52	hr114

[a]VERO cells were cotransfected with pSV2neo and various clones containing viral DNA. The coordinates of each HSV fragment used in each transfection are shown.

[b]That these genes are expressed in the cell lines has been ascertained by immunofluorescence with appropriate antisera (for D14, Goldstein and Weller 1988) or by their ability to complement the growth of null mutants in the appropriate gene (for S22, E22, and BL1; Carmichael et al. 1988; L. Zhu and S. Weller; D. Goldstein and S. Weller; both in prep.). UL numbers were assigned based on the DNA sequence of D. McGeoch (pers. comm.).

mutations are consistent with the positions of four open reading frames designated UL5, UL8, UL9, and UL52, based on sequence analysis of D. McGeoch (pers. comm.). These four open reading frames are predicted to encode polypeptides of the following sizes: 99 kD, 80 kD, 94 kD, and 114 kD, respectively (see Figs. 2 and 3) (D. McGeoch, pers. comm.).

For two viral genes, UL8 and UL52, we have developed a new strategy for isolation of *lacZ* insertion mutants. In both cases, the *lacZ* gene was first inserted in-frame into the coding regions of these genes such that *lacZ* would be expressed under the control of the

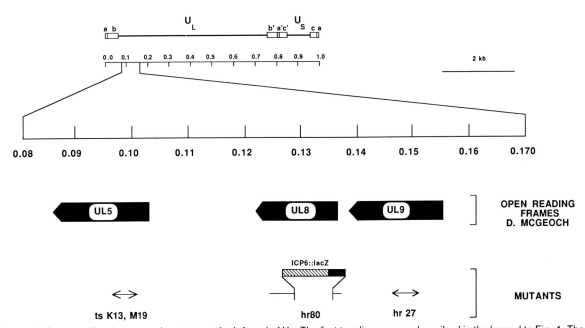

Figure 2 Open reading frames and mutants at the left end of U_L. The first two lines are as described in the legend to Fig. 1. The region between map coordinates 0.08 and 0.17 is expanded. Open reading frames corresponding to UL5, UL8, and UL9 are shown (D. McGeoch, pers. comm.). On the bottom line, map locations and schematic diagrams are shown for three complementation groups of DNA negative mutants. For *ts*K13, *ts*M19, and *hr*27, the line with the double arrows corresponds to the smallest fragment that can rescue these mutations.

Table 2 Mutants Described in This Study

Mutant	Type of mutation	Map location[a] (HSV protein)	Viral titer[b] (PFU/ml)		Viral DNA phenotype[c]	Reference[d]
			P	NP		
*hr*R3	*lacZ* insertion	insertion at 0.574 (ICP6, UL39)	2.0×10^8	1.5×10^8	+	Goldstein and Weller (1988)
ICP6Δ	deletion	deletion of 0.564–0.585 (ICP6, UL39)	1.0×10^8	9.0×10^7	+	Goldstein and Weller (1988)
*hr*114	insertion of ICP6::*lacZ* fusion	insertion at 0.719 (114 kD, UL52)	8.3×10^7	$<10^3$	–	D.J. Goldstein and S.K. Weller (unpubl.)
*ts*K13	temperature-sensitive	0.095–0.098 (99 kD, UL5)	1.0×10^8	$<10^2$	–	Weller et al. (1987) L. Zhu and S.K. Weller (unpubl.)
*ts*M19	temperature-sensitive	0.095–0.098 (99 kD, UL5)	2.0×10^8	$<10^2$	–	Weller et al. (1987) L. Zhu and S.K. Weller (unpubl.)
*hr*80	deletion/ICP6::*lacZ* insertion	deletion of 0.126–0.137 (80 kD, UL8)	1.1×10^8	$<10^2$	–	E.P. Carmichael and S.K. Weller (unpubl.)
*hr*27	spontaneous hr	0.145–0.155 (94 kD, UL9)	1.5×10^8	$<10^2$	–	Carmichael et al. (1988)

[a]Map locations were determined by marker rescue for *ts*K13, *ts*M19, and *hr*27 and are presented as the coordinates of the smallest fragment that rescued the mutation. For insertion and deletion mutations, the locations of the lesions were determined by DNA analysis. The viral gene to which each mutation has been mapped is given in parentheses.

[b]Viral titers are given for permissive (P) and nonpermissive (NP) conditions. For all *hr* mutants, the P condition is growth on complementing cell lines and the NP condition is growth on VERO cells. For *ts* mutants the P condition is growth at 34°C on VERO cells and the NP condition is growth at 39.5°C on VERO cells.

[c]Viral DNA synthesis is based on the ability of mutants to synthesize viral DNA under nonpermissive growth conditions relative to wild-type virus: (+) > 20% and (–) no detectable viral DNA synthesized.

[d]Reference in which the most recent genetic or phenotypic data are presented.

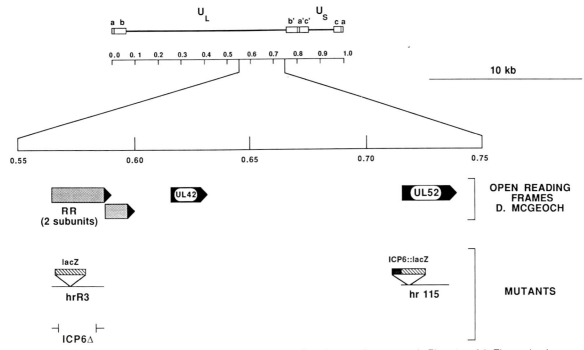

Figure 3 Open reading frames and mutants at the right end of U_L. The first two lines are as in Figs. 1 and 2. The region between map coordinates 0.55 and 0.75 is expanded. Open reading frames corresponding to RR, UL42, and UL52 are shown (D. McGeoch, pers. comm.). On the bottom line, map locations and schematic diagrams of three mutants are shown: two in the RR gene and one in UL52.

endogenous promoters for UL8 and UL52. Following marker transfer, these constructs failed to produce blue plaque recombinants as were observed above when *lacZ* was inserted into the ICP6 gene. One possible explanation for this failure is that these constructs result in insufficient expression of β-galactosidase to generate blue plaques. We therefore constructed a plasmid containing an ICP6::*lacZ* fusion that places the *lacZ* gene under the control of the ICP6 promoter, since we had shown previously that *lacZ* could be expressed efficiently in a similar ICP6::*lacZ* fusion (Goldstein and Weller 1988). The construction of the ICP6::*lacZ* fusion will be described in detail (D.J. Goldstein and S.K. Weller, in prep.). This ICP6::*lacZ* fusion was inserted into the coding regions of UL8 and UL52; in the case of UL8, a clone containing a 1.6-kb deletion was used for the insertion (see Figs. 2 and 3). Using this strategy, *lacZ* insertion mutants *hr*80 (complementation group 1–26) and *hr*114 (complementation group 1–37) were isolated and shown to be totally dependent on complementing cell lines for virus growth and DNA synthesis (E. Carmichael et al., unpubl.). Thus, both *hr*80 and *hr*114 are deficient in viral gene products essential for viral DNA synthesis—UL8 and UL52, respectively.

Two nonleaky temperature-sensitive mutants (*ts*K13 and M19, first described by Schaffer et al. 1973) representing complementation group 1–10 have been mapped to the coding sequences of the 99-kD gene product, UL5 (Weller et al. 1987; L. Zhu and S.K. Weller, unpubl.). These mutants make no detectable viral DNA at the nonpermissive temperature (npt) (Table

2) (Weller et al. 1987). Experiments in which cells infected with *ts*K13, *ts*M19, or KOS at the permissive temperature and then shifted to the npt at various times after infection indicate that UL5 is required continuously during DNA synthesis (L. Zhu and S.K. Weller, unpubl.).

Another DNA-negative viral mutant, *hr*27, was isolated as a spontaneous mutant following propagation in S22 cells that contain the genes for the UL8 and UL9 (Carmichael et al. 1988). The mutation in *hr*27 has been localized by marker rescue analysis to an 800-bp fragment within the coding sequences of the putative 94-kD polypeptide, UL9. Complementation studies demonstrated that *hr*27 forms a new complementation group designated 1–36 (Carmichael et al. 1988).

Thus, the isolation of host range and nonleaky *ts* mutants has allowed the identification of four genes whose products are essential for viral DNA synthesis in infected cells. As expected based on their DNA phenotypes, all four groups of mutants also exhibit defects in the synthesis of late viral proteins (data not shown).

Discussion

trans-Acting factors involved in viral DNA synthesis

We have demonstrated that viral RR is not essential for viral growth and DNA synthesis in exponentially growing cells in culture; however, null mutants in this gene are compromised when propagated in serum-starved cells whose levels of cellular reductase may be decreased

(Goldstein and Weller 1988 and unpubl.). Mutants have been isolated in genes for four gene products of unknown function (UL5, UL8, UL9, and UL52). All mutants can be propagated on appropriate host cell lines containing the wild-type version of each gene product but not in untransformed VERO cells, and all four are defective in the synthesis of viral DNA under nonpermissive growth conditions. Thus, we have identified four genes whose products appear to be essential for viral DNA synthesis in infected cells under certain conditions.

An alternative approach has recently been used to identify gene products required for amplification of HSV-origin-containing plasmids (Challberg 1986). Challberg has found that clones containing HSV DNA can be used in transient transfection experiments to support origin-containing plasmid amplification (Challberg 1986). This powerful technique has allowed the identification of seven viral genes believed to be required directly for viral DNA synthesis; these include the major DNA-binding protein, DNA polymerase, and five genes whose functions are unknown (M. Challberg, pers. comm.). Four of the unknown genes identified by Challberg's assay correspond to the four gene products identified genetically above: UL5, UL8, UL9, and UL52. In addition, he has identified a fifth gene encoding a putative 51-kD protein (UL42) in which no mutants have been reported (see Fig. 3). Recent evidence suggests that UL42 is equivalent to an HSV-2 54-kD DNA-binding protein that copurifies with the HSV polymerase and has been called a polymerase-associated protein (Vaughan et al. 1985; D. Parris and H. Marsden, pers. comm.). There is a remarkable correspondence between the genes shown to be essential for plasmid amplification by the transfection assay and genes required for viral DNA synthesis in vivo as shown by the isolation of conditionally lethal mutants in viral genes (see Figs. 2 and 3). The gene for viral RR was shown to be dispensable in both systems, although it is clearly required for optimal DNA synthesis in the plasmid amplification system (Challberg, pers. comm.) and is required for optimal viral growth and viral DNA synthesis in vivo (Goldstein and Weller 1988).

Functional analysis of proteins involved in viral DNA synthesis

The functions of UL5, UL8, UL9, UL42, and UL52 have yet to be determined. By analogy with other better-characterized replication systems, we might expect HSV DNA replication to require primase, helicase, polymerase accessory functions, topoisomerase, ligase, and a protein that binds specifically to an HSV origin of replication. Elias et al. (1986) have recently reported the identification and partial purification of a virus-induced DNA-binding protein that is specific for sequences found within ori_S. The partially purified ori_S-binding protein has been shown to specifically bind to an 18-bp sequence within ori_S marked with a wavy line in Figure 1B. This sequence is highly conserved in all four origins. Figure 1B shows the locations of tandem short direct

repeats (arrows 1, 2, 3, 1′, 2′, and 3′) reported first for ori_L of HSV-1 (Weller et al. 1985). Sequences in repeats 1, 2, and 3 are complementary to sequences in repeats 1′, 2′, and 3′, respectively, and are drawn to reflect an inner region of dyad symmetry within each half of the larger palindrome. The binding site for the origin-binding protein spans the 2′ and 3′ repeat segments that are repeated four times either in direct or indirect orientation within ori_L of both HSV-1 and HSV-2 but only three times within ori_S from both viruses. It is not clear whether this origin recognition protein corresponds to one of the proteins of unknown function described above, nor is it known whether it is encoded by the virus or by the cell.

Preliminary genetic and biochemical evidence suggests the existence of an HSV replication complex consisting of at least the major DNA-binding protein and the HSV polymerase and perhaps other proteins such as UL42 and the alkaline nuclease (Littler et al. 1983; Ruyechan and Weir 1984; Vaughan et al. 1984, 1985; Chiou et al. 1985; O'Donnell et al. 1987). It is hoped that future studies of cis- and trans-acting factors required for HSV DNA replication will lead to the elucidation of the roles of these proteins, the interactions between them, and the development of new antiviral therapies.

Acknowledgments

We thank numerous colleagues working in HSV whose contributions are too numerous to cite in this report due to space considerations. This work was supported by Public Health Service grant AI-21747 and March of Dimes Basil O'Connor grant A-545. S.K.W. is a recipient of the American Cancer Society junior facility research award.

References

Carmichael, E.P., M.J. Kosovsky, and S.K. Weller. 1988. Isolation and characterization of herpes simplex virus type 1 host range mutants defective in viral DNA synthesis. *J. Virol.* **62:** 91.

Challberg, M.D. 1986. A method for identifying the viral genes required for herpesvirus DNA replication. *Proc. Natl. Acad. Sci.* **83:** 9094.

Chiou, H.C., S.K. Weller, and D.M. Coen. 1985. Mutations in the herpes simplex virus major DNA-binding protein gene leading to altered sensitivity to DNA polymerase inhibitors. *Virology* **145:** 213.

Conley, A.J., D.M. Knipe, P.C. Jones, and B. Roizman. 1981. Molecular genetics of herpes simplex virus. VII. Characterization of a temperature-sensitive mutant produced by in vitro mutagenesis and defective in DNA synthesis and accumulation of γ polypeptides. *J. Virol.* **37:** 191.

Dubbs, D.R. and S. Kit. 1964. Mutant strains of herpes simplex deficient in thymidine kinase-inducing activity. *Virology* **22:** 493.

Dutia, B.M. 1983. Ribonucleotide reductase induced by herpes simplex virus has a virus-specified constituent. *J. Gen. Virol.* **64:** 513.

Elias, P., M.E. O'Donnell, E.S. Mocarski, and I.R. Lehman. 1986. A DNA binding protein specific for an origin of replication of herpes simplex virus type 1. *Proc. Natl. Acad. Sci.* **83:** 6322.

Fisher, F.B. and V.G. Preston. 1986. Isolation and characterisation of herpes simplex virus type 1 mutants which fail to induce dUTPase activity. *Virology* **148**: 190.

Goldstein, D.J. and S.K. Weller. 1988. The HSV-1 induced ribonucleotide reductase activity is dispensable for virus growth and DNA synthesis: Isolation and characterization of an ICP6 LacZ insertion mutant. *J. Virol.* **62**: 196.

Jamieson, A.T., G.A. Gentry, and J.H. Subak-Sharpe. 1974. Induction of both thymidine and deoxycytidine kinase activity by herpes simplex virus. *J. Gen. Virol.* **24**: 465.

Lee, C.K. and D.M. Knipe. 1983. Thermolabile in vivo DNA-binding activity associated with a protein encoded by mutants of herpes simplex virus type 1. *J. Virol.* **46**: 909.

Littler, E., D.J.M. Purifoy, A. Minson, and K.L. Powell. 1983. Herpes simplex virus non-structural proteins. III. Function of the major DNA-binding protein. *J. Gen. Virol.* **64**: 983.

Lockshon, D. and D.A. Galloway. 1986. Cloning and characterization of ori_{L2}, a large palindromic DNA replication origin of herpes simplex virus type 2. *J. Virol.* **58**: 513.

Moss, H. 1986. The herpes simplex virus type 2 alkaline DNase activity is essential for replication and growth. *J. Gen. Virol.* **67**: 1173.

O'Donnell, M.E., P. Elias, B.E. Funnell, and I.R. Lehman. 1987. Interaction between the DNA polymerase and single stranded DNA binding protein (infected cell protein 8) of herpes simplex virus 1. *J. Biol. Chem.* **262**: 4260.

Panicali, D., A. Grzelecki, and C. Huang. 1986. Vaccinia virus vectors utilizing β-galactosidase assay for rapid selection of recombinant viruses and measurement of gene expression. *Gene* **47**: 193.

Preston, C.M. and M.G. Cordingley. 1982. mRNA- and DNA-directed synthesis of herpes simplex virus coded exonuclease in *Xenopus laevis* oocytes. *J. Virol.* **43**: 386.

Preston, V.G. and F.B. Fisher. 1984. Identification of the herpes simplex virus type 1 gene encoding the dUTPase. *Virology* **138**: 58.

Preston, V.G., J.W. Palfreyman, and B.M. Dutia. 1984. Identification of a herpes simplex virus type 1 polypeptide which is a component of the virus-induced ribonucleotide reductase. *J. Gen. Virol.* **65**: 1457.

Purifoy, D.J.M. and K.L. Powell. 1981. Temperature-sensitive mutants in two distinct complementation groups of herpes simplex virus type 1 specify thermolabile DNA polymerase. *J. Gen. Virol.* **54**: 219.

Purifoy, D.J.M., R.B. Lewis, and K.L. Powell. 1977. Identifica-

tion of the herpes simplex virus DNA polymerase gene. *Nature* **269**: 621.

Ruyechan, W.T. and A.C. Weir. 1984. Interaction with nucleic acids and stimulation of the viral DNA polymerase by the herpes simplex virus type 1 major DNA-binding protein. *J. Virol.* **52**: 727.

Schaffer, P.A., G.M. Aron, N. Biswal, and M. Benyesh-Melnick. 1973. Temperature-sensitive mutants of herpes simplex virus type 1: Isolation, complementation and partial characterization. *Virology* **52**: 57.

Sheldrick, P. and N. Berthelot. 1975. Inverted repetitions in the chromosome of herpes simplex virus. *Cold Spring Harbor Symp. Quant. Biol.* **39**: 667.

Spaete, R.R. and N. Frenkel. 1982. The herpes simplex virus amplicon: A new eukaryotic defective-virus cloning-amplifying vector. *Cell* **30**: 295.

Stow, N.D. 1982. Localization of an origin of DNA replication within the TR_S/IR_S repeated region of the herpes simplex virus type 1 genome. *EMBO J.* **1**: 863.

Vaughan, P.J., D.J.M. Purifoy, and K.L. Powell. 1985. DNA-binding protein associated with herpes simplex virus DNA polymerase. *J. Virol.* **53**: 501.

Vaughan, P.J., L.M. Banks, D.J.M. Purifoy, and K.L. Powell. 1984. Interactions between herpes simplex virus DNA-binding proteins. *J. Gen. Virol.* **65**: 2033.

Vlazny, D.A. and N. Frenkel. 1981. Replication of herpes simplex virus DNA: Localization of replication signals within defective virus genomes. *Proc. Natl. Acad. Sci.* **78**: 742.

Weller, S.K., K.J. Lee, D.J. Sabourin, and P.A. Schaffer. 1983. Genetic analysis of temperature-sensitive mutants which define the gene for the major herpes simplex virus type 1 DNA-binding protein. *J. Virol.* **45**: 354.

Weller, S.K., E.P. Carmichael, D.P. Aschman, D.J. Goldstein, and P.A. Schaffer. 1987. Genetic and phenotypic characterization of mutants in four essential genes that map to the left half of HSV-1 UL_L DNA. *Virology* **161**: 198.

Weller, S.K., A. Spadaro, J.E. Schaffer, A.W. Murray, A.M. Maxam, and P.A. Schaffer. 1985. Cloning, sequencing, and functional analysis of ori_L, a herpes simplex virus type 1 origin of DNA synthesis. *Mol. Cell. Biol.* **5**: 930.

Whitton, J.L. and J.B. Clements. 1984. Replication origins and a sequence involved in coordinate induction of the immediate early gene family are conserved in an intergenic region of herpes simplex virus. *Nucleic Acids Res.* **12**: 2061.

Interaction of Cellular Proteins with the Adenovirus Origin of DNA Replication

P.C. van der Vliet, J. Claessens, E. de Vries, P.A.J. Leegwater, G.J.M. Pruijn, W. van Driel, and R.T. van Miltenburg

Laboratory for Physiological Chemistry, State University of Utrecht, 3521 GG Utrecht, The Netherlands

Adenovirus DNA replication is enhanced considerably by nuclear proteins from uninfected cells. Two of these, nuclear factor I (NFI) and nuclear factor III (NFIII), act by binding to specific sequences in the Ad2 origin. We have studied the mode of binding in detail by footprinting techniques, contact-point analysis, and mutagenesis of the recognition sites. NFI and NFIII bind closely together and share one bp in their contacts. NFI binds to one side of the DNA helix with major groove base contacts. Using bromodeoxycytidine (BrdC)-substituted DNA, evidence was obtained for a mechanism in which NFI finds its binding site by sliding along the DNA. NFIII has contact points at both sides of the helix, with base contacts in the major as well as the minor groove. Sequences surrounding the NFIII core sequences influence binding, and a high-affinity binding site in Ad4 corresponds with high stimulation of replication. NFIII binds also with variable affinity to a number of cellular promoter and enhancer elements, and a consensus sequence TATGCAAAT was obtained.

Another HeLa nuclear protein that binds to the Ad origin, nuclear factor IV(NFIV), was purified to apparent homogeneity. NFIV requires molecular ends for binding to double-stranded DNA and binds to a sequence present at the Ad DNA termini. However, its sequence specificity is not very strong. At increasing concentrations the presence of many regularly spaced binding sites was observed. No strong effect of NFIV on the replication of terminal protein (TP)-containing templates was observed, whereas TP-free DNA replication was inhibited.

Replication of adenovirus DNA in human cells is an efficient process leading to 10^5-10^6 progeny molecules within 20–30 hours after infection. The mechanism has been studied extensively both in vivo and in vitro (for reviews, see Sussenbach and van der Vliet 1983; Kelly 1984; Campbell 1986) and has served as a model for detailed studies on the enzymatic mechanisms of DNA replication in mammalian cells. Both viral and cellular proteins are required for initiation of replication. The two viral proteins are the 140-kD adenovirus DNA polymerase and the 80-kD precursor terminal protein (pTP), which serves as a primer. Initiation takes place at either terminus of the linear, 36-kbp double-stranded viral genome by formation of a covalent bond between pTP and dCMP, the first nucleotide of the nascent chain. The 3'-OH group of this dCMP residue serves to prime further elongation by a displacement mechanism. Although a very limited initiation reaction can occur in the presence of these two viral proteins, the reaction is strongly enhanced by two cellular proteins, NFI (Nagata et al. 1982; Guggenheimer et al. 1984; Rawlins et al. 1984; Leegwater et al. 1985; Diffley and Stillman 1986) and NFIII (Pruijn et al. 1986), also called ORP-C (Rosenfeld et al. 1987; Wides et al. 1987). These proteins recognize specific sequences in the adenovirus origin of replication, located between 25 and 50 nucleotides from the replication start site. Their mecha-

nism of action is unknown, but extensive mutagenesis of the recognition sites (de Vries et al. 1985; Schneider et al. 1986; Rosenfeld et al. 1987; Wides et al. 1987) has indicated that binding of the proteins is essential for their stimulatory function.

After formation of an initiation complex, two other proteins participate in the elongation reaction. One essential viral protein is the 72-kD DNA-binding protein (DBP) that cooperates with the DNA polymerase to permit processive and efficient DNA chain elongation, including unwinding of potential hairpins (Lindenbaum et al. 1986). This protein also protects single-stranded DNA originating from the displacement reaction against nucleolytic breakdown and forces the single-stranded DNA in a regular, rigid structure (Van Amerongen et al. 1987) NFII is a cellular protein possessing topoisomerase I activity and is required only late during elongation (Nagata et al. 1983). We have analyzed the binding of NFI and NFIII to the origin in more detail. The two proteins bind closely together, sharing one bp in their contacts with the DNA helix. NFIII recognizes, in addition to the adenovirus origin, regulatory elements in many cellular promoters and enhancers, all sharing a conserved octanucleotide element. A third protein, NFIV, was purified; this binds to the molecular ends of the origin and displays a remarkable binding mode.

61

Experimental Procedures

Ad DNA replication in vitro

DNA replication was studied in a system composed of the purified viral proteins pTP, Ad DNA polymerase, and Ad DBP as described before (Pruijn et al. 1986). As templates we used either viral DNA containing the terminal protein (DNA-TP) and digested with XhoI or EcoRI-AvaII digests of the Ad2 and Ad4 origin containing plasmids pHRI and P4A85Δ (Hay 1985b). Nuclear proteins were added as indicated in the legends.

Purification of nuclear factors

Proteins were extracted from HeLa nuclei with 0.3 M NaCl (Nagata et al. 1982; Leegwater et al. 1985). NFI was further purified by DEAE cellulose, phosphocellulose, and double-stranded DNA cellulose chromatography followed by recognition-site affinity chromatography (Diffley and Stillman 1986; Rosenfeld and Kelly 1986). The final preparation contained a prominent band at 160 kD and two bands at 120 and 104 kD, respectively (de Vries et al. 1987a). NFIII was partially purified by DEAE and phosphocellulose chromatography as described (Pruijn et al. 1986), followed by pKB67-88 DNA cellulose chromatography (Rosenfeld and Kelly 1986) and single-stranded DNA cellulose chromatography. Throughout the purification procedure, NFIII activity was monitored by assaying the DNA replication stimulation rather than DNA binding to prevent contamination with other proteins recognizing the octamer sequence. SDS-polyacrylamide gel electrophoresis revealed one band of 95 kD, possessing NFIII activity after renaturation (G.J.M. Pruijn et al., in prep.). NFIV was purified by DEAE-cellulose, phosphocellulose, and double-stranded and single-stranded DNA cellulose chromatography. Purification was monitored by binding to the Ad4 origin using the modified exonuclease III protection assay described below. SDS-polyacrylamide gel electrophoresis of the most purified preparation revealed two bands of 72 and 84 kD molecular mass (E. de Vries et al., in prep.). The final preparation contained 100 ng per μl.

Plasmids

MXE-2 contains the 1338 left terminal Ad2 sequence (r-strand) in M13 mp8 (De Vries et al. 1985). p4A85Δ containing the terminal 85 bp of Ad4 as well as the Ad2 deletion mutants were a gift from Dr. R.T. Hay (Hay 1985). Cellular NFIII sites were analyzed in pHB2.3, containing a *Psammechinus miliaris* histone 2B gene (Busslinger et al. 1980), pK$^+$Z/3, containing the rearranged murine κ light-chain gene from 7^{0}Z/3 cells (Parslow et al. 1984), V$_H$19.2, containing a rearranged human Ig heavy-chain gene promoter (Mensink et al. 1986), and pXLU2.5, containing a *Xenopus laevis* U2 snRNA gene (Mattaj et al. 1985). The murine Igμ enhancer is present in CAIG$^+$ (Banerji et al. 1983), and the SV40 enhancer was cloned by inserting the 323-bp

PvuII-StuI fragment of SV40 into the BamHI site of pUC12.

Exonuclease III protection using in vitro synthesized binding sites

To assay the sequence-specific binding of NFI and NFIV we used a modification of the exonuclease III protection procedure (Wu 1985). To prevent stops caused by the degradation of exonuclease III from both sides of a double-stranded probe, we performed primer extension on a recombinant M13mp9 plasmid containing the Ad origin, followed by restriction enzyme digestion of the duplex DNA. This leads to a double-stranded binding site with a single-stranded tail, which can only be digested by exonuclease III from one side. End-labeled primers complementary to nucleotides 65–81 in the Ad2 origin were hybridized to ssMXE-2 (de Vries et al. 1985), elongated with *Escherichia coli* DNA polymerase (Klenow fragment) and digested with BamHI. Five μg of crude nuclear extracts or column fractions were bound to 10 ng (10.000 cpm) DNA in the presence of 1 μg poly(dI-dC)·poly(dI-dC) in 15 mM Tris-HCl (pH 7.5), 2 mM Na-phosphate (pH 7.0), 5 mM MgCl$_2$, 100 mM NaCl for 15 minutes at 0°C (final volume 50 μl). Exonuclease III (50 U) was then added and after 10 minutes at 37°C the reaction was stopped by addition of 50 μl 0.2% SDS, 20 mM EDTA. After phenol extraction the products were analyzed on a sequence gel.

Footprints and contact-point analysis

The conditions for DNase I footprints have been described (de Vries et al. 1987b). Footprinting using methidium-propyl-EDTA (MPE) (Hertzberg and Dervan 1984) was performed by mixing end-labeled DNA and protein in a final volume of 50 μl in a buffer without dithiothreitol (DTT). For NFI and NFIV the same buffer was used as for exonuclease protection, whereas for NFIII the binding buffer consisted of 25 mM HEPES-NaOH (pH 7.5), 50 mM NaCl, 0.5 mM MgCl$_2$, 4% glycerol, and 2% sucrose. 5 μl 1 mM MPE and 5 μl 2 mM (NH$_4$)$_2$Fe(SO$_4$)$_2$·6H$_2$O were mixed, diluted with 90 μl H$_2$O, and 2–5 μl of this mixture were added to the DNA-protein complex. After incubation for 5 minutes at 30°C, the reaction was stopped by addition of an equal volume of 100 mM EDTA, 1.2 M ammonium acetate, phenol extracted, and the products were analyzed on a sequence gel.

Methylation protection and alkylation interference were performed as described (de Vries et al. 1987). Gel retardation analysis was performed by incubating NFIII with 0.1 ng end-labeled DNA (10.000 cpm) in the presence of 1 μg poly(dI-dC)·poly(dI-dC) and 1 μg bovine serum albumin in a buffer containing 10 mM Tris-HCl (pH 7.5), 1 mM EDTA, 1 mM DTT, 0.025% Nonidet P-40, 50 mM NaCl, and 4% Ficoll. Bound and free DNA were separated in a 5% polyacrylamide gel using 25 mM Tris, 190 mM glycine, 2 mM EDTA (pH 8.3) as running buffer. For competition experiments competitor DNA was mixed with the labeled probe before adding NFIII.

Results

DNA replication in vitro is enhanced by binding of NFI and NFIII to their recognition sequences

Replication in vitro of plasmid DNA containing the adenovirus origin of DNA replication can be accomplished provided that the DNA is linearized at or near the origin (Tamanoi and Stillman 1982; van Bergen et al. 1983). An easy assay to distinguish between repair and replication makes use of analysis of reaction products by agarose gel electrophoresis in the presence of SDS. The presence of the covalently bound pTP to newly replicated DNA leads to a mobility shift during electrophoresis. We used this assay to study the effects of NFI and NFIII on Ad2 and Ad4 DNA in the presence of purified Ad2-derived viral proteins. As shown in Figure 1, the Ad2 template containing both NFI and NFIII recognition sequences is stimulated by both proteins. Ad4 DNA, lacking an NFI site, is stimulated only by NFIII. The stimulation is larger than with Ad2, in agreement with the higher binding affinity of the Ad4 site for NFIII (see below). Thus, in this system the stimulation of

DNA replication by nuclear factors correlates with their binding affinity.

The NFI and NFIII binding sites in Ad2 share a common AT base pair

Earlier studies of the NFI and NFIII binding sites by DNase I footprinting indicated substantial overlap (Pruijn et al. 1986; Rosenfeld et al. 1987). We have analyzed the core recognition sequences by chemical footprinting using MPE-Fe(II) complexes as well as by studying the effects on the binding affinity of deletions in the NFI and NFIII recognition sites.

The results of MPE and DNase I footprinting are summarized in Figure 2A. The regions protected against MPE-induced degradation are considerably smaller than the DNase I protected regions, which can be readily explained by the need for DNase I to bind to DNA in order to catalyze nucleolytic breakdown, leading to steric hindrance by NFI and NFIII. The MPE footprints border each other at the top strand, and one nucleotide in the bottom strand between the two binding sites is protected less than 50%. The effects of deletions and mutations on the affinity of NFIII were studied by competition analysis using a band-shift assay. As shown in Table 1, a $T \rightarrow C$ transition at nucleotide 39 reduces the binding affinity more than threefold. Further deletions from this side reduce the binding affinity further. An $A \rightarrow G$ mutation at position 46 is tenfold less effective in binding, indicating the importance of this base pair. This mutation also abolishes the enhancing effect of NFIII on DNA replication (Pruijn et al. 1986). Not all mutations have a negative effect. The Ad4-binding site with changes at positions 43, 44, and 48 has an increased binding affinity. This site corresponds to the octamer consensus sequences found in many cellular NFIII recognition sequences (see below).

Earlier studies on NFI using deletions (Leegwater et al. 1985), point mutations (Rosenfeld et al. 1987), and contact-point analysis (de Vries et al. 1987b) have indicated the importance of an AT bp at nucleotide 39, in particular a major groove contact with the C_5 methyl group of thymidine. Our studies with NFIII indicate that the same AT bp also is required for optimal NFIII binding. Despite their close spacing, no evidence has been found so far for a strong cooperativity. Both NFI and NFIII bind and stimulate independently. They are also

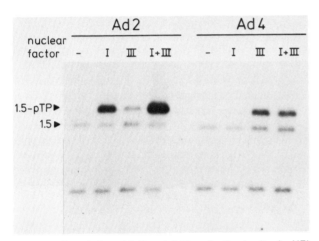

Figure 1 Stimulation of Ad2 and Ad4 replication in vitro by NFI and NFIII. Ad2 or Ad4 origin-containing plasmids were linearized at the origin and incubated in the presence of purified viral proteins and NFI and NFIII as indicated. The arrows show the origin-containing fragment, protein-free (1.5) or complexed with pTP after DNA replication (1.5-pTP).

Table 1 Relative Binding Affinities of NFIII to Mutant Ad Recognition Sequences

Mutant	Sequence	Relative binding affinity (%)[a]
	40 50	
Ad2wt	C A A T A T G A T A A T G A G G	100
Ad2Δ40	t t c c A T G A T A A T G A G G	30
Ad2Δ41	a t t c c T G A T A A T G A G G	15
Ad2Δ43	g A A T t c c A T A A T G A G G	25
Ad2pm 46	C A A T A T G A T A g T G A G G	10
Ad4	t A A T A T G c a A A T a A G G	250

[a]Calculated from the ratio of competitor to probe at 50% competition.

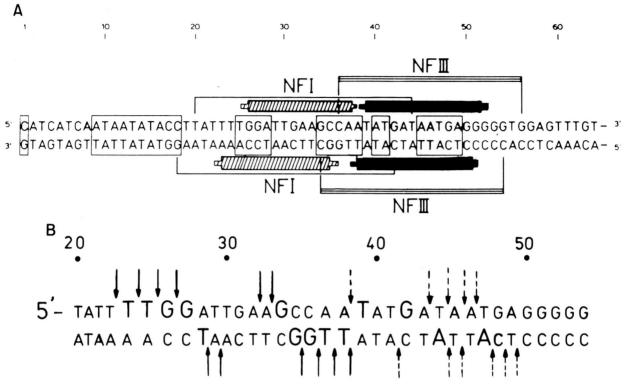

Figure 2 Binding of NFI and NFIII to the Ad2 origin. (*A*) The sequence of part of the Ad2 inverted terminal repetition is shown. Nucleotides highly conserved in the various Ad serotypes are boxed. Large brackets indicate the regions that are protected against DNase I digestion. The hatched area shows the MPE footprint of NFI, the black area that of NFIII. The borders indicate the 50% protection limits. (*B*) Contacts between NFI or NFIII and their binding sites are given in bold type (base contacts) or by arrows (phosphate contacts). The dotted arrows show contacts with NFIII. Base contacts as detected by protection for NFIII are G 42, A 44, and A 47.

easily separated chromatographically, indicating that they are not strongly complexed within the cell.

Contact-point analysis reveals different modes of binding of NFI and NFIII

Analysis of base contacts (A,G,T) and phosphate backbone contacts has indicated that NFI binds symmetrically at one side of the helix, presumably as a dimer. This agrees well with the dyad symmetry of the recognition sequence (de Vries et al. 1987b; Gronostajski 1987). We have performed a similar analysis on the NFIII-binding site by methylation protection and ethylation interference assays. A summary of the results for both proteins is given in Figure 2B. In contrast to NFI, NFIII protects both G residues and A residues against methylation. Since dimethylsulfate methylates guanine residues at the N7 position in the major groove and adenine residues at the N3 position in the minor groove, this indicates that NFIII has both major and minor groove contacts. Ethylation of phosphate groups at several positions impairs binding of NFIII, indicating a close interaction between the protein and the phosphate group. Strong interference was observed for the phosphate groups 5' to the bps 39, 44, 45, 46, and 47 in the top strand and 49 in the bottom strand, whereas the other contacts interfered more weakly, about 50%. In contrast to the phosphate backbone contacts observed

for NFI binding, the NFIII contacts are scattered over the recognition sequence and are not confined to one side of the helix. Remarkably, the two phosphate groups in each strand next to bp 39 contact both proteins. The results indicate that NFIII has a mode of binding that is quite distinct from that of NFI.

Analysis of BrdC-substituted DNA indicates a possible sliding mechanism for NFI binding

To understand the mode of binding of NFI in more detail, we attempted to study contacts between C residues in the recognition sequence and the protein. No methods have been described so far for analysis of C contacts. We approached this problem similarly as for T contacts, i.e., by synthesizing BrdC-substituted DNA containing the NFI recognition sequence using primer extension (de Vries et al. 1987b). In contrast to bromodeoxyuridine (BrdU) substitution, BrdC-substituted DNA bound NFI considerably less than the unmodified control DNA, even at low substitution grades. We then investigated whether specific C residues were responsible for the inhibition by performing an interference assay, followed by specific breakdown of protein-bound and protein-free DNA at BrdC residues using piperidine (de Vries et al. 1987a). Surprisingly, no specific C contacts were observed in or near the NFI recognition sequence. Rather, inhibition of binding occurred at many residues, but residues close to the recognition sequence interfered more strongly than residues at a large distance from the binding site. When the amount of interference is plotted against the distance from the binding site, a gradient is observed, suggesting that the interference is inversely related to the distance of a BrdC residue from the NFI-binding site (Fig. 3). Although several other explanations, like structural changes in the DNA helix by the introduction of a bromine group, cannot be excluded, we favor a model based on the assumption that NFI selects its specific binding sites by one-dimensional sliding along the DNA. The interference results could then be explained assuming that a bromine group impairs with sliding. If NFI would start such sliding randomly, a BrdC residue close to the NFI-binding site would have a larger effect than a BrdC residue at a large distance. Presently this model remains speculative, since the actual binding mechanism of NFI is unknown.

Cellular binding sites for NFIII include promoter and enhancer elements containing a conserved octanucleotide

For NFI, a number of cellular binding sites have been described (Borgmeyer et al. 1984; Gronostajski et al. 1984; Siebenlist et al. 1984; Hennighausen et al. 1985; Jones et al. 1987) and a consensus sequence TGGC/A N_5 GCCAA was derived (Gronostajski et al. 1985). The presence of a strong NFIII-binding sequence in Ad4 led

us to search for cellular binding sites containing the core NFIII recognition sequence. A number of conserved potential binding sites were found in promoter and enhancer elements, all containing the octanucleotide ATGCAAAT in either orientation. These include the histone 2B promoter, immunoglobulin light- and heavy-chain promoters, immunoglobulin heavy-chain enhancer, U2 snRNA enhancer, and the SV40 enhancer. We analyzed these sites for NFIII-binding using DNase I footprint analysis and methylation protection and compared their relative binding affinities using competition assays. The results are summarized in Figure 4. All sequences bound NFIII. The regions protected by DNase I coincide with the octanucleotide sequence and extend for about 20 nucleotides, except for the Ig heavy-chain promoter and SV40 enhancer where 28–32 nucleotides are protected. Methylation protection indicated that, as in Ad2, the G at position 3 of the octamer and the A at position 6 were protected. In the bottom strand this was the case with the G at position 4 and in some cases the A at position 8. A consensus for optimal NFIII binding, TATGCAAAT, could be derived. The differences in relative binding affinities fall into two classes: (1) mutations in the consensus sequence and (2) mutations outside this region. Mutations inside the consensus sequence all reduced the binding by varying degrees, depending on the position and the kind of mutation. Mutations in nucleotides that were shown to contact the protein

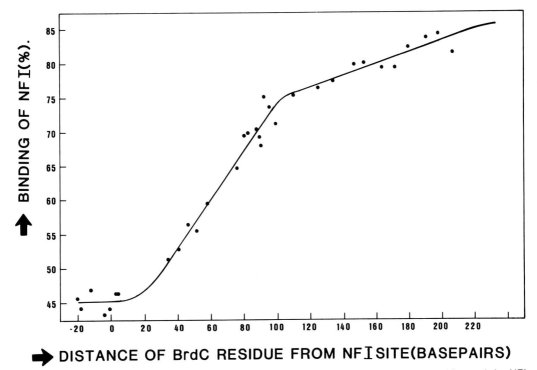

Figure 3 Interference of NFI binding by BrdC is dependent on the distance between the BrdC residue and the NFI recognition sequence. End-labeled, partially BrdC-substituted DNA containing the NFI sequence was synthesized by primer extension. BrdC was present at random positions in the DNA, in a ratio of about 1 BrdC to 50 C residues. To this DNA mixture, NFI was added and protein-bound DNA was separated from protein-free DNA by filtration. Both fractions were analyzed after specific degradation next to BrdC residues on a sequence gel. Each band was quantitated and the percentage filterbound material per fragment was plotted against the distance of the fragment from the NFI site.

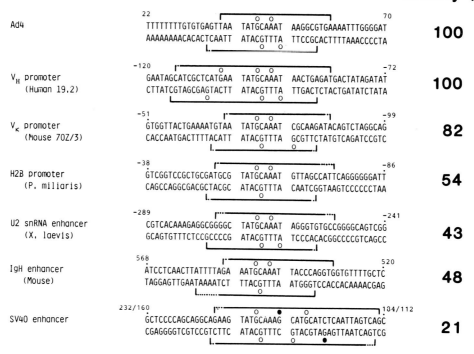

**Relative binding
affinity (%)** [1]

¹**Calculated from the molar ratio competitor DNA/probe
at 50 % competition.**

Figure 4 NFIII recognition sequences are present in cellular promoter and enhancer elements. The sequences of transcription regulatory elements as well as the Ad4 origin are aligned according to the central octamer motif. DNase I footprint borders are indicated by brackets, nucleotides protected against dimethylsulfate methylation by open circles. The closed circles in the SV40 enhancer indicate enhanced methylation sensitivity. The relative binding affinities were determined by incubating fixed concentrations of NFIII and ³²P-labeled Ad4 origin fragments with increasing amounts of competitor DNA, followed by gel retardation analysis and counting of the retarded and protein-free DNA bands.

caused the highest reduction in binding. Mutations outside the consensus sequence had up to twofold effects. Remarkably, the group of three strong binding sequences in Ad4 and the immunoglobulin promoters all contained two consecutive A residues in front of the consensus sequence.

NFIV, a cellular protein recognizing the molecular ends of adenovirus DNA

We have searched for other proteins binding to the adenovirus origin employing an exonuclease protection assay. Primer extension followed by restriction enzyme digestion was used to synthesize a labeled duplex DNA sequence extending from − 12 to +81 of the Ad2 or Ad4 origin. A strong stop was observed at position − 4 upon incubation with crude HeLa nuclear extracts. Using this assay, the protein causing this stop was purified to apparent homogeneity (see Experimental Procedures) and designated NFIV. NFIV was bound to the first 10−12 bp of Ad2 DNA in the presence of NFI. By competition analysis we observed that NFIV requires double-stranded ends for binding, irrespective of the presence of a specific sequence as present in the Ad origin.

When the Ad origin was present in circular DNA, the binding was at least tenfold reduced. The mode of binding of NFIV was further studied by exonuclease protection and MPE footprint analysis using probes containing about 180 bp in front of the first adenovirus bp. Exonuclease assays indicated various stops at regular intervals, depending on the NFIV concentration (Fig. 5A). At high concentrations, this entire region turned out to be protected against DNase I. Upon MPE footprint analysis (Fig. 5B), we observed a regular binding pattern extending from the preferred binding site at position 1 upstream toward the molecular end. A spacing of about 25−30 bp was observed, including 14−18 protected bp, with intervals of hypersensitive sites. This pattern was also strongly influenced by the NFIV concentration. At low concentrations a specific binding site at the preferred location in the Ad origin was seen, whereas upon increasing concentrations the respective sites were filled toward the end of the molecule. A possible model to explain the binding mode of NFIV is given in Figure 6.

The effects of NFIV on DNA replication in vitro depend on the templates used. With TP-free linearized

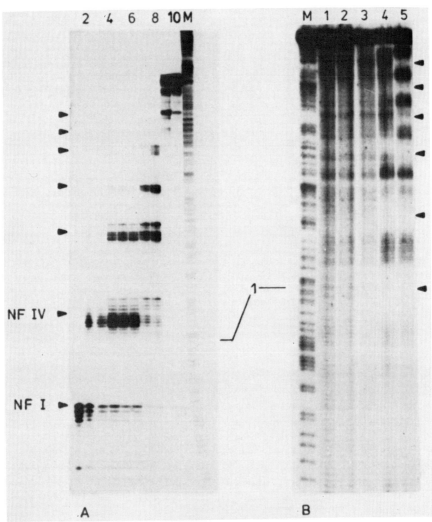

Figure 5 Binding of NFIV at multiple, regularly spaced sites. (*A*) Exonuclease protection. 10 ng of end-labeled DNA synthesized by primer extension (see Methods) and containing 180 bp in front of the first nucleotide of the Ad2 origin (1) was bound to increasing concentrations of NFIV and 10 ng of NFI. The arrows give the position of the exonuclease stop sites. (Lane *1*) No NFIV; (lanes *2–10*) 0.02, 0.04, 0.08, 0.12, 0.16, 0.2, 0.3, and 0.5 μl NFIV. M = marker. (*B*) MPE protection pattern. A 300-bp double-stranded fragment, end-labeled and containing 163 bp in front of the Ad insert was bound to increasing concentrations of NFIV in the absence of NFI. The protection against MPE-induced breakdown was analyzed as described in methods. (Lane *1*) No NFIV; (lanes *2–5*) 0.1, 0.3, 1.0, and 3.0 μl NFIV.

plasmid DNA a strong inhibition was observed, and with the natural viral TP-DNA either a weak stimulation or no effect was observed.

Discussion

Initiation of adenovirus DNA replication appears to require intimate collaboration between viral and cellular proteins. Two nuclear sequence-specific DNA-binding proteins, NFI and NFIII, enhance the initiation reaction considerably. Depending on the conditions, NFI stimulates 10- to 30-fold (de Vries et al. 1985; Adhya et al. 1986; Wides et al. 1987), whereas for NFIII values, between three- and sixfold stimulation has been observed (Pruijn et al. 1986; Wides et al. 1987). These two effects seem to be independent and cumulative.

Both NFI and NFIII were originally detected by virtue of their stimulatory action in an in vitro reconstituted system, but an NFI site is also essential in vivo (Hay 1985a; Wang and Pearson 1985). The role of an NFIII site is less clear so far. Its conserved character (Sussenbach 1985) is indirect evidence for a function, but analysis of Ad2 or Ad4 deletion mutants in vivo has not revealed significant effects of an NFIII site (Hay 1985a), and a stimulation of Ad4 DNA replication was only observed with Ad2 helper DNA (Hay 1985b).

Our detailed analysis of the NFIII-binding site in Ad2 shows that NFI and NFIII bind very closely together, even sharing one base pair. Nevertheless, we did not observe strong cooperativity between the two proteins, either in their binding or in their stimulatory action. Also, their binding modes differ considerably. This could

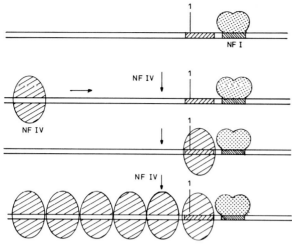

Figure 6 Model for binding of NFIV. The situation is given for linear DNA containing 163 bp in front of position 1 of the adenovirus DNA sequence, and in the presence of NFI. NFIV requires molecular ends for binding and will first bind to a site next to the NFI site. At increasing concentrations, NFIV fills the DNA at regularly spaced positions. Without NFI a similar binding pattern is observed (see Fig. 5B), but NFI increases the binding affinity.

mean that the sites are so close just by virtue of the efficient use of DNA in the adenovirus, suggesting that insertions between the NFI and NFIII sites would not impair function. Presently, we are investigating this point. It should be noted that the position of NFI with regard to its distance to the molecular end is very important. Insertion or deletion of only a few bp around position 20–25 already inhibits DNA replication strongly (Adhya et al. 1986; Wides et al. 1987; E. de Vries et al., unpubl.).

Our results indicate that, like NFI (Leegwater et al. 1986; Jones et al. 1987), NFIII might be involved in cellular transcription. Highly purified NFIII binds efficiently to a number of promoter and enhancer elements required for transcription. Although we have not formally proven that the same purified protein is active in transcription, indirect evidence indicates that this might be the case. The octamer sequence is essential for transcription and proteins present in crude extracts of HeLa cells can bind to octamer sequences in a similar way as NFIII (Davidson et al. 1986; Mocikat et al. 1986; Sive and Roeder 1986; Staudt et al. 1986). Also, a partially purified HeLa nuclear factor with DNA-binding properties like NFIII stimulated SV40-enhancer-dependent transcription in vitro (Bohmann et al. 1987). Formal proof will depend on reconstitution of these systems with purified proteins. The participation of NFIII and possibly NFI in replication as well as transcription could indicate the multifunctional character of these proteins. It should be mentioned that the stimulatory effect of NFI and NFIII on Ad DNA replication occurs in the absence of transcription, thus excluding transcriptional activation in the classic sense (Kornberg 1983). Rather, participation of these sequence-specific proteins in both pro-

cesses could reflect the common need for certain structural changes in the replication origin as well as promoter DNA, or could facilitate the assembly of proper nucleoprotein complexes. Such multiple interactions might govern high-precision DNA-dependent syntheses like replication and transcription according to basically similar rules, guided by DNA-protein as well as protein-protein interactions.

Using an exonuclease protection assay, we detected and purified a third HeLa nuclear protein, NFIV, that also binds to the origin of adenovirus DNA, in addition to NFI and NFIII. Preferential binding to nucleotides 1–12 was observed in the presence of NFI, but this might be caused primarily by a blocking effect. The sequence specificity of this protein, if any, seems less pronounced than that of NFI or NFIII. Other sequences were also recognized and a binding mode prevailed in which many proteins were located closely together and regularly spaced (see Fig. 6). This was particularly apparent when probes were used containing several hundred bp in front of the preferential binding site. A protein recognizing the same terminal sequence of Ad2 was also reported by Rosenfeld et al. (1987) and designated ORP-A. Whether this protein shows a similar behavior as NFIV is not known. The sequence to which NFIV binds preferentially in the presence of NFI is essential for replication, but the function of NFIV in adenovirus DNA replication is not clear. Using terminal-protein-containing templates, no effect, or in some cases a weak stimulation, was observed, and plasmid DNA replication was blocked completely. Thus, the presence of the terminal protein might be one way for adenovirus to prevent inhibition of replication by this protein, but this remains speculative. The increased binding affinity of NFIV in the presence of NFI, even in the absence of an NFI recognition site, suggests some interaction between the two proteins, and presently we are investigating this further.

Acknowledgments

We thank Drs. R. Hay, M. Birnstiel, T. Parslow, R.K.B. Schuurman, C.P. Süter, W. Schaffner, I. Mattaj, G. Tebb, J. Ter Schegget, and A. de Ronde for making the various plasmids available to us. A gift of MPE from Dr. P. Dervan is gratefully acknowledged. This work was supported in part by the Netherlands Foundation for Chemical Research (SON) with financial support from the Netherlands Organization for the Advancement of Pure Research (ZWO).

References

Adhya, S., P.S. Shneidman, and J. Hurwitz. 1986. Reconstruction of adenovirus replication origins with a human nuclear factor I binding site. *J. Biol. Chem.* **261:** 3339.

Banerji, J., L. Olson, and W. Schaffner. 1983. A lymphocyte specific cellular enhancer is located downstream of the joining region in immunoglobulin heavy chain genes. *Cell* **33:** 729.

Bohmann, D., W. Keller, T. Dale, H.R. Schöler, G. Tebb, and

I.W. Mattaj. 1987. A transcription factor which binds to the enhancers of SV40, immunoglobulin heavy chain and U2 snRNA genes. *Nature* **325:** 268.

Borgmeyer, U., J. Nowock, and A.E. Sippel. 1984. The TGGCA-binding protein: A eukaryotic nuclear protein recognizing a symmetrical sequence on double-stranded linear DNA. *Nucleic Acids Res.* **10:** 4295.

Busslinger, M., R. Portmann, J.C. Irminger, and M.L. Birnstiel. 1980. Ubiquitous and gene specific regulatory 5'-sequences in a sea urchin histone DNA clone coding for histone protein variants. *Nucleic Acids Res.* **8:** 959.

Campbell, J.L. 1986. Eukaryotic DNA replication. *Annu. Rev. Biochem.* **55:** 736.

Davidson, I., C. Fromental, P. Augereau, A. Wildeman, M. Zenke, and P. Chambon. 1986. Cell-type specific protein binding to the enhancer of SV40 in nuclear extracts. *Nature* **313:** 544.

de Vries, E., S.M. Bloemers, and P.C. van der Vliet. 1987a. Incorporation of 5-bromodeoxyuridine in the adenovirus 2 replication origin interferes with nuclear factor I binding. *Nucleic Acids Res.* **15:** 7223.

de Vries, E., W. van Driel, S.J.L. van den Heuvel, and P.C. van der Vliet. 1987b. Contact point analysis of the HeLa nuclear factor I recognition site reveals symmetrical binding at one side of the DNA helix. *EMBO J.* **6:** 161.

de Vries, E., W. van Driel, M. Tromp, J. van Boom, and P.C. van der Vliet. 1985. Adenovirus DNA replication in vitro: Site directed mutagenesis of the nuclear factor I binding site of the Ad2 origin. *Nucleic Acids Res.* **13:** 4935.

Diffley, J.F.X. and B.M. Stillman. 1986. Purification of a cellular, double-stranded DNA-binding protein required for initiation of adenovirus DNA replication by using a rapid filterbinding assay. *Mol. Cell. Biol.* **6:** 1363.

Gronostajski, R.M. 1987. Site-specific DNA binding of nuclear factor I: Effect of the spacer region. *Nucleic Acids Res.* **15:** 5545.

Gronostajski, R.M., K. Nagata, and J. Hurwitz. 1984. Isolation of human DNA sequences that bind nuclear factor I, a host protein involved in adenovirus DNA replication. *Proc. Natl. Acad. Sci.* **81:** 4013.

Gronostajski, R.M., S. Adhya, K. Nagata, R.A. Guggenheimer, and J. Hurwitz. 1985. Site-specific DNA binding of nuclear factor I: Analysis of cellular binding sites. *Mol. Cell. Biol.* **5:** 964.

Guggenheimer, R.A., B.W. Stillmann, K. Nagata, F. Tamanoi, and J. Hurwitz. 1984. DNA sequences required for the in vitro replication of adenovirus DNA. *Proc. Natl. Acad. Sci.* **81:** 3069.

Hay, R.T. 1985a. The origin of adenovirus DNA replication: Minimal DNA sequence requirement in vivo. *EMBO J.* **4:** 421.

———. 1985b. Origin of adenovirus DNA replication. Role of nuclear factor I binding site in vivo. *J. Mol. Biol.* **186:** 129.

Hennighausen, L., U. Siebenlist, D. Danner, P. Leder, D. Rawlins, P.J. Rosenfeld, and T.J. Kelly. 1985. High affinity binding site for a specific nuclear protein in the human IgM gene. *Nature* **314:** 289.

Hertzberg, R.P. and P.B. Dervan. 1984. Cleavage of DNA with methidiumpropyl-EDTA-Iron (II): Reaction conditions and product analyses. *Biochemistry* **23:** 3934.

Jones, K.A., J.T. Kadonaga, P.J. Rosenfeld, T.J. Kelly, and R. Tjian. 1987. A cellular DNA-binding protein that activates eukaryotic transcription and DNA replication. *Cell* **48:** 79.

Kelly, T.J., Jr. 1984. Adenovirus DNA replication. In *The adenoviruses* (ed. H.S. Ginsberg), vol. 19, p. 271. Plenum Press, New York.

Kornberg, A. 1983. *DNA replication.* W.H. Freeman, San Francisco.

Leegwater, P.A.J., W. van Driel, and P.C. van der Vliet. 1985. Recognition site of nuclear factor I, a sequence-specific DNA binding protein from HeLa cells that stimulates adenovirus DNA replication. *EMBO J.* **4:** 1515.

Leegwater, P.A.J., P.C. van der Vliet, R.A.W. Rupp, J. Nowock, and A.E. Sippel. 1986. Functional homology between the

sequence-specific DNA-binding proteins nuclear factor I from HeLa cells and the TGGCA protein from chicken liver. *EMBO J.* **5:** 381.

Lindenbaum, J.O., J. Field, and J. Hurwitz. 1986. The adenovirus DNA-binding protein and adenovirus DNA polymerase interact to catalyze elongation of primed DNA templates. *J. Biol. Chem.* **261:** 10218.

Mattaj, I.W., S. Lienhard, J. Jirichi, and E.M. de Robertis. 1985. An enhancer-like sequence within the *Xenopus* U2 gene promoter facilitates the formation of stable transcription complexes. *Nature* **316:** 163.

Mensink, E.J.B.M., R.K.B. Schuurman, J.D.L. Schot, A. Thompson, and F. Alt. 1986. Immunoglobulin heavy chain rearrangements in X-linked agammaglobulinemia. *Eur. J. Immunol.* **16:** 963.

Mocikat, R., F.G. Falkner, R. Mertz, and H.G. Zachau. 1986. Upstream regulatory sequences of immunoglobulin genes are recognized by nuclear proteins which bind also to other gene regions. *Nucleic Acids Res.* **14:** 8829.

Nagata, K., R.A. Guggenheimer, and J. Hurwitz. 1983. Adenovirus DNA replication in vitro: Synthesis of full-length DNA with purified proteins. *Proc. Natl. Acad. Sci.* **80:** 4266.

Nagata, K., R.A. Guggenheimer, T. Enomoto, J.H. Lichy, and J. Hurwitz. 1982. Adenovirus DNA replication in vitro: Identification of a host factor that stimulates synthesis of the preterminal protein-dCMP complex. *Proc. Natl. Acad. Sci.* **79:** 6438.

Parslow, T.G., D.L. Blair, W.J. Murphy, and D.K. Granner. 1984. Structure of the 5' ends of immunoglobulin genes: A novel conserved sequence. *Proc. Natl. Acad. Sci.* **81:** 2650.

Pruijn, G.J.M., W. van Driel, and P.C. van der Vliet. 1986. Nuclear factor III, a novel sequence-specific DNA-binding protein from HeLa cells stimulating adenovirus DNA replication. *Nature* **322:** 656.

Rawlins, D.R., P.J. Rosenfeld, R.J. Wides, M.O. Challberg, and T.J. Kelly. 1984. Structure and function of the adenovirus origin of replication. *Cell* **37:** 309.

Rosenfeld, P.J. and T.J. Kelly. 1986. Purification of nuclear factor I by DNA recognition site affinity chromatography. *J. Biol. Chem.* **261:** 1398.

Rosenfeld, P.J., E.A. O'Neill, R.J. Wides, and T.J. Kelly. 1987. Sequence-specific interactions between cellular DNA-binding proteins and the adenovirus origin of DNA replication. *Mol. Cell. Biol.* **7:** 875.

Schneider, R., I. Gander, U. Muller, R. Mertz, and E.L. Winnacker. 1986. A sensitive and rapid gel retention assay for nuclear factor I and other DNA-binding proteins in crude nuclear extracts. *Nucleic Acids Res.* **14:** 1303.

Siebenlist, U., L. Hennighausen, J. Battey, and P. Leder. 1984. Chromatin structure and protein binding in the putative regulatory region of the C-*myc* gene in Burkitt lymphoma. *Cell* **37:** 381.

Sive, H.L. and R.G. Roeder. 1986. Interaction of a common factor with conserved promoter and enhancer sequences in histone 2B, immunoglobulin and U2 snRNA genes. *Proc. Natl. Acad. Sci.* **83:** 6382

Staudt, L.M., M. Singh, R. Sen, T. Wirtz, P.A. Sharp, and D. Baltimore. 1986. A lymphoid specific protein binding to the octamer motif of immunoglobin gene. *Nature* **323:** 640.

Sussenbach, J.S. 1985. The structure of the genome. In *The adenoviruses* (ed. H.S. Ginsberg), vol. 19, p. 35. Plenum Press, New York.

Sussenbach, J.S. and P.C. van der Vliet. 1983. The mechanism of adenovirus DNA replication and the characterization of replication proteins. *Curr. Top. Microbiol. Immunol.* **109:** 53.

Tamanoi, F. and B.M. Stillman. 1982. Function of the adenovirus terminal protein in the initiation of DNA replication. *Proc. Natl. Acad. Sci.* **79:** 2221.

Van Amerongen, M., R. Grondelle, and P. C. van der Vliet. 1987. Interaction between adenovirus DNA binding protein and single-stranded polynucleotides studied by circular dichroism and ultraviolet absorption. *Biochemistry* **26:** 4646.

van Bergen, B.G.M., P.A. van der Ley, W. van Driel, A.D.M. van

Mansfeld, and P.C. van der Vliet. 1983. Replication of origin containing adenovirus DNA fragments that do not carry the terminal protein. *Nucleic Acids Res.* 11:1975.

Wang, K. and G.D. Pearson. 1985. Adenovirus sequences required for replication in vivo. *Nucleic Acids Res.* **13:** 5173.

Wides, R.J., M.D. Challberg, D.R. Rawlins, and T.J. Kelly.

1987. Adenovirus origin of DNA replication: Sequence requirements for replication in vitro. *Mol. Cell. Biol.* **7:** 864.

Wu, C. 1985. An exonuclease assay reveals heat-shock element and TATA box DNA-binding proteins in crude nuclear extracts. *Nature* **317:** 84.

Requirements for the Initiation of Adenovirus Type-2 and Type-4 DNA Replication

R.T. Hay, L. Clark, P.H. Cleat, M.P.G. Harris,* E.C. Robinson, and C.J. Watson
Department of Biochemistry and Microbiology, University of St. Andrews, St. Andrews, Fife, KY16 9AL, Scotland

We have used an in vivo transfection assay to define the roles of the individual protein-binding domains located within the adenovirus. type 2 (Ad2) and type 4 (Ad4) origins of replication. A plasmid containing only the terminal 18 bp of the viral genome replicates very poorly in the presence of Ad2. Addition of a cellular nuclear factor I (NFI)-binding site, in either orientation, or an NFIII-binding site partially restores replication activity. In contrast, all plasmids that contain the terminal 18 bp of the viral genome replicate equally well in the presence of Ad4, irrespective of the presence of NFI and NFIII.

An in vitro system to study the initiation of Ad4 DNA replication has been developed. A cytoplasmic extract from Ad4-infected cells efficiently catalyzed the template-dependent transfer of dCMP to precursor terminal protein (pTP). Fractionation of a HeLa cell nuclear extract resolved an inhibitor of replication from a factor that stimulated initiation four- to fivefold. Results of deletion analysis in vitro were completely consistent with the in vivo findings: Only the terminal 18 bp were required. Addition of purified NFI or NFIII failed to stimulate the initiation reaction. Thus Ad4 appears to have evolved a remarkably simple origin of replication consisting of the terminal 18 bp of the viral genome.

The adenovirus genome is a 36-kb linear double strand of DNA attached via the 5′ ends to terminal proteins and containing inverted terminal repeats (ITRs) of about 100 bp. DNA synthesis is initiated at either end of the molecule by transfer of dCMP onto the 80,000 molecular weight pTP. The 3′ OH of the protein-linked dCMP then serves as the primer for DNA synthesis. Replication proceeds by a strand displacement mechanism and the displaced single strand then acts as a template for a second round of DNA synthesis (for review, see Tamanoi 1986).

The Ad2 origin of replication has been defined in vivo by a transfection assay in which linear plasmid molecules containing inverted copies of the adenovirus ITR are introduced into cells in the presence of helper virus (Hay et al. 1984). Using this assay deletion analysis demonstrated that the terminal 45 bp of the Ad2 genome fulfilled the requirements of an origin of DNA replication (Hay 1985a). This conclusion was reinforced by the construction of viable virus genomes with deletions in the left ITR. Whereas viral genomes containing a left ITR of only 45 bp were fully infectious, genomes containing 36 bp of the left ITR were noninfectious (Hay and McDougall 1986). When transfection assays were carried out with the subgroup E Ad4, it was shown that, in contrast to Ad2, only the terminal 18 bp of the viral

genome was required for efficient replication in vivo (Hay 1985b).

Utilization of the in vitro system developed to study Ad2 replication (Challberg and Kelly 1979) has led to the recognition that three domains within the terminal 51 bp of the viral genome contribute to the efficiency of replication. The terminal 18 bp of the genome appear to be necessary, but in isolation can support only limited initiation (Tamanoi and Stillman 1983; van Bergen et al. 1983; Challberg and Rawlins 1984; Lally et al. 1984). The additional presence of DNA sequences between nucleotides 19 and 39 stimulates DNA replication in the presence of the cellular protein NFI, which binds to this sequence (Nagata et al. 1983; Guggenheimer et al. 1984; Rawlins et al. 1984; de Vries et al. 1985; Leegwater et al. 1985; Schneider et al. 1986). DNA sequences between nucleotides 40 and 51 appear to constitute a third domain that can increase the efficiency of replication and is the recognition site for a cellular protein known as NFIII (Pruijn et al. 1986) or ORP-C (Rosenfeld et al. 1987; Wides et al. 1987).

Although Ad2 and Ad4 have different DNA sequence requirements for the initiation of DNA replication in vivo, DNA sequence analysis revealed that the terminal 25 bp of the two viruses were identical. Whereas DNA sequences corresponding to an NFIII-binding site were present within the type 4 ITR, no match was found to the NFI consensus recognition site.

To investigate the differences in the DNA sequence requirement for the initiation of DNA replication in Ad2

---

*Present address: NERC Institute of Virology, Mansfield Road, Oxford, England.

CANCER CELLS 6 / Eukaryotic DNA Replication. © 1988 by Cold Spring Harbor Laboratory 0-87969-308-8/88 $1.00

and Ad4, we have attempted to assess in vivo the contribution to replication efficiency made by each domain. We have purified the cellular proteins that interact with these domains and have developed an in vitro system for the replication of Ad4 DNA that can be used to directly compare the replication requirements of Ad2 and Ad4.

Materials and Methods

Cells and virus

Monolayers of HeLa and 293 (Graham et al. 1977) cells were grown in Glasgow modified Eagle's medium containing 5% and 10% fetal calf serum, respectively. HeLa suspension cells were grown in minimal essential medium containing 5% newborn calf serum. Ad2 and Ad4 were grown and titrated on 293 cells by the method of Williams (1970), and virus stocks were purified by the method of Russell et al. (1967).

Templates

Adenovirus DNA, DNA-protein complex, and viral cores were prepared as described (Goding and Russell 1983). Plasmids containing the Ad2 ITR (pHR1) and deleted forms thereof (pHRnΔ) and the Ad4 ITR (p4A1) and deleted forms thereof (p4AnΔ) have been described (Hay 1985b; Harris and Hay 1988), as have the plasmids pC4 and pD21 (Adhya et al. 1986). Supercoiled plasmid DNA was prepared as described (Hay 1985b). Oligonucleotides were synthesized on a Biosearch 8600 DNA synthesizer.

Assay for DNA replication in vivo

Plasmid DNA was cleaved with EcoRI and cotransfected with adenovirus DNA into 293 cells. DNA was extracted from the cells, cleaved with DpnI, and analyzed by Southern blotting using pUC8 as probe (Hay 1985a).

Preparation of protein fractions

Extracts for in vitro replication were prepared from HeLa cells infected with 100 plaque-forming units per cell of Ad4. Hydroxyurea (5 mM) was added 2 hours postinfection and nuclear and cytoplasmic extracts prepared after 22 hours as described (Challberg and Kelly 1979). Nucleic acids were removed by passage of the extracts over DEAE-cellulose in 0.2 M NaCl and proteins concentrated by precipitation with ammonium sulfate. Nuclear extract prepared from uninfected HeLa cells as described (Nagata et al. 1982) was applied to DEAE-Sepharose and bound proteins eluted with a linear gradient of 0.05 to 0.3 M NaCl. Material that passed through the DEAE-Sepharose column was applied directly onto a column of BioRex 80 and bound proteins eluted with a linear gradient of 0.05–0.6 M NaCl. Fractions were tested for their ability to stimulate in vitro replication (Harris and Hay 1988) and in gel retention assays (Barrett et al. 1987) for binding to duplex oligonucleotides representing individual domains of the replication origins. Sequence-specific DNA-binding proteins were further purified by recognition site affinity chromatography using the above duplex oligonucleotides, essentially as described (Kadonaga and Tjian 1986).

Results

Sequences required for Ad2 and Ad4 DNA replication in vivo

To define the role of the individual domains of the Ad2 and Ad4 origins of replication a series of hybrid plasmids were utilized for in vivo transfection experiments. Each of these plasmids contained the minimal origin of replication, nucleotides 1–18 common to both Ad2 and Ad4, fused to either the NFI- or NFIII-binding domains or to a combination of both. The plasmids tested were as follows: (1) pHR18Δ contains the terminal 18 bp, which is identical in both Ad2 and Ad4; (2) p4A2 contains the terminal 140 bp of the Ad4 genome, which does not contain an NFI-binding site, but does contain a binding site for NFIII; (3) pHR1 contains the terminal 103 bp of the Ad2 genome and thus contains binding sites for both NFI and NFIII; (4) pC4 contains the terminal 18 bp of the viral genome linked to a cellular NFI-binding site; (5) pD21 is similar to pC4 but with the cellular NFI-binding site in the opposite orientation (Adyha et al. 1986). Plasmids were cleaved with EcoRI to expose the origin of replication and cotransfected into 293 cells with Ad2 or Ad4. After 72 hours, DNA was extracted from the cells and incubated in the presence of DpnI to cleave any unreplicated DNA (Hay 1985a). Replicated DNA was detected by Southern blotting using pUC8 as probe and identified by its resistance to cleavage by DpnI. The results of this analysis and the structure of the plasmids utilized are presented in Figure 1. pHR1, which contains NFI- and NFIII-binding sites, within the Ad2 ITR, replicates efficiently in the presence of Ad2, whereas pHR18Δ, which contains only the terminal 18 bp from the viral genome, replicates very poorly (1%). Addition of a cellular NFI-binding site, in either orientation, restores replication efficiency to between 10 and 20% of that obtained with pHR1. p4A1, which lacks an NFI-, but contains an NFIII-binding site, also restores replication efficiency to between 10 and 20% (Fig. 1). These results suggest that the presence of binding sites for both NFI and NFIII can independently stimulate the replication of plasmids also containing the terminal 18 bp of the viral genome. The situation with Ad4 is quite different, in that all plasmids that contain the terminal 1–18 sequence replicate equally well, irrespective of the presence of NFI- or NFIII-binding sites (Fig. 1).

Ad4 DNA replication in vitro

To investigate the biochemical differences that are apparent between Ad2 and Ad4, we have developed an in vitro system for the replication of Ad4 DNA, thus permitting a direct comparison with the in vitro system that already exists for Ad2 (Challberg and Kelly 1979). Nuclear and cytoplasmic extracts from Ad4-infected HeLa cells were prepared as described previously for Ad2

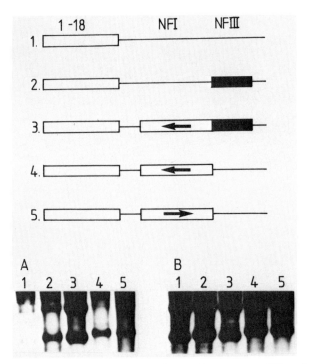

Figure 1 Plasmids containing the 1–18 sequence, NFI and NFIII domains were cleaved with *Eco*RI and cotransfected with Ad2 (*A*) or Ad4 (*B*) DNA into 293 cells. DNA was extracted after 72 hr, digested with *Dpn*I and analyzed by Southern blotting using pUC8 DNA as probe.

(Challberg and Kelly 1979). Initiation was assayed in these extracts by the transfer of dCMP onto the pre-terminal protein, which is the first synthetic event in viral DNA replication. Incubation of viral cores or DNA-protein complex with nuclear extracts from Ad4-infected cells resulted in very poor transfer of dCMP onto pTP.

However, incubation of the same templates with cyto-plasmic extracts from Ad4-infected cells resulted in the efficient transfer of dCMP onto the pTP (Table 1). These results contrast sharply with the situation observed in vitro with Ad2, where cytoplasmic extracts are inactive and nuclear extracts are active. Whereas the addition of uninfected cell nuclear extract to cytoplasmic extracts of Ad2-infected cells stimulated initiation, a similar addition caused inhibition of initiation with Ad4. Quantitatively, the transfer of dCMP observed with Ad4 cytosol alone was similar to that observed when Ad2 cytosol was supplemented with uninfected cell nuclear extract.

The requirements for initiation of replication (pTP-dCMP transfer) in cytoplasmic extracts of Ad4-infected cells are documented in Table 1. Initiation was completely dependent on the presence of template, infected cell extract, and a divalent cation. Although $MgCl_2$ at the optimal concentration of 3 mM was used in these experiments, its substitution by 1 mM $MnCl_2$ resulted in a twofold increase in pTP-dCMP transfer. ATP stimulated the reaction six- to tenfold.

As mentioned above, the addition of nuclear extract to the cytoplasmic extract inhibited initiation. Fractionation of the nuclear extract by ion-exchange chromatography on DEAE-Sepharose identified a potent inhibitor of initiation that was resolved from a fraction that could stimulate pTP-dCMP transfer four- to fivefold. The stimulatory activity could be further purified on phosphocellulose and denatured DNA cellulose matrices and did not copurify with NFI or NFIII.

To establish whether proteins that interact with the Ad2 and Ad4 origins of replication can influence replication in vitro, we have synthesized duplex oligonucleotides corresponding to the recognition sites for NFI and NFIII and the terminal 18 bp of the genome. Proteins from uninfected HeLa cells, binding specifically to these

Table 1 Requirements for Initiation of Ad4 DNA Replication In Vitro

Conditions	Relative incorporation of dCMP	Template	Relative incorporation of dCMP
Complete	1.0	p4A1	1.0
−template	<0.01	p4A1, uncut	<0.01
−ATP	0.13	p4A79Δ	1.05
−MgCl$_2$	<0.01	p4A35Δ	0.92
−MgCl$_2$, +MnCl$_2$	2.0	p4A6Δ	<0.01
+100 μM aphidicolin	1.2	pHR1	0.97
+100 μM ddTTP	1.05	pHR54Δ	1.03
+NE	0.07	pHR45Δ	1.1
+NFI	1.03	pHR18Δ	0.95
+NFIII	0.98	pHR7Δ	<0.01
+stimulatory factor	4.1	pUC8	<0.01

*Eco*RI cleaved plasmid template DNA (0.05 μg) and cytoplasmic extract (4.2 μg) were incubated at 37°C for 60 minutes with various omissions or additions. Second round affinity fractions of NFI and NFIII were used. Crude nuclear extract (NE, 13.4 μg) was from uninfected HeLa cells. The stimulatory factor was DEAE-Sepharose fraction (2.1 μg total protein). Deleted derivatives of pHR1 (contains Ad2 ITR) are designated pHRnΔ, where n is the number of bases of the ITR remaining. p4A1 (contains the Ad4 ITR) and deleted derivatives, p4AnΔ utilize the same conventions. [^{32}P]dCMP transferred to pTP was detected by autoradiography and quantitated by liquid scintillation counting. In a standard reaction 0.5 fmole of dCMP is transferred to pTP.

sequences, were identified using a gel retention assay (Fried and Crothers 1981; Garner and Revzin 1981; Barrett et al. 1987) and purified by recognition site affinity chromatography (Kadonaga and Tjian 1986). Neither NFI, NFIII, nor a protein that bound to the 1–18 sequence was capable of stimulating pTP-dCMP transfer when added to cytoplasmic extract from Ad4-infected cells (Table 1).

The most efficient templates in the initiation reaction were viral cores, although plasmids containing the Ad4 ITR were also active, provided that they were linearized to expose the viral terminus (Table 1). To determine the template requirements for pTP-dCMP transfer, a series of plasmids containing progressively deleted Ad2 and Ad4 ITRs were tested in a cytoplasmic extract from Ad4-infected cells. As previously observed in vivo (Fig. 1), all plasmids containing the terminal 18 bp of the genome were equally active. Plasmids in which the deletions extended into the terminal 18 bp or pUC8 were completely inactive in vitro (Table 1). The stimulation observed with the HeLa cell nuclear factor was equally evident with viral cores, plasmids containing the complete ITR, and plasmids containing the terminal 18 bp.

Heat denaturation of *Eco*RI-cleaved p4A1 reduced template activity 30-fold but did not completely abolish replication, suggesting that denatured template could function in vitro. To investigate this finding further we synthesized 24 base oligonucleotides that contained 18 bases from either the 3′ or 5′ end of the viral genome. The oligonucleotide representing the 3′ end of the genome was active, whereas the oligonucleotide representing the 5′ end was completely inactive in the template-directed transfer of dCMP onto pTP in the cytoplasmic extract.

Discussion

This study demonstrates that there are clear differences in the initiation of DNA replication between Ad2 and Ad4, both in vivo and in vitro. Three distinct domains within the Ad2 origin of replication can contribute to the efficiency of DNA replication (Fig. 2). The first domain located between nucleotides 1 and 18 is common to both Ad2 and Ad4 and is absolutely required for viral replication, although in isolation it supports only limited replication. Domains containing the binding sites for NFI or NFIII can independently stimulate replication when linked to the 1–18 sequence. Whereas the importance of NFI in Ad2 replication has now been well established, the role of NFIII in vivo is still open to question. Previous

deletion analysis had indicated that the NFIII site present in the Ad2 ITR was not required for DNA replication in vivo (Hay 1985b). In fact, viral genomes containing a left ITR in which the NFIII-binding site was deleted give rise to progeny virus with wild-type growth characteristics (Hay and McDougall 1986). In this context, it should be noted that NFIII binds to the site present within the Ad4 ITR with higher affinity than to the site present within the Ad2 ITR. In contrast, Ad4 only requires the terminal 18 bp for fully efficient replication, both in vivo and in vitro. The presence on plasmids of the binding sites for NFI and NFIII fails to stimulate replication in vivo, as does the addition of purified NFI and NFIII in vitro. An additional nuclear factor that could stimulate Ad4 DNA replication in vitro was identified that did not appear to correspond to any of the sequence-specific DNA-binding proteins that have been shown to stimulate Ad2 DNA replication in vitro (Nagata et al. 1982; Pruijn et al. 1986).

Studies using synthetic oligonucleotides revealed a surprising specificity for initiation on single-stranded templates. The oligonucleotide corresponding to the 3′ end of the genome, which would be recognized as the template in vivo was active, whereas the 5′, nontemplate strand displaced in vivo was inactive. A similar situation has been described recently with Ad2 (M. Kenny and J. Hurwitz, pers. comm.), suggesting that Ad2 and Ad4 have evolved a similar mechanism for the recognition of single-stranded DNA.

Understanding the mechanism of DNA replication initiation will require characterization of the factors that interact with the origin of replication. The relatively simple construction of the Ad4 origin of replication may prove to be advantageous in further studies of this nature.

Acknowledgments

We wish to thank the Medical Research Council, the Cancer Research Campaign, and the Science and Engineering Research Council for the support of this work. Thanks are due to Margaret Wilson for typing and Bill Blyth for photography.

References

Adhya, S., P.S. Shneidman, and J. Hurwitz. 1986. Reconstruction of adenovirus replication origins with a human nuclear factor I binding site. *J. Biol. Chem.* **261:** 3339.

Barrett, P., L. Clark, and R.T. Hay. 1987. A cellular protein binds to a conserved sequence in the adenovirus type 2 enhancer. *Nucleic Acids Res.* **15:** 2719.

Challberg, M.D. and T.J. Kelly. 1979. Adenovirus DNA replication *in vitro*. *Proc. Natl. Acad. Sci.* **76:** 655.

Challberg, M.D. and D.R. Rawlins. 1984. Template requirements for the initiation of adenovirus DNA replication. *Proc. Natl. Acad. Sci.* **81:** 100.

de Vries, E., W. van Driel, M. Tromp, J. van Boom, and P.C. van der Vliet. 1985. Adenovirus DNA replication *in vitro*: Site-directed mutagenesis of the nuclear factor I binding site of the Ad2 origin. *Nucleic Acids Res.* **13:** 4935.

Fried, M. and D.M. Crothers. 1981. Equilibria and kinetics of

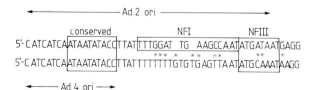

Figure 2 Organization of the Ad2 and Ad4 origins of replication showing regions of homology and protein-binding domains.

lac repressor-operator interactions by polyacrylamide gel electrophoresis. *Nucleic Acids Res.* **9**: 6505.

Garner, M.M. and A. Revzin. 1981. A gel electrophoresis method for quantifying the binding of proteins to specific DNA regions. Applications to components of the *E. coli* lactose operon regulatory system. *Nucleic Acids Res.* **9**: 3047.

Goding, C.R. and W.C. Russell. 1983. Adenovirus cores can function as templates in *in vitro* DNA replication. *EMBO J.* **2**: 339.

Graham, F.L., J. Smiley, W.C. Russell, and R. Nairn. 1977. Characteristics of a human cell line transformed by DNA from human adenovirus type 5. *J. Gen. Virol.* **36**: 59.

Guggenheimer, R.A., B.W. Stillman, K. Nagata, F. Tamanoi, and J. Hurwitz. 1984. DNA sequences required for the *in vitro* replication of adenovirus DNA. *Proc. Natl. Acad. Sci.* **81**: 3069.

Harris, M.P.G. and R.T. Hay. 1988. DNA sequences required for the initiation of adenovirus type 4 DNA replication in vitro. *J. Mol. Biol.* (in press).

Hay, R.T. 1985a. The origin of adenovirus DNA replication: Minimal DNA sequence requirement *in vivo*. *EMBO J.* **4**: 421.

———. 1985b. Origin of adenovirus DNA replication: Role of the nuclear factor I binding site *in vivo*. *J. Mol. Biol.* **186**: 129.

Hay, R.T. and I.M. McDougall. 1986. Viable viruses with deletions in the left inverted terminal repeat define the adenovirus origin of DNA replication. *J. Gen. Virol.* **67**: 321.

Hay, R.T., N.D. Stow, and I.M. McDougall. 1984. Replication of adenovirus mini-chromosomes. *J. Mol. Biol.* **175**: 493.

Kadonaga, J.T. and R. Tjian. 1986. Affinity purification of sequence-specific DNA binding proteins. *Proc. Natl. Acad. Sci.* **83**: 5889.

Lally, C., T. Dorper, W. Groger, G. Antoine, and E.-L. Winnacker. 1984. A size analysis of the adenovirus replicon. *EMBO J.* **3**: 333.

Leegwater, P.A.J., W. van Driel, and P.C. van der Vliet. 1985. Recognition site of nuclear factor I, a sequence-specific DNA-binding protein from HeLa cells that stimulates DNA replication. *EMBO J.* **4**: 1515.

Nagata, K., R.A. Guggenheimer, and J. Hurwitz. 1983. Specific binding of a cellular DNA replication protein to the origin of replication of adenovirus DNA. *Proc. Natl. Acad. Sci.* **80**: 6177.

Nagata, K., R.A. Guggenheimer, T. Enomoto, J.H. Lichy, and J. Hurwitz. 1982. Adenovirus DNA replication *in vitro*: Identification of a host factor that stimulates synthesis of the preterminal protein-dCMP complex. *Proc. Natl. Acad. Sci.* **79**: 6438.

Pruijn, G.J.M., W. van Driel, and P.C. van der Vliet. 1986. A novel sequence-specific DNA-binding protein from HeLa cells stimulating adenovirus DNA replication: Nuclear factor III. *Nature* **322**: 656.

Rawlins, D.R., P.J. Rosenfeld, R.J. Wides, M.D. Challberg, and T.J. Kelly. 1984. Structure and function of the adenovirus origin of replication. *Cell* **37**: 309.

Rosenfeld, P.J., E.A. O'Neill, R.J. Wides, and T.J. Kelly. 1987. Sequence-specific interactions between cellular DNA-binding proteins and the adenovirus origin of DNA replication. *Mol. Cell. Biol.* **7**: 875.

Russell, W.C., R.C. Valentine, and H.G. Periera. 1967. The effect of heat on the anatomy of the adenoviruses. *J. Gen. Virol.* **1**: 509.

Schneider, R., I. Gander, U. Muller, R. Mertz, and E.L. Winnacker. 1986. A sensitive and rapid gel retention assay for nuclear factor I and other DNA binding proteins in crude nuclear extracts. *Nucleic Acids Res.* **14**: 1303.

Tamanoi, F. 1986. On the mechanism of adenovirus DNA replication. In *Adenovirus DNA* (ed. W. Doerfler), p. 97. Martinus Nijhoff, Boston.

Tamanoi, F. and B.W. Stillman. 1983. A specific DNA sequence is required for the initiation of adenovirus DNA replication in vitro. *Proc. Natl. Acad. Sci.* **80**: 6446.

van Bergen, B.G.M., P.A. van der Ley, W. van Driel, A.D.M. van Mansfeld, and P.C. van der Vliet. 1983. Replication of origin containing adenovirus DNA fragments that do not carry the terminal protein. *Nucleic Acids Res.* **11**: 1975.

Wides, R.J., M.D. Challberg, D.R. Rawlins, and T.J. Kelly. 1987. Adenovirus origin of replication: Sequence requirements for replication in vitro. *Mol. Cell. Biol.* **7**: 864.

Williams, J.F. 1970. Enhancement of adenovirus plaque formation on HeLa cells by magnesium chloride. *J. Gen. Virol.* **9**: 251.

Replication and Resolution of Poxvirus Telomeres

G. McFadden, D. Stuart, C. Upton, P. Dickie, and A.R. Morgan

Department of Biochemistry, University of Alberta, Edmonton, Alberta T6G 2H7, Canada

The molecular termini of the Shope fibroma virus (SFV) DNA genome consist of covalently closed hairpin structures of two orientations (flip and flop), and these sequences have been cloned in the inverted repeat conformation within circular plasmids in yeast and recombination-deficient *Escherichia coli*. Telomeric resolution is readily monitored by an in vivo transfection assay in which circular plasmids containing a minimal domain of two inverted copies of a 58 to 76-bp SFV target sequence are efficiently converted into linear minichromosomes with viral hairpin termini (De-Lange and McFadden 1987). Resolution can also be mimicked in vitro by virtue of the ability of negatively supercoiled plasmids bearing SFV telomeric sequences to facilely extrude into the cruciform configuration, which can be converted to bona fide linear minichromosomes by the concerted action of T7 endonuclease 1 plus DNA ligase. Models to rationalize the process of telomere resolution in poxviruses in vivo are discussed.

The complete replication of the ends of linear DNA molecules requires special adaptations to account for the need of all DNA polymerases described to date for pre-existing 3′-hydroxyl primer (Watson 1972; Cavalier-Smith 1974; Bateman 1975). Hairpin termini represent one strategy for circumventing this problem, and such telomeric structures have been observed in *Tetrahymena* rDNA (Blackburn and Gall 1978), *Paramecium* mtDNA (Pritchard and Cummings 1981), linear plasmids of yeast (Kikuchi et al. 1985), linear plastids in barley (Ellis and Day 1986), and the viral DNA genomes of parvoviruses (Berns et al. 1985), iridoviruses (González et al. 1986), and poxviruses (Geshelin and Berns 1974; Baroudy et al. 1982; DeLange et al. 1986). The appeal of poxvirus DNA as a model system to analyze the replication and resolution of DNA with hairpin termini is that viral DNA replication is believed to be completely under the control of viral-encoded gene products and occurs exclusively within autonomous cytoplasmic "factories" (Dales and Pogo 1982; Holowczak 1982; McFadden and Dales 1982; Wittek 1982; Moss 1985).

The first poxvirus for which the terminal DNA structure has been deduced, vaccinia virus, is a member of the *Orthopoxvirus* genus (for review, see Baroudy et al. 1983; Moss et al. 1983). Vaccinia has a linear double-stranded DNA genome of about 185 kb, with terminal hairpin structures that exist in two orientations (flip and flop) and that contain about a dozen non-base-paired nucleotides (Baroudy et al. 1982). SFV, a poxvirus of the genus *Leporipoxvirus*, has been extensively studied recently because of its ability to induce benign fibromas in rabbits (for review, see McFadden 1987). As illustrated in Figure 1, the genome of SFV is 160 kb in length, including terminal inverted repeats (TIRs) of 12.4 kb, and possesses hairpin termini with fewer extrahelical bases than vaccinia (Wills et al. 1983; DeLange et al. 1984b, 1986). DNA sequencing studies of the entire SFV TIR revealed little or no sequence homology with

the TIR of vaccinia except for a region several dozen base pairs immediately downstream from the termini (Upton and McFadden 1986; Upton et al. 1987). Interest in the replication of the telomeres of SFV as a model system for hairpin termini began with the demonstration that the telomeres could be propagated in circular yeast plasmids in the replicated inverted repeat conformation (DeLange et al. 1984a, 1986), using a variation of the telomeric cloning protocol developed by Szostak and Blackburn (1982) to propagate the telomeres of yeast and of the *Tetrahymena* DNA. The palindromic arrangement of the SFV telomeric sequences can also be stably propagated at high copy number in multiply *rec*-deficient *E. coli* (DeLange et al. 1986), although these sequences are unstable in wild-type hosts (Dickie et al. 1987b). In addition, an efficient in vivo transfection system has been developed for both SFV and vaccinia virus that catalyzes the resolution of the cloned inverted repeat arrangement of the viral telomeres into bona fide viral hairpin termini (DeLange et al. 1986; Merchlinsky and Moss 1986). The ability to generate functional linear viral minichromosomes in this fashion has permitted a wide range of experiments to examine the mechanism and enzymology of poxviral telomere replication, resolution, and segregation.

Experimental Procedures

Plasmid and minichromosome constructions

All plasmid constructs containing the SFV telomeric inserts were propagated in *E. coli* DB1256 (*recA recBC sbcB*) as described in DeLange et al. (1986). The parental plasmid pSAD-2 used to construct the derivatives illustrated in Figure 5 has been described elsewhere (DeLange and McFadden 1987) and contains two inverted copies of the core 76-bp sequence (see Fig. 1C) required for maximal telomere resolution. The insert of pSAD-2 contains an 86-bp deletion from

77

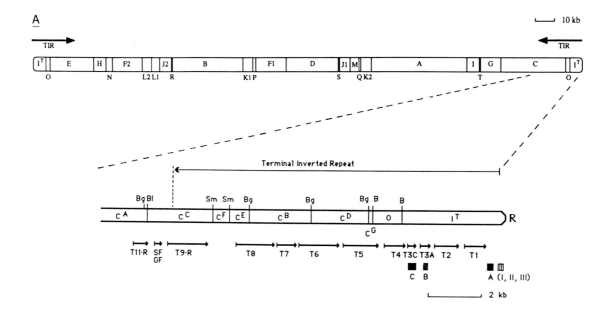

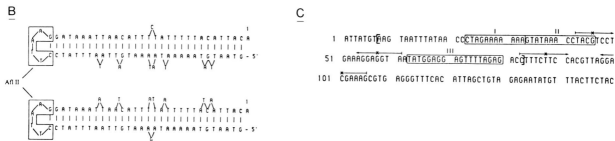

Figure 1 Telomeric region of the SFV genome. (*A*) The *Bam*HI fragments of the 160-kb SFV DNA genome are displayed and the 12.4-kb TIR indicated. The expressed open reading frames T1 to T11-R plus the Shope fibroma growth factor (SFGF) gene are illustrated for the right (R) terminus. Regions denoted A, B, and C are rich in palindromic sequences, and those defined as I, II, and III are within the minimal domain required for telomeric resolution. Bg = *Bgl*II; B1 = *Bgl*I; Sm = *Sma*I; B = *Bam*HI. (*B*) The flip-flop hairpin termini of the SFV genome are shown up to nucleotide 1 as defined by Upton et al. (1987). The boxed *Afl*II site can be found in the lineform configuration only in the inverted repeat arrangement of the SFV telomere (see Fig. 3). (*C*) The sequence of the 150 nucleotides downstream from the terminal hairpins are displayed to highlight the 76-bp minimal resolution core (in brackets) from nucleotides 8 to 83. Imperfect palindromes in this region are shown as inverted arrows. Domains I, II, and III (described in text) are boxed.

the central axis of the native SFV telomeric inverted repeat and is itself a perfect palindrome formed by a fusion of two copies of the core resolution domains such that it possesses an *Afl*II site (CTTAAG) at the symmetry axis. To insert various nonviral sequences into the pSAD-2 central axis, the plasmid was treated with topoisomerase 1 to facilitate the resorption of cruciforms in the plasmid preparation, digested with *Afl*II, and the linearized monomers purified by preparative gel electrophoresis as described by DeLange et al. (1986). The nonpalindromic inserts that were blunt-end ligated with the linearized pSAD-2 included *Alu*I fragments of φX174 (pDφA-series) or *Hin*fI fragments of φX174 (pDAH-series): pDφA-28 (9 bp), pDφA-9 (42 bp), pDφA-2 (55 bp), pDφA-48 (75 bp), pDAH-30 (118 bp). The artificial palindromic inserts blunt-end ligated into the linearized pSAD-2 were derived from pPAL102, which contains a 102-bp head-to-head fusion of the *Sph*I-*Eco*RI fragment of the pUC19 multiple cloning site. pPAL102 was

created by digesting pUC19 with *Eco*RI, blunt-end ligating at high concentration (150 μg/ml), and digesting the resulting concatemers with *Sph*I. The *Sph*I-*Eco*RI-*Sph*I palindrome was purified by preparative acrylamide gel electrophoresis and blunt-end ligated into the *Afl*II site of pSAD-2. The smaller variants of pPAL102 were created by the progressive removal of central axis sequences from pPAL102 by digestion with a sequential series of restriction enzymes specific for the pUC19 multiple cloning site: pPAL94 (*Kpn*I), pPAL70 (*Sma*I), pPAL48 (*Xho*I), pPAL40 (*Pst*I). The numbers in each case of the pPAL series refer to the size (in bp) of the palindrome inserted at the *Afl*II site of pSAD-2. The single axis copy of pSAD-2 (pSDA-1) and the dimeric tandem copy (pSDA-46) (see Fig. 5) were created by excising one side of the symmetry axis of the pSAD-2 insert with *Afl*II plus *Sst*I and re-ligating the digestion products under blunt-end conditions. Clones were screened on the basis of insert sizes and candidate clones confirmed by DNA sequencing: pSDA-1 represented the circularized monomer with no insert; pSDA-2 contained the inverted repeat orientation of the insert (which behaved identically to pSAD-2 in the transfection assay and is not shown in Fig. 5); pSDA-46 contained the tandem orientation of the insert. The control plasmid pAT34 in Figure 2 is described elsewhere (DeLange and McFadden 1987).

Transfection protocols

The in vivo resolution assay has been described elsewhere (DeLange et al. 1986) and involves the transfection of 50 ng calcium-phosphate-precipitated plasmid DNA in the absence of carrier DNA into SFV-infected SIRC cells. At 3 and 24 hours post-transfection, DNA was isolated, digested with *Dpn*I (when required), electrophoresed in 0.7% agarose, blotted, and hybridized with ^{32}P-labeled vector probe. *Dpn*I digestion will cleave only input plasmid DNA isolated from *dam*$^+$ *E. coli*, whereas DNA that had replicated in the transfected cells is resistant (DeLange and McFadden 1986). Efficient resolution of the input DNA into minichromosomes with hairpin termini is characterized by the generation of linear *Dpn*I-resistant molecules of sizes ranging from monomers, dimers, and trimers right up to higher order oligomers. Lack of resolution is scored by the presence of exclusively high-molecular-weight *Dpn*I-resistant concatemers of vector DNA (see Fig. 2).

Results

Properties of cloned SFV telomeres

The observation that poxviral telomeric sequences are not resolved in yeast means that the viral sequences were "frozen" in the replicative intermediate configuration as an imperfect palindrome (DeLange et al. 1984a, 1986). Such inverted repeat arrangements of poxviral telomeric sequences are also observed within replicative intermediates during lytic infection in vivo (Moyer and Graves 1981; Baroudy et al. 1983; DeLange and McFadden 1986). Interestingly, the inverted repeat arrangement of the vaccinia telomere can be propagated in *E. coli* possessing little or no impairment of recombination functions (Pickup et al. 1983; Winters et al. 1985; Merchlinsky and Moss 1986), whereas the SFV telomeric sequences are unstable except in highly recombination deficient (*recA recBC sbcB*) host cells (DeLange et al. 1986; Dickie et al. 1987b). The reasons for this are unclear but may be related to the fact that, although both poxviral telomeres are comparably (AT) rich, the SFV telomere has fewer extrahelical bases in the flip/flop terminal hairpins (see Fig. 1B), and therefore the SFV dimeric inverted repeat is a more perfect palindrome than that of vaccinia (Baroudy et al. 1983; DeLange et al. 1986). Palindromes that are perfect, or near perfect, are known to be highly unstable in wild-type *E. coli* (e.g., Collins 1981; Warren and Green 1985; Shurvinton et al. 1987).

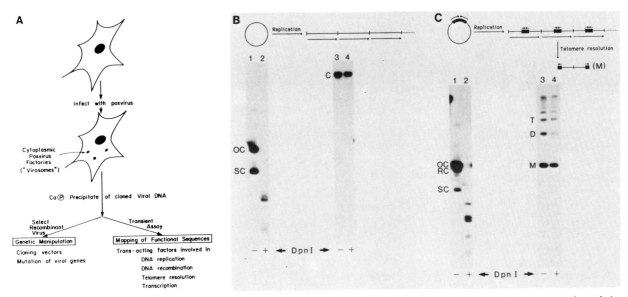

Figure 2 Transfection assay for replication and telomere resolution in SFV-infected cells. (*A*) Schematic representation of the protocol for calcium phosphate precipitation of cloned DNA for genetic manipulation of poxviruses and for transient assays in the cytoplasm of poxvirus-infected cells. (*B*) The sequence nonspecific replication of transfected circular plasmid DNA sequences. Plasmid DNA containing no poxviral sequences (pAT34) was transfected into SFV-infected rabbit cells, harvested at 3 hr (before viral DNA replication; lanes *1* and *2*) and 24 hr (after replication; lanes *3* and *4*), digested with *Dpn*I or left undigested and analyzed by Southern blotting, using vector probe. OC = open circular; SC = supercoiled; C = concatamers. (*C*) The conversion of transfected plasmid DNAs containing the minimal core domain for SFV telomere resolution (see Figs. 1C and 5) into linear minichromosomes. Conditions are as in panel *B* except the transfecting plasmid was pSA1B-56A, which contains 322 bp from the cloned SFV telomeric inverted repeat. Minichromosome sizes are indicated as M (monomer), D (dimer), and T (trimer). RC = relaxed cruciform, which comigrates with OC during agarose gel electrophoresis.

When purified in vitro, plasmids bearing vaccinia or SFV telomeric palindromes readily extrude into the cruciform configuration, with one hairpin arm being equivalent to the flip and the other to the flop arrangement of the viral terminal hairpin (DeLange et al. 1986). The energetics of cruciformation of SFV telomeric derivatives has been examined by two-dimensional agarose gel electrophoresis and shown to be characterized by a moderate energy of formation and low activation energy such that, provided sufficient torsional energy is supplied by negative supercoiling in the individual topoisomers, extrusion occurs as a facile transition (Dickie et al. 1987b). Furthermore, due to the relatively large size of these cloned palindromes, the circular domain of plasmid can be completely relaxed by the lineform-to-cruciform transition and the hairpin arms attain a length determined by the superhelical density of the plasmid. The base of an extruded cruciform is identical to a Holliday crossover junction, and as a result, the cruciform structure is of interest as a possible intermediate during telomere resolution in vivo (see below).

In vivo telomere resolution assay

To ascertain whether or not poxviral proteins that participate in telomere replication and resolution are diffusible and can recognize exogenous cloned viral sequences in *trans*, an in vivo transfection assay has been developed in which plasmid DNA is transfected into poxvirus-infected cells (DeLange and McFadden 1986; DeLange et al. 1986; Merchlinsky and Moss 1986). As illustrated in Figure 2, both DNA replication and telomere resolution can be monitored in this assay and the general characteristics of the system can be summarized as follows: (1) All transfected circular DNA will replicate within the infected cell cytoplasm in a sequence-independent fashion to generate long tandem head-to-tail arrays that migrate by agarose gel electrophoresis as *Dpn*I-resistant high-molecular-weight DNA concatemers. (2) For reasons that are still unclear, cells infected with a leporipoxvirus such as SFV are at least an order of magnitude more efficient at the amplification of transfected plasmid DNA than are those infected with an orthopoxvirus such as vaccinia. (3) The origin-independent replication of input DNA is under the control of poxvirus-induced *trans*-acting factors and occurs concomitantly with viral DNA replication. (4) The majority of plasmid sequences do not integrate into the replicating poxviral genomes but instead are amplified in an autonomous fashion.

When plasmids containing poxviral telomeric inserts are transfected into virus-infected cells, replication of the input plasmid DNA occurs concomitantly with resolution into linear minichromosomes with viral hairpin termini (see Fig. 2C). Both vaccinia and SFV telomeres are resolved in cells infected with the heterologous virus, but in each case SFV-infected cells catalyze higher levels of telomeric resolution than those infected by vaccinia. The majority of linear minichromosomes possess intact hairpins at both ends and are covalently closed throughout their length such that double-length

single-stranded circles can be readily observed by electron microscopy under fully denaturing conditions (DeLange et al. 1986), a situation that mimics that observed for the intact viral genome as well (Geshelin and Berns 1974). Using sets of staggered unidirectional deletions from either axis, as well as bidirectional central axis deletions from the *Afl*II site at the symmetry axis of the cloned SFV telomeres, it has been shown that all of the target sequences required for this resolution event lie within a 58–76-bp core domain just downstream from the nonpalindromic nucleotides that form the extrahelical bases of the viral terminal hairpins (see Fig. 1C). This target sequence must be present as two copies in the inverted repeat orientation to function as substrate for telomeric resolution (DeLange et al. 1986; DeLange and McFadden 1987). Importantly, this core region near the termini of SFV and vaccinia includes conserved sequences (designated I, II, and III), which constitute virtually the only area of DNA sequence homology between the TIR regions of the two viruses. In fact, an intact copy of region I is also found at a comparable position downstream from the hairpin termini of African swine fever virus, an iridovirus that spends a portion of its replicative cycle in the cytoplasm (González et al. 1986).

In vitro telomere resolution

The in vivo resolution assay described above does not distinguish whether the input DNA transfected into the poxvirus-infected host cell is in the lineform or the cruciform (DeLange et al. 1986). However, the availability of template in the cruciform configuration allows for a simple and direct mechanism for the generation of artificial linear minichromosomes in vitro. As shown in Figure 3, the lineform-cruciform isomerization can be conveniently monitored in SFV telomeric plasmids with *Afl*II,

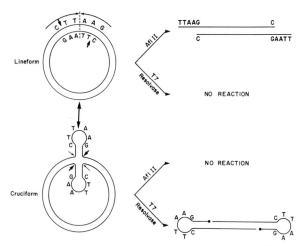

Figure 3 In vitro resolution of cloned SFV telomeres to hairpin termini. The *Afl*II site at the central axis of the inverted repeat arrangement of the cloned SFV telomere is cleavable only when the plasmid is in the lineform configuration. The cruciform arrangement is cleavable by a "Holliday-resolvase" such as T7 endonuclease 1, which generates a linear minichromosome species containing staggered nicks.

which recognizes the target CTTAAG sequence when the central axis is in the fully base-paired conformation but not when extrusion has created partially single-stranded hairpin arms (see Fig. 1B). When in the cruciform, the intact plasmid can be readily cleaved by enzymes that normally recognize Holliday crossover junctions during genetic recombination (Dickie et al. 1987b). One such enzyme is the T7 gene 3 protein, endonuclease 1, which has been extensively studied on synthetic crossover structures in vitro (Panayotatos and Wells 1981; deMassy et al. 1984, 1987; Dickie et al. 1987a) and which will specifically cleave the crossover strands 5′ to the cruciform junction of poxviral telomeric plasmids to yield linear hairpin-terminated minichromosomes in vitro. As illustrated in Figure 3, the sites of the resulting nicks depend on the position of the crossover junction at the time of cleavage, which will in turn be a function of the extent of negative supercoiling of the substrate plasmid. These nicks can be sealed by DNA ligase to yield a minichromosome species in vitro that is indistinguishable from minichromosome monomers generated in vivo by the transfection assay. Thus large quantities of minichromosome can be generated in vitro for transfection studies to analyze the abilities of various constructs to replicate autonomously in vivo.

To date, only one candidate poxviral gene product has been identified that might catalyze a comparable resolving reaction in vitro. Lakritz et al. (1985) described a nuclease activity from vaccinia virus that introduces cross-links into a variety of superhelical DNA substrates. This activity also recognizes the cloned poxviral telomeric insert sequences of SFV and vaccinia but, unlike T7 endonuclease, the products produced by this nuclease are heterogeneous, suggesting a requirement for other accessory proteins before the fidelity of resolution observed in vivo can be reconstituted in vitro (M. Reddy and W.R. Bauer, pers. comm.).

Models for telomeric resolution

Numerous models have been advanced to rationalize the resolution of hairpin termini from an inverted repeat replicative intermediate. Two of these models, illustrated in Figure 4, are based on the terminal palindrome model of Cavalier-Smith (1974) as modified for hairpin termini by Bateman (1975) and the cruciform extrusion model (McFadden and Morgan 1982; Szostak 1983). Note that neither model involves the synthesis of new phosphodiester bonds but merely serves to isomerize phosphodiesters existing in the palindromic intermediate into the segregated hairpin arrangement. An important difference between these two models is that the actual strand cleavage event in a cruciform intermediate would be determined by the crossover position (Fig. 4C), whereas in the staggered nicking model it is fixed by a site-specific endonuclease (Fig. 4D). Note also that the models must account for the fact that the extrahelical bases in the resolved hairpins lie within a 53-bp stretch of the SFV inverted repeat, and thus the two strand cleavages that segregate the parental chains

must occur at least 54 bp apart to maintain the proper flip/flop symmetry of the daughter termini.

The observation that up to 86 bp of the central axis of the SFV telomere can be deleted without affecting resolution allows for certain classes of mutant target substrates to be used to test some of the predictions of these models. In Figure 5 is shown a series of SFV telomeric constructs derived from pSAD-2, a plasmid containing two inverted copies of the 76-bp minimal domain for resolution, in which all of the nonpalindromic central axis sequences have been deleted (DeLange and McFadden 1987). The fact that the 86-bp central axis deletion in pSAD-2 does not abrogate resolution means that there is considerable freedom permitted in the distance between the two inverted copies of the minimal domains. Since pSAD-2 contains a central axis AflII site for insertional mutagenesis, a variety of palindromic and nonpalindromic sequences have been used to modify the distance between the resolution domains. As shown in Figure 5, artificial palindromic inserts consisting of head-to-head fusions of the pUC19 multiple cloning site up to 94 bp in length have very little effect on resolution activity in vivo. However, nonpalindromic inserts larger than 42 bp are incompatible with resolution, as are single-copy minimal domain or tandem-copy minimal domain constructs. These results indicate that although the precise sequence of the central axis of the DNA target for telomere resolution is not important, the palindromic nature of these sequences is critical. This suggests that symmetrical strand exchange (for example, by branch migration) at or near the axis of dyad symmetry is somehow involved in the process of resolution.

Discussion

Eukaryotic telomeres in general are characterized by a variety of structural features that contribute to the stability of the ends of the linear DNA chromosome and to the complete replication of these termini (for review, see Szostak 1983; Blackburn 1984, 1985; Blackburn and Szostak 1984). The extent to which covalently closed structures such as terminal hairpins are utilized by different eukaryotic genomes is still uncertain, but in those systems in which they clearly play a role (such as *Paramecium* mtDNA, parvoviruses, iridoviruses, and poxviruses), the telomeric sequences enter into replicative intermediate structures in which the hairpin termini are converted transiently into the inverted repeat conformation (Moyer and Graves 1981; Pritchard and Cummings 1981; Baroudy et al. 1983; Berns et al. 1985; DeLange and McFadden, 1986). The fact that the inverted repeat arrangement of the poxviral telomere generated by propagation in yeast (DeLange et al. 1984a, 1986) or cloned from viral concatemeric junctions (Winters et al. 1985; Merchlinsky and Moss 1986) can function as precursors for telomeric resolution in vivo argues for its role as a bona fide intermediate of telomeric replication. The overall topological status of the replicating poxviral genome is still poorly defined,

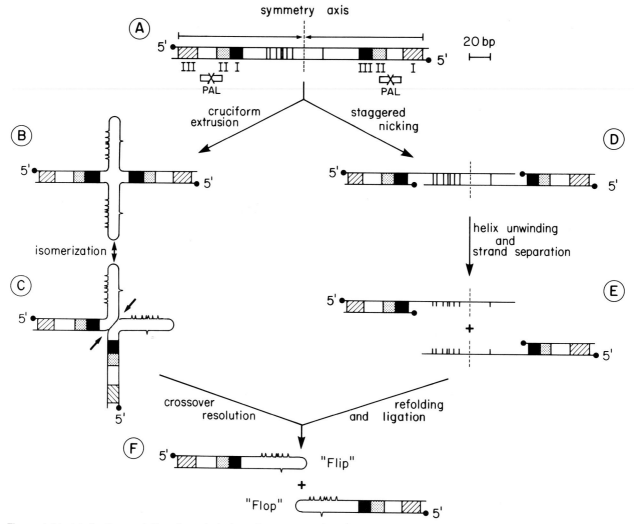

Figure 4 Models for the resolution of poxviral telomeric sequences into flip-flop hairpin termini. (*A*) The inverted repeat arrangement of the SFV telomere, showing the resolution domains (I, II, and III), the overlapping palindrome (PAL), and the 8 nonpalindromic bases (vertical lines) that form the extrahelical bases on the daughter hairpins; (*B*) and (*C*) the cruciform extrusion model, showing resolution at a crossover point arbitrarily positioned at the edge of region I; (*D*) and (*E*) the staggered nicking model showing a site of resolution comparable to that shown in part *C*; (*F*) the segregated hairpin termini.

but in theory such inverted repeats might be found in viral concatemeric arrays, circular intermediates, terminal recombination products, or in terminal replication bubbles (e.g., Esteban et al. 1977).

The target DNA sequences for SFV telomeric resolution can be localized to two inverted copies of a minimal domain of 58–76 bp in length (DeLange et al. 1986; DeLange and McFadden 1987). The data in Figure 5 indicate that the spacing between the two copies of the minimal domain is quite flexible, at least within the range of up to 80–90 bp, provided the spacer DNA is palindromic. The fact that the nonpalindromic spacers' variants do not support efficient resolution activity is compatible with the expectations of models in which some form of strand exchange, such as branch migration, must occur between sequences on each side of the overall symmetry axis. Consider, for example, cruciform extrusion (Fig. 4), which was proposed several years

ago as a possible transient intermediate for telomere resolution (McFadden and Morgan 1982; Szostak 1983). The potential in vivo involvement of cruciform structures remains a controversial issue (e.g., Courey and Wang 1983; Sinden et al. 1983), but Dickie et al. (1987b) have presented arguments that there are no major thermodynamic or energetic considerations that mitigate against lineform-to-cruciform transitions for the poxviral telomeric sequences considered here. Figure 6A indicates how the stabilization of cruciforms can be accomplished in vitro by the energy of negative supercoiling, but the question of torsional stress within topological domains in eukaryotic systems is not well understood, and it is difficult to assess if superhelical tension could play such a role in vivo (for review, see Wang 1985). However, the model in Figure 6B illustrates how site-specific helicase activity could also achieve the same goal of strand separation and refolding

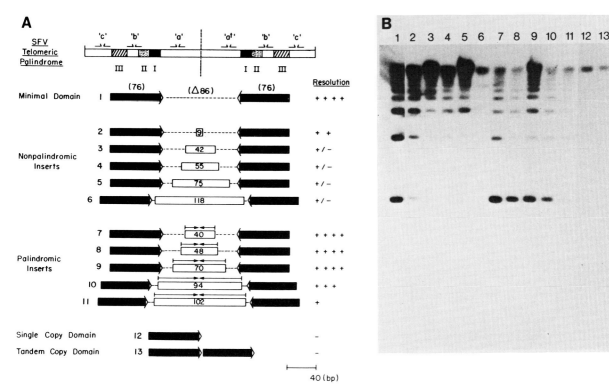

Figure 5 Effect of central axis symmetry variants on the resolution of the SFV telomere. (*A*): Variants of pSAD-2, which includes the minimal domain for SFV telomeric resolution, were constructed (see Experimental Procedures) and tested for resolution to minichromosomes as described in Fig. 2. 1 = pSAD-2; 2 = pDφA-28; 3 = pDφA-9; 4 = pDφA-2; 5 = pDφA-48; 6 = pDAH-30; 7 = pPAL40; 8 = pPAL48; 9 = pPAL70; 10 = pPAL94; 11 = pPAL102; 12 = pSDA-1; 13 = pSDA-46. (*B*) Southern blot of the resolved minichromosomes from panel *A*: monomers (M), dimers (D), and trimers (T).

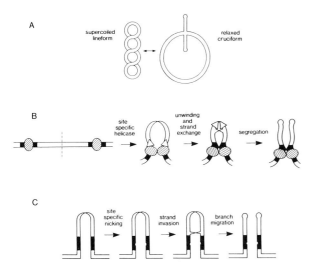

Figure 6 Possible roles of poxviral sequence domains during telomeric resolution. (*A*) Torsional strain induced by negative supercoiling can stabilize the cruciform conformation of cloned poxviral telomeres in vitro, but whether the required topological domains could be generated in vivo is unclear. (*B*) Symmetrical recognition of the two copies of the resolution domain by viral proteins could target helix unwinding by site-specific helicase activity, which could then refold into a cruciform. (*C*) Alignment of the two target DNA domains could be coupled with strand exchange initiated either by site-specific nicking (as in the Bateman model) to generate a single crossover, or else by intact strand exchange to create two crossovers (not shown). Branch migration to the symmetry axis plus the action of topoisomerase would then segregate the daughter hairpins.

without supercoiling. Two examples of site-specific helicase are the *E. coli dnaB* gene product (LeBowitz and McMacken 1986; Baker et al. 1987) and the SV40 T-antigen (Wold et al. 1987), both of which can unwind *ori* sequences in the absence of a replication fork.

The ability of transfected plasmid DNA with poxviral telomeric sequences to be resolved to minichromosomes in poxvirus-infected cells is closely correlated with the capacity of the same cells to support the sequence nonspecific replication of input circular DNA into tandem concatameric arrays (DeLange and McFadden 1986; DeLange et al. 1986). Recently, it has also been shown that poxvirus-infected cells can also catalyze high levels of genetic recombination between transfected plasmid DNAs (Evans et al. 1988). Cells infected with leporipoxviruses such as SFV or myxoma virus are consistently capable of catalyzing substantially higher levels of replication/resolution/recombination than are those infected with orthopoxviruses such as vaccinia, with the levels being negligible in the cytoplasm of uninfected cells. Linkage between telomeric resolution and generalized recombination is also predicted by the model in Figure 6C, which hypothesizes site-specific nicking within aligned copies of the minimal resolution domain followed by strand invasion, perhaps catalyzed by a poxviral equivalent of the *E. coli* recA protein. Branch migration of the resulting crossover junction toward the central axis would also accomplish resolution in a fashion consistent with all of the data.

One advantage of the poxvirus system is the capability of genetic analysis for many, if not all, of the events of the replicative cycle (Dales and Pogo 1982). For example, a number of the "defective-late" temperature-sensitive mutants of vaccinia virus have been shown by pulsed-field gel electrophoresis to generate oligomeric forms of the viral genome that are not resolved efficiently to mature monomers (A.M. DeLange, pers. comm.), suggesting that mutational analysis of the gene products required for telomeric resolution is feasible. The isolation and characterization of these gene products will prove invaluable not only for dissecting the biochemistry of replication of hairpin termini but may very well also turn out to be relevant to the issues of general semiconservative DNA replication and recombination as well.

Acknowledgments

We thank A.M. DeLange, M. Reddy, P. Traktman, and D. Evans for helpful discussions, A. Wills for technical assistance, and B. Bellamy for preparing the manuscript. This work was supported by operating funds from the Medical Research Council of Canada and salary stipends to G.M., D.S., and P.D. from the Alberta Heritage Foundation for Medical Research.

References

Baker, T.A., B.E. Funnell, and A. Kornberg. 1987. Helicase action of dnaB protein during replication from the *E. coli* chromosomal origin *in vitro. J. Biol. Chem.* **262:** 6877.

Baroudy, B.M., S. Venkatesan, and B. Moss. 1982. Incomplete base-paired flip-flop terminal loops link the two DNA strands of the vaccinia virus genome into one uninterrupted polynucleotide chain. *Cell* **28:** 315.

———. 1983. Structure and replication of vaccinia virus telomeres. *Cold Spring Harbor Symp. Quant. Biol.* **47:** 723.

Bateman, A.J. 1975. Simplification of palindromic telomere theory. *Nature* **253:** 379.

Berns, K.I., N. Muzyczka, and W.W. Hauswirth. 1985. Replication of parvoviruses. In *Virology* (ed. B.N. Fields), p. 415. Raven Press, New York.

Blackburn, E.H. 1984. Telomeres: Do the ends justify the means? *Cell* **37:** 7.

———. 1985. Artificial chromosomes in yeast. *Trends Genet.* **1:** 8.

Blackburn, E.H. and J.G. Gall. 1978. A tandemly repeated sequence at the termini of the extrachromosomal ribosomal RNA genes in *Tetrahymena. J. Mol. Biol.* **120:** 33.

Blackburn, E.H. and J.W. Szostak. 1984. The molecular structure of centromeres and telomeres. *Annu. Rev. Biochem.* **53:** 163.

Cavalier-Smith, T. 1974. Palindromic base sequences and replication of eukaryotic chromosomes. *Nature* **250:** 467.

Collins, J. 1981. Instability of palindromic DNA in *E. coli. Cold Spring Harbor Symp. Quant. Biol.* **45:** 409.

Courey, A.I. and J.C. Wang. 1983. Cruciform formation in a negatively supercoiled DNA may be kinetically forbidden under physiological conditions. *Cell* **33:** 817.

Dales, S. and B.G.T. Pogo. 1982. *The biology of poxviruses.* Springer-Verlag, New York.

DeLange, A.M. and G. McFadden. 1986. Sequence nonspecific replication of transfected plasmids in poxvirus-infected cells. *Proc. Natl. Acad. Sci.* **83:** 614.

———. 1987. Efficient resolution of replicated ·poxvirus telo-

meres to native hairpin structures requires two inverted symmetrical copies of a core target DNA sequence. *J. Virol.* **61:** 1957.

DeLange, A.M., B. Futcher, R. Morgan, and G. McFadden. 1984a. Cloning of the vaccinia virus telomere in a yeast plasmid vector. *Gene* **27:** 13.

DeLange, A.M., C. Macaulay, W. Block, T. Mueller, and G. McFadden. 1984b. Tumorigenic poxviruses: construction of the composite physical map of the Shope fibroma virus genome. *J. Virol.* **50:** 408.

DeLange, A.M., M. Reddy, D. Scraba, C. Upton, and G. McFadden. 1986. Replication and resolution of cloned poxvirus telomeres *in vivo* generates linear minichromosomes with intact viral hairpin termini. *J. Virol.* **59:** 249.

deMassy, B., R.A. Weisberg, and F.W. Studier. 1987. Gene 3 endonuclease of bacteriophage T7 resolves conformationally branched structures in double-stranded DNA. *J. Mol. Biol.* **193:** 359.

deMassy, B., F.W. Studier, L. Dorgai, L. Appelbaum, and R.A. Weisberg. 1984. Enzymes and sites of genetic recombination: Studies with gene-3 endonuclease of phage T7 and with site-affinity mutants of phage lambda. *Cold Spring Harbor Symp. Quant. Biol.* **49:** 715.

Dickie, P., G. McFadden, and A.R. Morgan. 1987a. The site-specific cleavage of synthetic Holliday junction analogs and related branched DNA structures by bacteriophage T7 endonuclease 1. *J. Biol. Chem.* **262:** 14826.

Dickie, P., A.R. Morgan, and G. McFadden. 1987b. Cruciform extrusion in plasmids bearing the replicative intermediate configuration of a poxvirus telomere. *J. Mol. Biol.* **196:** 541.

Ellis, T.H.N. and A. Day. 1986. A hairpin plastid genome in barley. *EMBO J.* **5:** 2769.

Esteban, M., L. Flores, and J.A. Holowczak. 1977. Model for vaccinia virus DNA replication. *Virology* **83:** 467.

Evans, D., D. Stuart, and G. McFadden. 1988. High levels of genetic recombination between co-transfected plasmid DNAs in poxvirus-infected mammalian cells. *J. Virol.* **62:** 367.

Geshelin, P. and K.I. Berns. 1974. Characterization and localization of the naturally occurring crosslinks in vaccinia virus DNA. *J. Mol. Biol.* **88:** 785.

González, A., A. Talavera, J.M. Almendral, and E. Viñuela. 1986. Hairpin loop structure of African swine fever virus DNA. *Nucleic Acids Res.* **14:** 6835.

Holowczak, J.A. 1982. Poxvirus DNA. *Curr. Top. Microbiol. Immunol.* **97:** 27.

Kikuchi, Y., K. Hirai, N. Gunge, and F. Hishinuma. 1985. Hairpin plasmid—A novel linear DNA of perfect hairpin structure. *EMBO J.* **4:** 1881.

Lakritz, N., P.D. Foglesong, M. Reddy, S. Baum, J. Hurwitz, and W.R. Bauer. 1985. A vaccinia virus DNase preparation which cross-links superhelical DNA. *J. Virol.* **53:** 935.

LeBowitz, J.H. and R. McMacken. 1986. The *E. coli* dnaB replication protein is a DNA helicase. *J. Biol. Chem.* **261:** 4738.

McFadden, G. 1987. Poxviruses of rabbits. In *Virus diseases in laboratory and captive animals* (ed. G. Darai), p. 37. Martinus Nijhoff, Boston.

McFadden, G. and S. Dales. 1982. Organization and replication of poxvirus DNA. In *Organization and replication of viral DNA* (ed. A.S. Kaplan), p. 173. CRC Press, Boca Raton, Florida.

McFadden, G. and A.R. Morgan. 1982. DNA cruciform structures: Implications for telomer replication in eukaryotes and instability of long palindromic DNA sequences in prokaryotes. *J. Theor. Biol.* **97:** 343.

Merchlinsky, M. and B. Moss. 1986. Resolution of linear minichromosomes with hairpin ends from circular plasmids containing vaccinia virus concatemer junctions. *Cell* **45:** 879.

Moss, B. 1985. Replication of poxviruses. In *Virology* (ed. B.N. Fields,) p. 685. Raven Press, New York.

Moss, B., E. Winters, and E.V. Jones. 1983. Replication of vaccinia virus. *UCLA Symp. Mol. Cell. Biol. New Ser.* **10:** 449.

Moyer, R.N. and R.L. Graves. 1981. The mechanism of cytoplasmic orthopoxvirus DNA replication. *Cell* **27:** 391.

Panayotatos, N. and R.D. Wells. 1981. Cruciform structures in supercoiled DNA. *Nature* **289:** 466.

Pickup, D.J., D. Bastia, and W.K. Joklik. 1983. Cloning of the terminal loop of vaccinia virus DNA. *Virology* **124:** 215.

Pritchard, A.E. and D.J. Cummings. 1981. Replication of linear mitochondrial DNA from *Paramecium*: Sequence and structure of the initiation-end crosslink. *Proc. Natl. Acad. Sci.* **78:** 7341.

Shurvinton, C.E., M.M. Stahl, and F.W. Stahl. 1987. Large palindromes in the lambda phage genome are preserved in a rec⁺ host by inhibiting lambda DNA replication. *Proc. Natl. Acad. Sci.* **84:** 1624.

Sinden, R.R., S.S. Broyles, and D.E. Pettijohn. 1983. Perfect palindromic *lac* operator DNA sequence exists as a stable cruciform structure in supercoiled DNA *in vitro* but not *in vivo*. *Proc. Natl. Acad. Sci.* **80:** 1797.

Szostak, J.W. 1983. Replication and resolution of telomeres in yeast. *Cold Spring Harbor Symp. Quant. Biol.* **47:** 1187.

Szostak, J.W. and E.H. Blackburn. 1982. Cloning yeast telomeres on linear plasmid vectors. *Cell* **29:** 245.

Upton, C. and G. McFadden. 1986. Tumorigenic poxviruses: Analysis of viral DNA sequences implicated in the tumorigenicity of Shope fibroma virus and malignant rabbit virus. *Virology* **152:** 308.

Upton, C., A.M. DeLange, and G. McFadden. 1987. Tumorigenic poxviruses: Genomic organization and DNA sequence of the telomeric region of the Shope fibroma virus genome. *Virology* **160:** 20.

Wang, J.C. 1985. DNA topoisomerases. *Annu. Rev. Biochem.* **54:** 665.

Warren, G.J. and R.L. Green. 1985. Comparison of physical and genetic properties of palindromic DNA sequences. *J. Bacteriol.* **161:** 1103.

Watson, J.D. 1972. Origin of concatemeric T7 DNA. *Nat. New Biol.* **239:** 197.

Wills, A., A.M. DeLange, C. Gregson, C. Macaulay, and G. McFadden. 1983. Physical characterization and molecular cloning of the Shope fibroma virus genome. *Virology* **130:** 403.

Winters, E., B.M. Baroudy, and B. Moss. 1985. Molecular cloning of the terminal hairpin of vaccinia virus DNA as an imperfect palindrome in an *E. coli* plasmid. *Gene* **37:** 221.

Wittek, R. 1982. Organization and expression of the poxvirus genome. *Experientia* **38:** 285.

Wold, M.S., J.J. Li, and T.J. Kelly. 1987. Initiation of SV40 DNA replication *in vitro*: Large-tumor-antigen and origin-dependent unwinding of the template. *Proc. Natl. Acad. Sci.* **84:** 3643.

Sequence-independent Replication and Sequence-specific Resolution of Plasmids Containing the Vaccinia Virus Concatemer Junction: Requirements for Early and Late *trans*-Acting Factors

M. Merchlinsky and B. Moss

Laboratory of Viral Diseases, National Institute of Allergy and Infectious Diseases,
National Institutes of Health, Bethesda, Maryland 20892

The concatemer junction from replicative forms of vaccinia virus DNA was cloned into plasmid vectors and shown to be a precise duplex copy of the viral terminal hairpin structure with each strand corresponding to one of the alternative sequence isomers. Circular *Escherichia coli* plasmids with palindromic junction fragments were replicated in vaccinia-virus-infected cells and resolved into linear minichromosomes with vector DNA in the center and vaccinia virus DNA hairpins at each end. The replication of input plasmids required early viral *trans*-acting factors and was sequence-independent, whereas the resolution of plasmids containing the concatemer junction was sequence-specific and relied on late viral factors.

Poxviruses are large, double-stranded DNA viruses that replicate in the cytoplasm of infected cells. Vaccinia, like other poxviruses, encodes for all or nearly all of the factors required for its own replication (for review, see Moss 1985). Among the enzymes that may be directly involved in replication of vaccinia virus DNA, a DNA polymerase (Earl et al. 1986), a DNA-dependent ATPase (Rodriguez et al. 1986; Broyles and Moss 1987), and a topoisomerase (Shuman and Moss 1987) have been mapped and sequenced. Vaccinia virus has a 185,000-bp genome with cross-linked ends (Geshelin and Berns 1974). The nucleotide sequence of the termini has revealed that the ends of the genome are covalently continuous, with each strand joined to form a hairpin loop (Baroudy et al. 1982). The details of vaccinia virus replication are poorly understood, but a series of studies showed that nicks are introduced near the ends of the genome soon after infection and sealed as cross-links in daughter molecules (Esteban and Holowczak 1977a,b; Pogo 1977, 1980; Pogo and O'Shea 1978). Furthermore, during viral replication the terminal sequences were detected in concatemeric forms by restriction digests of intracellular forms of rabbitpox (Moyer and Graves 1981) and vaccinia (Baroudy et al. 1983; Moss et al. 1983) virus DNA. The association of these concatemeric forms with the virosomal nucleoprotein complex during DNA replication and their transitory appearance during early stages of replication suggest that such structures may be replicative intermediates.

We have cloned the concatemer junction of replicating vaccinia virus DNA to determine its precise structure and prepare substrates for studying the processing of this intermediate into mature telomeres (Merchlinsky et al. 1988). The concatemer junction was shown to be a precise duplex copy of the viral terminal hairpin structure, with each strand corresponding to one of the alternative sequence isomers. The circular plasmids containing the concatemer junction, when transfected into vaccinia-virus-infected cells, replicated and were resolved into linear vaccinia minichromosomes with covalently continuous hairpin ends (Merchlinsky and Moss 1986). Similar findings also were obtained by DeLange et al. (1986) with synthetic concatemer junctions from vaccinia virus and Shope fibroma virus. During the course of these studies, it was noted that plasmids without poxvirus DNA sequences could replicate in infected cells (DeLange and McFadden 1986; Merchlinsky and Moss 1986).

The purpose of the present study was to distinguish between *cis*- and *trans*-acting factors required for plasmid replication and telomere resolution. We report that plasmid replication is not enhanced by any vaccinia virus DNA sequence, but is dependent on early viral functions. In contrast, the conversion of plasmids containing the concatemer junction into linear minichromosomes was sequence-specific and relied on late viral gene function(s).

Methods

Construction of recombinant plasmids
Plasmids containing the concatemer junction of vaccinia virus were prepared as described previously (Merchlinsky et al. 1988). To construct the plasmids spanning the genome, DNA was isolated from purified vaccinia virus strain WR by resuspending virus at 2.5 mg/ml in 50 mM Tris-HCl (pH 8.0), 0.5% SDS, 6% sucrose, and 1

CANCER CELLS 6 / Eukaryotic DNA Replication. © 1988 by Cold Spring Harbor Laboratory 0-87969-308-8/88 $1.00

mg/ml proteinase K at 37°C for 4 hours. The sample was extracted with phenol, phenol:chloroform, and chloroform before precipitation with ethanol. The pellet was resuspended in TE (10 mM Tris-HCl [pH 8.0], 1 mM EDTA), digested with HindIII, and ligated to HindIII-digested, calf intestinal phosphatase-treated pUC13. Recombinants containing vaccinia virus DNA were detected by colony hybridization and analyzed by agarose gel electrophoresis of DNA isolated by a boiling minilysis procedure. Plasmids containing the HindIII D through HindIII O fragments were prepared. The HindIII B and HindIII C fragments were isolated after agarose gel electrophoresis by dissolving the gel slice in sodium perchlorate (Yang et al. 1979) followed by glass bead extraction (Vogelstein and Gillespie 1979). The samples were digested with SalI and ligated to SalI-digested calf intestinal phosphatase-treated pUC13, and the SalI and SalN from Hind B and SalK from Hind C were isolated. The HindIII-SalI fragments from Hind B and Hind C were purified by perchlorate extraction after agarose gel electrophoresis and ligated to HindIII-SalI-digested pBR322. The BamHI subclones of HindIII A and cosmid library of vaccinia virus were supplied by E. Jones; the plasmid pA7 was provided by P. Earl.

The clones pOX and pHD-2X were derived from pHD. The plasmid pHD was constructed by treating the 412-bp HinfI concatemer junction fragment derived from pBD (Merchlinsky et al.1988) with Klenow fragment to generate blunt ends and ligating the fragment to a HincII-digested pUC13 plasmid missing the XbaI site. The plasmid pHD-2X was generated by digesting pHD with XbaI and ligating the large vector-insert fragment to the 132-bp XbaI central fragment containing the vaccinia virus hairpin sequence. The pOX was constructed from pHD by digestion with XbaI, addition of an annealed 37-bp oligonucleotide with a single base change converting a T to an A in the outermost XbaI site, and ligation to the central XbaI fragment to regenerate an intact 412-bp palindromic insert.

Transfection of recombinant plasmids into eukaryotic cells

Tissue culture cells at 80–100% confluency in six-well dishes were infected with vaccinia virus strain WR or temperature-sensitive mutants (Condit et al. 1983) at a multiplicity of 30 pfu per cell or mock-infected with medium. After 30 minutes at 37°C, the cells were overlaid with 5 ml minimal essential medium (MEM) (Quality Biologicals) containing 10% fetal calf serum and transfected with plasmids by calcium phosphate precipitation (Graham and van der Eb 1973). The DNA precipitate was formed by mixing an equal volume (0.25 ml) of 2 × HBS (280 mM NaCl, 40 mM HEPES [pH 7.1], 2 mM Na$_2$HPO$_4$), and 250 mM CaCl$_2$ containing the plasmid DNA. Approximately 1 μg of plasmid DNA was used per well, and carrier DNA was not required for efficient transfection. The medium was replaced 4 hours posttransfection. After 24 hours, the cells were harvested by scraping, rinsed with phosphate-buffered saline, and the DNA was isolated by a modified Hirt procedure

(Merchlinsky and Moss 1986) or by cytoplasmic fractionation. The cellular membranes were lysed by incubation in 300 μl of 100 mM NaCl, 50 mM KCl, 20 mM Tris-HCl (pH 8.0), 0.1 mM EDTA, 0.1% Triton X-100, 0.5% NP-40 (Razin et al. 1979) on ice for 10 minutes. The nuclei were removed by low-speed centrifugation and the samples were brought to 0.5 mg/ml proteinase K and incubated at 37°C for 6 hours. The samples were phenol, phenol:chloroform, and chloroform extracted before precipitation with ethanol. The pellets were resuspended in TE before digestion with restriction enzymes (New England Biolabs or Beohringer Mannheim), agarose gel electrophoresis, transfer to Gene Screen Plus (Dupont), and hybridization with vector DNA labeled with ^{32}P by nick translation. Enzyme incubations and Southern blotting protocols were performed as suggested by the manufacturer or as described in Maniatis et al. (1982).

Results

Plasmids are replicated in an origin-independent manner in vaccinia virus-infected cells

Specific origins of replication have not yet been identified in the vaccinia virus genome. Indeed, the presence of such origins is questionable, as circular DNA molecules lacking any vaccinia DNA can replicate in infected cells. Alternatively, the replication observed might be a background level that could be greatly enhanced in plasmids containing origin sequences. To test the latter hypothesis, overlapping fragments representing the entire vaccinia genome were subcloned into plasmid and cosmid vectors and tested for their ability to replicate in infected cells. The sets of fragments used for this study are indicated in Figure 1. These included the HindIII D to HindIII O fragments, eight subclones of HindIII A, four subfragments of HindIII B, three subfragments of HindIII C, and six overlapping cosmid clones derived from a partial Sau3A digest of vaccinia DNA (Jones et al. 1987). Additional plasmids containing the concatemer junction of vaccinia virus not shown in Figure 1 were also used for this study.

This collection of plasmids and cosmids was used to transfect monolayers of tissue culture cells infected with vaccinia virus. Cytoplasmic DNA was isolated 24 hours posttransfection, digested with DpnI, which extensively cleaves the methylated input plasmid but not the newly replicated unmethylated DNA, and an enzyme with a unique site in each plasmid (usually SmaI) electrophoresed on an agarose gel, transferred to nitrocellulose, and hybridized with nick-translated vector DNA. A representative experiment is shown in Figure 2. In this example, plasmids containing equimolar amounts of the HindIII D through HindIII O fragments plus a constant amount of pUC13 as an internal control were transfected into 293 cells and cytoplasmic DNA was digested with SmaI, which cuts uniquely in vector sequence, and DpnI. All plasmids, including the pUC13, replicated to a similar extent in vaccinia virus-infected cells, but not in

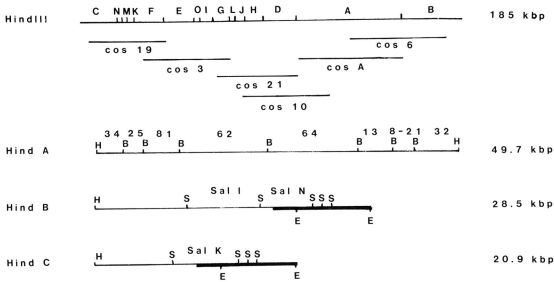

Figure 1 Viral DNA fragments used to determine *cis*-acting sequences required for replication. The clones were prepared as described in the text. The subclones of *Hind*III A, B, and C fragments are shown with restriction enzymes *Hind*III (H), *Bam*HI (B), *Sal*I (S), and *Eco*RI (E). The heavy line in *Hind*III B and C refers to the viral terminal inverted repetition.

uninfected cells (not shown). Nonspecific replication was observed for all input plasmids, including subclones of the concatemer junction in BSC-1, 293, CV-1, or RK cells after infection with vaccinia virus. The replicated plasmid DNA ran as a high-molecular-weight ($>$ 25 kb) heterogeneous smear when digested solely with *Dpn*I. Partial digestion with a restriction enzyme that cut once in the transfected plasmid yielded a series of fragments at integer multiples of the input plasmid consistent with a tandem array of head-to-tail molecules. Thus, we could find no evidence for *cis*-acting vaccinia DNA sequences that greatly enhanced plasmid replication.

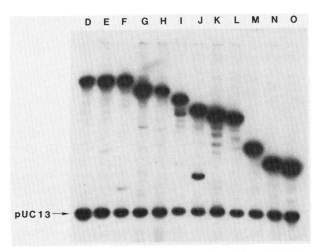

Figure 2 Sequence-independent replication of plasmid DNA in infected cells. Cells were infected with vaccinia virus and transfected with plasmids containing (from left to right) the *Hind*III D through *Hind*III O fragments as well as a constant amount of pUC13. The DNA was isolated and digested with *Dpn*I and *Sma*I before electrophoresis and hybridization with pUC13 labeled with ^{32}P by nick translation.

Resolution of circular plasmids into linear minichromosomes is sequence specific

We demonstrated previously that circular plasmids containing the concatemer junction of vaccinia virus replicative intermediate DNA are converted into linear minichromosomes in cells infected with vaccinia virus. The structure of the concatemer junction and the resolution process are outlined in Figure 3. Also, an autoradiograph showing the formation of linear molecules from cloned 2.6-kb *Bst*EII and 250-bp *Pvu*I fragments is presented in Figure 3. Evidence that the resolved bands have the indicated structure was reported previously (Merchlinsky and Moss 1986). Significantly, the 132-bp *Xba*I concatemer junction (pWBXba11) was not resolved. There are at least two possible interpretations of these results. One is that at least a certain size inverted repeat is required for resolution and the minimum lies between 132 and 250 bp. Alternatively, the failure of pWBXba11 to resolve could reflect the loss of specific sequences essential for resolution.

The first model would be likely if the generation of linear minichromosomes from circular plasmids involves the extrusion of the imperfect palindrome as a cruciform and its resolution by an enzyme analogous to T4 endonuclease VII. This enzyme recognizes the base of an extruded cruciform as a Holliday intermediate and, by the introduction of site-specific nicks, generates linear molecules with hairpin ends (Mizuuchi et al. 1982b; Lilly and Kemper 1984). The plasmids containing the concatemer junction of vaccinia have been shown to extrude cruciforms in vitro (Merchlinsky et al. 1988). Another means to resolve circular plasmids into linear minichromosomes would be the introduction of sequence-specific nicks on each strand, which, after branch migration and ligation, would generate linear molecules with hairpin ends. To discriminate between sequence-

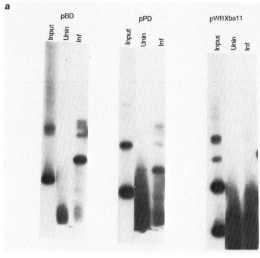

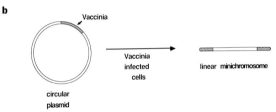

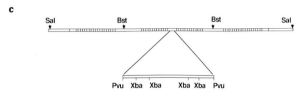

Figure 3 Conversion of plasmids containing the concatemer junction of vaccinia virus into linear minichromosomes in infected cells. (*a*) The plasmids pBD, pPD, and pWBXba11 were transfected into cells. For each sample, three lanes are shown: input DNA, *Dpn*I-digested DNA from uninfected (Unin) or infected (Inf) cells. (*b*) Schematic representation of linear molecules formed by pBD or pPD in infected cells. (*c*) Structure of concatemer junction of vaccinia virus. The plasmid pBD contains the sequences between the *Bst*EII sites, pPD the sequences between the *Pvu*I sites, and pWBXba11, the sequence between the innermost *Xba*I sites. The bars refer to the direct repeats near the termini of vaccinia virus.

specific or solely structural requirements for resolution, we have constructed plasmids containing symmetrical deletions or inversions so that the inverted repeat structure of the insert is conserved. The molecules were transfected into infected cells, and the cytoplasmic DNA was harvested 24 hours posttransfection and digested with *Dpn*I and *Nde*I. Those molecules that have been replicated but not resolved will be converted into linear molecules, whereas resolved minichromosomes will be digested into a fragment that runs slightly faster than the unresolved linear and a small fragment that is electrophoresed off the gel. The results for pOX, a plasmid containing a single base change destroying the *Xba*I site closest to the direct repeats; pHD-2X, a plasmid missing the 37-bp *Xba*I fragment from both sides of the insert;

and pXO, which contains the 37-bp *Xba*I fragment inverted, are shown in Figure 4. The pOX is replicated and efficiently resolved, whereas the pXO and pHD-2X are replicated but not resolved into linear minichromosomes. The resolution of molecules containing the concatemer junction depends on sequence-specific interactions, as pXO and pHD-2X contain inverted repeats of 412 and 338 bp, both of which are larger than the 250-bp inverted repeat of pPD, which is resolved (Merchlinsky and Moss 1986). Furthermore, pOX and pXO differ only in nucleotide sequence, as they have identical palindromic inserts except for the inversion of 37 bp.

Viral *trans*-acting factors are required for the replication and resolution of input plasmids

To determine the requirements of viral gene functions for the nonspecific replication of input plasmids, we utilized a series of temperature-sensitive mutants described by Condit et al. (1983). Cells were transfected with a plasmid containing the concatemer junction of vaccinia virus and infected with the conditionally lethal mutants in DNA replication ts42 from complementation group 5 or ts17 from complementation group 21. The DNA isolated posttransfection was digested with *Nde*I, which cuts uniquely in vector sequence, and in some cases, *Dpn*I. The input plasmid and those molecules

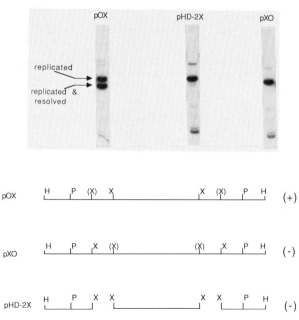

Figure 4 Sequence-specific resolution of plasmids containing the concatemer junction of vaccinia virus in infected cells. Plasmids were transfected into cells infected with vaccinia virus and digested with *Nde*I and *Dpn*I. The location of the replicated as well as the replicated and resolved bands are indicated. The structure of each plasmid is shown with restriction sites indicated for *Hin*fI (H), *Pvu*I (P), and *Xba*I (X). The *Xba*I site destroyed by oligonucleotide-directed mutagenesis is indicated by (×).

that have been replicated but not resolved into linear minichromosomes will be converted into linear sized fragments by *Nde*I. As before, resolved minichromosomes will be cleaved asymmetrically, generating two fragments: a small piece, and one that runs slightly faster than the linear form of the input plasmid. The results using pOX are shown in Figure 5. At the permissive temperature of 31°C, the plasmid was replicated and resolved with about 50% of the replicated material converted to linear minichromosomes. Although even more linear DNA was present in cells infected at the nonpermissive temperature of 40°C, very little of the material was converted into *Dpn*I-resistant material or resolved. Therefore, the replication of input plasmids is dependent on viral genes shown to be required for viral DNA replication, including the viral DNA polymerase (ts group 5) (Traktman et al. 1983) and a gene of unknown function necessary for DNA replication (ts group 21) (Evans and Traktman 1987).

The lack of resolution of pOX in ts group 5 or ts group 21 infected cells at the nonpermissive temperature may be due to a requirement for plasmid replication prior to resolution; or, since DNA⁻ mutants do not progress beyond the early phase of the viral life cycle, the resolution of plasmids may also depend on late encoded viral gene products. To determine the contribution of late viral gene products to resolution, we utilized a set of temperature-sensitive mutants defective in late protein synthesis and tested their ability to resolve pOX at the conditionally lethal temperature. The results in Figure 6 demonstrate that, although the plasmids are replicated at both the permissive and nonpermissive temperatures, the plasmids are more poorly resolved at the elevated

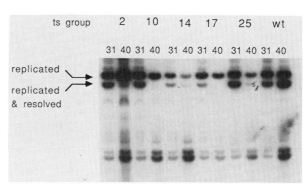

Figure 6 Resolution of plasmids containing the concatemer junction requires late viral *trans*-acting factors. Cells were transfected with pOX and infected with ts gp2 (ts21), ts gp10 (ts53), ts gp14 (ts63), ts gp17 (ts7), ts gp25 (ts 22), or wild-type vaccinia (wt) at 31°C or 40°C. The DNA was digested with *Nde*I and *Dpn*I before electrophoresis and hybridization with pUC13 labeled with ³²P by nick translation. The positions of the replicated as well as the replicated and resolved bands are indicated.

temperature. These complementation groups map to many loci in the genome (Thompson and Condit 1986) but are all associated with a profound reduction in late protein synthesis. The conversion of circular plasmids containing the concatemer junction into linear minichromosomes, in contrast to DNA replication, is dependent on late encoded viral function(s).

Discussion

The first objective of this study was to determine the precise structure of the junction between unit length vaccinia virus genomes in concatemeric replicative intermediates. To accomplish this, we cloned restriction endonuclease fragments containing the junction and various lengths of flanking DNA into bacterial plasmids. All of the inverted repeat structures, including one 7200 bp long, were stably maintained and propagated in *E. coli*. Although perfect inverted repeats are very unstable in *E. coli* (Collins 1981; Lilley 1981; Collins et al. 1982; Mizuuchi et al. 1982a), the predicted structure of the joint in the vaccinia inserts is not perfectly symmetrical since the central portion of the insert corresponds to the incompletely base-paired hairpin loop. This feature was confirmed by the nucleotide sequence of the cloned junction fragment (Merchlinsky et al. 1988). The concatemer junction was shown to be a precise duplex copy of the hairpin structure found at the end of the genome. The conversion of this structure into hairpin ends provides a structural basis for the observed sequence isomers.

Although viral concatemers are found during DNA replication in cells infected with vaccinia virus, there was no direct evidence that they are replicative intermediates. To address this question, plasmids containing concatemer junctions were introduced by standard calcium phosphate transfection procedures into cells that had been infected with vaccinia virus. The circular plasmids were converted into linear minichromosomes with

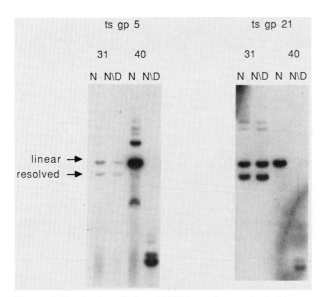

Figure 5 Replication of plasmid DNA requires early viral *trans*-acting factors. Cells were transfected with pOX and infected with ts gp5 (ts 42) or ts gp21 (ts 17) at 31°C or 40°C, and the DNA samples were digested with *Nde*I (N) or *Nde*I and *Dpn*I (N/D) before electrophoresis and hybridization to pUC13 labeled with ³²P by nick translation. The positions of the linear and the resolved bands are indicated.

vector DNA in the center and vaccinia DNA hairpins at the ends. This reaction was only observed in infected cells, suggesting that vaccinia virus enzymes were involved.

The replication of plasmids with the concatemer junction led us to inquire whether the vaccinia genome contains cis-acting DNA sequences required for DNA replication. Viral origins have been identified previously by subcloning genomes into plasmid vectors and testing for the ability of the chimeras to replicate in infected cells (Kucherlapati and Skoultchi 1984); however, using this approach with vaccinia virus, we were unable to detect any viral sequence that was preferentially replicated. All circular plasmids, irrespective of insert, were converted into large heterogeneous DpnI-resistant material. The nonspecific replication of input plasmid was observed in the cytoplasm of viral infected cells and, as demonstrated by conditionally lethal mutants in viral DNA replication, relied on at least two viral gene products: the DNA polymerase and one other gene required for viral DNA replication. The generation of long head-to-tail arrays of plasmid in infected cell cytoplasm is consistent with a rolling circle mechanism that replicates input plasmid using the viral replication machinery. Similar unregulated replication in poxvirus cells has been reported by DeLange and McFadden (1986).

To more faithfully duplicate the structure of viral DNA, a set of linear plasmids with hairpin ends was also constructed and tested for their ability to replicate in infected cells. The plasmid pSV9 (Merchlinsky and Moss 1986), a head-to-head dimer of pBD containing two copies of vector DNA and the concatemer junction, was digested with SalI or AccI and converted to pUC-vaccinia hairpins by heating and quick chilling. The SalI or AccI hairpin was ligated to XhoI or ClaI digests of viral DNA, and the mixture was transfected into infected cells. Analogous to the results seen with circular plasmids, no preferential replication was observed.

DNA viruses generally require a selective advantage for the preferential replication of their genomes over cellular sequences. Vaccinia virus, however, is replicated in the cytoplasm of infected cells and codes for all, or nearly all, of the functions required for its replication. Thus, vaccinia may not require cis-acting sequence elements to selectively replicate its DNA. Also, some DNA viruses have been observed, at high multiplicities of infection, to generate defective genomes with multiple copies of viral origins (Holland 1985). In contrast, vaccinia defective genomes with repeated viral sequences have not been observed, even at high multiplicities of infection (M. Merchlinsky, unpubl.).

The inability to detect viral origins with circular plasmids containing segments of vaccinia DNA is not sufficient to rule out specific regions as origins for genome replication. There is evidence that nicks are introduced and DNA replication is initiated near the ends of the genome early in infection (Esteban and Holowczak 1977a,b; Pogo 1977; Pogo and O'Shea 1978; Pogo et al. 1981, 1984). The origin of vaccinia virus DNA replication may be the nicked double-stranded genome gen-

erated by sequence-specific nicking in vivo. Plasmids transfected into infected cells may be randomly nicked, creating double-stranded templates that serve as surrogate substrates for the viral replication machinery.

Although all circular plasmids transfected into infected cells were replicated, only those containing vaccinia virus concatemer junctions larger than 250 bp were converted into linear minichromosomes (Merchlinsky and Moss 1986). Also, a plasmid with a concatemer junction of 132 bp was not resolved. To determine if resolution was determined solely by the size of the inverted repeat or if sequence-specific interactions were required, a symmetrical deletion and inversion were made that conserved the inverted repeat. Although both pXO and pHD-2X had an inverted repeat larger than 250 bp, neither plasmid was resolved, indicating that sequence-specific interactions are required for resolution. The 37-bp XbaI fragment that has been deleted in pHD-2X and inverted in pXO has a sequence element that is highly conserved between vaccinia and the poxvirus Shope fibroma virus (DeLange et al. 1986). Since both Shope fibroma and vaccinia virus can resolve the concatemer junction from the heterologous virus (DeLange et al. 1986), this conserved sequence element may specify the sequence requirements for resolution.

The resolution of plasmids containing the concatemer junction was only observed in cells infected with vaccinia virus. The contribution of late gene products to the process was measured by assaying for the ability of a plasmid to be converted into linear minichromosomes by temperature-sensitive viruses at the nonpermissive temperature. Plasmids containing the concatemer junction were replicated, but not efficiently resolved, at elevated temperatures. The process of conversion of circular plasmids with concatemer junctions into linear minichromosomes, in contrast to DNA replication, relies on late viral gene function(s).

Some initial efforts have been made to identify enzymes that might be involved in the resolution of vaccinia telomeres. A late single-stranded endonuclease isolated from vaccinia virions was shown to nick supercoiled DNA (Rosemond-Hornbeak et al. 1974; Rosemond-Hornbeak and Moss 1974). Recently, Lakritz and coworkers (1985) extended that observation and demonstrated that the nicks occur at specific locations and that the ends of some of the molecules become cross-linked. We have noted that the supercoiled plasmid containing the vaccinia concatemer joints are specifically cleaved and cross-linked at the nucleotides corresponding to the borders of the 104-nucleotide hairpin loops by a partially purified preparation of the vaccinia nuclease (Merchlinsky et al. 1988).

References

Baroudy, B.M., S. Venkatesan, and B. Moss. 1982. Incompletely base-paired flip-flop terminal loops link the two DNA strands of the vaccinia virus genome into one uninterrupted polynucleotide chain. *Cell* **28**: 315.
———. 1983. Structure and replication of vaccinia virus telomeres. *Cold Spring Harbor Symp. Quant. Biol.* **47**: 723.

Broyles, S.S. and B. Moss. 1987. Identification of the vaccinia virus gene encoding nucleoside phosphohydrolase I. *J. Virol.* **61**: 1738.

Collins, J. 1981. Instability of palindromic DNA in *Escherichia coli. Cold Spring Harbor Symp. Quant. Biol.* **45**: 409.

Collins, J., G. Volckaert, and P. Nevers. 1982. Precise and nearly-precise excision of the symmetrical inverted repeats of Tn5; common features of recA-independent deletion events in *Escherichia coli. Gene* **19**: 139.

Condit, R.C., A. Motyczka, and G. Spizz. 1983. Isolation, characterization, and physical mapping of temperature-sensitive mutants of vaccinia virus. *Virology* **128**: 429.

DeLange, A.M. and G. McFadden. 1986. Sequence-nonspecific replication of transfected plasmid DNA in poxvirus-infected cells. *Proc. Natl. Acad. Sci.* **83**: 614.

DeLange, A.M., M. Reddy, D. Scraba, C. Upton, and G. McFadden. 1986. Replication and resolution of cloned poxvirus telomers in vivo generates linear minichromosomes with intact viral hairpin termini. *J. Virol.* **59**: 249.

Earl, P.L., E.V. Jones, and B. Moss. 1986. Homology between DNA polymerases of poxviruses, herpesviruses, and adenoviruses: Nucleotide sequence of the vaccinia virus DNA polymerase gene. *Proc. Natl. Acad. Sci.* **83**: 3659.

Esteban, M. and J.A. Holowczak. 1977a. Replication of vaccinia DNA in mouse L cells. I. In vivo DNA synthesis. *Virology* **78**: 57.

———. 1977b. Replication of vaccinia DNA in mouse L cells. III. Intracellular forms of viral DNA. *Virology* **82**: 308.

Evans, E. and P. Traktman. 1987. Molecular genetic analysis of a vaccinia virus gene with an essential role in DNA replication. *J. Virol.* **61**: 3152.

Geshelin, P. and K.I. Berns. 1974. Characterization and localization of the naturally occurring crosslinks in vaccinia virus DNA. *J. Mol. Biol.* **88**: 785.

Graham, F.L. and A.J. van der Eb. 1973. A new technique for the assay of infectivity of human adenovirus 5 DNA. *Virology* **52**: 456.

Holland, J.J. 1985. Generation and replication of defective genomes. In *Virology* (ed. B.N. Fields et al.), p. 77. Raven Press, New York.

Jones, E.V., C. Puckett, and B. Moss. 1987. DNA-dependent RNA polymerase subunits encoded within the vaccinia virus genome. *J. Virol.* **61**: 1765.

Kucherlapati, R. and A.I. Skoultchi. 1984. Introduction of purified genes into mammalian cells. *CRC Crit. Rev. Biochem.* **16**: 349.

Lakritz, N., P.D. Fogelsong, M. Reddy, S. Baum, J. Hurwitz, and W.R. Bauer. 1985. A vaccinia virus DNAse preparation which cross-links superhelical DNA. *J. Virol.* **53**: 935.

Lilley, D.M.J. 1981. In vivo consequences of plasmid topology. *Nature* **292**: 380.

Lilley, D.M.J. and B. Kemper. 1984. Cruciform-resolvase interactions in supercoiled DNA. *Cell* **36**: 413.

Maniatis, T., E.F. Fritsch, and J. Sambrook. 1982. *Molecular cloning: A laboratory manual.* Cold Spring Harbor Laboratory, Cold Spring Harbor, New York.

Merchlinsky, M. and B. Moss. 1986. Resolution of linear minichromosomes with hairpin ends from circular plasmids containing vaccinia virus concatemer junctions. *Cell* **45**: 879.

Merchlinsky, M., C.F. Garon, and B. Moss. 1988. Molecular cloning and sequence of the concatemer junction from vac-

cinia virus replicative DNA. Viral nuclease cleavage sites in cruciform structures. *J. Mol. Biol.* **199**: (in press).

Mizuuchi, K., M. Mizuuchi, and M. Gellert. 1982a. Cruciform structures in palindromic DNA are favored by DNA supercoiling. *J. Mol. Biol.* **156**: 229.

Mizuuchi, K., B. Kemper, J. Hayes, and R.A. Weisberg. 1982b. T4 endonuclease VII cleaves Holliday structures. *Cell* **29**: 357.

Moss, B. 1985. Replication of poxviruses. In *Virology* (ed. B.N. Fields et al.) p. 685. Raven Press, New York.

Moss, B., E. Winters, and E.V. Jones. 1983. Replication of vaccinia virus. *UCLA Symp. Mol. Cell. Biol. New Ser.* **10**: 449.

Moyer, R.W. and R.L. Graves. 1981. The mechanism of cytoplasmic orthopox replication. *Cell* **27**: 391.

Pogo, B.G.T. 1977. Elimination of naturally occurring crosslinks in vaccinia virus DNA after viral penetration into cells. *Proc. Natl. Acad. Sci.* **74**: 1739.

———. 1980. Terminal crosslinking of vaccinia DNA strands by an in vitro system. *Virology* **100**: 339.

Pogo, B.G.T. and M.T. O'Shea. 1978. The mode of replication of vaccinia virus DNA. *Virology* **84**: 1.

Pogo, B.G.T., E.M. Berkowitz, and S. Dales. 1984. Investigation of vaccinia virus DNA replication employing a conditional lethal mutant defective in DNA. *Virology* **132**: 436.

Pogo, B.G.T., M. O'Shea, and P. Freimuth. 1981. Initiation and termination of vaccinia virus DNA replication. *Virology* **108**: 241.

Razin, S.U., V.L. Mantieva, and G.P. Georgiev. 1979. The similarity of DNA sequences remaining bound to scaffold upon nuclease treatment of interphase nuclei and metaphase chromosomes. *Nucleic Acids Res.* **7**: 1713.

Rodriguez, J.F., J.S. Kahn, and M. Esteban. 1986. Molecular cloning, encoding sequence, and expression of vaccinia virus nucleic acid-dependent nucleoside triphosphatase gene. *Proc. Natl. Acad. Sci.* **83**: 9566.

Rosemond-Hornbeak, H. and B. Moss. 1974. Single-strand deoxyribonucleic acid-specific nuclease from vaccinia virus. Endonucleolytic and exonucleolytic activities. *J. Biol. Chem.* **249**: 3292.

Rosemond-Hornbeak, H., E. Paoletti, and B. Moss. 1974. Single-strand deoxyribonucleic acid-specific nuclease from vaccinia virus. Purification and characterization. *J. Biol. Chem.* **249**: 3287.

Shuman, S. and B. Moss. 1987. Identification of a vaccinia virus gene encoding a type I DNA topoisomerase. *Proc. Natl. Acad. Sci.* **84**: 7478.

Thompson, C.L. and R.C. Condit. 1986. Marker rescue mapping of vaccinia virus temperature-sensitive mutants using overlapping cosmid clones representing the entire virus genome. *Virology* **150**: 10.

Traktman, P., P. Sridhar, R.C. Condit, and B.E. Roberts. 1983. Transcriptional mapping of the DNA polymerase gene of vaccinia virus. *J. Virol.* **49**: 125.

Vogelstein, B. and D. Gillespie. 1979. Preparative and analytical purification of DNA from agarose. *Proc. Natl. Acad. Sci.* **76**: 615.

Yang, R.C.-A., J. Lis, and R. Wu. 1979. Elution of DNA from agarose gels after electrophoresis. *Methods Enzymol.* **68**: 176.

Polyomavirus DNA Synthesis In Vitro: Studies with CHO, 3T3, and Their tsDNA Mutants

J.J. Dermody,* K.G. Lawlor,* H. Du,* B. Wojcik,* K.K. Jha,*
L. Malkas,† R. Hickey,† E.F. Baril,† and H.L. Ozer*

*Department of Biological Sciences, Hunter College, CUNY, New York, New York 10021;
†Worcester Foundation for Experimental Biology, Shrewsbury, Massachusetts 01545

Utilizing a strategy developed for the isolation of mammalian cell mutants temperature-sensitive (ts) for DNA synthesis, we have identified seven mutants in mouse (3T3) and Chinese hamster (CHO) cells that restrict polyoma DNA synthesis in a temperature-dependent manner. Extracts from wild-type CHO and 3T3 cells have been successfully used to develop in vitro systems for papovavirus DNA synthesis that mimic the permissivity in vivo for viral DNA synthesis. ts20, a tsDNA mutant from 3T3 cells, has been found to have a defect in a purified multiprotein form of DNA polymerase α as only 20–25% of the activity is found as polα$_2$. In contrast, a non-ts revertant (ts20R) shows greater than 90% of the activity chromatographing as polα$_2$, as in wild-type cells. ts20 also shows a marked reduction in T antigen-dependent replication of a plasmid containing a polyoma origin in vitro. Five of the cell mutants, including ts20, have been corrected by DNA from a human cosmid library as a prelude to the isolation of the genes responsible for the ts defects.

Temperature-sensitive mutants have been a powerful tool in understanding the molecular mechanism of many cell and viral processes. Only limited studies have been described for mammalian cells in culture and few mutants have been defined as defective in functions directly related to DNA synthesis. Several years ago, this laboratory described the isolation of ts mutants in 3T3 that affected cellular and polyomavirus DNA synthesis (Slater and Ozer 1976; Zeng et al. 1984). Such mutants involved loci on the X chromosome (Jha et al. 1980). More recently, we shifted our attention to the Chinese hamster cell line CHO. Several considerations indicated that this cell line would be a better choice to serve as a parent of a mutant collection. First, it has favorable growth properties over a broad range of temperatures (33–41°C) and its efficiency of colony formation approaches 100%. It has also successfully been used for replica plating, permitting isolation of mutants even under nonselective conditions. Second, it had often been used for genetic studies, although few mutants directly affecting DNA synthesis had been described. Moreover, recessive mutants, as expected for ts mutants, have been isolated at unusually high frequency. Since these loci were dispersed throughout the genome, it suggested that mutants at autosomal loci might be easier to obtain in these cells than other cell lines (e.g., 3T3).

We recently described the isolation of over 200 mutants in CHO (and another Chinese hamster cell line V79) that are ts for growth by utilizing a variety of selective and nonselective strategies, including replica plating (Dermody et al. 1986; Ozer et al. 1987). Approximately 10% were selectively ts for DNA synthesis (tsDNA). To further identify those mutants that were most likely to be directly involved in DNA synthesis, as

contrasted to other functions relevant to DNA replication such as cell cycle progression, we assessed the ability of each mutant to support viral DNA synthesis (Dermody et al. 1986). As shown by Longiaru and Horwitz (1981) and this laboratory (Radna et al. 1987), human adenovirus replicates its DNA in CHO cells after virion infection. Furthermore, although CHO cells are resistant to papovavirus infection by virions, they do support viral DNA synthesis after transfection. More specifically, polyomavirus DNA synthesis occurs at levels consistent with a permissive cell, whereas only low levels of SV40 DNA synthesis can be observed (LaBella and Ozer 1985). Five of the CHO tsDNA mutants restricted polyoma DNA synthesis in a temperature-dependent manner. Adenovirus DNA synthesis was restricted in only one of these mutants (JB3-B) and in neither of the previously studied 3T3 mutants (ts2, ts20) (J. Dermody and H. Ozer, unpubl.). The conditions of infection precluded a defect in cell cycle progression being responsible; the differential effect on adenovirus and polyomavirus DNA synthesis ruled out that a defect in nucleotide pool metabolism was responsible. The latter remains a possibility for the tsDNA phenotype in JB3-B.

In an effort to determine biochemically the function that is heat-labile, we have attempted to adapt the in vitro system for DNA synthesis initially developed for SV40 by Li and Kelly (1984) to CHO cells. In particular, we sought to know whether cell extracts prepared from any of the mutants would be defective for viral DNA synthesis in vitro in a temperature-dependent or non-temperature-dependent manner. Such a system would also serve as a model for the study of putative cellular origins of replication isolated from CHO sequences (e.g., for the DHFR amplicant) (Burhans et al. 1986).

95

Materials and Methods

Cell lines and viruses

Cell culture procedures were as previously reported for CHO, 3T3, and their respective *ts* mutants (Dermody et al. 1986). *ts* mutants were routinely propagated at 33–35°C and used for experiments within a limited number of passages from frozen storage. Human adenovirus 2 (Ad2) was propagated in HeLa cells as described elsewhere (Radna et al. 1987). Defective adenovirus vector AdLTSVR587 (Mansour et al. 1985) was obtained from S. Mansour and R. Tjian and propagated in CV-1 cells with an Ad2 helper for expansion of a virus stock and preparation of extracts for polyoma large T antigen. The recombinant adenovirus vector Ad5SVR115 was obtained from Y. Gluzman and propagated in 293 cells as described by Stillman and Gluzman (1985).

In vitro replication assays

The basic methodology was as described by Li and Kelly (1984). Subconfluent or recently confluent monolayers of cells were routinely used for preparation of hypotonic cytosol extracts in 5 mM KCl, 1.5 mM $MgCl_2$, 1 mM dithiothreitol (DTT), 20 mM HEPES (pH 7.5), for both SV40 and polyoma in vitro DNA synthesis. The concentration of protein varied with the cell line and cell density as noted in the text. 50 μl replication reactions consisted of cell extract, form I DNA of an origin fragment cloned in a pBR322-derived plasmid (150 ng); immunoaffinity purified T antigen; 100 μM dCTP, dATP, dTTP, dGTP; 200 μM CTP, UTP, GTP; 4 mM ATP; 40 mM phosphocreatine; 100 μg creatine phosphokinase; 7 mM $MgCl_2$; 0.5 mM DTT; and 5–10 μCi of [α-^{32}P]dCTP and/or dATP (S.A. 3000 Ci per nmole). Reactions were incubated at designated temperatures for 0–4 hours. After isolation of products, the DNA was digested with *Dpn*I and *Sal*I (to generate unit length fragments) and analyzed by electrophoresis on 1.4% agarose gel. Incorporation was quantitated by excision of the *Dpn*I-resistant, unit length fragment.

The "SV40 system" utilized the plasmid pJL0, which contained SV40 sequences (nucleotides 5171–128) in pKP45 (Li and Kelly 1984). T antigen was purified by immunoaffinity chromatography on a column containing the monoclonal anti-T antibody pAb 419 (Li and Kelly 1984). The concentration of T antigen was 1.2 mg/ml and was typically used at 1–2 μl per reaction. The "polyoma system" utilized the plasmid pJLPY0, which contained polyoma sequences (nucleotides 4973–368) corresponding to the complete polyoma origin. It was constructed by isolation of the *Acc*I origin fragment from polyoma strain A2, attachment of *Bam*HI linkers, and cloning into the *Bam*HI site of the polylinker in pKP54 and was kindly provided by J. Li. Polyoma T antigen was purified by immunoaffinity chromatography on a column containing a monoclonal antibody from hybridoma F4 reactive with both polyoma T and t (Palles et al. 1986) as described by Murakami et al. (1986a). The concentration of T antigen was 0.1 mg/ml and was typically used at 8 μl per reaction. Both T antigen preparations were dialyzed against 50% glycerol, 5 mM NaCl, 0.1 mM EDTA, 0.1 mM DTT, 0.1 mM phenylmethylsulfonyl fluoride (PMSF), 10 mM HEPES (pH 7.5), and stored at −20°C.

Purification of DNA polymerase

The mouse cell lines *ts20*, *ts20R*, and *ts2* were inoculated into 15-cm dishes and harvested after 3 days at 33°C or after an additional 16 hours at 39°C. The cells were scraped into 0.15 mM NaCl, 0.01 M $NaHPO_4$ (pH 7.4), centrifuged at low speed, and stored as a cell pellet at −70°C. The cell pellet was extracted and the multiprotein form of DNA polymerase (polα) prepared from the combined nuclear extract (NE)-postmicrosomal supernatant (PMS) by a modification (L. Malkas et al., in prep.) of the procedure previously published for HeLa cells (Vishwanatha et al. 1986). In brief, the NE-PMS fraction was adjusted to 2 M in KCl, and polyethylene glycol 8000 was added to a concentration of 5% (w/v) with constant stirring at 4°C. The suspension was centrifuged at 16,000g for 30 minutes and the resulting supernatant dialyzed against 50 mM Tris (pH 7.5), 0.15 M KCl, 1 mM DTT, 1 mM EDTA, 1 mM EGTA, 1 mM aminoacetonitrile hemisulfate, 1 mM PMSF (buffer A) containing 0.25 M sucrose. The dialyzed fraction was clarified by centrifugation, overlayered onto a cushion of 2 M sucrose in buffer A and subjected to discontinuous gradient centrifugation at 241,200g (VTi 50 rotor) for 4 3/4 hours at 4°C. Following centrifugation, the supernatant (S-4 fraction) and the 2 M sucrose interphase (P-4 fraction) were successively removed by aspiration. The P-4 fraction was equilibrated with 50 mM Tris-HCl (pH 7.5), 50 mM KCl, 1 mM DTT, 1 mM EDTA, 1 mM aminoacetonitrile, 1 mM PMSF, 10% glycerol (buffer B) by dialysis and was loaded onto a DEAE (DE-52) cellulose column that was coupled in descending order to native- and denatured DNA-cellulose columns. The column matrixes had been equilibrated with buffer B and after loading of the P-4 fraction onto the DEAE-cellulose column, they were successively eluted with 2-column volumes of buffer A containing 10% glycerol. The effluent from the denatured DNA-cellulose column was dialyzed against buffer A and chromatographed on DEAE-BioGel to separate the DNA polymerase α_2-containing fraction that elutes at 0.15 M KCl. Total activity in Table 1 is calculated from the unbound (polα_1), 0.15 M KCl eluate, and 0.3 M KCl eluate (polα_3) of DEAE-BioGel. DNA polymerase activity is determined by assay with activated DNA or poly(dA).(dT)4 as template as described previously (Vishwanatha et al. 1986).

Results

Replication of papovaviral sequences in extracts prepared from CHO cells

Cell extracts prepared from CHO cells supplemented with immunoaffinity-purified T antigen support the replication of a plasmid containing origin sequences derived from the homologous papovavirus DNA as assayed by

Table 1 DNA Polymerase α_2 in tsDNA Mutants

Mutant cell line	Temperature (°C)	Poly(dA)/oligo(dT) template activity[a]		
		Pol α_2[b]	total[c]	Pol α_2/total (%)
ts20	33	2.85	11.1	25.6
	39	2.07	10.4	19.9
ts20R	33	7.34	7.8	94.1
	39	3.76	4.1	91.7
ts2	33	16.2	17.2	94.2
	39	17.1	19.1	89.5

DNA polymerase was purified and assayed as described in the text and methods from cells grown at the respective temperatures.

[a]One unit corresponds to 1 nM of dNTP incorporated per hour at 35°C.

[b]DEAE-BioGel eluate at 0.15 M KCl.

[c]Total activity recovered in all DEAE-BioGel fractions.

*Dpn*I resistance as shown in Figure 1. In the case of SV40, the efficiency of synthesis is rather low (lanes e and f) and markedly reduced as compared to extracts prepared from permissive monkey cells, as previously shown by Li and Kelly (1985). Synthesis in extracts from CHO cells was dependent on T antigen and an intact SV40 origin. Mixing experiments with extracts from monkey cells indicate that CHO extracts are not inhibitory (data not shown). These results are quite consistent with those observed for intracellular SV40 DNA synthesis in CHO cells, since only 1000 copies are detected at 72–96 hours post-transfection with SV40 sequences (LaBella and Ozer 1985). Hurwitz and co-workers (Murakami et al. 1986b) first reported that papovaviral DNA synthesis could be stimulated when a partially purified fraction containing polymerase/primase from permissive cells was added. Figure 1 (lanes g and h) shows that a similar effect can be observed for SV40 replication in CHO extracts supplemented with the polymerase/primase fraction eluted from phosphocellulose in 0.5 M KCl (Wold et al. 1987). This fraction was kindly provided by M. Wold and D. Weinberg.

When the same cell extracts were utilized for polyoma DNA synthesis by substituting immunoaffinity-purified polyoma large T antigen and a plasmid containing the polyoma origin of DNA synthesis, replication was observed as well (Fig. 1, lanes c and d). However, several differences were noted. First, the level of replication with the polyoma system is considerably higher than with the SV40 system, consistent with the level of replication of these two viral DNAs intracellularly. Second, polyoma DNA replication is temperature-dependent in extracts prepared from wild-type cells (compare lane c at 33°C with lane d at 37.5°C). It should be noted that the amount of polyoma T is not at a saturation level in this experiment, in contrast to the amount of SV40 T antigen. This temperature dependence is not related to the level of DNA per se since it is also observed in mouse cell extracts (data not shown). This phenomenon has also been found with polyoma T prepared from insect cells using a bacculovirus vector (Rice et al. 1987) (C. Prives, pers. comm.). This temperature dependence of synthesis with wild-type extracts is most

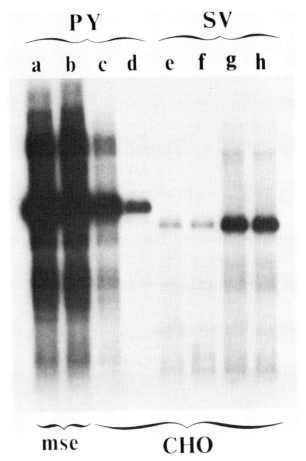

Figure 1 Papovavirus DNA synthesis in vitro. Replication was determined as described in the text and methods using the "polyoma system" (*a,b,c,d*), "SV40 system" alone (*e,f*) or supplemented with polα/primase from HeLa cells (*g,h*). All cell extracts were prepared from cells grown at 33°C and were adjusted to the same protein concentration (140 µg): L cells (*a*), A31N (*b*), CHO (*c–h*). Incubation temperature in vitro was 33°C (*a,b,c,e,g*) or 37.5°C (*d,f,h*) for 2 hr.

likely due to the heat lability of the polyoma T antigen itself or its association with cellular replication factors. Preincubation of CHO extracts at 37°C for 60 minutes does not result in as extensive inactivation of replication capacity. In addition, recent experiments involving a preparation of polyoma T antigen with appreciably greater replication activity show less difference (less than twofold) when assayed in CHO at both temperatures.

We have also examined polyoma DNA replication in mouse cells under the conditions used for CHO extracts. Polyoma DNA synthesis is higher in both mouse L cells and 3T3 cells (Subline A31N) than with CHO extracts (see Fig. 1, lanes a and b) when suboptimal T levels are used. However, replication levels in both CHO and mouse cell extracts are increased and approximate each other when more nearly optimal levels of T antigen are used for DNA synthesis (~30 pmol of nucleotide incorporated per hour), consistent with that reported by Murakami et al. (1986a) for the mouse cell line FM3A and comparable to that of SV40 in its permissive system. Taken together, these results confirm those of Hurwitz, Prives, and co-workers that an effective in vitro system can be established for polyomavirus (Murakami et al. 1986a). Furthermore, cellular factors can be derived from Chinese hamster cells as well as mouse cells for replication of sequences containing a polyoma origin fragment.

Replication of polyoma sequences in extracts prepared from tsDNA mutants

We have begun the analysis of the *ts* cell mutants by examining *ts20* in vitro. This mutant was isolated from *A31N* and has been shown to restrict intracellular polyoma DNA synthesis at an early stage of strand elongation (Zeng et al. 1984). Figure 2 shows that viral DNA synthesis is reduced in *ts20* in a temperature-independent fashion, i.e., at 33°C. The results are essentially the same at 30°C (data not shown). The marked decrease in replication at 37°C in wild-type extracts makes one cautious in concluding that it is also more temperature-sensitive in *ts20*. When the replication capacity of *A31N* is compared over a range of incubation temperature in vitro with extracts prepared from cells grown at 33°C, it was found that a sharp fall in activity occurs between 36°C and 37.5°C (data not shown). When *A31N* and *ts20* are compared at 36°C (see Fig. 2) and the incorporation is normalized to 33°C as 100%, there is a greater fall in *ts20* (to 48%) than in *A31N* (to 71%).

DNA polymerase in mouse cells

Baril and co-workers have reported that a multiprotein form of DNA polymerase ($pol\alpha_2$) can be purified from HeLa cells that synthesizes extended single strands in vitro (Vishwanatha et al. 1986). This activity is dependent on $pol\alpha$ and requires accessory proteins (C1, C2). These polypeptides co-chromatograph as a complex in association with primase and other factors as reported

in detail elsewhere in this volume. In view of the nature of the defect observed in polyoma DNA synthesis intracellularly (Zeng et al. 1984), we assessed the properties of $pol\alpha_2$ in *ts20*. Extracts can be prepared from mouse cells and purified by similar procedures as those developed for HeLa cells, including subcellular fractionation, chromatography on DNA cellulose (double-stranded followed by single-stranded DNA), and DEAE-BioGel (E. Baril and H. Ozer, upubl.). When such preparations are obtained, the DNA polymerase α activity is detected predominantly in the fraction eluting at 0.15 M KCl, which contained the $pol\alpha_2$ complex and $pol\alpha_2$ enzymatic activity as assayed using a $poly(dA) \cdot oligo(dT)$ template (which requires accessory proteins) or activated calf thymus DNA (which is independent of accessory proteins). When $pol\alpha$ is prepared from *ts20* cells at either the permissive temperature (33°C) or from cells shifted to the restrictive temperature (39°C) for 16 hours, which results in 90% inhibition of intracellular DNA synthesis, it chromatographs anomalously and only 20–25% of the activity is found as $pol\alpha_2$ when assayed within $poly(dA) \cdot oligo(dT)$ as shown in Table 1. The predominant $pol\alpha$ activity chromatographs differently depending on the temperature at which the cells were incubated prior to their being harvested for preparation of extracts. At 33°C, the major peak (63% of the total activity) eluted prior to the $pol\alpha_2$ (i.e., in the fraction previously designated $pol\alpha_1$), whereas at 39°C, the major peak elutes at 0.3 M KCl (i.e., $pol\alpha_3$).

The defect at 33°C is reminiscent of the in vitro studies on polyoma DNA synthesis in the preceding section. Two types of control data support the premise that this defect in $pol\alpha_2$ is relevant to the *ts* phenotype. First, it is not due merely to the inhibition of DNA synthesis, since it is observed at 33°C. Moreover, *ts2*, which is similarly temperature-sensitive for DNA synthesis, does not show this defect. Second, it is linked genetically to the *ts* mutation, since a revertant (*ts20R*) of *ts20* that was selected for the ability to form colonies at 39°C (Zeng et al. 1984) does not show this defect. In both *ts2* and *ts20R*, as in *A31N* (data not shown), 90% or more of the activity chromatographs as $pol\alpha_2$ when prepared from cells at either temperature.

Genetic analysis of tsDNA mutants

Partial analysis of the tsDNA mutants indicated that the defect in each mutant is recessive to wild type in cell hybrids (Jha et al. 1980; B. Wojcik et al., unpubl.). We have, therefore, attempted to correct the temperature-sensitive defect in growth by introduction of members of a human cosmid library (Lau and Kan 1983) by DNA-mediated gene transfer. To facilitate transfer and subsequent identification of the transfected sequences, we have exploited a linked dominant selective marker, *eco gpt* with SV40 regulatory sequences (SV_2gpt). Mutant cells were transfected by the Ca-phosphate DNA co-precipitation technique (Graham and Van der Eb 1973) or protoplast fusion in suspension (Litzkas et al. 1984) and selected for *gpt* expression at 33°C. Cultures were

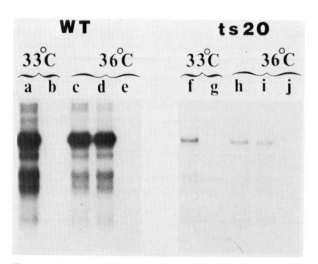

Figure 2 Polyoma DNA synthesis in *ts20* from mouse cells in vitro. Replication was determined as described in Fig. 1 utilizing cell extracts from *A31N* (*a–e*) (45 µg) or *ts20* (*f–j*) (32 µg). Replication reactions were performed in duplicate and were T-dependent in all cases, both as 33°C (*a,b,f,g*) and 36°C (*c,d,e,h,i,j*). T antigen was omitted in reactions *b,e,g,j*.

peratures (38.5–39.5°C) and rare temperature-resistant colonies identified by their continued growth. As shown in Table 2, the overall frequency of surviving colonies ($gpt^+ ts^+$) is quite low, consistent with the *ts* defect being corrected by a unique copy sequence. We have successfully obtained primary transfectants for five of the mutants. Since the human sequences were functional in a cosmid library, the intact gene would be expected to be smaller than 40–45 kb and amenable to conventional recombinant DNA cloning strategies. Such efforts are currently in progress.

Discussion

We have shown that the in vitro systems developed for extracts from permissive cells for SV40 and polyoma can be extended to other cell systems, namely CHO cells. Moreover, cell extracts prepared for one experimental system (e.g., SV40) can be used successfully without modification for the other. Some subtle differences may exist, since the only published data for polyoma replication (Murakami et al. 1986a) involved extracts prepared in the presence of 0.2 M NaCl, i.e., differently from Li and Kelly, and this study. Indeed, extracts prepared from CHO cells in that manner were initially inactive for replication of polyoma sequences (K. Lawlor and H. Ozer, unpubl.). The most evident difference, however, is the difference in efficiency of the two-viral system in CHO extracts as the polyoma system gives 10- to 100-fold more replication than the SV40 system. This discrepancy mimics the behavior of the two viruses for intracellular viral DNA synthesis (LaBella and Ozer 1985). Furthermore, the level of polyoma replication in vitro approximates that of conventional permissive cells as 3T3, further emphasizing that CHO cells can be used to study host factors in polyoma replication. An additional finding was the marked reduction in efficiency of the polyoma system in CHO (and mouse) cell extracts at 37°C and higher temperatures under conditions of limiting polyoma T antigen. Since it is generally considered more difficult to obtain large quantities of polyoma T antigen in a stable form than SV40 T antigen, this phenomenon has some practical as well as experimental

implications. Our experience, however, is that the vector developed by Mansour et al. (1985) and used in this study and others (Murakami et al. 1986a) can be used effectively. It must be emphasized that since the vector is replication defective, complexities are inevitably introduced by the presence of wild-type adenovirus as helper. Variability has been observed among preparations of polyoma T antigen that may be attributed to this or other factors.

We have initiated an analysis of a series of tsDNA mutants isolated in this laboratory that restrict intracellular polyoma DNA synthesis in a temperature-dependent manner. Initial results with *ts20* suggest that it is defective for polyoma DNA synthesis in vitro. The fact that the major effect is observed at a temperature that is nonrestrictive for intact cells is not in itself inconsistent with a heat-labile component, since it could be more unstable when extracted or assayed in such extracts. Support for the former is suggested by the anomalous chromatographic behavior of $pol\alpha_2$ complex purified from *ts20*. Indeed, the defect in $pol\alpha_2$ complex could be responsible for the failure to obtain efficient replication of the polyoma origin in vitro. However, other aspects of the *ts20* phenotype suggest that the defect may be more complicated (Zeng et al. 1984, 1985). Further studies with more purified fractions, revertants, and *ts20* corrected by human sequences should be quite informative in defining the significance of the $pol\alpha_2$ complex in this mutant.

In conclusion, we have found that a defect in cell and viral DNA synthesis can also be observed for replication of a plasmid containing a polyoma origin in vitro, suggesting that an in vitro complementation sytem can be developed for identifying functions defective in a *ts* cell mutant. Such an experimental system would appear to be amenable to mutants obtained in this laboratory from both mouse and Chinese hamster cells. The latter is of particular interest since it can be utilized for both polyoma and SV40 under appropriate experimental conditions.

Acknowledgments

We wish to thank colleagues who have provided vectors, constructs, or other reagents essential to the establishment of the in vitro systems, including J. Li, Y. Gluzman, S. Mansour, R. Tjian, E. Harlow, and C. Prives. This work was initiated while H.L.O. was an American Cancer Society scholar in the laboratory of T.J. Kelly, and we are especially indebted to J. Li, P. Rosenfeld, D. Weinberg, M. Wold, and other members of that laboratory for their valuable cooperation and assistance. This work was supported by Public Health Service grants from the National Cancer Institute: CA-23002 (H.L.O.), CA-15187 (E.B.), and P-32128-708. It was performed in part under the auspices of the RCMI Center for Gene Structure and Function at Hunter College. L.M. is a recipient of a National Institutes of Health postdoctoral fellowship.

Table 2 Correction of tsDNA Mutants with DNA from a Human Cosmid Library

Mutant cell line	Method of DNA transfer	gpt^+ colonies at 33°C	$gpt^+ ts^+$ colonies at 39°C
ts2 (3T3)	I[a]	4,500	2
ts20 (3T3)	II[b]	3,800	2
JB3-B (CHO)	I	25,000	3
JB7-K (CHO)	II	4,000	1
JB11-J (CHO)	I	8,000	4

10^8 cells of each cell line received DNA sequences of the human cosmid pCV103k *gpt* at 33°C.
[a]Calcium-phosphate DNA coprecipitation technique.
[b]Protoplast fusion technique.

References

Burhans, W.C., J.E. Seleque, and N.E. Heintz. 1986. Isolation of the origin of replication associated with the amplified Chinese hamster dihydrofolate reductase domain. *Proc. Natl. Acad. Sci.* **83:** 7790.

Dermody, J.J., B.E. Wojcik, H. Du, and H.L. Ozer. 1986. Identification of temperature-sensitive DNA⁻ mutants of Chinese hamster cells affected in cellular and viral DNA synthesis. *Mol. Cell. Biol.* **6:** 4594.

Graham, F.L. and A.J. Van der Eb. 1973. A new technique for the assay of infectivity of human adenovirus 5 DNA. *Virology* **52:** 456.

Jha, K.K., M. Siniscalco, and H.L. Ozer. 1980. Temperature-sensitive mutants of Balb/3T3 cells. III. Hybrids between ts2 and other mouse mutant cells affected in DNA synthesis and correction of ts2 defect by human X chromosome. *Somatic Cell Genet.* **6:** 603.

LaBella, F. and H.L. Ozer. 1985. Differential replication of SV40 and polyoma DNA in Chinese hamster ovary cells. *Virus Res.* **2:** 329.

Lau, Y.-F. and Y.W. Kan. 1983. Versatile cosmid vectors for the isolation, expression, and rescue of gene sequences: Studies with the human α-globin gene cluster. *Proc. Natl. Acad. Sci.* **80:** 5225.

Li, J.J. and T.J. Kelly. 1984. Simian virus 40 DNA replicates in vitro. *Proc. Natl. Acad. Sci.* **81:** 6973.

———. 1985. Simian virus 40 DNA replication in vitro: Specificity of initiation and evidence for bidirectional replication. *Mol. Cell. Biol.* **5:** 1238.

Litzkas, P., K.K. Jha, and H.L. Ozer. 1984. Efficient transfer of cloned DNA into human diploid cells: Protoplast fusion in suspension. *Mol. Cell. Biol.* **4:** 2549.

Longiaru, M. and M.S. Horwitz. 1981. Chinese hamster ovary cells replicate adenovirus DNA. *Mol. Cell. Biol.* **1:** 208.

Mansour, S.L., T. Grodzicker, and R. Tjian. 1985. An adenovirus vector system used to express polyoma virus tumor antigen. *Proc. Natl. Acad. Sci.* **82:** 1359.

Murakami, Y., T. Eki, M. Yamada, C. Prives, and J. Hurwitz. 1986a. Species-specific in vitro synthesis of DNA containing the polyoma virus origin of replication. *Proc. Natl. Acad. Sci.* **83:** 6347.

Murakami, Y., C.R. Wobbe, L. Weissbach, F.B. Dean, and J. Hurwitz. 1986b. Role of DNA polymerase and DNA primase in SV40 DNA replication in vitro. *Proc. Natl. Acad. Sci.* **83:** 2869.

Ozer, H.L., J.J. Dermody, and B. Wojcik. 1987. Mammalian ts DNA mutants. *UCLA Symp. Mol. Cell. Biol. New Ser.* **47:** 475.

Pallas, D.C., C. Schley, M. Mahoney, E. Harlow, B.S. Schaffhausen, and T.M. Roberts. 1986. Polyoma small t antigen: Overproduction in bacteria, purification, and utilization for monoclonal and polyclonal antibody production. *J. Virol.* **60:** 1075.

Radna, R., B. Foellmer, L.A. Feldman, U. Francke, and H.L. Ozer. 1987. Restriction of human adenovirus replication in Chinese hamster cell lines and cell hybrids with human cells. *Virus Res.* **8:** 277.

Rice, W.C., H.E. Lorimer, C. Prives, and L. Miller. 1987. Expression of polyoma large T antigen by using a baculovirus vector. *J. Virol.* **61:** 1712.

Slater, M. and H.L. Ozer. 1976. Temperature-sensitive mutants of Balb/3T3 cells. II. Description of a mutant affected in cellular and polyoma virus DNA synthesis. *Cell* **7:** 289.

Stillman, B.W. and Y. Gluzman. 1985. Replication and supercoiling of SV40 DNA in cell extracts from human cells. *Mol. Cell. Biol.* **5:** 2051.

Vishwanatha, J.K., S.A. Coughlin, M. Wesolowski-Owen, and E.F. Baril. 1986. A multiprotein form of DNA polymerase from HeLa cells: Resolution of its associated catalytic activities. *J. Biol. Chem.* **261:** 6619.

Wold, M.S., J.J. Li, and T. Kelly. 1987. Initiation of SV40 DNA replication in vitro: Large tumor antigen and origin dependent unwinding of the template. *Proc. Natl. Acad. Sci.* **84:** 3643.

Zeng, G.-C., J. Donegan, H.L. Ozer, and R. Hand. 1984. Characterization of a ts mutant of Balb/3T3 cells and correction of the defect by in vitro addition of extracts from wild-type cells. *Mol. Cell. Biol.* **4:** 1815.

Zeng, G.-C., M. Zannis-Hadjopoulos, H.L. Ozer, and R. Hand. 1985. Defective DNA topoisomerase I activity in a DNA ts mutant of Balb/3T3 cells. *Somatic Cell Mol. Genet.* **11:** 557.

observed when the extents of DpnI-resistant material were compared after dl3-5/SV40 or pSV2cat transfection (Fig. 2). Both plasmids carry identical SV40 sequences.

Replication of derivatives of dl3-5/SV40 with mutations in the rep gene

To test whether the less-than-expected replication of dl3-5/SV40 depended on an intact AAV rep gene, two derivatives of dl3-5/SV40 were transfected into COS-7 cells. dl3-5/ins32/SV40 contains an 8-base insert at mp 32 that acts as a frameshift mutation in the rep gene. dl10-37/SV40 has a major deletion in the rep gene between mp 10-37 into which is inserted the same SV40 regulatory sequence present in dl3-5/SV40. Both of these replicated much better in COS-7 cells than dl3-5/SV40 (Fig. 2). The extent of dl10-37 replication was indistinguishable from that of pSV2cat.

dl3-5/SV40 inhibits replication in trans

When dl3-5/SV40 was cotransfected with dl10-37/SV40 (Fig. 2), the replication of the latter was inhibited. Cotransfection of dl3-5/SV40 with pSV2cat did not inhibit replication of pSV2cat. We conclude that the AAV rep gene inhibited the SV40 T antigen-mediated replication of plasmids in COS-7 cells only if the plasmids contained AAV sequences.

Inhibition requires the AAV terminal repeats

In an effort to identify the target sequences conferring susceptibility of replication to the trans inhibitory effects of the rep gene, a construct was made that lacked the inverted terminal repeats of the dl3-5/SV40 genome. This construct replicated well in COS-7 cells (Fig. 3), but was able to effectively inhibit the replication of dl3-5/ins32/SV40 (data not shown). It still did not inhibit pSV2cat replication. We conclude that a necessary part of the target sequence of the rep gene inhibition is within the inverted terminal repeats of the AAV genome.

Discussion

Parvoviruses infect a wide spectrum of vertebrates. The genus *Parvovirus* contains viruses that replicate autonomously but exhibit for the most part strict host and even tissue specificity. In cell culture the autonomous parvoviruses require that a cell go through S phase in order for viral replication to occur. The *Dependoviruses*, on the other hand, generally require a helper virus coinfection to replicate, but exhibit a broad host range (Siegl et al. 1985). Recent reports have suggested that the function of the helper virus is indirect, to alter the intracellular milieu in a way that renders the cells permissive for AAV. Indeed, AAV has now been shown to replicate in certain cells in the absence of helper virus (Schlehofer et al. 1986; Yakobson et al. 1987). Hence, the notion of AAV defectiveness requires some modification. It now appears that the AAV genome can respond to the intracellular milieu in two ways; if it is permissive, AAV replicates; if not, the AAV genome is integrated into cellular DNA to form a latent infection.

Recent work has served to illustrate that the AAV genome has a variety of regulatory capabilities. Prod-

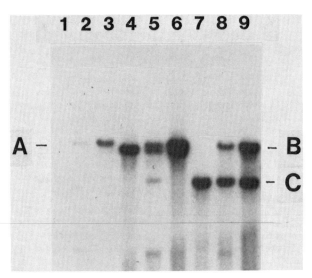

Figure 2 Inhibition of DNA replication by the AAV rep gene. COS-7 cells were transfected with either 0.25 μg pSM620 (lane 1), dl03-05/SV (lane 2), dl03-05/ins32/SV40 (lane 3), dl10-37/SV40 (lane 4), or pSV2 cat (lane 6). Some cells were cotransfected with 0.25 μg pSV2cat and 10 μg of either dl03-05/SV40 (lane 8) or dl03-05/ins32/SV40 (lane 9). Low molecular DNAs were isolated 48 hr after transfection and analyzed. The positions of linear forms of dl10-37/SV (A), dl03-05/SV and dl03-05/SVins32 (B), and pSV2cat (C) are indicated.

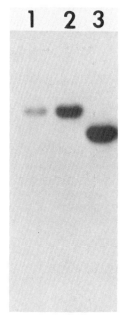

Figure 3 Transfection of COS-7 cells with dl3-5/SV40 (lane 1), dl3-5/ins32/SV40 (lane 2), and pSVaav (lane 3). pSVaav moves more rapidly primarily because it is cloned into a smaller derivative of pBR322.

ucts of the *rep* gene are required for AAV gene expression and replication under permissive conditions (Labow et al. 1986; Tratschin et al. 1986). Under nonpermissive conditions the *rep* gene products have been demonstrated to have several negative regulatory properties with respect to gene expression (Tratschin et al. 1986; Labow et al. 1987). In this paper, we have demonstrated the ability of one or more *rep* gene products to negatively regulate the replication of hybrid AAV/SV40 genomes in COS-7 cells. The inhibition requires a target sequence in *cis* that is at least partially contained within the AAV inverted terminal repeats. It seems likely that this represents a negative regulation that may form a normal part of the AAV life cycle; i.e., under nonpermissive conditions *rep* gene products can repress both AAV gene expression and DNA replication, thus favoring establishment of a latent proviral state from which the AAV genome can be rescued when the intracellular milieu becomes permissive. Thus, the AAV genome would serve as a sense organ that can actively respond to intracellular conditions. Determination of the specific mechanism of the inhibition of DNA replication reported in this paper awaits development of an in vitro assay.

The inhibition of DNA replication we have reported is similar to that reported for papillomaviruses. Indeed, the two viruses seem to be quite similar in life cycle except that papilloma more frequently establishes a latent state as a plasmid, although it does integrate on occasion. Interestingly, the gene arrangements for the two viruses are quite similar and unlike that of the polyomaviruses. It seems likely that negative regulation may be a general phenomenon for nuclear DNA viruses that commonly establish latent infections.

Acknowledgments

We wish to thank Ms. P. Burfeind and Mr. E. Homar for technical assistance. This work was supported by Public Health Service grant AI-22251 from the National Institutes of Health.

References

Birnboim, H.C. and J. Doly. 1979. A rapid alkaline extraction procedure for screening recombinant plasmid DNA. *Nucleic Acids Res* **7**: 1513.

Carter, B.J. and C.A. Laughlin. 1984. Adeno-associated virus defectiveness and the nature of the helper function. In *The parvoviruses* (ed. K.I. Berns), p. 67. Plenum Press, New York.

Cheung, A.M-K., M.D. Hoggan, W.W. Hauswirth, and K.I. Berns. 1980. Integration of the adeno-associated virus genome into cellular DNA in latently infected human Detroit-6 cells. *J. Virol.* **33**: 739.

Feinberg, A.P. and B. Vogelstein. 1983. A technique for radiolabeling DNA restriction fragments to high specific activity. *Anal. Biochem.* **13**: 212.

Gluzman, Y. 1981. SV40-transformed simian cells support the replication of early SV40 mutants. *Cell* **23**: 175.

Gorman, C.M., L.F. Moffat, and B.H. Howard. 1982. Recombinant genomes which express chloramphenicol acetyltransferase in mammalian cells. *Mol. Cell. Biol.* **2**: 1044.

Hermonat, P.L. 1984. "Genetic analysis and utilization of adeno-associated virus (AAV) as a mammalian cloning vector." Ph.D. thesis, University of Florida, Gainesville.

Hermonat, P.L. and N. Muzyczka. 1984. Use of adeno-associated virus as a mammalian DNA cloning vector: Transduction of neomycin resistance into mammalian tissue culture cells. *Proc. Natl. Acad. Sci.* **81**: 6470.

Hermonat, P.L., M.A. Labow, R. Wright, K.I. Berns, and N. Muzyczka. 1984. Genetics of adeno-associated virus: Isolation and preliminary characterization of mutants of adeno-associated type 2 mutants. *J. Virol.* **51**: 329.

Hirt, B. 1967. Selective extraction of polyoma DNA from infected mouse cell cultures. *J. Mol. Biol.* **26**: 365.

Labow, M.A., L.H. Graf, and K.I. Berns. 1987. Adeno-associated virus gene expression inhibits cellular transformation by heterologous genes. *Mol. Cell. Biol.* **7**: 1320.

Labow, M.A., P.L. Hermonat, and K.I. Berns. 1986. Positive and negative autoregulation of the adeno-associated virus type 2 genome. *J. Virol.* **60**: 251.

Lusby, E.W. and K.I. Berns. 1982. Mapping of 5 primed -termini of two adeno-associated virus RNAs in the left half of the genome. *J. Virol.* **41**: 518.

Maniatis, T., E.F. Fritsch, and J. Sambrook. 1982. *Molecular cloning: A laboratory manual.* Cold Spring Harbor Laboratory, Cold Spring Harbor, New York.

McCutchan, J.H. and J.S. Pagano. 1968. Enhancement of the infectivity of SV40 DNA with DEAE-dextran. *J. Natl. Cancer Inst.* **41**: 351.

Mendelson, E., J.P. Trempe, and B.J. Carter. 1986. Identification of the *trans*-active rep proteins of adeno-associated virus by antibodies to a synthetic oligopeptide. *J. Virol.* **56**: 823.

Schlehofer, J.R., M. Ehrbar, and H. zur Hausen. 1986. Vaccinia virus, herpes simplex virus and carcinogens induce DNA amplification in a human cell line and support replication of a helper virus dependent parvovirus. *Virology* **152**: 110.

Siegl, G., R.C. Bates, K.I. Berns, B.J. Carter, D.C. Kelly, E. Kurstak, and P. Tattersall. 1985. Characteristics and taxonomy of parvoviridae. *Intervirology* **23**: 61.

Southern, E.M. 1975. Detection of specific sequences among DNA fragments separated by gel electrophoresis. *J. Mol. Biol.* **98**: 503.

Srivastava, A., E.W. Lusby, and K.I. Berns. 1983. Nucleotide sequence and organization of the adeno-associated virus 2 genome. *J. Virol.* **45**: 555.

Tratschin, J.-D., I.L. Miller, and B.J. Carter. 1984. Genetic analysis of adeno-associated virus: Properties of deletion mutants constructed in vitro and evidence for an adeno-associated virus replication function. *J. Virol.* **51**: 611.

Tratschin, J.-D., J. Tal, and B.J. Carter. 1986. Negative and positive regulation in *trans* of gene expression from adeno-associated virus vectors in mammalian cells by a viral REP gene product. *Mol. Cell. Biol.* **6**: 2884.

Yakobson, B., R. Koch, and E. Winocour. 1987. Replication of adeno-associated virus in synchronized cells without the addition of a helper virus. *J. Virol.* **61**: 972.

DNA Unwinding Function of the SV40 Large Tumor Antigen

H. Stahl, M. Scheffner, M. Wiekowski, and R. Knippers

Fakultät für Biologie, Universität Konstanz, D 7750 Konstanz, Federal Republic of Germany

Isolated SV40 large tumor antigen (T antigen) has the biochemical properties of a DNA helicase. Short double-stranded DNA duplices (20–34 bp) with 3'-protruding single-stranded tails of 10 nucleotides or less are efficient substrates for the T antigen helicase, suggesting that the entry site for the T antigen helicase is characterized by single-strand–double-strand junctions rather than by extended stretches of single-stranded DNA. However, T antigen is also able to unwind fully double-stranded DNA using internal binding sites for the initiation of the strand separation reaction. At low ionic strength, this reaction does not depend on the presence of the SV40 origin of replication. At salt concentrations of 75–100 mM potassium acetate, an origin-containing DNA fragment is more efficiently unwound by T antigen than a control fragment. We propose that T antigen induces conformational changes in the DNA region to which it is bound, and that the induced DNA conformation resembles the single-strand–double-strand junction required for the DNA helicase activity of T antigen.

An essential function of T antigen for viral DNA replication was first recognized in 1972 (Tegtmeyer 1972). Investigated temperature-sensitive mutants (tsA mutants) failed to initiate replication under nonpermissive conditions but were quite efficient in strand elongation. Therefore, it was concluded that T antigen played a role in an initiation step but was dispensable for the elongation phase of the replication cycle. Additional genetic experiments (Shortle et al. 1979) and numerous in vitro experiments (Ariga and Sugano 1983; Li and Kelly 1984; Stillman et al. 1985) clearly showed that a specific interaction of T antigen with a DNA site in the SV40 origin of replication is essential for the induction of each round of replication. However, T antigen is not only required at an initiation step but also at subsequent reactions during the replication cycle. Replicating SV40 minichromosomes carry T antigen tightly bound to sites in the vicinity of replication forks, where it performs a function related to the separation of parental DNA strands (Stahl and Knippers 1983; Stahl et al. 1985; Wiekowski et al. 1987). Moreover, isolated T antigen is able to unwind DNA duplices in a reaction requiring ATP hydrolysis (Stahl et al. 1986). This biochemical property of T antigen is comparable to the function of prokaryotic DNA helicases, which are essential components of the replication machineries of bacteria and bacteriophages.

In this paper, we summarize the evidence for a DNA helicase function of T antigen. We describe some experiments that were performed to better understand the substrate requirements for the T antigen helicase. Our model studies may be useful to explore the function of T antigen during the initiation and the elongation phase of SV40 DNA replication.

Methods and Materials

T antigen and assay conditions

T antigen was isolated from SV40-infected African green monkey kidney cells (cell line TC7) using a modification of the immunoaffinity procedure of Simanis and Lane (1985). The standard unwinding assay was performed in 0.05-ml volumes of 20 mM Tris-HCl (pH 7.5), 10 mM $MgCl_2$, 0.5 mM dithioerythritol, 2 mM ATP, 0.1 mg/ml bovine serum albumin with 6–9 ng of ^{32}P-labeled DNA substrate, and 50–200 ng purified T antigen. In some experiments we added 600 ng/ml of the *Escherichia coli* single-strand specific DNA binding (SSB) protein (Pharmacia) to the reaction mixture.

The reaction was carried out for 30–60 minutes at 37°C and stopped by 50 mM EDTA and 1% SDS. The fraction of unwound DNA was determined by polyacrylamide gel electrophoresis (10%; 90 mM Tris-borate, 10 mM EDTA [pH 8.3]) and autoradiography.

DNA substrates

A double-stranded 34-mer M13-DNA fragment (Anderson et al. 1980) was obtained from Bethesda Research Laboratory. The complementary strand was annealed to M13mp8-DNA and 3'-end-labeled using the Klenow fragment of *E. coli* DNA polymerase I and [^{32}P]dATP (Stahl et al. 1986). The 34-mer fragment, as obtained from the supplier, contains 5' protruding ends. For control experiments, this fragment was converted to full double strandedness by the Klenow polymerase in the presence of all four deoxyribonucleotides and [^{32}P]dATP. The following oligonucleotides were chemi-

105

106 CANCER CELLS 6 / *Eukaryotic DNA Replication*

cally synthesized (McBride and Caruthers 1983; Wiekowski et al. 1988):

5′-T T T T T T A C A A C G T C G T G A C T (C T) n
      A T G T T G C A G C A C T G A

The overhanging 5′ end was "filled up" using the Klenow polymerase with [^{32}P]dATP. Substrates were prepared without CT tail (n = 0) or with CT tails of 5 (n = 2 + C), 10 (n = 5), 20 (n = 10), or 30 (n = 15) nucleotides.

Two SV40 DNA fragments of comparable lengths were used, namely the 109-bp *Hin*fl-G fragment (SV40 nucleotides 4459–4568) and the 109-bp *Hin*dIII-*Nco*l fragment (SV40 nucleotides 5171–37). The latter fragment includes the two high-affinity T-antigen-binding sites and the SV40 "core" origin (Li et al. 1986; Deb et al. 1986, 1987). The overhanging single-stranded ends of the fragments were filled up to produce blunt ends before cloning in the *Sma*l site of plasmid pUC8. For our experiments, the fragments were recovered from the plasmids by *Eco*RI and *Hin*dIII restriction and converted to full double-strandedness by the Klenow polymerase with ^{32}P-labeled dNTPs. Since the *Eco*RI and *Hin*dIII restriction sites bracket the SV40 inserts in the pUC8

vector, the DNA fragments used were 34 nucleotides longer than the origin SV40 DNA segments.

The structures of other DNA substrates will be described below.

Results and Discussion

T antigen as DNA helicase

In vivo-initiated replicative intermediates of SV40 minichromosomes, incubated with nucleotides and with protein extracts from proliferating human or monkey cells, continue semiconservative DNA replication in vitro to produce mature SV40 chromatin containing circularly closed DNA molecules as replication products (Su and DePamphilis 1978; Stahl et al. 1985). In contrast to the more recently developed replication systems using SV40 DNA as template (Li and Kelly 1984; Stillman et al. 1985), the chain elongation system does not require the addition of purified T antigen. However, T antigen is present at replication forks of isolated replicating SV40 minichromosomes, where it appears to perform an essential function, since certain T-antigen-specific monoclonal antibodies inhibit replicative chain elongation in vitro (Fig. 1) (Stahl et al. 1985; Wiekowski et al. 1987).

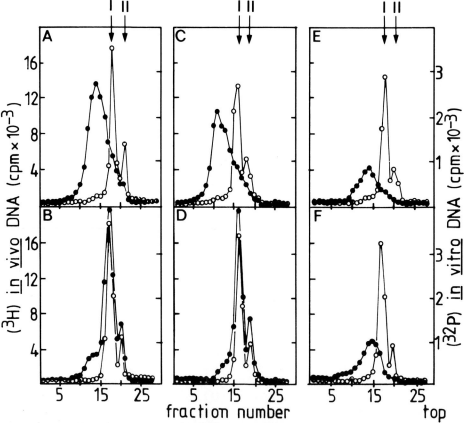

Figure 1 SV40 minichromosome replication in vitro. Minichromosomes, prepared from [^{3}H]thymidine-labeled (1 hr) SV40-infected cells, were incubated in vitro with a protein extract from uninfected TC7 cells and ^{32}P-labeled deoxynucleotides under the conditions described in Stahl et al. (1985). The DNA was extracted and centrifuged through neutral sucrose gradients containing 1.2 M NaCl and 0.1% Sarcosyl. (*A,C,E*) SV40 DNA, after 3-min pulse replication in vitro (●); (*B,D,F*) SV40 DNA, after 30-min chases in vitro (●). Form I and form II SV40 DNA (○), extracted from in vivo [^{3}H]thymidine-labeled minichromosomes, served as sedimentation marker. (*A,B*) Control: replication of minichromosomes without immunoglobulins; (*C,D*) preincubation with monoclonal antibody PAb101; (*E,F*) preincubation with monoclonal antibody PAb 1630. The tops of the gradients are on the right.

The function of T antigen at replication forks is most likely related to the unwinding of parental DNA strands (Wiekowski et al. 1987). Indeed, isolated T antigen has properties of a DNA helicase (Fig. 2) (Stahl et al. 1986) and the same T-antigen-specific monoclonal antibodies that inhibit in vitro replicative chain elongation also block the DNA helicase activity of isolated T antigen (Fig. 3).

Substrate requirements

We demonstrated the DNA helicase activity of isolated T antigen using as a substrate M13mp8 DNA carrying a hydrogen-bonding [^{32}P]-labeled complementary 34-mer DNA strand. The annealed strand was released in a T-antigen-catalyzed reaction depending on the presence of magnesium salts and ATP hydrolysis (Fig. 2) (Stahl et al. 1986). Under identical reaction conditions, the fully double-stranded 34-mer DNA was not unwound by T antigen (Fig. 2), suggesting that the single-stranded region of the M13mp8 substrate may be essential for the initiation of the unwinding reaction. However, the single-stranded region, required for efficient unwinding, may not be very extended since its complete coating with the E. coli SSB protein did not significantly affect the DNA helicase activity of subsequently added T antigen (Wiekowski et al. 1988). In this respect, T antigen differs from the E. coli dnaB protein, a bacterial replica-

tive DNA helicase, which is inactive on substrates, precoated with SSB protein (LeBowitz and McMacken 1986).

To systematically investigate the substrate requirements for T antigen, we used chemically synthesized substrates consisting of a 20-bp double-stranded section with 3' overhanging single-stranded tails of various lengths, ranging from 30 to 5 nucleotides. The results showed that the efficiency of unwinding decreased with shorter single-stranded tails, but a single-stranded region as short as 5 nucleotides was nevertheless quite sufficient to promote the DNA helicase activity of T antigen (Fig. 4). We conclude that the entry site for T antigen is not an extended stretch of single-stranded DNA but rather a structural feature of the substrate characterized by the transition point from single- to double-strandedness.

DNA constructs, similar to those used in the experiment of Figure 4 but with 5' overhanging single strands, were shown to be poor substrates, implying that the T antigen helicase has a preferred polarity of unwinding, moving in the 3' to 5' direction of the strand to which it is bound (Wiekowski et al. 1988). This is just opposite to the polarity of the E. coli dnaB DNA helicase, which preferentially moves in the 5' to 3' direction (LeBowitz and McMacken 1986).

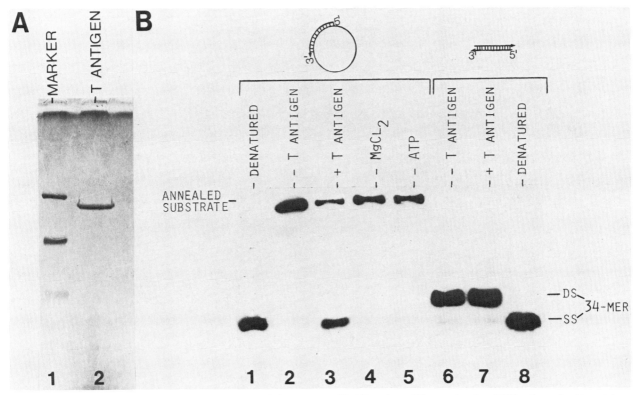

Figure 2 DNA helicase activity of isolated T antigen. (A) Immunopurified T antigen. Silver stain of an SDS polyacrylamide gel (see Stahl et al. 1986). Electrophoresis markers are proteins of M_r 94,000, 68,000, and 43,000 (from the top). (B) DNA helicase activity. The structures of the substrates used are shown on top; arrow heads indicate sites of radioactive labeling (see Methods and Materials). We show the autoradiogram of a polyacrylamide gel after electrophoresis. (Lanes 1 and 8) Heat-denatured substrates; (lanes 2 and 6) incubation in the standard reaction mixture without T antigen; (lanes 3 and 7) incubation with T antigen under standard conditions, or without MgCl$_2$ (lane 4), or without ATP (lane 5).

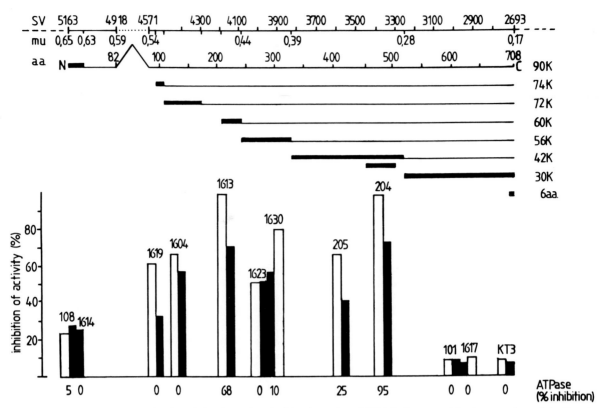

Figure 3 Inhibition of in vitro replicative chain elongation (solid columns) and DNA helicase activity (open columns) by T-antigen-specific monoclonal antibodies. The origin and the characterization of the antibodies (designated by their PAb numbers) were given in Stahl et al. (1986) and Wiekowski et al. (1987). The numerical values at the bottom of the figure refer to the inhibitory effects of the antibodies on the ATPase activity of T antigen, a biochemical property most likely connected to the DNA helicase function. The antibodies are arranged according to the locations of their epitopes in T antigen as indicated by the thick parts in the group of horizontal lines symbolizing T antigen or fragments of T antigen. Amino termini are at the left and carboxyl termini at the right (aa, amino acids). The upper line represents the genetic early region of the SV40 genome in SV40 nucleotide numbers (SV) or physical map units (mu).

A summary of the known properties of T antigen DNA helicase in comparison to the dnaB helicase is given in Table 1.

T antigen initiates unwinding at internal sites of long DNA double strands

T antigen serves as an initiator of SV40 DNA replication (Tegtmeyer 1972), and recent evidence suggests that isolated T antigen may be able to partially unwind closed circular DNA (Dean et al. 1987; Wold et al. 1987; M.Scheffner and H. Stahl, unpubl.). Since isolated T antigen appears to be sufficient for this reaction, we expect to obtain an unwinding of fully double-stranded DNA. To investigate this possibility, we used as substrates two completely double-stranded SV40 DNA fragments, each 143 bp long. One fragment contained both high-affinity T-antigen-binding sites and the entire core origin of replication (see Methods and Materials). The second fragment included the SV40 DNA segment from nucleotides 4459–4568.

We found that T antigen was able to efficiently unwind both the origin-containing and the control fragment under standard assay conditions (low salt), provided that the E. coli SSB protein was present to prevent the

reannealing of separated complementary strands (Fig. 5, lanes 2).

This result is clearly in contrast to the data presented above in Figures 2 and 4, where we showed that T antigen fails to unwind 20- and 34-bp-long DNA duplices unless they carry 3′ single-strand extensions. However, the size and the base sequences of the double strands used are significantly different. T antigen, initiating DNA unwinding from an internal site of duplex DNA, has to induce conformational changes of the double-stranded DNA section to which it is bound; and the 20-bp and 34-bp fragments may be too short for an effective interaction of T antigen with DNA, in particular as several T antigen molecules are needed to form stable T-antigen–DNA complexes (Mastrangelo et al. 1985).

An additional and equally unexpected result of the experiment of Figure 5 is the fact that, at low ionic strengths, unwinding occurred with essentially equal efficiencies, regardless of whether the SV40 origin of replication was present or not. However, low salt conditions are nonstringent for T-antigen–DNA interactions. Under these conditions, T antigen binds to essentially all DNA sequences with no particular preference for the origin of replication. At higher salt concentrations, unspecific interactions of T antigen with DNA are far less

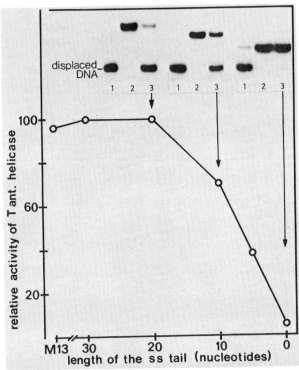

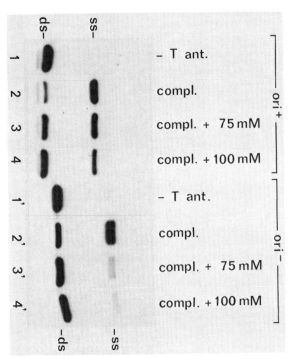

Figure 4 Substrate requirements. The substrates possess a 20-bp double-stranded section and 3' single-strand extensions of 30, 20, 10, 5, or 0 nucleotides as indicated (see Methods and Materials). At saturating T antigen concentrations, the substrates, containing 30- and 20-mer single-strand extensions, are unwound with the same efficiencies (100%) as the M13mp8 substrate of Fig. 2 (M13). The inserts show the autoradiograms of some selected experiments with substrates containing a 20-mer (*left*) or a 10-mer (*center*) single-stranded tail, as well as with completely double-stranded DNA (*right*). (Lane *1*) Heat-denatured substrates; (lane *2*) incubation under standard conditions without T antigen; (lane *3*) incubation with T antigen.

Figure 5 Unwinding of fully double-stranded DNA. The complete system (compl.) was the standard reaction mixture (Materials and Methods) plus *E. coli* SSB protein and T antigen. In some assays, 75 mM or 100 mM potassium acetate (final concentrations) was added to the complete system as indicated. *Left*: (lanes *1–4*) DNA substrate, containing the SV40 origin of replication (ori⁺). *Right*: (lanes *1'–4'*) DNA substrate without origin (ori⁻) (see Materials and Methods). (Lanes *1* and *1'*) DNA after incubation in the absence of T antigen. (ss) Single-stranded reaction products; (ds) double-stranded DNA substrates.

stable than the interaction of T antigen with the specific binding sites in and adjacent to the SV40 origin of replication (Dorn et al. 1982; Wright et al. 1984). Indeed, with 75–100 mM potassium acetate in the reaction

buffer, the unwinding of the control fragment was largely suppressed, whereas the origin fragment was efficiently unwound in a T-antigen-catalyzed reaction (Fig. 5, lanes 3 and 4). We do not yet know whether T antigen at low salt concentrations initiates DNA strand separation at random sites or whether it recognizes and binds to sections of the DNA that deviate from the classical

Table 1 Biochemical Properties of T Antigen DNA Helicase and *E. coli* dnaB Protein DNA Helicase

	T antigen	dnaB protein
Reaction conditions	rATP/dATP (2 mM; Mg⁺⁺ (7 mM) low salt	rATP (2 mM); Mg⁺⁺ (7 mM) low salt
Enzymatic activities	(specific) DNA-binding ATPase-activity	binding to single-stranded DNA DNA-dependent ATPase-activity
Helicase substrate	double-stranded DNA with 3' terminal extension of a few nucleotides fully double-stranded DNA	"replication forks" with a 3' terminal extension of about 40 and a 5' terminal extension of 80 nucleotides
Interaction with substrate	binding to the transition point from double- to single-stranded DNA	binding at the 5' single-stranded region and migration along the single strand to the double-stranded
Direction of unwinding	3' to 5'	5' to 3'
Rate of unwinding in vitro	approximately 100 bp/min	2000 bp/min
Reaction	probably processive and in complex with DNA polymerase	probably processive, in complex with primase

LeBowitz and McMacken (1986); Wiekowski et al. (1988).

B-form structure, for example, to stretches of AT-base pairs (which are present in both fragments) (Ryder et al. 1986) or to sequences of alternating purine-pyrimidine base pairs that assume non-B-form structures in several defined regions of SV40 DNA, including regions in the two fragments investigated (Müller et al. 1987).

In any case, bound T antigen must eventually induce a DNA conformation that includes single-strand to double-strand junctions and is therefore equivalent to the ends of the artificial substrates used in the experiments of Figure 4. In this context, we mention that similar results have recently been obtained using closed circular DNA molecules as substrates for T antigen. At low ionic strengths, T antigen was able to partially unwind circular DNA molecules with or without an SV40 origin of replication. At higher ionic strengths, however, origin-containing DNA circles were more efficiently unwound than unspecific DNA (Wold et al. 1987; M. Scheffner and H. Stahl, unpubl.).

We expect, however, that experiments with linear DNA molecules will be quite useful to investigate in detail the molecular mechanisms by which T antigen initiates and performs the unwinding of DNA duplices. These experiments are not restricted to the relatively small DNA molecules used in the experiments of Figure 5. In fact, T antigen is able to unwind long double-stranded DNA stretches, including full-length linearized SV40 DNA (5.2 kbp) (Wiekowski et al. 1988).

Stable T-antigen–origin complexes

As an initiator of DNA replication, T antigen most likely catalyzes a localized unwinding of the SV40 origin region (Dean et al. 1987; Wold et al. 1987; M. Scheffner and H. Stahl, in prep.). However, we have shown above that isolated T antigen does not necessarily require a particular DNA sequence to initiate the unwinding of a DNA double strand. Why is the interaction of T antigen with the specific origin-binding site essential for the initiation of an SV40 DNA replication cycle? First, unspecific DNA binding is probably unstable under the ionic strength conditions of the nucleus or the in vitro DNA replication system. In vivo, unspecific binding may also be suppressed because SV40 DNA is densely packed in chromatin except for the origin region, which may be nucleosome-free in replication-competent SV40 minichromosomes (Sogo et al. 1986). In addition, origin binding may be a requirement for the formation of a functional complex with other components of the replication apparatus (Wold et al. 1987).

In any case, origin-bound T antigen must eventually unwind the origin region, a reaction that is essential for its subsequent helicase function. This reaction may be comparable to the transition from a closed to an open promoter complex after binding of transcribing RNA polymerase (for review, see McClure 1985). A characteristic feature of the open promoter complex is its resistance against high salt; we expect that "open origin" complexes are also salt resistant.

To investigate this possibility, we treated SV40 minichromosomes, isolated from SV40-infected cells, with 1.2 M NaCl. This salt concentration is sufficiently high to dissociate most DNA-bound proteins, including histones. The salt concentration used is also much higher than the 0.2–0.4 M NaCl required to disrupt in-vitro-formed T-antigen–DNA complexes (Dorn et al. 1982)

We detected a significant fraction of minichromosomes carrying T antigen in a complex that was resistant against 1.2–1.5 M NaCl. This fraction included replicating minichromosomes that carry a salt-stably bound T antigen in the vicinity of replication forks as described before (Stahl and Knippers 1983; Stahl et al. 1985). We also found by electron microscopic examination of salt-treated SV40 minichromosomes a number of nonreplicating DNA molecules with tightly bound T antigen at the origin region (Fig. 6).

Restriction mapping indicated that T antigen was located some 100 (±50) bp on the genetically late side of the *Bgl*I cut (Fig. 6). This region includes the AT-rich domain of the origin of replication where localized strand unwinding should be facilitated (Deb et al. 1986, 1987; Li et al. 1986). This region also includes start sites for the synthesis of the first DNA strands as mapped by Hay and DePamphilis (1982).

The salt stability of these complexes excludes a binding of T antigen to the exterior surface of the DNA and suggests that T antigen may be located between the two strands of the double helix initiating strand separation as a first step to establish replication forks.

Conclusion

T antigen uniquely combines two important functions for SV40 DNA replication, namely, the function of an initiator protein that locally unwinds the DNA section to which it is bound and the function of a DNA helicase required for a strand unwinding reaction at replication forks.

The formation of an "open origin" complex implies the establishment of structures characterized by double-strand–single-strand transitions, just as in the model substrates for the T antigen DNA helicase (Fig. 4). Bound T antigen can now proceed in the 3' to 5' direction on the strand to which it is bound and can processively disrupt the hydrogen bonds of complementary DNA strands. The polarity of this reaction corresponds to the polarity of the template for leading strand synthesis, suggesting a close functional cooperation between T antigen and the replicative DNA polymerase. In fact, inhibition of DNA polymerase by aphidicolin strongly interferes with the strand separation reaction in vivo (Dröge et al. 1985). However, we cannot exclude the possibility that cellular DNA helicases may operate at SV40 DNA replication forks under certain conditions and at terminal stages in the replication cycle, as suggested by Tack and Proctor (1987).

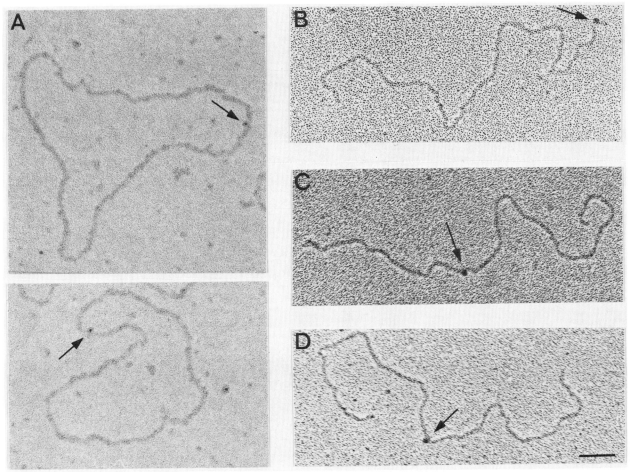

Figure 6 Electron microscopic examination of SV40 DNA molecules carrying salt-stably bound T antigen in the origin region. SV40 minichromosomes were prepared from SV40-infected cells (Stahl et al. 1985), treated with 1.2 M NaCl, and sedimented through a neutral sucrose gradient in 1.2 M NaCl, but without sarcosyl as in Fig. 1. The isolated DNA was incubated with polyclonal T-antigen-specific antibodies and immunostained using ferritin-labeled protein A (A) or ferritin-labeled second antibodies (B) as described in Stahl et al. (1985). We show relaxed circular (A) as well as *Bgl*I (B), *Eco*RI (C), and *Bam*HI (D) restricted SV40 DNA. The arrows indicate the ferritin-stained T antigen. We show typical examples taken from a collection of about 30 molecules of each type.

Acknowledgments

We thank W. Deppert and D. Lane for their kind gifts of hybridoma cells producing monoclonal antibodies PAb101, PAb108, KT3, and PAb204, and PAb205, respectively. G. Brandner and H.K. Hochkeppel supplied hybridoma supernatants containing monoclonal antibodies of the 16-series. H. Zentgraf performed the electron micrographs. We are grateful to M. Schwarz for the chemically synthesized oligonucleotides, T. Kapitza for preparing T antigen, and I. Lühr for typing the manuscript. The work was supported by Deutsche Forschungsgemeinschaft, Fonds der Chemie, and a Konrad Adenauer Fellowship to M.W.

References

Anderson, S., M.J. Gait, L. Mayol, and I.G. Young. 1980. A short primer for sequencing DNA cloned in the single-stranded vector M13mp8. *Nucleic Acids Res.* **8:** 1731.

Ariga, H. and S. Sugano. 1983. Initiation of simian virus 40 DNA replication in vitro. *J. Virol.* **48:** 481.

Dean, F.B., P. Bullock, Y. Murakami, C.R. Wobbe, L. Weissbach, and J. Hurwitz. 1987. Simian virus 40 DNA replication: SV40 large T antigen unwinds DNA containing the SV40 origin of replication. *Proc. Natl. Acad. Sci.* **84:** 16.

Deb, S., A.L. DeLucia, C.P. Baur, A. Koff, and P. Tegtmeyer. 1986. Domain structure of the simian virus 40 core origin of replication. *Mol. Cell. Biol.* **6:** 1663

Deb S., S. Tsui, A. Koff, A.L. DeLucia, R. Parsons, and P. Tegtmeyer. 1987. The T antigen binding domain of the simian virus 40 core origin of replication. *J. Virol.* **61:** 2143.

Dorn, A., D. Brauer, B. Otto, E. Fanning, and R. Knippers. 1982. Subclasses of simian virus 40 large tumor antigen. *Eur. J. Biochem.* **128:** 53.

Dröge, P., J.M. Sogo, and H. Stahl. 1985. Inhibition of DNA synthesis by aphidicolin induces supercoiling in simian virus 40 replicative intermediates. *EMBO J.* **4:** 3241.

Hay, R.T. and M.L. DePamphilis. 1982. Initiation of SV40 DNA replication in vivo: Location and structure of 5′ends of DNA synthesized in the origin region. *Cell* **28:** 767.

LeBowitz, J. and R. McMacken. 1986. The *Escherichia coli* dnaB replication protein is a DNA helicase. *J. Biol. Chem.* **261:** 4738.

Li, J.J. and T.S. Kelly. 1984. Simian virus 40 DNA replication in vitro. *Proc. Natl. Acad. Sci.* **81:** 6973.

Li, J.J., K.W.C. Peden, R.A.F. Dixon, and T. Kelly. 1986. Functional organization of the simian virus 40 origin of DNA replication. *Mol. Cell. Biol.* **6:** 1117.

Mastrangelo, I.A., P.V.C. Hough, V.G. Wilson, J.S. Wall, J.F. Hainfeld, and P. Tegtmeyer. 1985. Monomers through trimers of large T antigen in region I and monomers through tetramers in region II bind to SV40 origin DNA as stable structures in solutions. *Proc. Natl. Acad. Sci.* **82:** 3626.

McBride, L.J. and M.H. Caruthers. 1983. An investigation of several deoxynucleoside phosphoramidites useful for synthesizing deoxyoligonucleotides. *Tetrahedron Lett.* **24:** 245.

McClure, W.R. 1985. Mechanism and control of transcription initiation in prokaryotes. *Annu. Rev. Biochem.* **54:** 171.

Müller, B.C., A.L. Raphael, and J.K. Barton. 1987. Evidence for altered DNA conformations in the simian virus 40 genome: Site-specific DNA cleavage by the chiral complex Λ-tris (4,7diphenyl-1,10-phenanthroline) cobalt III. *Proc. Natl. Acad. Sci.* **84:** 1764.

Ryder, K., S. Silver, A.L. DeLucia, E. Fanning, and P. Tegtmeyer. 1986. An altered DNA conformation in origin region I is a determinant for the binding of SV40 large T antigen. *Cell* **44:** 719.

Shortle, D.R., R.F. Margolskee, and D. Nathans. 1979. Mutational analysis of the simian virus 40 origin: Pseudorevertants of mutants with a defective replication origin. *Proc. Natl. Acad. Sci.* **76:** 6128.

Simanis, V. and P.D. Lane. 1985. An immunoaffinity purification procedure for SV40 large T antigen. *Virology* **144:** 88.

Sogo, J.M., H. Stahl, T. Koller, and R. Knippers. 1986. Structure of replicating simian virus 40 minichromosomes. *J. Mol. Biol.* **189:** 189.

Stahl, H. and R. Knippers. 1983. Simian virus 40 large tumor antigen on replicating viral chromatin: Tight binding and localization on the viral genome. *J. Virol.* **47:** 65.

Stahl, H., P. Dröge, and R. Knippers. 1986. DNA helicase activity of SV40 large tumor antigen. *EMBO J.* **5:** 1939.

Stahl, H., P. Dröge, H. Zentgraf, and R. Knippers. 1985. A large tumor antigen specific monoclonal antibody inhibits DNA replication of simian virus 40 minichromosomes in an in vitro elongation system. *J. Virol.* **54:** 473.

Stillman, B., R.D. Gerard, R.A. Guggenheimer, and Y. Gluzman. 1985. T antigen and template requirements for SV40 DNA replication in vitro. *EMBO J.* **4:** 2933.

Su, R.T. and M.L. DePamphilis. 1978. Simian virus 40 DNA replication in isolated replicating minichromosomes. *J. Virol.* **28:** 53.

Tack, L.C. and G.N. Proctor. 1987. Two major replicating simian virus 40 chromosome classes. *J. Biol. Chem.* **262:** 6339.

Tegtmeyer, P. 1972. Simian virus 40 deoxyribonucleic acid synthesis: The viral replicon. *J. Virol.* **10:** 591.

Wiekowski, M., P. Dröge, and H. Stahl. 1987. Monoclonal antibodies as probes for a function of large T antigen during the elongation process of simian virus 40 DNA replication. *J. Virol.* **61:** 411.

Wiekowski, M., M. Schwarz, and H. Stahl. 1988. Simian virus 40 large T antigen DNA helicase. Characterization of the ATPase dependent DNA unwinding activity and its substrate requirements. *J. Biol. Chem.* **263:** 436.

Wold, M.S., J.L. Li, and T.J. Kelly. 1987. Initiation of simian virus 40 DNA replication in vitro: Large-tumor-antigen and origin-dependent unwinding of the template. *Proc. Natl. Acad. Sci.* **84:** 3643.

Wright, P.J., A.L. DeLucia, and P. Tegtmeyer. 1984. Sequence-specific binding of simian virus 40 A protein to nonorigin and cellular DNA. *Mol. Cell. Biol.* **4:** 2631.

SV40 Origin-dependent DNA Unwinding and Nucleoprotein Complex Formation by SV40 T Antigen

F.B. Dean,* M. Dodson,[†] J.A. Borowiec,* Y. Ishimi,* G.S. Goetz,* P. Bullock,* S.W. Matson,[‡] H. Echols,[†] and J. Hurwitz*

*Graduate Program in Molecular Biology and Virology, Sloan-Kettering Institute for Cancer Research, New York, New York 10021; [†]Department of Molecular Biology, University of California, Berkeley, California 94720; [‡]Department of Biology, University of North Carolina, Chapel Hill, North Carolina 27514

The complete replication of DNA containing the SV40 origin of replication can be carried out with SV40 T antigen and six protein fractions purified from HeLa cells. These include DNA polymerase α–primase, single-strand DNA binding protein, topoisomerase II, RNase H, a 5' to 3' exonuclease, and DNA ligase. The SV40 T antigen has two activities required for the localized initiation of DNA replication: site-specific DNA binding and a DNA helicase. The combination of the site-specific binding and helicase activities allows T antigen to carry out the SV40 origin-dependent unwinding of duplex DNA. The DNA unwinding activity is initiated at the replication origin and both circular and linear duplex DNA molecules are efficient substrates for unwinding. Although duplex DNA unwinding is bidirectional, the helicase activity is unidirectional, moving in a 3' to 5' direction on the strand to which T antigen is bound. T antigen forms an ATP-dependent nucleoprotein complex at the origin of replication when tested under conditions required for DNA replication. We suggest that the formation of this complex is essential for the initiation of DNA unwinding and replication.

The only protein encoded by SV40 that is required for viral DNA replication is the large tumor antigen (T antigen), and the initiation of replication depends on the binding of T antigen to SV40 replication origin (Rigby and Lane 1983; DePamphilis and Bradley 1986; Fried and Prives 1986). DNA replication dependent on the SV40 origin and on T antigen has been carried out in vitro using extracts derived from simian or human cells (Li and Kelly 1984; Stillman and Gluzman 1985; Wobbe et al. 1985; Yamaguchi and DePamphilis 1986), or with purified protein fractions derived from HeLa cells. The purified factors include DNA polymerase α–primase, DNA topoisomerase I, and a single-strand DNA binding protein (SSB) (Wobbe et al. 1987).

The DNA region essential for initiating SV40 DNA replication has been defined at the sequence level (Bergsma et al. 1982; Stillman et al. 1985; DeLucia et al. 1986; Li et al. 1986). It consists of a 64-bp segment termed the core origin. There are two T-antigen-binding sites, I and II, located near the SV40 origin (Tjian 1978; DeLucia et al. 1983; Jones and Tjian 1984). Site II corresponds to the core origin, and site I lies outside the core origin and is not required for DNA replication in vivo or in vitro (Stillman et al. 1985; DeLucia et al. 1986; Li et al. 1986; Dean et al. 1987b).

SV40 T antigen carries out an origin-dependent duplex DNA unwinding activity in vitro in the presence of ATP, $MgCl_2$, and SSB (Dean et al. 1987c; Wold et al. 1987). Circular DNA is unwound in the presence of any topoisomerase than can remove positive supercoils. T

antigen is able to unwind duplex DNA due to an intrinsic DNA helicase activity (Stahl et al. 1986; Dean et al. 1987c; Wiekowski et al. 1987). Oligonucleotides hybridized to circular single-stranded DNA are displaced by T antigen, and this activity is not DNA sequence-specific. However, under conditions required for SV40 DNA replication in vitro, fully duplex DNA fragments are not unwound unless they contain a functional origin of replication (Dean et al. 1987c; Wold et al. 1987).

To initiate DNA replication it is likely that T antigen first binds specifically to the origin region and then, in the presence of an SSB, unwinds the DNA. This sequence of events would be similar to the pathways suggested for initiation of replication at two prokaryotic origins, *Escherichia coli oriC* and bacteriophage λ. In these systems a sequence-specific DNA-binding protein, dnaA protein for *E. coli* (Fuller et al. 1984) and the O protein for λ (Dodson et al. 1985), initially localizes the origin by formation of a specialized nucleoprotein structure (Echols 1986). This complex opens the DNA helix and provides access for the dnaB protein, a DNA helicase (LeBowitz and McMacken 1986), to bind to the DNA. Extensive DNA unwinding can then occur in the presence of additional factors such as SSB and DNA gyrase (Baker et al. 1986; Dodson et al. 1986). The SV40 system differs, however, in that the origin localization, helix opening, and helicase activities are provided solely by the T antigen. In this paper, we present further characterization of the various activities of SV40 T antigen.

113

Experimental Procedures

DNA replication assay

Preparations of pSV01ΔEP DNA and SV40 T antigen were as described (Wobbe et al. 1985). HeLa SSB (Wobbe et al. 1987), DNA polymerase α–primase (Murakami et al. 1986), RNase H (fraction V, DiFrancesco and Lehman 1985), and topoisomerase II (fraction 3, Miller et al. 1981) were purified from HeLa cells as described. DNA ligase and the 5′ to 3′ exonuclease were purified from HeLa cells (Y. Ishimi and J. Hurwitz, in prep.). Reaction mixtures (40 μl) contained 40 mM creatine phosphate (di Tris salt, pH 7.7), 7 mM MgCl$_2$, 0.5 mM dithiothreitol, 4 mM ATP, 200 μM each of CTP, UTP, and GTP, 100 μM each of dATP, dGTP, and dTTP, 20 μM [α-^{32}P]dCTP, 0.24 μg of superhelical plasmid pSV01ΔEP DNA, 0.8 μg of creatine kinase, 16 μg bovine serum albumin, 0.6 μg T antigen, 0.16 μg HeLa SSB, 0.5 unit DNA polymerase α, 0.6 unit DNA primase, 1.7 units RNase H, 0.14 μg DNA ligase, 200 units topoisomerase II, and 0.15 μg of a HeLa 5′ to 3′ exonuclease. After incubation at 37°C for 3 hours, the reaction was terminated and 1/10 volume was removed to determine the total amount of acid-insoluble material formed. The remaining replication reaction products were analyzed by electrophoresis on 1.2% agarose gels in the presence of 0.5 μg/ml ethidium bromide. The ethidium bromide intercalates into the DNA, and under these conditions all covalently closed, circular DNA molecules become supercoiled and migrate identically, regardless of their initial superhelical density. Thus relaxed, replicative form I′ (RFI′) DNA migrates as a single band and can be quantitated. After autoradiography of the dried gel, radioactive regions were excised and quantitated, and the proportion of reaction products consisting of covalently closed, circular molecules (RFI′) was determined.

Helicase assay with a partially duplex DNA substrate

Reaction mixtures (20 μl) contained 40 mM Tris-HCl (pH 7.5), 2 mM MgCl$_2$, 5 mM dithiothreitol, 50 μg/ml bovine serum albumin, 2.5% glycerol, 1.8 mM ATP, and approximately 0.2 μM DNA (as nucleotide). Reactions were incubated at 37°C for 30 minutes and terminated by the addition of 10 μl of 45 mM EDTA, 45% glycerol, 0.1% sodium dodecyl sulfate, 0.1% xylene cyanol, 0.1% bromphenol blue, and 60 μg/ml of proteinase K. The reaction products were analyzed by electrophoresis through a 6% nondenaturing polyacrylamide gel (Matson 1986) and autoradiography of the dried gel. The substrate consisted of a 7200-nt linear single-stranded DNA molecule with short stretches of duplex DNA at both ends (Matson 1986). Briefly, it was constructed by annealing a 341-bp *Hae*III restriction fragment with circular single-stranded M13 mp7 DNA, followed by cleavage with *Cla*I restriction endonuclease and end-labeling. *Cla*I cuts once within the 341-bp duplex region, generating a linear M13 mp7 molecule with duplex regions of 200 bp and 141 bp at the ends.

Unwinding of duplex DNA

Reaction mixtures (30 μl) contained 40 mM creatine phosphate (di Tris or disodium salt, pH 7.7), 7 mM MgCl$_2$, 1 mM dithiothreitol, 4 mM ATP, 0.7 μg creatine kinase, 0.36 μg of linear or relaxed, circular duplex DNA, 0.5–1.2 μg T antigen, 0.6 μg *E. coli* SSB (Pharmacia or U.S. Biochemicals), and 10 units of HeLa topoisomerase I in reactions containing circular DNA as substrate. Incubation was for 2 hours at 37°C. Reactions utilizing DNA substrates pSVLD, pSVLD 6-1, and pRLM4 (Dodson et al. 1987) were terminated by the addition of glutaraldehyde to 0.1%, further incubated for 15 minutes at 37°C, and analyzed by electron microscopy (see below). Reactions utilizing the 311-bp radioactively labeled SV40 origin-containing duplex DNA fragment generated by *Eco*RI digestion of pSV01ΔEP DNA, or the 291-bp origin-lacking fragment generated by *Pvu*II digestion of pVOP DNA (Goetz et al. 1988) were analyzed by electrophoresis through a 5% nondenaturing polyacrylamide gel. After autoradiography of the dried gel, radioactive regions were excised to quantitate the amount of DNA fragment unwound.

Nucleoprotein complex formation

Reactions (20–30 μl) contained 40 mM creatine phosphate (di Tris salt, pH 7.7), 7 mM MgCl$_2$, 1 mM dithiothreitol, 4 mM ATP, 25 μg/ml of creatine kinase, 0.5 μg substrate DNA, and 0.4 μg T antigen. After incubation for 1 hour at 37°C, reactions were terminated by the addition of glutaraldehyde to 0.1% and further incubated for 15 minutes at 37°C. The SV40 origin-containing plasmid substrates pSV01ΔEP (Wobbe et al. 1985) and pOR1 (DeLucia et al. 1986) have been described.

Electron microscopy

Reaction products fixed with 0.1% glutaraldehyde were passed over a Sepharose 4B column (4 × 0.5 cm) previously equilibrated with 40 mM HEPES-KOH buffer (pH 7.6) and 11 mM magnesium acetate. The peak fraction was diluted 1:4 in column buffer to a final DNA concentration of about 1 μg/ml, and electron microscopy was carried out by the polylysine technique (Williams 1977). Grids were rotary shadowed with tungsten. The lengths of projected molecules were measured on a Numonics 2400 digitizing tablet.

Agarose gel electrophoresis

After fixation with 0.1% glutaraldehyde, samples were prepared for electrophoresis by twofold dilution with H$_2$O and the addition of one-seventh volume of gel loading buffer, containing 20% Ficoll, 0.1 M EDTA, 0.25% bromphenol blue, and 0.25% xylene cyanol. Samples were electrophoresed in 1.5% agarose gels containing 25 mM Tris, 190 mM glycine, and 1 mM EDTA (pH 8.5), at 4 v/cm. DNA was visualized under ultraviolet illumination after staining in 0.5% ethidium bromide.

DNase-I-protection assay

Reaction mixtures (20 μl) contained 40 mM creatine phosphate (di Tris salt, pH 7.8), 7 mM MgCl$_2$, 0.1 mM dithiothreitol, 0.3 μg of pBR322ΔEP DNA, 15 ng of ^{32}P-labeled SV40 origin-containing DNA, 4 mM ATP, and T antigen. The labeled DNA substrate was generated by cleavage of pSV01ΔEP with restriction endonuclease *Eco*RI, labeling of the 5′ ends with [γ-^{32}P]ATP and T4 polynucleotide kinase, further cleavage with *Sph*I, and gel purification. The resulting origin-containing DNA fragment was labeled on the strand containing A residues in position 21–28 of the SV40 genome. After 30 minutes at 37°C, 30 ng of DNase I (Worthington) was added and the mixture further incubated for 60 seconds. The reaction was terminated with 20 μl of phenol/chloroform (1:1 v/v) and 1 μl of 0.5 M EDTA, and DNA fragments collected by precipitation with ethanol. The digestion products were analyzed on 6% polyacrylamide-urea gels.

Results

Replication in vitro of DNA containing the SV40 replication origin was recently carried out with purified protein fractions derived from HeLa cells (Wobbe et al. 1987). The required proteins included the SV40 T antigen, DNA polymerase α–primase, and HeLa SSB. However, the replication products in this system did not include monomer-sized covalently closed, circular DNA molecules. It was clear that additional factors would be necessary to complete the final stages of replication.

Complete replication of SV40 DNA has now been reconstituted in vitro. In addition to T antigen, DNA polymerase α–primase, and SSB, the addition of four more protein fractions resulted in the production of RFI′ DNA (Table 1). These additional protein fractions were RNase H, DNA ligase, topoisomerase II, and a 5′ to 3′ exonuclease, all purified from HeLa cells. A typical reaction resulted in the incorporation of 20 pmol dCMP, with about 15% of the reaction products consisting of RFI′. Although the omission of T antigen, polymerase α–primase, or SSB resulted in a loss of incorporation,

Table 1 Requirements for Replication of SV40 Origin-containing DNA with Purified Proteins

Reaction	DNA synthesis (pmol dCMP incorporated)	RFI′ (%)
Complete	20	15
−T antigen	0.2	N.D.
−SSB	0.2	N.D.
−polymerase α/primase	0.2	N.D.
−RNase H	21	8.7
−ligase	20	2.0
−topoisomerase II	9.7	3.6
−5′ to 3′ exonuclease	19	1.7

Reaction mixtures (40 μl) were as described in Experimental Procedures, with components omitted as indicated. RFI′, replicative form I′ (covalently closed, circular duplex DNA); N.D. indicates not done.

the other four protein fractions had little effect. However, the omission of either the DNA ligase, topoisomerase II, or the exonuclease all inhibited the formation of RFI′ significantly, roughly 80–90%. We do not see a strong requirement for RNase H at present.

We wished to analyze further the role of T antigen in DNA replication. T antigen has recently been shown to have a complex, multifunctional role in SV40 DNA synthesis, involving both site-specific binding to the replication origin and DNA unwinding carried out by a DNA helicase activity (Stahl et al. 1986; Dean et al. 1987c). These activities allow T antigen to carry out the origin-dependent unwinding of fully duplex DNA (Dean et al. 1987c). Due to the successful analysis by electron microscopy of DNA unwinding in the bacteriophage λ replicative system (Dodson et al. 1986), we used this approach to examine duplex DNA unwinding by T antigen (Dodson et al. 1987).

Plasmid pSVLD, a 10-kb circular DNA containing the SV40 origin, was incubated with T antigen, ATP, E. coli SSB, and HeLa topoisomerase I. DNA unwinding reactions can be carried out as well with HeLa SSB substituted for E. coli SSB, and with HeLa topoisomerase II substituted for topoisomerase I. E. coli SSB was used because the structure of single-strand DNA coated with it is well characterized. Products of the unwinding reaction were spread for electron microscopy and photographed (Fig. 1A). Plasmid molecules containing unwound regions were observed, with the unwound regions coated with E. coli SSB. The SSB-coated DNA was thickened in width and compacted in length compared to duplex DNA. Thus, the circles appear smaller as unwinding proceeds to completion. In addition, a large knob was often seen at the junction between the unwound region and the intact, duplex DNA. This is likely due to the presence of T-antigen molecules at the unwinding fork.

To determine the location of the unwound region with respect to the position of the SV40 origin on the DNA, the unwound circular DNA was cleaved with restriction endonuclease *Eco*RI (Fig. 1B). The locations of the unwound regions could then be mapped precisely. The duplex regions on partially unwound molecules were measured and were aligned with the shorter arm to the left (Fig. 2). The unwound regions span the replication origin, and the presence of equal lengths of unwound DNA on either side of the origin shows that unwinding proceeds bidirectionally from the origin.

Next we compared DNA unwinding on circular and linear duplex DNA substrates (Table 2). To verify that the formation of unwound products observed with linear DNA was dependent on the SV40 origin, three different substrates were used. These included pSVLD, which carries an intact SV40 origin; pSVLD 6-1, which has a 6-bp deletion in the origin, rendering it defective; and pRLM4, which contains only the bacteriophage λ origin. (All three DNA molecules were cleaved with restriction endonuclease *Aat*II to generate the linear substrates; similar results were observed with *Sal*I-linearized DNA.)

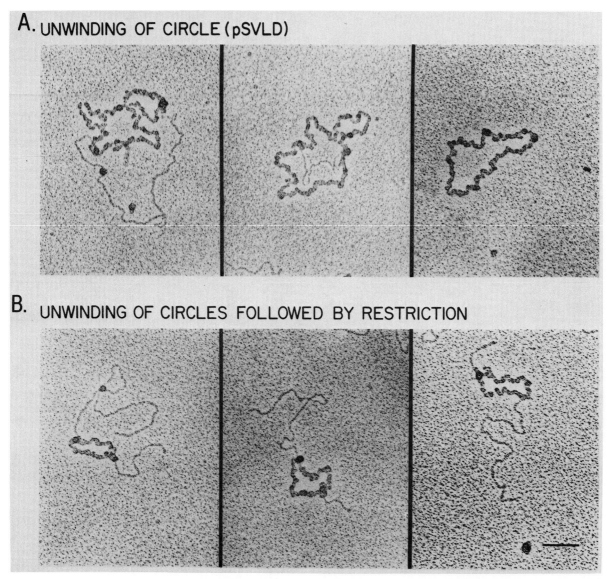

Figure 1 Electron micrographs of DNA products formed in the unwinding reaction. (*A*) Two partially unwound and one fully unwound circular plasmid DNAs. (*B*) Partially unwound molecules cleaved with restriction endonuclease *Eco*RI. Reaction mixtures were as described in Experimental Procedures, containing 0.36 µg of relaxed pSVLD DNA and 0.7 µg of T antigen (bar = 0.1 µm).

DNA unwinding was carried out identically with circular and linear substrates, except that topoisomerase was omitted from the reactions with linear DNA. Unwinding occurred efficiently on both circular and linear pSVLD molecules (Table 2), whereas reactions using pRLM4 yielded no unwound products. Unwinding on circular DNA was reduced 18-fold by the 6-1 mutation, whereas the reduction was sixfold on linear DNA. Origin specificity was clear for DNA unwinding with both circular and linear DNA. Thus, circular and linear DNA are equally effective substrates, and topological strain in the DNA is not necessary to initiate unwinding.

Although T-antigen unwinding of duplex DNA is origin-dependent, the T-antigen helicase activity is not specific for the SV40 origin under other conditions. For instance, the enzyme can bind to DNA substrates that have a region of single-strand DNA and begin translocation (Stahl et al. 1986; Dean et al. 1987c). This was used to determine the directionality of unwinding by T antigen (Goetz et al. 1988; Wiekowski et al. 1988) (Fig. 3). Helicase directionality is defined with respect to the DNA strand to which the enzyme is bound. On the substrate shown in Figure 3A, T-antigen migration in the 3' to 5' direction will result in the displacement of the 143-nt oligonucleotide. When T antigen was incubated with the substrate, the 143-nt fragment was displaced (Fig. 3B, lane 3). Greater amounts of T antigen did not result in any displacement of the 202-nt fragment. This shows that T antigen translocates along DNA in the 3' to 5' direction.

The ratio between T antigen and DNA also had an effect on the origin-specificity of duplex DNA unwinding

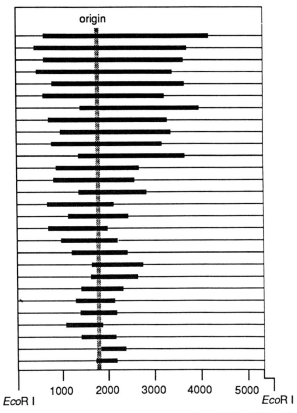

Figure 2 Location of unwound regions in pSVLD DNA with respect to the SV40 replication origin. Products of the DNA unwinding reactions were cleaved with restriction endonuclease EcoRI, which cleaves pSVLD twice and results in a 5243-bp SV40 origin-containing fragment, the entire SV40 genome. Unwound molecules were photographed and lengths of the two duplex DNA arms were measured. The replication origin was taken to be closer to the end of the shorter DNA arm and the molecules were aligned as shown. Thin lines represent duplex DNA, and solid bars represent the unwound, protein-coated DNA. The location of the replication origin is indicated at top.

Table 2 Origin Specificity and Topological Requirements for DNA Unwinding

DNA substrate	Molecules examined (no.)	Unwound (%)
pSVLD circle	400	37
pSVLD 6-1 circle	400	2
pRLM 4 circle	300	<0.3
pSVLD linear	400	45
pSVLD 6-1 linear	400	8
pRLM 4 linear	300	<0.3

Unwinding reactions were carried out with either relaxed, circular DNA or DNA linearized with restriction endonuclease AatII, as indicated. Plasmid pSVLD carries an intact SV40 DNA replication origin; pSVLD 6-1 has a 6-bp deletion in the origin and is defective for replication; pRLM 4 contains the bacteriophage λ replication origin. Molecules carrying an SSB-coated region were counted as unwound.

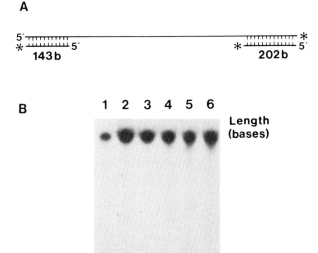

Figure 3 Unwinding of duplex DNA by SV40 T antigen is in a 3' to 5' direction. (A) The substrate used was a 7200-nt linear, partial duplex DNA constructed as described in Experimental Procedures. Asterisks show the location of radioactive label. (B) Helicase activity was analyzed in reactions containing the partial duplex substrate as described in Experimental Procedures. (Lane 1) Heat denatured substrate; (lane 2) T antigen omitted; (lane 3) 75 ng of T antigen added; (lane 4) 150 ng of T antigen; (lane 5) 300 ng of T antigen; (lane 6) 150 ng of T antigen in the absence of ATP.

(Fig. 4). The two strands of a 311-bp origin-containing (Ori⁺) duplex DNA fragment (0.4 ng) were unwound by 1.2 μg T antigen, a 600 to 1 molar ratio of T antigen to DNA (Fig. 4, lane 2). An increase in DNA concentration of up to 1000-fold, by the addition of competitor DNA lacking the SV40 origin, inhibited this reaction no more than 30%. Surprisingly, a reaction with 0.4 ng of a 291-bp origin-lacking (Ori⁻) duplex DNA was also unwound by T antigen in the absence of competitor DNA (Fig. 6, lane 7). However, the addition of competitor DNA inhibited this reaction more than tenfold. Therefore, the origin-specificity of duplex DNA unwinding can be lost at high ratios of T antigen to DNA.

Other nucleoside triphosphates were tested for their ability to support the unwinding of duplex DNA (Table 3). Unwinding reactions were carried out using the 311-bp origin-containing DNA fragment, analyzed by gel electrophoresis, and quantitated. dTTP worked as well as ATP, whereas dATP, dCTP, and UTP were about twofold less effective. CTP, GTP, and dGTP were only marginally effective. Apparently, a variety of nucleotides support DNA unwinding by SV40 T antigen. Similar results have been observed for the T-antigen DNA helicase activity (Goetz et al. 1988).

Another major role for T antigen in DNA replication and unwinding of duplex DNA is site-specific DNA bind-

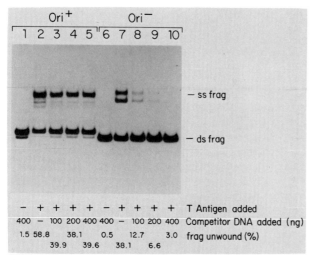

Figure 4 Effect of added competitor DNA on the unwinding of
duplex DNA fragments containing or lacking the SV40 replication origin. Unwinding reactions were carried out as described
in Experimental Procedures and contained 1.2 μg of T antigen
as indicated. Reactions contained 25 fmol (0.4 ng) of the
311-bp SV40 origin-containing (Ori⁺) DNA fragment or 25
fmole (0.4 ng) of the 291-bp origin-lacking (Ori⁻) DNA fragment. Unlabeled linear plasmid pVOP, lacking the replication
origin, was added as competitor DNA as indicated.

ing (Tjian 1978; DeLucia et al. 1983; Jones and Tjian
1984). When the products of DNA unwinding reactions
were examined by electron microscopy, a "bilobed"
nucleoprotein structure was observed on many of the
molecules on which unwinding had not started (Dean et
al. 1987a) (Fig. 5a). To determine whether these structures were located near the SV40 origin, the substrate
was linearized so that the SV40 origin was located 33%
from one end of the molecule. Examination of the complexes formed on these molecules showed that they
were located at or near the origin (Fig. 5b).

The requirements for the formation of these complexes were determined. The substrate DNA was linearized

Table 3 Unwinding of Duplex DNA Fragments in the
Presence of Various Nucleotides

Nucleoside triphosphate added	Substrate unwound (%)
None	2.5
ATP	41.8
ATP, omit T antigen	1.4
UTP	19.4
dATP	26.0
dTTP	40.5
dCTP	20.1
GTP	2.6
CTP	3.7
dGTP	3.6

Unwinding reactions were as described in Experimental
Procedures, containing 25 fmol of the 311-bp SV40
origin-containing duplex DNA fragment, 400 ng duplex
pVOP origin-lacking DNA, and 0.8 μg T antigen. Nucleotides were added to 4 mM.

so that the SV40 origin was positioned 8% from one end
of the molecule. Interestingly, incubation of the DNA
with T antigen alone resulted in the formation of small
nucleoprotein complexes located near the replication
origin (Fig. 5c). However, incubation of the DNA with T
antigen in the presence of 4 mM ATP resulted in large,
bilobed complexes similar to the ones formed under
DNA unwinding conditions (Fig. 5d).

A preliminary estimate of the sizes of these complexes
was carried out by comparison with the size of 10-nm
gold particles that were rotary shadowed on the same
electron microscope grid (data not shown). The small
complexes appeared to contain fewer than 4 monomers
of T antigen, whereas the large complexes apparently
contained between 8 and 16 T-antigen molecules. DNA
molecules containing the large complexes were examined for whether they caused a condensation or
shortening of the end-to-end lengths of the protein-
bound DNA fragments. Complexes were formed on the
311-bp origin-containing restriction fragment generated
by EcoRI cleavage of pSV01ΔEP. No difference was
noted between the lengths of protein-bound and protein-
free DNA fragments. In addition, no sharp bending
induced by the complexes was seen. Thus, the T-antigen
nucleoprotein complexes do not cause a DNA condensation or bending of the DNA that can be visualized
by electron microscopy.

The sites at which the small and large complexes
formed were determined in relation to the SV40 origin
sequences. Distances from the nearest DNA end to
each of the two edges of the rotary-shadowed complexes were measured, and the positions of the two nucleoprotein complexes are shown relative to the SV40
origin region (Fig. 5e). The small structure that forms in
the absence of ATP covered T-antigen-binding site I,
and the large, ATP-dependent complex covered binding
sites I and II. Since the DNA sequences of binding site II
(the "core" origin sequence) are essential for DNA
unwinding and DNA replication, whereas site I is dispensable (DeLucia et al. 1986; Dean et al. 1987b), we
suggest that ATP stimulates T-antigen binding to the
DNA sequences required for DNA replication.

We tested whether the two sites of T-antigen nucleoprotein complexes could be distinguished by a gel
mobility shift assay (Fig. 6). Plasmid DNA was digested
so that the SV40 origin was on a fragment about 900 bp
long. The DNA fragment carrying the complete SV40
origin sequence had a reduced mobility after binding of
T antigen in the absence of ATP (Fig. 6, lane 2).
T-antigen binding in the presence of ATP resulted in
greater retardation of the fragment (lane 3). This is
consistent with the observation of two different types of
nucleoprotein complexes by electron microscopy. ATP
hydrolysis did not appear to be required for formation of
the mobility-shift complex since the nonhydrolyzable analog, AppNp, could substitute for ATP. Fixation of the
complexes with glutaraldehyde prior to electrophoresis
was required (lanes 5–6).

The DNA fragment containing only the minimal, core
origin sequence (T-antigen-binding site II) did not exhibit

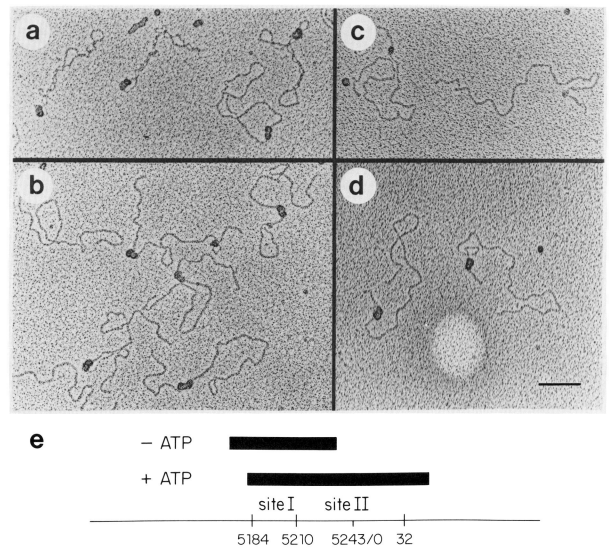

Figure 5 Electron micrographs of nucleoprotein structures formed on pSV01ΔEP DNA. (a) Complexes formed as described in Experimental Procedures on circular duplex DNA in the presence of T antigen, ATP, *E. coli* SSB, and HeLa topoisomerase I. (b) Complexes formed as in a, on DNA linearized by restriction endonuclease *Pst*I. (c) Complexes formed in the presence of T antigen alone on DNA linearized with restriction endonuclease *Aat*II. (d) Complexes on *Aat*II-linearized DNA formed in the presence of T antigen and ATP (bar = 0.1 μm). (e) Comparison of the DNA regions contained in nucleoprotein structures, indicated by solid bars, with the positions of T-antigen DNA-binding sites I and II at the SV40 replication origin. Numbers indicate nucleotide positions on the SV40 genome.

any mobility shift after incubation with T antigen in the absence of ATP. Instead, a mobility shift was observed only after incubation in the presence of ATP (Fig. 6, lanes 8 and 9). Thus, formation of a nucleoprotein structure at the core replication origin requires ATP.

The interaction of T antigen with the SV40 origin region was examined in greater detail using a DNase-I-protection assay (Borowiec and Hurwitz 1988) (Fig. 7). In the absence of ATP, small amounts of T antigen yielded a weak protection of T-antigen-binding site I. With increasing T antigen, site I became completely protected, and site II was partially bound. In the presence of ATP, low amounts of T antigen protected all of site I and partially protected site II. With increasing T

antigen, both sites I and II were fully protected. Previous studies have shown that T antigen can bind to site II in the absence of ATP. The difference between the earlier studies and this one is that the reaction conditions used for the experiments shown here were those required for DNA replication.

Discussion

SV40 T antigen has at least two activities that play fundamental roles in SV40 DNA replication: site-specific DNA binding and DNA helicase activities. These two activities act in concert, so that T antigen can carry out the SV40 origin-dependent unwinding of duplex DNA.

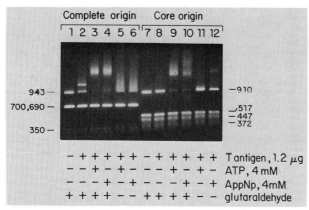

Figure 6 Agarose gel electrophoresis of nucleoprotein structures. Reactions were carried out as described in Experimental Procedures, with modifications as indicated. (Lanes *1–6*) Substrate pSV01ΔEP DNA, containing the complete SV40 origin region, cleaved with restriction endonuclease *Nci*I; (lanes *7–12*) pOR1 substrate DNA, containing only the SV40 core origin region, cleaved by *Hin*fI and *Pvu*I. DNA fragment sizes are shown at the sides in bp. The 943- and 910-bp DNA fragments contain the SV40 origin regions of the two plasmids.

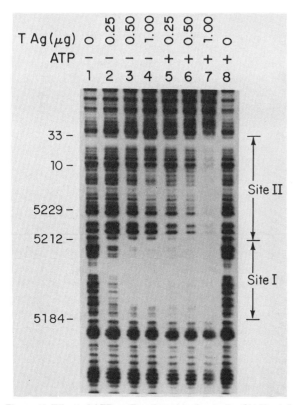

Figure 7 Effect of ATP on T-antigen binding to the SV40 origin region. DNase-I-protection reactions were carried out as described in Experimental Procedures, with preincubation in the presence of ATP and T antigen as indicated. After limited DNase-I digestion, products were electrophoresed through a polyacrylamide-urea gel. Numbers on the left indicate nucleotide positions on the SV40 genome. Locations of T-antigen DNA-binding sites I and II are indicated at right.

It has been well established that T antigen binds to the SV40 replication origin (Tjian 1978; DeLucia et al. 1983; Jones and Tjian 1984). We have shown that under reaction conditions required for DNA replication in vitro, T antigen requires ATP to form a specific complex at the DNA sequences essential for DNA replication. The results from three different techniques, electron microscopy, gel mobility shift, and DNase footprinting, all led to the same conclusion. T antigen forms a small complex in the absence of ATP at T-antigen-binding site I, near the replication origin. The protein requires the presence of ATP to form a larger structure, which encompasses binding sites I and II. Binding site II comprises the region essential for SV40 DNA replication, the core origin, whereas site I is outside of the core origin and is not required for replication in vivo or in vitro (Stillman et al. 1985; DeLucia et al. 1986; Li et al. 1986; Dean et al. 1987b). Therefore, ATP is required for T antigen to form a specific complex at the SV40 origin sequences necessary for replication.

The ATP-dependent T-antigen–DNA complex does not cause wrapping of the DNA; there is no visible condensation or bending of the DNA in the complex. This is in contrast to what has been found for the nucleoprotein structures formed in other systems (Echols 1986), where, for example, the initiator proteins of *E. coli oriC* and bacteriophage λ (Fuller et al. 1984; Dodson et al. 1985) do cause a condensation of the bound DNA. The prokaryotic initiation proteins may use distortion of the DNA helix induced by DNA wrapping around the nucleoprotein complex to help initiate DNA strand separation. However, it seems that in the T-antigen nucleoprotein complex the protein may instead be positioned around the DNA and use a different mechanism to destabilize the helix.

The T-antigen helicase activity unwinds DNA in the 3′ to 5′ direction. Thus, T antigen migrates along the same parental DNA strand and in the same direction that DNA polymerase α does during synthesis of the leading DNA strand. T antigen and polymerase α may be associated at the replication fork. In fact, T antigen may guide DNA polymerase α–primase to the DNA. Evidence for an interaction between T antigen and DNA polymerase α includes the observations that polymerase α can be immunoprecipitated with T antigen by antibodies against T antigen (Smale and Tjian 1986) and that SV40 replication works only with DNA polymerase α–primase from a permissive cell type (Murakami et al. 1986). The unwinding of duplex DNA by T antigen is initiated at the SV40 origin and moves bidirectionally. This is consistent with SV40 DNA replication, which is also bidirectional both in vivo and in vitro (Danna and Nathans 1972; Fareed et al. 1972; Li and Kelly 1985; Stillman and Gluzman 1985; Wobbe et al. 1985).

Both linear and circular duplex DNA are equally effective as substrates for DNA unwinding. Thus, no topological strain is necessary to initiate unwinding, and the role of a topoisomerase is only to remove the positive superhelical strain generated by unwinding. This is another departure from the prokaryotic systems *E. coli oriC* and bacteriophage λ, where DNA supercoiling is required to initiate the unwinding reactions (Baker et al. 1986; Dodson et al. 1986).

The origin specificity for duplex DNA unwinding by T antigen can be lost under some conditions in vitro. These include the presence of a single-strand region on the DNA substrate or particularly high ratios of T antigen to DNA in the reaction. However, we feel it is more important that origin specificity can be demonstrated under conditions required for DNA replication than that it can be lost under other conditions.

A time lag is observed before SV40 DNA replication is initiated in vitro, and this lag can be eliminated by preincubation of the reaction components in the absence of dNTPs (Stillman et al. 1986; Wobbe et al. 1986; Wold et al. 1987). During the preincubation, a stable protein–DNA pre-elongation complex is formed. The requirements for formation of the protein–DNA complex include T antigen, ATP, and a protein fraction that contains SSB activity. Due to the requirement for SSB, and the fact that the T-antigen nucleoprotein complex alone is not stable in the absence of glutaraldehyde fixation, the protein–DNA complex that forms during the preincubation step cannot be simply the T antigen origin-specific nucleoprotein complex. Rather, we suggest that the protein–DNA pre-elongation complex corresponds to a partially unwound DNA molecule with SSB coating the single-stranded regions, analogous to the unwound structures shown in Figure 1B.

Complete replication of DNA molecules containing the SV40 replication origin can now be carried out in vitro using seven highly purified protein fractions. The activities of the proteins required for RFI′ production are consistent with the functions expected to be necessary. The T antigen, SSB, and polymerase α–primase together are sufficient to carry out extensive incorporation of deoxynucleotides (Wobbe et al. 1987). RNase H and the exonuclease would be expected to remove the RNA primers with which every DNA chain is obligatorily initiated. After gap-filling by polymerase, DNA ligase would seal the remaining DNA single-strand breaks. The role of topoisomerase II would be to remove positive superhelical strain ahead of the advancing replication fork, and also to unlink the two catenated daughter DNA circles.

PCNA (proliferating cell nuclear antigen) has also been reported to have a role in SV40 DNA replication in vitro, being required for the elongation of DNA chains (Prelich et al. 1987). However, since the only genetically defined requirements for replication are for T antigen and the DNA replication origin, it may be difficult for some time to correlate requirements for replication demonstrated in vitro with a primary role in vivo. It is possible that further purification will reveal other factors required for complete DNA replication in the system reported here. However, we anticipate that the set of proteins ultimately found to be required will reflect the simplicity with which the present system is constituted.

Acknowledgments

We thank Ms. C. Turck and Ms. N. Belgado for their assistance. This work was supported by grants from the National Institutes of Health: GM-34559 to J.H., GM-17078 to H.E., and GM-33476 to S.W.M. S.W.M. is the recipient of an American Cancer Society Faculty Research Award. F.B.D. and J.A.B. are supported by fellowships from the National Institutes of Health, P.B. by a fellowship from the American Cancer Society, and G.S.G. by a training grant from the National Institutes of Health.

References

Baker, T.A., K. Sekimizu, B.E. Funnell, and A. Kornberg. 1986. Extensive unwinding of the plasmid template during staged enzymatic initiation of DNA replication from the origin of the *Escherichia coli* chromosome. *Cell* **45:** 53.

Bergsma, D.J., D.M. Olive, S.W. Hartzell, and K.N. Subramanian. 1982. Territorial limits and functional anatomy of the simian virus 40 replication origin. *Proc. Natl. Acad. Sci.* **79:** 381.

Borowiec, J.A. and J. Hurwitz. 1988. ATP stimulates the binding of simian virus 40 (SV40) large tumor antigen to the SV40 origin of replication. *Proc. Natl. Acad. Sci.* **85:** 64.

Danna, K. and D. Nathans. 1972. Bidirectional replication of simian virus 40 DNA. *Proc. Natl. Acad. Sci.* **69:** 3097.

Dean, F.B., M. Dodson, H. Echols, and J. Hurwitz. 1987a. ATP-dependent formation of a specialized nucleoprotein structure by simian virus 40 (SV40) large tumor antigen at the SV40 replication origin. *Proc. Natl. Acad. Sci.* **84:** 8981.

Dean, F.B., J.A. Borowiec, Y. Ishimi, S. Deb, P. Tegtmeyer, and J. Hurwitz. 1987b. Simian virus 40 large tumor antigen requires three core replication origin domains for DNA unwinding and replication *in vitro*. *Proc. Natl. Acad. Sci.* **84:** 8267.

Dean, F.B., P. Bullock, Y. Murakami, C.R. Wobbe, L. Weissbach, and J. Hurwitz. 1987c. Simian virus 40 (SV40) DNA replication: SV40 large T antigen unwinds DNA containing the SV40 origin of replication. *Proc. Natl. Acad. Sci.* **84:** 16.

DeLucia, A.L., S. Deb, K. Partin, and P. Tegtmeyer. 1986. Functional interactions of the simian virus 40 core origin of replication with flanking regulatory sequences. *J. Virol.* **57:** 138.

DeLucia, A.L., B.A. Lewton, R. Tjian, and P. Tegtmeyer. 1983. Topography of simian virus 40 A protein-DNA complexes: Arrangement of pentanucleotide interaction sites at the origin of replication. *J. Virol.* **46:** 143.

DePamphilis, M.L. and M.K. Bradley. 1986. Replication of SV40 and polyoma virus chromosomes. In *The papoviridae* (ed. N.P. Salzman), vol. 1, p. 99. Plenum Press, New York.

DiFrancesco, R.A. and I.R. Lehman. 1985. Interaction of ribonuclease H from *Drosophila melanogaster* embryos with DNA polymerase-primase. *J. Biol. Chem.* **260:** 14764.

Dodson, M., J. Roberts, R. McMacken, and H. Echols. 1985. Specialized nucleoprotein structures at the origin of replication of bacteriophage λ: Complexes with λO protein and with λO, λP, and *Escherichia coli* DnaB proteins. *Proc. Natl. Acad. Sci.* **82:** 4678.

Dodson, M., F.B. Dean, P. Bullock, H. Echols, and J. Hurwitz. 1987. Unwinding of duplex DNA from the SV40 origin of replication by T antigen. *Science* **238:** 964.

Dodson, M., H. Echols, S. Wickner, C. Alfano, K. Mensa-Wilmot, B. Gomes, T. LeBowitz, J.D. Roberts, and R. McMacken. 1986. Specialized nucleoprotein structures at the origin of replication of bacteriophage λ: Localized unwinding of duplex DNA by a six-protein reaction. *Proc. Natl. Acad. Sci.* **83:** 7638.

Echols, H. 1986. Multiple DNA-protein interactions governing high precision DNA transactions. *Science* **233**: 1050.

Fareed, G.C., C.F. Garon, and N.P. Salzman. 1972. Origin and direction of simian virus 40 deoxyribonucleic acid replication. *J. Virol.* **10**: 484.

Fried, M. and C. Prives. 1986. The biology of simian virus 40 and polyomavirus. *Cancer Cells* **4**: 1.

Fuller, R.S., B.E. Funnell, and A. Kornberg. 1984. The dnaA protein complex with the *E. coli* chromosomal replication origin (oriC) and other DNA sites. *Cell* **38**: 889.

Goetz, G.S., F.B. Dean, J. Hurwitz, and S.W. Matson. 1988. The unwinding of duplex regions in DNA by the simian virus 40 large tumor antigen-associated DNA helicase activity. *J. Biol. Chem.* **263**: 383.

Jones, K.A. and R. Tjian. 1984. Essential contact residues within SV40 large T antigen binding sites I and II identified by alkylation-interference. *Cell* **36**: 155.

LeBowitz, J.H. and R. McMacken. 1986. The *Escherichia coli* dnaB replication protein is a DNA helicase. *J. Biol. Chem.* **261**: 4738.

Li, J.-J. and T.J. Kelly. 1984. Simian virus 40 DNA replication *in vitro*. *Proc. Natl. Acad. Sci.* **81**: 6973.

———. 1985. SV40 DNA replication *in vitro*: Specificity of initiation and evidence for bidirectional replication. *Mol. Cell. Biol.* **5**: 1238.

Li, J.-J., K.W.C. Peden, R.A.F. Dixon, and T. Kelly. 1986. Functional organization of the simian virus 40 origin of DNA replication. *Mol. Cell. Biol.* **6**: 1117.

Matson, S.W. 1986. *Escherichia coli* helicase II (*uvr*D gene product) translocates unidirectionally in a 3′ to 5′ direction. *J. Biol. Chem.* **261**: 10169.

Miller, K.G., L.F. Liu, and P.T. Englund. 1981. A homogeneous type II DNA topoisomerase from Hela cell nuclei. *J. Biol. Chem.* **256**: 9334.

Murakami, Y., C.R. Wobbe, L. Weissbach, F.B. Dean, and J. Hurwitz. 1986. Role of DNA polymerase alpha and DNA primase in simian virus 40 DNA replication *in vitro*. *Proc. Natl. Acad. Sci.* **83**: 2369.

Prelich, G., M. Kostura, D.R. Marshak, M.B. Mathews, and B. Stillman. 1987. The cell-cycle regulated proliferating cell nuclear antigen is required for SV40 DNA replication *in vitro*. *Nature* **326**: 471.

Rigby, P.W.J. and D.P. Lane. 1983. Structure and function of simian virus 40 large T-antigen. *Adv. Viral Oncol.* **3**: 31.

Smale, S.T. and R. Tjian. 1986. T-antigen-DNA polymerase alpha complex implicated in simian virus 40 DNA replication. *Mol. Cell. Biol.* **6**: 4077.

Stahl, H., P. Droge, and R. Knippers. 1986. DNA helicase activity of SV40 large tumor antigen. *EMBO J.* **5**: 1939.

Stillman, B.W. and Y. Gluzman. 1985. Replication and super-coiling of SV40 DNA in cell-free extracts from human cells. *Mol. Cell. Biol.* **5**: 2051.

Stillman, B., J.F.X. Diffley, G. Prelich, and R.A. Guggenheimer. 1986. DNA-protein interactions at the replication origins of adenovirus and SV40. *Cancer Cells* **4**: 453.

Stillman, B., R.D. Gerard, R.A. Guggenheimer, and Y. Gluzman. 1985. T antigen and template requirements for SV40 DNA replication *in vitro*. *EMBO J.* **4**: 2933.

Tjian, R. 1978. The binding site on SV40 DNA for a T antigen-related protein. *Cell* **13**: 165.

Wiekowski, M., P. Droge, and H. Stahl. 1987. Monoclonal antibodies as probes for a function of large T antigen during the elongation process of simian virus 40 DNA replication. *J. Virol.* **61**: 411.

Wiekowski, M., M.W. Schwartz, and H. Stahl. 1988. Simian virus 40 large T antigen DNA helicase. *J. Biol. Chem.* **263**: 436.

Williams, R. 1977. Use of polylysine for adsorption of nucleic acids and enzymes to electron microscope specimen films. *Proc. Natl. Acad. Sci.* **74**: 2311.

Wobbe, C.R., F. Dean, L. Weissbach, and J. Hurwitz. 1985. *In vitro* replication of duplex circular DNA containing the simian virus 40 origin site. *Proc. Natl. Acad. Sci.* **82**: 5710.

Wobbe, C.R., F.B. Dean, Y. Murakami, L. Weissbach, and J. Hurwitz. 1986. Simian virus 40 DNA replication *in vitro*: Study of events preceding elongation of chains. *Proc. Natl. Acad. Sci.* **83**: 5710.

Wobbe, C.R., L. Weissbach, J.A. Borowiec, F.B. Dean, Y. Murakami, P. Bullock, and J. Hurwitz. 1987. Replication of simian virus 40 origin-containing DNA *in vitro* with purified proteins. *Proc. Natl. Acad. Sci.* **84**: 1834.

Wold, M.S., J.-J. Li, and T.J. Kelly. 1987. Initiation of simian virus 40 DNA replication *in vitro*: Large-tumor-antigen- and origin-dependent unwinding of the template. *Proc. Natl. Acad. Sci.* **84**: 3643.

Yamaguchi, M. and M.L. DePamphilis. 1986. DNA binding site for a factor(s) required to initiate simian virus 40 DNA replication. *Proc. Natl. Acad. Sci.* **83**: 1646.

SV40 Origin of Replication

P. Tegtmeyer,* S. Deb,* A.L. DeLucia,* S.P. Deb,* A. Koff,* S. Tsui,*
R. Parsons,* K. Partin,* C.P. Baur,* F.B. Dean,[†] and J. Hurwitz[†]

*Department of Microbiology, State University of New York, Stony Brook, New York 11794;
[†]Graduate Program in Molecular Biology, Sloan Kettering Cancer Center, New York, New York 10021

SV40 DNA replication requires a viral origin of replication, the virus-encoded large T antigen, and factors from permissive host cells. We have planned and constructed a series of mutations in the origin of replication to analyze the interactions among these replicon components. The complete origin consists of an essential 64-bp core region and flanking ancillary regions. The core origin has three or more domains with sequence-specific functions that are required for replication in vivo. These domains correspond to an inverted repetition, a cluster of four recognition pentanucleotides for the binding of T antigen, and an AT-rich segment that contains a bending locus. Extensively purified T antigen unwinds DNA containing the viral core origin. The domain requirements for origin unwinding are strikingly similar to the domain requirements for in vivo replication. These similarities argue that most of the replication domains in the core origin serve to facilitate the unwinding of duplex DNA by T antigen. The domains could enhance the opening of duplex DNA by virtue of an intrinsic DNA structure, through an interaction with T antigen, or by both mechanisms. However, the origin domain corresponding to the inverted repeat is only partly accounted for in the unwinding reaction. Thus, it may have additional unidentified functions.

The SV40 replicon is a simple and attractive model for eukaryotic DNA replication. A number of investigators have begun to characterize the factors and events that are essential for the initiation of SV40 DNA replication. The hope is that this information will provide general principles that will lead to an understanding of other eukaryotic replicons as well.

SV40 DNA replication requires the interaction of a single virus-encoded protein, large T antigen, with a unique viral origin of replication to initiate each round of DNA synthesis (Danna and Nathans 1972; Tegtmeyer 1972; Tjian 1978; DePamphilis and Bradley 1986). T antigen has an intrinsic DNA helicase activity that enables it to unwind any DNA that is not fully duplex (Stahl et al. 1986; Dean et al. 1987b; Wiekowski et al. 1987; Wold et al. 1987). However, under appropriate conditions, circular DNA templates are unwound by T antigen only in the presence of an SV40 origin of replication (Dean et al. 1987b; Dodson et al. 1987; Wold et al. 1987). Thus, T antigen apparently binds to the origin of fully duplex DNA and opens the DNA helix in order to initiate the unwinding reaction. Presumably, DNA polymerase α−primase then can synthesize RNA primers for DNA elongation at a number of sites on one DNA strand within the unwound origin of replication (Hay and DePamphilis 1982; DePamphilis and Bradley 1986; Murakami et al. 1986). A specific interaction between SV40 T antigen and DNA polymerase may facilitate this step in the initiation process (Smale and Tjian 1986). Additional host factors may also contribute to the initiation of replication. Wold et al. (1987) find that a cellular fraction enhances the specificity of the origin unwinding reaction by T antigen.

A thorough characterization of the SV40 origin of replication is central to an understanding of the events that occur in the initiation of replication. We have undertaken a systematic genetic and functional analysis of the origin region. In this paper, we subdivide the origin into distinct regions and domains. We identify the domains that determine the binding of T antigen, the conformation of DNA within the origin, and the unwinding of origin DNA. Our findings suggest that the primary function of the minimal essential core origin is to initiate the unwinding of duplex DNA by T antigen. However, by the process of exclusion, we suggest that at least one core domain may have a function not previously recognized.

Materials and Methods

Plasmids
The construction of the matched set of plasmids, pOR1–5, and pOR1-Enh was described by DeLucia et al. (1986). The common pOR vector consists of pML2 (Lusky and Botchan 1981) sequences 651–4361 with a HindIII site added to the 651 position and an NcoI site added to the 4361 position. This segment served as an acceptor for the SV40 origin restriction fragments described in the Results section. The plasmid pSV01ΔEP (ori⁺) contains the EcoRII fragment G of SV40 DNA (Wobbe et al. 1985).

Site-directed mutagenesis
Single bp substitutions were made in the core origin of replication extending from SV40 sequences 5209 through 34 in the pOR1 plasmid. Mutations from nucleotides 5209 through 5229 were created by base misincorporation as described by Deb et al. (1986a); mutations from nucleotides 5221 through nucleotide 32 were made by using synthetic oligonucleotides as described by Deb et al. (1986b).

123

DNA replication

The assay for DNA replication in COS-1 cells has been described previously by DeLucia et al. (1986). To ensure equivalence in transfection efficiencies with each purified plasmid preparation, the input DNAs were quantitated by densitometry of ethidium-bromide-stained form I DNA separated in agarose gels. Replicated DNA was extracted from cells 72 hours after transfection.

DNA binding

DNA binding was analyzed under conditions suitable for in vitro DNA replication (Li and Kelly 1984, 1985; Stillman and Gluzman 1985; Wobbe et al. 1985). Binding reactions were carried out for 1 hour in 30 mM HEPES, 1 mM dithiothreitol (DTT), 0.1 mg/ml bovine serum albumin, 8% glycerol, 7 mM $MgCl_2$, 4 mM ATP, and 40 mM creatine phosphate at pH 7.5, 37°C. For DNase footprinting, a fragment containing the SV40 origin of replication was excised from the plasmids with *Hin*fI and *Eco*RI and radiolabeled at the 3' end of the *Eco*RI site. Purified large T antigen (Simanis and Lane 1985) was added in a 100-fold molar excess. DMS footprinting was carried out under conditions designed for the optimal binding of T antigen to the origin (DeLucia et al. 1983). The details of the DNase and DMS footprinting procedures have been described previously by DeLucia et al. (1983).

DNA bending

The intrinsic bending of origin DNA was determined by a gel electrophoresis assay (Widom 1985; Deb et al. 1986b). Wild-type and mutant pOR1 plasmids were cut with *Hha*I, mixed together in equal amounts, and separated by electrophoresis in 12% polyacrylamide gels.

Origin unwinding

The origin unwinding assay has been described by Dean et al. (1987b). Standard reaction mixtures contained 40 mM creatine phosphate (diTris salt, pH 7.7), 7 mM $MgCl_2$, 1 mM DTT, 4 mM ATP, 0.7 µg creatine kinase, 10 units of HeLa cell topoisomerase I, 0.6 µg of *Escherichia coli* single-stranded DNA-binding protein (SSB), 0.9 µg bovine serum albumin, 0.36 µg relaxed substrate DNA, and 1.1 µg T antigen. After incubation for 2 hours at 37°C, the products were analyzed by agarose gel electrophoresis, transfer to a nitrocellulose membrane, hybridization with radiolabeled pBR322 DNA, and scintillation counting.

Results

Origin components for DNA replication

Previous studies (for review, see DePamphilis and Bradley 1986) identified the general location of the SV40 origin and showed that it consists of T-antigen-binding region I on the early side of the origin, T-antigen-binding region II from nucleotides 5209 through 37, and the promoter-enhancer region on the late side of the origin. Deletion of either T antigen region I or of the promoter-enhancer region reduced replication, whereas deletions within T antigen region II abolished replication completely. Thus, the minimal essential core origin was known to map between nucleotides 5208 and 38, although its exact limits were not clearly established.

We constructed a matched set of plasmids to investigate further the relationships among these origin components (DeLucia et al. 1986). We tested the replication efficiency of the plasmids in COS-1 cells that constitutively express T antigen and support the replication of wild-type (WT) origins (Gluzman 1981). After 72 hours at 36–37°C, DNA was extracted and digested with *Mbo*I to distinguish unmethylated progeny DNA from methylated input DNA. The products were analyzed by gel electrophoresis, blotting, and hybridization with radiolabeled pBR322 DNA. The results are summarized in Table 1. The single deletion either of T antigen region I or of the promoter-enhancer region reduced replication efficiency by less than 50%. The simultaneous deletion of both regions caused a more dramatic 90–95% decrease in origin function. Replacement of the promoter with enhancer sequences restored significant function. Thus, T antigen region I, the upstream promoter region, or an isolated 72-bp enhancer facilitate, but are not essential for, DNA replication. Their functions are not known. All contribute to an open conformation of origin chromatin (for review, see DePamphilis and Bradley 1986). However, this common activity is apparently not sufficient to explain their role in replication because region I and the enhancer function only when they are located on the appropriate side of the core origin (DeLucia et al. 1986; S.C. Chandrasekharappa and K.N. Subramanian, pers. comm.).

Table 1 Components of the SV40 Origin of Replication

Plasmids	SV40 Origin Components				Replication (%)
	region I (5171–5208)[a]	core origin (5209–37)	promoter (38–160)	enhancer (107–182)	
pOR5	+	+	+[b]	+[b]	100
pOR4	+	+	+	—	90–100
pOR3	—	+	+	—	60–70
pOR2	+	+	—	—	50–60
pOR1-Enh	—	+	—	+	25–50
pOR1	—	+	—	—	5–10

[a]The numbers in parentheses refer to nucleotide positions in the SV40 genome.
[b]pOR5 contains sequences 38–234.

Core origin domains for replication

We constructed plasmids with substitutions of single bps at approximately every other position throughout the core origin from nucleotides 5209 through 34 (Deb et al. 1986a,b, 1987). Figure 1 summarizes the replication efficiencies of these mutant origins. Important land-marks in the core origin are shown at the top of the figure. These consist of an imperfect inverted repeat at the early end of the core, four 5'-GAGGC-3' pentanu-cleotides in the center of the core, and an AT-rich sequence at the late end of the core. Nucleotide numbers and the double-stranded wild-type (WT) sequence

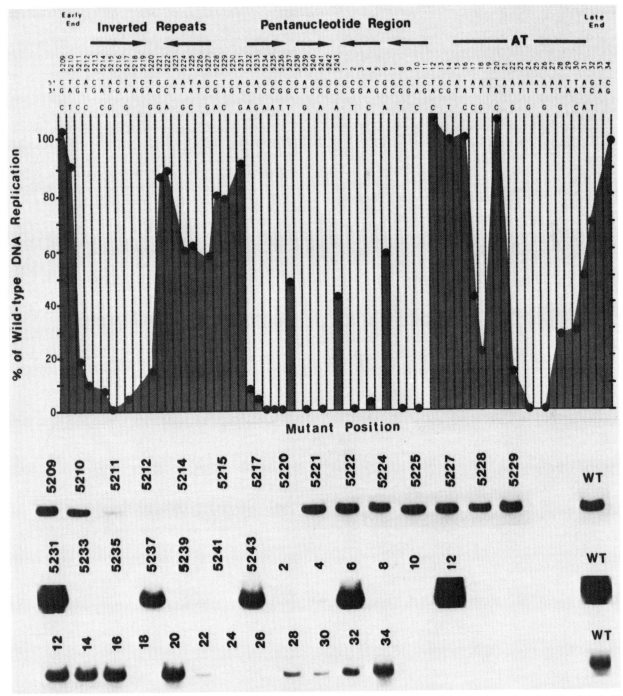

Figure 1 Replication of wild-type and mutant SV40 origins in COS-1 cells. The core origin consists of nucleotides 5211–31. Structural features of the core are shown at the top of the figure. The histogram shows the mean replication efficiency of these mutants determined in three independent experiments. Representative data for mutations at various nucleotide positions are shown at the bottom of the figure.

are indicated. The mutant bases shown in Figure 1 below the WT sequence correspond to the lower strand of WT DNA.

We determined the mean replication efficiency of each mutant in COS-1 cells in three independent experiments. The histogram summarizes the replication of each mutant relative to the replication of plasmids with WT origins. Representative data for the mutants are shown at the bottom of the figure. Each line of these results represents a separate experiment with its own wild-type control. For operational purposes, we define a functional domain as a contiguous set or nearly contiguous set of sequences in which base substitutions cause a significant decrease in replication. The remaining sequences presumably have spacer functions. The core origin appears to consist of three or more domains. A major domain extends 10 bp from positions 5211 through 5220. It corresponds to one arm of the imperfect inverted repeat. An apparent minor domain from nucleotides 5224 through 5227 falls within the second arm of the inverted repeat. The central domain of the core origin consists of four subdomains that correspond to the four repeated pentanucleotides each separated

by a single bp. The final domain extends from nucleotide 17 through 31 and is separated into two subdomains at position 20. Interestingly, both of these subdomains consist of contiguous adenine tracts.

Core origin domains for T antigen binding
We have not yet determined the effect of the origin mutations on T antigen binding. Nevertheless, footprinting analysis defines the importance of specific core sequences in protein binding (Fig. 2). In the footprint assay, each end-labeled DNA molecule is cut or modified only once with a low concentration of DNase or DMS. When analyzed by gel electrophoresis and autoradiography, the resultant fragments present a ladder of DNA. A gap appears in the ladder if the corresponding DNA is protected from DNase or DMS by bound proteins.

We first used DNase footprinting to examine the general arrangement of T antigen on DNA under replication conditions (Fig. 2, top). In the absence of ATP, T antigen bound to the origin very poorly. The addition of ATP dramatically enhanced DNA binding. All of the DNase-sensitive sites in the core origin were specifically pro-

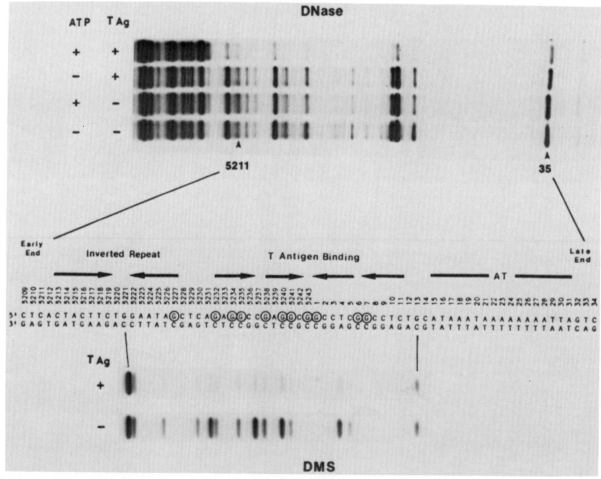

Figure 2 Binding of SV40 large T antigen to the core origin of replication. DNase and DMS footprinting procedures are described in Materials and Methods. T antigen protects nucleotides 5211–35 from DNase and the circled guanines from DMS. Only one strand of the DNA was examined in the footprints.

tected from DNase. This result strongly suggests that T antigen physically extends over most of the origin sequences. Thus, it could contact DNA anywhere within core sequences, or it could position other proteins over the origin by protein–protein interactions. Perhaps T antigen positions DNA polymerase α–primase to initiate RNA primer synthesis in this way.

We used DMS footprinting to identify potential guanine contacts on one strand of the origin sequences under conditions that allowed DNA binding in the absence of ATP (Fig. 2, bottom). T antigen protected all of the guanines in the four pentanucleotides of the central replication domain from DMS. It also protected the guanines between pentanucleotides and at position 5227, but not at other positions within the core origin DNA fragment. Thus, the pentanucleotide region plays a major role in T antigen recognition and binding. Additional footprinting techniques, in the presence and absence of ATP, may reveal more contact sites within the core origin.

Core origin domains for DNA bending

At the late end of the core origin, an AT-rich segment contains two tracts of homopolymeric dA·dT. These tracts correspond to two domains or to two parts of a single domain required for efficient DNA replication. Indeed, similar tracts are a common feature of many origins of replication. Intrinsic bending of DNA may occur at the junctions of homopolymeric dA·dT with adjacent B-DNA (Widom 1985; Koo et al. 1986). The bending causes a decreased mobility of DNA during electrophoresis through polyacrylamide gels of the appropriate porosity. The length of a dA·dT tract may influence net bending and gel mobility in two ways. First, it determines the stability of the altered helical structure of the tract that is responsible for bending. Second, the positions of the two junctional bends around the helix determine the direction of the bends relative to each other. Junctions separated by half a turn produce greater net bending than junctions separated by a complete turn. The late end of the SV40 core origin has an arrangement of dA·dT tracts that has not been investigated previously. An A_3 and an A_8 tract are separated by a single thymine residue. Thus, the existence and location of potential bending sequences were uncertain.

We reasoned that mutations in the AT segment would change the lengths of the dA·dT tracts and would either increase or decrease the degree of net bending of DNA. Thus, by measuring the effects of mutations on the gel mobility of origin DNA, we could map the locations of bps that determine DNA conformation. To detect small changes in structure, we mixed WT and mutant origins and examined their mobilities by coelectrophoresis of the two DNAs in the same lane of a gel (Fig. 3). HhaI cutting of the plasmids produces a 253-bp fragment that contains the AT origin segment near its center. At 5°C, the WT fragment has the mobility of a DNA fragment 35–40 bp larger than 253 bp (data not shown). Origin DNA with mutations from nucleotides 12 through 20 ran at the same retarded position as the WT origin DNA. In

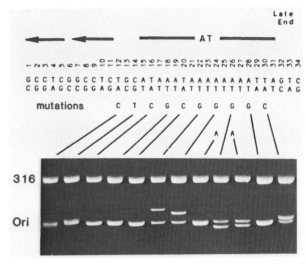

Figure 3 DNA bending determinants within the core origin of replication. Plasmids were cut with HhaI, and wild-type fragments were mixed with each mutant DNA as internal standards. The mixed fragments were analyzed together by electrophoresis through a 12% polyacrylamide gel at 5°C. Separation of wild-type and mutant origins indicates that the mutated bp encodes an altered DNA structure.

contrast, mutations from positions 22 through 30 caused a separation of the WT and mutant origin fragments, but not a 316-bp control fragment, during gel electrophoresis. Thus, each of these nucleotide positions determines DNA conformation. At 37°C, the anomalous migration and divergence of WT and mutant fragments is apparent but less pronounced than at 5°C; at 55°C, all fragments comigrate at the expected position of a 253-bp DNA (data not shown). These changes are characteristic of a bent DNA structure. Thus, a DNA binding locus from nucleotides 22 through 30 maps to the same location as a DNA replication domain. We conclude that DNA bending in the proper conformation may be a structural signal for DNA replication.

Core origin domains for DNA unwinding

Unwinding of a circular SV40 origin-containing duplex DNA by T antigen results in production of unwound circles with unusual electrophoretic mobility that have been designated form U DNA (Dean et al. 1987a,b; Wold et al. 1987). To study the effect of mutations in the SV40 origin on DNA unwinding by T antigen, we first determined that the reaction could be quantitated and that the amount of unwound DNA increased linearly with increasing T antigen or time of incubation (Fig. 4). Relaxed plasmid pSVO1 ΔEP, containing an intact SV40 origin region, was incubated at 37°C with ATP, HeLa topoisomerase I, and E. coli SSB. Deproteinized DNA reaction products were analyzed by agarose gel electrophoresis after incubation with increasing amounts of T antigen (Fig. 4A) or time (Fig. 4B). Reactions were then quantitated by blotting of the gel and hybridization with a ^{32}P-labeled RNA probe complementary to pBR322. After autoradiography, the radioactive regions of the blot containing the substrate and product form U

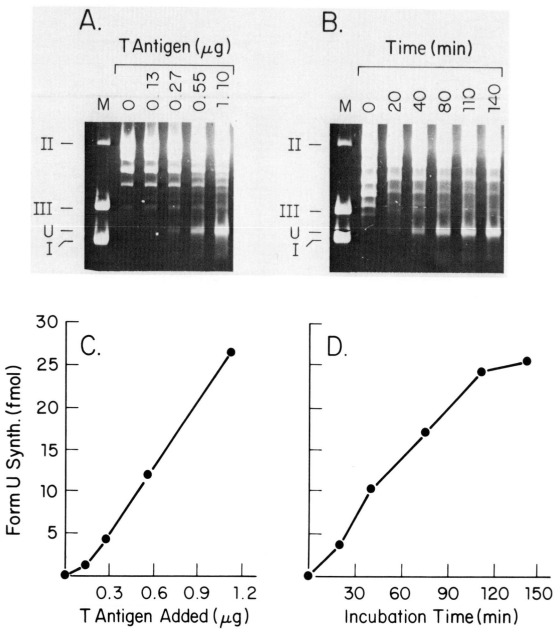

Figure 4 Unwinding of DNA with a wild-type origin by SV40 T antigen. Plasmid DNA (pSV01 Δ EP, *ori* [+]) containing a wild-type origin was incubated (*A*) for 2 hr at 37°C with increasing amounts of T antigen, or (*B*) with 1.1 μg of T antigen for increasing times. Panels *A* and *B* are quantitated in panels *C* and *D*, respectively. The symbols I, II, III, and U indicate supercoiled, nicked circular, linear, and highly unwound DNA. (Reprinted, with permission, from Dean et al. 1987a.)

DNA were excised and quantitated (Fig. 4, C and D). The reaction appeared linear, and 1.1 μg of T antigen and a 2-hour incubation were selected to analyze the unwinding reaction on DNA molecules containing mutant origins.

We analyzed 40 different plasmids, each containing a unique point mutation within the 64-bp core origin of replication, for their ability to allow DNA unwinding by T antigen. After quantitation of the unwinding reaction, a histogram showing the efficiency of origin unwinding of all the point mutants was constructed (Fig. 5). The effectiveness of the mutant origins in supporting DNA

replication in vivo is shown at the top of the figure for comparison. The inhibition of the DNA unwinding reaction by the point mutations is shown in the lower histogram. Qualitatively, there was a striking similarity in the response to the mutant origins in the two systems.

Discussion

Our in vivo and in vitro analyses of the SV40 replication origin reveal a coherent pattern of functional domains within the core origin of replication (Fig. 6). For in vivo DNA replication, major (solid bars) and minor (stippled

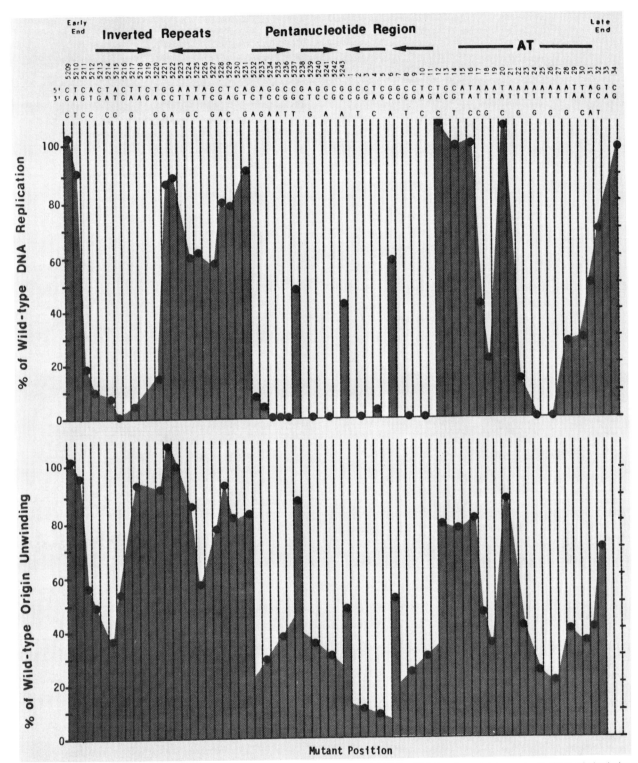

Figure 5 Unwinding of DNA with mutant origins by SV40 T antigen. Plasmid DNAs (0.36 μg) containing substitutions of single bps were incubated with 1.1 μg of T antigen for 2 hr at 37°C. Approximately 11% of the wild-type substrate was unwound, and this value was normalized to 100%. The histogram at the bottom of the figure shows the unwinding efficiency of the mutant origins relative to the wild-type origin. The histogram at the top of the figure shows the replication efficiency of mutant origins for comparison.

bars) domains have been identified (Fig. 1; Deb et al. 1986a,b, 1987). At the early end of the core origin, a major domain from nucleotides 5211 to 5220 and a minor domain from positions 5224 to 5227 correspond

roughly to the two arms of an imperfect inverted repeat. A major domain at the center of the core can be subdivided into four distinct subdomains that correspond to the 5'-GAGGC-3' pentanucleotides. DMS footprinting

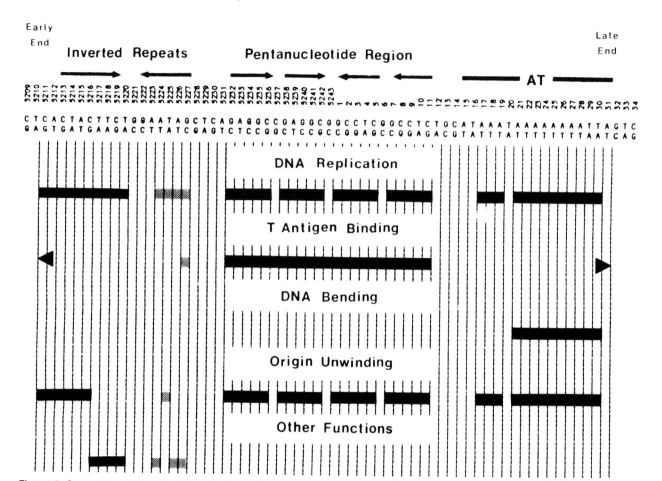

Figure 6 Comparison of functional domains in the SV40 core origin of replication. The data for the mapping of relevant domains is shown in Figs. 2–5. Dark bars indicate major domains. Stippled bars indicate minor domains in which mutations cause a 50% or less decrease in function. The arrowheads in the T-antigen-binding summary show the entire span of DNase protection by T antigen. Replication domains that are not accounted for in the T-antigen binding, DNA-bending, or origin-unwinding domains suggest additional functions of the origin.

also identifies the pentanucleotides as recognition sequences for T antigen binding. However, DNase footprinting suggests that the bound protein spans the entire core origin DNA (indicated by the arrowheads in the figure). At the late end of the core origin, a major AT domain from nucleotides 17 to 31 is separated into two parts at position 20. The sequences from positions 17 to 31 also encode a conformation of DNA that results in bending. The in vitro origin unwinding reaction requires most, but not all, of the nucleotides essential for in vivo DNA replication. Thus, the SV40 core origin of replication may serve primarily to facilitate the unwinding of duplex DNA, presumably initiated by the interaction of just the purified T antigen.

The only significant difference in the domain structure for the replication and unwinding functions is evident at the early end of the core origin. bps 5217 and 5220 are important for DNA replication but not for origin unwinding (Fig. 6). This discrepancy may indicate that two distinct domains overlap in this region. Both would be required for replication, but only one domain would contribute to T-antigen-induced unwinding.

Mutations in the core origin inhibit replication in vivo to a greater extent than they reduce unwinding. This quantitative variation may reflect differences in the assays. In theory, the high concentrations of T antigen used in vitro could compensate for *cis* mutations. However, experiments using lower amounts of T antigen did not change the relative levels of mutant and WT origin function. Alternatively, the in vitro assays could lack or be deficient in factors that would augment WT functions. Finally, the in vitro unwinding assay measured single-cycle events, whereas replication in vivo is a multicycle process. Each cycle would add new substrate molecules to the replicating pool, and the replication of WT origins would be amplified relative to the mutant origins.

The inverted repeat at the early end of the core origin may contain two overlapping domains and may play a complex role in replication and unwinding. Bound T antigen protects this domain from DNase but has few apparent base-specific contacts with this DNA segment. Nevertheless, T antigen appears to require one of the overlapping domains for origin unwinding. In addition, the inverted symmetry of the region is compatible with the idea that a cellular protein binds the putative second domain to cooperate in the initiation of DNA replication.

The important role of the central T-antigen-binding domain in T-antigen-induced unwinding is not surprising. Both DNA-binding and intracellular replication studies have established the importance of the four pentanucleotides of the core origin in determining the proper arrangement of bound T antigen for function. Deb et al. (1987) have proposed that each pentanucleotide positions a monomer at the proper distance, rotation, and orientation relative to other T antigen monomers and that such positioning leads to subsequent events in replication.

The AT domain at the late end of the core origin shares structural features with many origins of replication. The relatively weak base pairing of these tracts would facilitate strand separation. However, the SV40 domain is not only AT-rich but also has a very precise sequence requirement that can be divided into two parts. The part between nucleotides 21 and 28 consists of a dA·dT tract that encodes an intrinsic bending of DNA. The role of this bipartite domain in origin unwinding is not clear. It could either destabilize duplex DNA directly by virtue of its intrinsic structure, or it could be a recognition site for interaction with T antigen. Indeed, a dA·dT tract in T-antigen-binding site I, which has a different arrangement of binding signals from the core origin, markedly enhances T antigen binding (Ryder et al. 1986).

The unwinding of duplex DNA is a common event in the initiation of replication of internal origins. In some cases, such as *E. coli* or bacteriophage λ, unwinding is accomplished by a complex of proteins (Echols 1986). First an origin-binding protein (dnaA for *E. coli* or the O protein for λ) binds to the origin and forms a specific complex. A region of single-strand DNA is exposed and the dnaB protein is brought into position, either by dnaC for *E. coli* or by the P protein for λ. DNA unwinding is then initiated by the dnaB helicase activity (Baker et al. 1986; Lebowitz and McMacken 1986). In the case of SV40, a single protein recognizes and unwinds the origin. The biochemical mechanism for the unwinding of duplex origin DNA remains to be determined.

Acknowledgments

This work was supported by National Institutes of Health grants CA-28146, CA-18808, CA-19176, and GM-34559. F.B.D. is supported by a fellowship from the National Institutes of Health.

References

Baker, T.A., K. Sekimizu, B.E. Funnell, and A. Kornberg. 1986. Extensive unwinding of the plasmid template during staged enzymatic initiation of DNA replication from the origin of the *Escherichia coli* chromosome. *Cell* **45:** 53.

Danna, K. and D. Nathans. 1972. Bidirectional replication of simian virus 40 DNA. *Proc. Natl. Acad. Sci.* **69:** 3097.

Dean, F.B., J.A. Borowiec, Y. Ishimi, S. Deb, P. Tegtmeyer, and J. Hurwitz. 1987a. SV40 large T antigen requires three core

replication origin domains for DNA unwinding and replication *in vitro*. *Proc. Natl. Acad. Sci.* **84:** 8267.

Dean, F.B., P. Bullock, Y. Murakami, C.R. Wobbe, L. Weissbach, and J. Hurwitz. 1987b. SV40 DNA replication: SV40 large T antigen unwinds DNA containing the SV40 origin of replication. *Proc. Natl. Acad. Sci.* **84:** 16.

Deb, S., A.L. DeLucia, C.-P. Baur, A. Koff, and P. Tegtmeyer. 1986a. Domain structure of the simian virus 40 core origin of replication. *Mol. Cell. Biol.* **6:** 1663.

Deb, S., A.L. DeLucia, A. Koff, S. Tsui, and P. Tegtmeyer. 1986b. The adenine-thymine domain of the simian virus 40 core origin directs DNA bending and coordinately regulates DNA replication. *Mol. Cell. Biol.* **6:** 4578.

Deb, S., S. Tsui, A. Koff, A.L. DeLucia, R. Parsons, and P. Tegtmeyer. 1987. The T-antigen-binding domain of the simian virus 40 core origin of replication. *J. Virol.* **61:** 2143.

DeLucia, A.L., S. Deb, K. Partin, and P. Tegtmeyer. 1986. Functional interactions of the simian virus 40 core origin of replication with flanking regulatory sequences. *J. Virol.* **57:** 138.

DeLucia, A.L., B.A. Lewton, R. Tjian, and P. Tegtmeyer. 1983. Topography of simian virus 40 A protein-DNA complexes: Arrangement of pentanucleotide interaction sites at the origin of replication. *J. Virol.* **46:** 143.

DePamphilis, M.L. and M.K. Bradley. 1986. Replication of SV40 and polyoma virus chromosomes. In *The papovaviridea* (ed. N.P. Salzman), vol. 1, p. 99. Plenum Press, New York.

Dodson, M., F.B. Dean, P. Bullock, H. Echols, and J. Hurwitz. 1987. Unwinding of duplex DNA from the SV40 origin of replication by T antigen. *Science* **238:** 964.

Echols, H. 1986. Multiple DNA-protein interactions governing high precision DNA transactions. *Science* **233:** 1050.

Gluzman, Y. 1981. SV40 transformed simian cells support the replication of early SV40 mutants. *Cell* **23:** 175.

Hay, R.T. and M.L. DePamphilis. 1982. Initiation of SV40 DNA replication *in vivo*: Location and structure of 5′ ends of DNA synthesized in the *ori* region. *Cell* **28:** 767.

Koo, H.-S., H.-M. Wu, and D.M. Crothers. 1986. DNA bending at adenine-thymine tracts. *Nature* **320:** 501.

Lebowitz, J.H. and R. McMacken. 1986. The *Escherichia coli* dnaB replication protein is a DNA helicase. *J. Biol. Chem.* **261:** 4738.

Li, J.-J. and T.J. Kelly. 1984. Simian virus 40 DNA replication *in vitro*. *Proc. Natl. Acad. Sci.* **81:** 6973.

———. 1985. SV40 DNA replication *in vitro*: Specificity of initiation and evidence for bidirectional replication. *Mol. Cell. Biol.* **5:** 1238.

Lusky, M. and M. Botchan. 1981. Inhibition of SV40 replication in simian cells by specific pBR322 sequences. *Nature* **293:** 79.

Murakami, Y., C.R. Wobbe, L. Weissbach, F.B. Dean, and J. Hurwitz. 1986. Role of DNA polymerase alpha and DNA primase in simian virus 40 DNA replication *in vitro*. *Proc. Natl. Acad. Sci.* **83:** 2369.

Ryder, K., S. Silver, A.L. DeLucia, E. Fanning, and P. Tegtmeyer. 1986. An altered DNA conformation in origin region I is a determinant for the binding of SV40 large T antigen. *Cell* **44:** 719.

Simanis, V. and D.P. Lane. 1985. An immunoaffinity purification procedure for SV40 large T antigen. *Virology* **144:** 88.

Smale, S.T. and R. Tjian. 1986. T-antigen-DNA polymerase α complex implicated in simian virus 40 DNA replication. *Mol. Cell. Biol.* **6:** 4077.

Stahl, H., P. Droge, and R. Knippers. 1986. DNA helicase activity of SV40 large tumor antigen. *EMBO J.* **5:** 1939.

Stillman, B.W. and Y. Gluzman. 1985. Replication and supercoiling of SV40 DNA in cell-free extracts from human cell. *Mol. Cell. Biol.* **5:** 2051.

Tegtmeyer, P. 1972. Simian virus 40 deoxyribonucleic acid synthesis: The viral replicon. *J. Virol.* **10:** 599.

Tjian, R. 1978. The binding site of SV40 DNA for a T-antigen-related protein. *Cell* **13:** 165.

Widom, J. 1985. Bent DNA for gene regulation and DNA packaging. *Bioessays* **2:** 11.

Wiekowski, M., P. Droge, and H. Stahl. 1987. Monoclonal antibodies as probes for a function of large T antigen during the elongation process of simian virus 40 DNA replication. *J. Virol.* **6:** 411.

Wobbe, C.R., F. Dean, L. Weissbach, and J. Hurwitz. 1985. *In vitro* replication of duplex circular DNA containing the simian virus 40 origin site. *Proc. Natl. Acad. Sci.* **82:** 5710.

Wold, M.S., J.-J. Li, and T.J. Kelly. 1987. Initiation of simian virus 40 DNA replication *in vitro*: Large-tumor-antigen- and origin-dependent unwinding of the template. *Proc. Natl. Acad. Sci.* **84:** 3643.

Cellular Proteins Required for SV40 DNA Replication In Vitro

M.S. Wold, J.J. Li, D.H. Weinberg, D.M. Virshup, J.L. Sherley, E. Verheyen, and T. Kelly

Department of Molecular Biology and Genetics, Johns Hopkins University School of Medicine, Baltimore, Maryland 21205

To define the cellular proteins required for DNA replication we have made use of a cell-free system that is capable of replicating plasmid DNA molecules containing the SV40 origin of replication. Systematic fractionation–reconstitution experiments indicate that there are a minimum of five required cellular proteins. These include one partially purified protein fraction (CF IIa) and four proteins that have been purified to near homogeneity: topoisomerase II, DNA polymerase α–primase complex, proliferating cell nuclear antigen (PCNA/cyclin), and a newly identified replication protein, RP-A. RP-A is a multi-subunit protein that has single-stranded DNA binding activity and is required for a T antigen-dependent, origin-dependent unwinding reaction. The roles of RP-A and the other proteins in the replication of SV40 DNA are discussed.

The replication of chromosomal DNA in animal cells is not well understood. One approach to this problem is to analyze the replication of the simpler chromosomes of animal viruses (Challberg and Kelly 1982; Campbell 1986; Kelly et al. 1988). The papovavirus SV40 has been extensively studied for this purpose because the replication of its genome is similar in many ways to the replication of chromosomal replicons (DePamphilis and Wassarman 1982; Campbell 1986; Kelly et al. 1988). This is due to the fact that only one viral protein, the SV40 T antigen, is required for DNA replication; thus, the replication of the SV40 genome is largely dependent on the cellular replication machinery.

The SV40 T antigen is a multifunctional protein that has been clearly implicated in the initiation of viral DNA replication (Rigby and Lane 1983; Campbell 1986). The initial step in DNA replication is the binding of T antigen to a nucleotide sequence element within the viral origin of DNA replication. Since the affinity of T antigen for this element is much greater than for other sites in the DNA, the binding event imparts a high degree of specificity to the initiation process. Once bound to the DNA, T antigen catalyzes local unwinding of the DNA in the origin region (Dean et al. 1987; Wold et al. 1987). This unwinding reaction is a function of the intrinsic helicase activity of T antigen (Stahl et al. 1986) and requires ATP and at least one cellular protein (Wold et al. 1987). Unwinding at the origin is presumably a prerequisite for priming and subsequent chain elongation. In addition to its role in initiation of replication, the helicase activity of T antigen may function during chain elongation to unwind the parental strands in front of the advancing replication forks (Stahl et al. 1985; Wiekowski et al. 1987).

Several cellular proteins have been implicated in SV40 DNA replication. Inhibitor studies carried out in vivo and in vitro as well as more direct reconstitution experiments in vitro have demonstrated a role for cellular DNA polymerase α–primase complex in the synthesis of nascent SV40 DNA chains (Huberman 1981; Li and Kelly 1984; Miller et al. 1985; Murakami et al. 1986). Detailed in vitro studies have revealed two roles for cellular topoisomerases in the replication process (Yang et al. 1987). One role, the unlinking of the parental strands during chain elongation, can be performed by either topoisomerase I or topoisomerase II. The second role, segregation of daughter molecules, is exclusively a function of topoisomerase II. Recent reconstitution experiments have demonstrated that a cellular protein variously referred to as PCNA or cyclin is involved in SV40 DNA replication (Prelich et al. 1987a). This protein, which was originally identified as a polypeptide specific for growing cells, appears to stimulate the elongation of nascent chains. Finally, a single-stranded DNA binding protein that stimulates SV40 DNA replication in vitro has been purified from HeLa cells (Wobbe et al. 1987). The role of this protein in the replication process is not yet clear.

As an approach to defining all of the cellular proteins involved in SV40 DNA replication, we have made use of the cell-free SV40 DNA replication system originally described by Li and Kelly (1984, 1985). In this system all of the cellular proteins required for replication are provided as a cytoplasmic extract from primate cells. We report here the results of systematic fractionation of such an extract derived from HeLa cells. Our data indicate that there are a minimum of five cellular proteins that are required in addition to the T antigen for the replication of SV40 DNA. The required proteins include DNA polymerase α–primase complex, topoisomerase II, PCNA, and a newly identified protein, replication protein A.

Methods

Reaction conditions

The conditions for replication and unwinding reactions were as described previously (Li et al. 1986; Wold et al. 1987).

CANCER CELLS 6 / Eukaryotic DNA Replication. © 1988 by Cold Spring Harbor Laboratory 0-87969-308-8/88 $1.00

Fractionation of HeLa cell cytoplasmic extract
The preparation of HeLa cytoplasmic extract and the generation of fractions CF I and CF II by phosphocellulose chromatography have been described previously (Li and Kelly 1984; Wold et al. 1987). CF I in buffer F(30 mM HEPES [pH 7.8], 100 mM KCl, 1 mM dithiothreitol [DTT], 0.25% inositol) was bound to a column of hydroxylapatite and the active fraction was eluted with buffer F containing 70 mM potassium phosphate. The resulting fraction (CF I′) was dialyzed into buffer F containing 15 mM KCl, 0.25 mM EDTA, and 0.01% NP-40 and then fractionated by chromatography on a column of DEAE-Sephacel. The column was eluted with a linear gradient of KCl (100–300 mM in buffer F). Two peaks of replication activity were identified by appropriate complementation assays. The first peak, eluting at 150 mM KCl, was designated CF IA and the second peak, eluting at 260 mM KCl, was designated CF IB. PCNA was purified from CF IB by hydrophobic interaction and ion exchange chromatography by methods analogous to those described previously (Prelich et al. 1987a). RP-A was purified from CF IA by methods that will be described elsewhere (Wold and Kelly 1988).

DNA polymerase α–primase complex was purified by immunoaffinity chromatography by a modification of previously described methods (Murakami et al. 1986). The affinity column was prepared by coupling SJK237 nonneutralizing monoclonal antibody against DNA polymerase α (Tanaka et al. 1982) to cyanogen bromide-activated Sepharose CL4B. Fraction CF II was adjusted to 20 mM Tris (pH 8.5), 365 mM KCl, 10% glycerol and loaded on the column. The flow-through fraction (CF IIA) was dialyzed against 30 mM HEPES (pH 7.8) 0.25% inositol, 0.25 mM EDTA, 1 mM DTT, 30 mM KCl, 10% glycerol and stored at −80°C. The column was washed with 30 mM HEPES (pH 7.8), 20 mM Tris (pH 8.5), 0.25% inositol, 0.25 mM EDTA, 1 mM DTT, 365 mM KCl, 10% glycerol, and the DNA polymerase α–primase complex was eluted with 20 mM Tris (pH 8.5), 1 mM EDTA, 1 mM DTT, 0.5 M KCl, 10% glycerol, 50% ethylene glycol. Fractions containing polymerase activity were dialyzed against 20 mM Tris (pH 8.5), 1 mM EDTA, 50% glycerol, 50 mM KCl, 1 mM DTT, 0.1 mM phenylmethylsulfonylfluoride and stored at −20°C.

Protein analysis
Analysis of polypeptides was performed by SDS-polyacrylamide gel electrophoresis according to the method of Laemmli (1970). Procedures for centrifugal elutriation and immunoblotting were as described by J. Sherley and T.J. Kelly (in prep.). The monoclonal antibody used for detection of PCNA (19F4) was described by Ogata et al. (1987). PCNA bands were detected with anti-mouse IgG antibody and ^{125}I-labeled protein A.

Results

Fractionation of the SV40 DNA replication system
We have previously demonstrated that a cytoplasmic extract derived from HeLa cells contains all of the cel-

lular proteins that are required for SV40 DNA replication in vitro (Li and Kelly 1984; Li et al. 1987). To identify and characterize these cellular replication proteins, we have carried out a series of fractionation–reconstitution experiments. The current status of this fractionation is summarized in Figure 1. Four protein fractions have been identified that are absolutely required for DNA replication. We have purified active proteins to near homogeneity from three of these cytoplasmic fractions: RP-A from fraction CF IA, PCNA from fraction CF IB, and polymerase α–primase complex from fraction CF II. Purification of the fourth fraction (CF IIA) is in progress. In addition, we have previously demonstrated that topoisomerase activity is required for both the elongation of nascent chains (topoisomerase I or II) and the segregation of daughter molecules (topoisomerase II) (Yang et al. 1987). As indicated in Figure 1, the topoisomerases, although present in cytoplasmic extracts, are more easily obtained from nuclear extracts. Thus, at this writing the evidence indicates that at least five cellular proteins are required in addition to the SV40 T antigen for efficient SV40 DNA replication in vitro.

Replication protein A
The replication activity in fraction CF IA was purified at least 100-fold by chromatography on a column of Affi-gel Blue. Fractions were assayed for replication activity in reaction mixtures containing the complementing fractions CF IB and CF II, as well as T antigen and topoisomerase I. Analysis of the active fractions by SDS-polyacrylamide gel electrophoresis revealed the presence of four polypeptides with molecular weights of 70,000, 53,000, 32,000, and 13,000 (Fig. 2). To determine the relationship of these polypeptides to each other, samples of the purified material were analyzed by sedimentation in glycerol gradients under several different conditions. The four polypeptides co-sedimented in a relatively narrow zone coincident with replication activity in gradients that contained 50 mM KCl, 500 mM KCl, or 500 mM NaCl with 1.7 M urea. We conclude that the four polypeptides are subunits of a single protein that we have designated replication protein A (RP-A). The sedimentation coefficient of RP-A at low ionic strength is 6.7, which would be consistent with a molecular weight of 86,000 if RP-A were an approximately spherical globular protein. Comparison of this native molecular weight with the sizes of the subunits suggests that RP-A is an asymmetric protein. However, determination of the actual molecular weight and subunit stoichiometry of RP-A must await more detailed hydrodynamic studies. It should be noted that chromatographic and electrophoretic evidence suggests that the 53-kD polypeptide is a proteolytic product of the larger 70-kD subunit.

RP-A was identified and purified on the basis of its ability to complement other cellular replication proteins in the reconstitution of SV40 DNA replication in vitro. Figure 2 shows an analysis of the products of such a reconstitution reaction by agarose gel electrophoresis. The reaction mixture contained purified RP-A, CF IB, CF II, topoisomerase I, and T antigen, as well as a template

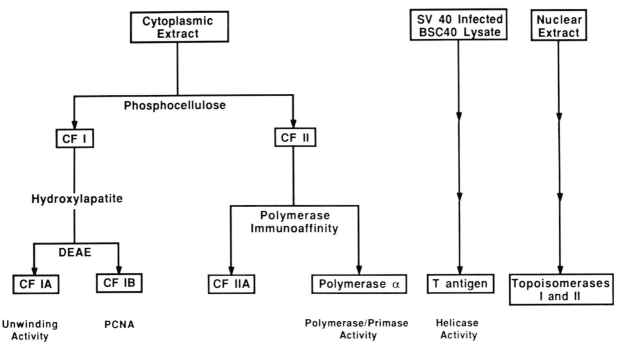

Figure 1 Protein fractions required for SV40 DNA replication in vitro. Cytoplasmic extract derived from HeLa cells was fractionated by the indicated chromatographic procedures (see Methods for details). Relevant biochemical activities of the fractions are indicated in the lower portion of the figure.

containing the SV40 origin of DNA replication. (Similar results were obtained when the purified polymerase α–primase complex and CF IIA were substituted for CF II.) The distribution of reaction products was quite similar to that observed previously with crude cytoplasmic extracts (Li and Kelly 1984; Li et al. 1987). Both monomeric circular products and higher molecular weight forms were observed. In the absence of RP-A no DNA synthesis above background was observed, indicating that SV40 DNA replication in vitro is completely dependent on this cellular protein.

In previous studies of the replication reaction, we have demonstrated that CF I, the parent fraction of RP-A, contains activities that are required for the early events in SV40 DNA replication (Wold et al. 1987). In particular, when CF I is incubated with T antigen, ATP, topoisomerase I, and the template, it is possible to detect extensive unwinding of the template. The unwinding reaction is completely dependent on the presence of the wild-type viral origin of DNA replication and probably represents an obligatory step in the initiation of viral DNA synthesis. To examine the ability of RP-A to facilitate the origin-dependent unwinding reaction, the purified protein was incubated for 30 minutes with T antigen, ATP, topoisomerase I, and a plasmid template containing the SV40 origin (Fig. 3). A rapidly migrating, underwound form of the template (arrow) was generated during the incubation of the complete reaction mixture, but no such product was observed if either RP-A or T antigen was omitted.

It has been shown previously (Dean et al. 1987; Wold et al. 1987) that the origin-dependent unwinding reaction catalyzed by T antigen can be facilitated by *Escherichia coli* single-stranded DNA binding protein

(SSB). For this reason, we examined the ability of the purified RP-A to bind to single-stranded DNA. Using a nitrocellulose filter-binding assay, it was found that RP-A has significant single-stranded DNA binding activity (comparable in this qualitative assay to *E. coli* SSB and adenovirus DBP) and may also have some affinity for duplex DNA (Table 1). It should be noted that although *E. coli* SSB will function in the unwinding assay, it cannot replace RP-A in the replication reaction (data not shown). This suggests that the role of RP-A in SV40 DNA replication may be more complex than simply providing single-stranded DNA binding activity.

Table 1 Replication Protein A Binds to Single-stranded DNA

Protein	DNA bound to nitrocellulose filter	
	SS DNA	DS DNA
None	1%	1%
RP-A	79%	11%
E. coli SSB	30%	3%
Adeno DBP	91%	n.d.
BSA	1%	0.5%

Nitrocellulose filter binding assays were carried out as described previously (Rosenfeld and Kelly 1986). The substrate for binding was a ^{32}P-labeled 120-bp oligonucleotide that was used in its native form (DS DNA) or after thermal denaturation (SS DNA). The data are presented as percentage of DNA retained on the filter. Binding reaction mixtures contained 80 pg DNA and 100 ng RP-A, 600 ng *E. coli* SSB, or 400 ng adenovirus DNA binding protein. n.d. indicates not determined.

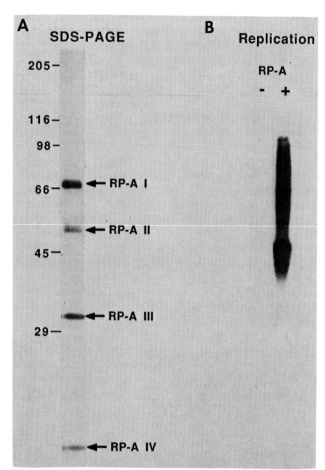

Figure 2 RP-A is required for SV40 DNA replication. (*A*) SDS-polyacrylamide gel electrophoresis of purified RP-A. The protein sample was electrophoresed on an 8–14% gradient gel and polypeptides were visualized by silver staining. (*B*) DNA products synthesized in the presence and absence of 100 ng of purified RP-A. The conditions for the replication reactions were as described previously (Li et al. 1986). Reaction mixtures contained 5 μg CF IB, 20 μg CF II, 08. μg T antigen, and 100 ng topoisomerase I. The reaction products were analyzed by agarose gel electrophoresis and visualized by autoradiography.

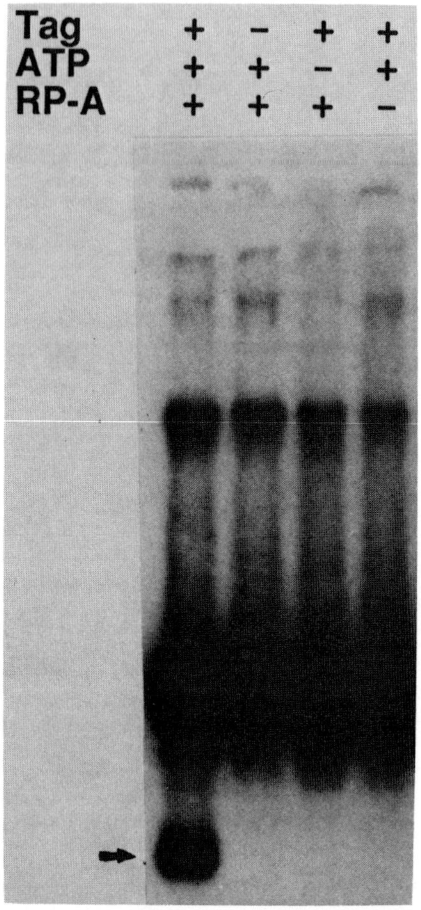

Figure 3 RP-A is required for T antigen-dependent unwinding of the template. Unwinding reactions were performed as described previously. The reaction mixtures contained 2.2 μg T antigen, 4 mM ATP, 250 ng RP-A (where indicated), and a plasmid DNA molecule (pUC.HSO) containing the wild-type SV40 origin of DNA replication. The products of the unwinding reaction were analyzed by agarose gel electrophoresis and visualized by the Southern hybridization procedure. (Wold et al. 1987).

PCNA

PCNA or cyclin, a protein unique to growing cells, has recently been implicated in SV40 DNA replication (Prelich et al. 1987a). It was found that authentic PCNA (kindly provided by Dr. B. Stillman) could replace the requirement for CF IB in our reconstituted SV40 replication reactions. A replication activity was subsequently purified to homogeneity from fraction CF IB by hydrophobic interaction and ion exchange chromatography. When the purified protein was analyzed by SDS-polyacrylamide gel electrophoresis, a single polypeptide chain with an apparent molecular weight of 36,000 was observed (Fig. 4A). The homogeneous protein was required for efficient reconstitution of SV40 DNA replication in vitro, and the products of the reconstituted reactions were similar to those observed with crude extracts (Fig. 4B). The 36-kD polypeptide comigrated with PCNA in SDS-polyacrylamide gels and reacted with an anti-PCNA monoclonal antibody (kindly provided by Dr.

E.M. Tan). We conclude that the 36-kD polypeptide purified from fraction IB is PCNA.

Although PCNA is clearly required for efficient DNA replication in vitro, we were able to detect a very low level of DNA synthesis in its absence (data not shown). Analysis of the synthetic products by agarose gel electrophoresis under denaturing conditions revealed that they consisted of short DNA chains 100–500 nucleotides in length. Synthesis of these short chains was completely dependent on T antigen and the SV40 origin of DNA replication, suggesting that they were initiated at or near the viral origin. In agreement with this suggestion, we found that the chains synthesized in the absence of PCNA hybridized predominantly, although not exclusively, to the region of the template containing the SV40 origin. These data indicate that PCNA is not absolutely required for initiation of SV40 DNA replication, but is required for the efficient elongation of nascent chains. In support of the view that PCNA does not

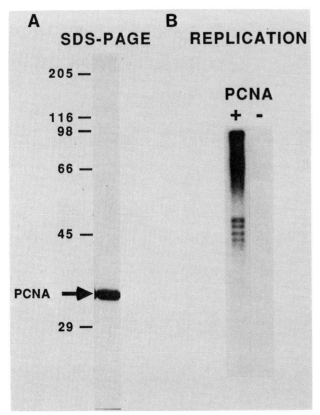

Figure 4 PCNA is required for SV40 DNA replication. (*A*) SDS-polyacrylamide gel electrophoresis of purified PCNA. Protein samples were electrophoresed through a 10% SDS-polyacrylamide gel and visualized by silver staining. (*B*) DNA products synthesized in the presence and absence of 12 ng of purified PCNA. The conditions for the replication reactions were as described previously (Li et al. 1986). Reaction mixtures contained 15 μg CF IA, 20 μg CF II, 0.8 μg T antigen, and 100 ng topoisomerase I. The reaction products were analyzed by agarose gel electrophoresis and visualized by autoradiography.

play a significant role in the early stages of the replication reaction, we found that the purified protein had no effect on the rate or extent of the origin-dependent unwinding reaction described above.

PCNA is present in actively growing cells, but is absent from nonproliferating cells (Bravo and MacDonald-Bravo 1984; Celis et al. 1987). Moreover, it has been reported that the rate of synthesis of PCNA increases during the S phase of the cell cycle (Bravo and Celis 1980). These observations are consistent with the possibility that the level of PCNA might be one of the factors controlling the level of DNA synthesis during the mammalian cell cycle. For this reason we carried out experiments to determine the relative amounts of PCNA in HeLa cells at different stages of the cell cycle. Highly synchronized HeLa cells were obtained by the method of post-elutriation progression (J. Sherley and T.J. Kelly, in prep.). In this method, G_1 cells are isolated from an unsynchronized cell population by centrifugal elutriation and then allowed to progress through the cell cycle. The initial population of G_1 cells was about 95% pure as

determined by flow microfluorimetry. The first S phase cells appeared about 8 hours after the G_1 cells were returned to culture, and S phase lasted 8–12 hours. Newly divided G_1 cells first appeared at 20–24 hours, corresponding to the doubling time of the original unsynchronized cell population (22 hr). Essentially all of the cells divided within an 8-hour period. Extracts were prepared from the synchronized cells at different stages of the cell cycle and assayed for PCNA by immunoblotting (Fig. 5). The amount of PCNA detectable by this procedure did not change significantly as the cells progressed through the cell cycle. In particular, the amount of PCNA present in G_1 phase was roughly the same as the amount present in S phase. As a control, we measured the amount of PCNA in cells rendered quiescent by starvation for serum growth factors. In agreement with previous reports, we observed very little PCNA in such cells (Bravo et al. 1981). As expected, when the cells were stimulated to proliferate by addition of fresh serum, the level of PCNA dramatically increased. These data confirm the correlation of PCNA with cell proliferation, but also demonstrate that in proliferating cells there is no correlation between the PCNA level and the rate of DNA synthesis. The simplest interpretation of these data is that PCNA does not play a significant regulatory role during the normal cell cycle.

DNA polymerase α–primase complex

DNA polymerase α–primase was purified from CF II by immunoaffinity chromatography on an anti-polymerase α antibody Sepharose column (see methods; Wong et al. 1986). All detectable protein loaded on this column flowed through (fraction CF IIA), but 85% of the polymerase α activity remained bound and was recovered by elution with 50% ethylene glycol (Murakami et al. 1986). The recovered polymerase activity was inhibited by aphidicolin and catalyzed DNA synthesis on both activated natural DNA and poly(dA) · oligo(dT) templates. Fractions active in DNA synthesis also contained significant primase activity. Analysis by SDS-polyacrylamide gel electrophoresis revealed the presence of polypeptides characteristic of mammalian DNA polymerase α–primase (subunit sizes of approximately 180 kD, 70 kD, 55 kD, and 45 kD; Fig. 6A). In addition, the preparations contained immunoglobulin heavy and light chain (derived from the column matrix), as well as a major polypeptide of approximately 30 kD that may be a contaminant or a protein associated with the polymerase–primase complex. Reconstitution experiments revealed that both the purified polymerase α–primase complex and fraction CF IIA were required for efficient SV40 DNA replication in vitro (Fig. 6B). Work is in progress to identify the active components present in fraction CF IIA.

Discussion

Systematic analysis of HeLa extracts indicates that a minimum of five cellular proteins are required for SV40 DNA replication. Figure 7 summarizes the current state

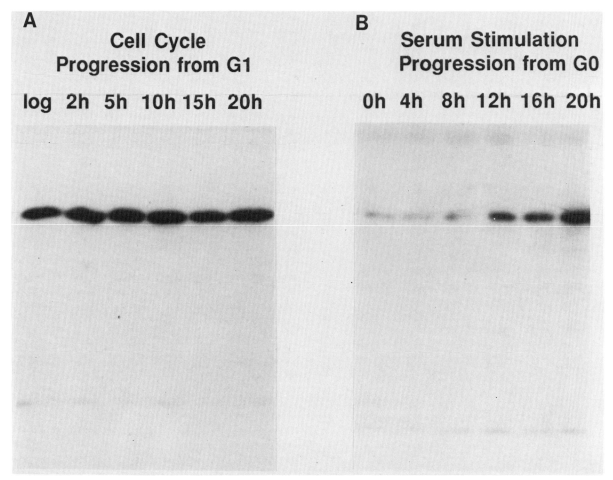

Figure 5 Analysis of the levels of PCNA during the cell cycle. (*A*) PCNA levels in cells synchronized by post-elutriation progression. An unsynchronized population of HeLa cells in exponential growth (log) was subjected to centrifugal elutriation and cells in G_1 phase were collected. The G_1 cells were immediately returned to culture and allowed to progress through the cell cycle. Cytoplasmic extracts were prepared at various times post-elutriation and PCNA was detected by SDS-PAGE followed by immunoblotting. Control experiments indicated that essentially all of the cellular PCNA was recovered in cytoplasmic extracts. (*B*) PCNA levels in quiescent vs. proliferating cells. Mouse 3T3 cells were rendered quiescent by starvation for serum and then stimulated to proliferate by addition of fresh serum (Bravo and MacDonald-Bravo 1984). Extracts were prepared at various times after serum addition and analyzed for PCNA as described above.

of knowledge concerning the role of the cellular proteins and T antigen in the replication process. Since information about replication mechanisms is fragmentary at this time, the scheme shown in Figure 7 is likely to undergo many refinements and should be considered largely speculative. The first step in replication is the recognition of the minimal origin by T antigen (Tjian 1978; Shortle et al. 1979; Campbell 1986). This is followed by the local unwinding of the origin region catalyzed by T antigen (Dean et al. 1987; Wold et al. 1987). The unwinding reaction requires ATP hydrolysis and is greatly facilitated by RP-A. The next step in the replication process is the initiation of DNA synthesis in the unwound region. The precise protein requirements for initiation are not yet known, since a direct assay for initiation is not available. It seems likely that the polymerase α–primase complex plays a direct role in initiation; additional proteins may be required as well. The subsequent elongation of the nascent DNA to full-length

strands requires polymerase α–primase complex, PCNA, and topoisomerase I or II, but the requirement for other replication proteins (T antigen CF IIA and RP-A) in this process is unknown. The last step in replication is the separation of completed daughter molecules, which requires topoisomerase II (Yang et al. 1987).

The most recent addition to the panel of proteins required for SV40 DNA replication is RP-A. RP-A has no intrinsic helicase or ATPase activity (data not shown), but is required for the origin-dependent unwinding of DNA by T antigen. Thus, it is likely that one role of RP-A is to facilitate the generation of a single-stranded region at the origin preparatory to initiation of DNA synthesis. It is also possible that RP-A plays a role in the elongation phase of the replication reaction. It has been suggested on the basis of inhibitor studies that the helicase activity of T antigen is responsible for unwinding the parental strands at the replication forks (Stahl et al. 1985;

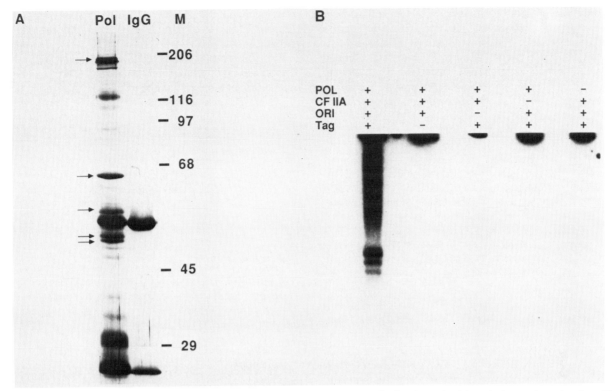

Figure 6 Polymerase α—primase is required for SV40 DNA replication. (*A*) SDS-polyacrylamide gel electrophoresis of purified polymerase α—primase (Pol). Protein samples were electrophoresed through a 10% SDS-polyacrylamide gel and visualized by silver staining. The arrows indicate polymerase α—primase subunits. Lanes marked IgG and M contained immunoglobulin IgG and molecular weight markers, respectively. (*B*) Requirements for DNA replication. Reaction mixtures contained 31 μg CF I and, where indicated, 9 μg CF IIA, 9 units DNA polymerase α—primase (Pol), 0.8 μg T antigen (Tag), 100 ng pUC.HSO plasmid DNA (ORI +) or 100 ng pUC.HSOd4 plasmid DNA (ORI −) (Wold et al. 1987).

Wiekowski et al. 1987), and, if this is correct, RP-A may act to facilitate the process. The finding that rather extensive unwinding of the template can occur in the presence of T antigen, RP-A, topoisomerase I, and ATP is consistent with this possibility.

The mechanism by which RP-A facilitates the T-antigen-mediated unwinding of the template is not completely understood. The finding that RP-A has single-stranded DNA binding activity suggests that one function of the protein may be to stabilize the single-stranded region generated by the helicase activity of T antigen. Indeed, previous work has demonstrated that *E. coli*

SSB can partially substitute for RP-A in the unwinding reaction (Dean et al. 1987; Wold et al. 1987). However, given that the subunit structure of RP-A is considerably more complex than any of the previously described prokaryotic and eukaryotic SSBs, we suspect that RP-A may play additional roles in SV40 DNA replication. In support of this view, we find that *E. coli* SSB is unable to substitute for RP-A in the complete reconstituted replication reaction.

The involvement of PCNA in SV40 DNA replication was originally discovered by Prelich and co-workers (1987a,b), who also suggested that the protein may

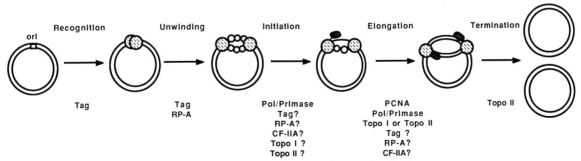

Figure 7 Roles of viral and cellular proteins in SV40 DNA replication. See text for details.

function during DNA chain elongation. Our data are in accord with this suggestion. In reconstitution experiments we have observed a small but significant level of DNA synthesis in the absence of PCNA. This residual DNA synthesis does not appear to be due to contamination of other fractions with PCNA because we have consistently failed to detect such contamination by sensitive immunoblotting procedures. The observed DNA synthesis is completely dependent on T antigen and the presence of a viral replication origin in the template, indicating it is the result of specific initiation events. However, the products of the reaction consist of DNA strands 200–500 bases in length that are preferentially derived from the origin region. These results indicate that PCNA is not absolutely required for initiation of DNA synthesis but is required for the synthesis of long nascent strands. It has been observed previously that PCNA greatly increases the processivity of the mammalian DNA polymerase δ (Tan et al. 1987; Bravo et al. 1987; Prelich et al. 1987b). Although it is not yet clear that polymerase δ is involved in SV40 DNA replication, our data are consistent with the general hypothesis that PCNA may be acting as a processivity factor during the replication reaction.

A large number of studies have demonstrated that PCNA levels are very low in quiescent cells and increase markedly when such cells are stimulated to proliferate (Bravo et al. 1981; Takasaki et al. 1981). Under these conditions the increase in PCNA is correlated with a corresponding increase in PCNA mRNA levels (Almendral et al. 1987). It has also been suggested on the basis of pulse-labeling experiments that the rate of synthesis of PCNA varies significantly during the normal cell cycle and is highest during the S phase (Bravo and Celis 1980). However, no quantitative studies of the levels of PCNA at different stages of the cell cycle have been published. Our data indicate that there is no significant change in the total amount of PCNA relative to bulk cellular protein as HeLa cells progress through the cell cycle. Although these data do not rule out a regulatory role for PCNA in the temporal control of DNA replication during the cell cycle, they render such a possibility less likely. A number of fluorescent antibody studies have demonstrated that the distribution of PCNA in the nucleus changes dramatically as cells traverse the S phase (Bravo and MacDonald-Bravo 1985; Celis et al. 1986). Given the likelihood that PCNA is directly involved in cellular DNA synthesis, these changes in the distribution of PCNA probably reflect changes in the sites of active DNA synthesis as suggested previously (Celis et al. 1986).

Our fractionation experiments confirm previous work indicating that DNA polymerase α–primase complex is required for SV40 DNA replication (Huberman 1981; Li and Kelly 1984; Miller et al. 1985; Murakami et al. 1986). It is not yet clear whether DNA polymerase α is the only polymerase activity required for SV40 DNA replication, but this situation should soon be clarified by further fractionation experiments. The finding that PCNA is required for SV40 DNA replication clearly raises the possibility that the activity defined as DNA polymerase δ (Byrnes et al. 1976) may be involved in DNA replication as well.

The results presented in this paper indicate that the SV40 replication system may be comparable in complexity to the better characterized prokaryotic replication systems (Baker et al. 1986; Dodson et al. 1986). The T antigen is a multifunctional protein that contains both origin recognition and helicase activities. In addition, at least five cellular proteins are required for DNA replication, and two of these, DNA polymerase α and RP-A, are composed of multiple subunits. Further fractionation experiments should lead to the identification of the remaining cellular proteins involved in the replication process.

Acknowledgments

We are indebted to Pamela Simancek and Alicia Russo for expert technical assistance. We also thank our colleagues in the laboratory for many useful suggestions during the course of this work.

References

Almendral, J.M., D. Huebsch, P.A. Blundell, H. MacDonald-Bravo, and R. Bravo. 1987. Cloning and sequencing of the human nuclear protein cyclin: Homology with DNA-binding proteins. *Proc. Natl. Acad. Sci.* **84:** 1575.

Baker, T.A., K. Sekimizu, B.E. Funnell, and A. Kornberg. 1986. Extensive unwinding of the plasmid template during staged enzymatic initiation of DNA replication from the origin of the *E. coli* chromosome. *Cell* **45:** 53.

Bravo, R. and J.E. Celis. 1980. A search for differential polypeptide synthesis throughout the cell cycle of HeLa cells. *J. Cell Biol.* **84:** 795.

Bravo, R. and H. MacDonald-Bravo. 1984. Induction of the nuclear protein "cyclin" in quiescent mouse 3T3 cells stimulated by serum and growth factors. Correlation with DNA synthesis. *EMBO J.* **13:** 3177.

———. 1985. Changes in the nuclear distribution of cyclin(PCNA) but not its synthesis depend on DNA replication. *EMBO J.* **4:** 655.

Bravo, R., R. Frank, P.A.. Blundell, and H. MacDonald-Bravo. 1987. Cyclin/PCNA is the auxiliary protein of DNA polymerase δ. *Nature* **326:** 515.

Bravo, R., S.J. Fey, J. Bellatin, P.M. Larsen, J. Arevalo, and J.E. Celis. 1981. Identification of a nuclear and of a cytoplasmic polypeptide whose relative proportions are sensitive to changes in the rate of cell proliferation. *Exp. Cell Res.* **136:** 311.

Byrnes, J.J., K.M. Downey, V.L. Black, and A.G. So. 1976. A new mammalian DNA polymerase with 3′ to 5′ exonuclease activity: DNA polymerase δ. *Biochemistry* **15:** 2817.

Campbell, J.L. 1986. Eukaryotic DNA replication. *Annu. Rev. Biochem.* **55:** 733.

Celis, J.E., P. Madsen, H.V. Nielsen, and A. Celis. 1986. Nuclear patterns of cyclin(PCNA) antigen distribution subdivide S-phase in cultured cells—some applications of PCNA antibodies. *Leuk. Res.* **10:** 237.

Celis, J.E., P. Madsen, A. Celis, H.V. Nielsen, and B. Gesser. 1987. Cyclin(PCNA, auxiliary protein of DNA polymerase δ) is a central component of the pathway(s) leading to DNA replication and cell division. *FEBS Lett.* **220:** 1.

Challberg, M.D. and T.J. Kelly. 1982. Eukaryotic DNA replication: Viral and plasmid model systems. *Annu. Rev. Biochem.* **51:** 901.

Dean, F.B., P. Bullock, Y. Murakami, C.R. Wobbe, L. Weissbach, and J. Hurwitz. 1987. Simian virus 40 (SV40) DNA replication: SV40 large T antigen unwinds DNA containing the SV40 origin of replication. *Proc. Natl. Acad. Sci.* **84:** 16.

DePamphilis, M.L. and P.M. Wassarman. 1982. Organization and replication of papovavirus DNA. In *Organization and replication of viral DNA* (ed. A.S. Kaplan), p. 37. CRC Press, Boca Raton, Florida.

Dodson, M., H. Echols, S. Wickner, C. Alfano, K. Mensa-Wilmot, B. Gomes, J. LeBowitz, J.D. Roberts, and R. McMacken. 1986. Specialized nucleoprotein structures at the origin of replication of bacteriophage lambda: Localized unwinding of duplex DNA by a six-protein reaction. *Proc. Natl. Acad. Sci.* **83:** 7638.

Huberman, J.A. 1981. New view of the biochemistry of eucaryotic DNA replication revealed by aphidicolin, an unusual inhibitor of DNA polymerase α. *Cell* **23:** 647.

Kelly, T.J., M.S. Wold, and J.J. Li. 1988. Initiation of viral replication. *Adv. Virus Res.* **34:** (in press).

Laemmli, U.K. 1970. Cleavage of structural proteins during the assembly of the head of bacteriophage T4. *Nature* **227:** 680.

Li, J.J. and T.J. Kelly. 1984. Simian virus 40 DNA replication *in vitro. Proc. Natl. Acad. Sci.* **81:** 6973.

———. 1985. Simian virus 40 DNA replication *in vitro:* Specificity of initiation and evidence for bidirectional replication. *Mol. Cell. Biol.* **51:** 1238.

Li, J.J., M.S. Wold, and T.J. Kelly. 1987. Analysis of SV40 DNA replication in vitro. In *Mechanisms of DNA replication and recombination* (ed. T.J. Kelly and R. McMacken), p. 289. Academic Press, New York.

Li, J.J., K.W.C. Peden, R.A.F. Dixon, and T.J. Kelly. 1986. Functional organization of the simian virus 40 origin of DNA replication. *Mol. Cell. Biol.* **6:** 1117.

Miller, M.R., R.G. Ulrich, T.S. Wang, and D. Korn. 1985. Monoclonal antibodies against human DNA polymerase α inhibit DNA replication in permeabilized human cells. *J. Biol. Chem.* **260:** 134.

Murakami, Y., C.R. Wobbe, L. Weissbach, F.B. Dean, and J. Hurwitz. 1986. Role of DNA polymerase α and DNA primase in simian virus 40 DNA replication in vitro. *Proc. Natl. Acad. Sci.* **83:** 2869.

Ogata, K., P. Kurki, J.E. Celis, R.M. Nakamura, and E.M. Tan. 1987. Monoclonal antibodies to a nuclear protein (PCNA/cyclin) associated with DNA replication. *Exp. Cell. Res.* **168:** 475.

Prelich, G., M. Kostura, D.R. Marshak, M.B. Mathews, and B. Stillman. 1987a. The cell-cycle regulated proliferating cell nuclear antigen is required for SV40 replication *in vitro. Nature* **326:** 471.

Prelich, G., C.-K. Tan, M. Kostura, M.B. Mathews, A.G. So, K.M. Downey, and B. Stillman. 1987b. Functional identity of proliferating cell nuclear antigen and a DNA polymerase-δ auxiliary protein. *Nature* **326:** 517.

Rigby, P.W. and P.D. Lane. 1983. Simian virus 40 large T antigen. *Adv. Viral Oncol.* **3:** 31.

Rosenfeld, P.J. and T.J. Kelly. 1986. Purification of nuclear factor I by DNA recognition site affinity chromatography. *J. Biol. Chem.* **261:** 1398.

Shortle, R., R.F. Margolskee, and D. Nathans. 1979. Mutational analysis of the SV40 replicon: Pseudorevertants of mutants with a defective replication origin. *Proc. Natl. Acad. Sci.* **76:** 126.

Stahl, H., P. Droge, and R. Knippers. 1986. DNA helicase activity of SV40 large tumor antigen. *EMBO J.* **5:** 1939.

Stahl, H., P. Droge, H.W. Zentgraf, and R. Knippers. 1985. A large tumor antigen specific monoclonal antibody inhibits DNA replication of simian virus 40 minichromosomes in an *in vitro* elongation system. *J. Virol.* **54:** 473.

Takasaki, Y., Y.-S. Deng, and E.M. Tan. 1981. A nuclear antigen associated with cell proliferation and blast transformation: Its distribution in synchronized cells. *J. Exp. Med.* **154:** 1899.

Tan, C.-K., C. Castillo, A.G. So, and K.M. Downey. 1986. An auxiliary protein for DNA polymerase-δ from fetal calf thymus. *J. Biol. Chem.* **261:** 12310.

Tanaka, S., S. Hu, T.S. Wong, and D. Korn. 1982. Preparation and preliminary characterization of monoclonal antibodies against human DNA polymerase α. *J. Biol. Chem.* **257:** 8386.

Tjian, R. 1978. The binding site on SV40 DNA for a T antigen-related protein. *Cell* **13:** 165.

Wiekowski, M., P. Droge, and H. Stahl. 1987. Monoclonal antibodies as probes for a function of large T antigen during the elongation process of simian virus 40 DNA replication. *J. Virol.* **61:** 411.

Wobbe, C.R., L. Weissbach, J.A. Borowiec, F.B. Dean, Y. Murakami, P. Bullock, and J. Hurwitz. 1987. Replication of simian virus 40 origin-containing DNA in vitro with purified proteins. *Proc. Natl. Acad. Sci.* **84:** 1834.

Wold, M.S. and T. Kelly. 1988. Purification and characterization of replication protein-A, a cellular protein required for SV40 DNA replication in vitro. *Proc. Natl. Acad. Sci.* (in press).

Wold, M.S., J.J. Li, and T.J. Kelly. 1987. Initiation of simian virus 40 DNA replication in vitro: Large-tumor-antigen- and origin-dependent unwinding of the template. *Proc. Natl. Acad. Sci.* **84:** 3643.

Wong, S.W., L.R. Pabarski, P.A. Fisher, T.S. Wong, and D. Korn. 1986. Structural and enzymological characterization of immunoaffinity-purified DNA polymerase α/DNA primase complex from KB cells. *J. Biol. Chem.* **261:** 7958.

Yang, L., M.S. Wold, J.J. Li, T.J. Kelly, and L.F. Liu. 1987. Roles of DNA topoisomerases in SV40 DNA replication *in vitro. Proc. Natl. Acad. Sci.* **84:** 950.

Characterization of Cellular Proteins Required for SV40 DNA Replication In Vitro

M.P. Fairman, G. Prelich, T. Tsurimoto, and B. Stillman

Cold Spring Harbor Laboratory, Cold Spring Harbor, New York 11724

Replication of SV40 DNA in vitro from plasmids containing a functional origin of replication requires SV40 large tumor antigen (TAg) and cellular proteins present in a soluble extract from human 293 cells. The cellular proteins that are essential for SV40 DNA replication have been separated into multiple components, some of which have been purified. The reconstituted replication reaction includes a cellular component that forms a presynthesis complex at the replication origin with TAg, a multi-subunit single-strand DNA-binding protein, and the proliferating cell nuclear antigen (PCNA). The identification and characterization of these cellular replication proteins define multiple stages of SV40 DNA replication that are analogous to events that occur during the replication of prokaryotic DNAs.

In proliferating cells that are committed to undergo a round of DNA replication and cell division, a series of regulatory events occurs prior to the synthetic S phase of the cell cycle that is poorly understood. It is likely that a portion of the pre-S phase that follows replication commitment involves the synthesis or activation of cellular proteins that are directly involved in DNA replication and that these events are some of the ultimate regulatory events in cell proliferation control. Therefore, if these cellular proteins can be identified, it may be possible to work back through the regulatory pathways that control cell proliferation, thereby providing a direct link between the mitogenic signals at the cell surface and the initiation of DNA synthesis.

One approach to identify cellular proteins involved in DNA replication is to utilize cell-free extracts from eukaryotic cells that support DNA replication of well-defined DNA templates. We have used the best-characterized system, the replication of SV40 DNA, to identify cellular proteins involved in DNA replication. SV40 is an ideal model chromosome because it contains one origin of DNA replication, and its mechanism of DNA synthesis resembles the mechanism of replication presumed to occur from multiple origins present in cellular chromosomes (for review, see DePamphilis and Bradley 1986). Furthermore, only one virus-encoded protein, the SV40 TAg, is required for DNA replication; therefore, cellular proteins must play a role in the replication of this DNA.

An efficient cell-free system for replication of plasmid DNAs that contain the SV40 origin of DNA replication was first developed from permissive monkey cells and required the addition of purified SV40 TAg (Li and Kelly 1984). Subsequently, SV40 DNA replication was demonstrated in extracts prepared from human HeLa or 293 cells, which can grow as suspension cultures, and was likewise dependent on the addition of purified SV40 TAg (Li and Kelly 1985; Stillman and Gluzman 1985; Wobbe et al. 1985). Using this latter system, it was shown that only 65 bp of SV40 DNA, which constitutes the minimal core origin sequences, could support effi-

cient DNA replication; however, replication was stimulated approximately twofold when SV40 TAg-binding site I was adjacent to the core origin (Stillman et al. 1985; Li et al. 1986). Surprisingly, the SV40 enhancer and promoter sequences that are required for transcription of early and late genes and for efficient DNA replication in vivo are not required for replication of DNA in vitro.

SV40 TAg is the only virus-encoded protein that is required for DNA replication in vivo (Tegtmeyer 1972) and in vitro (Li and Kelly 1984, 1985; Stillman and Gluzman 1985; Stillman et al. 1985). It binds to two specific sites, I and II, in the SV40 origin region, and DNA binding to site II is required for initiation of DNA replication (for review, see Rigby and Lane 1983). In addition, TAg is a DNA helicase that unwinds duplex DNA from a single-strand gap; a reaction that requires ATP hydrolysis by the TAg ATPase activity (Stahl et al. 1986 and this volume). Both the DNA-binding activity and the helicase/ATPase activities are required for initiation of DNA replication in vitro (Stillman et al. 1985; Stahl et al. 1986; Smale and Tjian 1986). Indeed, TAg can bind to duplex SV40 origin sequences and, in the presence of ATP, can promote bidirectional unwinding of the DNA in the absence of DNA synthesis (Dean et al. 1987; Wold et al. 1987; Dodson et al. 1987; Tegtmeyer et al.; Dean et al.; Stahl et al.; all this volume). This reaction requires a single-strand DNA-binding protein such as the *Escherichia coli* SSB to stabilize the unwound, single-strand DNA. The origin-dependent TAg unwinding reaction is probably one of the steps involved in the initiation of DNA replication.

To identify and characterize the cellular proteins that are required for SV40 DNA replication in vitro, we have fractionated the human 293 cell extracts into multiple components and purified a subset of these components. The identification and characterization of these cellular proteins has led to the idea that SV40 DNA replication can be divided into a series of discrete stages of initiation and elongation.

143

Materials and Methods

Cell extracts and T antigen

Extracts were prepared from human 293 cells and separated into fractions A, B, and II as described previously (Stillman and Gluzman 1985; Prelich et al. 1987a). SV40 T antigen was prepared from HeLa cells coinfected with wild-type adenovirus and the recombinant adenovirus vector Ad5SVR112 and purified by immunoaffinity chromatography as described previously (Simanis (Simanis and Lane 1985; Stillman and Gluzman 1985). The Ad5SVR112 vector was obtained from Dr. Y. Gluzman (Cold Spring Harbor Laboratory) and contains the SV40 T antigen gene expressed from the adenovirus major late promoter.

Fractionation of replication component A

The protein concentration of fraction A was determined and adjusted to 30 mg/ml with buffer A containing 25 mM NaCl. Solid ammonium sulfate (ultrapure, Schwarz/Mann Biotech, Ohio) was added to 40% saturation and the solution stirred slowly on ice for 30 minutes. The precipitated proteins were collected by centrifugation at 13,000g for 30 minutes and the supernatant adjusted to 65% saturation by addition of more solid, and the precipitated proteins recovered as before. Both pellets were resuspended separately in 1–2 ml buffer A plus 25 mM NaCl and dialyzed against the same buffer overnight at 4°C. The 0–40% pellet was designated A_1 and the 40–65% pellet A_2. A_1 was further fractionated by loading onto a denatured DNA cellulose (ssDNA cellulose) column (Sigma, 4.3 mg DNA/g) at a protein concentration of 8 mg protein/ml bed volume. The column was washed with two-column volumes of buffer A containing 25 mM NaCl (fraction SSI), followed by two-column volumes of buffer A plus 1.5 M NaCl (fraction SSII) and then two-column volumes of 1.5 M NaCl plus 50% v/v ethylene glycol (Aldrich) (fraction SSIII). The protein content of each fraction was determined as before and the pooled protein peaks dialyzed against buffer A containing 25 mM NaCl plus 20% sucrose. The three protein peaks from this column were designated SSI, II, and III; fractions SSI and SSIII were stored in aliquots at −70°C.

SSIII was further concentrated by binding to a DEAE-cellulose column in buffer A containing 25 mM NaCl and eluting the protein with buffer A containing 0.2 M NaCl. The peak of protein was detected by SDS-polyacrylamide gel electrophoresis (PAGE) followed by staining with Coomassie brilliant blue dye and the peak fractions pooled. This fraction was loaded onto a linear 15–35% (v/v) glycerol gradient in buffer A containing 0.1 M NaCl. Gradients were centrifuged at 40,000 rpm in a Beckman SW41 rotor for 40 hours at 4°C. The protein content of each fraction was determined by SDS-PAGE followed by silver staining using the method of Wray et al. (1981). The three comigrating polypeptides corresponding to the peak of activity were designated replication factor A (RF-A) and were stored in small aliquots at −70°C.

Fractionation of replication components B and II

PCNA was purified from fraction B as described by Prelich et al. (1987a). Fraction II was reapplied to a phosphocellulose column and separated into five fractions (IIA–E), two of which (IIA and IIC) were essential for DNA replication in the presence of fraction I and purified topoisomerases I and II (T. Tsurimoto and B. Stillman, unpubl.).

DNA replication reactions

Replication reactions contained (final concentrations) 40 mM HEPES-KOH (pH 7.5), 8 mM MgCl$_2$, 0.5 mM dithiothreitol, 100 μM each of dCTP, dGTP, and dTTP, 25 μM [α-^{32}P]dATP (approximately 100 cpm/pmol), 4 mM ATP, 200 μM each of CTP, GTP, and UTP, 40 mM creatine phosphate, and 1 μg/ml creatine phosphokinase (rabbit muscle type 1, Sigma Chemical Co.). Each reaction contained 300 ng of plasmid pSV010, which contains the entire SV40 genome cloned into the *Bam*HI site of pUC118 (Prelich and Stillman 1988), 1 μg of purified T antigen and cellular extracts as indicated. All reactions were prepared on ice and started by placing the tubes at 37°C. Reactions were terminated by addition of EDTA to 10 mM and the radioactivity incorporated into acid-insoluble material determined as described previously (Stillman and Gluzman 1985). For experiments to test for the formation of the presynthesis complex (Stillman et al. 1986; Wobbe et al. 1987), reactions that contained 40 mM HEPES-KOH (pH 7.5), 8 mM MgCl$_2$, 200 μM each of CTP, GTP, UTP, 4 mM ATP, 40 mM creatine phosphate, and 1 μg/ml creatine phosphokinase were preincubated at 37°C for 15 minutes with plasmid DNA and the indicated proteins. Then the above indicated concentrations of deoxyribonucleoside triphosphates (dNTPs) were added, along with additional protein components, and incubated at 37°C for the indicated times.

Protein assays and gel electrophoresis

Protein concentrations were determined by the method of Bradford (1976) using bovine serum albumin as the standard. NaDocSO$_4$/polyacrylamide gels (5% w/v acrylamide stacking gel, 12.5% w/v resolving gel, 37.5:1 acrylamide to bisacrylamide) were prepared and proteins subjected to electrophoresis by the method of Laemmli (1970). Proteins were visualized either by staining in 0.5% Coomassie brilliant blue followed by destaining overnight in acetic acid/methanol/H$_2$O (2:1:17) or by silver staining by the method of Wray et al. (1981).

Agarose gel electrophoresis (neutral gels in Tris-borate-EDTA buffer or alkaline gels) were prepared and run as described by Maniatis et al. (1982).

Recombinant plasmids and phage DNAs

The recombinant phage DNAs and plasmid DNAs have been described by Prelich and Stillman (1988).

Results

Fractionation of the cellular extract into multiple components

To identify the cellular proteins involved in SV40 DNA replication, the cellular proteins present in the 293 cell cytosol extract were fractionated into multiple components by column chromatography. A summary of the fractionation is shown in Figure 1. The previously described fractionation of the S100 extract into fractions IIA and IIB by phosphocellulose and DEAE-cellulose column chromatography (Prelich et al. 1987a) was used as the basis for identification of novel replication factors. Fraction II was separated into two active fractions—IIA, which contains the DNA polymerases, and fraction IIC, which is essential for DNA replication but has not been purified to date. Additionally, in reconstituted replication reactions that contain fractions I, IIA, and IIC, the purified calf thymus topoisomerases I and II were required for DNA replication and segregation of the daughter DNA molecules (data not shown). This is similar to the results of Yang et al. (1987), who demonstrated a requirement for these topoisomerases in SV40 DNA replication. In this paper, the identification of novel

replication factors present in fractions A and B will be described.

Fraction A, which contained replication components of unknown function, was separated by ammonium sulfate precipitation into two components, one of which (A$_1$) was required for replication in the presence of fractions II and B. The A$_1$ fraction was further divided into three fractions by denatured DNA cellulose chromatography, and this step yielded two separate fractions (SSI and SSIII), which were essential for replication in the reconstituted system containing fractions II and B (Table 1). Since fraction SSIII contained a low concentration of protein, the replication factor present in this fraction was purified to apparent homogeneity by chromatography on DEAE-cellulose, followed by glycerol gradient sedimentation. This analysis revealed that three polypeptides of 70,000 (70K), 34,000 (34K), and 11,000 (11K) apparent molecular weight (Fig. 2B) cofractionated with the essential replication component derived from fraction SSIII. The purification and characterization of these polypeptides will be reported elsewhere (Fairman and Stillman 1988), but it should be noted that we have been unable to separate these three polypeptides from each other by a variety of procedures

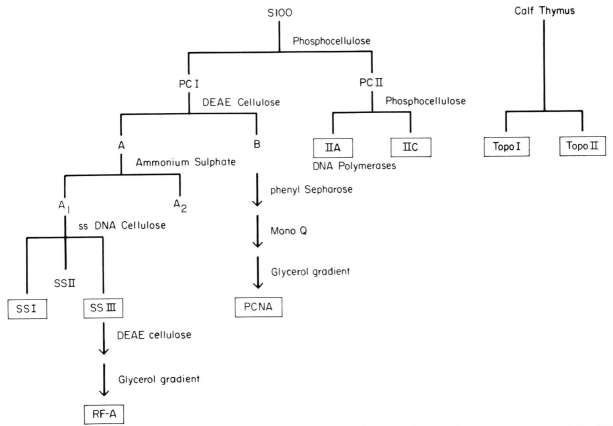

Figure 1 Fractionation of 293 cell extracts into multiple components. A flow chart of the fractionation is shown, starting with the S100 cytosol extract. The fractionation of the S100 into fractions I and II and the fractionation of I into SSI, RF-A, and PCNA are described in the Methods section. Fraction II was divided by phosphocellulose chromatography into five fractions, of which fractions IIA and IIC were required for complete replication in the presence of fraction I and purified calf thymus topoisomerases I and II (T. Tsurimoto and B. Stillman, unpubl.). One essential component for replication, SV40 TAg, is not shown on this chart. All essential cellular components are highlighted by a box.

Table 1 Reconstitution of SV40 DNA Replication with Cellular Fractions

Component	DNA Synthesis (pmol dAMP/hr)
S100	65.5
I + II	55.9
I	0.1
II	0.3
A + II	8.0
B + II	0.4
A + B + II	58.5
A$_1$ + B + II	44.7
A$_2$ + B + II	2.9
A$_1$ + A$_2$ + B + II	39.5
SSI + B + II	1.5
SSIII + B + II	4.4
SSI + SSIII + B + II	63.2

Reactions (50 μl) were set up as described in the Methods section and contained pSV010 (300 ng), TAg (1.2 μg), and optimal amounts of the indicated cellular fractions. Following incubation for 1 hr at 37°C, the amount of DNA synthesis was determined.

and retain their replication activity. Thus, it appears that the active replication component present in fraction SSIII is a tight complex of three proteins that bind to DNA and that are essential for DNA replication. This multi-subunit protein was designated RF-A. In addition, the SSI fraction that did not bind to DNA cellulose is also absolutely required for DNA replication (Table 1).

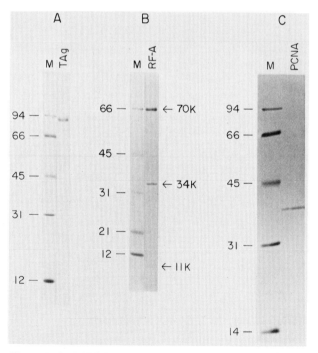

Figure 2 SDS-PAGE of purified replication proteins. (*A*) SV40 T antigen. (*B*) Cellular replication factor RF-A, which contains polypeptides of 70K, 34K, and 11K. (*C*) PCNA. The protein molecular weight standards were phosphorylase B (94), bovine serum albumin (66), ovalbumin (45), carbonic anhydrase (31), soybean trypsin inhibitor (21), lysozyme (14), and cytochrome *c* (12).

Early events during SV40 DNA replication

Previous results indicated that there is a 10–15 minute delay prior to the synthesis of the first nascent strands at the replication origin following the transfer of replication reactions to 37°C (Stillman and Gluzman 1985). Subsequently, it was demonstrated that by preincubating the replication reactions for 15 minutes at 37°C in the absence of the precursor dNTPs, this lag could be overcome in a step that required SV40 *ori* containing plasmid DNA, T antigen, and the cellular extract (Stillman et al. 1986; Wobbe et al. 1986; Fairman et al. 1987; Wold et al. 1987). This presynthesis reaction corresponded to the formation of a complex of proteins at the replication origin, which could be immediately used for subsequent DNA replication upon addition of dNTPs. We have previously shown that T antigen with fractions I and II or T antigen with fractions A and II were necessary and sufficient for this presynthesis step (Fairman et al. 1987). However, upon separation of fraction A into multiple components, it became clear that only a subset of the components in A were required for this step, but more surprisingly, fraction II was no longer required.

Figure 3A demonstrates that when the presynthesis reaction was incubated with *ori* containing plasmid DNA (pSV010), TAg, SSI, RF-A, PCNA (derived from fraction B; see below), and fraction II, subsequent replication started immediately after addition of the precursor dNTPs, and the omission of fraction II from the presynthesis reaction had no effect. Similarly, the lag in replication could be eliminated when either the RF-A protein (Fig. 3B) or PCNA (Prelich et al. 1987a) was absent from the presynthesis reactions, demonstrating that they are not required for this stage of replication. Thus, only SSI was implicated in this reaction. To test this directly, presynthesis reactions containing only *ori* plasmid DNA, TAg, and SSI were preincubated for 15 minutes at 37°C, and then the other replication components were added to the reaction at zero time together with dNTPs. Figure 3,C and D, demonstrates that under these conditions, immediate DNA synthesis was observed. In contrast, when either SSI or TAg was omitted from the presynthesis reaction, but added with dNTPs at time zero, replication only occurred following a 10–15-minute time lag. Thus *ori* containing plasmid DNA, TAg, and proteins present in fraction SSI are necessary and sufficient for presynthesis complex formation. Therefore, these studies to date have identified at least two essential replication factors that were present in fraction A, each of which is required at a different stage of SV40 DNA replication in vitro.

Function of PCNA in SV40 DNA replication

Prelich et al. (1987a) have identified a single essential replication factor from fraction B as PCNA, which has alternatively been designated cyclin (Mathews et al. 1984) or the polymerase δ auxiliary protein (Bravo et al. 1987; Prelich et al. 1987b; Tan et al. 1986). This latter identity suggested that PCNA was involved in the elongation of DNA replication by binding to polymerase δ.

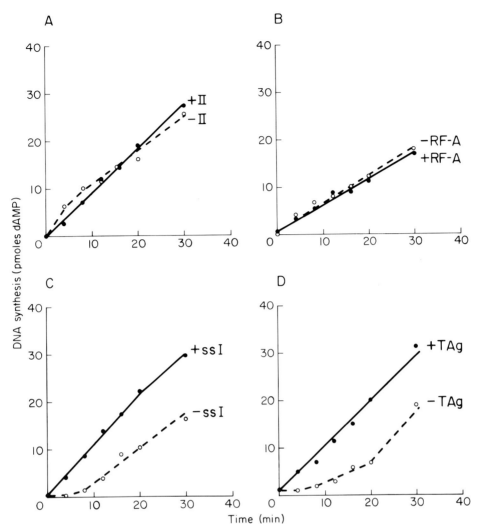

Figure 3 Kinetics of DNA replication following a preincubation step. (A) Time course of DNA synthesis following a 15-min preincubation at 37°C of 600 ng pSV010 template DNA, 2 μg TAg, and optimal amounts of fractions SSI, purified RF-A, purified PCNA (both from glycerol gradient step) in the absence (○) or presence (●) of optimal amounts of fraction II. In the latter case, the missing component was added at time zero with the dNTPs. Aliquots from the 100-μl reactions were removed at the indicated times and DNA precipitated with trichloroacetic acid and the radioactivity determined by liquid scintillation counting. (B) Reactions were set up as in A, but TAg, fraction II, SSI, and PCNA were included in the preincubation in the absence (○) or presence (●) of RF-A. Again, the missing component was added at time zero with dNTPs and the reactions were terminated at the indicated times. (C) Time course of DNA synthesis following a preincubation of pSV010 and TAg in the absence (○) or presence (●) of fraction SSI. Following the preincubation at 37°C for 15 min, fractions II and purified RF-A and PCNA (and SSI when omitted) were added with the dNTPs and the replication kinetics determined. (D) Same as C, except that the preincubation was with pSV010 template DNA, fraction SSI in the absence (○) or presence (●) of TAg. Again, the components II, RF-A, PCNA (and TAg where missing) were added with dNTPs at zero time.

Indeed, PCNA is not required for the presynthesis stage of SV40 DNA replication (Fig. 3,C and D; Prelich et al. 1987a). In the absence of PCNA, but in the presence of fractions II and A, a low level of DNA replication was observed (Prelich et al. 1987a). To characterize the replication products formed in the presence or absence of PCNA, reactions containing pSV011 plasmid DNA, TAg, and fractions II and A (± PCNA) were preincubated for 15 minutes in the absence of dNTPs and then for 10 or 20 minutes following addition of dNTPs. The replication products were then isolated and analyzed by neutral agarose gel electrophoresis (Fig. 4A), alkaline agarose gel electrophoresis (Fig. 4B), or following di-

gestion with the restriction enzymes DdeI and SphI, followed by polyacrylamide gel electrophoresis (Fig. 4C).

In the presence of PCNA, complete replication products consisting of covalently closed but relaxed circular DNA that migrated near form II marker DNA and a smear of slower migrating replication intermediates were observed (Fig. 4A, lane 2). When denatured, this DNA migrated as covalently closed circular DNA and a smear of shorter intermediate nascent strands (Fig. 4B, lane 4), and all the restriction enzyme fragments were labeled (Fig. 4C, lane 6), indicating complete DNA synthesis. In contrast, reactions that lacked PCNA yield-

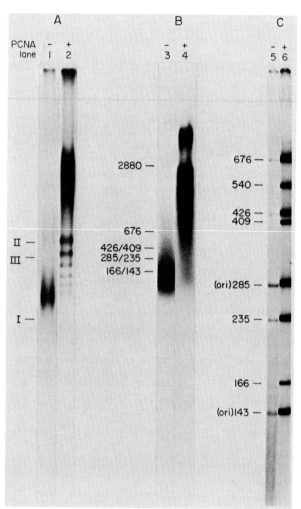

Figure 4 Analysis of replication products of reactions with or without PCNA. Replication reactions containing pSV011 template DNA, TAg, and optimal amounts of fractions II and A, in the absence (−) or presence (+) of purified PCNA (glycerol gradient step) were incubated for 15 min at 37°C, and then dNTPs were added. Aliquots of the reactions were taken at various times and the replication products isolated by protease digestion in the presence of SDS, phenol extraction, and ethanol precipitation. The products were then subjected to electrophoresis in neutral agarose gels (*A*), alkaline agarose gels following denaturation (*B*), or polyacrylamide gels following digestion with the enzymes *Sph*I and *Dde*I (*C*). The gels were dried and exposed to X-ray film with an intensifying screen. The products were isolated following replication at 37°C for 20 min (lanes *1* and *2*) or 10 min (lanes *3−6*). The positions of forms I, II, and III (2880) in part *A* and of *Dde*I and *Sph*I fragments of pSV011 (parts *B* and *C*) are indicated.

ed significantly different replication products. These migrated slightly slower than form I DNA in neutral agarose gels (Fig. 4A, lane 1) but only contained very short nascent strands ~ 100–300 bases long following denaturation and alkaline agarose gel electrophoresis (Fig. 4B, lane 3). When these products were digested with *Dde*I and *Sph*I, the 285- and 143-bp origin spanning fragments were predominantly labeled, with the origin proximal 676-, 426-, and 235-bp fragments labeling less well and relatively little label in the origin distal

540-, 409-, and 166-bp fragments (Fig. 4C, lane 5). In addition, a smear of low-molecular-weight DNA was also observed in this lane. These results suggested that in the absence of PCNA, synthesis begins at the replication origin and proceeds bidirectionally in a population of molecules, but the nascent strands are very short and do not represent the entire genome. Similar replication intermediates have been reported by Decker et al. (1986) when the elongation stage was inhibited with aphidicolin. However, when the small fragments were used as a probe on a Southern blot that contained restriction fragments of the pSV011 template DNA, hybridization to all fragments, including the origin distal fragments, was detected (data not shown). Thus, it appears that some of the short nascent DNA strands were displaced from the template DNA, probably contributing to the smear of short strands (Fig. 4C, lane 5).

If the short nascent DNA strands from the reaction lacking PCNA, or the complete daughter DNA strands from the reaction containing PCNA, were used as hybridization probes on dot blots containing cloned, separated strands from the SV40 genome, an interesting result was obtained (Fig. 5). The nascent DNA from the reaction containing PCNA hybridized to the coding and noncoding strands from both the early and late side of the replication origin. In stark contrast, the short nascent strands derived from the reaction lacking PCNA only hybridized to the noncoding strands from the early and late side of the origin, but not the coding strands from the same regions. Hybridization to the M13 phage vector DNA was not observed. The noncoding strands will hybridize to the nascent DNA strands that are synthesized discontinuously (lagging strand replication), whereas the coding strands in the template DNA will hybridize to the leading strand that is synthesized continuously at the replication fork (Fig. 5B). Therefore, it appears that PCNA is required for leading strand synthesis, and that lagging strand synthesis still occurs in the absence of PCNA, but the short fragments are not ligated together.

Discussion

Due to the lack of suitable genetic techniques in mammalian cells, a biochemical approach has been employed to identify the cellular proteins that are required for eukaryotic DNA replication. A cellular extract that can support SV40 DNA replication in vitro in the presence of purified SV40 T antigen has been fractionated into multiple components, and at least seven separate cellular replication components can be identified. The recognition of these separate cellular proteins and their preliminary functional characterization suggests that they are required at several distinct stages of SV40 DNA replication. As discussed below, several of these stages are similar to the multiple events that have been characterized in the better known prokaryotic replication systems.

The cellular fraction, SSI, contains at least one essential replication factor and is also required with SV40 TAg

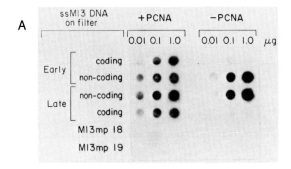

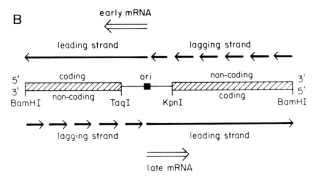

Figure 5 Strand specificity of replication reaction products. Replication reactions containing the plasmid pSV02 (the SV40 genome cloned into the *Bam* site of pAT153), TAg, and fractions A and II in the absence or presence of PCNA (where indicated) were incubated at 37°C for 30 min following a preincubation step at 37°C for 15 min without dNTPs. The isolated replication products were denatured with NaOH and layered on top of a 15–35% alkaline sucrose gradient. The gradients were sedimented for 14 hr at 30,000 rpm in a Beckman SW41 rotor. The replication reaction products from the peak of radioactivity in the gradient (4–5S without PCNA and 16–18S with PCNA) were pooled and precipitated with ethanol, then the products were used as hybridization probes on dot blots containing the following immobilized, single-strand DNAs: the early coding and noncoding strands from the *Taq-Bam* fragment and the late coding and noncoding strands from the *Kpn-Bam* fragment, all cloned into M13, mp18, and 19 vector DNAs (hatched regions in diagram). The M13mp18 and M13mp19 vector DNA without inserts were included as controls. The amount of DNA immobilized on the filters is shown. Following hybridization of the replication products with the filters in 50% formamide, 50 mM HEPES (pH 7.4), 1× Denhardt's reagent, 3× SSC, 150 μg/ml denatured salmon sperm DNA at 42°C, the filters were washed twice with 2× SSC at room temperature, twice in 0.1× SSC and 0.1% SDS at 55°C for 20 min and for 5 min in 0.1× SSC at room temperature. The filters were dried and exposed to X-ray film. The diagram below shows the replication products from both the leading and lagging strands that are expected from a completely reconstituted replication reaction.

for the first step in DNA replication in vitro. Previous results have demonstrated that it takes a 10–15-minute incubation at 37°C before synthesis of the first nascent strands at the replication origin are observed (Stillman and Gluzman 1985; Stillman et al. 1986; Wobbe et al. 1986; Wold et al. 1987). This incubation period corresponds to the establishment of a presynthesis complex of proteins at the replication origin (step 1, Fig. 6). One

event during this stage is the binding of SV40 TAg to its binding site II in the core origin (see Dean et al. this volume), but it is not known what role the SSI fraction plays during this reaction. Proteins in SSI could also bind to the origin or TAg and exist in the protein complex, but it is equally possible that the SSI factor(s) function in a catalytic manner, rather than stoichiometrically at the origin. This step is analogous to the formation of the initial complex at the *E. coli oriC* replication origin, which consists of the *dnaA* protein and which is augmented by the HU protein (see Baker et al. this volume). Similarly, a multiprotein complex is formed at the bacteriophage λ origin following binding of the phage O and P proteins (see McMacken et al. this volume). Furthermore, the presynthesis events during the first 15 minutes of SV40 DNA replication in vitro could also include the initial unwinding of the origin DNA and formation of the primer at the replication origin, paralleling similar events at *oriC* and the bacteriophage λ *ori* (Baker et al.; McMacken et al.; both this volume).

Indeed, the TAg-dependent unwinding of DNA at the SV40 *ori* has been observed and requires both the site-specific DNA-binding and ATPase/helicase activities of TAg and a single-strand DNA-binding protein such as the *E. coli* SSB (see Stahl et al.; Tegtmeyer et al.; Dean et al.; Wold et al.; all this volume). Since RF-A binds tightly and preferentially to single-strand DNA (Fairman and Stillman 1988), the second stage of SV40 DNA replication could involve RF-A by binding to the displaced single strands following the unwinding of the duplex template by the TAg-associated helicase activity (step 2, Fig. 6). This would be analogous to the unwinding events at the *E. coli* and bacteriophage λ origins of replication that require the *dnaB* helicase and *E. coli* SSB (Baker et al.; McMacken et al.; both this volume).

In the presence of TAg, fraction II, and fraction A (SSI plus RF-A), but in the absence of PCNA, initiation of DNA replication starts at the replication origin and proceeds bidirectionally in a population of molecules away from the origin (Prelich et al. 1987a; Prelich and Stillman 1988; this report; steps 3 and 4, Fig. 6). Thus, the formation of the first nascent strands at the SV40 *ori* and subsequent elongation can proceed in the absence of PCNA, but interestingly, DNA synthesis only occurs on the discontinuously synthesized lagging strand. The requirement for PCNA for the continuously synthesized leading strand replication is consistent with its role as a processivity factor for DNA polymerase δ (Tan et al. 1986; Prelich et al. 1987b). Downey et al. (this volume) have used synthetic, duplex DNA templates and have demonstrated that PCNA and polymerase δ function in a manner expected for a leading strand polymerase. Taken together, these results suggest a role for DNA polymerase δ in SV40 DNA replication as the leading strand polymerase. A role in SV40 DNA replication for polymerase α and its associated DNA primase activity has been demonstrated by Murakami et al. (1986a,b), and it is therefore likely that polymerase α functions as the lagging strand DNA polymerase and at the replication origin for synthesis of the first nascent DNA strands.

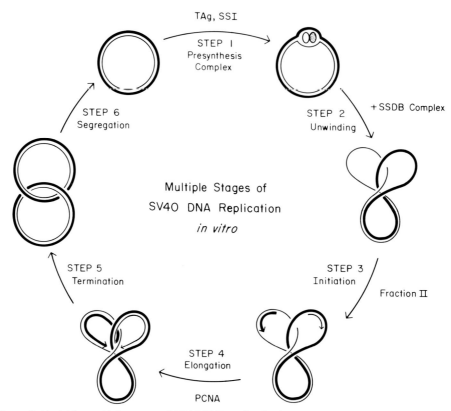

Figure 6 Model for multiple stages of SV40 DNA replication in vitro (see text for details).

Thus, two DNA polymerases may function at eukaryotic replication forks, one for the leading strand and the other for the lagging strand. A coupled leading/lagging strand polymerization model was first suggested by Alberts (Sinha et al. 1979; Alberts et al. 1983) and has resulted in the replisome model for *E. coli* replication (Kornberg 1982). Indeed, the replisome complex at a prokaryotic replication fork contains asymmetric forms of DNA polymerase III, which could synthesize leading and lagging strands (McHenry 1985; McHenry et al., this volume).

The final stages of SV40 replication are the termination of DNA synthesis and segregation of the daughter DNA molecules, (steps 5 and 6, Fig. 6). The DNA topoisomerases I and II are required for the elongation stage of DNA synthesis, and either enzyme is sufficient in vitro; however, only topoisomerase II will segregate the catenated daughter DNA molecules (Yang et al. 1987; T. Tsurimoto and B. Stillman, unpubl.). The roles of topoisomerases I and II for SV40 DNA replication in vitro are identical to the roles they play during replication in the yeast *Saccharomyces cerevisiae* (DiNardo et al. 1984; Brill et al. 1987) and in SV40 replication in vivo (Snapka 1986).

It appears that the events that take place during SV40 DNA replication in vitro parallel similar events that occur during replication of prokaryotic chromosomes and most likely reflect similar events during replication of eukaryotic chromosomal DNA. The recognition of multiple stages of SV40 DNA replication and the identifica-

tion of cellular proteins required at these stages will eventually lead to a detailed understanding of these events and how they are regulated through the cell cycle. Of particular interest are the events that precede the synthesis of DNA, because these may be the regulatory events that follow cellular commitment to replicate its genome and divide. However, it is also possible that the actual replicative stages themselves may be regulated throughout S phase to ensure that elongation from the numerous replication origins proceeds in a correct temporal order. It is clear that further characterization of the cellular proteins required for SV40 DNA replication in vitro will provide insights into these important cellular processes.

Acknowledgments

We thank Barbara Weinkauff for typing the manuscript. This work was supported by grants to B.S. from the Rita Allen Foundation and the National Institutes of Health (CA-13106).

References

Alberts, B.M., J. Barry, P. Bedinger, T. Formosa, C.V. Jongeneel, and K.N. Kreuzer. 1983. Studies on DNA replication in the bacteriophage T4 in vitro system. *Cold Spring Harbor Symp. Quant. Biol.* **47**: 655.
Bradford, M.M. 1976. A rapid and sensitive method for the quantitation of microgram quantities of protein utilizing the principle of protein dye binding. *Anal. Biochem.* **72**: 248.

Bravo, R., R. Frank, P.A. Blundell, and H. MacDonald-Bravo. 1987. Cyclin/PCNA is the auxiliary protein of DNA polymerase-δ. *Nature* **326:** 515.

Brill, S.J., S. DiNardo, K. Voelkel-Meiman, and R. Sternglanz. 1987. Need for DNA topoisomerase activity as a swivel for DNA replication for transcription of ribosomal RNA. *Nature* **326:** 414.

Dean, F.B., P. Bullock, Y. Murakami, C.R. Wobbe, L. Weissbach, and J. Hurwitz. 1987. Simian virus 40 (SV40) DNA replication: SV40 large T antigen unwinds DNA containing the SV40 origin of replication. *Proc. Natl. Acad. Sci.* **84:** 16.

Decker, R.S., M. Yamaguchi, R. Possenti, and M.L. DePamphilis. 1986. Initiation of simian virus 40 DNA replication *in vitro*: Aphidicolin causes accumulation of early-replicating intermediates and allows determination of the initial direction of DNA synthesis. *Mol. Cell. Biol.* **6:** 3815.

DePamphilis, M.L. and M.K. Bradley. 1986. Replication of SV40 and polyoma virus chromosomes. In *The papovaviridae* (ed. N.P. Salzman), p. 99. Plenum Press, New York.

DiNardo, S., K. Voelkel, and R. Sternglanz. 1984. DNA topoisomerase II mutant of *Saccharomyces cerevisiae*: Topoisomerase II is required for segregation of daughter molecules at the termination of DNA replication. *Proc. Natl. Acad. Sci.* **81:** 2616.

Dodson, M., F.B. Dean, P. Bullock, H. Echols, and J. Hurwitz. 1987. Unwinding of duplex DNA from the SV40 origin of replication by T antigen. *Science* **238:** 964.

Fairman, M.P. and B. Stillman. 1988. Cellular proteins required for multiple stages of SV40 DNA replication *in vitro*. *EMBO J.* (in press).

Fairman, M.P., G. Prelich, and B. Stillman. 1987. Identification of multiple cellular factors required for SV40 replication *in vitro*. *Philos. Trans. R. Soc. Lond. B* (in press).

Kornberg, A. 1982. *Supplement to DNA replication.* W.C. Freeman, San Francisco.

Laemmli, U.K. 1970. Cleavage of the structural proteins during assembly of the head of bacteriophage T4. *Nature* **227:** 680.

Li, J.J. and T.J. Kelly. 1984. Simian virus 40 DNA replication *in vitro*. *Proc. Natl. Acad. Sci.* **81:** 6973.

———. 1985. Simian virus 40 DNA replication *in vitro*: Specificity of initiation and evidence for bidirectional replication. *Mol. Cell. Biol.* **5:** 1238.

Li, J.J., K.W.C. Peden, R.A. Dixon, and T. Kelly. 1986. Functional organization of the simian virus 40 origin of DNA replication. *Mol. Cell. Biol.* **6:** 1117.

Maniatis, T., E.F. Fritsch, and J. Sambrook. 1982. *Molecular cloning: A laboratory manual.* Cold Spring Harbor Laboratory, Cold Spring Harbor, New York.

Mathews, M.B., R.M. Bernstein, B.R. Franza, Jr., and J.I. Garrels. 1984. Identity of the proliferating cell nuclear antigen and cyclin. *Nature* **309:** 374.

McHenry, C.S. 1985. DNA polymerase III holoenzyme of *Escherichia coli*: Components and function of a true replicative complex. *Mol. Cell. Biochem.* **66:** 71.

Murakami, Y., T. Eki, M. Yamada, C. Prives, and J. Hurwitz. 1986a. Species-specific in vitro synthesis of DNA containing the polyoma virus origin of replication. *Proc. Natl. Acad. Sci.* **83:** 6347.

Murakami, Y., C.R. Wobbe, L. Weissbach, F.B. Dean, and J. Hurwitz. 1986b. Role of DNA polymerase α and DNA primase in simian virus 40 DNA replication *in vitro*. *Proc. Natl. Acad. Sci.* **83:** 2869.

Prelich, G. and B. Stillman. 1988. Coordinated leading and

lagging strand synthesis during SV40 DNA replication *in vitro* requires PCNA. *Cell* (in press).

Prelich, G., M. Kostura, D.R. Marshak, M.B. Mathews, and B. Stillman. 1987a. The cell-cycle regulated proliferating cell nuclear antigen is required for SV40 DNA replication *in vitro*. *Nature* **326:** 471.

Prelich, G., C.K. Tan, M. Kostura, M.B. Mathews, A.G. So, K.M. Downey, and B. Stillman. 1987b. Functional identity of proliferating cell nuclear antigen and a DNA polymerase-δ auxiliary protein. *Nature* **326:** 517.

Rigby, P.W.J. and D.P. Lane. 1983. Structure and function of simian virus 40 large T-antigen. In *Advances in virology and oncology* (ed. G. Klein), vol. 3, p. 31. Raven Press, New York.

Simanis, V., and D.P. Lane. 1985. An immunoaffinity purification procedure for SV40 large T antigen. *Virology* **144:** 88.

Sinha, N.K., C.F. Morris, and B.M. Alberts. 1979. Efficient *in vitro* replication of double-stranded DNA templates by a purified T4 bacteriophage replication system. *J. Biol. Chem.* **255:** 4290.

Smale, S.T. and R. Tjian. 1986. T-antigen–DNA polymerase α complex implicated in simian virus 40 DNA replication. *Mol. Cell. Biol.* **6:** 4077.

Snapka, R.M. 1986. Topoisomerase inhibitors can selectively interfere with different stages of simian virus 40 DNA replication. *Mol. Cell. Biol.* **6:** 4221.

Stahl, H., P. Dröge, and R. Knippers. 1986. DNA helicase activity of SV40 large tumor antigen. *EMBO J.* **8:** 1939.

Stillman, B.W. and Y. Gluzman. 1985. Replication and supercoiling of simian virus 40 DNA in cell extracts from human cells. *Mol. Cell. Biol.* **5:** 2051.

Stillman, B., J.F.X. Diffley, G. Prelich, and R.A. Guggenheimer. 1986. DNA-protein interactions at the replication origins of adenovirus and SV40. *Cancer Cells* **4:** 453.

Stillman, B., R.D. Gerard, R.A. Guggenheimer, and Y. Gluzman. 1985. T antigen and template requirements for SV40 DNA replication in vitro. *EMBO J.* **4:** 2933.

Tan, C.K., C. Castillo, A.G. So, and K.M. Downey. 1986. An auxiliary protein for DNA polymerase-δ from fetal calf thymus. *J. Biol. Chem.* **261:** 12310.

Tegtmeyer, P. 1972. Simian virus 40 deoxyribonucleic acid synthesis: The viral replicon. *J. Virol.* **10:** 591.

Wobbe, C.R., F. Dean, L. Weissbach, and J. Hurwitz. 1985. *In vitro* replication of duplex circular DNA containing the simian virus 40 DNA origin site. *Proc. Natl. Acad. Sci.* **82:** 5710.

Wobbe, C.R., F.B. Dean, Y. Murakami, L. Weissbach, and J. Hurwitz. 1986. Simian virus 40 DNA replication *in vitro*: Study of events preceding elongation of chains. *Proc. Natl. Acad. Sci.* **83:** 4612.

Wobbe, C.R., L. Weissbach, J.A. Borowiec, F.B. Dean, Y. Murakami, P. Bullock, and J. Hurwitz. 1987. Replication of simian virus 40 origin-containing DNA in vitro with purified proteins. *Proc. Natl. Acad. Sci.* **84:** 1834.

Wold, M.S., J.J. Li, and T.J. Kelly. 1987. Initiation of simian virus 40 DNA replication *in vitro*: Large-tumor-antigen- and origin-dependent unwinding of the template. *Proc. Natl. Acad. Sci.* **84:** 3643.

Wray, W., T. Boulikas, V.P. Wray, and R. Hancock. 1981. Silver staining of proteins in polyacrylamide gels. *Anal. Biochem.* **118:** 197.

Yang, L., M.S. Wold, J.J. Li, T.J. Kelly, and L.F. Liu. 1987. Roles of DNA topoisomerases in simian virus 40 DNA replication *in vitro*. *Proc. Natl. Acad. Sci.* **84:** 950.

Competition between DNA Polymerase α and p53 for Binding to SV40 T Antigen

G. Gough, J.V. Gannon, and D.P. Lane

Imperial Cancer Research Fund, Clare Hall Laboratories, South Mimms, Potters Bar, Herts EN6 3LD, United Kingdom

The SV40 large T protein is the only viral protein required both in vivo and in vitro for SV40 DNA synthesis. The same protein is also responsible for the oncogenic action of the virus. Both of these activities of the protein imply an intimate reaction with components of the host cell. Using immunochemical methods, the binding of T antigen to two host components, the replicative enzyme DNA polymerase α and the p53 protein, has been analyzed. DNA polymerase α and p53 exert similar effects on the antigenic structure of T antigen, and in vitro binding assays show that p53 can block the binding of DNA polymerase α to T.

All viruses are obligate parasites, and viral products must subvert the host cell's normal components to ensure viral propagation. In the case of the small DNA tumor virus SV40 the principal, and only essential, viral protein required for this subversion is the large T protein, a polypeptide of 708 amino acids that is found principally in the cell nucleus, in a variety of oligomeric and extensively modified forms. Large T is a multifunctional protein required for viral DNA replication in permissive cells and for transformation in both permissive and nonpermissive cells (Rigby and Lane 1983). Large T binds specifically to DNA sequences at the viral origin, and when bound, initiates a local unwinding of the DNA apparently through its intrinsic ATP-dependent DNA helicase activity (Stahl et al. 1986; Dean et al. 1987; Wold et al. 1987). The locally underwound DNA template, by analogy to prokaryotic chromosomal replication systems (Baker et al. 1986), probably provides a suitable template for the entry of the cellular replicative polymerase(s).

The T protein may be actively involved in this process, since recent evidence suggests that T is associated with DNA polymerase α in vivo (Mole et al. 1987) and can bind to the holoenzyme in vitro (Smale and Tjian 1986; Gannon and Lane 1987). This interaction may also explain the restricted host range of the virus as addition of the holoenzyme from permissive cells to extracts of nonpermissive cells renders them competent for the in vitro replication of SV40 DNA (Murakami et al. 1986).

The DNA-binding and ATPase activities of T antigen, although essential for viral replication, are apparently not required for viral transformation (Manos and Gluzman 1985). An extensive genetic analysis of the T antigen regions required for cellular transformation suggests that multiple discrete domains of the protein are involved (Pipas et al. 1983). In both lytically infected and transformed cells T antigen is found complexed to a host protein, p53 (Lane and Crawford 1979; McCormick and Harlow 1980; Harlow et al. 1981a). The normal role of p53 is not clear, but when aberrantly expressed in tissue culture systems, the p53 gene acts as an oncogene to immortalize primary cells and to complement an activated *ras* gene in their complete transformation (Eliyahu et al. 1984; Jenkins et al. 1984; Parada et al. 1984). Site-directed mutagenesis has recently led to the isolation of T antigens that contain single amino acid substitutions that render the protein defective in p53 binding. Such mutant T antigens are also defective in replication and in cellular transformation, implying a role for the T–p53 interaction in both these processes. We have used an extensive library of monoclonal antibodies to show that DNA polymerase α and p53 compete for binding to T antigen and use this fact to suggest a model for the normal function of p53.

Materials and Methods

Eukaryotic cells and viral stocks

293 cells were from Dr. P. Gallimore. HeLa cells were from the ICRF cell production unit. T3T3 cells, a transformed 3T3 cell line that overproduces p53, were derived in this laboratory. Ad5-SVR111 virus was from Dr. Y. Gluzman. All cells were grown at 37°C in 10% CO_2 in air in a humidified incubator. The medium used was Dulbecco's modified Eagle's medium supplemented with 10% fetal bovine serum.

Monoclonal antibodies

The PAb 4 series of hybridoma cell lines were from Dr. E. Harlow (Harlow et al. 1981b). The PAb 2 series of hybridoma cell lines were developed within this laboratory (Lane and Hoeffler 1980; Clark et al. 1981; Mole et al. 1987). The locations of the epitopes recognized by these antibodies on T antigen have been described previously (Harlow et al. 1981b; Mole et al. 1987). The anti-p53 hybridoma cell line, 200.47, was from Dr. W. Dippold (Dippold et al. 1981). Another anti-p53 hybridoma cell line, RA3.2C2, was from Dr. V. Rotter (Rotter et al. 1981). The anti-DNA polymerase α hybridoma cell lines SJK132, SJK237, SJK287, and STK-1 (Tanaka et al. 1982) were obtained from the American Type Culture Collection. The hybridoma cell lines were grown as

153

described above, and the antibodies they secrete were purified from the culture medium by protein-A Sepharose chromatography (Ey et al. 1978). Purified antibodies were iodinated using the iodogen-coated tube method to specific activities of 1–2 μCi/μg.

Cell extracts

Extracts of cells were prepared as S100s in HYPO buffer (10 mM HEPES KOH [pH 7.4], containing 1.5 mM MgCl$_2$, 5 mM KCl and 100 mM NaCl) at a fixed ratio of 10^8 cells/ml, exactly as described by Stillman et al. (1986). Extracts were snap frozen in a dry ice/ethanol bath and stored in small aliquots at −70°C.

In vitro SV40 DNA replication reactions

Standard replication reactions used immunoaffinity-purified T antigen (Simanis and Lane 1985), an S100 extract of HeLa cells, an ATP regenerating system, an SV40 origin containing plasmid, and a standard mix of ribo- and deoxyribonucleotides with [^{32}P]dATP as the label (Li and Kelly 1984; Stillman et al. 1986). For anti-T inhibition of DNA replication the T was incubated for 1 hour with the pure test antibody before addition to the complete reaction mix.

Solid phase radioimmunoassays

All the assays described employed flexible plastic 96-well microtiter trays coated with pure monoclonal antibodies as a solid phase immunoabsorbent, and bound antigen was detected using ^{125}I-labeled pure monoclonal antibody. Plates were coated by overnight incubation with 50 μl/well of antibody (30 μg/ml in 10 mM phosphate buffer [pH 7.5]) and blocked by incubation in phosphate-buffered saline (PBS) containing 20% w/w dried skimmed milk for 3 hours. Plates were then rinsed in PBS and stored dry at −20°C. Extracts, mixtures of extracts, and samples of pure protein were added to the wells in a final volume of 50 μl and incubated on the appropriate coated plate overnight at 4°C. The wells were then washed repeatedly in PBS containing 0.1% NP-40 and then 50 μl of the appropriate labeled antibody added (~ 0.1 ng [50,000 cpm]/well). After 2 hours at room temperature, the plates were washed as before and then the individual wells counted in a Gamma counter. All assay points were determined in duplicate.

T–pol, T–p53, and pol–T–p53 complex formation in vitro

Complexes were formed in vitro by simple mixing of the appropriate extracts and pure T antigen followed by incubation for 2 hours at 4°C. Samples of the mixtures were then analyzed as described above. For anti-T inhibition of complex formation, the T was incubated for 1 hour with the pure test antibody before addition to the extract.

Immunodepletion of extracts

Extracts were depleted of p53 or DNA polymerase α by passage through protein-A Sepharose columns to which

the appropriate monoclonal antibody had been covalently coupled (Simanis and Lane 1985). The effectiveness of the depletion was monitored using the solid phase radioimmunoassay.

Results

Detection of a complex between T and human DNA polymerase α

Solid phase radioimmunoassays allow a rapid and quantitative analysis of T–DNA polymerase α complex formation to be undertaken. Figure 1a shows the results of such an assay using the anti-DNA polymerase α antibody SJK 287 as solid phase and the ^{125}I-labeled anti-T antibody, PAb 419, as probe. In such assays, it is possible to titrate both the T and DNA polymerase α components of the complex. When control antibodies are used as a solid phase, only very low background binding of the anti-T label is detected (Fig. 1a).

Specific antibody inhibition of complex formation

In earlier studies on the complex between T and p53, only a small subgroup of anti-T antibodies was found to be able to block the in vitro assembly of the complex, whereas a somewhat larger group was able to bind to T in the absence but not in the presence of bound p53 (Lane and Gannon 1986). Having established an in vitro assay for the T–DNA polymerase α, a similar survey of the anti-T library for inhibitory antibodies that could block assembly or whose epitopes were absent from T complexed to DNA polymerase α was conducted. Figure 1b shows that PAb 205 and PAb 414 inhibit T–DNA polymerase α complex formation in vitro, whereas PAb 423 fails to do so. Many other anti-T antibodies binding to other discrete sites on T are also unable to inhibit complex formation (data not shown). Figure 1c shows that PAb 250, although binding efficiently to free T, cannot interact with T complexed to DNA polymerase α present in extracts of virus-infected cells. A similar result was obtained with PAb 204 (data not shown). PAb 419 (Fig. 1c) and many other anti-T antibodies can bind the T in the complex. Surprisingly, neither PAb 250 nor PAb 204 can block complex assembly, suggesting that either the binding of DNA polymerase α to T actually displaces the antibody or that T exists in two discrete forms: a PAb 250, PAb 204 epitope-displaying form and another form that lacks these epitopes and can bind DNA polymerase α.

An extraordinary correlation exists between the behavior of these sets of anti-T antibodies with regard to the T–DNA polymerase α complex and their previously described interactions with the T–p53 complex. There is also a remarkable concordance between their in vitro reactions with the T–DNA polymerase α complex and their ability to inhibit the T-dependent replication of SV40 DNA in vitro. Thus, Figure 2 shows that PAb 205 and PAb 414 both inhibit replication, whereas PAb 250 and the closely related antibody PAb 251 do not. None of these antibodies inhibits the DNA-binding, ATPase, or

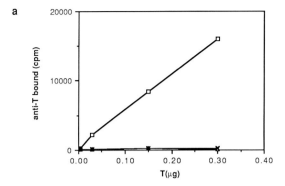

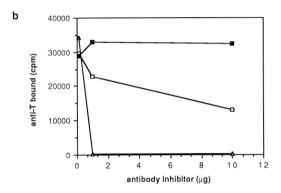

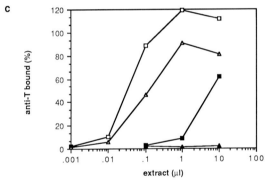

Figure 1 Immunoassay of the T–DNA polymerase α complex. (a) Formation of the T–DNA polymerase α complex in vitro. Pure T antigen was mixed with an S100 extract of HeLa cells and complex formation measured by radioimmunoassay. The labeled anti-T antibody was PAb 419. In (□—□) the solid phase antibody was the anti-DNA polymerase α antibody SJK 287. As a control solid phase the antimurine p53 antibody RA3.2C2 was used (▲—▲). As a control for nonspecific binding of the T to the SJK 287 solid phase (×—×) the S100 extract was omitted. (b) Inhibition of T–DNA polymerase α complex formation by anti-T antibodies. Pure T (0.3 μg) was incubated with a range of concentrations of pure monoclonal anti-T antibodies before mixing with HeLa S100 and T–DNA polymerase α complex formation measured as above. The inhibitors used were (■—■) PAb 423; (□—□) PAb 414; and (△—△) PAb 205. None of these antibodies block the binding of the label PAb 419 to T. (c) Epitopes displayed by T and the T–DNA polymerase α complex extracted from virus-infected cells. Extracts of Ad 5 SVR 111-infected 293 cells were titrated on an anti-T solid phase (PAb 423) and probed with two different labeled anti-T antibodies (□—□ PAb419) and (△—△ PAb 250). The same extracts were also titrated on an anti-DNA polymerase α solid phase (SJK287) and again probed with the two different anti-T antibodies (■—■ PAb 419) and (▲—▲ PAb 250).

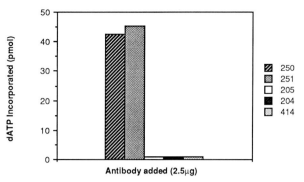

Figure 2 Anti-T antibody inhibition of SV40 DNA replication in vitro. Pure T antigen (1 μg) was preincubated with 2.5 μg of pure anti-T antibody. The mix was then added to a standard SV40 in vitro replication reaction utilizing a HeLa cell S100 and the level of dATP incorporation into DNA measured after 1 hr.

helicase activities of T antigen (data not shown). PAb 204 does inhibit replication but cannot recognize the T–DNA polymerase α complex. It does, however, inhibit the ATPase (Clark et al. 1981) and helicase activities (Stahl et al. 1986) of T, perhaps implying that both T–DNA polymerase α complex and "free T" are required in the replication reaction.

Murine p53 blocks the binding of T to DNA polymerase α

The antigenic similarities between the T–DNA polymerase α and T–p53 complexes suggested that the two host proteins might occupy overlapping sites on T. To test for this directly, the effect of p53 on T–DNA polymerase α complex formation was measured (see also Gannon and Lane 1987). Figure 3a shows that a crude extract of mouse T3T3 cells containing high levels of p53 blocks the assembly of the complex. When the T3T3 extract is immunodepleted of p53 by passage through an anti-p53 immunoabsorbent column (Fig. 3b), this inhibitory activity is lost (Fig. 3c). These results strongly suggest that p53 can block the binding of T to DNA polymerase α.

Murine DNA polymerase α can bind T

When in a set of control experiments for the previous study pure SV40 T was mixed with T3T3 extracts depleted of p53, the formation of T–murine DNA polymerase α complex could be measured (Fig. 4). Such a complex could not be detected in undepleted extracts under these conditions (Fig. 4), adding further support to the idea that p53 and DNA polymerase α compete for binding to T antigen and extending the detection of T–DNA polymerase α complexes to a nonpermissive system. The extent of T–DNA polymerase α complex formation with murine polymerase in these depleted extracts is much less than that seen with the HeLa extracts. Current studies are aimed at determining the relative affinity of T for murine versus human DNA polymerase α.

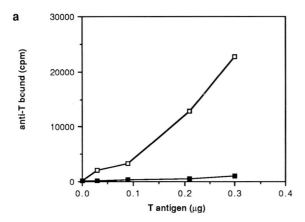

a

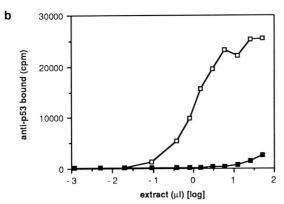

b

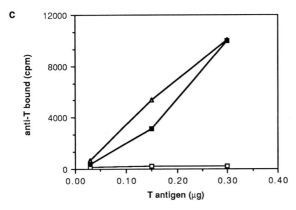

c

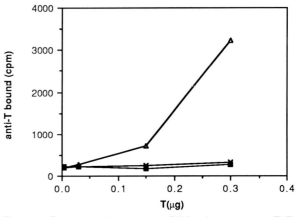

Figure 4 T can complex to mouse DNA polymerase α in T3T3 extracts depleted of p53. Undepleted (■—■), mock depleted (×—×), or p53 depleted (△—△) extracts of T3T3 cells were mixed with a range of concentrations of pure T antigen and the formation of T–DNA polymerase α complex measured as before, using the anti-DNA polymerase α, SJK287, as solid phase and the anti-T, PAb 419, as label.

Figure 3 Murine p53 blocks the binding of T to human DNA polymerase α. (*a*) Extracts of mouse T3T3 cells containing p53 block T–DNA polymerase α complex assembly. HeLa S100 (50 μl) was mixed with buffer (□—□) or an equal volume of a mouse T3T3 cell extract (■—■) and then a range of amounts of pure T added. The formation of T–DNA polymerase α complex was measured as described in Fig. 1. (*b*) Immuno-depletion of p53 from T3T3 cell extracts. A T3T3 extract was passed slowly through a protein-A Sepharose column to which the anti-p53 monoclonal antibody PAb 421 had been covalently linked. The level of p53 in the starting extract (□—□) and in the extract depleted by passage through the column (■—■) was measured in a p53 radioimmunoassay using the anti-p53 RA3.2C2 as a solid phase and another anti-p53 200.47 as the labeled probe. (*c*) T3T3 extracts immunodepleted of p53 cannot block T–DNA polymerase α complex assembly. HeLa S100 was mixed with buffer (△—△), with T3T3 extract (□—□), or with T3T3 extract depleted of p53 (as above) (■—■). Pure T was added over a range of concentrations and the formation of the T–DNA polymerase α complex measured as before.

Discussion

The exploration of the mechanism of SV40 DNA replication made possible by the recent development of in vitro systems has demonstrated striking parallels between this eukaryotic system and that of prokaryotic chromosomal replication. In the prokaryotic system, the dnaA protein occupies specific sites within *ori*C and permits entry of a DNA helicase (dnaB); localized unwinding occurs and the replicative polymerase / primase holoenzyme now starts bidirectional replication from the underwound substrate. In the SV40 system, the large T protein plays an analogous role to both dnaA and dnaB, apparently combining the activity of an *ori*-specific DNA-binding protein and a helicase within one polypeptide.

Attention is now focusing on the control of normal eukaryotic chromosomal DNA replication. From the SV40 and prokaryotic systems we can deduce the requirements for this process. First, in the absence of T and an *ori* the normal cell must have alternative functions that select sites within the chromosome to act as substrates for the initiation of replication. Although most simply this requirement could be satisfied by specific chromosomal *ori* sequences and a sequence-specific DNA-binding protein, neither of these have yet been identified and, indeed, extensive studies on the *Xenopus* system have implied that specific *ori* sequences may not be required in eukaryotic chromosomes (Blow and Laskey 1986). There are only a few reports of eukaryotic DNA helicases (Hubscher and Stalder 1985), and none has been purified to homogeneity.

The replicative DNA polymerases involved in both the SV40 system and in host cell DNA replication are also incompletely defined. Several reports in the SV40 system define an essential role for DNA polymerase α (Murakami et al. 1986), and the findings reported here on the interaction between T and DNA polymerase α suggest that this virus host interaction may at least guide the enzyme to the origin. It is important to realize that in all the studies describing the existence of the T–DNA polymerase α complex, none has shown a direct interaction of T with the catalytic subunit, and it is entirely possible that T interacts with this polypeptide via an associated subunit of the polymerase/primase complex. Indeed, it appears that only a subset of DNA polymerase α is competent to bind T and that, similarly, only a subset of T molecules is able to bind to DNA polymerase α (Smale and Tjian 1986; Gannon and Lane 1987). This could reflect either a relatively low affinity of T for the DNA polymerase α holoenzyme, or more provocatively, the presence of "bridging" molecule present in limiting amounts. It is an intriguing possibility that T may alter the properties of the enzyme potentially by displacing a cellular subunit, possibly a cellular helicase.

The involvement of polymerase δ in SV40 replication has been suggested by the identification of the polymerase δ accessory protein (PCNA, cyclin) as an essential requirement for the elongation phase of the in vitro reaction (Bravo et al. 1987; Prelich et al. 1987a,b). It is not known if T also interacts with polymerase δ, and it is possible that at origin the true replicative polymerase is a larger assembly containing elements of both polymerase δ and polymerase α (Ottiger et al. 1987).

The finding that the cellular protein p53 can compete with DNA polymerase α for binding to T antigen is the first report of a direct effect of p53 on the biochemical activity of T antigen. It raises a number of important questions about the roles of these protein/protein complexes in both viral transformation and lytic infection. If, as suggested by the antibody inhibition data, the formation of a complex between T antigen and DNA polymerase α is an essential step in SV40 DNA synthesis, then p53 could potentially block this process. The level of viral DNA synthesis taking place within a given infected permissive cell will then depend on the relative molar concentrations of p53 and DNA polymerase α and on their relative affinities for T antigen. In this context, it is interesting to recall that p53 levels rise fairly late in lytic infection of permissive cells (Harlow et al. 1981a), the majority of the T antigen molecules being in "free" form and able presumably to bind DNA polymerase α during the early phase of infection. In contrast, in the abortive infection of nonpermissive mouse cells, p53 levels rise rapidly and nearly all T antigen molecules appear complexed to and saturated by p53 (Linzer et al. 1979; Lane and Gannon 1986).

The p53 from nonpermissive species binds more tightly to T than that of permissive species (Lane et al. 1982), but it seems unlikely that the competition between p53 and DNA polymerase α for T could provide a complete explanation of host permissivity, since permissivity appears to be a dominant trait in experiments where heterokaryons are established between permissive and nonpermissive cells. Two recent studies support this view. First, Murakami et al. (1986) demonstrated SV40 DNA replication in extracts of nonpermissive cells supplemented with purified DNA polymerase α/primase isolated from permissive cells. However, the

level of p53 in the nonpermissive cell extract was not assessed, and, therefore, the ratio of DNA polymerase α to p53 in the replication reaction is unknown. Second, Gerard et al. (1987) massively overproduced T in a nonpermissive cell and demonstrated that these cells contained free T as well as T–p53 complex. Although T isolated from these cells could function in the in vitro replication system, the cells themselves could not act as permissive hosts.

Nevertheless, it will be possible now to look directly for effects of p53 on host range by attempting to block SV40 DNA synthesis in vivo and in vitro by introducing saturating levels of p53 from nonpermissive cells into permissive systems. Indeed, transfection of murine p53 expression plasmids into COS cells leads to a dramatic reduction in the T-dependent replication of cotransfected SV40 origin-containing plasmids. These results (Struzbecher et al., this volume) provide a striking in vivo correlate to our in vitro studies.

The anti-pol antibodies used in this study will, under our assay conditions, react with murine DNA polymerase α. T will bind murine DNA polymerase α in vitro in extracts, provided they have been depleted of murine p53, and this association is also blocked by p53 so the T-pol interaction might conceivably be important in viral transformation as well as in lytic infection. The connection forged between p53 and DNA polymerase α by their competitive binding to SV40 T antigen may provide some insight into the normal role of the p53 proto-oncogene. One interesting speculation is that an inhibitory factor that binds to DNA polymerase α may also bind p53. Thus, the high levels of p53 found as cells enter S phase (Reich and Levine 1984) may be needed to remove this factor, and the high p53 levels found in a range of tumor cells may be causally linked to their uncontrolled DNA replication. Such a model predicts that T antigen will displace this factor and activate DNA polymerase α, which could in turn provide an insight into the ability of T antigen to stimulate quiescent cells into division. Indirect support of this proposal comes from the work of Mercer et al. (1984), who found that although intranuclear microinjection of anti-p53 antibodies blocked the ability of serum growth factors to induce quiescent cells into DNA synthesis, it did not ablate their growth response to T antigen, although this could be inhibited by the injection of anti-T antibodies.

References

Baker, T., K. Sekimizu, B. Funnell, and A. Kornberg. 1986. Extensive unwinding of the plasmid template during staged enzymatic initiation of DNA replication from the origin of the *Escherichia coli* chromosome. *Cell* **45**: 53.

Blow, J. and R. Laskey. 1986. Initiation of DNA replication in nuclei and purified DNA by a cell-free extract of *Xenopus* eggs. *Cell* **47**: 577.

Bravo, R., R. Frank, P. Blundell, and H. Macdonald-Bravo. 1987. Cyclin/PCNA is the auxiliary protein of DNA polymerase-δ. *Nature* **326**: 515.

Clark, R., D.P. Lane, and R. Tjian. 1981. Use of monoclonal antibodies as probes of simian virus 40 T antigen ATPase activity. *J. Biol. Chem.* **56**: 11854.

Dean, F.B., P. Bullock, Y. Murakami, C.R. Wobbe, L. Weiss-bach, and J. Hurwitz. 1987. Simian virus 40 (SV40) DNA replication: SV40 large T antigen unwinds DNA containing the SV40 origin of replication. *Proc. Natl. Acad. Sci.* **84:** 16.

Dippold, W.G., G. Jay, A.B. DeLeo, G. Khoury, and L.J. Old. 1981. p53 transformation-related protein: Detection by monoclonal antibody in mouse and human cells. *Proc. Natl. Acad. Sci.* **78:** 1695.

Eliyahu, D., A. Raz, P. Gruss, D. Givol, and M. Oren. 1984. Participation of p53 cellular tumour antigen in transformation of normal embryonic cells. *Nature* **312:** 646.

Ey, P.L., S.J. Prowse, and C.R. Jenkin. 1978. Isolation of pure 1gG1 1gG2a and 1gG2b immunoglobulins from mouse serum using protein A sepharose. *Immunochemistry* **15:** 429.

Gannon, J.V. and D.P. Lane. 1987. p53 and DNA polymerase α compete for binding to SV40 T antigen. *Nature* **329:** 456.

Gerard, R., R. Guggenheimer, and Y. Gluzman. 1987. Analysis of nonpermissivity in mouse cells overexpressing simian virus 40 T antigen. *J. Virol.* **61:** 851.

Harlow, E., D.C. Pim, and L.V. Crawford. 1981a. Complex of simian virus 40 large-T antigen and host 53,000-molecular-weight protein in monkey cells. *J. Virol.* **37:** 564.

Harlow, E., L.V. Crawford, D.C. Pim, and N.M. Williamson. 1981b. Mononclonal antibodies specific for simian virus 40 tumor antigens. *J. Virol.* **39:** 861.

Hubscher, U. and H. Stalder. 1985. Mammalian DNA helicase. *Nucleic Acids Res.* **13:** 5471.

Jenkins, J.R., K. Rudge, and G.A. Currie. 1984. Cellular immortalization by a cDNA clone encoding the transformation-associated phosphoprotein p53. *Nature* **312:** 651.

Lane, D.P. and L.V. Crawford. 1979. T antigen is bound to a host protein in SV40-transformed cells. *Nature* **278:** 261.

Lane, D.P. and J. Gannon. 1986. Monoclonal antibody analysis of the SV40 large T antigen-p53 complex. *Cancer Cells* **4:** 387.

Lane, D.P. and W.K. Hoeffler. 1980. SV40 large T shares an antigenic determinant with a cellular protein of molecular weight 68,000. *Nature* **288:** 167.

Lane, D.P., J. Gannon, and G. Winchester. 1982. The complex between p53 and SV40 T antigen. *Adv. Viral Oncol.* **2:** 23.

Li, J.J. and T.J. Kelly. 1984. Simian virus 40 DNA replication *in vitro. Proc. Natl. Acad. Sci.* **81:** 6973.

Linzer, D., W. Maltzman, and A. Levine. 1979. The SV40 A gene product is required for the production of a 54,000 M.W. cellular tumor antigen. *Virology* **98:** 308.

Manos, M.M. and Y. Gluzman. 1985. Genetic and biochemical analysis of the transformation-competent, replication-defective simian virus 40 large T antigen mutants. *J. Virol.* **53:** 120.

McCormick, F. and E. Harlow. 1980. Association of a murine 53,000-dalton phosphoprotein with a simian virus 40 large T antigen in transformed cells. *J. Virol.* **34:** 213.

Mercer, W.E., C. Avignolo, and R. Baserga. 1984. Role of the p53 protein in cell proliferation as studied by microinjection of monoclonal antibodies. *Mol. Cell. Biol.* **4:** 276.

Mole, S., J. Gannon, M. Ford, and D. Lane. 1987. Structure and function of SV40 large T antigen. *Proc. R. Soc. Lond. B.* (in press).

Murakami, Y., C. Wobbe, L. Weissbach, F. Dean, and J. Hurwitz. 1986. Role of DNA polymerase α and DNA primase in simian virus 40 DNA replication *in vitro. Proc. Natl. Acad. Sci.* **83:** 2869.

Ottiger, H., P. Frei, M. Hassig, and U. Hubscher. 1987. Mammalian DNA polymerase α: A replication competent holoenzyme from calf thymus. *Nucleic Acids Res.* **15:** 4789.

Parada, L.F., H. Land, R.A. Weinberger, D. Wolf, and V. Rotter. 1984. Cooperation between gene encoding p53 tumor antigen and *ras* in cellular transformation. *Nature* **312:** 649.

Pipas, J.M., K.W. Peden, and D. Nathans. 1983. Mutational analysis of simian virus 40 T antigen: Isolation and characterization of mutants with deletions in the T-antigen gene. *Mol. Cell. Biol.* **3:** 202.

Prelich, G., M. Kostura, D. Marshak, M. Mathews, and B. Stillman. 1987a. The cell-cycle regulated proliferating cell nuclear antigen is required for SV40 DNA replication *in vitro. Nature* **326:** 471.

Prelich, G., C. Tan, M. Kostura, M. Mathews, A. So, K. Downey, and B. Stillman. 1987b. Functional identity of proliferating cell nuclear antigen and a DNA polymerase-δ auxiliary protein. *Nature* **326:** 517.

Reich, N. and A. Levine. 1984. Growth regulation of a cellular tumour antigen, p53, in nontransformed cells. *Nature* **308:** 199.

Rigby, P.W.J. and D.P. Lane. 1983. Structure and function of the simian virus 40 large T-antigen. *Adv. Viral Oncol.* **3:** 31.

Rotter, V., M.A. Boss, and D. Baltimore. 1981. Increased concentration of an apparently identical cellular protein in cells transformed by either Abelson murine leukaemia virus or other transforming agents. *J. Virol.* **38:** 336.

Simanis, V. and D.P. Lane. 1985. An immunoaffinity purificiation procedure for SV40 large T antigen. *Virology* **144:** 88.

Smale, S.T. and R. Tjian. 1986. T-antigen-DNA polymerase α complex implicated in simian virus 40 DNA replication. *Mol. Cell. Biol.* **6:** 4077.

Stahl, H., P. Droge, and R. Knippers. 1986. DNA helicase activity of SV40 large tumour antigen. *EMBO J.* **5:** 1939.

Stillman, B., J. Diffley, G. Prelich, and R.A. Guggenheimer. 1986. DNA-protein interactions at the replication origins of adenovirus and SV40. *Cancer Cells* **4:** 453.

Tanaka, S., S.-Z. Hu, T.S.-F. Wang, and D. Korn. 1982. Preparation and preliminary characterization of monoclonal antibodies against human DNA polymerase α. *J. Biol. Chem.* **257:** 8386.

Wold, M., J. Li, and T. Kelly. 1987. Initiation of simian virus 40 DNA replication *in vitro*: Large-tumour-antigen and origin-dependent unwinding of the template. *Proc. Natl. Acad. Sci.* **84:** 3643.

p53 Inhibits DNA Synthesis from the SV40 Origin of Replication

H.-W. Stürzbecher, A.W. Braithwaite, C. Addison, C. Palmer, K. Rudge, D. Lynge-Hansen, and J.R. Jenkins

Marie Curie Research Institute, The Chart, Oxted, Surrey, RH8 0TL, United Kingdom

We have studied the effect of p53 on T-antigen-directed DNA replication in monkey COS cells using plasmids containing an SV40 origin of replication and encoding wild-type or mutant p53 proteins. The results show that wild-type mouse p53 strongly inhibits SV40 origin-directed DNA replication. Experiments using cotransfected SV40 origin-containing plasmids or p53 amber mutants indicate that this inhibition requires a functional p53 protein and is restricted to p53 molecules that retain their ability to complex with T antigen. However, expression of wild-type human p53 is not inhibitory. In addition to any role in the G_0–G_1 transition, these data suggest that p53 may play a direct role in the initiation or maintenance of replicative DNA synthesis.

The cellularly encoded phosphoprotein p53 is expressed in minor amounts in an unstable form in normal cells, but it is present at elevated levels in a stable form in cells transformed by different agents (for review, see Crawford 1983). p53 complementary DNA (cDNA) expression constructs immortalize primary cells in vitro (Jenkins et al. 1984a) and cooperate with an activated *ras* oncogene in malignant transformation (Jenkins et al. 1984a; Eliyahu et al. 1984; Parada et al. 1984). p53 forms specific complexes with simian virus 40 (SV40) large T antigen (Lane and Crawford 1979; Linzer and Levine 1979). In lytically infected cells, a subpopulation of p53 T antigen complexes is associated with both replicating and mature SV40 DNA (Tack et al. 1986).

In serum-stimulated fibroblasts, p53 mRNA and protein levels are maximal late in G_1 to early S phase (Reich and Levine 1984), and microinjection of anti-p53 antibodies indicates a role for p53 in the regulation of cellular DNA synthesis (Mercer et al. 1982). We have examined the consequences of expressing wild-type and mutant p53 proteins from other species in SV40 transformed monkey cells. The data presented show that expression of mouse p53 results in a substantial and selective inhibition of SV40 origin-dependent DNA replication.

Methods

Cell culture and transfection
Monkey COS cells that express a functional SV40 large T antigen (Gluzman 1981) were used as the recipient cell line in all transfection experiments. Details are as given in Stürzbecher et al. (1987).

Plasmids
Human p53 cDNA and mouse wild-type and mutant p53 cDNAs were cloned into the pBC12CMV vector described by Cullen (1986). This vector contains the 112-bp *NcoI* to *HindIII* DNA fragment encompassing a functional SV40 replication origin. Construction of the murine p53 cDNA gene and the internal deletion mutants have been described in detail (Jenkins et al. 1984a,b, 1985). CMVori lacks an expressed p53 cDNA gene; CMVmsp53 encodes a wild-type mouse p53 cDNA gene; CMVdl162 and CMVdl516 contain internal deletions of mouse p53; CMVmsp53$_{am}$, CMSdl162$_{am}$, and CMVdl516$_{am}$ contain an additional amber mutation at residue 609 (Jenkins et al. 1984b); CMVp281$_{gly}$ and CMVp281$_{lys}$ are point mutants in which the amino acid at position 281 has been changed from glu → gly and glu → lys, respectively (C. Addison and J. Jenkins, in prep.). CMVhump53 contains a human cDNA gene; CMVNeo encodes the gene conferring resistance to the neomycin-kanamycin family in *Escherichia coli* (Southern and Berg 1982).

Monoclonal antibodies
The hybridomas PAb 421 (Harlow et al. 1981b), PAb 200-47 (Dippold et al. 1981), PAb 242, and PAb 248 (Yewdell et al. 1986) were generously provided by D.P. Lane (Imperial Cancer Research Fund).

Replication analysis of plasmid DNA
Seventy-two hours post-transfection plasmid DNA was isolated using modified Hirt supernatant procedures (Hirt 1967). Plasmid DNA was digested with excess *DpnI* restriction endonuclease and used to transform competent DH5 *E. coli* (Hanahan 1983). Parent and daughter molecules are distinguished by their differential sensitivity to the methylation-sensitive enzyme *DpnI* (Li and Kelly 1984). Transformation frequency after *DpnI* digestion is therefore a measure of plasmid replication. Transformation efficiency was about 10^7–10^8 bacterial colonies per μg input plasmid. Cells were plated on L-agar supplemented with 0.01 M $MgCl_2$ and 50 μg/ml ampicillin or kanamycin, and incubated overnight at 37°C. Colonies were counted manually.

159

CANCER CELLS 6 / Eukaryotic DNA Replication. © 1988 by Cold Spring Harbor Laboratory 0-87969-308-8/88 $1.00

Extraction of cells and Western blotting

10^6 transfected COS cells were lysed on ice with 1 ml modified RIPA buffer (10 mM Tris-HCl [pH 8.0]; 150 mM NaCl; 1 mM EDTA; 1% NP-40; 1% Na-deoxycholic acid; 0.1% SDS; 0.25 mg/ml phenylmethylsulfonyl fluoride; 30 μg/ml aprotinin). Extracts were cleared by centrifugation at 105,000g for 30 minutes at 4°C. Immunoprecipitation using PAb 200-47 and analysis by SDS-PAGE were carried out as described previously (Jenkins et al. 1985). The approximate amount of mouse p53 was determined by immunoblot analysis according to Burnette (1981), with PAb 421 followed by ^{125}I-labeled protein A.

Flow cytometry

Seventy-two hours post-transfection, cells were washed with phosphate-buffered saline (PBS), trypsinized, and fixed in cold (−20°C) 70% ethanol and stored at −20°C. Just prior to analysis of DNA content, fixed cells were treated with 100 μg/ml ribonuclease A and the DNA stained with propidium iodide (Taylor 1980).

Results

Mouse p53 expression vectors were tested for their ability to replicate by transfection into the SV40 transformed monkey COS cell line. COS cells contain an integrated SV40 genome with a defective origin of replication, but express a functional SV40 T antigen and are therefore permissive for replication of plasmids containing a functional SV40 origin of replication. Seventy-two hours post-transfection episomal DNA was recovered and the *Dpn*I-resistant fraction quantitated by transformation of *E. coli* DH5. The results are shown in Figure 1A. CMVori, lacking an expressed p53 cDNA gene, serves as a positive control for SV40 origin-dependent DNA replication. The number of *Dpn*I-resistant colonies recovered from transfection of COS cells with CMVdl516 was comparable to CMVori. In contrast, CMVmsp53, encoding wild-type mouse p53, gave only 2% *Dpn*I-resistant colonies compared to CMVori, and the mean value for five independent experiments was about 4% of CMVori. CMVdl162 gave about 10% relative to CMVori. As a control, the expression of mouse p53 was examined in parallel transfections by indirect immunofluorescence using separately the murine p53 specific monoclonal antibodies PAb 242 and PAb 248 (Yewdell et al. 1986) and the rodent p53 specific monoclonal antibody PAb 200-47 (Dippold et al. 1981). CMVdl516, CMVmsp53, and CMVdl162 all showed about 35–40% mouse p53-positive cells. We conclude that CMVmsp53 and CMVdl162 are restricted in their ability to replicate in COS cells.

Next we asked whether restriction of plasmid DNA replication by CMVmsp53 and CMVdl162 was dependent on expression of a full-length encoded p53 protein product. COS cells were transfected with wild-type and mutant p53 constructs in which the p53 cDNA genes contained an additional amber mutation at nucleotide residue 609 (Jenkins et al. 1984b). The results of these

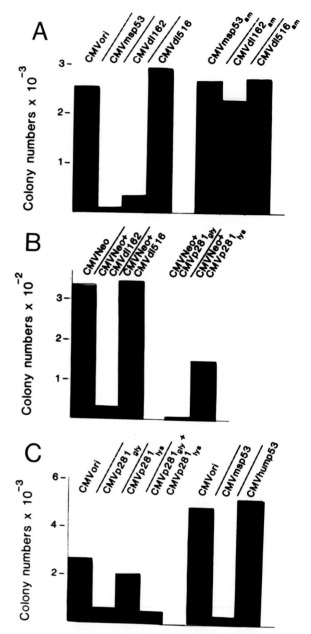

Figure 1 Mouse p53 inhibits SV40 origin-dependent DNA replication. COS cells were transfected using the DEAE/Dextran procedure. 72 hours post-transfection plasmid DNA was isolated, digested with *Dpn*I, and used to transform competent *E. coli* DH5. The number of *Dpn*I-resistant colonies represents a measure of plasmid replication. Plasmids are as detailed in Methods.

transfections are also shown in Figure 1A. The single base change implicated in the gly→Am transition results in complete restoration of the replicative capacity of both CMVmsp53 and CMVdl162. CMVdl516am replicates essentially identical to CMVdl516. Obviously, expression of a full-length p53 protein product is required for restriction of DNA replication.

To distinguish between *cis*- or *trans*-mediated inhibition, p53 expression constructs were cotransfected into

COS cells along with CMVNeo. The results are shown in Figure 1B. CMVdl516 has no effect on CMVNeo replication, whereas CMVdl162 suppresses replication of the cotransfected CMVNeo. Two point mutants of p53 (see Methods), one of which inhibits plasmid replication, gave similar results. From these results we conclude that the inhibition of replicative capacity shown by CMVdl162 operates in *trans*.

One possible interpretation of the inhibition of plasmid replication is that overproduction of exogenous p53 might have nonspecific toxic effects on the cellular metabolism. To test this, transfected COS cells were examined for DNA content by flow cytometry. Figure 2 shows that there is no detectable alteration in the distribution of DNA contents. As previously shown, any inhibition of cell division in a subpopulation of 35–40% of cells positive for antigen would be clearly detectable in this assay (Murray et al. 1982). These results argue that there is no significant inhibition of cell cycle progression by the mouse wild-type p53 cDNA gene product, and that restriction of replicative synthesis is SV40-origin-specific.

Another possible interpretation might be that p53 has simply to accumulate in the transfected cells above a certain threshold to cause inhibition of plasmid replication. Therefore, the amount of exogenous p53 was analyzed by Western blotting. Figure 3 shows that there is

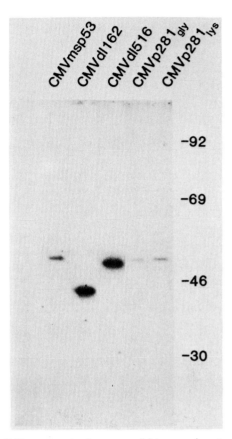

Figure 3 The amount of mouse wild-type and mutant p53 proteins does not correlate with inhibition of plasmid replication. Extracts of transfected COS cells were immunoprecipitated with the monoclonal antibody PAb 200-47, specific for murine p53, and the immunoprecipitates analyzed by SDS-PAGE. After transfer to nitrocellulose filters, p53 proteins were blotted with PAb 421 and ^{125}I-labeled protein A.

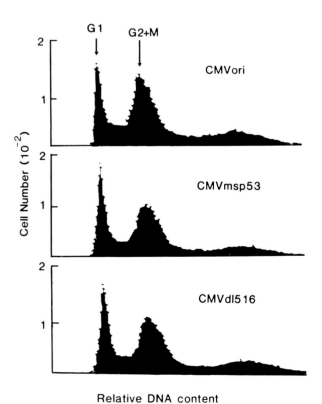

Figure 2 Mouse wild-type and mutant p53s do not inhibit proliferation of transfected monkey COS cells. 72 hours posttransfection cells were fixed in cold ethanol, the DNA stained with propidium iodide, and the DNA content of the cells analyzed by flow cytometry.

no relationship between steady-state levels of the expressed p53 proteins and inhibition.

The mouse p53 expression constructs fall into two classes: those encoding a T-antigen-binding p53 protein and those encoding a non-T-antigen-binding protein (Stürzbecher et al. 1987). All T-antigen-binding proteins inhibit plasmid replication, whereas the others do not, indicating that the ability to inhibit SV40 origin-dependent DNA replication and to associate with T antigen might be related. To further substantiate this observation, two point mutants of mouse p53, CMVp281$_{gly}$ and CMVp281$_{lys}$ (see Methods), were tested for their effects on plasmid replication. CMVp281$_{gly}$ p53 associates with T antigen, but CMVp281$_{lys}$ p53 does not. Figure 1C shows that CMVp281$_{gly}$ markedly inhibits plasmid replication, whereas CMV281$_{lys}$ does not. Cotransfection of both plasmids reduces the number of DpnI-resistant colonies to the level of CMVp281$_{gly}$ alone. These results provide clear evidence that the inhibitory effect of mouse p53 on plasmid replication is related to T-antigen-binding capacity. Furthermore, the inhibition of DNA replication is dominant. Next, we asked whether inhibition of plasmid replication is a general feature of T-antigen-binding-p53 protein overexpression. An expression vector was constructed encoding a full-length human p53 protein. The human p53 protein is detectable by indirect immunofluorescence in an equivalent percentage of the transfected cell population, and association experiments using in-vitro-translated human p53 and T antigen from a COS cell lysate confirm that human p53 is capable of binding to T antigen under these conditions (data not shown). Figure 1C shows that CMVhump53 causes no detectable inhibition whatsoever of SV40 origin-dependent replicative DNA synthesis. Thus, suppression of replication is a characteristic of the murine p53 protein and is not a general feature of the T/p53 interaction per se.

Discussion

SV40 DNA replication requires the virally encoded large T antigen (Campbell 1986) as well as a range of host cell proteins (Murakami et al. 1986). An essential step in the initiation of viral DNA synthesis involves binding of T antigen to the replication origin (for review, see Campbell 1986). T antigen can bind to cDNA polymerase α in soluble cell extracts (Smale and Tjian 1986), indicating that T-antigen–polymerase association may play a role in initiation and/or elongation of SV40 DNA replication. p53 also forms complexes with large T antigen (Lane and Crawford 1979; Linzer and Levine 1979) and T/p53 complexes can be identified on replicating SV40 chromosomes (Tack et al. 1986). In vitro T antigen–p53 complexes bind to DNA fragments containing the SV40 origin of replication (Reich and Levine 1982), and mouse p53 can displace DNA polymerase α from T antigen in in vitro plate-binding assays (Gannon and Lane 1987). In this paper, we show that expression of mouse p53 in monkey COS cells leads to a significant drop in the level of SV40 origin-dependent replication and that this effect correlates with the ability of the expressed mouse protein to complex with T antigen. Taken in isolation, the mouse p53 results might suggest that p53 functions as a regulatory factor that sequesters functional free T antigen into an inactive complex. Thus, overexpression of p53 might lead to a decrease in overall replicative synthesis. However, the human p53 result suggests otherwise, since in this case overexpression has no effect on DNA synthesis. It seems more likely that inhibition of plasmid replication by mouse p53 and perhaps DNA polymerase α displacement also result from some intrinsic species difference between the way mouse and human (and presumably monkey) p53 interact with T antigen. It is known that the complex between human p53 and T antigen is much less stable than mouse p53/T aggregates (Harlow et al. 1981a). Therefore, in cells permissive for SV40, it may be DNA polymerase α that displaces p53 from a complex with T antigen. This hypothesis implies that p53 participates in some intermediate step between T-antigen binding and DNA polymerase-α-mediated DNA synthesis. It is significant that mouse cells are nonpermissive for SV40 replication and human cells are semipermissive (Tooze 1980). Although p53 is certainly

not essential for SV40 replication, our data suggest that differences between mouse and human p53 are able to play a role in defining viral host range. A number of reports have implicated p53 in early events following the stimulation of quiescent cells and specifically in the transition from G_0 to G_1 (Mercer et al. 1982). The data we present here suggest that p53 may also be directly involved in the initiation or maintenance of replicative DNA synthesis.

Acknowledgments

We thank Ed Harlow for a human cDNA gene and Pat Imrie (Institute for Cancer Research, Sutton) for flow cytometry. We also thank Jean Marr for typing the manuscript. A. Braithwaite was supported by the Howard Florey Fellowship from Australia.

References

Burnette, W.N. 1981. "Western blotting": Electrophoretic transfer of proteins from sodium dodecylsulfate-polyacrylamide gels to unmodified nitrocellulose and radiographic detection with antibody and radioiodinated protein A. *Anal. Biochem.* **112**: 195.

Campbell, J.L. 1986. Eukaryotic DNA replication. *Annu. Rev. Biochem.* **55**: 733.

Crawford, L. 1983. The 53,000-dalton cellular protein and its role in transformation. *Int. Rev. Exp. Pathol.* **25**: 1.

Cullen, B.R. 1986. *Trans*-activation of human immunodeficiency virus occurs via a bimodal mechanism. *Cell* **46**: 973.

Dippold, W.G., G. Jay, A.B. DeLeo, G. Khoury, and L.J. Old. 1981. p53 transformation-related protein: Detection by monoclonal antibody in mouse and human cells. *Proc. Natl. Acad. Sci.* **78**: 1695.

Eliyahu, D., A. Raz, P. Gruss, D. Givol, and M. Oren. 1984. Participation of p53 cellular tumour antigen in transformation of normal embryonic cells. *Nature* **312**: 646.

Gannon, J.V. and D.P. Lane. 1987. p53 and DNA polymerase α compete for binding to SV40 T antigen. *Nature* **329**: 456.

Gluzman, Y. 1981. SV40-transformed simian cells support the replication of early SV40 mutants. *Cell* **23**: 175.

Hanahan, D. 1983. Studies on transformation of *Escherichia coli* with plasmids. *J. Mol. Biol.* **166**: 557.

Harlow, E., D.C. Pim, and L.V. Crawford. 1981a. Complex of simian virus 40 large-T antigen and host 53,000 molecular weight protein in monkey cells. *J. Virol.* **37**: 564.

Harlow, E., L.V. Crawford, D.C. Pim, and N.M. Williamson. 1981b. Monoclonal antibodies specific for simian virus 40 tumor antigens. *J. Virol.* **39**: 861.

Hirt, B. 1967. Selective extraction of polyoma DNA from infected mouse cells. *J. Mol. Biol.* **26**: 365.

Jenkins, J.R., K. Rudge, and G.A. Currie. 1984a. Cellular immortalization by a cDNA clone encoding the transformation-associated phosphoprotein p53. *Nature* **312**: 651.

Jenkins, J.R., K. Rudge, P. Chumakov, and G.A. Currie. 1985. The cellular oncogene p53 can be activated by mutagenesis. *Nature* **317**: 816.

Jenkins, J.R., K. Rudge, S. Redmond, and A. Wade-Evans. 1984b. Cloning and expression of full length mouse cDNA sequences encoding the transformation associated protein p53. *Nucleic Acids Res.* **12**: 5609.

Lane, D.P. and L.V. Crawford. 1979. T-antigen is bound to a host protein in SV40-transformed cells. *Nature* **278**: 261.

Li, J.J. and T.J. Kelly. 1984. Simian virus 40 DNA replication in vitro. *Proc. Natl. Acad. Sci.* **81**: 6973.

Linzer, D.I.H. and A.J. Levine. 1979. Characterization of a 54K dalton cellular SV40 tumor antigen present in SV40 transformed cells and uninfected embryonal carcinoma cells. *Cell* **17**: 43.

Mercer, W.E., D. Nelson, A.B. DeLeo, L.J. Old, and R. Baserga. 1982. Microinjection of monoclonal antibody to protein p53 inhibits serum-induced DNA synthesis in 3T3 cells. *Proc. Natl. Acad. Sci.* **79:** 6309.

Murakami, Y., C.R. Wobbe, L. Weissbach, F.B. Dean, and J. Hurwitz. 1986. In vitro replication of DNA containing the simian virus 40 origin. *Cancer Cells* **4:** 465.

Murray, J.D., A.J.D. Bellett, A.W. Braithwaite, L.K. Waldron, and I.W. Taylor. 1982. Altered cell cycle progression and aberrant mitosis in adenovirus-infected rodent cells. *J. Cell. Physiol.* **111:** 89.

Parada, L.F., H. Land, R.A. Weinberg, D. Wolf, and W. Rotter. 1984. Cooperation between gene encoding p53 tumour antigen and *ras* in cellular transformation. *Nature* **312:** 649.

Reich, N.C. and A.J. Levine. 1982. Specific interaction of the SV40 T antigen-cellular p53 protein complex with SV40 DNA. *Virology* **117:** 286.

————. 1984. Growth regulation of a cellular tumour antigen, p53, in nontransformed cells. *Nature* **308:** 199.

Smale, S.T. and R. Tjian. 1986. T-antigen-DNA polymerase α complex implicated in simian virus 40 DNA replication. *Mol. Cell. Biol.* **6:** 4077.

Southern, P.J. and P. Berg. 1982. Transformation of mammalian cells to antibiotic resistance with a bacterial gene under control of the SV40 early region promoter. *J. Mol. Appl. Genet.* **1:** 327.

Stürzbecher, H.-W., P. Chumakov, W.J. Welch, and J.R. Jenkins. 1987. Mutant p53 proteins bind hsp 72/73 cellular heat-shock-related proteins in SV40-transformed monkey cells. *Oncogene* **1:** 201.

Tack, L.C., J.H. Wright, and E.G. Gurney. 1986. Free and viral chromosome-bound simian virus 50 T antigen: Changes in reactivity of specific antigenic determinants during lytic infection. *J. Virol.* **58:** 635.

Taylor, I.W. 1980. A rapid single step staining technique for DNA analysis by flow microfluorimetry. *J. Histochem. Cytochem.* **28:** 1021.

Tooze, J., ed. 1980. *Molecular biology of tumor viruses*, 2nd edition: *DNA tumor viruses*. Cold Spring Harbor Laboratory, Cold Spring Harbor, New York.

Yewdell, J.W., J.V. Gannon, and D.P. Lane. 1986. Monoclonal antibody analysis of p53 expression in normal and transformed cells. *J. Virol.* **59:** 444.

Initiation of Polyomavirus and SV40 DNA Replication, and the Requirements for DNA Replication during Mammalian Development

M.L. DePamphilis,* E. Martinez-Salas,* D.Y. Cupo,[†§] E.A. Hendrickson,[†**]
C.E. Fritze,[†‡‡] W.R. Folk,[‡] and U. Heine*

*Department of Cell and Developmental Biology, Roche Institute of Molecular Biology, Nutley, New Jersey 07110; †Department of Molecular Genetics, Harvard Medical School, Boston, Massachusetts 02115; ‡Department of Microbiology, University of Texas, Austin, Texas 78712

The results summarized in this paper reveal that simian virus 40 (SV40) and polyomavirus (PyV) origin of DNA replication (*ori*) core contain all *cis*-acting sequence information necessary for initiating bidirectional, semi-discontinuous DNA replication in the presence of the homologous large tumor antigen (T-ag) and permissive cell factors. Therefore, the "initiation zone" model proposed by Hay and DePamphilis (1982) for initiation of DNA replication in SV40 is equally applicable to PyV. In differentiated or pluripotent embryonal carcinoma mouse cell lines, PyV DNA replication requires PyV T-ag and *ori* consisting of a cell-specific enhancer element plus a "core" element dedicated to replication. Microinjection of DNA into nuclei of mouse embryos revealed that these requirements are established after the first cell cleavage event. In one-cell embryos, the amount of PyV DNA replication increased tenfold, and only *ori*-core and T-ag were required; enhancers had no effect on either DNA replication or gene expression in one-cell embryos. SV40 *ori* in the presence of SV40 T-ag was marginally active in developing two-cell embryos, but replication was not increased in one-cell embryos. Replication of DNA containing putative cellular *ori* sequences but lacking a PyV or SV40 *ori*-core element was not detected in either one-cell or two-cell developing embryos. These results imply that, from fertilized egg to whole animal, mammalian cells require unique *cis*-acting sequences for DNA replication. In differentiated mouse cells, where PyV *ori* does require an enhancer, bidirectional DNA replication originated at the same place in PyV *ori*-core as it did in SV40 *ori*-core, and DNA replication in both viruses was discontinuous predominantly, if not exclusively, on the retrograde arm of replication forks. Thus, transcriptional elements can facilitate initiation of viral DNA replication to an extent that depends on the nature of *ori*-core and the permissive cell environment, but transcriptional elements themselves do not function as origins of replication.

Results and Discussion

Requirements for initiation of SV40 and PyV DNA replication

The current interest of our laboratory is on the mechanism of initiation of chromosome replication in mammalian cells, and how regulation of this process is coupled to regulation of cell division. We have focused our attention on four primary questions: What is an origin of DNA replication in mammalian cells? How does it function? How is its activity regulated? Do mammalian chromosomes require origins of replication in the same sense as viruses, mitochondria, and prokaryotic genomes? To obtain definitive answers to these questions, we have utilized the SV40 and PyV chromosomes as model systems. These viruses replicate in the nucleus of their host as small (5.3 kb) circular chromosomes whose histone composition and nucleosome structure are indistinguishable from those of the host cell (for review, see DePamphilis and Wassarman 1982; DePamphilis and Bradley 1986). With the exception of virally encoded T-ag, all of the requirements for viral chromosome replication are provided by the host. Events at SV40, PyV, and cellular replication forks are essentially the same (DePamphilis and Wassarman 1980, 1982).

SV40 and PyV each contain a *cis*-acting, genetically defined sequence that functions as an *ori* in the presence of T-ag and permissive cell factors (Fig. 1; for review, see DePamphilis and Bradley 1986; DePamphilis 1987). These *ori*-regions are similar in that each contains a core element dedicated to DNA replication and absolutely required for replication in vivo (DePamphilis and Bradley 1986) and in vitro (Stillman et al. 1985; Li et al. 1986) (Fig.1). This element is exactly 64 bp in SV40 (Deb et al. 1986) and about 66 bp in PyV (p.

Present addresses: §Department of Chemistry, Bates College, Lewiston, Maine 04240; **Dana Farber Cancer Institute, 44 Binney Street, RM 1012, Boston, Massachusetts 02115; ‡‡Department of Molecular Genetics and Cellular Biology, University of Chicago, Chicago, Illinois 60637.

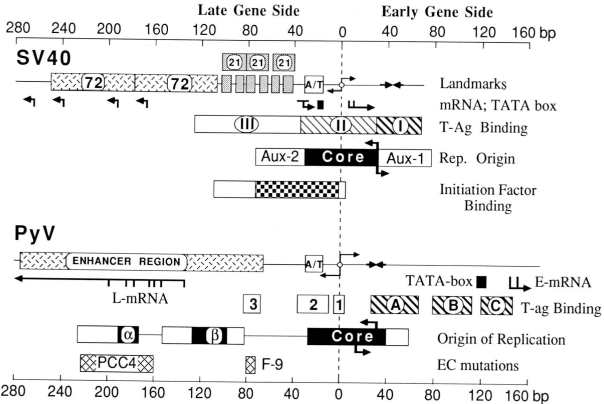

Figure 1 Comparison of SV40 and PyV *ori* regions (DePamphilis and Bradley 1986). The center of the major palindrome in *ori* was defined as 0 and the distance in nucleotides to the left or right indicated for simplicity in comparing the two genomes. SV40 landmarks include two 72-bp perfect repeats that contain enhancer elements, three 21-bp repeats, and a TATA box (solid box) that comprise the early promoter, six $G_{3-4}CG_2Pu_2$ repeats (shaded boxes), a 17-bp A/T sequence (open box), a 27-bp palindrome (pinwheel), a 14-bp inverted repeat ($\rightarrow\leftarrow$) and early and late mRNA initiation sites (arrows). DNA binding sites for wild-type SV40 T-ag are shaded according to binding affinity (I > II > III). *Cis*-acting sequences that function as SV40 *ori* include sequences that are required absolutely (Core) and auxiliary sequences (Aux) that facilitate replication three- to fivefold. The transition from discontinuous to continuous DNA synthesis that defines the OBR is indicated by arrows protruding from *ori*-core that point in the direction of DNA synthesis. The "core" of the DNA binding site for a factor(s) required to initiate SV40 DNA replication is indicated by a checkered box and its other limits by an open box. The symbols for PyV landmarks are similar to those for SV40 and include the transcriptional enhancer region, a 15-bp A/T sequence, a 34-bp palindrome, a 17-bp inverted repeat, a TATA box, and early and late mRNA start sites. DNA binding sites for wild-type PyV T-ag are shaded according to binding affinity for PyV A3 (B,C > A > 1,2,3). *Cis*-acting sequences that function as PyV origin of replication (α, β, and core) are defined by deletion and point mutations (minimum required sequence is indicated by a solid rectangle and the outer limits by open rectangles).

145 in DePamphilis and Bradley 1986). Although their sequences are not identical, the two *ori*-core elements are strikingly similar in structural organization (p. 150 in DePamphilis and Bradley 1986; Figs. 5 and 6).

In contrast to SV40, PyV *ori requires* at least one element; *ori*-core alone has no detectable activity in differentiated mouse cells (Fig. 1). Two elements; α and β, have been identified that function as strong enhancers for gene expression in differentiated mouse cells; *either* of these elements allows *ori*-core to initiate DNA replication in differentiated mouse cells (Herbomel et al. 1984; Mueller et al. 1984; Veldman et al. 1985; Hassell et al. 1986). In SV40, deletion of the enhancer elements has no effect on DNA replication, although deletion of the 21-bp repeats (containing the 'GGGCGG' boxes that comprise the promoter) reduces SV40 replication two- to threefold. SV40 *ori*-core is flanked by two 43–45-bp auxiliary sequences (*aux-1* and *aux-2*) that each

facilitate replication two- to fivefold. *aux-2* contains three 'GGGCGG' boxes. Other differences between SV40 and PyV *ori*-regions should also be noted. SV40 replicates only in monkey or human cells, whereas PyV replicates only in mouse cells. SV40 T-ag binds strongly to *ori*-core (although this site [site II] is five- to sevenfold weaker than site I [Gottlieb et al. 1985]), and all three PyV T-ag DNA-binding sites (A, B, and C) with affinities comparable to SV40 sites I and II lie outside the PyV *ori*. A tenfold increase in PyV T-ag is required to observe binding to sites 1, 2, and 3 (Dilworth et al. 1984; Cowie and Kamen 1986). Finally, SV40 *ori*-core contains early mRNA start sites, whereas all mRNA start sites in PyV lie outside *ori*-core and are directed away from *ori*. These differences in the organization and activation of SV40 and PyV *ori*-regions suggest that significant differences may exist in the mechanisms for initiation of replication in these two viral chromosomes.

However, three recent observations demonstrate that SV40 and PyV use the same mechanism for initiation of DNA replication. First, elimination of both promoter and enhancer elements in SV40 reduces DNA replication in vivo by 10- to 100-fold, depending on experimental conditions (DeLucia et al. 1986; Lee-Chen and Wood-worth-Gutai 1986; Li et al. 1986; Hertz and Mertz 1986). Second, as discussed below, PyV *ori*-core can function, under some in vivo conditions, equally well with or without enhancer elements. Third, when PyV DNA replication in differentiated mouse cells was analyzed in parallel with SV40 DNA replication in differentiated monkey cells, both were found to replicate semi-discontinuously: RNA-primed DNA synthesis events occurred predominantly, if not exclusively, on retrograde arms of replication forks (that side of replication forks where the direction of DNA synthesis must be opposite to the direction of fork movement). Finally, the PyV origin of bidirectional DNA replication in differentiated mouse cells (conditions where *ori*-core requires an enhancer element for activity) is located within PyV *ori*-core at virtually the same site it is found in SV40 *ori*-core. Therefore, the model proposed by Hay and DePamphilis (1982) for initiation of SV40 DNA replication applies equally well to PyV.

Requirements for initiation of DNA replication in mammalian embryos

Results with some embryonic systems suggest that the requirements for DNA replication in embryos are not the same as in differentiated cells. All DNA molecules (including SV40 and PyV) injected into *Xenopus* eggs replicate under apparent control of the cell division cycle but with no apparent requirement for specific sequences (Méchali and Kearsey 1984; Blow and Laskey 1986). Furthermore, replication bubbles are at least five times more frequent in *Drosophila* embryos than in *Drosophila*

differentiated cells (Blumenthal et al. 1974). These results suggest that embryonic cells can recognize many sequences as origins of replication that cannot be recognized in differentiated cells. Conversely, embryonic cells require unique *cis*-acting sequences that are different from those required by differentiated cells. PyV DNA replicates in mouse differentiated cells but not in mouse embryonal carcinoma cell lines, a problem that can be corrected by *cis*-acting mutations in PyV enhancer elements (Fig. 1; Linney and Donerly 1983; Amati 1985; Melin et al. 1985). These results present a paradox. If embryonal carcinoma cells are representative of mouse embryos, DNA replication in mammalian embryos should require unique DNA sequences. However, if *Xenopus* and *Drosophila* embryos are representative of other embryonic systems, then DNA replication in mammalian embryos should not require unique DNA sequences.

We addressed this dilemma by injecting unique DNA sequences into mouse embryos (Wirak et al. 1985; Chalifour et al. 1986, 1987). Mouse embryos are remarkably different from either *Xenopus* or *Drosophila* embryos in that they contain much less maternally inherited protein and RNA. For example, in two days a fertilized *Xenopus* egg produces a swimming tadpole, whereas a fertilized mouse egg produces only four to eight cells (Davidson 1986). Therefore, a requirement for *cis*-acting sequences may be observed only in the absence of high concentrations of replication factors.

Early mammalian development offers four candidates for injection studies (Fig. 2). Oocytes are arrested in prophase of the first meiosis. They do not replicate their own DNA, although they do transcribe and translate their own genes. Unfertilized eggs are arrested in metaphase of the second meiosis, where they neither replicate their DNA nor transcribe their genes. Fertilization is followed by initiation of cellular DNA synthesis, but RNA synthesis does not occur until after S phase in

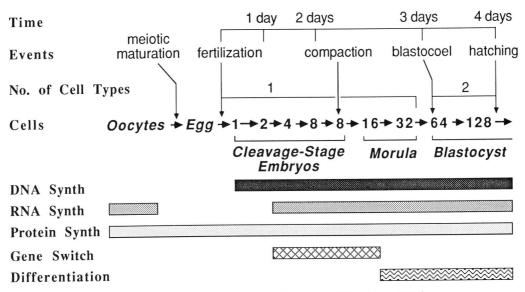

Figure 2 Events during early mouse development (Davidson 1986).

two-cell embryos. Therefore, we began by injecting circular DNA containing PyV, SV40, or bacterial plasmid sequences into one of the nuclei of a two-cell embryo. Surviving embryos were cultured for up to 3 days to allow development to the blastocyst stage. DNA was purified, cut at a unique restriction site to convert substrates and products of DNA replication into linear molecules that were fractionated by gel electrophoresis, detected by blotting-hybridization, and quantitated by densitometry of the resulting autoradiograms. When plasmid DNA that had been replicated by *Escherichia coli* was injected, one portion of the DNA was also digested with DpnI restriction endonuclease to identify molecules that had undergone at least one round of replication. Replication (or gene expression) was not detected in embryos earlier than 1 day post-injection, and the maximum amounts of replication (or gene expression) were observed 2 days post-injection. Extensive DNA replication in developing two-cell embryos resulted in abnormal multicellular embryos, whereas DNA replication in one-cell embryos blocked development to the two-cell stage. Circular DNA molecules that failed to replicate for any reason were nevertheless stable for up to 3 days.

Only circular DNA molecules containing either a functional PyV (Wirak et al. 1985) or SV40 (Chalifour et al. 1986) *ori* replicated when injected into two-cell mouse embryos, and replication occurred only when a functional T-ag gene from the same virus was included on the same or on a separate plasmid. These results are consistent with the requirements for viral DNA replication in differentiated mammalian cells, but they are in marked contrast to results obtained in analogous experiments with *Xenopus*. As a control, we also injected DNA into

the nucleus of mouse oocytes. Consistent with the biology of these cells, neither PyV nor SV40 sequences replicated, although SV40 early and late genes were efficiently expressed (Chalifour et al. 1986, 1987). The fact that SV40 replicates in two-cell mouse embryos at approximately 3% of the level of PyV suggests that permissive cell factors present in differentiated mouse cells are expressed at low levels in early mouse embryos. SV40 DNA replication has not been detected in mouse differentiated cells, even when the concentration of SV40 T-ag is equal to or greater than that expressed in the permissive COS-1 cell line (Gerard et al. 1987). SV40 T-ag expressed in these mouse cells is functional in an SV40 in vitro DNA replication assay. Thus, developing two-cell mouse embryos can recognize sequences as *ori* that are not recognized as *ori* in mouse embryonal carcinoma or differentiated cell lines.

We then proceeded to determine whether or not enhancer elements were required to activate PyV *ori*-core in embryos as they were in differentiated cells. A plasmid containing the complete PyV genome to provide T-ag was coinjected with a second plasmid containing a specific configuration of the PyV *ori* region. In two-cell mouse embryos, α-β core and β core configurations replicated, but α core did not (Wirak et al. 1985). Furthermore, β-β core replicated at least six times better than β core, whereas neither enhancers nor core alone were able to replicate (Fig. 3). These results suggested that β functioned as an enhancer element in developing two-cell mouse embryos, whereas α element did not, and that core required an enhancer element in *cis* for replication activity. However, it was possible that failure of α core or core to replicate was the result of competition for initiation factors with the wild-type PyV *ori* on the

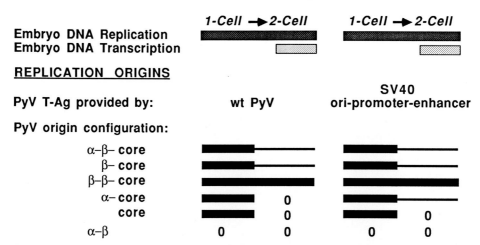

Figure 3 *Cis*-acting sequence requirements for replication of DNA injected into one-cell and two-cell mouse embryos. Lines indicate when a Dpn1 resistant DNA band was observed in the gel (thicker bars represent five- to tenfold increase in the amount of replication). (0) indicates DNA replication not detected. PyV T-ag was provided either by pB1a containing a complete PyV genome cloned into pML-1 (Wirak et al. 1985), or by pSVE containing a complete SV40 control region (72-72-21-21-21-*ori*; Fig. 1) directly upstream of the PyV T-ag gene cloned into pML-1 (courtesy of J. Hassell). The indicated PyV *ori* sequences were cloned into pML-1 as described previously (Wirak et al. 1985). β-β core was taken from PyV host range mutant F101 (Linney and Donerly 1983).

plasmid providing T-ag. Therefore, this experiment was repeated using a plasmid to provide PyV T-ag in which the wild-type PyV *ori*-promoter-enhancer region was replaced by the SV40 *ori*-promoter-enhancer region. Under these conditions, α-β core, β core, and β-β core replicated as before, but α core now initiated replication as well. However, once again, neither enhancers nor core alone replicated (Fig. 3). Therefore, core required association with an enhancer element to initiate replication in developing 2-cell embryos. The α element was simply a weaker enhancer under these conditions than the β element. This hypothesis was confirmed using transient expression assays in which *E. coli* chloramphenicol transacetylase (CAT) gene was driven by a herpes simplex virus (HSV) thymidine kinase promoter. The β element functioned as an enhancer in developing two-cell mouse embryos, whereas the α element did not (DePamphilis et al. 1987).

When similar experiments were repeated in one-cell mouse embryos, we were surprised to find that enhancer elements were no longer required for either DNA replication or gene expression. PyV *ori*-core alone replicated as well as any other configuration of the PyV *ori*, even in the presence of a plasmid bearing the wild-type PyV *ori* (Fig. 3). Two copies of β failed to stimulate DNA replication above that of *ori*-core alone, and neither α nor β contained *ori* activity. Similarly, transient expression assays with CAT vectors confirmed that the HSV tk promoter was also about ten times more active in one-cell embryos, regardless of the presence or absence of enhancers. Therefore, one-cell embryos can recognize sequences as *ori* that are not recognized as *ori* in either developing two-cell mouse embryos or mouse embryonal carcinoma and differentiated cell lines.

The developmental stage of a one-cell mouse embryo is analogous to a *Xenopus* egg prior to midblastula transition, which marks the onset of *Xenopus* gene transcription (Davidson 1986). Therefore, we examined the ability of mouse one-cell embryos to replicate DNA that contained putative cellular *ori*-sequences. Plasmids containing the complete SV40 genome replicated in one-cell embryos as well as they did in two-cell embryos, even though PyV replication was at least five-

to tenfold better in one-cell embryos. However, replication was not detected in plasmids containing a variety of cellular DNA sequences that had been isolated as putative cellular *ori* signals (Table 1). Therefore, one-cell mouse embryos appear to have a high concentration of polyoma-specific permissive cell factor(s).

There are three general conclusions that can be derived from the properties of PyV and SV40 in mouse embryos, embryonic cell lines, and differentiated cells. First, the requirements for DNA replication observed in embryonal carcinoma and differentiated cells are established after the first cleavage event in mouse embryos. In developing two-cell embryos, PyV *ori* requires a functional core-element together with a functional enhancer and T-ag; the enhancer element's cell-specificity determines whether or not it will activate an *ori*-core or a gene promoter (Amati 1985; DePamphilis 1987). Second, DNA replication in one-cell embryos (fertilized eggs) still requires unique *cis*-acting sequences, but enhancer elements are no longer needed for either DNA replication or transcription. Finally, DNA sequences that are not recognized as *ori* in mouse embryonal carcinoma and differentiated cells (e.g., SV40, *ori*, and PyV *ori*-core) can nevertheless function as *ori* sequences at the earliest stages of mammalian embryonic development. This may explain why *Drosophila* embryos initiate replication at many more DNA sites than do *Drosophila* differentiated cells. The concentration of initiation factor(s) appears exceptionally high during that stage of embryonic development that relies on maternally inherited proteins, but so far we have not detected DNA replication with any plasmid lacking a functional SV40 or PyV *ori*-core. These data are consistent with a requirement for as yet unidentified unique *cis*-acting sequences to initiate DNA replication in mammalian chromosomes.

The origin of bidirectional replication and distribution of RNA-primed nascent DNA chains at replication forks

The preceding results demonstrated that, in the presence of PyV T-ag and mouse permissive cell factors, PyV *ori*-core can initiate DNA replication as efficiently alone as when associated with an enhancer element.

Table 1 One-Cell Mouse Embryos Have a High Concentration of PyV-specific "Permissive Cell Factor(s)"

Plasmid	Sequence	Selection	Source	DNA Replication
pJYM	SV40		Lusky and Botchan (1981)	0.3% to 3% of PyV
m4, m8	mouse	ARS in yeast	Roth et al. (1983)	not detected
MARS 1 to 4	mouse	ARS in mouse	Grummt et al. (1987)	not detected
EcoC, EcoF	hamster	amplified DHFR gene	Heintz et al. (1983)	not detected
ors8, ors12	monkey	early S-phase replication	Frappier and Zannis-Hadjopoulos (1987)	not detected

Circular plasmids were injected into nuclei of one-cell or two-cell mouse embryos, and the surviving embryos were cultured in vitro for up to 72 hrs (5 to 7 cell divisions).

This is similar to SV40 DNA replication in differentiated monkey cells where *ori*-core is sufficient for initiation (though less efficient than when associated with either an enhancer or promoter) and particularly to SV40 *ori*-directed DNA replication under some in vitro conditions where core alone is required (Stillman et al. 1985; Li et al. 1986). If PyV *ori*-core contains all information necessary for the T-ag initiation complex to begin replication, one would expect that the origin of bidirectional replication (OBR) is located in the PyV *ori*-core, as it is in SV40 *ori*-core, even under conditions when enhancer elements are an integral part of *ori*, and despite the fact that the strongest T-ag binding sites and mRNA start sites lie outside of *ori* (Fig. 1). Therefore, we mapped the location of the PyV ORB in PyV replicating intermediates isolated from differentiated cells.

The OBR is defined by the transition points from discontinuous to continuous DNA synthesis on each side of a replication bubble (Fig. 4). The template locations of RNA-p-DNA covalent linkages in RNA-primed nascent DNA chains were identified in PyV replicating DNA purified from virus-infected mouse fibroblasts using techniques previously developed on SV40 (Hay and DePamphilis 1982). Nascent DNA chains were radiolabeled uniquely at their RNA-p-DNA junctions by hydrolyzing the RNA in alkali to generate 5′-hydroxyl termini that were then radiolabeled with ^{32}P. 5′ ^{32}P-labeled DNA was annealed to unique PyV single-stranded DNA templates cloned into M13 phage. Hybrid molecules were isolated and then cut at a unique restriction site to release the 5′ ends of chains that had annealed across that sequence. The 5′ ^{32}P-labeled DNA fragments released were fractionated by gel electrophoresis and compared directly with the sequence of nascent DNA in this region to identify the nucleotide in the template complementary to the 5′-terminal nucleotide in the nascent chain.

Analysis of nascent PyV (Hendrickson et al. 1987a,b) and SV40 (Hay et al. 1984) DNA chains that annealed to sequences 1100–1400 bp from *ori* revealed that PyV and SV40 replication forks are essentially the same; DNA synthesis was discontinuous predominantly, if not

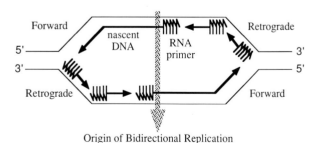

Origin of Bidirectional Replication

Figure 4 The OBR is defined by the transition points from discontinuous to continuous DNA synthesis on each side of a replication bubble. That side of replication forks where the direction of DNA synthesis is opposite to the direction of fork movement is referred to as "retrograde arm" and the other side is referred to as "forward arm."

exclusively, on the retrograde template. About one third of PyV or SV40 nascent DNA chains contained six to nine ribonucleotides covalently linked to their 5′ end, 80% of which began with ATP and 20% with GTP. Greater than 80% of PyV or SV40 RNA-primed DNA chains hybridized specifically to the retrograde template. Moreover, at least 95% of the RNA-primed DNA chains from either PyV or SV40 whose initiation sites could be mapped to unique nucleotide locations originated from the retrograde template. In the case of SV40, 5′ ends of RNA primers were mapped to positions 2–12 bases upstream of clusters of RNA-p-DNA junctions (Hay and DePamphilis 1982; Hay et al. 1984).

A similar analysis was carried out with nascent DNA chains that annealed to the *ori*-region of these viruses to identify the OBR. In both PyV (Fig. 5) and SV40 (Fig. 6), the OBR was located within *ori*-core at its junction with a strong T-ag DNA-binding site. Since the distribution of RNA-p-DNA junctions was always confined to retrograde templates, even within *ori*-core, RNA-primed DNA synthesis initiation events occurred only on one side of *ori*-core, the side that was also the template for early mRNA synthesis. Therefore, assuming that DNA synthesis begins in *ori*-core, it must begin in the same direction as early mRNA synthesis. Furthermore, since the distribution and frequency of RNA-primed DNA synthesis initiation sites and the sizes and composition of RNA primers are the same in the *ori*-region as they are at other genomic locations, the same mechanism used to initiate Okazaki fragments at replication forks appears to initiate DNA synthesis at *ori*.

Comparison of the OBR in PyV with that in SV40 revealed that the transition points on the late (L)mRNA side were identical. These transition points were 1 nucleotide from the first GAGGC element encountered in T-ag DNA-binding site A in PyV (Fig.5) and site I in SV40 (Fig. 6), and 21 nucleotides from the first GAGGC element encountered within either *ori*-core. Since the arrangement of GAGGC elements determines T-ag DNA-binding sites (Ryder et al. 1986; Deb et al. 1987), T-ag binding to the *ori*-region apparently determines the transition point on the L-mRNA template. However, SV40 T-ag binds most tightly to site I, most of which can be deleted with little effect on DNA replication. To determine whether site I is involved in establishing the OBR, RNA-p-DNA junctions were mapped in cs1085 (DiMaio and Nathans 1980), a viable SV40 mutant in which site I is deleted (Fig. 6). Remarkably, both transition points in cs1085 were identical to wild-type SV40 (data not shown). Therefore, the transition point from discontinuous to continuous DNA synthesis on the L-mRNA template is determined by interaction of the T-ag initiation complex with *ori*-core.

The transition points on the early (E) mRNA side of *ori* were located at different positions in the two viral *ori*-cores. The one in SV40 is within 1 bp of its counterpart on the L-mRNA side (Fig. 6), whereas the transition point on the E-mRNA side of PyV *ori* is about 20 nucleotides closer to the A-rich element in *ori*-core than its counterpart on the L-mRNA side is to the T-rich element

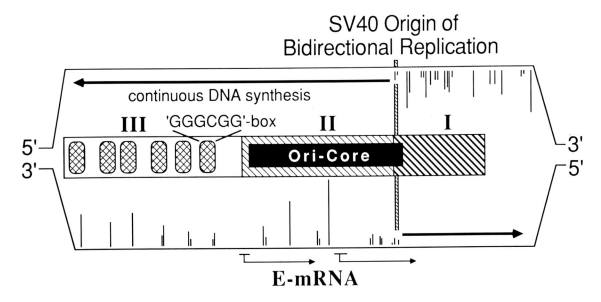

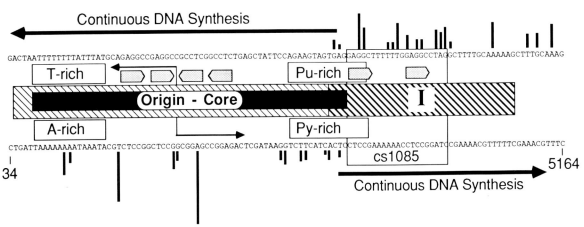

Figure 5 Map of the RNA-p-DNA covalent linkages in the PyV(A3) *ori*-region (Hendrickson et al. 1987). Height of bar is proportional to relative number of linkages found at each template nucleotide. T-ag DNA-binding sites A, B, C, 1, 2, and 3 (darker shading indicates stronger binding) are indicated as well as *ori*-core activation elements α and β. The DNA sequence in the *ori*-core region is shown in the lower panel and GAGGC boxes (pointed shaded boxes), A/T rich sequence, puridine (Pu)/pyrimidine (Py) rich sequence, and major palindromic sequence (◄⅃►) are indicated.

(Fig. 5). This difference suggested that the transition point on the E-mRNA side of *ori* is determined by the interaction of the adjacent transcriptional element with *ori*-core, since these elements are quite different in the two viral genomes ('GGGCGG' boxes in SV40 and the β enhancer in PyV). To test this hypothesis, RNA-p-DNA junctions were mapped in 0X21 (Hartzell et al. 1983), a viable SV40 mutant in which all three 21-bp repeats were deleted (nucleotides 35–177) and a single 72-bp repeat element is contiguous with *ori*-core. The transition point on the L-mRNA side of 0X21 *ori* was identical to wild-type SV40, but the transition point on the E-mRNA side was shifted downstream about 40 bases to

nucleotide 5171. Thus, the L-mRNA side transition point is determined by *ori*-core alone, whereas the E-mRNA side transition point is determined by interaction of a transcriptional element with *ori*-core. The significance of these transition points from discontinuous to continuous DNA synthesis can be explained by the "initiation zone model" for initiation of DNA replication.

The initiation zone model for initiation of DNA replication

All of the available data on both SV40 and PyV DNA replication are consistent with the model proposed by Hay and DePamphilis (1982) for initiation of DNA repli-

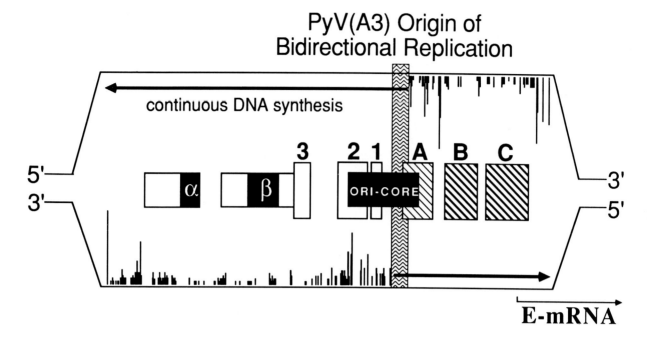

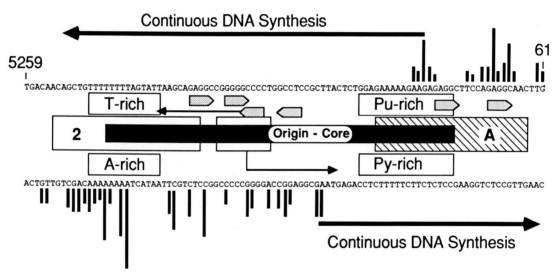

Figure 6 Map of the RNA-p-DNA covalent linkages in the SV40 wt800 *ori*-region (Hay and DePamphilis 1982). Symbols are the same as in Fig. 5, except that T-ag DNA-binding sites are referred to as I, II, and III, and 'GGGCGG' boxes that comprise part of the SV40 promoter are indicated.

cation in SV40 chromosomes (Fig. 7). This model was based on the locations of RNA-primed DNA synthesis initiation events in the *ori*-region and their remarkable similarity to initiation events at replication forks throughout the SV40 genome. The results summarized in this paper reveal that, in both SV40 and PyV, *ori*-core contains all of the *cis*-acting sequence information required for initiating bidirectional, semi-discontinuous DNA replication in the presence of T-ag and permissive cell factors. Transcriptional elements themselves do not function as origins of replication, but only facilitate initia-

tion to an extent that depends on the nature of *ori*-core and the permissive cell.

In the "initiation zone model" (Fig. 7), a T-ag initiation complex binds to *ori*-core and unwinds a region of double-stranded DNA, thus creating a replication bubble (two diverging replication forks). DNA primase–DNA polymerase α then selects one of several possible initiation sites on the single-stranded template encoding early mRNA and initiates synthesis of the first nascent DNA chain. This strand becomes the forward arm of replication forks moving in the same direction as E-mRNA

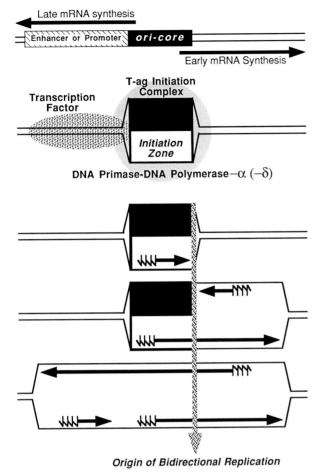

Figure 7 The initiation zone model for initiation of SV40 and PyV DNA replication (Hay and DePamphilis 1982).

synthesis. Thus, the transition from discontinuous to continuous DNA synthesis on the E-mRNA side of *ori* marks one border of the first initiation zone. DNA primase can initiate synthesis as close as 15 nucleotides from this border (5' ends of RNA primers in Hay and DePamphilis 1982), although most initiation events appear to occur further away (relative frequencies of RNA-p-DNA linkages in Figs. 5 and 6). The concept of a stochastic selection by DNA primase–DNA polymerase α of one initiation site among several potential sites is based on the metabolism of Okazaki fragments and the arrangement of nucleosomes at replication forks, and the observation that initiation sites are too frequent for all of them to be used in each replicating DNA molecule and still produce Okazaki fragments with an average size of 135 bases (for review, see DePamphilis and Wassarman 1980, 1982; DePamphilis and Bradley 1986; DePamphilis 1987).

When sufficient single-stranded DNA template is generated by the fork moving in the early gene direction, a second RNA-primed DNA synthesis initiation event will occur on this retrograde template at one of several possible sites *outside ori*-core. This nascent strand then becomes the forward arm of replication forks moving in

the direction of L-mRNA. Thus, the transition from discontinuous to continuous DNA synthesis on the L-mRNA side of *ori* marks one border of the second initiation zone: the place where T-ag initiation complex begins to mask the L-mRNA side of *ori*-core. The absence of RNA-p-DNA linkages on the L-mRNA side of *ori*-core means that binding of T-ag initiation complex to *ori*-core must physically block initiation events on the L-mRNA side and allow them on the E-mRNA side, because the consensus sequences for RNA-primed DNA synthesis initiation sites (purine-dT or purine-dC [Hay et al. 1984]) are present on the L-mRNA template as well as the E-mRNA template, and a large palindromic sequence exists within *ori*-core (Figs. 5 and 6), insuring that some initiation sites on the E-mRNA template are also represented on the L-mRNA template. In SV40, DNA primase–DNA polymerase α initiates synthesis as close as 16 nucleotides from the DNase I footprint border of T-ag DNA-binding site II (nucleotide 5213, Deb et al. 1987). As replication forks move in the direction of L-mRNA synthesis, a third initiation zone is created on the retrograde arm and an Okazaki fragment is again initiated at one of several possible sites. This process continues, resulting in bidirectional replication from the OBR.

Several other observations also support the initiation zone model. SV40 T-ag has helicase activity that can initiate unwinding of circular DNA molecules specifically at SV40 *ori* (Stahl et al. 1986; Dean et al. 1987; and articles by Stahl et al.; Kelly and Hurwitz, this volume). This activity depends on interaction with the same sequences in *ori*-core that are required for DNA replication (Tegtmeyer et al. this volume). The prediction that DNA replication begins in the direction of E-mRNA synthesis is consistent with the observations that the first fully synthesized SV40 DNA sequences include *ori* and the region about 300 bases on its early gene side (Decker et al. 1986), and that RNA-primed nascent DNA chains are synthesized preferentially on the E-mRNA template side of *ori* during initiation of SV40 DNA replication in vitro (Taljanidisz et al. 1987). In addition, a fraction of PyV DNA replicates unidirectionally in vivo, and these forks move in the same direction as E-mRNA synthesis (Buckler-White et al. 1982).

Because the initiation factor binding site in SV40 (Yamaguchi and DePamphilis 1986; DePamphilis et al. 1987) includes the early gene promoter, TATA box, and for E-mRNA start sites (Fig. 1), it is tempting to suggest that initiation may be activated by transcription through *ori*. However, DNA replication in SV40 chromosomes or SV40 *ori*-driven plasmid DNA is completely resistant to α-amanitin (Decker et al. 1987), and no mRNA initiation sites are directed through the PyV *ori*-core (Fig. 1). Nevertheless, binding of proteins to transcriptional promoter or enhancer elements (e.g., Sp1 binding to 'GGGCGG' boxes), may facilitate activation of *ori* by stabilizing binding of T-ag initiation complex to *ori*-core, and/or by unmasking the *ori*-core sequence in viral chromatin to allow binding of T-ag initiation complex. For example, the SV40 initiation factor binding site overlaps

T-Ag binding site 2 (Fig. 1), suggesting that the permissive cell factor that binds to the initiation factor site may facilitate binding of T-Ag to site 2. Association of DNA primase–DNA polymerase α with T-ag-initiation complex (Smale and Tjian 1986) could position this enzyme to initiate RNA-primed DNA synthesis in *ori*-core. The fact that binding of T-ag to PyV *ori*-core is significantly weaker than binding to SV40 *ori*-core could account for the fact that transcriptional elements play a much greater role in activating PyV *ori*-core than SV40 *ori*-core.

Initiation of DNA replication in cellular chromosomes

In keeping with the principles of DNA replication in other systems, mammalian chromosomes likely utilize *ori* sequences to regulate their replication. By analogy to SV40, a cellular helicase could substitute for viral T-ag in melting cellular *ori*-core elements to allow DNA primase–DNA polymerase α to initiate DNA synthesis. Cellular *ori* activity is likely regulated by transcriptional elements, which could account for the observation that active genes are replicated early during S-phase (see Hatton et al., this volume). Normally, enhancer-dependent *ori*-core elements will initiate replication only when cells express the enhancer-specific protein. Therefore, one-cell mouse embryos (and presumably pre-midblastula transition cells in *Xenopus* and *Drosophila* embryos) would initiate replication in all *ori*-core elements because enhancer elements are not needed in these cells for either DNA transcription or replication.

In addition to *ori* sequences, cellular DNA may also require attachment to nuclear envelope sites, as suggested by the requirement for nuclear organization of DNA prior to its replication in *Xenopus* eggs (Blow and Laskey 1986; Newport 1987). This could allow introduction of negative superhelical turns that are required for initiation of SV40 DNA replication in vitro (DePamphilis 1987). Thus, DNA injected into mouse nuclei that do not contain a viral *ori* would not replicate because nuclear membrane attachment sites are already occupied by cellular DNA. Viruses provide a mechanism to circumvent this requirement. We are currently attempting to test this hypothesis by injecting DNA into the germinal vesicle of mouse oocytes in order to convert the foreign DNA into maternal chromatin, and then allow the injected oocytes to undergo meiotic maturation in vitro to become eggs, fertilize the eggs in vitro (or treat them with chemicals to induce parthenogenesis) to initiate nuclear assembly, and then observe whether or not alien chromatin will replicate along with mouse chromatin. The simpler route of injecting DNA into unfertilized mouse eggs is not available because injected DNA is rapidly degraded.

References

Amati, P. 1985. Polyoma regulatory region: A potential probe for mouse cell differentiation. *Cell* **43**: 561.

Blow, J.J. and R.A. Laskey. 1986. Initiation of DNA replication in nuclei and purified DNA by a cell-free extract of *Xenopus* eggs. *Cell* **47**: 577.

Blumenthal, A.B., H.J. Kriegstein, and D.S. Hogness. 1974. The units of DNA replication in *Drosophila melanogaster* chromosomes. *Cold Spring Harbor Symp. Quant. Biol.* **38**: 205.

Buckler-White, A.J., M.R. Krauss, V. Pigiet, and R.M. Benbow. 1982. Asynchronous bidirectional replication of polyoma virus DNA. *J. Virol.* **43**: 885.

Chalifour, L.E., D.O. Wirak, P.M. Wasserman, and M.L. DePamphilis. 1986. Expression of simian virus 40 early and late genes in mouse oocytes and embryos. *J. Virol.* **59**: 619.

Chalifour, L.E., D.O. Wirak, U. Hansen, P.M. Wassarman, and M.L. DePamphilis. 1987. *Cis*- and *trans*-acting sequences required for expression of simian virus 40 genes in mouse oocytes. *Genes Dev.* **1** (10): 1096.

Cowie, A. and R. Kamen. 1986. Guanine nucleotide contacts within viral DNA sequences bound by polyomavirus large T antigen. *J. Virol.* **57**: 505.

Davidson, E.H., 1986. *Gene activity in early development.* Academic Press, New York.

Dean, F.B., P. Bullock, Y. Murakami, C.R. Wobbe, L. Weissbach, and J. Hurwitz. 1987. Simian virus 40 (SV40) DNA replication: SV40 large T antigen unwinds DNA containing the SV40 origin of replication. *Proc. Natl. Acad. Sci.* **84**: 16.

Deb, S., A.L. DeLucia, C.-P. Baur, A. Koff, and P. Tegtmeyer. 1986. Domain structure of the simian virus 40 core origin of replication. *Mol. Cell. Biol.* **6**: 1663.

Deb, S., S. Tsui, A. Koff, A.L. DeLucia, R. Parsons, and P. Tegtmeyer. 1987. The T-antigen binding domain of the simian virus 40 core origin of replication. *J. Virol.* **61**: 7.

Decker, R.S., M. Yamaguchi, R. Possenti, and M.L. DePamphilis. 1986. Initiation of simian virus 40 DNA replication *in vitro*: Aphidicolin causes accumulation of early-replicating intermediates and allows determination of the initial direction of DNA synthesis. *Mol. Cell. Biol.* **6**: 3815.

Decker, R.S., M. Yamaguchi, R. Possenti, M. Bradley, and M.L. DePamphilis. 1987. In vitro initiation of DNA replication in simian virus 40 chromosomes. *J. Biol. Chem.* **262**: 10863.

DeLucia, A.L., S. Deb, K. Partin, and P. Tegtmeyer. 1986. Functional interactions of the simian virus 40 core origin of replication with flanking regulatory sequences. *J. Virol.* **57**: 138.

DePamphilis, M.L. 1987. Replication of simian virus 40 and polyoma virus chromosomes. In *Molecular aspects of the papovaviruses* (ed. Y. Aloni). Martinus Nijhoff, The Netherlands. (In press.)

DePamphilis, M.L. and M.K. Bradley. 1986. Replication of SV40 and polyoma virus chromosomes. In *The papoviridae* (ed. N.P. Salzman), vol. 1, p. 99. Plenum Press, New York.

DePamphilis, M.L. and P.M. Wassarman. 1980. Replication of eukaryotic chromosomes: A close-up of the replication fork. *Annu. Rev. Biochem.* **49**: 627.

———. 1982. Organization and replication of papovavirus DNA. In *Organization and replication of viral DNA* (ed. A.S. Kaplan), p. 37. CRC Press, Boca Raton, Florida.

DePamphilis, M.L., R.S. Decker, M. Yamaguchi, R. Possenti, D.O. Wirak, R. Perona, and J.A. Hassell. 1987. Transcriptional elements and their role in activation of simian virus 40 and polyoma virus origins of replication. *UCLA Symp. Mol. Cell. Biol. New Ser.* **47**: 367.

Dilworth, S.M., A. Cowie, R.I. Kamen, and B.E. Griffin. 1984. DNA binding activity of polyoma virus large tumor antigen. *Proc. Natl. Acad. Sci.* **81**: 1941.

DiMaio, D. and D. Nathans. 1980. Cold-sensitive regulatory mutants of simian virus 40. *J. Mol. Biol.* **140**: 120.

Frappier, L. and M. Zannis-Hadjopoulos. 1987. Autonomous replication of plasmids bearing monkey DNA origin-enriched sequences (ors). *Proc. Natl. Acad. Sci.* **84**: (in press).

Gerard, R.D., R.A. Guggenheimer, and Y. Gluzman. 1987. Analysis of nonpermissivity in mouse cells overexpressing simian virus 40 T-antigen. *J. Virol.* **61**: 851.

Gottlieb, P., M.S. Nasoff, E.F. Fisher, A.M. Walsh, and M.H. Caruthers. 1985. Binding studies of SV40 T-antigen to SV40 binding site II. *Nucleic Acids Res.* **13**: 6621.

Grummt, F., A. Holst, F. Muller, H. Luksza, W. Siwka, G. Zastrow, and E. Helftenbein. 1987. Eukaryotic genomic DNA sequences replicating autonomously in mouse L cells. *UCLA Symp. Mol. Cell. Biol. New Ser.* **46:** 381.

Heintz, N.H., J.D. Milbrandt, K.S. Greisen, and J.L. Hamlin. 1983. Cloning of the initiation region of a mammalian chromosomal replicon. *Nature* **302:** 439.

Hartzell, S.W., J. Yamaguchi, and K.N. Subramanian. 1983. SV40 deletion mutants lacking the 21-bp repeated sequences are viable, but have noncomplementable deficiencies. *Nucleic Acids Res.* **11:** 1601.

Hassell, J.A., W.J. Muller, and C.R. Mueller. 1986. The dual role of the polyomavirus enhancer in transcription and DNA replication. *Cancer Cells* **4:** 561.

Hay, R.T. and M.L. DePamphilis. 1982. Initiation of simian virus 40 DNA replication *in vivo*: Location and structure of 5′-ends of DNA synthesized in the origin region. *Cell* **28:** 767.

Hay, R.T., E.A. Hendrickson, and M.L. DePamphilis. 1984. Sequence specificity for the initiation of RNA primed-SV40 DNA synthesis *in vivo. J. Mol. Biol.* **175:** 131.

Hendrickson, E.A., C.E. Fritze, W.R. Folk, and M.L. De-Pamphilis. 1987a. The origin of bidirectional DNA replication in polyoma virus. *EMBO J.* **6:** 2011.

———. 1987b. Polyoma virus DNA replication is semi-discontinuous. *Nucleic Acids Res.* **15:** 6393.

Herbomel, P., B. Bourachot, and M. Yaniv. 1984. Two distinct enhancers with different cell specificities coexist in the regulatory region of polyoma. *Cell* **39:** 653.

Hertz, G.Z. and J. Mertz. 1986. Bidirectional promoter elements of simian virus 40 are required for efficient replication of the viral DNA. *Mol. Cell. Biol.* **6:** 3513.

Lee-Chen, G.-J. and M. Woodworth-Gutai. 1986. Simian virus 40 DNA replication: Functional organization of regulatory elements. *Mol. Cell. Biol.* **6:** 3086.

Li, J.J., K.W.C. Peden, R.A.F. Dixon, and T. Kelly. 1986. Functional organization of the simian virus 40 origin of DNA replication. *Mol. Cell. Biol.* **6:** 1117.

Linney, E. and S. Donerly. 1983. DNA fragments from F9 PyEC mutants increase expression of heterologous genes in transfected F9 cells. *Cell* **35:** 693.

Lusky, M. and M. Botchan. 1981. Inhibition of SV40 replication in simian cells by specific pBR322 DNA sequences. *Nature* **293:** 79.

Méchali, M. and S. Kearsey. 1984. Lack of specific sequence requirement for DNA replication in *Xenopus* eggs compared with high sequence specificity in yeast. *Cell* **38:** 55.

Melin, F., C. Pinon, C. Reiss, C. Kress, N. Montreau, and D. Blangy. 1985. Common features of polyomavirus mutants selected on PCC4 embryonal carcinoma cells. *EMBO J.* **4:** 1799.

Mueller, C.R., A.M. Mes-Masson, M. Bouvier, and J.A. Hassell. 1984. Location of sequences in polyomavirus DNA that are required for early gene expression *in vivo* and *in vitro. Mol. Cell. Biol.* **4:** 2594.

Newport, J. 1987. Nuclear reconstitution *in vitro*: Stages of assembly around protein-free DNA. *Cell* **48:** 205.

Roth, G.E., H.M. Blanton, L.J. Hager, and V.A. Zakian. 1983. Isolation and characterization of sequences from mouse chromosomal DNA with *ARS* function in yeasts. *Mol. Cell. Biol.* **3:** 1898.

Ryder, K., S. Silver, A.L. DeLucia, E. Fanning, and P. Tegtmeyer. 1986. An altered DNA conformation in origin region I is a determinant for the binding of SV40 large T-antigen. *Cell* **44:** 719.

Smale, S.T. and R. Tjian. 1986. T-antigen-DNA polymerase α complex implicated in simian virus 40 DNA replication. *Mol. Cell. Biol.* **6:** 4077.

Stahl, H., P. Droge, and R. Knippers. 1986. DNA helicase activity of SV40 large tumor antigen. *EMBO J.* **5:** 1939.

Stillman, B., R.D. Gerard, R.A. Guggenheimer, and Y. Gluzman. 1985. T antigen and template requirements for SV40 DNA replication *in vitro. EMBO J.* **4:** 2933.

Taljanidisz, J., R.S. Decker, Z.S. Guo, M.L. DePamphilis, and N. Sarkar. 1987. Initiation of simian virus 40 DNA replication *in vitro*: Identification of RNA-primed nascent DNA chains. *Nucleic Acids Res.* **15:** 7877.

Veldman, G.M., S. Lupton, and R. Kamen. 1985. Polyomavirus enhancer contains multiple redundant sequence elements that activate both DNA replication and gene expression. *Mol. Cell. Biol.* **5:** 649.

Wirak, D.O., L.E. Chalifour, P.M. Wassarman, W.J. Muller, J.A. Hassell, and M.L. DePamphilis. 1985. Sequence-dependent DNA replication in preimplantation mouse embryos. *Mol. Cell. Biol.* **5:** 2924.

Yamaguchi, M. and M.L. DePamphilis. 1986. DNA binding site for a factor(s) required to initiate simian virus 40 DNA replication. *Proc. Natl. Acad. Sci.* **83:** 1646.

Sequence-specific Binding of a Cellular Protein Associated with DNA Polymerase α to the SV40 Core Origin of DNA Replication

E. Fanning, W. Traut, I. Dornreiter, S. Dehde, P. Alliger, and B. Posch

Institute for Biochemistry, 8000 Munich 2, Federal Republic of Germany

A monkey cell factor (MCF) that interacts sequence-specifically with double-stranded DNA sequences in the simian virus 40 (SV40) core origin of DNA replication was identified using gel retention assays. The factor is abundant in primate cell extracts but not in rodent cell extracts. Binding activity of the protein on mutant templates is correlated with the replication activity of the origin. MCF also binds to single-stranded DNA. Larger DNA-protein complexes, containing other proteins in addition to MCF, were also detected. One of these proteins appears to be related to DNA polymerase α. The results suggest that MCF may be involved in SV40 replication.

Initiation of SV40 DNA replication is controlled primarily by three elements: a *cis*-acting SV40 DNA sequence that serves as the origin of replication, the multifunctional SV40 regulatory protein T antigen, and one or more protein factors from monkey or human cells permissive for SV40 DNA replication (for review, see DePamphilis and Bradley 1986).

The 64-bp minimal core origin of DNA replication has been defined by detailed mutational analysis in several laboratories (for review, see DePamphilis and Bradley 1986) (Fig. 1A). The replication activity of the origin is enhanced by auxiliary sequences adjacent to the core origin: large-T-antigen-binding site I on the early side, and the Sp1-binding sites (Dynan and Tjian 1983) on the late side.

The core origin itself is composed of several domains identified by mutational analysis. A 10-bp DNA sequence in the early palindrome is conserved among closely related primate papovaviruses and is specifically required for origin activity (Deb et al. 1986a). This element is separated from T-antigen-binding site II by a spacer region that overlaps the early palindrome (Fig. 1A). On the late side of the origin, a second domain composed of AT-rich sequences is specifically required, either as a protein-binding site (Yamaguchi and DePamphilis 1986; Lee et al. 1987) or as a determinant of altered DNA conformation (Deb et al. 1986b). T antigen binding to site II is essential for SV40 replication in vivo and in vitro (for review, see DePamphilis and Bradley 1986). T antigen mediates DNA unwinding at the origin (Stahl et al. 1986; Dean et al. 1987; Wold et al. 1987) and may help to direct DNA polymerase α−primase to the SV40 origin (Smale and Tjian 1986).

The function of the conserved sequence in the early palindrome in replication is not known. The conserved nature of this element and its sensitivity to mutation suggested that it could represent the binding site for a cellular protein. The present study was undertaken to address this question.

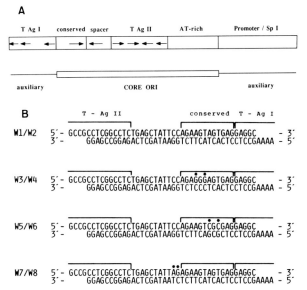

Figure 1 Schematic diagram of the SV40 origin of DNA replication. (*A*) Binding sites for T antigen (arrows show the orientation of the GAGGC binding signals) and the transcription factor Sp1 are indicated. The palindrome between T-antigen-binding sites I and II is indicated by arrows. Part of the palindrome sequence is conserved among primate papovaviruses and is essential for origin function, and part of it serves merely as a spacer (Deb et al. 1986a). (*B*) Template oligonucleotides used for protein-binding studies. Mutations are indicated by asterisks.

Experimental Procedures

Nuclear extracts

Nuclear extracts were made from subconfluent cultures of TC7 monkey cells (Robb and Huebner 1973) essentially as described (Dignam et al. 1983), except that buffer C contained 0.35 M rather than 0.43 M NaCl. Similar extracts were prepared from other primate and rodent cell lines (W. Traut and E. Fanning, in prep.). All

CANCER CELLS 6 / Eukaryotic DNA Replication. © 1988 by Cold Spring Harbor Laboratory 0-87969-308-8/88 $1.00

buffers contained 1 mM phenylmethylsulfonyl fluoride (PMSF) and 10 mM $Na_2S_2O_4$ as protease inhibitors. Extracts were stored in aliquots at $-70°C$.

Monoclonal antibodies

IgG was purified from hybridoma culture supernatants using a MAPS II kit (BioRad, Munich). PAb 419 (Harlow et al. 1981) recognizes the amino terminus of SV40 T antigen and SJK 132-20 (Wong et al. 1986) is directed against the catalytic subunit of DNA polymerase α. It does not cross-react with polymerase δ (Byrnes 1985).

Oligonucleotides

Chemically synthesized oligonucleotides (Fig. 1B) were purified by polyacrylamide gel electrophoresis and either 5′ end-labeled with T4 polynucleotide kinase, followed by reannealing, if desired, or first reannealed and labeled with Klenow polymerase and either [α-^{32}P]dCTP or dTTP or both (Amersham, Braunschweig) (3000 Ci/mmol), together with unlabeled dNTPs to ensure that the recessed ends were filled in (Maniatis et al. 1982). Labeled oligonucleotides were purified by gel filtration.

Gel retention assays

Binding reactions contained 500 ng of poly(dA · dT)-poly(dA · dT) (Pharmacia-PL), 10 fmol of labeled oligonucleotides in 50 mM HEPES-KOH (pH 7.5), 150 mM NaCl, 1 mM EDTA, 5 mM dithiothreitol, 10% glycerol, and 6 µg of nuclear protein adjusted to 150 mM NaCl in a volume of 30 µl. After 15 minutes at 25°C, the reaction products were analyzed by nondenaturing polyacrylamide gel electrophoresis as described (Schneider et al. 1986).

Results

Interactions between monkey cell proteins and the SV40 core origin of DNA replication

A panel of oligonucleotides spanning the conserved sequence between T-antigen-binding sites I and II was synthesized to assay for specific binding of cellular proteins (Fig. 1B). One pair of oligonucleotides, W1/2, contained the wild-type sequence; two pairs, W3/4 and W5/6, carried mutations in the conserved sequence; and one pair, W7/8, carried mutations outside the conserved region. The same mutations were introduced into the intact origin of SV40 DNA replication by oligonucleotide-directed mutagenesis and replication of the plasmids was tested after transfection into COS-1 monkey cells (Gluzman 1981). In agreement with the results of Deb et al. (1986a), the wild-type plasmid DNA and the plasmid carrying the W7/8 mutations replicated well, whereas the mutant origins carrying the W3/4 and W5/6 lesions were defective (W. Traut and E. Fanning, in prep.).

Incubation of TC7 monkey cell extracts with the labeled double-stranded wild-type template W1/2 and analysis in gel retention assays resulted in three major protein-DNA complexes of different mobility and abundance (Fig. 2A, lane 0). A similar pattern of protein-DNA

complexes was observed with Klenow polymerase-labeled W1/2 template (Fig. 2,B and C) and an origin DNA restriction fragment (not shown). A fourth complex of mobility slower than band *a* was observed in some experiments (not shown). A complex migrating faster than band *c*, but slower than the free oligonucleotide in band *d* (Fig. 2A) is likely to be a proteolytic degradation product, since it could be generated by limited treatment of the cell extract with proteinase K or trypsin (not shown).

The sequence specificity of the protein-DNA interactions was tested by competition with increasing amounts of unlabeled wild-type and mutant oligonucleotides (Fig. 2A). Binding of cellular protein to the labeled template will be reduced if the competing unlabeled oligonucleotide bears a specific binding site for the protein. Protein-DNA complexes *b* and *c* were competed by the wild-type template W1/2 and by the replication-competent mutant W7/8. The replication-defective mutants W3/4 and W5/6 did not compete effectively for binding to the monkey proteins that formed band *c*, although some competition was detectable in band *b*. These results suggest that the conserved sequence in the early palindrome of SV40 origin DNA represents part or all of a specific binding site for at least one monkey cell protein.

Interactions of SV40 origin DNA with cellular proteins from cell lines of various species

Extracts prepared from several primate and rodent cell lines were assayed for specific binding to the wild-type template W1/2. The DNA was labeled with Klenow polymerase to ensure that the labeled template was completely double-stranded. The protein-DNA complexes formed with extracts of the human epithelioid lines 293 and HeLa, as well as the human fibroblast line MRC-5 (not shown), closely resembled those formed with monkey cell extracts (Fig. 2B). The complexes formed with extracts of hamster BHK, rat 2, and mouse 3T3 fibroblasts, in contrast, differed from the primate pattern in mobility (band *c'* vs. *c* in primates) and in abundance. No protein-DNA complexes were detected with extracts of pig liver or *Xenopus* oocytes (not shown). Thus, in general, primate cell proteins that bind specifically to the SV40 origin of replication appear to differ both qualitatively and quantitatively from related proteins in rodent cell extracts.

Protein interactions with single-stranded SV40 origin DNA

Gel retention assays carried out with monkey cell proteins and single-stranded end-labeled oligonucleotides W1–W8 revealed a pattern of protein-DNA complexes remarkably similar to that observed with double-stranded template (W. Traut and E. Fanning, in prep.). This result suggested that the single-stranded binding activity might be related to the double-strand activity. To test this possibility, competition binding assays were performed using Klenow-labeled wild-type double-stranded template and increasing amounts of unlabeled single-stranded competitor DNA (Fig. 2C). The results demon-

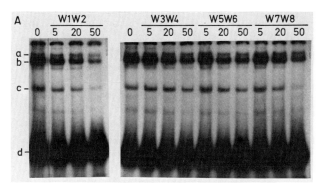

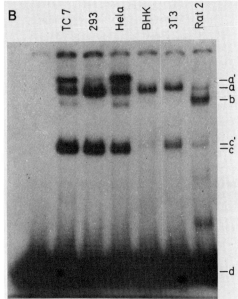

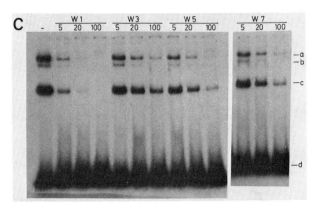

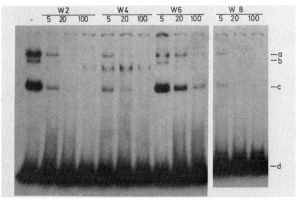

strate that all of the single-stranded oligonucleotides competed for protein binding to the double-stranded DNA, although with different efficiencies. The even-numbered oligonucleotides competed more effectively than the odd-numbered ones, possibly suggesting a preference for certain single-stranded sequences. We conclude that the double-stranded origin-binding proteins from monkey cells also bind to single-stranded DNA.

Alteration of protein-DNA complex migration by monoclonal antibody

The sequence-specific binding of monkey cell factors to SV40 origin DNA, the correlation of binding affinity with the replication activity of the origin, and the strong binding activity of replication-competent primate extracts compared to the weak activity of rodent extracts suggested that the monkey cell factor may be involved in SV40 DNA replication. One cellular protein long thought to participate in SV40 replication is DNA polymerase α (Edenberg et al. 1978; Otto and Fanning 1978; De-Pamphilis and Bradley 1986). Indeed, DNA polymerase α–primase is reported to be closely associated with the primate cell-specific factor(s) required for SV40 replication in vitro (Murakami et al. 1986).

For these reasons, we wished to test whether DNA polymerase α could be associated with the protein-origin DNA complexes detected by gel retention (Fig. 2). We reasoned that if specific monoclonal antibody against the catalytic subunit of polymerase α were added to monkey cell extract, it would bind to the enzyme complex, thus increasing its molecular weight. A gel retention assay carried out with the antibody-bound polymerase should then reveal a slower migrating DNA-protein complex if polymerase α were associated with origin DNA-protein complexes. The results demonstrate clearly that migration of band *b* was delayed in the presence of anti-polymerase but not in the presence of a control antibody against SV40 T antigen (Fig. 3, lanes 3 and 5). Furthermore, in the presence of antibody, a new double band migrating more slowly than band *a* appeared (lane 3). A delay in migration of band *b* was also observed with double-stranded template (lane 9). Band *c* was not affected. These results indicate that the protein component of band *b* probably includes DNA polymerase α.

Figure 2 Sequence-specific binding of cellular proteins to double- and single-stranded SV40 origin DNA. (*A*) Binding of TC7 proteins to the labeled double-stranded wild-type template W1W2 was tested in the absence (lane *0*) and presence of a 5-, 20-, or 50-fold excess of unlabeled competitor oligonucleotide as indicated. (*B*) Binding of Klenow-labeled W1/2 to 6 μg of protein extract from various cell lines as indicated. The left lane contained oligonucleotide but not extract. (*C*) Binding of monkey cell proteins to Klenow-labeled double-stranded wild-type template in the absence (−) or presence of a 10-, 20-, or 100-fold excess of unlabeld single-stranded oligonucleotides as indicated.

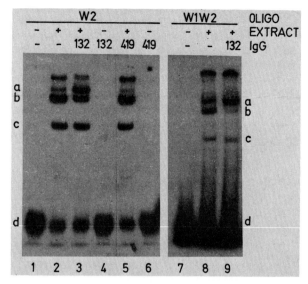

Figure 3 Gel retention assay of protein-origin DNA complexes in the presence of anti-polymerase-α antibody. Purified monoclonal antibody (0.8 μg) specific for DNA polymerase α (SJK 132-20) or SV40 T antigen (PAb 419) or buffer (−) was incubated with TC7 extract for 30 minutes prior to addition of W2 or Klenow-labeled W1/2 as indicated.

Discussion

We have used an electrophoretic assay to identify proteins from permissive monkey cells that bind to the SV40 core origin of DNA replication. Competition of unlabeled mutant oligonucleotides with the labeled wild-type template indicated that at least one cellular protein binds specifically to a conserved sequence in the early domain of the origin. Competition with single-stranded oligonucleotides from the origin region demonstrated that the double-strand origin-binding activity also binds to single-stranded DNA. Curiously, protein binding and competition were most effective with the even-numbered oligonucleotides, which represent the template strand for continuous DNA synthesis in the early direction (DePamphilis and Bradley 1986). However, other single-stranded oligonucleotides from the adenovirus origin of replication and SV40 coding sequences also competed (W. Traut and E. Fanning, unpubl.), implying that the single-strand binding activity is not strictly sequence specific. Nevertheless, several oligonucleotides failed to compete (W3, W5, W7, sequences from the human c-*myc* promoter), suggesting a puzzling preference for certain types of single-stranded sequence.

SV40 origin DNA-protein complexes of slower mobility were also detected. These larger complexes could represent oligomers of the band *c* monkey cell factor. Alternatively, they could arise through binding of a different protein to the same sequences, or they may represent complexes of MCF with heterologous proteins. The proteins that form the larger complexes can be separated by ion exchange chromatography from the band *c* factor (P. Alliger et al., unpubl.), favoring the latter two possibilities. Gel retention assays performed in the presence of monoclonal antibody to DNA polymerase α

suggest that this protein may be a component of band *b* (Fig. 3). Since further fractionation of the band *b* proteins can generate band *c* (P. Alliger et al., unpubl.), it seems likely that band *b* includes at least two different proteins: polymerase α and MCF.

Several observations suggest that MCF may be involved in SV40 DNA replication. Binding of the monkey protein to mutant templates is correlated with the replication activity of the corresponding origin DNA. Abundant protein-DNA complexes of similar mobility were detected with extracts of primate cells that support SV40 replication in vitro (Li and Kelly 1985; Stillman et al. 1985; Murakami et al. 1986), whereas nonpermissive cell extracts formed complexes of different mobility and lower abundance, or failed to form complexes with origin template. Cytoplasmic extracts prepared from monkey cells for in vitro replication assays (Li and Kelly 1984) contained the same origin-binding activity as the nuclear extracts (W. Traut and E. Fanning, unpubl.). Finally, DNA polymerase α, thought to play a role in SV40 replication, appears to be associated with MCF. Purification of the monkey cell factor and in vitro SV40 replication assays will be required to test this prediction.

Acknowledgments

We thank Karin Thalmeier and Ernst Winnacker for helpful discussions, Dorit Weigand and Ronald Mertz for oligonucleotide synthesis, Uli Hübscher, Pia Thömmes, and Ed Harlow for hybridomas, and Maria Ihmsen for preparation of the manuscript. The financial support of the Deutsche Forschungsgemeinschaft (Fa-138/3-1 and 138/2-1), Bundesministerium für Forschung und Technologie, and Fonds der Chemischen Industrie is gratefully acknowledged.

References

Byrnes, J.J. 1985. Differential inhibitors of DNA polymerase alpha and delta. *Biochem. Biophys. Res. Commun.* **132:** 628.

Dean, F., P. Bullock, Y. Murakami, C.R. Wobbe, L. Weissbach, and J. Hurwitz. 1987. Simian virus 40 (SV40) DNA replication: SV40 large T antigen unwinds DNA containing the SV40 origin of replication. *Proc. Natl. Acad. Sci.* **84:** 16.

Deb, S., A.L. DeLucia, C.-P. Baur, A. Koff, and P. Tegtmeyer. 1986a. Domain structure of the simian virus 40 core origin of replication. *Mol. Cell Biol.* **6:** 1663.

Deb, S., A.L. DeLucia, A. Koff, S. Tsui, and P. Tegtmeyer. 1986b. The adenine-thymine domain of the simian virus 40 core origin directs DNA binding and coordinately regulates DNA replication. *Mol. Cell Biol.* **6:** 4578.

DePamphilis, M.L. and M.K. Bradley. 1986. Replication of SV40 and polyoma virus chromosomes. In *The papovaviridae* (ed. N.P. Salzman), vol. 1, p. 99. Plenum Press, New York.

Dignam, J., R. Lebowitz, and R. Roeder. 1983. Accurate transcription initiation by RNA polymerase II in a soluble extract from isolated mammalian nuclei. *Nucleic Acids Res.* **11:** 1475.

Dynan, W.S. and R. Tjian. 1983. The promoter-specific transcription factor Sp1 binds to upstream sequences in the SV40 early promoter. *Cell* **35:** 79.

Edenberg, H., S. Anderson, and M.L. DePamphilis. 1978. Involvement of DNA polymerase alpha in simian virus 40 DNA replication. *J. Biol. Chem.* **253:** 3273.

Gluzman, Y. 1981. SV40-transformed simian cells support the replication of early SV40 mutants. *Cell* **23:** 175.

Harlow, E., L.V. Crawford, D.C. Pim, and N.M. Williamson. 1981. Monoclonal antibodies specific for simian virus 40 tumor antigens. *J. Virol.* **39:** 861.

Lee, W., P. Mitchell, and R. Tjian. 1987. Purified transcription factor AP-1 interacts with TPA-inducible enhancer elements. *Cell* **49:** 741.

Li, J.J. and T. Kelly. 1984. Simian virus 40 DNA replication in vitro. *Proc. Natl. Acad. Sci.* **81:** 6973.

―――. 1985. Simian virus 40 DNA replication in vitro: Specificity of initiation and evidence for bidirectional replication. *Mol. Cell. Biol.* **5:** 1238.

Maniatis, T., E.F. Fritsch, and J. Sambrook. 1982. *Molecular cloning: A laboratory manual.* Cold Spring Harbor Laboratory, Cold Spring Harbor, New York.

Murakami, Y., C.R. Wobbe, L. Weissbach, F.B. Dean, and J. Hurwitz. 1986. Role of DNA polymerase and DNA primase in simian virus 40 DNA replication in vitro. *Proc. Natl. Acad. Sci.* **83:** 2869.

Otto, B. and E. Fanning. 1978. DNA polymerase alpha is associated with replicating SV40 nucleoprotein complexes. *Nucleic Acids Res.* **5:** 1715.

Robb, J. and K. Huebner. 1973. Effect of cell chromosome number on simian virus 40 replication. *Exp. Cell. Res.* **81:** 120.

Schneider, R., I. Gander, U. Müller, R. Mertz, and E.-L. Winnacker. 1986. A sensitive and rapid gel retention assay for nuclear factor I and other DNA-binding proteins in crude nuclear extracts. *Nucleic Acids Res.* **14:** 1303.

Smale, S. and R. Tjian. 1986. T-antigen-DNA polymerase alpha complex implicated in simian virus 40 DNA replication. *Mol. Cell. Biol.* **6:** 4077.

Stahl, H., P. Dröge, and R. Knippers. 1986. DNA helicase activity of SV40 large tumor antigen. *EMBO J.* **5:** 1939.

Stillman, B., R. Gerard, R. Guggenheimer, and Y. Gluzman. 1985. T antigen and template requirements for SV40 DNA replication in vitro. *EMBO J.* **4:** 2933.

Wold, M.S., J.J. Li, and T.J. Kelly. 1987. Initiation of simian virus 40 DNA replication in vitro: Large-tumor-antigen- and origin-dependent unwinding of the template. *Proc. Natl. Acad. Sci.* **84:** 3643.

Wong, S., L.R. Paborsky, P.A. Fisher, T.S.-F. Wang, and D. Korn. 1986. Structural and enzymological characterization of immunoaffinity-purified DNA polymerase alpha-DNA primase complex from KB cells. *J. Biol. Chem.* **261:** 7958.

Yamaguchi, M. and M.L. DePamphilis. 1986. DNA binding site for a factor(s) required to initiate simian virus 40 DNA replication. *Proc. Natl. Acad. Sci.* **83:** 1646.

Carcinogen-induced Factors Responsible for SV40 DNA Replication and Amplification in Chinese Hamster Cells

Y. Berko-Flint, S. Karby, and S. Lavi

Department of Microbiology, The George S. Wise Faculty of Life Sciences,
Tel Aviv University, Ramat Aviv 69978, Israel

Exposure to environmental agents leads to the amplification of SV40 DNA sequences in virally transformed Chinese hamster cells and to enhanced viral replication in infected Chinese hamster cells. Elevated levels of T antigen were demonstrated in the carcinogen-treated cells resulting from enhanced transcription. The studies presented in this manuscript demonstrate that in addition to T antigen, cellular factors activated following DNA perturbations are responsible for the enhanced viral replication. In Chinese hamster embryo (CHE) cells treated with *N*-methyl-*N'*-nitro-*N*-nitrosoguanidine (MNNG) several days before viral infection, enhanced viral replication was detected long after the decay of the carcinogen. The carcinogen-induced factors can be transmitted, upon fusion, between treated CHO cells and untreated cells containing integrated viral genomes, turning on viral DNA amplification in the heterokaryons. The requirement of cellular factors activated in the carcinogen-treated cells for viral amplification was demonstrated directly utilizing the SV40 in vitro replication system. Enhanced viral replication in vitro occurred only in cytosolic extracts from treated cells supplemented with excess T antigen. The carcinogen-induced cellular factors are associated mainly with the initiation of viral DNA replication, since the sequences spanning the SV40 origin of replication are preferentially amplified.

Environmental agents are associated with the initiation of carcinogenesis. Carcinogens cause phenomena that accompany malignancy, such as mutations (Ames et al. 1973; Heidelberger 1975), chromosomal aberrations, translocations (Abe and Sasaki 1977; Popescu et al. 1977), and amplification of cellular and viral genes (Lavi 1981; Lavi and Etkin 1981; Tlsty et al. 1984; Kleinberger et al. 1986). The involvement of environmental agents in the naturally occurring viral-related tumor development was suggested (Jarrett et al. 1978; zur Hausen 1986). Synergism between various types of viral infections and chemical agents that resulted in enhanced cell transformation in vitro and tumor appearance in vivo was demonstrated as well (Salaman et al. 1963; Casto et al. 1973).

SV40 amplification in carcinogen-treated cells was used in our studies as a model system for the understanding of the carcinogen-mediated events associated with viral activation and gene amplification. In permissive cells, SV40 replication requires a single viral encoded protein, T antigen (Tegtmeyer 1972), and cellular components (Challberg and Kelly 1982; DePamphilis and Wassarman 1982). Multiple rounds of viral replication occur in these cells during a single cell cycle (Tooze 1981). In SV40 transformed nonpermissive or semipermissive cells the integrated viral DNA replication is regulated under cell cycle control and occurs only once during the cell cycle. However, upon the exposure of semipermissive transformed cells to environmental agents, overreplication of viral sequences occurs, resulting in SV40 DNA amplification (Lavi 1982; Lavi et al. 1983).

Earlier studies in our laboratory demonstrated that the carcinogen-mediated viral amplification is a transient process requiring an intact origin of DNA replication and a functional T antigen. The amplified DNA is heterogeneous in size and is enriched mostly for sequences spanning the SV40 origin of replication (Lavi et al. 1987). Treatment of a synchronized cell population at the G_1–S boundary results in enhanced viral DNA amplification (Y. Berko-Flint and S. Lavi, in prep.). The enhanced replication is associated with increased transcription and expression of viral genes. Recent studies in our laboratory demonstrate the induction of *trans*-acting factors responsible for the enhanced expression of viral and cellular genes, including T antigen and dihydrofolate reductase (DHFR). The elevated expression resulted at least in part from induced transcription (Kleinberger et al. 1988). In the studies presented in this manuscript, we demonstrate induction of cellular factors affecting SV40 DNA replication in the carcinogen-treated cells. The possible role of the carcinogen-activated factors in gene amplification in general and in viral chemical cocarcinogenesis will be discussed.

Materials and Methods

Cell culture
CO60, CHO, and CHE cells were grown in Dulbecco's modified Eagle's medium (DMEM; Gibco Laboratories)

183

supplemented with 10% fetal calf serum (FCS; Biolabs, Jerusalem).

Cell synchronization and fusion
Cells were seeded (10^6 cells per 9-cm plate) and maintained in isoleucine, glutamine-deficient medium (Gibco) for 18 hours (Toby and Crissman 1972). A sample of cells was then analyzed by fluorescence-activated cell sorter (FACS) to determine cell cycle distribution.

Fusion
Mixed CHO and CO60 cells (10^6 cells of each) were plated in 6-cm dishes. After 8 hours the cells were fused using 40% polyethylene glycol 6000 (Serva) for 2 minutes, as described by Pontecorvo (1975).

Carcinogen treatment
10^6 cells per 9-cm dish were seeded in 5 ml DMEM supplemented with 10% FCS. After 24 hours, MNNG (Aldrich Chemical Co. Inc., Milwaukee, WI) or 7,12 dimethylbenz(a)anthracene (DMBA; Sigma), freshly dissolved in dimethyl sulfoxide (1 mg/ml), was added to the medium at the indicated concentrations.

Plasmid
pSVK1 was kindly provided by D. Dorsett (Dorsett et al. 1985). pSVK1 is a complete SV40 genome cloned via the *Kpn*I site into a pML2, a pBR322-derived shuttle vector.

Hybridization
Dispersed cell assay and slot blot hybridization procedures were performed as described previously (Lavi 1981; Kleinberger et al. 1986).

Immunoprecipitation of T antigen
At the indicated times, the cells were labeled for 2 hours with [^{35}S]methionine (50 μCi)/ml, 800 Ci/mmol, Amersham, England) in methionine-free medium, supplemented with 10% dialyzed FCS. Protein extracts were prepared as described (Maltzman et al. 1981) and equal numbers of radioactive ^{35}S cpm were immunoprecipitated using PAb 419 anti-T antibodies (Harlow et al. 1981). The immunoprecipitates were separated by 12.5% polyacrylamide gel electrophoresis, fluorographed, dried, and subjected to autoradiography.

In vitro replication assay
Cell extracts were prepared as described by Li and Kelly (1984). T antigen was purified according to Dixon and Nathans (1985). Reaction mixtures contained 50 μl of: 30 mM HEPES (pH 7.5), 7.0 mM $MgCl_2$, 0.5 mM dithiothreitol (DTT), 4 mM ATP, 200 μM each of CTP, UTP, and GTP, 100 μM each of dATP, dGTP, TTP, and 25 μM [α-^{32}P]dCTP (specific activity 1000 cpm/pmol), 40 mM creatine phosphate, 20 μg/ml creatine phosphokinase, 0.1 μg of pSVK1 plasmid, and 150 μg of cell extract. 1 μg of T antigen was added where indicated. Reactions were incubated at 37°C for 3 hours and then stopped by

adjusting the reaction mixture to 15 mM EDTA and 0.2% sodium dodecyl sulfate (SDS). Proteinase K at 200 μg/ml was added for 30 minutes at 37°C. The DNA was then extracted with phenol and chloroform, filtered through Sephadex G-50, and precipitated with ethanol. *Bst*NI digestion was carried out for 6 hours under the conditions specified by the manufacturer (New England BioLab).

Results

Enhanced viral DNA replication in carcinogen-treated cells
The effect of carcinogens on free viral DNA replication in the semipermissive Chinese hamster cells was studied. Embryonic cells (CHE) were treated with DMBA prior to viral infection. Similar levels of SV40 DNA were detected in control and treated cells 2 hours after the treatment (Fig. 1), indicating that viral absorp-

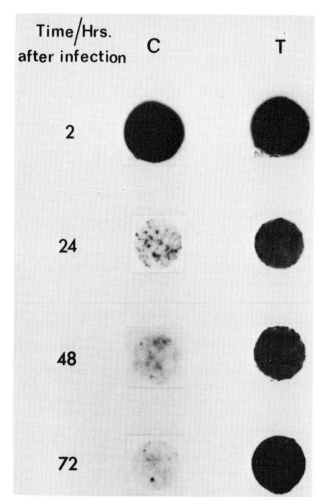

Figure 1 Enhancement of viral replication in DMBA-treated CHE cells. Untreated and DMBA-treated (0.3 μg/ml for 6 hr) CHE cells were infected with SV40 virus. At the indicated times after treatment, cells were harvested and 10^6 cells were filtered onto nitrocellulose filters. Hybridization was carried out with ^{32}P-labeled SV40 DNA probe as described (Lavi 1981). (C) Control untreated; (T) treated.

tion was not affected by the treatment. Enhanced viral replication was observed 24 hours after treatment and continued for the next 2 days. Maximal replication was detected 72 hours after treatment. Other agents arresting DNA replication such as MNNG, aflatoxin B_1, benzo(a)pyrene, and UV irradiation induced a similar effect on the SV40-infected cells (data not shown). These results coupled with our earlier studies demonstrate that following exposure to environmental agents, enhanced viral replication occurs in cells containing integrated SV40 (CO60) (Fig. 2B direct) or in CHE cells infected with SV40 virus or with viral DNA. It is possible that DNA damage leads to the activation of cellular factors governing viral DNA replication. Such factors might be present at limiting quantities in the semipermissive Chinese hamster cells.

Activation of *trans*-acting factors affecting SV40 replication in carcinogen-treated cells

The participation of carcinogen-activated cellular factors in the amplification process was demonstrated using two approaches. The first approach involved pre-

treatment of CHE cells with MNNG, a labile carcinogen (Peterson et al. 1981), at various times prior to transfection with viral DNA (Fig. 2A). In cells pretreated shortly before transfection (2−24 hr), 4.0- to 5.5-fold enhanced viral replication was observed. The inducing signal was even stronger in cells pretreated 48−96 hours prior to viral DNA introduction, resulting in 9.0- to 13.7-fold enhancement of viral DNA replication.

The second approach engaged fusion between carcinogen-treated CHO cells (donor cells) and untreated CO60 cells containing integrated viral DNA (recipient cells). In the heterokaryons between the treated donor cells and the untreated recipient cells, 2.0- to 2.5-fold enhancement of SV40 DNA replication occurred (Fig. 2B fusion). When a synchronous population of donor cells, present at the G_1−S boundary, was treated with MNNG 24 hours prior to cell fusion, elevated levels of SV40 DNA amplification were recorded in the heterokaryons (5.1 and 12.1 for cells treated with 3.5 μg/ml and 7.0 μg/ml MNNG, respectively, Fig. 2B fusion). The pattern of the indirectly induced amplification obtained by fusion is similar to that observed upon direct treatment of the cells with carcinogens (Fig. 2B).

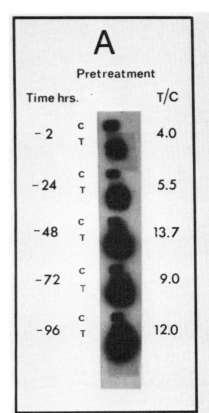

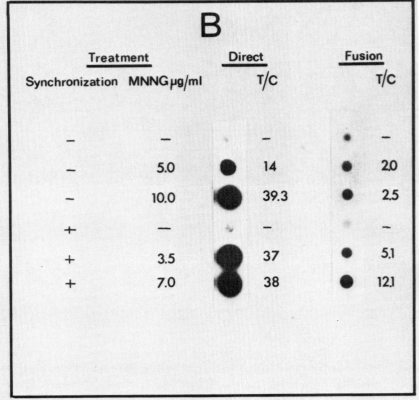

Figure 2 Direct and indirect induction of viral DNA replication in CHE and CO60 cells. (A) CHE cells were treated with DMBA (0.3 μg/ml for 6 hr) 16 hr after plating. At the indicated times (2−96 hr) after treatment, untreated and treated cells were transfected with pSVK1 (Dorsett et al. 1985) using DEAE-dextran transfection procedure (McCutchan and Pagano 1965). 72 hr after transfection, DNA from 2×10^5 cells was extracted and slot blot hybridization was performed (Kleinberger et al. 1986) using ^{32}P-labeled SV40 DNA probe. (B) Unsynchronized and synchronized cells were treated for 2 hr with different concentrations of MNNG. *Direct*: 72 hr after treatment of CO60 cells, dot blot hybridization of 2×10^5 cells was performed using ^{32}P-labeled SV40 DNA probe. *Fusion*: Untreated or MNNG-treated (24 hr after treatment) CHO cells were fused with a similar number of untreated CO60 cells. 48 hr after fusion dot blot hybridization was performed. (C) Control untreated; (T) treated. The autoradiograms were scanned and T/C ratio was calculated.

However, a lower amplification level was obtained upon cell fusion. Increasing doses of carcinogens yield a higher amplification level, and synchronized cells are more responsive to the carcinogen insult than the non-synchronized cells. These studies demonstrate that carcinogens activate *trans*-acting factors facilitating free viral DNA replication and amplification of integrated SV40.

Carcinogen-mediated induction of T antigen synthesis

T antigen is required for SV40 DNA replication in infected cells and for viral DNA amplification in carcinogen-treated virally transformed cells (Tegtmeyer 1972; Lavi 1981). Recent studies demonstrated the role of T antigen as a *trans*-activator of gene expression (Brady et al. 1984; Robbins and Botchan 1986; Segawa and Yamaguchi 1987). Alteration in T antigen expression following the treatment might affect viral DNA replication. T antigen synthesis was determined in control and DMBA-treated CHE cells infected with SV40. As demonstrated in Figure 3A, elevated levels of T antigen were observed in the carcinogen-treated virally infected

CHE cells 48 hours after treatment. An increase in T antigen synthesis was obtained as early as 24 hours after treatment of CO60 cells. Since under the experimental conditions SV40 DNA replication was enhanced (Fig. 3A and B), it was impossible to assess whether T antigen synthesis was elevated due to increased template availability or due to alterations in the mode of T antigen expression. Therefore, T antigen synthesis was measured in the presence or absence of DNA replication. As demonstrated in Figure 3C, aphidicolin, which inhibits DNA polymerase α (Ikegami et al. 1978), abolished viral DNA amplification in DMBA-treated CO60 cells but did not affect T antigen induction. Thus, the activation of T antigen synthesis in treated CO60 cells is an amplification-independent process.

Carcinogen-mediated induction of cellular factors responsible for SV40 DNA replication in vitro

The in vitro system for SV40 replication developed by Li and Kelly (1984) permits the analysis of the different components involved in SV40 replication (T antigen and

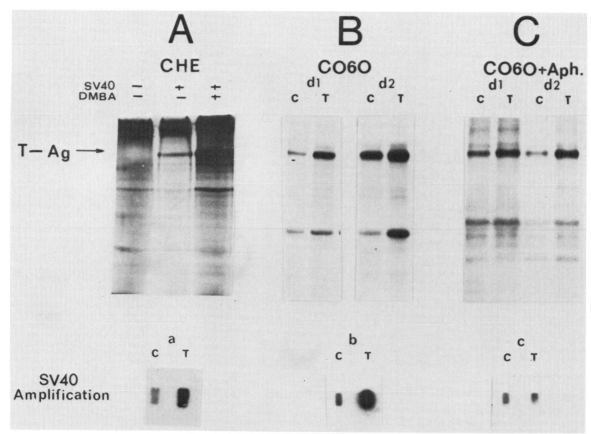

Figure 3 T antigen synthesis and SV40 DNA amplification in carcinogen-treated and untreated cells. 10^6 cells were seeded onto 9-cm plates and 24 hr later the cells were treated for 6 hr with 0.3 μg/ml DMBA. 24 and/or 48 hr after treatment the cells were labeled for 2 hr with [^{35}S]methionine. (*A*) SV40-infected CHE cells labeled 48 hr after treatment. (*B*) CO60 cells. (*C*) CO60 grown in the presence of aphidicolin (1 μg/ml). CO60 cells were labeled 24 and 48 hr after treatment. Equal numbers of ^{35}S-labeled proteins were immunoprecipitated with PAb 419 anti-T antigen antibodies as described in Methods. SV40 amplification was measured 48 hr after treatment using the slot blot hybridization procedure (*a, b,* and *c*). (C) Control untreated; (T) treated.

cellular factors). Earlier studies (Li and Kelly 1985) demonstrated that extracts prepared from Chinese hamster cells did not support SV40 replication in vitro. This system was used to investigate the possiblity that carcinogens alter the cellular functions involved in viral replication. The in vitro reaction mixture included exogenous SV40 template, excess amounts of purified T antigen (Dixon and Nathans 1985), and crude cytosolic extracts prepared from treated and untreated CO60 cells. Analysis of the acid-insoluble products revealed that only marginal amounts of dCMP (3–5 pmol) were incorporated into newly synthesized DNA in extracts from untreated cells, in the presence or in the absence of T antigen, and in extracts from treated cells in the absence of T antigen. A remarkable increase in incorporation, 30 pmol, was observed upon addition of excess T antigen to the extracts from carcinogen-treated cells. In the fully permissive extract derived from HeLa cells in the presence of excess T antigen, 100 pmol were incorporated. In the absence of T antigen, only 3 pmol dCMP were incorporated. The newly synthesized DNAs derived from the Chinese-hamster-treated extracts and from the HeLa extract, in the presence of T antigen, were shown to be *Dpn*I resistant (data not shown).

We have previously shown in CO60 cells treated with carcinogens increased replication of viral sequences surrounding the origin of replication (Lavi et al. 1987). To analyze the mode of viral replication in extracts from carcinogen-treated cells, the reaction products were digested with *Bst*NI, an enzyme that cleaves the template plasmid pSVK1 (Dorsett et al. 1985) into 19 fragments that can be separated by polyacrylamide gel electrophoresis. As demonstrated in Figure 4, in extracts from treated cells the sequences spanning the viral origin were replicated to a higher extent than remote sequences. In HeLa extracts all the viral fragments were distributed evenly. Thus, in CO60 extracts, in the presence of excess T antigen, enhanced origin activation was observed, indicating that in addition to enhanced T antigen activity in treated cells, cellular factors associated with the initiation of SV40 DNA replication are activated.

Discussion

In this report, we have demonstrated the induction of factors affecting SV40 DNA replication in carcinogen-treated CHE cells infected with SV40 or in transformed CHE cells (CO60) containing an integrated viral genome. Three lines of evidence demonstrate that the carcinogen-activated factors are acting in *trans* and that their induction does not require direct interaction between the DNA-damaging agents and the viral genome: (1) Pretreatment of CHE cells with MNNG, a labile carcinogen with t1/2 of 1.1 hours (Peterson et al. 1981), 96 hours prior to transfection with viral DNA resulted in enhanced viral DNA replication (Fig. 2A). The carcinogen-induced responses functioned a long time after the decay of the inducing agent. (2) Fusion between carcinogen-treated CHO cells and untreated

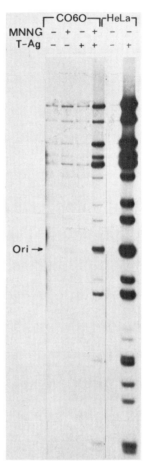

Figure 4 Genomic distribution of SV40 DNA sequences replicated in vitro. Extracts from HeLa cells and from untreated and MNNG-treated (7.0 μg/ml, for 2 hr) CO60 cells, were prepared 24 hr posttreatment as described in Methods. In vitro replication reactions were performed using pSVK1 as template DNA in the absence or presence of 1.0 μg purified T antigen. The extracted DNA was digested with *Bst*NI and fractionated by electrophoresis on 6% polyacrylamide gel. The gel was dried and subjected to autoradiography. The origin-containing fragment is marked by an arrow.

CO60 cells harboring an integrated SV40 genome led to enhanced viral replication in the heterokaryons (Fig. 2B). (3) Cytosolic extracts from carcinogen-treated Chinese hamster cells supported SV40 replication in the in vitro replication system supplemented with excess T antigen (Fig. 4).

Authentic SV40 replication in vitro depends on the addition of excess exogenous T antigen and cellular factors present in the cytosolic extracts (Li and Kelly 1984; Stillman et al. 1985). Utilizing this system, we were able to demonstrate that cellular factors activated following carcinogen treatment are essential for the amplification process. However, in addition to these cellular factors, increased T antigen synthesis was demonstrated in the carcinogen-treated cells.

The elevated levels of T antigen resulted from replication-independent enhanced expression (Fig. 3C). Studies in our laboratory demonstrated that the enhanced expression of T antigen and several cellular genes such as β-actin, p53, and others is regulated, at least in part, on the level of transcription (Kleinberger et al. 1988). It is possible that the cellular factors involved in the activation of SV40 replication are regulated similarly. Nomura and Oishi (1984) and Lambert et al. (1983) suggested that the cellular factors activated in the carcinogen-treated cells are the permissive factors facilitating viral replication in permissive cells. Such factors were shown to be transmitted upon fusion between monkey cells or carcinogen-treated cells and the nonpermissive virally transformed cells. Recent studies by Murakami et al. (1986) demonstrated that in extracts derived from nonpermissive cells, replacement of the endogenous polymerase α–DNA primase complex with such a complex from permissive cells results in the generation of SV40 replication. However, in our experiments, in vitro and in vivo, we demonstrated preferential replication and amplification of origin sequences, (Lavi et al. 1987 and Fig. 4). It is possible that cellular factors specifically associated with the initiation of DNA replication and S phase are activated in the carcinogen-treated cells. The elongation of S phase following carcinogen treatment and the enhanced amplification of both viral and cellular genes in treated synchronized cells support this hypothesis (Kleinberger et al. 1986; Y. Berko-Flint et al., in prep.).

We propose that following treatment with carcinogens, a cascade of events is activated, leading to enhanced expression of several cellular genes, including genes associated with the regulation of the S phase. Overexpression of such genes might lead to multiple initiations of DNA replication, resulting in gene amplification (Johnston et al. 1986; Lavi et al. 1987) and enhanced replication of viruses. Expression and replication of endogenous or exogenous tumor viruses activated in the carcinogen-treated cells might lead to enhanced cell transformation by these viruses. Recent studies in our laboratory demonstrate indeed that enhanced viral transformation occurred in carcinogen-treated embryonic cells infected with SV40.

Acknowledgments

We thank S. Etkin for her excellent technical help. The expert secretarial work of Judy Rapoport is much appreciated. This project was supported by grants from the National Council of Development and Deutsches Krebschungszentrum, Heidelberg, Germany; a grant from the Van-Bytes Foundation; and a grant from the Israel Cancer Research Fund.

References

Abe, S. and M. Sasaki. 1977. Chromosomal aberrations and sister chromatide exchange in Chinese hamster cells exposed to various chemicals. *J. Natl. Cancer Inst.* **58**: 1635.

Ames, B.N., S.E. Durston, E. Yamasaki, and F.D. Lee. 1973. Carcinogens are mutagens: A simple test combining liver homogenates for activation and bacteria for detection. *Proc. Natl. Acad. Sci.* **70**: 2281.

Brady, J., J.B. Bolen, M. Radonovich, N. Salzman, and G. Khoury. 1984. Stimulation of SV40 late gene expression by SV40 tumor antigen. *Proc. Natl. Acad. Sci.* **81**: 2040.

Casto, B.C., J.W. Pieczynski, and J.A. Dipaolo. 1973. Enhancement of adenovirus transformation by pretreatment of hamster cells with carcinogenic polycyclic hydrocarbons. *Cancer Res.* **33**: 819.

Challberg, M.D. and T.J. Kelly. 1982. Eukaryotic DNA replication: Viral and plasmid model systems. *Annu. Rev. Biochem.* **51**: 901.

DePamphilis, M.L. and P.M. Wassarman. 1982. Organization and replication of papovavirus DNA. In *Organization and replication of viral DNA* (ed. A. Kaplan), p. 37. CRC Press, Boca Raton, Florida.

Dixon, R.F. and D. Nathans. 1985. Purification of SV40 large T-antigen by immunoaffinity chromatography. *J. Virol.* **58**: 1001.

Dorsett, D., I. Deichaite, and E. Winocour. 1985. Circular and linear SV40 DNAs differ in recombination. *Mol. Cell. Biol.* **5**: 869.

Harlow, E., L.W. Crawford, D.C. Pim, and N.M. Williamson. 1981. Monoclonal antibodies specific for SV40 tumor antigens. *J. Virol.* **39**: 861.

Heidelberger, C. 1975. Chemical carcinogenesis. *Annu. Rev. Biochem.* **44**: 79.

Ikegami, S., T. Taguchi, and M. Ohashi. 1978. Aphidicolin prevents mitotic cell division by interfering with the activity of DNA polymerase α. *Nature* **275**: 458.

Jarrett, W.F.H., P.E. McNeil, W.T.R. Grimshaw, I.E. Selman, and W.I.M. McInyre. 1978. High incidence area of cattle cancer with a possible interaction between an environmental carcinogen and papilloma virus. *Nature* **274**: 215.

Johnston, R.N., J. Feder, A.B. Hill, S.W. Sherwood, and R.T. Schimke. 1986. Transient inhibition of DNA synthesis and subsequent increase DNA content per cell. *Mol. Cell. Biol.* **6**: 3373.

Kleinberger, T., S. Etkin, and S. Lavi. 1986. Carcinogen mediated methotrexate resistance and dhfr amplification in Chinese hamster cells. *Mol. Cell. Biol.* **6**: 1958.

Kleinberger, T., Y. Berko-Flint, M. Blank, S. Etkin, and S. Lavi. 1988. Carcinogen induced *trans*-activation of gene expression. *Mol. Cell. Biol.* (in press).

Lambert, M.E., S. Gattoni-Celli, P. Kirschmeier, and I.B. Weinstein. 1983. Benzo(a)pyrene induction of extra-chromosomal viral DNA synthesis in rat cells transformed by polyoma virus. *Carcinogenesis* **4**: 587.

Lavi, S. 1981. Carcinogen mediated amplification of viral DNA sequences in SV40 transformed CHE cells. *Proc. Natl. Acad. Sci.* **78**: 6144.

———. 1982. Carcinogen-mediated activation of SV40 replicons: A model system for initiation of carcinogenesis. In *Gene amplification* (ed. R.T. Schimke), p. 225. Cold Spring Harbor Laboratory, Cold Spring Harbor, New York.

Lavi, S. and S. Etkin. 1981. Carcinogen mediated induction of SV40 DNA synthesis in SV40 transformed CHE cells. *Carcinogenesis* **2**: 417.

Lavi, S., T. Kleinberger, Y. Berko-Flint, and M. Blank. 1987. Stable and transient coamplification of DHFR and SV40 in carcinogen treated cells. In *Accomplishments in oncology: The role of DNA amplification in carcinogenesis* (ed. J.R. Schlehofer), p. 117. J.B. Lippincott, Philadelphia.

Lavi, S., N. Kohn, T. Kleinberger, Y. Berko, and S. Etkin. 1983. Amplification of SV40 and cellular genes in SV40 transformed Chinese hamster cells treated with chemical carcinogens. *UCLA Symp. Mol. Cell. Biol. New Ser.* **11**: 659.

Li, J. and T.J. Kelly. 1984. SV40 DNA replication in vitro. *Proc. Natl. Acad. Sci.* **81**: 6973.

———. 1985. SV40 DNA replication *in vitro*. Specificity of initiation and evidence for bidirectional replication. *Mol. Cell. Biol.* **5**: 1238.

Maltzman, W., M. Oren, and A.J. Levine. 1981. The structural relationships between 54,000 molecular weight cellular tumor antigens detected in viral and non-viral transformed cells. *Virology* **112**: 145.

McCutchan, J.H. and J.S. Pagano. 1965. Enhancement of the infectivity of SV40 deoxyribonucleic acid with diethylaminoethyl-dextran. *J. Natl. Cancer Inst.* **41**: 351.

Murakami, Y., C.R. Wobbe, L. Weissbach, F.B. Dean, and J. Hurwitz. 1986. Role of DNA polymerase α and DNA primase in SV40 DNA replication *in vitro*. *Proc. Natl. Acad. Sci.* **83**: 2869.

Nomura, S. and M. Oishi. 1984. UV irradiation induces an activity which stimulates SV40 rescue upon cell fusion. *Mol. Cell. Biol.* **4**: 1159.

Peterson, A.R., J.R. Landolth, H. Paterson, C.P. Spears, and C. Heidelberger. 1981. Oncogenic transformation and mutation of C3H/10T1/2 clone 8 mouse embryo fibroblasts by alkylating agents. *Cancer Res.* **41**: 3095.

Popescu, N.C., D. Turnbull, and J.A. Dipaolo. 1977. Sister chromatide exchange and chromosome aberration analysis with the use of several carcinogens and non-carcinogens. Brief communication. *J. Natl. Cancer Inst.* **59**: 289.

Pontecorvo, G. 1975. Production of mammalian somatic cell hybrids by means of polyethylenglycol treatment. *Somatic Cell Genet.* **1**: 397.

Robbins, P.D. and M. Botchan. 1986. *Trans*activation of SV40 enhancer. *Mol. Cell. Biol.* **6**: 1283.

Salaman, M.H., K.E. Rowson, F.J. Roe, J.K. Ball, J. Harvey, and G. de Benedictis. 1963. The combined action of viruses and other carcinogens. In *Viruses, nucleic acids and cancer*, p. 544. University of Texas, M.D. Anderson Hospital and Tumor Institute. Williams and Wilkins, Baltimore.

Segawa, K. and N. Yamaguchi. 1987. Induction of c-Ha-ras transcription in rat cells by SV40 large T antigen. *Mol. Cell. Biol.* **7**: 356.

Stillman, B., R.D. Gerard, R.A. Guggenheimer, and Y. Gluzman. 1985. T-antigen and template requirements for SV40 DNA replication *in vitro*. *EMBO J.* **4**: 2933.

Tegtmeyer, P. 1972. SV40 deoxyribonucleic acid synthesis: The viral replicon. *J. Virol.* **10**: 591.

Tlsty, T.D., P.C. Brown, and R.T. Schimke. 1984. UV irradiation facilitates methotrexate resistance and amplification of the dihydrofolate reductase gene in cultured 3T6 mouse cells. *Mol. Cell. Biol.* **4**: 1050.

Toby, R.A. and H.A. Crissman. 1972. Use of flow microfluorometry in detailed analysis of effects of chemical agents on cell cycle progression. *Cancer Res.* **32**: 2726.

Tooze, J. 1981. *Molecular biology of tumor viruses,* 2nd edition, revised: *DNA tumor viruses.* Cold Spring Harbor Laboratory, Cold Spring Harbor, New York.

Zur Hausen, H. 1986. Intracellular surveillance of persisting viral infections. *Lancet* **II**: 489.

Positive and Negative Control of DNA Replication

J. Roberts and H. Weintraub

Fred Hutchinson Cancer Center, Seattle, Washington 98104

We showed previously in a specific model system that DNA replication is regulated by an interplay between positive factors that initiate DNA replication and negative elements that prevent re-replication of DNA sequences within a single S phase. We have continued to evaluate the nature of the interaction between the positive and negative elements of replication control. We find, using as a model a simian virus 40-bovine papilloma virus (SV40-BPV) chimeric replicon, that replication in the eukaryotic cell can be regulated by a *cis*-acting negative control mechanism in which replication is permitted in unreplicated replicons but actively prevented in replicons that have already been duplicated. In addition, to monitor the activity of positive replication factors through the cell cycle, we have used the in vitro SV40 replication system to assess the activity of extracts prepared from cells at specific stages of the cell cycle. Results of these assays suggest that the positive and negative regulators of DNA replication undergo coordinate changes in activity through the cell cycle.

Mechanisms of DNA replication control are apparently quite diverse, reflecting the particular genetic constraints of each organism. Probably the most straightforward type of regulation is the positive control demonstrated by many bacteriophages and eukaryotic viruses. Here, replication is limited by the abundance of a phage- or virus-encoded initiation factor. By exploiting this positive feedback loop, genome copy number increases exponentially until the loop is broken, a cellular replication factor becomes limiting, or cell death ensues.

Most mechanisms of replication control are designed to maintain a constant gene copy number and, consequently, superimpose some form of negative control to override the effects of positively acting replication factors. Prokaryotic plasmids, for example, keep themselves at a remarkably constant copy number within the host bacterium. Again, copy number is limited by the abundance of plasmid-encoded positive replication initiation factors. However, all plasmids appear to encode an inhibitor that can act, in *trans*, to limit the accumulation of this positive initiation factor(s) (Itoh and Tomizawa 1980; Shafferman et al. 1982; Abeles et al. 1984; Pal et al. 1986). The abundance of this inhibitor increases as plasmid copy number increases, so that initiation events cease when the plasmid attains a set copy number. A primary feature of this type of control is that all plasmids, both unreplicated and previously replicated, are treated as indistinguishable members of a common replicon pool. Thus, to maintain a constant copy number, during any given generation some individual plasmids will replicate more than once and others not at all. Therefore, in a cell that contains multiple independent, unique replicons, each unique genetic element, to ensure its perpetuation from generation to generation, must encode its own unique initiation factor. Overlap between the replication factors encoded by different plasmids accounts, in part, for the phenomenon of plasmid incompatibility (see Novick and Hoppensteadt 1978).

These considerations suggest that *trans*-acting negative control is, in principle, probably not the mechanism of replication control in the eukaryotic genome. It is unappealing to imagine that each of the 10,000 to 100,000 replication origins in the vertebrate genome has its own unique, independently regulated initiation factor and that for any given replicon a single initiation event per generation could be faithfully maintained.

cis-Acting negative controls act through a mechanism very different from *trans*-acting controls. The foundation of *cis*-acting negative control is that each replicon is regulated independently of all others; initiation is permitted in unreplicated replicons and actively prevented in replicons that have already been duplicated. This form of replication control makes two strong experimental predictions that clearly distinguish it from *trans*-acting negative control. First, each replicon will be replicated just once per cell cycle. Second, copy number control should be maintained despite an excess of all positive factors necessary for DNA replication.

We showed previously in a specific model system that DNA replication is regulated by an interplay between positive factors that initiate DNA replication and negative elements that prevent re-replication of DNA sequences with a single S phase (Roberts and Weintraub 1986). This conclusion emerged from experiments in which we constructed chimeric replicons consisting of DNA sequences derived from both SV40 and BPV. SV40 is a runaway replicon in the presence of the viral-encoded initiation factor T antigen, whereas BPV is usually a controlled replicon, each viral genome replicating once per cell cycle. Transient replication assays revealed that replication of composite SV-BPV plasmids can be controlled by the dominant negative action of specific BPV-encoded signals that override the unregu-

191

lated runaway replication induced by the positive factor, SV40 T antigen. We report here experiments that demonstrate that the replication of SV-BPV plasmids in monkey cells conforms to the predictions of a *cis*-acting negative control mechanism.

Our model system demonstrates that DNA replication in eukaryotic cells can be regulated through a *cis*-acting negative control mechanism. Negative control mechanisms that limit replication to just one round must be reset to permit replication in subsequent cell cycles. Cell fusion and nuclear transplantation experiments suggest that negative control is maintained through the G_2 phase of the cell cycle but is relaxed during the process of mitosis so that G_1 nuclei are once again fully competent to replicate their DNA (see Discussion). We have begun to investigate how the resetting of negative controls might be coupled through the cell cycle with parallel changes in the activity of positively acting replication factors.

To monitor the activity of positively acting replication factors, we have used an in vitro system that will faithfully replicate DNA molecules containing the SV40 replication origin in the presence of the initiator SV40 T antigen and a cytosolic extract prepared from a cell type permissive to SV40 replication (Li and Kelly 1984; Stillman and Gluzman 1985). We find significant differences in the activity of extracts prepared from various points in the cell cycle. S-phase extracts have a specific activity tenfold higher than G_1 or mitotic cell extracts; G_2 extracts are as active as S-phase extracts. These changes suggest models in which the activity of the positive and negative factors that regulate DNA replication undergo coordinate fluctuations through the cell cycle.

Results

SV-BPV plasmids replicate once per cell cycle

We have described previously the construction of stable COS cell lines that maintain SV-BPV composite plasmids as episomes (Roberts and Weintraub 1986). Briefly, the gene encoding G-418 resistance (*Neo*^{r}) was inserted into an SV-BPV vector that contained the SV40 replication origin and all the information necessary for regulated BPV replication (i.e., in the 5.4-kb *Hind*III-*Bam*HI fragment of the BPV genome). This plasmid was transfected into COS-7 cells (Gluzman 1981) and G-418-resistant cell clones were picked and propagated as cell lines. In these cell lines the SV-Neo-BPV plasmid is maintained as an episome at approximately 1000 copies per cell. We observed that the SV-Neo-BPV episome is present in all cell lines as both a closed circular monomer and a high-molecular weight, extrachromosomal concatamer. In the absence of BPV elements, SV-Neo plasmids did not yield stable cell lines in COS cells, presumably because the uncontrolled replication of the plasmid led to death of the host cell.

The replication pattern of the SV-Neo-BPV episomes was evaluated using a standard density transfer analysis. SNB-1000, an exponentially growing COS cell line that carried 1000 copies of the SV-Neo-BPV episome,

was prelabeled for 48 hours with tritiated thymidine and then transferred to heavy growth medium containing 50 μM bromodeoxyuridine (BrdU). The cells were allowed to grow for 24 hours (just less than one cell cycle time), and then total cellular DNA was prepared and fractionated on a CsCl equilibrium gradient. Replication of cellular genomic DNA was monitored by following the position of both tritium counts and ethidium-bromide-stained material in the CsCl gradient. Also, gradient fractions were hybridized to a rDNA probe as an additional control. All three procedures indicate that during the 24 hours of growth in BrdU, 90% of the cellular genomic DNA had replicated once, and 10% of the cellular DNA had not yet replicated (Fig. 1). Hybridization of gradient fractions to a radiolabeled probe specific for the SV-Neo-BPV episome revealed that its pattern of replication was indistinguishable from the host cell DNA. 90% of the episomes had replicated once, 10% had not yet replicated, and no detectable episomal DNA had replicated more than once (Fig. 1). These results have been confirmed with three independent COS cell lines that carry SV-Neo-BPV episomes. In no case do we observe premature movement of the episomal DNA into the heavy/heavy region of the CsCl density gradient. Southern blot analysis of gradient fractions revealed that both forms of the SV-Neo-BPV episome, the monomer and the high-molecular-weight concatamer, replicate once per cell cycle (data not shown).

The copy number of the pSV-Neo-BPV episome is not controlled by cellular levels of T antigen

Our results demonstrate that each SV-Neo-BPV episome replicates just once per cell cycle in its COS cell host. To demonstrate that this pattern of DNA replication completely conforms to the two predicted features of *cis*-acting negative control (see above), it is essential to show that this regulated replication occurs in an environment that contains an excess of all positive factors necessary for DNA replication. COS cells have the capability to amplify an SV40 origin plasmid to 10^4–10^5 copies per cell within 48 hours following the introduction of such a plasmid into the COS cell nucleus. Since all our SNB cell lines have stabilized the SV-Neo-BPV episome at just 10^3 copies per cell, it would appear that the episome copy number is set by a mechanism operating independently of the positive replicative competence of the host cell (see Discussion).

To demonstrate in a functional assay that the copy number of the SV-Neo-BPV episome is stable despite an excess of all positive factors required for DNA replication, we supertransfected SNB cells with the plasmid pSV-T, a plasmid that contains an SV40 replication origin and encodes the initiation factor T antigen (Fig. 2). Although this plasmid will be amplified to high copy number in SNB cells, this was not true for the replication of the endogenous episome pSV-Neo-BPV. The endogenous SV-Neo-BPV episome was insensitive to this influx of excess T antigen and remained stable at lower copy number. This experiment directly proves that copy

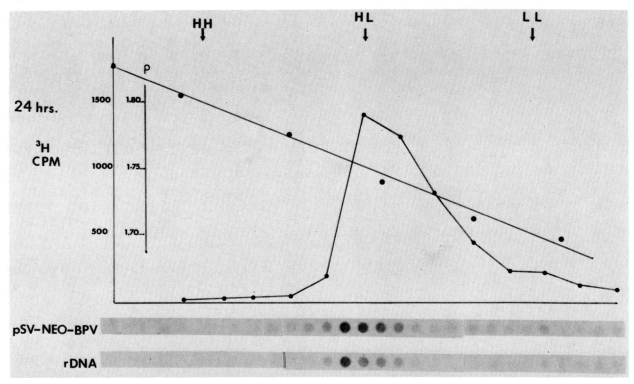

Figure 1 Density transfer analysis of pSV-Neo-BPV replication. Exponentially growing SNB-1000 cells were labeled for 48 hr with 1 microcurie/ml tritiated thymidine and then transferred to medium containing 50 μM BrdU and grown for an additional 24 hr. Total cellular DNA was fractionated on a CsCl equilibrium gradient and fractions were collected and analyzed by "dot-blot" hybridization. Shown is the distribution of incorporated ^{3}H-T across the gradient, and the position of densities corresponding to native, half-, and fully BrdU-substituted DNA. Beneath are the corresponding gradient fractions hybridized either with pBR322 probe (which detects the SV-Neo-BPV episome) or rDNA probe.

number control of the regulated SV-Neo-BPV plasmid occurs through a negative control mechanism that is dominant to an excess of positive replication factors.

Positive control of DNA replication through the cell cycle

An in vitro system that will faithfully replicate DNA molecules containing the SV40 replication origin has been developed recently (Li and Kelly 1984). This system utilizes exogenous SV40 T antigen as the initiator protein and a cytosolic extract from primate cells, which supplies all the other factors necessary for DNA replication. Since this system relies on cellular factors for all events in DNA replication other than those performed by T antigen, we anticipated that it would prove useful in assessing cell-cycle-associated changes in the activity of these positive replication factors.

We used a combination of elutriation and fluorescence-activated cell sorter (FACS) analysis to isolate large quantities of cells that were in either the G_1, S, or G_2 phases of the cell cycle. Cytosolic extracts were prepared from these cells and used to replicate an SV40 origin-containing plasmid, pSV-ori, in vitro. By measuring the incorporation of radiolabeled dCTP into DNA during this reaction, we found that S-phase extracts had a specific activity tenfold greater than G_1 extracts. This

was true for Manca cells (a Burkitt's lymphoma cell line), 293 cells (an embryonic human kidney cell line transformed by the adenovirus E1A and E1B genes), and K562 cells (a human erythropoietic cell line) (Fig. 3A). This tenfold difference is based on incorporation of dCMP per μg of cell protein. Since G_1 cells actually contain about one half as much protein as S-phase cells, the difference in replication activity on a per-cell basis is about 20-fold. The products of the reactions carried out either with G_1, S, or G_2 phase extracts were indistinguishable (Fig. 3B) and therefore do not indicate what function might be limiting in G_1. However, we find that addition of purified proliferating cell nuclear antigen (PCNA) or topoisomerase I does not increase the activity of G_1 extracts. In addition, the levels of α polymerase activity are identical in G_1 and S-phase extracts (data not shown). Finally, mixing of G_1 and S-phase extracts indicates that no replication inhibitor is present in G_1 cells. It is possible that the deficiency in G_1-promoted replication reflects the absence of a factor necessary for the efficient assembly of these various proteins into a higher order enzyme complex.

We have also found that G_2 extracts from K562 cells were almost as active as S-phase extracts. However, mitotic extracts prepared from nocadozole-arrested HeLa and 293 cells shows a low specific activity similar to G_1 extracts. We are continuing to investigate the

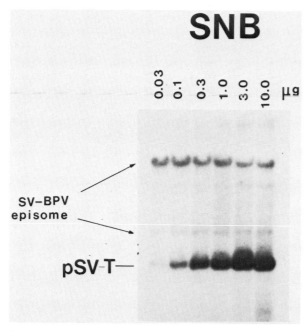

Figure 2 Replication of plasmids pSV and pSV-T in SNB-1000 cells. Increasing amounts of pSV-T (a plasmid containing the SV40 replication origin, early promoter, and T antigen gene) were transfected into a SNB cell line that contained 1000 copies per cell of the SV-Neo-BPV episome. Total cellular DNA was harvested at 72 hr post-transfection, and the replication of the transfected plasmid was determined by monitoring the accumulation of DPN-resistant plasmid DNA by Southern blot. The endogenous SV-Neo-BPV episome in SNB-1000 cells is indicated.

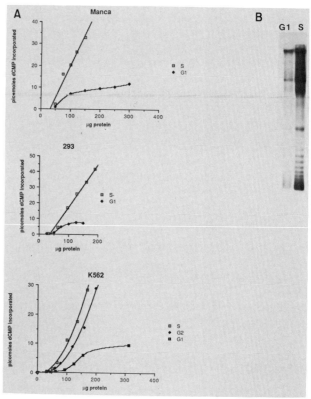

Figure 3 In vitro replication of an SV40 origin plasmid in extracts from G_1, G_2, and S-phase cells. (*A*) Manca, 293, and K562 cells were grown in spinner culture and sorted into G_2, S, and G_2 phases of the cell cycle by preparative centrifugal elutriation followed by FACS analysis. The in vitro replication reactions used the indicated amount of cytosolic extract, 100 ng of pSV-ori DNA, and were carried out for 1 hr at 37°C. All reactions were done twice, on two separate days, and the results averaged. (*B*) The products of reactions using 100 μg of either G_1 or S-phase Manca cytosolic extracts were analyzed on 1% agarose gels. The topoisomers of form I DNA reflect the assembly of the plasmid into chromatin during the course of replication (Stillman and Gluzman 1985). The slower migrating DNA forms are replication intermediates.

nature of the factor(s) that is limiting in G_1 for DNA replication, and we are also studying the mechanism of conversion of the high S or G_2 levels of activity into the relatively low level of G_1 activity as cells proceed through mitosis.

Discussion

Our data indicate that the initiation of DNA synthesis during the cell cycle is regulated by positive factors, whereas the subsequent limitation of replication to just one round per cell cycle is subject to *cis*-acting negative control.

Although our data primarily address the cyclic activity of the enzymes actually involved in DNA replication, positive control of the transition from G_1 into S phase of the cell cycle has also been suggested, based on cell fusion and nuclear transplantation experiments. Fusion of G_1 phase HeLa cells with S-phase cells will induce DNA replication in the G_1 nucleus; replication in the S-phase nucleus also continues (Rao and Johnson 1970). The same result has been obtained for *Stentor* (DeTerra 1967). Nuclear transplantation experiments yield results similar to those obtained by cell fusion. In *Stentor*, transplantation of G_1 nuclei into S-phase cells results in induction of replication in the G_1 nucleus (DeTerra 1967). However, G_1 cytoplasm cannot sustain replication in a transplanted S-phase nucleus. These

experiments demonstrate that the G_1 nucleus is competent to replicate its DNA and that entry into S phase of the cell cycle is brought about by positive factors present in excess of the S-phase cell.

Our experiments are entirely consistent with these conclusions. We find that G_1 extracts have a tenfold lower capacity to support the in vitro replication of SV40 DNA than do S-phase extracts. Mixing G_1 and S-phase extracts demonstrates that this difference is not due to an inhibitor present in G_1 cells, but rather to S-phase cells containing positive factors for DNA replication that are deficient or absent in G_1 cells. We therefore believe that this in vitro system will prove useful in assessing some of the biochemical changes that accompany the progression of the cell through the cell cycle.

A more difficult problem has been understanding the nature of the control mechanism that limits DNA replication to just one round per cell cycle. Our SV-BPV model system demonstrates that specific *cis*-acting BPV elements are necessary to establish regulated, once-per-cell-cycle replication of this viral chimera. Furthermore, copy number control of SV-BPV episomes occurs through a mechanism that is independent of the positive replicative capacity of the host cell. The SNB episome is stable at a copy number of 1000 molecules per cell, even though the SNB cell contains sufficient SV40 T antigen, and all other replication factors, to amplify an unregulated SV40 origin plasmid to 100,000 copies per cell. These observations argue strongly for the operation of a *cis*-acting negative control mechanism in the regulation of DNA replication. The foundation of this type of control is that each replicon is regulated independently of all others; initiation is permitted in unreplicated replicons and actively prevented in replicons that have already been duplicated.

Cell fusion and nuclear transplantation experiments have suggested that the cell also uses a *cis*-acting negative control mechanism to regulate the replication of its genomic DNA. Fusion of an S-phase HeLa cell with a G_2 cell will not induce replication in the G_2 nucleus; replication in the S-phase nucleus continues (Rao and Johnson 1970). Similarly, transplantation of a G_2 nucleus into an S-phase cell will not cause replication to commence in the G_2 nucleus (Ord 1969). Also, transplantation of a late S-phase nucleus into an early S-phase cell will not prolong the duration of DNA synthesis in the late S nucleus (Ord 1969). All of these experiments indicate that genomic DNA is restricted by a *cis*-acting negative control mechanism to just one round of DNA replication per cell cycle. This is also consistent with our in vitro replication experiments that show that even though G_2 extracts are almost as competent to replicate SV40 as S-phase extracts, in the intact cell the G_2 nucleus is apparently unable to respond to these factors. It would be interesting to determine whether after infection SV40 is able to replicate in G_2.

Negative controls on DNA replication must be relaxed to permit a new round of DNA synthesis in the next cell cycle. The experiments described above show that negative control is still operative in the G_2 phase of the cell cycle, but has been reset by the time the cell reaches the next G_1 phase (since G_1, but not G_2 nuclei will replicate in S-phase cytoplasm). Our experiments suggest that the positive controls on replication fluctuate coordinately with the negative controls; positive and negative controls appear to be activated and repressed at similar points in the cell cycle. Thus, extracts from G_2 cells are almost as active as S-phase extracts in replicating DNA, whereas mitotic and G_1 extracts are much less active. Again, these observations confirm those made by nuclear transplantation; replication in an S-phase nucleus can be supported by G_2 cytoplasm but not by G_1 cytoplasm (DeTerra 1967; Ord 1969). In sum, these observations suggest that the positive and negative controls on DNA replication are coordinately activated in the G_1 to S transition, and coordinately repressed as the cell enters mitosis.

In principle, it might appear redundant for the cell to activate and repress both positive and negative replication controls, since adequate models of replication con-

trol could be made in which the negative controls were inactivated (or reset) at the onset of S phase, and positive factors were constitutively active throughout the cell cycle. The cyclic activity of both positive and negative control might suggest that a single element common to both control mechanisms is being regulated, or alternatively, that the resetting of negative control is mechanistically tied to an event that occurs only in mitosis (e.g., the separation of sister chromatids, or activation of a mitosis-specific kinase). If negative controls were obligately reset during mitosis, then positive controls would also need to be simultaneously repressed to preserve the G_1 phase of the cell cycle.

Based on these experiments, we would schematically view the cell cycle as follows: At the start of S phase all positive elements are available and the chromosomes are fully competent and receptive to these factors. After a segment of DNA replicates, a *cis*-acting negative control makes that segment inaccessible to additional initiations during that S phase and into G_2. Some time at the end of G_2, or during mitosis, the activity of at least one positive replication factor is lost; in addition, at the same time, *cis*-acting negative control is also reset. Resetting of *cis*-acting negative control renders the genome once again competent to replicate its DNA; however, the concomitant absence of a positive control element(s) results in a G_1 phase where no DNA replication occurs. During G_1 the proper conditions are again generated to allow a positive environment for the onset of DNA replication. Presumably, these conditions are dependent on the multitude of known and unknown external and internal elements that contribute to the decision to enter start. It is amusing that at this very superficial level of analysis we have been able to construct a crude outline of a cell cycle without referring to the need to cycle the presumed cellular initiation factor, which in our sytem corresponds to SV40 T antigen.

Methods

Cells

293, Manca, and K562 cell lines were maintained in spinner cultures at densities from 2.5 to 5×10^5 cells per ml. 293 cells were grown in Joklid modified suspension medium + 5% calf serum, and K562 and Manca cells in RPMI + 10% calf serum. Typically 10^9 cells were separated by centrifugal elutriation (see Meistrich 1983) in a Beckman JE-10X rotor. 15 to 25 200-ml fractions were collected, and each fraction was analyzed on a FACS by propidium iodide staining to determine which fractions contained G_1, S, and G_2 phase cells.

SNB cells were grown in DME + 15% fetal calf serum + 0.5 mg/ml G-418. Transfections and transient replication assays were performed as described previously (Robert and Weintraub 1986).

Density transfer analysis

One confluent plate of SNB cells was split 1:8 into medium containing 1–3 μCi/ml tritiated thymidine and grown for 2 days. Cells were then split 1:4 into medium containing 40–60 μM BrdU and grown for 2/3 of one cell cycle (18 hrs). Total cellular DNA was prepared and fractionated on a CsCl equilibrium density gradient in a Beckman 80Ti rotor at 40K rpm, 20°C for 45 hours. 0.3-ml fractions were collected from the bottom. The refractive index of every fifth fraction was determined and a small aliquot of each fraction was analyzed by liquid scintillation counting to determine the distribution of cellular genomic DNA in the gradient. The remainder of each fraction was passed over a 1-ml G-50 spin column to remove the CsCl and then denatured with NaOH, neutralized, and dot-blotted to nitrocellulose. The nitrocellulose filters were hybridized first to a pBR322 probe to detect the pSV-Neo-BPV episome. The probe was stripped from the filter by washing with boiling water, and then the filter was rehybridized to a rDNA probe to detect the position of cellular DNA. In some cases the gradient fractions were run on 1% agarose gels and Southern-blotted to confirm that all episomal forms replicated equivalently.

In vitro replication

Cell extracts were prepared and reactions performed exactly as described by Stillman and Gluzman (1985). However, in all cases crude cytosolic extracts instead of S-100s were used. The template for the reaction was the plasmid pSV-ori, which contains SV40 nucleotides 5171–499 (*Hin*dIII-*Hpa*I) cloned into the *Hin*dIII - *Eco*RI sites of the vector pAT153. Reactions contained 100 ng of DNA and 1–2 μg of T antigen and were carried out for 1 hour. Incorporation of dCMP was monitored by passing the reactions over 1-ml G-50 spin columns to remove the unincorporated nucleoside triphosphates.

Acknowledgments

I would like to thank Bruce Stillman for encouragement and help with the SV40 in vitro system, Greg Prelich for the gift of purified PCNA, and Gennarro Durso for the purified topoisomerase I. I thank Billy Forrester for expert advice on the use of the elutriator, and Pam Becker for technical insight. This work was partially supported by a grant from the National Institutes of Health to Hal Weintraub. J.R. is a Lucille Markey Scholar in biomedical science.

References

Abeles, A., K. Snyder, and D. Chattoraj. 1984. P1 plasmid replication: Replicon structure. *J. Mol. Biol.* **173:** 307.

DeTerra, N. 1967. Macronuclear DNA synthesis in *Stentor*: Regulation by a cytoplasmic initiator. *Proc. Natl. Acad. Sci.* **57:** 607.

Gluzman, Y. 1981. SV40-transformed simian cells support the replication of early SV40 mutants. *Cell* **23:** 175.

Itoh, T. and J.-I. Tomizawa. 1980. Formation of an RNA primer for initiation of replication of ColE1 DNA by ribonuclease H. *Proc. Natl. Acad. Sci.* **77:** 2450.

Li, J. and T. Kelly. 1984. Simian virus 40 DNA replication in vitro. *Proc. Natl. Acad. Sci.* **81:** 6973.

Meistrich, M. 1983. Experimental factors involved in separation by centrifugal elutriation. In *Cell separation: Methods and selected applications* (ed. T. Pretlow II and T. Pretlow), vol. 2, p. 33. Academic Press, New York.

Novick, R. and F. Hoppensteadt. 1978. On plasmid incompatibility. *Plasmid* **1:** 421.

Ord, M. 1969. Control of DNA synthesis in *Amoeba proteus*. *Nature* **221:** 964.

Pal, S., R. Mason, and D. Chattoraj. 1986. P1 plasmid replication. Role of initiator titration in copy number control. *J. Mol. Biol.* **192:** 275.

Rao, P. and R. Johnson. 1970. Mammalian cell fusion: Studies on the regulation of DNA synthesis and mitosis. *Nature* **225:** 159.

Roberts, J. and H. Weintraub. 1986. Negative control of DNA replication in composite SV40-bovine papilloma virus plasmids. *Cell* **46:** 741.

Shafferman, A., R. Kolter, D. Stalker, and D. Helinski. 1982. Plasmid R6K DNA replication. III. Regulatory properties of the pi initiation protein. *J. Mol. Biol.* **161:** 57.

Stillman, B. and Y. Gluzman. 1985. Replication and supercoiling of simian virus 40 DNA in cell extracts from human cells. *Mol. Cell. Biol.* **5:** 2051.

Dissection of DNA Replication and Enhancer Activation Functions of Epstein-Barr Virus Nuclear Antigen 1

J.L. Yates and S.M. Camiolo

Department of Human Genetics, Roswell Park Memorial Institute,
New York State Department of Health, Buffalo, New York 14263

The genome of Epstein-Barr virus (EBV) is maintained as a plasmid in latently infected cells through the action of a viral nuclear protein, EBNA1, and a *cis*-acting region, *oriP*. *oriP* contains two essential *cis*-acting components, each containing multiple EBNA1 binding sites. One is a region of dyad symmetry, and the other is a family of 30-bp repeats that can act as a transcriptional enhancer when activated by the presence of EBNA1. To investigate the relationship between activation of the 30-bp repeat enhancer by EBNA1 and *oriP*-dependent DNA replication, a deletion analysis of the *EBNA1* gene was undertaken. No deletion could be found to separate enhancer activation from replication activity, suggesting a common mechanism for activation of the two processes. The analysis revealed that only the DNA-binding domain and short, highly basic regions of the protein are very important for either activity when measured 3–4 days after introducing DNA into cells. However, additional regions of EBNA1, including its highly acidic carboxyl terminus, are required to stably maintain *oriP*-carrying plasmids under selection.

Two distinct systems of EBV DNA replication

EBV, like other herpesviruses, infects most humans for life, usually without symptoms. Lifelong infection by EBV is generally believed to involve the latent infection of epithelial cells of the oropharynx and B cells of the immune system. In contrast to neurotropic herpesviruses such as herpes simplex virus (HSV) that establish latency in nondividing neurons, EBV must maintain its latent genomes in cells that have the potential to divide. B cells latently infected by EBV are transformed into blasts in vivo and in vitro and will proliferate indefinitely in culture (for reviews, see zur Hausen 1981; Miller 1985). In such B-lymphoblastoid cell lines established by EBV infection, viral genomes are maintained as full-length (172 kb), covalently closed, circular plasmids usually at 5–50 copies per cell (Kashka-Dierich et al. 1977; Anvret and Miller 1981). When vegetative production of virus is induced, the circular genomes carried in latently infected cells are ready templates for amplification, which is presumed to involve a rolling circle mechanism as with HSV (Roizman and Batterson 1985). For these distinct biological functions of maintaining its DNA in latently infected cells and amplifying its DNA during virus production, EBV uses two distinct systems to replicate its DNA. This article addresses only the replication of EBV DNA during latency.

Latent EBV plasmid genomes are replicated by the cell's DNA replication machinery during S phase of the cell cycle (Hampar et al. 1974), resulting in a (usually) stable number of genome copies per cell. Replication of EBV latent plasmid genomes may thus be a useful model for the controlled replication of mammalian cellular DNA. Latent EBV DNA replication requires a single virally encoded protein, Epstein-Barr viral nuclear antigen 1 (EBNA1), and an 1800-bp, *cis*-acting region, *oriP* (Yates et al. 1984, 1985). In contrast, during vegetative viral replication, EBV DNA is replicated by a virally encoded DNA polymerase (Miller et al. 1977; Baer et al. 1984), presumably requires other EBV-encoded homologs of HSV proteins that are essential for replication of HSV DNA (Olivo and Challberg, this volume), and is amplified to 5,000–10,000 genomes per cell prior to cell death. *cis*-Acting signals responsible for initiation of vegetative EBV DNA synthesis have not been identified. *oriP* is not involved, or at least is not a sufficient signal, since induction of EBV replication in cell lines carrying stable *oriP*-containing plasmids increased the number of resident EBV genomes by up to 100-fold while the *oriP*-carrying plasmids increased by less than twofold (J. Yates, unpubl.).

Activation of *oriP* by EBNA1

Several observations suggest that EBNA1 activates *oriP* by binding to multiple sites in two separate regions of *oriP* having distinct functions. These two regions, a 20-member family of 30-bp repeats and a 140-bp region containing a 65-bp dyad symmetry located almost 1000 bp away, contain the only essential DNA of *oriP* (see Fig. 1). Both regions must be present in *cis*, yet they exhibit remarkable spatial independence, supporting replication about as well in the opposite relative orientation or when the distance between them is either eliminated or increased to over 5000 bp (Reisman et al. 1985; Reisman 1986). Studies using a carboxy-terminal fragment of EBNA1 produced in *Escherichia coli* indicate that EBNA1 can specifically bind to multiple sites in both regions of *oriP*, recognizing an 18-bp sequence present in each 30-bp repeat and present four times in the region

197

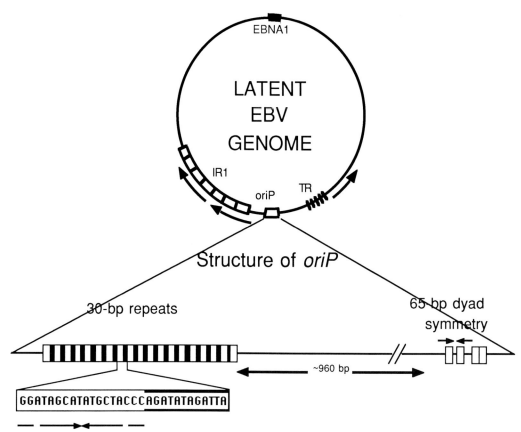

Figure 1 Maintenance of EBV plasmid genome in latently infected cells. Shown is the EBV circular genome (172 kbp) with the positions of the *EBNA1* gene, *oriP*, the large internal repeat (IR1), and the terminal repeats (TR) (scale not exact). Positions of the major start sites for latent transcription are indicated by arrows. Below is shown the structure of *oriP*, in opposite orientation to its occurrence on the genome. Open boxes represent EBNA1 binding sites present in the region of dyad symmetry and in each 30-bp repeat. The consensus sequence of the 30-bp repeats is shown, with arrows covering the symmetric EBNA1 binding site.

of dyad symmetry (Rawlins et al. 1985). The 65-bp dyad symmetry of *oriP* containing two symmetrically positioned EBNA1 binding sites is structurally analogous to the core replication origin of SV40 of which symmetric T-antigen binding sites are part of a larger dyad symmetry. If, by this analogy, the dyad symmetry region is presumed to be the actual origin of DNA replication, then the tandem array of EBNA1 binding sites that constitute the 30-bp repeats may be viewed as performing a requisite role in the activation of this origin. The fact that this activation of replication occurs with little regard to relative orientation or to distance between the 30-bp repeats and the region of dyad symmetry suggested an analogy to the activation of transcription by enhancer elements. This reasoning led to experiments that showed that the family of 30-bp repeats can act as a strong transcriptional enhancer. As with replication of DNA carrying intact *oriP*, enhancer activity of the 30-bp repeats is entirely dependent on the presence of EBNA1 (Reisman et al. 1985; Reisman and Sugden 1986).

The enhancer activity of the 30-bp repeats in conjunction with EBNA1 could have two possibly independent functions. Polyomaviral DNA replication requires the presence of at least one of the regions having enhancer activity adjacent to its origin (Muller et al. 1983; de

Villiers et al. 1984). Replication of SV40 viral DNA requires the presence of either the 21-bp repeats carrying recognition sites for transcription factor Sp1 or the 72-bp repeat enhancer (Bergsma et al. 1982; Hertz and Mertz 1986). Hence, the same property of the 30-bp repeats and EBNA1 that is manifested as transcriptional enhancement when a test promoter is placed on the same DNA molecule may be essential to allow initiation of replication at *oriP*. Alternatively, EBNA1 may activate replication through its interaction with the 30-bp repeats by a mechanism independent of enhancer function; the EBNA1-dependent enhancer activity may instead be a second function, important only for activation and regulation of transcription from one or more viral promoters. The transcription start site that is closest to *oriP* and active during latent infection has been proposed to lie 3300 bp from the 30-bp repeats, directing transcription away from *oriP* (clockwise in Fig. 1; Bodescot et al. 1986). Recent experiments strongly suggest the existence of a promoter at this site that is dependent on both the 30-bp repeats and EBNA1 for activity (B. Sugden and N. Warren, pers. comm.). Given the distance and orientation independence of the 30-bp repeat enhancer (Reisman and Sugden 1986) and evidence that some enhancers may concurrently activate two promoters separated by more than 15 kbp (Wang and Calame 1985), it is conceivable that transcription from more distant latent promoters located within IR1 (Sample et al. 1986; Speck et al. 1986) or across the joined termini (Fennewald et al. 1984) is activated to some degree by the 30-bp repeats and EBNA1 (see Fig. 1).

As an approach to investigating the role of enhancer activation in *oriP*-dependent DNA replication, a deletion analysis of the EBNA1 gene was undertaken. In defining regions of the EBNA1 protein that are most important for DNA replication and for enhancer activity, we sought to determine whether the two activities could be easily separated. The results of this analysis imply that enhancer activity is required for efficient DNA replication and that the two processes share a common, essential step. Somewhat unexpectedly, some mutants were found that support replication of *oriP*-containing DNA soon after its introduction into cells, but cannot support

the maintenance of these plasmids for many generations in cultured cells. These findings and their possible significance are discussed below.

Materials and Methods

Deletion constructions

Deletions were constructed using derivatives of pBR322 or pUC12 carrying the *EBNA1* gene. All deletion endpoints were made from restriction enzyme cleavage sites except for the amino-terminal endpoints of *dl*48, *dl*49, and *dl*96, which were created by digestion with *Bal*31 nuclease. The details of these constructions will be published elsewhere. All deletions were transferred to p367 using the *Avr*II and *Hind*III sites indicated in Figure 2 or using *Avr*II and *Sst*I, which cuts within the *EBNA1* gene. The chloramphenicol acetyltransferase (*CAT*) gene-*EBNA1* gene fusion, constructed on pRSV-

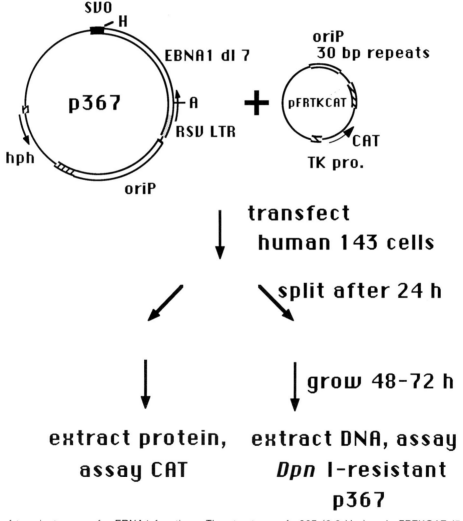

Figure 2 Outline of transient assays for EBNA1 functions. The structures of p367 (9.9 kbp) and pFRTKCAT (5.2 kbp) and the experimental protocol are shown. (SVO) Origin of SV40; (hph) hygromycin phosphotransferase gene; (hatched boxes) promoter and 3'-flanking region of the HSV TK gene; (CAT) chloramphenicol acetyltransferase gene; (A and H) *Avr*II and *Hind*III sites in p367. Because p367 contains *oriP* and the *hph* selectable marker, providing resistance to hygromycin B, its derivatives carrying *EBNA1* mutations can also be tested for long-term plasmid maintenance. The SV40 origin allows the mutant EBNA1 polypeptides to be easily detected in COS cells.

cat (Gorman et al. 1982), fuses the amino-terminal 38 codons of the *CAT* gene to codon eight of the *EBNA1* gene. *dl*43 and *sub*43 were constructed by deleting two base pairs from the *Sst*II site in the *EBNA1* gene; for *sub*43, an 8-bp *Sal*I linker (GGTCGACC) was inserted. Deletions removing most of IR3 from the *EBNA1* gene arose spontaneously in different *EBNA1* mutant backgrounds during the propagation of plasmids in *E. coli*. These deletions, similar to *dl*7 in size, are each denoted "*dl*GA" although they arose independently.

Transfection assays

For transient assays, human 143 cells grown in 10-cm dishes were transfected with 15 μg p367 or the plasmid being tested plus 5 μg pFRTKCAT using the calcium phosphate method as described previously (Yates et al. 1984). CAT assays were similar to those described previously (Gorman et al. 1982), using approximately 150 μg of extracted protein. Levels of enhancement were obtained by comparing the amount of CAT activity obtained with a given mutant to that obtained using p392, a plasmid like p367 but lacking all except 14 codons of the *EBNA1* gene. Low-molecular-mass DNA was extracted, then DNA from 5×10^6 cells was digested with *Bam*HI to linearize the plasmids and with *Dpn*I to digest unreplicated molecules, and analyzed on agarose gels followed by Southern blots using labeled pHEBo DNA as a probe, as described earlier (Yates et al. 1985). pHEBo is essentially p367 lacking the RSV-LTR, the *EBNA1* gene, and the SV40 origin (Fig. 2).

To test for stable replication of plasmids, duplicate 6-cm dishes of 143 cells were transfected with 2.5 μg of plasmid, trypsinized and replated after 24 hours, and selected in medium containing 250 μg hygromycin B per ml beginning 48 hours after transfection. Resistant colonies were pooled, propagated under selection for 18–22 population doublings from the time of colony seeding, and their low-molecular-mass DNA was harvested and analyzed by Southern blots of agarose gels.

Results

A series of small, in-frame deletions were constructed so as to cover almost the entire EBNA1 open reading frame (see Fig. 5, below). Because the EBNA1 protein contains some unusual repetitive amino acid sequences, several deletions were designed specifically to test the possible significance of these structures. About one-third of the 641-amino-acid protein is a repetitive glycine-plus-alanine sequence (denoted Gly-Ala) encoded by a triplet-repeat array of variable length (Hennessy et al. 1983; Baer et al. 1984). Removal of more than 95% of this region by the *dl*7 mutation was previously shown to have no detrimental effect on plasmid maintenance (Yates et al. 1985). Other repetitive amino acid sequences include an (Arg-Gly)$_5$ sequence preceding the Gly-Ala region, a highly basic stretch of 56 amino acids containing six copies of the sequence Arg-Gly-Arg-Gly just following the Gly-Ala array, a cluster of serines and a cluster of prolines and arginines immediately after this

basic region, and a highly acidic carboxyl terminus. Each of these structures was specifically deleted.

The methods used to test the EBNA1 mutants are outlined in Figure 2. For transient assays of replication and transcriptional enhancement, the plasmid p367 carrying the mutant to be tested was mixed with pFRTKCAT and transfected into human 143 cells. pFRTKCAT contains the family of 30-bp repeats of *oriP* and the *CAT* gene linked to the HSV-1 promoter of the thymidine kinase gene (Fig. 2B). pFRTKCAT provides a sensitive assay for the enhancer function of the 30-bp repeats as CAT synthesis from pFRTKCAT is increased 70- to 200-fold in the presence of EBNA1 (Reisman and Sugden 1986). The transfected cells were incubated for 3–4 days prior to harvest and split so that the same population of transfected cells could be used to measure both replication of *oriP*-carrying p367 (or mutant derivative) by measuring *Dpn*I-resistant p367 DNA and enhancement of transcription from the TK promoter on pFRTKCAT by measuring CAT enzyme levels. Examples of the transient replication assays and long term plasmid maintenance assays are described below.

Replication of p367 and derivatives carrying several EBNA1 deletion mutants in a transient assay are shown in Figure 3. Two plasmids were used as negative controls. pSM1, like p367 but lacking the RSV-LTR and the *EBNA1* gene, and p366, like p367 but lacking most of the *EBNA1* gene, produced weak signals of the expected mobility. To ensure that digestion with *Dpn*I was complete, DNA extracted from mock-transfected cells was mixed with p367 DNA and analyzed in parallel. No *Dpn*I-resistant DNA could be seen (first two lanes, Fig. 3). The low-level, EBNA1-independent replication observed with pSM1 and p366 was also observed with plasmids lacking both the SV40 origin and *oriP*; it therefore appears to be sequence-nonspecific (data not shown). EBNA1-dependent replication observed with p367 was 200 times the background, nonspecific level. In the experiment of Figure 3, all mutants tested except *dl*100 supported replication at 30–60% of the level of *dl*7. Since *dl*7 is typically twice as active as wild type in the transient assays, these mutants exhibit close to wild-type activity. *dl*100, a large deletion in the amino-terminal half, had no detectable activity.

An experiment testing the ability of several mutants to support long-term maintenance of plasmids under selection is shown in Figure 4. 143 cells were transfected with p367 or the deletion-carrying derivatives and cultured in the presence of hygromycin B. After 10–14 days, drug-resistant colonies were pooled from each plate and grown under selection for 18–22 population doublings from the time of colony formation. Extrachromosomal DNA was then isolated and analyzed for the presence of the introduced plasmids. Several mutants supported maintenance of the plasmids at multiple copies per cell, but with others, free plasmids were undetectable or present at less than one copy per cell. (In Fig. 4, 50 pg of p367 loaded in parallel lanes corresponds to 1 molecule per cell.) For mutants *dl*90 and *dl*3, only one of the duplicate selected populations

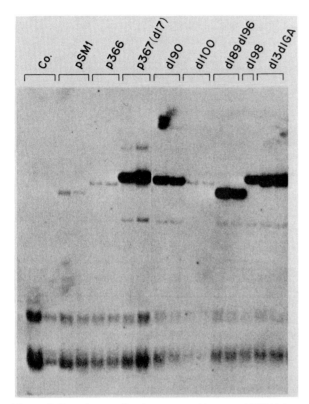

Figure 3 Transient replication assay with several EBNA1 mutants. Duplicate transfections with DNAs carrying the indicated mutations were carried out as described in Materials and Methods. Control samples from mock-transfected cells were digested with *Dpn*I and *Bam*HI after the addition of 1 ng and 0.2 ng of p367 DNA (lanes marked Co.). The plasmid carrying *dl*89*dl*96 is reduced in size because of an additional *Bam*HI site resulting from a linker present at the deletion junctions of *dl*89. The additional *Dpn*I-resistant DNA seen migrating ahead of p367 (9.9 kbp) in some lanes is pFRTKCAT (5.2 kbp), which was cointroduced into cells. Approximately fourfold more *Dpn*I-resistant pFRTKCAT is present in DNA from cells cotransfected with p367 than in DNA from cells cotransfected with pSM1 or p366, plasmids lacking EBNA1. This EBNA1-dependent replication, consistently about 1–2% of the level seen with the *oriP*-carrying plasmid in the same cells, is dependent on the 30-bp repeats carried by pFRTKCAT (data not shown). An over-exposed autoradiogram is shown so that the weak, EBNA1-dependent replication of pFRTKCAT could be seen.

carried plasmids at an average number of more than one copy per cell. In addition, most of the plasmid molecules that persisted with these mutants were represented by a series of lower mobility bands on the gels, presumably representing concatameric forms of the plasmids. These differences are interpreted to indicate a limited efficiency of plasmid maintenance for these mutants and are believed to have resulted from a small number of clones having given rise to most of the cells in the expanded populations. The four original populations contained 30–120 clones, but these varied greatly in size. For *dl*3 the impaired ability to support plasmid maintenance is consistent with its very low levels of replication and enhancer activation observed in transient assays. *dl*90, in contrast, showed close to wild-type activities in the transient assays and is discussed below along with

other mutants that support replication transiently, but do not support stable maintenance of plasmids under selection.

Regions of the EBNA1 protein required for enhancer activation, transient replication, and plasmid maintenance

The structures of all deletions constructed in the *EBNA1* gene and their resulting activities are presented in Figure 5. Although the experiments have not been completed for some mutants, three observations may be made to summarize the existing data. First, no mutation was found to separate enhancer activation and replication activity in transient assays. Whereas the activities resulting from different deletions ranged from barely detectable to greater than wild type, for all mutants tested, the two activities as percentages of the wild-type levels were within a factor of 2 of equality.

A second observation is that the only regions of EBNA1 that appear to be very important for activity measured in transient assays are the carboxy-terminal third of the protein, which contains the DNA-binding domain (Rawlins et al. 1985), and the very basic regions in the amino-terminal half of the protein. Most deletions affecting the amino-terminal two-thirds of the protein, amino acids 1–451, allow normal levels of replication and enhancement of transcription in transient assays. *dl*7, which lacks over 95% of the 227-amino-acid, Gly-Ala repetitive region, is consistently about twice as active as wild type in both transient assays. *dl*90, lacking the entire Gly-Ala coding region and some flanking sequences on both sides, is almost as active as wild type for both activities. Of the deletions that lie on the amino-terminal side of the Gly-Ala region, only *dl*3 (codons 40–61) reduces EBNA1 activity significantly. *dl*3 removes a basic region of the protein including a (Gly-Arg)$_5$ sequence. However, although *dl*3 exhibited only 10% activity in transient assays, the mutant *dl*3*dl*GA, which lacks most of the Gly-Ala region as well as codons 40–61 removed by *dl*3, was indistinguishable from wild type in both activities. Similar results were obtained with *dl*107. This deletion (amino acids 332–347) removes two copies of a basic, 8-amino-acid sequence that is repeated three and one-half times in the B95-8 sequence immediately following the Gly-Ala repeats. Enhancement was reduced to 30% of the wild-type level with *dl*107, but enhancement and replication were fully active with *dl*107*dl*GA, which additionally lacks most of the Gly-Ala region. *dl*45, which includes *dl*107 and removes the entire 53-amino-acid, highly basic region, caused a 90% reduction in enhancement activity. Within the first 451 amino acids of EBNA1, only these basic regions appear to be very important for enhancement and replication activities measured by transient assays; deletions affecting any other regions of the amino-terminal two-thirds of EBNA1 had only slight effects.

It remains a possibility that the inactivity of some EBNA1 mutants results from a failure of the altered proteins to be localized to the nucleus or from rapid

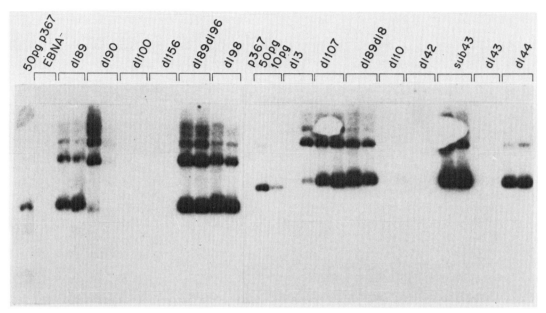

Figure 4 Ability of EBNA1 mutants to support plasmid maintenance. Southern blot analyses of DNA from duplicate cultures selected to carry indicated plasmids are shown. DNA from 5×10^6 cells was analyzed. 50 pg p367 corresponds to one molecule per cell. Control cultures (EBNA1 −) were selected to carry p392, which lacks the EBNA1 gene.

degradation of the proteins rather than an intrinsic loss of function. However, we have found that two mutants with very low activity, *dl*56 in the DNA binding domain and *dl*100, which removes most of the amino-terminal half, are both localized to the nucleus and accumulate to about the same levels as wild-type EBNA1 in COS cells (data not shown).

A third finding is that some deletions allow close to normal activity in transient assays but are less active in supporting the maintenance of plasmids for many generations under selection. *dl*90, lacking the entire Gly-Ala region and some flanking sequences in both sides of it, is as active as wild type within a factor of 2 in transient assays, yet it has an impaired ability to support long-term maintenance of plasmids, as mentioned above. Two other deletions, *dl*10, which removes most of a proline-arginine cluster near the middle of the polypeptide, and *dl*43, which removes its acidic tail, produce activities in the transient assays that are at least 50% of the wild-type levels, but the plasmids are soon lost during selection of transfected cells, with only 0.2 or fewer copies per cell remaining after approximately 20 population doublings (Figs. 4 and 5). Preliminary data suggest that two deletions adjacent to *dl*10, *dl*48 and *dl*49, have similar properties.

The following comparisons suggest that the failure of *dl*10 and *dl*43 to support long-term maintenance of *oriP*-carrying plasmids does not result from the slightly reduced replication or enhancement activities observed in transient assays. Two deletions that caused transient activities to be reduced to 10–30% of wild-type levels, *dl*107 and *dl*44, nevertheless allowed plasmids to be maintained in drug-selected populations at 3–6 copies per cell for the same period of time. *dl*43 is a 2-bp deletion in codon 619 that results in the replacement of

the 22-amino-acid, acidic carboxyl terminus with two glycines by shifting the translational reading frame. *sub*43, an in-frame substitution at codon 619, is similar to *dl*10 and *dl*43 in transient assays, slightly below wild type, yet it is fully active in maintaining *oriP*-carrying plasmids under selection (Figs. 4 and 5).

The regions of the EBNA1 protein inferred from these experiments to be most important for its different activities are diagramed in Figure 6.

Discussion

The analysis of replication and enhancer activation functions of EBNAs by testing a series of in-frame deletions throughout its gene has led to three main conclusions. The first two conclusions, that only short, basic regions of EBNA1 and its DNA binding domain are very important for enhancer activation and replication in transient assays and that the two functions require the same, or closely overlapping, parts of the protein, suggest that these two functions are closely related. The third finding, that some regions of EBNA1 are dispensable for enhancer activation and for transient replication of *oriP*-carrying DNA but are required to support stable replication of these DNAs under selection, is more difficult to interpret, but may imply the existence of a qualitative difference between the stable replication of EBV-derived plasmids in dividing cells and the first few rounds of replication that occur immediately after the introduction of DNA into cells.

Given the previous examples of involvement of transcription factors in DNA replication with other animal viruses, the failure to find EBNA1 mutants inactive in enhancement but active in replication is not surprising. However, there is no reason to think that the replication

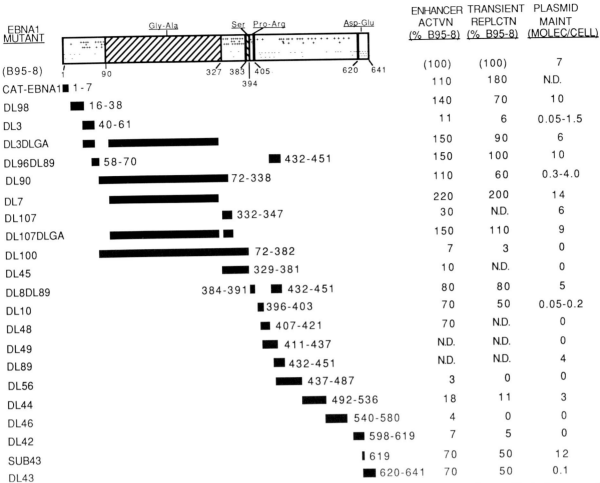

EBNA1 MUTANT	(deletion)	ENHANCER ACTVN (% B95-8)	TRANSIENT REPLCTN (% B95-8)	PLASMID MAINT (MOLEC/CELL)
(B95-8)		(100)	(100)	7
CAT-EBNA1	1-7	110	180	N.D.
DL98	16-38	140	70	10
DL3	40-61	11	6	0.05-1.5
DL3DLGA		150	90	6
DL96DL89	58-70 / 432-451	150	100	10
DL90	72-338	110	60	0.3-4.0
DL7		220	200	14
DL107	332-347	30	N.D.	6
DL107DLGA		150	110	9
DL100	72-382	7	3	0
DL45	329-381	10	N.D.	0
DL8DL89	384-391 / 432-451	80	80	5
DL10	396-403	70	50	0.05-0.2
DL48	407-421	70	N.D.	0
DL49	411-437	N.D.	N.D.	0
DL89	432-451	N.D.	N.D.	4
DL56	437-487	3	0	0
DL44	492-536	18	11	3
DL46	540-580	4	0	0
DL42	598-619	7	5	0
SUB43	619	70	50	12
DL43	620-641	70	50	0.1

Figure 5 Activities of EBNA1 mutants. The amino acids deleted for each mutant are shown beneath a diagram illustrating some of the salient features of the EBNA1 polypeptide. A small + or − indicates the position of each basic or acidic amino acid. On the right are shown the activities of each mutant, in most cases, an average of two experiments containing duplicates. Levels of enhancer activation and replication in transient assays are indicated as a percentage of the value obtained with B95-8 EBNA1. Enhancement with wild-type EBNA1 ranged from 60-fold to 200-fold. Transient assays of *dl*107, *dl*45, and *dl*48 were from single experiments. Levels of transient replication and plasmid maintenance were determined from densitometric scans of appropriately exposed autoradiograms of experiments similar to those shown in Figs. 4 and 5. The limit of detection for measuring plasmids maintained under selection was about 0.02 molecules per cell. N.D. indicates not done.

activity of EBNA1 would be required for enhancement. The 30-bp repeats of *oriP* alone, in the absence of the dyad symmetry region, can enhance transcription in the presence of EBNA1 but have virtually no ability to be replicated. In addition, in mouse BALB/c 3T3 cells, which are nonpermissive for maintenance of EBV-derived plasmids (Yates et al. 1985), EBNA1 can activate the 30-bp repeat enhancer of *oriP* but cannot support *oriP*-dependent replication in transient assays (J. Mecsas and B. Sugden, pers. comm.). This finding suggests that EBV plasmid replication requires an activity of EBNA1 (or of *oriP*) in addition to what is needed for enhancer activation, such as the interaction with a host protein involved in DNA replication. In the case of SV40, which is similar to EBV plasmids in that it replicates in monkey or human cells, but not in mouse cells, SV40 T antigen forms complexes with both the host protein p53 (Lane and Crawford 1979) and with DNA polymerase α (Smale and Tjian 1986). The inability of SV40 to repli-

cate in mouse cells has been explained by a failure of T antigen to associate properly with mouse DNA polymerase α (Murakami et al. 1986), perhaps due in part to an improper, competing association with mouse p53 (Gannon and Lane 1987). It might have been expected, then, that some EBNA1 deletions would result in the loss of replication activity without a loss in enhancement activity. One possible explanation for the failure to find such a mutant is that the region of EBNA1 that interacts with the host-specific factor required for replication is part of the DNA-binding domain of the protein, and so the deletions that remove or disrupt this structure result in a loss of both activities. Another quite distinct possibility is that the host-specific factor acts by recognizing *oriP*, perhaps in the region of dyad symmetry, rather than solely through an interaction with EBNA1.

The finding that only a small portion of the EBNA1 polypeptide outside of its DNA binding domain is very important for enhancer activation or for transient replica-

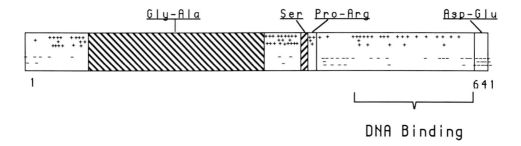

Figure 6 Regions of the EBNA1 polypeptide required for its functions. The Gly-Ala repeats, serine cluster, Pro-Arg cluster, and acidic carboxyl terminus are indicated. Each charged amino acid is indicated by a + or −. Regions of the protein required for enhancement of transcription and DNA replication in transient assays and for plasmid maintenance are indicated by solid lines where removal of a region results in less than 10% activity, and by dotted lines where removal of a region results in 10–30% activity or where the region is required only if the Gly-Ala region is present. Mutants have not been tested for the ability to bind to *oriP*. The DNA binding "domain" indicated is the region previously shown to bind specifically to *oriP* (Rawlins et al. 1985) except that the acidic tail has been excluded because of the activity of *dl* 43 in transient assays.

tion is similar to results obtained from studies with other transcriptional activating proteins. With the GAL4 (Ma and Ptashne 1987), GCN4 (Hope and Struhl 1986), and ADR1 (Hartshorne et al. 1986) proteins of yeast and with the rat or human glucocorticoid receptor proteins (Godowski et al. 1987; Hollenberg et al. 1987), large portions of the molecules can be removed without abolishing transcriptional activation. In contrast to the importance of highly basic regions of EBNA1 for enhancer activation, highly acidic regions of yeast GAL4 and GCN4 proteins appear to carry the transcriptional activating function. The very acidic 22-amino-acid tail of EBNA1 is essential for maintenance of *oriP*-carrying plasmids, but appears to contribute little to enhancer activation or to transient replication.

The requirements of more of the EBNA1 protein to support maintenance of plasmids than to support replication transiently is not presently understood. Additional experiments are necessary to rule out the possibility that this difference arises through an artifact of the transfection process, such as a very high level of transient EBNA1 gene expression that is not maintained, for example. However, one possible explanation is that the state of chromatin of introduced DNAs changes with time so that the DNA is less accessible to the cellular replication factors following the initial few rounds of DNA synthesis and that EBNA1 may act to alter chromatin structure. In this regard, it is worth noting the property of EBNA1 of associating with metaphase chromosomes (Reedman and Klein 1973; Grogan et al. 1983). We are in the process of testing the deleted forms of EBNA1 for the ability to associate with meta-

phase chromosomes in order to assess the functional significance of this property.

The deletion analysis of the *EBNA1* gene provides a starting point for investigating molecular mechanisms of the transcriptional activation and replication functions of the EBNA1 protein. In the future, we hope that the mutants will be useful in assigning biochemical properties, determined in vitro, to regions of the protein and in correlating the biochemical properties to function in vivo.

Acknowledgments

We thank Jules O'Rear and Lisa Davis for their comments on the manuscript. This work was supported by grants RO1 CA-43122 from the National Institutes of Health and IN-54Y from the American Cancer Society.

References

Anvret, M. and G. Miller. 1981. Copy number and location of Epstein-Barr viral genomes in neonatal human lymphocytes transformed after separation by size and treatment with mitogens. *Virology* 111: 47.

Baer, R., A.T. Bankier, M.D. Biggin, P.L. Dieninger, P.J. Farrell, T.J. Gibson, G. Hatfull, G.S. Hudson, S.C. Satchwell, C. Sequin, P.S. Tuffnell, and B.G. Barrell. 1984. DNA sequence and expression of the B95-8 Epstein-Barr virus genome. *Nature* 310: 207.

Bergsma, D.J., D.M. Olive, S. W. Hartzell, and K.N. Subramanian. 1982. Territorial limits and functional anatomy of the simian virus 40 replication origin. *Proc. Natl. Acad. Sci.* 79: 381.

Bodescot, M., O. Brison, and M. Perricaudet. 1986. An Epstein-Barr virus transcription unit is at least 84 kilobases long. *Nucleic Acids Res.* **14:** 2611.

de Villiers, J., W. Schaffner, C. Tyndall, S. Lupton, and R. Kamen. 1984. Polyoma virus DNA replication requires an enhancer. *Nature* **312:** 242.

Fennewald, S., V. van Santen, and E. Keiff. 1984. Nucleotide sequences of an mRNA transcribed in latent growth-transforming virus infection indicates that it may encode a membrane protein. *J. Virol.* **51:** 411.

Gannon, T.V. and D. P. Lane. 1987. p53 and DNA polymerase-alpha compete for binding to SV40 T antigen. *Nature* **329:** 456.

Godowski, P.T., S. Rusconi, R. Miesfield, and K.R. Yamamoto. 1987. Glucocorticoid receptor mutants that are constitutive activators of transcriptional enhancement. *Nature* **325:** 365.

Gorman, C.M., G.T. Merlino, M.C. Willingham, I. Pastan, and B.H. Howard. 1982. The Rous sarcoma virus long terminal repeat is a strong promoter when introduced into a variety of eukaryotic cells by DNA-mediated transfection. *Proc. Natl. Acad. Sci.* **79:** 6777.

Grogan, E.A., W.P. Summers, S. Dowling, D. Shedd, L. Gradeville, and G. Miller. 1983. Two Epstein-Barr viral nuclear neoantigens distinguished by gene transfer. *Proc. Natl. Acad. Sci.* **80:** 7650.

Hampar, B., A. Tanaka, M. Nonayama, and J.G. Derge. 1974. Replication of the resident repressed Epstein-Barr virus genome during the early S phase (S-1 period) of non-producer Raji cells. *Proc. Natl. Acad. Sci.* **71:** 631.

Hartshorne, T.A., H. Blumberg, and E.T. Young. 1986. Sequence homology of yeast regulatory protein ADR1 with *Xenopus* transcription factor TFIIIA. *Nature* **320:** 283.

Hennessy, K., M. Heller, V. van Santen, and E. Kieff. 1983. A simple repeat array in Epstein-Barr virus DNA encodes part of EBNA1 Epstein-Barr virus nuclear antigen. *Science* **220:** 1396.

Hertz, G.Z. and J.E. Mertz. 1986. Bidirectional promoter elements of simian virus 40 are required for efficient replication of the viral DNA. *Mol. Cell. Biol.* **6:** 3513.

Hollenberg, S.M., V. Giguere, P. Segui, and R.M. Evans. 1987. Colocalization of DNA-binding and transcriptional activation functions in the human glucocorticoid receptor. *Cell* **49:** 39.

Hope, I. and K. Struhl. 1986. Functional dissection of a eukaryotic transcriptional activator protein, GCN4 of yeast. *Cell* **46:** 885.

Kashka-Dierich, C., L. Falk, G. Bjursell, A. Adams, and T. Lindahl. 1977. Human lymphoblastoid cell lines derived from individuals without lymphoproliferative disease contain the same latent forms of Epstein-Barr virus DNA as those found in tumor cells. *Int. J. Cancer* **20:** 173.

Lane, D.P. and L.V. Crawford. 1979. T antigen is bound to a host protein in SV40-transformed cells. *Nature* **278:** 261.

Ma, T. and M. Ptashne. 1987. Deletion analysis of *GAL4* defines two transcriptional activating segments. *Cell* **48:** 847.

Miller, G. 1985. Epstein-Barr virus. In *Virology* (ed. B.N. Fields et al.), p. 563. Raven Press, New York.

Miller, R.L., R. Glaser, and F. Rapp. 1977. Studies of an Epstein-Barr virus-induced DNA polymerase. *Virology* **76:** 494.

Muller, W.J., C.R. Mueller, A.-M. Mes, and J.A. Hassell. 1983. Polyomavirus origin for DNA replication comprises multiple genetic elements. *J. Virol.* **47:** 586.

Murakami, Y., C.R. Wobbe, L. Wiessbach, F.B. Dean, and J. Hurwitz. 1986. Role of DNA polymerase-alpha and DNA primase in simian virus 40 DNA replication in vitro. *Proc. Natl. Acad. Sci.* **83:** 2869.

Rawlins, D., G. Milman, S.D. Hayward, and G.S. Hayward. 1985. Sequence specific DNA binding of the Epstein-Barr virus nuclear antigen (EBNA) to clustered sites in the plasmid maintenance region. *Cell* **42:** 859.

Reedman, B.M. and G. Klein. 1973. Cellular localization of an Epstein-Barr virus (EBV)-associated complement-fixing antigen in producer and non-producer lymphoblastoid cell lines. *Int. J. Cancer* **11:** 499.

Reisman, D. 1986. "*Cis-* and *trans-*activating genetic elements of the Epstein-Barr virus plasmid replicon." Ph.D. thesis, University of Wisconsin, Madison.

Reisman, D. and B. Sugden. 1986. *Trans-*activation of an Epstein-Barr viral transcriptional enhancer by the Epstein-Barr viral nuclear antigen 1. *Mol. Cell. Biol.* **6:** 3838.

Reisman, D., J. Yates, and B. Sugden. 1985. A putative origin of replication of plasmids derived from Epstein-Barr virus is composed of two *cis-*acting components. *Mol. Cell. Biol.* **5:** 1822.

Roizman, B. and W. Batterson. 1985. Herpes viruses and their replication. In *Virology* (ed. B. Fields et al.), p. 497. Raven Press, New York.

Sample, J., M. Hummel, D. Braun, M. Birkenbach, and E. Kieff. 1986. Nucleotide sequences of mRNA encoding Epstein-Barr virus nuclear proteins: A probable transcriptional initiation site. *Proc. Natl. Acad. Sci.* **83:** 5096.

Smale, S.T. and R. Tjian. 1986. T-antigen-DNA polymerase-alpha complex implicated in simian virus 40 DNA replication. *Mol. Cell. Biol.* **6:** 4077.

Speck, S.H., A. Pfitzner, and J.L. Strominger. 1986. An Epstein-Barr virus transcript from a latently infected, growth-transformed B-cell line encodes a highly repetitive polypeptide. *Proc. Natl. Acad. Sci.* **83:** 9298.

Yates, J.L., N. Warren, and B. Sugden. 1985. Stable replication of plasmids derived from Epstein-Barr virus in various mammalian cells. *Nature* **313:** 812.

Yates, J.L., N. Warren, D. Reisman, and B. Sugden. 1984. A *cis-*acting element from the Epstein-Barr viral genome that permits stable replication of recombinant plasmids in latently infected cells. *Proc. Natl. Acad. Sci.* **81:** 3806.

Wang. X.-F. and K. Calame. 1985. The endogenous immunoglobulin heavy chain enhancer can activate tandem V_H promoters separated by a large distance. *Cell* **43:** 659.

zur Hausen, H. 1981. Oncogenic herpesviruses. In *Molecular Biology of tumor viruses*, 2nd edition, revised: *DNA tumor viruses* (ed. J. Tooze), p. 747. Cold Spring Harbor Laboratory, Cold Spring Harbor, New York.

Initiation and Processing of Mitochondrial Displacement-loop Transcripts

J.N. Topper, D.D. Chang, R.P. Fisher, and D.A. Clayton

Department of Pathology, Stanford University School of Medicine,
Stanford, California 94305-5324

Transcription of each strand of vertebrate mitochondrial DNA (mtDNA), heavy (H) and light (L), initiates in the displacement-loop (D-loop) region, and the origin of H-strand replication is located downstream from a major promoter. This promoter is the start point both for gene transcription and for priming of H-strand DNA synthesis. The mitochondrial transcription system is composed of at least two protein entities with a transcription factor, capable of binding specific regions of mtDNA, being required in addition to mitochondrial RNA polymerase. Processing of a transcript complementary to the replication origin sequence is involved in D-loop metabolism and is effected by a site-specific endoribonuclease; this processing activity is a ribonucleoprotein. A currently identified RNA component of the endonuclease is a nucleus-encoded species that, by definition, might be imported to the organelle matrix. Activities isolated from mouse cells and human cells are capable of cleavage at conserved sequence elements in mitochondrial origin regions.

The D-loop region of mtDNA has evolved as a control region for both transcription and replication. Each strand of the circular genome (H and L) is transcribed from a single major promoter situated in the D-loop region (Fig. 1) (Chang and Clayton 1984). Approximately 150 bp separate the transcription start sites, but the two promoters, defined by mutational analyses, do not overlap; i.e., they function essentially independently in vitro (Chang and Clayton 1984, 1986b,c; Hixson and Clayton 1985).

Mammalian mitochondrial promoters have been identified for human (Bogenhagen et al. 1984; Chang and Clayton 1984; Hixson and Clayton 1985) and mouse (Chang and Clayton 1986a,b,c) mtDNAs. Basic promoter organization is preserved at least to *Xenopus* (Bogenhagen and Yoza 1986; Bogenhagen et al. 1986) in the evolutionary tree, and it is likely that all animal systems known to maintain the D-loop structure will have transcriptional regulatory elements that recapitulate at least the major features assigned to human and mouse promoter elements.

The L-strand promoter (LSP) is positioned upstream of the origin of mtDNA replication located in the D loop (O_H). Although this promoter is over 100 bp away, it was a candidate for involvement in priming DNA synthesis. That this is indeed the case was shown for human (Chang and Clayton 1985) and mouse (Chang et al. 1985) mtDNAs. Thus, there is intimate involvement between events surrounding transcription from the LSP and a commitment to DNA replication. A major step in that commitment may be cleavages by one or more RNA processing enzymes to form or facilitate the synthesis of RNA primers.

Results and Discussion

Regulatory region in the D loop

We have reported (Fisher and Clayton 1985; Fisher et al. 1987) the dissociation of the transcriptional machinery of human mitochondria into at least two distinct components: an intrinsically nonselective or weakly selective RNA polymerase, and a mitochondrial tran-

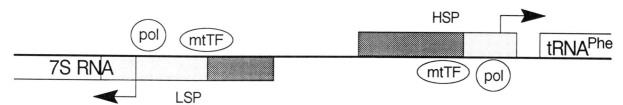

Figure 1 Transcriptional landmarks in the D-loop region. A portion of the D-loop region of human mtDNA is shown schematically, with some transcriptional landmarks indicated. The noncoding transcriptional control region contains major promoters for both strands (HSP and LSP), with arrows denoting the start sites and direction of transcription for each. The core promoters required for accurate initiation are stippled; upstream sequences essential for efficient promoter selection are shaded. The genes immediately flanking the control region encode phenylalanyl-tRNA and 7S RNA (Clayton 1984). A hypothetical model of promoter recognition involves mtTF binding to the upstream element and enhancing initiation by mtRNA polymerase (pol).

CANCER CELLS 6 / *Eukaryotic DNA Replication.* © 1988 by Cold Spring Harbor Laboratory 0-87969-308-8/88 $1.00

scription factor (mtTF) that confers promoter selectivity on the polymerase. Recognition of both major promoters (HSP and LSP) of human mtDNA requires the presence of mtTF; extensive purification has failed thus far to resolve distinct activities specifying the individual promoters. In contrast, the DNA sequences constituting the HSP and LSP show only limited homology to each other, and the two promoters are transcribed in vitro with markedly different efficiencies when present on the same DNA fragment. Deletion mapping (Bogenhagen et al. 1984; Chang and Clayton 1984) delimited the sequences minimally required for initiation at the correct transcriptional start sites to small regions encompassing the start sites. A "consensus" sequence could be derived from comparison of the core HSP and LSP sequences; its significance was essentially confirmed by in vitro transcriptional analysis of a series of promoter templates containing point substitutions (Hixson and Clayton 1985). However, both of these studies suggested a major role for upstream sequences in regulating the efficiency of selective transcription.

It has been demonstrated that mtTF functions by binding to template DNA; mtTF alone, but not mitochondrial RNA polymerase alone, can sequester promoter-containing DNA in preinitiation complexes. The promoter domains that mediate the response to mtTF were identified by transcription of HSP deletion mutants and LSP linker-substitution mutants in the reconstituted system dependent on exogenous mtTF. Interactions of mtTF with its target sequences have been successfully visualized as "footprints" in DNase protection assays carried out with both wild-type and mutant promoter-containing fragments. Together, these approaches define novel upstream regulatory elements of the major promoters of human mtDNA. The two mtTF-binding sites (HSP-proximal and LSP-proximal) are positioned identically in relation to their respective transcriptional start sites, between ~12 and ~40 bp upstream, but are found in opposite orientations with respect to the major direction of transcription, suggesting that mtTF may function bidirectionally (Fisher et al. 1987).

The major promoters of human mtDNA are composed of two functionally dissociable domains

The ability of mtTF to form stable preinitiation complexes and to protect discrete DNA sequences from nucleolytic cleavage has facilitated the dissociation of both major promoters of human mtDNA into functionally distinct domains. The requirements for upstream sequences at both the HSP and LSP have a common molecular basis; regulatory elements defined by the mtTF-binding sites are located between 12 and 40 bp upstream of the transcriptional start sites. It is therefore possible that the major protein effectors of transcription in this system can be accounted for by RNA polymerase and mtTF. The two other species (mouse and *Xenopus*) for which promoter identification data are currently available appear to fit the human paradigm with respect to basic sequence organization and nature of transcriptional

initiation, although some clear differences have been noted (see Bogenhagen and Yoza 1986; Chang and Clayton 1986b,c); preliminary data indicate the presence of mtTF in mouse mitochondrial extracts (Gray and Clayton 1987).

mtTF-binding sites are active in both orientations

The two mtTF-responsive elements identified have been compared at the DNA sequence level, with surprising results. Although the two elements are clearly analogous both in position and in transcriptional function, they are opposite in orientation with respect to the direction of major transcription. This arrangement would suggest that the factor, upon binding DNA in a sequence-directed orientation, can then activate transcription of either strand, from appropriate initiation signals nearby (Fisher et al. 1987).

Map positions of D-loop RNA and DNA

To understand the possible modes of replication initiation and any possible promoter involvement, it was necessary to map, with current technologies, the nucleic acid species synthesized from the D-loop region of human (Chang and Clayton 1985) and mouse (Chang et al. 1985) mtDNAs. The discussion that follows relates directly to mouse mtDNA synthesis, but the general features are applicable to the human case as well.

The 5' ends of D-loop H strands (DH-DNA) mapped by primer extension and S1 nuclease protection were identical to the DH-DNA 5' termini seen earlier by end-group analysis of isolated D-loop strands (Gillum and Clayton 1979). Mapping of H-strand RNA molecules resulted in two significant new insights. First, only one predominant 5' RNA end was detected, suggesting that most RNA from the D-loop region may initiate at a single site. Second, the 3' ends of H-strand RNA aligned remarkably well with DH-DNA 5' ends, and most important, some of this same H-strand RNA was covalently linked to DH-DNA. These observations indicated that DH-DNA is primed by RNA of significant size. Finally, all transitions from primer RNA synthesis to DNA synthesis occur within a 90-nucleotide region encompassing three previously identified sequence blocks (CSB-I, CSB-II, and CSB-III) conserved in vertebrate mtDNA (Fig. 2) (Walberg and Clayton 1981). The 3' termini of D-loop RNA in human mitochondria also map within these sequence blocks, although no covalent linkage to DNA has yet been established (Chang and Clayton 1985). The association between conserved nucleotide sequences and the switch region for elongation of primer RNAs seemed more than coincidental and raised the possibility that CSB elements may serve as control sequences involved in the transition from primer RNA synthesis to DNA synthesis. As such, these sequences might function as recognition sites for endonucleases responsible for primer RNA generation.

Figure 2 depicts a simplified model for initiation of H-strand DNA synthesis in vertebrate mtDNA consistent with the available data. Primer RNA synthesis begins at

D-LOOP RNA PROCESSING

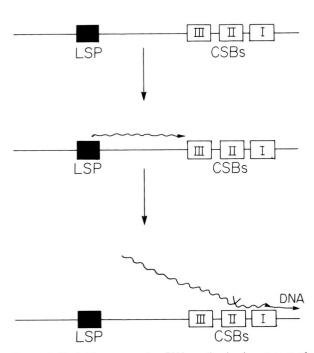

Figure 2 Model for processing RNA synthesized upstream of the origin of H-strand replication. All transcription of the L strand begins at a single LSP and proceeds into the D-loop region. Candidate sites for RNA processing are located near three previously identified short regions of high sequence conservation among animal species (CSBs). The caret marks the point of cleavage (between CSBs II and III) by the currently identified RNase MRP (Chang and Clayton 1987a,b).

a major promoter that is also involved in gene expression, and the transition from primer RNA synthesis to DNA synthesis occurs at distinct sites. A site-specific endoribonuclease, isolated from purified mitochondria, cleaves single-stranded RNA substrates containing the sequence of the O_H region (Fig. 3); cleavage occurs at one of the transition sites in a manner consistent with a role in genomic mtDNA replication (Chang and Clayton 1987a). We have termed this endonuclease RNase MRP (mitochondrial RNA processing) and have established that an endogenous nucleic acid component is essential for enzymatic activity (Chang and Clayton 1987b).

A role for RNA processing in DNA replication

What is the functional role of the RNA processing event at one of the transition sites from RNA synthesis to DNA synthesis? An interesting possibility is that the endonucleolytic processing centered at mouse nucleotide 16103 (Bibb et al. 1981) is necessary for a required hybrid to form between the RNA and template DNA. As RNA polymerase transcribes through the replication origin, the free energy available from the superhelicity of a closed circular mtDNA would facilitate the formation of a hybrid. Such a hybrid might soon be displaced unless

stabilized against branch migration; the cleavage event could stabilize the hybrid by removing a displaced RNA.

A second view relegates the endonuclease to a role in removing primer RNA from a nascent DNA strand, rather than being principally active in generating primer RNA. A common feature of the completion of DNA replication is the removal of RNA primers prior to the covalent joining of newly synthesized DNA. Since the O_H of mtDNA uses relatively long RNA primers that might branch-migrate away from the template strand during unidirectional DNA synthesis, the endonuclease MRP could be involved in reducing the size of the displaced primer RNA from the nascent H-strand DNA. This might facilitate covalent joining of the ends of the daughter H strand at the completion of a replication cycle. The development of an in vitro DNA replication system capable of initiation at this origin will be required to determine the specific function of this cleavage event in the overall mechanism of mtDNA replication.

Since the overall nucleotide sequences of the O_H regions of mouse and human mtDNA are quite different, it was interesting to test for cleavage of human substrate by mouse endonuclease and vice versa. Human RNA substrate was appropriately cleaved by the mouse endonuclease, and vice versa, indicating limited sequence information, common to both mouse and human RNA substrates, is sufficient for the proper recognition of the cleavage site (Chang and Clayton 1987a). Besides the three CSB elements, there are no conserved primary sequences of significant size nor any conserved potential secondary structures in this region. A role for CSB elements is further suggested by the fact that a yeast RNA sequence is cleaved by the vertebrate MRP activities at a site near a C-rich block typical of a CSB II element (Fig. 4). Although the manner in which this mitochondrial endoribonuclease selects its cleavage site is unknown, the fixed distance between the cleavage sites and CSB II implicates this sequence element in the recognition process. Additional mutational analysis of the CSB II region will be required to define the mechanism of cleavage site selection.

A prospective view of the generality of occurrence of the MRP activity, based on conserved sequence elements in the origin transcripts, is given in Table 1. The human and mouse activities have been detected (Chang and Clayton 1987a) and, based on the presence of a similar D-loop organization, *Xenopus* may be predicted to have a MRP activity. There are no CSB sequences in *Drosophila* mtDNA, and it is not known whether promot-

Table 1 Predicted Occurrence of MRP Activity

O_H	CSBs	MRP prospective
Human	I, II, III	known +
Mouse	I, II, III	known +
Xenopus	I, II, III	high
Drosophila	not present	low?
Yeast	I, II	medium?

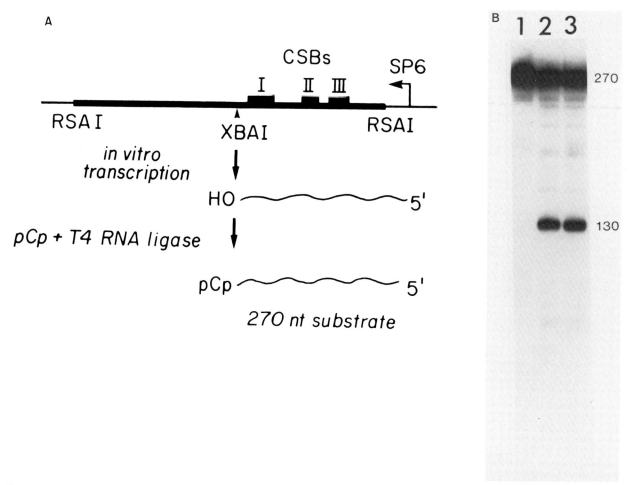

Figure 3 In vitro RNA processing assay. (*A*) The substrate for the in vitro processing assay was generated by using the SP6 transcription system. The template used was the pSP65 derivative containing the mouse mtDNA sequence from nucleotide 15497 to nucleotide 16216 (Bibb et al. 1981). The 270-nt substrate contains the three CSBs in the origin region. (*B*) The 270-nt substrate is assayed here with a mouse MRP DEAE-Sephacel fraction (Fraction V; Chang and Clayton 1987a,b); the product is 130 nt in size. (*1*) No enzyme, (*2, 3*) enzyme added.

ers are involved in replication priming in this system. Interestingly, yeast putative origin sequences have a CSB-II-like site (Baldacci et al. 1984) and, perhaps, a CSB I cognate as well. As shown in Figure 4, RNA sequence complementary to the *ori*5 region is a suitable substrate for cleavage, near the CSB II sequence, by both human and mouse MRP activities.

Ribonucleoprotein properties of the endonuclease

The sensitivity of RNase MRP to either nuclease digestion or thermal inactivation demonstrates a requirement for both RNA and protein components for site-specific cleavage by this mitochondrial endoribonuclease (Chang and Clayton 1987b). Two lines of evidence argue for the importance of at least one specific RNA. First, the elution profile of a 135-nucleotide RNA from a Mono Q ion exchange column is identical to the endonucleolytic activity profile, thus providing physical evidence for the association of the 135-nucleotide RNA with the endonuclease. Second, the endonucleolytic

activity can be inhibited by a specific oligonucleotide complementary to the 135-nucleotide RNA. These data, along with the large sedimentation coefficient of the endonuclease, suggest that RNase MRP is a ribonucleoprotein with at least one RNA component.

Attempts to identify the protein component of RNase MRP have not been successful in associating any specific polypeptide with the cleavage activity. In regard to the origin of the 135-nucleotide RNA of the endonuclease, the available RNA sequence information clearly indicates that this RNA is not encoded in mtDNA. No evidence for extragenomic genetic elements exists for mammalian mitochondria, despite numerous and extensive analyses of DNA isolates from this source. Most important, nuclear genes for these RNA species have been identified and sequenced (D.D. Chang et al., in prep.), thereby establishing an extramitochondrial origin.

All other known nuclear gene products involved in mitochondrial biogenesis are proteins, and translocation of such proteins synthesized on cytoplasmic ribosomes

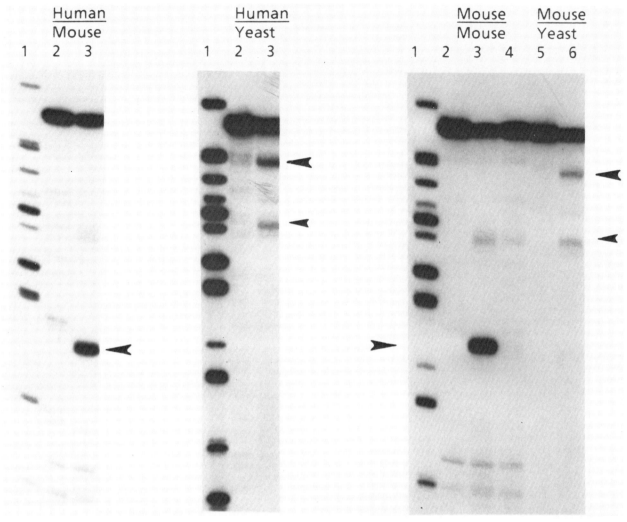

Figure 4 Cleavage of origin-related sequences. Mitochondrial extracts from human and mouse cells containing MRP activity were prepared as described (Chang and Clayton 1987a) and used to cleave RNA sequences complementary to mouse and yeast mtDNA origins of replication. (*Left*) Lane *1*, size markers; lane *2*, no human MRP, mouse 270-nt substrate as in Fig. 3; lane *3*, human MRP added, 130-nt mouse cleavage product noted by arrowhead. (*Middle*) Same, except with yeast RNA substrate generated from the *ori*5 region of yeast mtDNA (Baldacci et al. 1984). This sequence contains CSB I- and II-like regions and human MRP cleaves near the CSB II site (lane *3*, large arrowhead) and, possibly, a CSB I site (lane *3*, small arrowhead). (*Right*) Lane *1*, size markers, lane *2*, mouse RNA substrate, no MRP added; lane *3*, mouse RNA substrate, mouse MRP added, large arrowhead denotes 130-nt product; lane *4*, same as lane 3 except inactive enzyme added; lane *5*, yeast *ori*5 RNA sequence, no enzyme added; lane *6*, yeast *ori*5 RNA sequence, mouse MRP added. The large and small arrowheads note the same products as generated by the human MRP activity.

into mitochondria occurs posttranslationally. RNase MRP was isolated from mitochondria and cleaves a mitochondrial RNA substrate specifically at a previously established in vivo processing site (Chang and Clayton 1987a). Because the mitochondrial enzyme requires a nucleus-encoded RNA component for its activity, there must be a mechanism for transporting nucleic acid into mitochondria (Fig. 5). It will be of interest to learn the mode of assembly and transport of this novel mitochondrial endonuclease.

How is replication regulated?
The facts that priming of H-strand replication is promoter-dependent and that RNA processing appears to be intertwined with the transition to DNA synthesis

suggest a mode of controlling mtDNA replication. It is important to note that the D-loop origin represents the initial commitment to a genomic replication event; the origin of L-strand synthesis is functional only after mtDNA synthesis is essentially two-thirds completed (Clayton 1982). A simple prediction of this hierarchical arrangement is that the nucleus exerts its primary influence on mtDNA replication at the D loop.

The first required event is transcription from the LSP, which can serve the purposes of replication priming, gene transcription, or both. No RNA processing of D-loop sequences is known or suggested to be required for the purposes of gene expression; the first gene, that for tRNA[Pro], bounds the D loop (however, tRNA[Pro] may have a short 5′ leader, as does tRNA[Phe], which is the

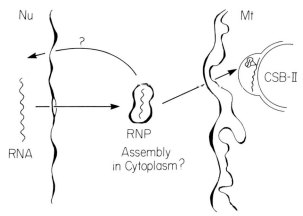

Figure 5 Requirement for RNA import into mitochondria. The gene for the 135-nucleotide RNA of the MRP activity is located in the nucleus. A simple model is that this RNA migrates to the cytoplasm for assembly with protein, as is the case with other known ribonucleoprotein (RNP) activities. Ultimately, the activity must be imported into the mitochondrial matrix space to cleave mitochondrial RNA. The mechanism of importation of this activity is currently unknown. The cellular site for any processing of this RNA or a precursor (Chang and Clayton 1987b) is unknown, and it is possible that some form of this activity is transported to the nucleus.

5′-most H-strand-encoded gene). In contrast, DNA replication appears to involve RNA processing in the CSB zone. Thus, the major relevant replication activities to date are mtTF, mitochondrial RNA polymerase, RNase MRP, and mtDNA polymerase. If MRP endonuclease is required for the actual provision of 3′-OH groups for extension by mtDNA polymerase, then it becomes an absolute requirement for replication; its absence would permit transcription but preclude any genomic replication events. We know little regarding the function and cellular abundance of mtDNA polymerase, but there are no data to argue that it is a rate-limiting enzymatic activity.

One of the more interesting possibilities is that mtTF and MRP endonuclease activities may dictate the overall level of gene expression and DNA replication by balancing the amounts of transcription product available for these purposes. Analyses of the regulation of the nuclear genes for these activities and their transport seem certain to bear on the overall process of organelle biogenesis.

Acknowledgments

These investigations were supported by grant GM-33088 from the National Institute of General Medical Sciences and grant NP-9 from the American Cancer Society, Inc. J.N.T., D.D.C., and R.P.F. are Medical Scientist Training Program trainees of the National Institute of General Medical Sciences (GM-07365).

References

Baldacci, G., B. Chérif-Zahar, and G. Bernardi. 1984. The initiation of DNA replication in the mitochondrial genome of yeast. *EMBO J.* **3:** 2115.

Bibb, M.J., R.A. Van Etten, C.T. Wright, M.W. Walberg, and D.A. Clayton. 1981. Sequence and gene organization of mouse mitochondrial DNA. *Cell* **26:** 167.

Bogenhagen, D.F. and B.K. Yoza. 1986. Accurate in vitro transcription of *Xenopus laevis* mitochondrial DNA from two bidirectional promoters. *Mol. Cell. Biol.* **6:** 2543.

Bogenhagen, D.F., E.F. Applegate, and B.K. Yoza. 1984. Identification of a promoter for transcription of the heavy strand of human mtDNA: In vitro transcription and deletion mutagenesis. *Cell* **36:** 1105.

Bogenhagen, D.F., B.K. Yoza, and S.S. Cairns. 1986. Identification of initiation sites for transcription of *Xenopus laevis* mitochondrial DNA. *J. Biol. Chem.* **261:** 8488.

Chang, D.D. and D.A. Clayton. 1984. Precise identification of individual promoters for transcription of each strand of human mitochondrial DNA. *Cell* **36:** 635.

———. 1985. Priming of human mitochondrial DNA replication occurs at the light-strand promoter. *Proc. Natl. Acad. Sci.* **82:** 351.

———. 1986a. Identification of primary transcriptional start sites of mouse mitochondrial DNA: Accurate in vitro initiation of both heavy- and light-strand transcripts. *Mol. Cell. Biol.* **6:** 1446.

———. 1986b. Precise assignment of the light-strand promoter of mouse mitochondrial DNA: A functional promoter consists of multiple upstream domains. *Mol. Cell. Biol.* **6:** 3253.

———. 1986c. Precise assignment of the heavy-strand promoter of mouse mitochondrial DNA: Cognate start sites are not required for transcriptional initiation. *Mol. Cell. Biol.* **6:** 3262.

———. 1987a. A novel endoribonuclease cleaves at a priming site of mouse mitochondrial DNA replication. *EMBO J.* **6:** 409.

———. 1987b. A mammalian mitochondrial RNA processing activity contains nucleus-encoded RNA. *Science* **235:** 1178.

Chang, D.D., W.W. Hauswirth, and D.A. Clayton. 1985. Replication priming and transcription initiate from precisely the same site in mouse mitochondrial DNA. *EMBO J.* **4:** 1559.

Clayton, D.A. 1982. Replication of animal mitochondrial DNA. *Cell* **28:** 693.

———. 1984. Transcription of the mammalian mitochondrial genome. *Annu. Rev. Biochem.* **53:** 573.

Fisher, R.P. and D.A. Clayton. 1985. A transcription factor required for promoter recognition by human mitochondrial RNA polymerase. Accurate initiation at the heavy- and light-strand promoters dissected and reconstituted *in vitro*. *J. Biol. Chem.* **260:** 11330.

Fisher, R.P., J.N. Topper, and D.A. Clayton. 1987. Promoter selection in human mitochondria involves binding of a transcription factor to orientation-independent upstream regulatory elements. *Cell* **50:** 247.

Gillum, A.M. and D.A. Clayton. 1979. Mechanism of mitochondrial DNA replication in mouse L-cells: RNA priming during the initiation of heavy-strand synthesis. *J. Mol. Biol.* **135:** 353.

Gray, M.W. and D.A. Clayton. 1987. Characterization of a mouse mitochondrial transcription system. *UCLA Symp. Mol. Cell. Biol. New Ser.* **52:** 395.

Hixson, J.E. and D.A. Clayton. 1985. Initiation of transcription from each of the two human mitochondrial promoters requires unique nucleotides at the transcriptional start sites. *Proc. Natl. Acad. Sci.* **82:** 2660.

Walberg, M.W. and D.A. Clayton. 1981. Sequence and properties of the human KB cell and mouse L-cell D-loop regions of mitochondrial DNA. *Nucleic Acids Res.* **9:** 5411.

Regulation of Yeast Plasmid Amplification

K.A. Armstrong, T. Som, F.C. Volkert, and J.R. Broach

Department of Molecular Biology, Princeton University, Princeton, New Jersey 08544

The long-term persistence of the multicopy yeast plasmid, 2-μm circle, is dependent on the plasmid's achieving a precise balance between subverting the host's replication machinery to its own ends and minimizing the debilitating effects of that subversion. To achieve this goal, the plasmid has developed several intriguing strategies for survival, including a completely novel mechanism of genome amplification. Amplification apparently occurs by a recombination-induced transient shift in the mode of plasmid replication from θ to double rolling circle. This capability may insure stable maintenance of the plasmid by enabling it to correct downward deviations in copy number that result from imprecision in the plasmid-encoded partitioning and replication systems. Several other biological systems in which this novel amplification mechanism may be operative are discussed. A second component of the plasmid survival strategy is a precise regulation of this amplification process to achieve an optimum copy level in the cell. The intricate regulatory circuitry that underlies this copy control system is described, and a model accounting for copy control based on this regulation of gene expression is discussed.

The 6318-bp double-strand DNA plasmid, 2-μm circle, is resident at high copy in the nucleus of most strains of *Saccharomyces* (cf. Broach 1981; Volkert and Broach 1987). The prevalence of the plasmid does not arise from any selective advantage conferred to the host by the presence of the plasmid (Futcher and Cox 1983; Mead et al. 1987). Rather, the plasmid's widespread distribution appears to be a result of its highly efficient transmission during mitotic growth and of its ability to be dispersed to plasmid-free cells through sexual conjugation and meiosis. The loss rate of the plasmid during mitotic growth is less than $1/10^4$ cells per generation, so plasmid-free cells seldom arise under these conditions. In addition, plasmid-free cells can reacquire plasmid through the meiotic cycle. 2-μm circle exhibits a pattern of non-Mendelian inheritance in which all four progeny spores from a cross between a plasmid-bearing strain and a plasmid-free strain obtain a full complement of plasmid molecules (Livingston 1977).

The primary contribution to the plasmid's tenacious persistence is its ability to ensure equal distribution of plasmid molecules between the two progeny cells at cell division. This equipartitioning process is promoted by the *trans*-acting products of two plasmid coding regions, designated *REP1* and *REP2* (Jayaram et al. 1983; Kikuchi 1983; Cashmore et al. 1986). In addition, equipartitioning requires the integrity of a series of direct tandem repeats of a 62-bp element lying near the origin of replication. This collection of repeats, designated *REP3* or *STB*, appears to function as a centromere-like element in the partitioning process (Kikuchi 1983; Jayaram et al. 1985; Murray and Cesarini 1986). Mutational inactivation of any of these partitioning components yields a plasmid that is often not transmitted to the daughter cell, or bud, at cell division (Jayaram et al. 1983; Kikuchi 1983; Murray and Szostak 1983). In addition, such mutant plasmids are often not incorporated into spores during meiosis. The mechanism of

plasmid partitioning is not known, even to the extent of whether partitioning involves reasonably precise disjunction of sister molecules or whether distribution of molecules between progeny cells is essentially random. However, one reasonable possibility is that the *REP1/REP2* proteins form dispersed binding sites within the nucleus for the plasmid and that these complexes are then randomly distributed between both progeny nuclei at cell division (Wu et al. 1987).

Efficient partitioning cannot be the only component of the plasmid's successful mode of propagation. Since plasmid replication is under stringent cell cycle control, each plasmid is replicated once and only once in each cell cycle during steady-state mitotic growth (Zakian et al. 1979). Making the reasonable assumption that partitioning and replication are not absolutely precise processes, plasmid copy levels would decline slowly over time under these circumstances. Even assuming precise partitioning at cell division and 100% efficiency in plasmid replication, the plasmid could at best hold its own during mitotic growth. However, under these circumstances meiotic transmission would be ineffective; plasmid copy levels would diminish by half during each meiotic cycle.

To rectify any downward fluctuation in copy levels that could arise from imprecise segregation of plasmid molecules at mitosis or from occasional failures in replication initiation, the plasmid possesses the capacity for copy number amplification. This capacity was inferred both from the teleological considerations enumerated above and from observations regarding apparent plasmid copy number expansion following certain cytoduction experiments (Sigurdson et al. 1981). However, unlike previously reported examples of amplification of specific regions of a eukaryotic genome—such as chorion protein gene amplification during *Drosophila* oogenesis (Spradling and Mahowald 1980) or gene amplification associated with drug resistance in cultured animal cell

213

(Schimke 1982; Stark and Wahl 1984)—2-μm circle plasmid copy number expansion does not involve an abrogation of the stringent control of replication initiation. Rather, 2-μm circle amplification proceeds through a novel mechanism in which site-specific recombination promotes a transitory shift in mode of replication elongation from θ to rolling circle (Futcher 1986; Volkert and Broach 1986). In the first part of this chapter, we review this mechanism and summarize the evidence that supports this model of amplification. In addition, we suggest other instances of selective gene amplification that might arise by this process.

The long-term persistence of the yeast plasmid during mitotic growth documents its success at achieving a delicate balance in its mode of propagation. The plasmid has had to subvert the cell's reproductive machinery to its own devices but without placing a meaningful burden on the host cell. For example, since plasmid replication requires the same apparatus as does chromosomal DNA (Livingston and Kupfer 1977; Zakian et al. 1979), plasmid copy levels must be high enough to ensure plasmid transmission to both progeny cells, but not so high that the plasmid copies seriously diminish the availability of replication complexes for chromosomal duplication. If this latter condition were not met, then plasmid-bearing strains would be at a selective disadvantage in growth competition with plasmid-free strains. This situation would, in the absence of extensive horizontal transmission, inexorably lead to plasmid extinction. The morbidity associated with high 2-μm circle copy levels in certain mutant strains of yeast can be taken as evidence that significant deviations from this delicate balance in host/plasmid interplay can lead to a crisis in cellular function (Holm 1982).

To maintain an appropriate balance during mitotic growth, the plasmid actively regulates its copy levels. That is, the plasmid possesses the capacity to sense its copy level in each cell and then respond to this assessment by altering its behavior. In situations in which copy levels are low, this would involve activation of its amplification system. In situations in which copy levels were high, the appropriate response would be repression of its amplification and perhaps diminution in its efficiency of replication initiation. In the second part of this chapter, we describe the regulatory circuitry that underlies this copy control. In addition, we suggest how these regulatory interactions yield a stable copy control system. Finally, we suggest several testable predictions that follow from this view of plasmid copy control.

Results and Discussion

Amplification of plasmid copy number

Futcher's model for plasmid amplification
The structural organization of 2-μm circle, diagramed in Figure 1, is integral to its mode of amplification and persistence. The plasmid consists of two unique regions separated by two regions of 599 bp each that are precise inverted repeats of each other (Hartley and

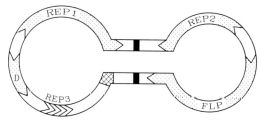

Figure 1 The yeast plasmid 2-μm circle. A diagram of the genomic organization of the yeast plasmid is shown, drawn to distinguish the inverted repeats (horizontal lines) from unique sequences (circular regions). On the diagram are indicated the locations of the open coding regions (dotted regions, arrows signifying the 5′ to 3′ orientation), the origin of replication (cross-hatched region), the *FLP*-recombination target site (solid region), and the *cis*-acting stability locus (chevrons).

Donelson 1980). The product of the largest plasmid coding region, *FLP*, catalyzes recombination at specific sites lying near the center of the inverted repeats (Broach and Hicks 1980; Broach et al. 1982). The result of this recombination event is inversion of the two unique regions with respect to each other. A single origin of replication lies at the junction between one of the repeats and the large unique region (Newlon et al. 1981; Broach et al. 1983; Brewer and Fangman 1987; Huberman et al. 1987). In addition, the plasmid contains the *cis*-active partitioning locus *REP3* and four extended open coding regions, each of which is transcribed into discrete polyadenylated RNA (Broach et al. 1979; Sutton and Broach 1985).

A novel model for the mechanism of 2-μm circle amplification, first proposed by Futcher (1986), is diagramed in Figure 2. Under normal conditions, plasmid replication forks proceed in a bidirectional manner away from the single origin to converge at the opposite side of the plasmid to yield two copies of the parent plasmid. Futcher noted that if *FLP*-mediated recombination occurred between a duplicated and nonduplicated repeat during fork elongation, then the relative directions of the two replication forks would be inverted. As a consequence, the forks would proceed in the same direction around the circular plasmid molecule, spinning off an ever enlarging catenane of plasmid genomes. Replication would terminate only after a second recombination event reinstated the bidirectional orientation of the forks. This amplification process can be viewed as a transient shift in the mode of plasmid replication from θ to rolling circle, generating extra copies of the plasmid from a single replication initiation event. Two features of this model are noteworthy. First, amplification is achieved without abrogating stringent regulation of initiation of DNA replication. Second, the mode of amplification accounts for the unusual structural organization of the plasmid and the otherwise apparently pointless inversional process.

Evidence for Futcher's model
Evidence in support of the above model for amplification comes from two sources. First, we have shown that 2-μm circle can amplify from single copy to its normal

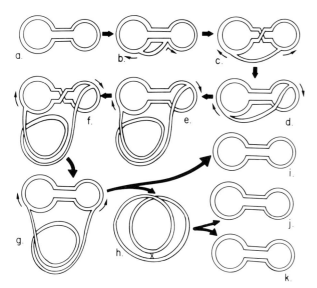

Figure 2 Futcher's (1986) model for recombinational amplification of 2-μm circle. (a,b) Semiconservative DNA replication proceeds bidirectionally from the plasmid origin. Arrows indicate replication fork movement. (c,d) A FLP-mediated recombination reaction reorients the forks so that they no longer converge. (e) Continuing replication in this mode yields a multimeric replication intermediate. (f,g) Another FLP recombination event restores the converging orientation of the replication forks. Completion of replication yields a 2-μm circle monomer (i) and a multimer (h). Further FLP-mediated or general recombination resolves the multimer to monomers (j,k).

full complement only if it is capable of FLP-mediated recombination, and only if such recombination occurs concomitant with mitotic growth (Volkert and Broach 1986). Specifically, we devised a method to introduce synchronously a single copy of 2-μm circle into the nucleoplasm of each cell in a culture. In our system, a single flp mutant 2-μm circle was integrated in a chromosome, flanked by FLP-recombination sites in direct orientation. FLP protein was supplied from a copy of the gene, inserted into a chromosome in another strain, under control either of its own promoter or of a galactose-inducible promoter. Upon mating a strain having a 2-μm circle insert with one having a FLP insert (and inducing with galactose when required), FLP protein recombined the flanking recombination sites, excising a flp⁻ 2-μm circle plasmid at a copy number of one. Under the continuing influence of FLP protein, the plasmid could then invert by recombination between its repeats, unless one of those repeats had been mutationally inactivated. The effect of FLP inversion, or failure to invert, on plasmid copy number was assessed by Southern hybridization, using a probe complementary to 2-μm circle and taking the intensity of the band(s) derived from the chromosomally inserted FLP gene as a single copy standard.

We found that the invertible circle (i.e., the one with two wild-type recombination sites) was capable of increasing in copy number, whereas the noninvertible circle was not, thus confirming the hypothesis that amplification requires FLP inversion. In addition, we found

that inducing expression of FLP for only a short period, followed by growth to saturation in medium that represses FLP production, severely limited the extent of amplification of the invertible circle. This was true despite the fact that this short pulse of FLP expression was sufficient to permit excision and inversion of the insert. This suggested (1) that turnover of FLP mRNA and protein must be fairly rapid and (2) that the act of inversion itself, not merely the simultaneous intracellular presence of both plasmid isomers, was required for amplification. Finally, we found that the period of rapid amplification coincided with the exponential phase. This was consistent with the prediction that FLP amplification occurs during the S phase of the cell cycle, rather than by unscheduled replication. These experiments show that the FLP system of 2-μm circle can enable the plasmid to increase its mean intracellular copy number in cells growing without selection.

A second approach to testing the Futcher model for amplification has been to assess the structure of plasmid DNA during the process of amplification. Futcher has found that the increased plasmid DNA present initially upon plasmid amplification — either after FLP-induced amplification as described above or immediately following synchronous mating of a plasmid-free strain with a plasmid-bearing strain — consists almost exclusively of high-molecular-weight DNA composed of multimers of unit length plasmid genomes (B. Futcher, pers. comm.). In addition, the ratio of the two invert isomers of the plasmid present in this multimeric fraction is not the standard 1:1 pattern observed during steady-state growth. Rather, the ratio is significantly biased in a manner expected if a single genome had been copied multiple times. These structural observations are consistent with the Futcher model of amplification. Results from the above two approaches do not prove the amplification model to be true: Nonetheless, the overwhelming nature of the circumstantial evidence provides sufficient assurance to assume that this model is correct.

Other examples of amplification by inversional recombination

The amplification mechanism apparently used by 2-μm circle is an exceedingly elegant solution to the problem of obtaining multiple copies in one generation from a single replicon that is normally restricted to a single initiation event per cell cycle. The fact that such a convoluted mechanism evolved suggests that the normal restriction to reinitiation of a replicon within a single generation is so stringent as to preclude any temporary abrogation of the rule. That is, in order to acquire the potential to amplify, the 2-μm circle ancestor plasmid found it easier to develop the elaborate recombinational switch in replication elongation mode than to develop a mechanism to promote multiple initiation events within a single cell cycle.

Given the normal parsimony of nature, it would seem unlikely that such an elegant mechanism for amplification would evolve for use only once. In fact, this does not appear to be the case. Several other small, circular, double-stranded DNA yeast plasmids have been identified in various osmophilic yeast (Toh-e et al. 1982, 1984). None of these exhibit homology to 2-μm circle, but all of the them possess the same genome organization and a similar site-specific recombination system as that carried by 2-μm circle (Araki et al. 1985). We would suggest that this recombination system is present to promote amplification of these yeast plasmids in a manner analogous to that seen for 2-μm circle. Similarly, chloroplast genomes from a number of organisms consist of two unique regions separated by two domains that are extended inverted repeats of each other (Rochaix 1978; Kolodner and Tewari 1979). In the chloroplast genome of *Chlamydomonas*, recombination occurs frequently between these repeats (Palmer 1983). In addition, as Wu and her colleagues have shown (Wu et al. 1986), the replication origin of this genome lies adjacent to one of the repeats, an organization that enhances the probability that a recombination event would invert the replication forks to yield rolling circle replication of the genome. Therefore, we would suspect that chloroplast genomes may amplify by this double rolling circle mechanism. Such a mechanism might account for the fact that both θ and rolling circle replication intermediates are observed in chloroplasts of a number of plants (Kolodner and Tewari 1975).

On a more speculative plane, we would like to suggest that some herpesviruses may use a similar amplification mechanism in the course of emerging from latency. Many herpesviruses, including HSV-1, HSV-2, and pseudorabies virus, contain extended inverted repeats that bracket unique domains. During lytic growth, recombination occurs readily between these repeats (Hayward et al. 1975; Delius and Clements 1976). In addition, in the latent state of the viral life cycle, at least one herpesvirus, EBV, has been shown to persist as a low-copy circular episome (Adams and Lindahl 1975; Lindahl et al. 1976). Finally, Roizman and his colleagues (Chou and Roizman 1985; Jenkins and Roizman 1986) have isolated a variant of HSV-1 that exhibits a reduced frequency of recombination between the inverted repeats. This virus exhibits essentially normal lytic growth but completely fails to undergo latency (B. Roizman, pers. comm.). We would suggest many herpesviruses, such as HSV-1, use a 2-μm circle style amplification mechanism to amplify their copy number in the initial stages of emergence from their latent state. Thus, the defect of Roizman's variant strain would be explained as a defect, not in entering the latent state, but in emerging from it. Obviously, if such a mechanism is correct, the recombination system responsible for the inversion offers a tantalizing target for therapeutic intervention to inhibit pernicious reemergence of latent herpesvirus infections.

Finally, amplification of some chromosomal sequences could proceed by a variation of this mechanism. Figure 3 presents a model for amplification of chromosomal sequences derived from Futcher's model for plasmid amplification. An origin of replication, lying asymmetrically between inverted repeats, yields replica-

tion of one repeat prior to duplicating the other. If a recombination event occurs between one of the replicated repeats and the unduplicated repeat, then the sequences lying between them would be inverted. Consequently, the replication forks would no longer proceed away from each other. Rather, one fork would follow the other to the end of the chromosome, yielding an acentric fragment. This fragment would be organized as a dimeric palindrome with the palindromic sequences flanking a small segment of unique sequence. The palindromic region corresponds to the chromosomal segment extending from the telomere-proximal repeat to the end of the chromosome. The unique segment corresponds to the region lying between the repeats. Formation of the acentric fragment should not adversely affect replication of the chromosome from which it is derived. We can assume that the chromosome is actually duplicated during this particular cell cycle by replication initiated at origins lying closer to the centromere. Thus, the end product of this event is the creation of two extra copies of whatever information lies near the telomere of this chromosome. Assuming asymmetric segregation of this acentric fragment coupled with its continued replication during each cell cycle, this information could be amplified to many hundreds of copies per cell, at least in a small subset of the descendants of the cell in which the fragment arose.

Several amplified chromosomal sequences have been shown to exist as acentric palindromes, which, as described above, are predicted to be the end product of this amplification process. For instance, the amplified rDNA genes in the macronucleus of many ciliated protozoans are organized as inverted dimers on acentric fragments (Yao 1982). These multiple copies are derived from a single rDNA gene resident in the micronucleus. In the context of this model, it is noteworthy that a pair of inverted repeats lies immediately upstream of the micronuclear rDNA copy. As predicted by the above model, the unique sequences lying between the palindromic copies of the rDNA genes in the amplified acentric fragment are precisely those sequences found between the upstream inverted repeats in the micronuclear copy (Yao et al. 1985). Thus, the organization of macronuclear rDNA copies and its relationship to the micronuclear template bear all the hallmarks of amplification of this inversional process. Obviously, this mechanism accounts only for the initial formation of the macronuclear rDNA structure. Amplification of this structure to its final copy level of several hundred per cell would have to proceed by a separate process.

A second example of an amplified segment that could have arisen by this mechanism is presented by the *ADH4* locus of yeast (Walton et al. 1986). This locus encodes a minor alcohol dehydrogenase isozyme. In strains lacking the major alcohol dehydrogenase genes, cells resistant to antimycin A have been shown to contain multiple copies of the *ADH4* gene. The striking feature of these multiple copies is that they are organized as palindromic repeats of the *ADH4* locus on multiple, acentric, extrachromosomal fragments. As above,

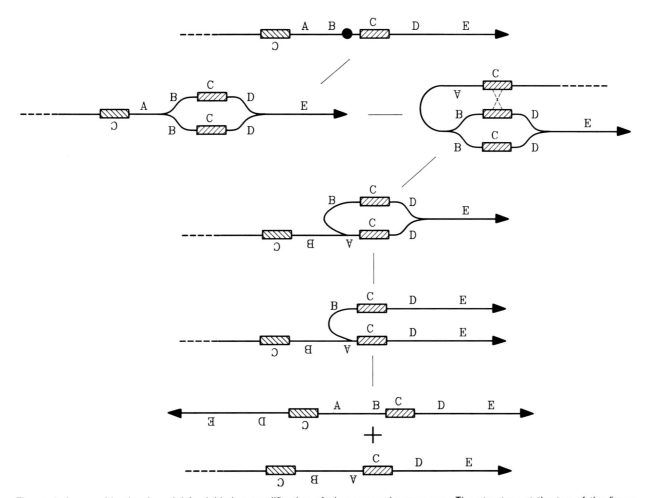

Figure 3 A recombinational model for initiating amplification of chromosomal sequences. The structure at the top of the figure represents the region of a chromosome lying near a telomere (designated by the arrowhead). Letters along the chromosome represent stretches of sequences, the orientations of which are indicated by the orientations and positions of the letters. Within this region a single origin of replication (●) lies asymmetrically between a pair of inverted repeats (hatched boxes, labeled C). Initial replication elongation from the origin yields duplication of one repeat but not the other. Recombination between a duplicated repeat and the nonduplicated repeat results in inversion of the sequences between them as well as inversion of the direction of progression of the replication fork. Continued elongation of each fork to the end of the chromosome generates the acentric palindromic fragment shown at the bottom of the figure. The chromosomal template is left unaltered, except for inversion of the sequences lying between the repeats.

the organization of the acentric *ADH4* fragment and its relationship to the single genomic copy are completely consistent with the formation of the extra-chromosomal copy by the mechanism diagrammed in Figure 3. Thus, several instances of specific chromosomal gene amplification can be accommodated within a model based on recombinational inversion of replication forks. This mechanism certainly does not account for all examples of specific gene amplification. Nonetheless, it certainly warrants inclusion in the panoply of processes by which selective expansion of chromosomal domains occurs.

Regulation of plasmid gene expression

The transcription pattern of 2-μm circle
The yeast plasmid genome is extensively transcribed, and its transcription is tightly regulated by the protein products of the plasmid itself. A transcription map of the

plasmid is shown in Figure 4. As is evident, each of the four coding regions is precisely encompassed by a polyadenylated mRNA species (Broach et al. 1979; Sutton and Broach 1985). Additional transcripts of unknown function are also derived from the plasmid, two of which (the 1950 and 1620 transcript) are coterminal with mRNA species from the larger unique portion of the genome. Experimental evidence argues against any precursor/product relationships between the larger transcripts and the smaller mRNA species, although available data do not unequivocally rule out such a possibility.

Plasmid gene expression is regulated by plasmid-encoded proteins
Initiation of transcription from most of the plasmid promoters is repressed by the activity of plasmid-encoded proteins. Repression of the promoter for the 1950 transcript by plasmid proteins was inferred from mutational

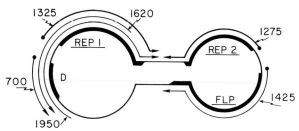

Figure 4 Transcription map of the yeast plasmid 2-μm circle. The map positions of the major 2-μm circle transcripts are indicated on a diagram of the B form of the 2-μm circle genome. Each transcript is designated by its length in bases, as determined by previous Northern analysis of 2-μm circle transcription (Broach et al. 1979). The precise location of the 3' end of all the transcripts shown (indicated by arrowheads) and the 5' ends of all but the 1950 and 1620 base transcripts are known (Sutton and Broach 1985). The locations of the four open coding regions are indicated by the heavy lines on the diagram of the genome, with tapers lying at the 3' end of the gene.

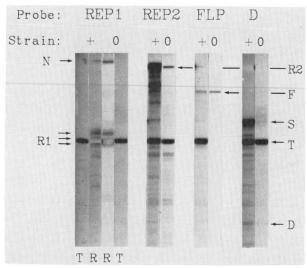

Figure 5 Repression of 2-μm circle gene expression by 2-μm circle encoded proteins. 2-μm circle transcript levels were measured by RNase protection assays as described in Som et al. (1988) in total RNA isolated from a [cir⁺] strain (tracks designated +) and the [cir⁰] strains containing a single, chromosomally integrated copy of an inactivated 2-μm plasmid (tracks designated 0). Labeled probes specific for *REP1*, *REP2*, *FLP*, or *D* mRNAs were used to yield the designated tracks. The probe for *REP1* mRNA also provides a measure of the level of the overlapping 1950 base transcript, and the probe for *D* also measures the overlapping 1620 base transcript. The position of migration of the protected fragments specific for *REP1* mRNA (R1), *REP2* mRNA (R2), *FLP* mRNA (F), *D* mRNA (D), the 1620 transcript (N), the 1950 transcript (S), and tubulin mRNA (T) are indicated and are the expected size predicted by the extent of overlap between each probe and its cognate transcript. The *REP1* mRNA probe yields a cluster of species in the size range expected for protection by *REP1* mRNA, consistent with our previous observation that *REP1* mRNA has heterogeneous cap sites (Sutton and Broach 1985). A probe for tubulin mRNA was included as an internal control in most of the reactions. However, since *REP1* and tubulin-protected fragments comigrate, these were processed in identical, parallel RNA samples (tracks T for the tubulin mRNA probe and tracks R for the *REP1* mRNA probe). For technical reasons, the tubulin mRNA probe was omitted from the *FLP*-probed [cir⁰] strain, although the levels of total RNA in the two *FLP* tracks were shown in a parallel reaction to be essentially identical.

analysis and from the behavior of certain gene fusions (Jayaram et al. 1985). More recently, we have completed a comprehensive analysis of regulation of plasmid transcription as a function of the presence of various plasmid gene products (Som et al. 1988). These results are summarized in the following.

To assess whether 2-μm circle gene expression is subject to significant regulation by plasmid-encoded proteins, we measured the relative levels of expression of each of the 2-μm circle genes in strains lacking 2-μm circles and in strains containing a normal complement of plasmids. To measure plasmid gene expression in a plasmid-free strain, we constructed derivatives of 2-μm circle that consisted of the entire 2-μm circle genome, but with all four plasmid genes inactivated by insertion either of vector sequences or of small synthetic oligonucleotides that yielded frameshift mutations within the coding regions. Each of these plasmids was integrated at single copy into a yeast chromosome. The transcription level of each plasmid gene in these single copy "null" plasmids was then compared to that of the cognate gene in an isogenic strain containing a normal complement of wild-type 2-μm circles ([cir⁺] strain).

We measured specific plasmid transcript levels by quantitative RNase protection assays (Melton et al. 1984). Representative results from this experiment, presented in Figure 5, show that expression of *FLP*, *REP1*, and *D*, but not of *REP2*, are substantially repressed by plasmid gene products. As evident from Figure 5, the level of *FLP* mRNA present in the strain containing single copies of the gene is essentially identical to that present in the [cir⁺] strain. That is, the transcription level per copy of *FLP* is approximately 100-fold less in the [cir⁺] strain than in the strain containing the single null plasmid. By similar argument, the per gene expression of *REP1* is approximately 20- to 50-fold lower in the [cir⁺] strain than in the single copy strain. Regulation of gene *D*, being expressed at a significantly lower level than either *FLP* or *REP1*, is more difficult to assess. However, it appears that expression of *D* mimics that of

FLP, showing approximately the same level of expression at a copy of one as it does in the [cir⁺] strain. These results strongly suggest that some plasmid product or combination of plasmid products substantially represses expression of *FLP* and *REP1*, and perhaps *D* as well. In addition, the 1950 base transcript appears to be repressed in the [cir⁺] strain, consistent with our prior observations. In contrast, the level of mRNA from *REP2* in the [cir⁺] strain is substantially higher than that in the single copy strain. The same is true of a transcript of 1620 nucleotides, which is coterminal with *D* mRNA (Broach et al. 1979; Sutton and Broach 1985). Thus, to a first approximation, the *REP2* and 1620 transcription units yield a level of mRNA production commensurate with their gene dosage, suggesting that their expression is essentially constitutive.

Partitioning proteins REP1 *and* REP2 *function as transcriptional regulators*

To confirm the regulatory pattern described above and to identify those plasmid components responsible for regulation of plasmid gene expression, we measured the level of expression of various 2-μm circle genes as a function of the presence of various combinations of plasmid gene products. To accomplish this we constructed a variety of strains. Each strain contained a target 2-μm circle gene, whose expression we measured. In addition, each strain contained a selected combination of active 2-μm circle genes whose expression we could regulate. To introduce plasmid-encoded proteins in a controlled manner into cells containing the metric gene, we constructed fusions of each of the 2-μm circle coding regions to the galactose-inducible *GAL10* promoter. As we and others have demonstrated, such promoter fusions provide high level synthesis from the gene to which the promoter is fused, as long as the strain containing the fusion is grown in the presence of galactose (Broach et al. 1983a). If the fusion-containing strain is grown in the absence of galactose—on glucose or raffinose, for example—little or no synthesis from the fused gene occurs. Each of these fused genes was integrated into a chromosomal site. Different fusions were integrated at different sites in the yeast genome so that strains containing any combination of the regulated 2-μm circle genes could be constructed with minimal effort.

The results of this analysis examining expression of the *FLP* gene are shown in Figure 6. Strains containing an integrated copy of the null 2-μm genome described above as well as integrated copies of either *GAL10-REP1*, *GAL10-REP2*, both *GAL10* constructs together, or neither *GAL10* construct were grown in inducing (galactose-containing) or noninducing (raffinose-containing) media. Total RNA was isolated from these cells and analyzed for the level of *FLP* mRNA by RNase protection. As is evident, the level of *FLP* mRNA is essentially unaffected by the presence of either *REP1* product or *REP2* product alone. However, in cells in which both products are present, the level of *FLP* mRNA is substantially depressed. The level of repression of *FLP* expression calculated from densitometer tracings of the autoradiogram shown in Figure 6 is approximately 50- to 100-fold. Thus, repression of *FLP* is effected by the concerted action of the *REP1* and *REP2* proteins. Similar results have been recently reported by Reynolds et al. (1987).

We have conducted similar analyses of the expression of other plasmid genes, using translational fusions of these genes to the *Escherichia coli lacZ* gene. We found that expression of both the *REP1* and the *D* genes are repressed if, and only if, the *REP1* and *REP2* proteins are present. In addition, neither the *D* gene product nor the *FLP* gene product affected expression of any of the 2-μm circle genes. Nor, under these conditions, did these two gene products substantially diminish the level of repression exerted by *REP1* and *REP2* proteins on *FLP* or *REP1* expression. These results can be inte-

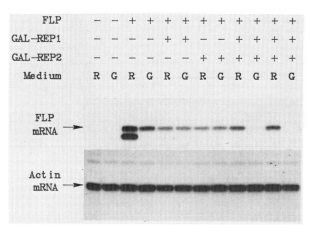

Figure 6 Repression of *FLP* mRNA levels by *REP1* and *REP2* proteins. Strains containing the indicated combinations of an integrated, defective 2-μm circle (designated FLP in the figure), *GAL10-REP1*, and *GAL10-REP2* were grown in 1% yeast extract, 2% peptone (YEP) plus either 2% raffinose (R) or 2% galactose (G). Samples of total RNA isolated from these cells were assayed for *FLP*-mRNA by RNase protection as described by Som et al. (1988). The band immediately below the *FLP*-specific band in the third track was an artifact in this particular sample and was not observed with other, essentially identical reactions.

grated into a model of copy control as described in the next section.

An additional regulatory interaction has been described recently by Murray et al. (1988). They reported that high levels of the *D* gene product can reverse *REP1/REP2*-mediated repression of *FLP*. This antagonism of repression is evident only when repression is effected by the relatively low levels of *REP1/REP2* complex found in a normal [cir⁺]. In strains containing high levels of *REP1* and *REP2* protein, high levels of *D* do not reverse repression (Murray et al. 1987; Som et al. 1988). This interaction has been incorporated into the model of plasmid copy control described below.

Control of plasmid copy levels

Regulatory interactions

A summary of the specific interactions of 2-μm-circle-encoded proteins with the 2-μm circle genome is illustrated in Figure 7. *FLP* protein binds to specific sites within the inverted repeats and catalyzes reciprocal recombination between them (Broach and Hicks 1980; Broach et al. 1982; Andrews et al. 1985; Senecoff et al. 1985). This recombination can induce a shift into rolling circle replication of the plasmid, which yields amplification of plasmid copy number (Futcher 1986; Volkert and Broach 1986). In addition, *REP1* and *REP2* proteins function together and through interaction with the plasmid domain, *REP3*, to promote equidistribution of plasmid molecules at cell division (Jayaram et al. 1983, 1985; Kikuchi 1983; Murray and Szostak 1983). *REP1* and *REP2* proteins act in concert also to repress transcription of plasmid genes *FLP*, *REP1*, and *D* and to repress transcription from a promoter lying adjacent to

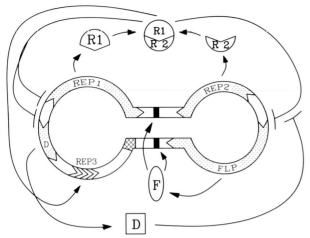

Figure 7 2-μm circle regulatory circuitry. Interactions of 2-μm circle plasmid products with the plasmid genome are indicated. *FLP* protein (F) catalyzes recombination between specific sites (filled regions) within the inverted repeats, a process required for plasmid copy number amplification. The products of *REP1* and *REP2* genes (R1 and R2) act in concert, perhaps as a heterologous dimeric complex, via the *REP3* locus to promote equipartitioning at cell division. In addition, these products repress transcription of *FLP*, *REP1*, and *D*. *D* protein antagonizes *REP1/REP2*-mediated repression of *FLP* gene expression, and perhaps of *REP1* and *D* gene expression as well.

REP3 locus (Jayaram et al. 1985). Finally, *D* protein interferes with *REP1/REP2* repression of *FLP* transcription and may similarly affect these proteins' ability to repress other 2-μm circle genes (Murray et al. 1987).

A model for plasmid copy control
Although the precise details have not necessarily been fully elaborated, regulation of 2-μm circle gene expression as described above can account for control of plasmid copy number. The central feature in such a model for plasmid copy control is regulation of *FLP*, whose activity stimulates, and is required for, copy number amplification. In cells with high copy levels, intercellular *REP1* and *REP2* protein concentrations are sufficient to maintain repression of *FLP* activity and, accordingly, to inhibit amplification. However, in cells acquiring a reduced level of plasmids, the diminished gene dosage of *REP1* and *REP2* yields reduced concentrations of these proteins, which in turn provokes derepression of *FLP* activity and induction of amplification. Thus, regulation of *FLP* expression by *REP1* and *REP2* provides for induction of amplification when copy level is low and repression of amplification when copy number is high.

A second feature of the model for plasmid copy control is autoregulation of *REP1*. This regulation probably serves as a homeostatic device, which enhances the plasmid's response to deviations of copy levels from the norm. First, *REP1* autoregulation provides a rigorous feedback loop on copy level increase. Concurrent with derepression of *FLP*, which is attendant on a drop in plasmid copy level, production of *REP1* protein is stimulated by derepression. Due to the consequent in-

crease in concentration of the *REP1/REP2* repressor complex, *FLP* expression is rapidly restored to its repressed level. In this manner, situations that provoke amplification also provoke subsequent increased repression of amplification. The result of this process is a transient burst of amplification to boost copy levels to normal, coupled with a burst of repressor synthesis to preclude significant overshoot of optimum copy number. Autoregulation of *REP1* also yields an enhanced sensitivity of the plasmid to decreases in plasmid concentration. If the concentration of *REP1* protein in the cell is maintained at a level just sufficient to establish effective repression of *FLP*, then a small drop in plasmid copy level would lead to reduced *REP1* protein levels, a corresponding increase in *FLP* expression, and activation of amplification. If, on the other hand, *REP1* protein concentration were at excess in the cell, then plasmid copy levels would have to drop drastically before amplification were activated.

The third feature of the model is the antagonism by *D* protein of *REP1/REP2* repression of *FLP*. This feature may also serve as a homeostatic device that enhances the responsiveness of the plasmid to changes in copy number. Consider, for example, the situation in which copy levels drop. Both *FLP* and *D* would become partially derepressed due to dilution of the repressor complex. The newly synthesized *D* protein then antagonizes the remaining repressor complex to allow further derepression of *FLP*. Thus, as a consequence of this positive feedback circuit, the magnitude of *FLP* induction following a decline in plasmid copy number is significantly enhanced. The plasmid obtains a large boost in induction of amplification following only a limited dilution of repressor.

A second facet of the role of *D* protein circuit in promoting homeostasis is its likely enhancement of the negative feedback loop based on autogenous regulation *REP1* that we described above. We can probably assume that *D* protein antagonizes *REP1/REP2* repression of *REP1* expression in a manner similar to its effect on *FLP* expression. Then, following a decline in copy number, not only would the *FLP* response be enhanced by *D* activity, but also derepression of *REP1* would be stimulated. Thus, in conjunction with an increase in the initial amplification response, the magnitude of the coincident repressor synthesis is increased, yielding a more stringent shut-off of further amplification.

Predictions and confirmations of the model
Several testable predictions emerge from the model for copy control elaborated above, some of which have been examined. The central component of the model is that the level of *FLP* expression controls the cellular copy level of the plasmid. Since *FLP* expression is substantially repressed under steady-state growth of plasmid-bearing cells, one would expect that presentation of additional *FLP* product in such cells should yield an increase in plasmid copy levels. In confirmation of this expectation, several groups have shown that in cells exhibiting increased expression of the *FLP* gene, 2-μm

circle plasmids are stably maintained at approximately 200–400 copies per cell, that is, several times the normal level (Reynolds et al. 1987; Murray et al. 1987; Som et al. 1988).

Second, *REP1* and *REP2* proteins are proposed to act as repressors of *FLP* expression. As a consequence, mutations within these genes should yield increased expression of *FLP* and an attendant increase in copy number. This prediction is not straightforward to test. In addition to their apparent role as transcriptional repressors, *REP1* and *REP2* proteins are required for efficient partitioning. Thus, loss of function of either of these genes yields an unstable plasmid that accumulates to relatively high copy due to asymmetric segregation at cell division. Nonetheless, Veit and Fangman (1985, and pers. comm.) have reported that *rep1* and *rep2* mutants of 2-μm circle maintain unusually high copy levels in plasmid-bearing cells, over and above that expected from loss of partitioning activity. These results suggest that inactivation of either gene perturbs the copy control process.

Third, the proposed role of *D* protein in control of plasmid copy level would suggest that its overproduction should yield an increase in *FLP* expression and an attendant increase in plasmid copy level. Murray et al. (1987) have reported such an effect. However, this observation is not so much a prediction of the model as a seminal fact underlying its formulation.

Fourth, since *REP1* and *REP2* proteins repress transcription of *FLP*, *REP1*, and *D*, we might anticipate that the promoter regions of these genes would contain sequences in common. Such sequences would consti-

tute domains to which either one or the other protein would bind to effect repression. In addition, since *REP1* and *REP2* proteins most likely bind to the *REP3* locus to effect plasmid partitioning, such a sequence might be expected to be present at that locus as well. Consistent with this hypothesis, we have previously obtained evidence suggesting that *REP1* protein binds double-stranded DNA with specificity for only those plasmid DNA fragments encompassing these three sites (L.C.C. Wu and J. Broach, unpubl.). With this expectation in mind, we examined the nucleotide sequence of 2-μm circle and found a nanonucleotide element 5′-TGCATTTTT-3′ (or its complement) that is present once within the *REP1/D* divergent promoter, twice within the *FLP* 5′-flanking domain, and six times within *REP3*. The precise location of this element within these three regions is diagramed in Figure 8. This sequence appears at no other site within the plasmid, nor is any other element of comparable size present uniquely at all three loci. Thus, this element is a possible candidate for mediating interactions of *REP1* and *REP2* proteins with the plasmid. It should be noted that transcriptional regulation of a number of genes in yeast has been shown to be mediated by elements of similar size (Donahue et al. 1983; Miller et al. 1985). A further prediction of these observations would be that specific deletion of this repressor binding site from the *FLP* promoter should yield a plasmid with an unfettered copy control system. We are in the process of testing this prediction.

Several previous observations regarding the behavior of certain mutant 2-μm plasmids are, at first glance, in conflict with the model for plasmid copy control pro-

TGCATTTTT..7bp..AAAAATGCA

REP1 + D CAT_{REP1}...170bp...TGCATTTTT..5bp...cAtAATGCA...69bp...ATG_D

REP2 + FLP CAT_{REP2}...160bp...TGCATTTTT..6bp...tgAAATCaA...

30bp...AAtAATGCg..7bp...TGCATTTTT...130bp...ATG_{FLP}

REP3   AAAAATGCA....46bp...TGCATTTTT..7bp...AgAAATGCA...37bp

...TGCATTTTT..7bp...AAAAATGCA...39bp

...TGCATTTTT..7bp...AgAAATGCA...53bp

...AAAAATGCA

Figure 8 Possible consensus sequence for *REP1/REP2* repressor binding. Shown at the top is a consensus sequence derived from a comparison of the sequences of those regions to which the *REP1/REP2* complex is expected to bind. Also shown is the organization of this repeated element within the *REP3* locus and the positions of the element relative to the initial ATG (or its inverse on the opposite strand) of the four major 2-μm circle coding regions.

posed above. Specifically, mutations in *FLP* and, to a lesser extent, in *D* would be predicted to show diminished copy levels or stability when compared to isogenic *FLP*⁺ or *D*⁺ plasmids. In fact, no loss of stability or copy number has been associated with loss of *FLP* activity. However, to date all such genetic analysis has been conducted with artificial hybrid plasmids, in which sequences for propagation in *E. coli* are inserted within the 2-μm circle genome. For unknown reasons and irrespective of the site of insertion of vector sequences, these hybrid plasmids are at least 2 orders of magnitude less stable than 2-μm circle itself and are maintained at a copy level 20% to 50% that of wild-type 2-μm circle (Volkert and Borach 1987). Thus, any effects of mutations in *FLP* or *D* could easily have been obscured by the debilitating effect of the presence of vector sequences. We are now reexamining the consequences of mutations in *FLP* and *D* in authentic 2-μm plasmids devoid of vector sequences, specifically with a view to testing the above copy control model.

Concluding Remarks

The plasmid copy control system proposed in this chapter represents a unique solution to maintaining constant levels of an extrachromosomal element. Numerous studies of bacterial plasmids have revealed a diversity of strategies for maintaining plasmids at specific copy levels within the cells. However, almost all of these strategies are based on regulating initiation of plasmid replication (Nordstrom 1985). Similarly, eukaryotic viruses that propagate in their latent state as extrachromosomal elements appear to regulate copy levels by modulating the frequency of replication initiation (Berg et al. 1986; Roberts and Weintraub 1986). We noted above that other eukaryotic extrachromosomal elements, including other yeast plasmids, many plant chloroplast genomes, and some latent viruses may also employ a recombination-induced shift in replication mode to effect amplification. Thus, we might anticipate that in order to regulate amplification, a similar regulatory scheme will be an integral component of these genomes as well.

Acknowledgments

This work was supported in part by grant GM-34596 from the National Institutes of Health to J.R.B. and grant 861391 from the American Heart Association to K.A.A.

References

Adams, A. and T. Lindahl. 1975. Epstein-Barr virus genomes with properties of circular DNA molecules in carrier cells. *Proc. Natl. Acad. Sci.* **72:** 1477.

Andrews, B.J., G.A. Proteau, L.G. Beatty, and P.D. Sadowski. 1985. The FLP recombinase of the 2 micron circle DNA of yeast: Interaction with its target sequences. *Cell* **40:** 795.

Araki, H., A. Jearnpipatkul, H. Tatsumi, T. Sakurai, K. Ushio, T. Muta, and Y. Oshima. 1985. Molecular and functional organization of yeast plasmid pSR1. *J. Mol. Biol.* **182:** 191.

Berg, L., M. Lusky, A. Stenlund, and M.R. Botchan. 1986. Repression of bovine papilloma virus replication is mediated by a virally encoded *trans*-acting factor. *Cell* **46:** 753.

Brewer, B.J. and W.L. Fangman. 1987. The localization of replication origins on ARS plasmids in *S. cerevisiae*. *Cell* **51:** 463.

Broach, J.R. 1981. The yeast plasmid 2μ circle. In *The molecular biology of the yeast* Saccharomyces: *Life cycle and inheritance* (ed. J.N. Strathern et al.), p. 445. Cold Spring Harbor Laboratory, Cold Spring Harbor, New York.

Broach, J.R. and J.B. Hicks. 1980. Replication and recombination functions associated with the yeast plasmid, 2 micron circle. *Cell* **21:** 501.

Broach, J.R., V.R. Guarascio, and M. Jayaram. 1982. Recombination within the yeast plasmid 2 micron circle is site-specific. *Cell* **29:** 227.

Broach, J.R., J.F. Atkins, C. McGill, and L. Chow. 1979. Identification and mapping of the transcriptional and translational products of the yeast plasmid 2μ circle. *Cell* **16:** 827.

Broach, J.R., Y.-Y. Li, L.C.-C. Wu, and M. Jayaram. 1983a. Vectors for high-level inducible expression of cloned genes in yeast. In *Experimental manipulation of the gene expression* (ed. M. Inouye), p. 83. Academic Press, New York.

Broach, J.R., Y.-Y. Li, J. Feldman, M. Jayaram, J. Abraham, K.A. Nasmyth, and J.B. Hicks. 1983b. Localization and sequence analysis of yeast origins of DNA replication. *Cold Spring Harbor Symp. Quant. Biol.* **47:** 1165.

Cashmore, A.M., M.S. Albury, G. Hadfield, and P.A. Meacock. 1986. Genetic analysis of partitioning functions encoded by the 2 μm circle of *Saccharomyces cerevisiae*. *Mol. Gen. Genet.* **203:** 154.

Chou, J. and B. Roizman. 1985. Isomerization of herpes simplex virus 1 genome: Identification of the *cis*-acting and recombination sites within the domain of the a sequence. *Cell* **41:** 803.

Delius, H. and J.B. Clements. 1976. A partial denaturation map of herpes simplex virus type 1 DNA: Evidence for inversion of the unique DNA regions. *J. Gen. Virol.* **33:** 125.

Donahue, T.F., R.S. Daves, G. Lucchini, and G.R. Fink. 1983. A short nucleotide sequence required for regulation of HIS4 by the general control system of yeast. *Cell* **32:** 89.

Futcher, A.B. 1986. Copy number amplification of the 2 micron circle plasmid of *Saccharomyces cerevisiae*. *J. Theor. Biol.* **119:** 197.

Futcher, A.B. and B.S. Cox. 1983. Maintenance of the 2 micron circle plasmid in populations of *Saccharomyces cerevisiae*. *J. Bacteriol.* **154:** 612.

Hartley, J.L. and J.E. Donelson. 1980. Nucleotide sequence of the yeast plasmid. *Nature* **286:** 860.

Hayward, G.S., R.J. Jacob, S.C. Wadsworth, and B. Roizman. 1975. Anatomy of herpes simplex virus DNA: Evidence for four populations of molecules that differ in the relative orientations of their long and short components. *Proc. Natl. Acad. Sci.* **72:** 4243.

Holm, C. 1982. Clonal lethality caused by the yeast plasmid 2μ DNA. *Cell* **29:** 585.

Huberman, J.A., L.D. Spotila, K.A. Nawotka, S. El-Assouli, and L.R. Davis. 1987. In vitro replication origin of the yeast 2 μm plasmid. *Cell* **51:** 473.

Jayaram, M., Y.-Y. Li, and J.R. Broach. 1983. The yeast plasmid 2 micron circle encodes components required for its high copy propagation. *Cell* **34:** 95.

Jayaram, M., A. Sutton, and J.R. Broach. 1985. Properties of REP3: A *cis* acting locus required for stable propagation of the yeast plasmid 2 micron circle. *Mol. Cell. Biol.* **5:** 2466.

Jenkins, F.J. and B. Roizman. 1986. Herpes simplex virus I recombinants with noninverting genomes frozen in different isomeric arrangements are capable of independent replication. *J. Virol.* **59:** 494.

Kikuchi, Y. 1983. Yeast plasmid requires a *cis*-acting locus and two plasmid proteins for its stable maintenance. *Cell* **35:** 487.

Kolodner, R.D. and K.K. Tewari. 1975. Chloroplast DNA from higher plants replicates by both the Cairns and rolling circle mechanism. *Nature* **256:** 708.

———. 1979. Inverted repeats in chloroplast DNA from higher plants. *Proc. Natl. Acad. Sci.* **76:** 41.

Lindahl, T., A. Adams, G. Bjursell, G.W. Bornkamm, C. Kaschka-Dierich, and U. Jehn. 1976. Covalently closed circular duplex DNA of Epstein-Barr virus in a human lymphoid cell line. *J. Mol. Biol.* **102:** 511.

Livingston, D.M. 1977. Inheritance of 2μm DNA plasmid from *Saccharomyces. Genetics* **86:**73.

Livingston, D.M. and D.M. Kupfer. 1977. Control of *Saccharomyces cerevisiae* 2 micron circle DNA replication by cell division cycle genes that control nuclear DNA replication. *J. Mol. Biol.* **116:** 249.

Mead, D.J., D.C.J. Gardner, and S.G. Oliver. 1986. The yeast 2μ plasmid: Strategies for the survival of a selfish DNA. *Mol. Gen. Genet.* **205:** 417.

Melton, D.A., P.A. Krieg, M.R. Rebagliati, T. Maniatis, K. Zinn, and M.R. Green. 1984. Efficient in vitro synthesis of biologically active RNA and RNA hybridization probes from plasmids containing a bacteriophage SP6 promoter. *Nucleic Acids Res.* **12:** 7035.

Miller, J.H., V.L. MacKay, and K.A. Nasmyth. 1985. Identification and comparison of two sequence elements that confer cell-type transcription in yeast. *Nature* **314:** 598.

Murray, A.W. and J.W. Szostak. 1983. Pedigree analysis of plasmid segregation in yeast. *Cell* **34:** 961.

Murray, J.A.H. and G. Cesarini. 1986. Functional analysis of the yeast plasmid partition locus STB. *EMBO J.* **5:** 3391.

Murray, J.A.H., M. Scarpa, N. Rossi, and G. Cesareni. 1987. Antagonistic controls regulate copy number of the yeast 2μ plasmid. *EMBO J.* **6:** 4205.

Newlon, C.S., R.J. Devenish, R.A. Suci, and C.J. Roffis. 1981. Replication origins used in vivo in yeast. *ICN-UCLA Symp. Mol. Cell Biol.* **22:** 501.

Nordstrom, K. 1985. Replication, incompatibility and partition. In *Plasmids in bacteria* (ed. D.R. Helinski et al.), p. 119. Plenum Press, New York.

Palmer, J.D. 1983. Chloroplast DNA exists in two orientations. *Nature* **301:** 92.

Reynolds, A., A. Murray, and J. Szostak. 1987. Function of the yeast plasmid gene products. *Mol. Cell. Biol.* **7:** 3566.

Roberts, J.M. and H. Weintraub. 1986. Negative control of DNA replication in composite SV40-bovine papilloma virus plasmid. *Cell* **46:** 741.

Rochaix, J.D. 1978. Restriction endonuclease map of the chloroplast DNA of *Chlamydomonas reinhardii. J. Mol. Biol.* **126:** 596.

Schmike, R.T., ed. 1982. Studies on gene duplications and amplifications—An historical perspective. In *Gene amplification*, p. 1. Cold Spring Harbor Laboratory, Cold Spring Harbor, New York.

Senecoff, J.F., R.C. Bruckner, and M.M. Cox. 1985. The FLP recombinase of the yeast 2 micron plasmid: Characterization of its recombination site. *Proc. Natl. Acad. Sci.* **82:** 7270.

Sigurdson, D.C., M.E. Gaarder, and D.M. Livingston. 1981. Characterization of the transmission during cytoductant formation of the 2 micron DNA plasmid from *Saccharomyces. Mol. Gen. Genet.* **183:** 59.

Som, T., K.A. Armstrong, F.C. Volkert, and J.R. Broach. 1988. Autoregulation of 2 μm circle gene expression provides a model for maintenance of stable plasmid copy levels. *Cell* **52:** 27.

Spradling, A.C. and A.P. Mahowald. 1980. Amplification of genes for chorion proteins during oogenesis in *Drosophila melanogaster. Proc. Natl. Acad. Sci.* **77:** 1096.

Stark, G.R. and G.M. Wahl. 1984. Gene amplification. *Annu. Rev. Biochem.* **53:** 447.

Sutton, A. and J.R. Broach. 1985. Signals for transcription and termination in the yeast plasmid 2 micron circle. *Mol. Cell. Biol.* **5:** 2770.

Toh-e, A., S. Tada, and Y. Oshima. 1982. 2-micron DNA-like plasmids in the osmophilic haploid yeast *Saccharomyces rouxii. J. Bacteriol.* **151:** 1380.

Toh-e, A., H. Araki, I. Utatsu, and Y. Oshima. 1984. Plasmids resembling 2-micron DNA in the osmotolerant yeasts *Saccharomyces bailii* and *Saccharomyces bisporus. J. Gen. Microbiol.* **130:** 2527.

Veit, B.E. and W.L. Fangman. 1985. Chromatin organization of the *Saccharomyces cerevisiae* 2 micron plasmid depends on plasmid-encoded products. *Mol. Cell. Biol.* **5:** 2190.

Volkert, F.C. and J.R. Broach. 1986. Site-specific recombination promotes plasmid amplification in yeast. *Cell* **46:** 541.

———. 1987. The mechanism of propagation of the yeast 2-micron circle plasmid. In *The biochemistry and molecular biology of industrial yeasts* (ed. G.G. Stewart et al.), p. 145. CRC Press, Boca Raton, Florida.

Walton, J.D., C.E. Paquin, K. Kaneko, and V.M. Williamson. 1986. Resistance to antimycin A in yeast by amplification of ADH4 on a linear, 42kb palindromic plasmid. *Cell* **46:** 857.

Wu, L.C.C., P.A. Fisher, and J.R. Broach. 1987. A yeast plasmid partitioning protein is a karyoskeletal component. *J. Biol. Chem.* **262:** 883.

Wu, M., J.K. Lou, D.Y. Chang, C.H. Chang, and Z.Q. Nie. 1986. Structure and function of a chloroplast DNA replication origin of *Chlamydomonas reinhardtii. Proc. Natl. Acad. Sci.* **83:** 6761.

Yao, M.-C. 1982. Amplification of ribosomal RNA gene in Tetrahymena. In *The cell nucleus* (ed. H. Busch and L. Rothblum), vol. 12, p. 127. Academic Press, New York.

Yao, M.-C., S.-G. Zhu, and C.-H. Yao. 1985. Gene amplification in *Tetrahymena thermophila:* Formation of extrachromosomal palindromic genes coding for rRNA. *Mol. Cell. Biol.* **5:** 1260.

Zakian, V.A., B.J. Brewer, and W.L. Fangman. 1979. Replication of each copy of the yeast 2 micron DNA plasmid occurs during the S phase. *Cell* **17:** 923.

Mapping Eukaryotic Replication Origins

J.A. Huberman and K.A. Nawotka

Department of Molecular and Cellular Biology, Roswell Park Memorial Institute,
Buffalo, New York 14263

We have developed a method that allows direct localization of replication origins in segments of chromosomal DNA for which cloned probes are available. The method employs two-dimensional neutral/alkaline agarose gel electrophoresis to separate the nascent strands of replicating DNA molecules away from nonreplicating molecules and parental strands. Analysis, by hybridization with short probe sequences, of the sequence content of nascent strands of various lengths allows determination of direction(s) of replication fork movement and location(s) of origins.

Although DNA replication is an essential aspect of cellular proliferation, virtually nothing is known about the mechanisms by which eukaryotic DNA replication is regulated. One important reason for our lack of knowledge is our uncertainty about the DNA sequences involved in initiation of replication. Although it has been known for nearly 20 years that there are multiple sites, called "origins," at which replication initiates within each eukaryotic chromosomal DNA molecule (Huberman and Riggs 1968), the extent to which these origins possess specific nucleotide sequences is not yet clear. In some eukaryotic cells, such as those in early *Xenopus* embryos, all tested DNA sequences can serve as origins (Harland and Laskey 1980), whereas in other cells origin function appears to be restricted to specific chromosome regions or to specific sequences (McKnight et al. 1978; Struhl et al. 1979; Zannis-Hadjopoulos et al. 1985; Burhans et al. 1986; James and Leffak 1986; Razin et al. 1986).

Unfortunately, none of the studies cited above has permitted definitive conclusions about the general nature of eukaryotic replication origins. That is because these studies (and many more which we do not have room to cite) were either carried out using exceptional biological systems whose unusual properties simplified origin identification (McKnight et al. 1978; Harland and Laskey 1980; Burhans et al. 1986) or were based on reasonable, but untested, assumptions about origin properties (Struhl et al. 1979; Zannis-Hadjopoulos et al. 1985; James and Leffak 1986; Razin et al. 1986). Methods were needed that would allow direct localization of origins used in vivo by normal cells, without reliance on assumptions. We have developed such a method (Nawotka and Huberman 1988), as have Brewer and Fangman (1987). In this paper, we provide a description of our method and of the results we have obtained with simian virus 40 (SV40) and with the yeast 2-μm plasmid (Huberman et al. 1987).

Experimental Procedures

Our method allows determination of the direction(s) of replication fork movement through segments of chromosomal DNA for which cloned probes are available. Because origins are defined as sites from which replication forks emerge (Huberman and Riggs 1968), determination of replication fork direction(s) allows direct inference of origin (and also terminus) location. The method we now use is based on an earlier method (Spotila and Huberman 1985); we have introduced modifications to both simplify and increase the sensitivity of the earlier method.

Figure 1 illustrates the principles of the improved method. A segment of chromosomal DNA delimited by restriction sites (R) is assumed to be replicated from the single origin (O) so that all replication forks pass through the segment from left to right (Fig. 1a). DNA containing replication forks is isolated by conventional gentle techniques from actively growing cells. The cells need not be synchronized; in fact, synchronization could lead to erroneous results by suppressing or enhancing signals from origins used in different portions of S phase. The isolated DNA is digested to completion with restriction enzyme R. Restriction fragments containing replication forks are enriched by selective adsorption to benzoylated, naphthoylated DEAE-cellulose (BND-cellulose). This enrichment is based on the ability of BND-cellulose to preferentially bind single-stranded DNA; there are short stretches of single-stranded DNA at replication forks. Twenty- to fiftyfold enrichment for fork-containing molecules can be achieved by a simple batch method (Huberman et al. 1987) modified from the batch procedure of Gamper et al. (1985).

The fork-containing fragments are then subjected to two-dimensional neutral/alkaline gel electrophoresis (Fig. 1b). The fragments are separated according to extent of replication in the first dimension, and nascent strands are separated according to size in the second dimension. The final two-dimensional gel is blotted to a nylon membrane, and the membrane is hybridized with short probe sequences derived from the region of interest. The circular area at the upper left of each of the diagramed autoradiograms in Figure 1b represents the strong signal from contaminating nonreplicating molecules. The vertical line extending downward from this position is due to signal from heterogenous-sized strands

225

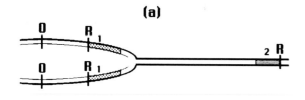

(a)

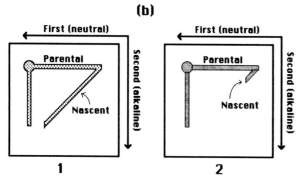

(b)

Figure 1 Origin mapping by determination of the sequence content of nascent strands of varying sizes. Symbols are self-explanatory or are explained in the text.

produced by occasional nicking of the nonreplicating molecules. The horizontal line extending rightward from the circular area represents signal from the parental strands of replicating molecules. Parental strands remain constant in size regardless of extent of replication. Nascent strands migrate more rapidly than parental strands. In the example shown in Figure 1, probe 1 from the left end of the segment detects the complete set of nascent strands, but probe 2 detects only the longest nascent strands. From such results, one could immediately conclude that replication forks move through the segment of interest from left to right, that the origin must be located at the left end of the segment or outside the segment to its left, and that origin localization would require testing the next segment to the left along the chromosome. The reader can easily imagine how the same basic technique, especially when augmented by use of additional short probes, would also allow detection of restriction fragments containing origins or termini.

The accuracy of the method is greatly increased if markers (DNA strands of known size) are also run in the second-dimension gel so that the minimum size of nascent strand detected by each probe can be accurately measured (see Fig. 3).

Results and Discussion

SV40

We first tested the improved method with replicating SV40 DNA, since the location of the single origin used by SV40 is well known (Danna and Nathans 1972). Our results are described in detail in a different report (Nawotka and Huberman 1988). In brief, all results were

consistent with bidirectional replication from the known origin location. In these trial experiments, we digested replicating SV40 DNA with various combinations of *Bgl*I (which cuts at the origin) and *Bam*HI (which cuts in the termination region). We were surprised to see that the shapes of the nascent strand arcs detected on blots of two-dimensional gels depended on the structures of the replicating molecules, as diagramed in Figure 2.

Each of the four panels of Figure 2 contains a diagram of a replicating DNA molecule above a diagram of a two-dimensional neutral/alkaline gel hybridized with a short probe capable of detecting the shortest nascent strands (an origin-proximal probe). In each two-dimensional gel diagram, first-dimension (neutral) electrophoresis is from right to left, and second-dimension (alkaline) electrophoresis is from top to bottom, as in Figure 1. The black square in the upper left of each gel represents the relatively strong signal from contaminating nonreplicating molecules. The vertical line extending downward from this square represents the signal from nicked strands. The horizontal line rightward from the square represents the signal from parental strands. The remaining line represents the arc of nascent strands.

The four panels of Figure 2 summarize, in diagrammatic form, the results obtained when SV40 DNA was cut with *Bam*HI and *Bgl*I to generate Y-shaped replicating molecules (upper left) or with *Bam*HI to generate molecules with expanding internal bubbles (upper right)

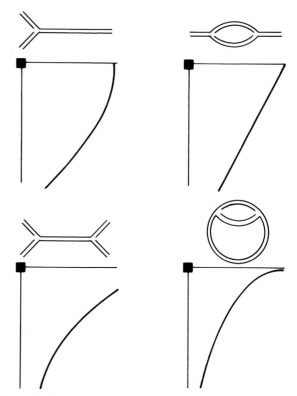

Figure 2 The structure of replicating molecules affects the shape of the nascent strand arc. Symbols are self-explanatory or are explained in the text. (Reprinted, with permission, from Nawotka and Huberman 1988.)

or with *Bgl*I to generate molecules with two replication forks converging from each end (lower left) or was left uncut as form I "Cairns"-type replicating molecules (lower left).

From separate experiments with linear marker DNAs, we have learned that the mobility of single DNA strands in the second dimension is an inverse function of the logarithm of strand size (Huberman et al. 1987). Therefore, the straight line nascent strand signal produced by replicating molecules with internal bubbles (Fig. 2, upper right) implies that the mobility of such replicating molecules in the first dimension is a logarithmic function of size (i.e., a logarithmic function of extent of replication). Similarly, the rightward-curved nascent strand arcs detected with "double-Y" and Cairns-type replicating molecules (Fig. 2, lower panels) imply that separation of the larger replicating molecules in the first dimension is greater than expected for a logarithmic relationship. A linear relationship between mobility and extent of replication in the first dimension would produce the rightward curvature seen in these lower panels; indeed, Tapper and DePamphilis (1978) have previously demonstrated a linear relationship between extent of replication and mobility in neutral gels for intact Cairns-type replicating SV40 molecules.

We were especially surprised to see that the nascent strand arc produced by Y-shaped replicating molecules curved upward (Fig. 2, upper left). This upward curvature implies that, for Y-shaped molecules that are more than half replicated, significant increases in extent of replication do not produce a significant change in mobility in the first-dimension gel. The same phenomenon has been detected by Brewer and Fangman (1987). In an elegant study of the effects of DNA structure on mobility in neutral agarose gels, these authors found that branched molecules are significantly retarded relative to linear molecules and that Y-shaped molecules show maximum retardation at 50% replication; as replication proceeds, the parental branch becomes shorter and the molecules behave more like simple linear molecules (Brewer and Fangman 1987).

2-μm plasmid

After testing the improved method with SV40, we used it to investigate origin usage in an unknown situation—the yeast 2-μm plasmid. This plasmid is found, at about 15–100 copies per cell, in most strains of *Saccharomyces cerevisiae*. It is located in the nucleus as a histone-associated minichromosome (Nelson and Fangman 1979). Each molecule of 2-μm plasmid ordinarily replicates just once during the normal cellular S phase (Zakian et al. 1979), and mutations that affect chromosomal DNA replication also affect 2-μm plasmid replication (Livingston and Kupfer 1977). Thus, the 2-μm plasmid appears to be an excellent model for yeast chromosomal replication.

The DNA of 2-μm plasmid is circular, and its entire sequence of 6318 bp has been determined (Hartley and Donelson 1980). An unusual feature of the sequence is

a stretch of 599 bp that is inverted and precisely repeated so as to divide the genome into two slightly unequal portions, a large unique region and a small unique region. An enzyme encoded by the 2-μm plasmid catalyzes intramolecular recombination between specific sites within the inverted repeats, leading to flipping of the small unique region with respect to the large unique region. The resulting two recombinational isomers, called forms A and B, are normally present in equal abundance (for review, see Broach 1982).

Two possible origins were previously identified in 2-μm plasmid by electron microscopy (Newlon et al. 1981) and by analysis of in vitro replication (Jazwinski and Edelman 1982). One possible origin was located in the middle of the small unique region (roughly 5300–5700 on the map of the A form; Hartley and Donelson 1980). The second possible origin was located at one of the boundaries between an inverted repeat and the large unique region. This origin appeared possibly coincidental with an *ARS* sequence previously mapped at 3660–3743 (Broach et al. 1983). *ARS* sequences allow colinear plasmids to replicate without integration into large chromosomes (Struhl et al. 1979). This property has suggested that *ARS* sequences might act as replication origins. Previously, it has not been possible to exclude alternate roles in replication for *ARS* sequences, such as acting as a topoisomerase-binding site, as a nuclear-matrix-binding site, or as a loading site for enzymes involved in replication.

Application of our improved two-dimensional gel method to yeast 2-μm plasmid has shown clearly that there is just a single replication origin, located at 3700 ± 100. If a second origin (at 5300–5700 or elsewhere) is used, it must be used at less than 2% of the frequency of primary origin usage (Huberman et al. 1987). Some of the data leading to these conclusions are summarized in Figure 3. Short probes 1–4 are from the large unique region, probe 5 is from the inverted repeat, and probes 6–8 are from the small unique region. The endpoints of the probe sequences are the horizontal endpoints of the data ellipses in Figure 3. The vertical endpoints of each data ellipse indicate estimated uncertainty in measurement of minimum strand length at the bottom end of the nascent strand arc detected by each probe. The solid lines are, in our opinion, the best lines through the data points; they extrapolate to position 3700, within the *ARS* sequence. The dashed line is calculated based on the assumption that replication forks move outward at equal rates from a hypothetical origin at 3900. Note that the minimum strand size detected by probe 1 is significantly less than predicted if the origin were located at 3900. Similarly, probe 5 data (Fig. 3) exclude the possibility of origin location at 3500. Thus, the 2-μm plasmid origin must be located at 3700 ± 100. The fact that this position corresponds exactly to the genetically mapped *ARS* sequence (Broach et al. 1983) suggests that *ARS* sequences derived from chromosomal DNA will prove to be chromosomal replication origins. We are now testing this possibility.

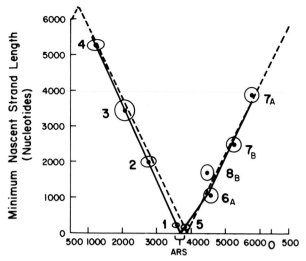

Nucleotide Number in 2μm Plasmid

Figure 3 Localization of the yeast 2-μm plasmid replication origin. The lengths of the shortest nascent strands detected by each probe were plotted as a function of probe position in the 2-μm plasmid DNA molecule. For each data ellipse, the vertical dimension represents estimated error in length measurement, and the left and right limits of the horizontal dimension correspond to the endpoints of the probe on the 2-μm plasmid map (Hartley and Donelson 1980). The solid lines through the points provide the closest fit to the data, in our estimate. The dashed lines are calculated based on the assumption that replication forks move outward at equal rates from an origin at 3900 (see text). (Reprinted, with permission, from Huberman et al. 1987.)

Acknowledgments

We thank the following people for their helpful discussions: Michael McCleland, Robert Benezra, Randall Morse, David Kowalski, Steven Pruitt, Les Davis, Robert Givens, Ravindra Hajela, and Jiguang Zhu. This work was supported by grants DCB-8616046 from the National Science Foundation, GM-31443 from the National Institutes of Health, and MV-229 from the American Cancer Society. Computer resources were provided by the N.I.H.-supported BIONET National Computer Resource for Molecular Biology.

References

Brewer, B.J. and W.L. Fangman. 1987. The localization of replication origins on *ARS* plasmids in *Saccharomyces cerevisiae. Cell* **51**: 463.

Broach, J.R. 1982. The yeast plasmid 2 μ circle. *Cell* **28**: 203.

Broach, J.R., Y.-Y. Li, J. Feldman, M. Jayaram, J. Abraham, K.A. Nasymth, and J.B. Hicks. 1983. Localization and sequence analysis of yeast origins of DNA replication. *Cold Spring Harbor Symp. Quant. Biol.* **47**: 1165.

Burhans, W.C., J.E. Selegue, and N.H. Heintz. 1986. Isolation of the origin of replication associated with the amplified Chinese hamster dihydrofolate reductase domain. *Proc. Natl. Acad. Sci.* **83**: 7790.

Danna, K.J. and D. Nathans. 1972. Bidirectional replication of SV40 DNA. *Proc. Natl. Acad. Sci.* **69**: 3097.

Gamper, H., N. Lehman, J. Piette, and J. Hearst. 1985. Purification of circular DNA using benzoylated naphthoylated DEAE-cellulose. *DNA* **4**: 157.

Harland, R.M. and R. Laskey. 1980. Regulated replication of DNA microinjected into eggs of *Xenopus laevis. Cell* **21**: 761.

Hartley, J.L. and J.E. Donelson. 1980. Nucleotide sequence of the yeast plasmid. *Nature* **286**: 860.

Huberman, J.A. and A.D. Riggs. 1968. On the mechanism of DNA replication in mammalian chromosomes. *J. Mol. Biol.* **32**: 327.

Huberman, J.A., L.D. Spotila, K.A. Nawotka, S.M. El-Assouli, and L.R. Davis. 1987. The in vivo replication origin of the yeast 2 μm plasmid. *Cell* **51**: 473.

James, C.D. and M. Leffak. 1986. Polarity of DNA replication through the avian alpha-globin locus. *Mol. Cell. Biol.* **6**: 976.

Jazwinski, S.M. and G.M. Edelman. 1982. Protein complexes from active replicative fractions associate in vitro with the replication origins of yeast 2-μm DNA plasmid. *Proc. Natl. Acad. Sci.* **79**: 3428.

Livingston, D.M. and D.M. Kupfer. 1977. Control of Saccharomyces cerevisiae 2 μm DNA replication by cell division cycle genes that control nuclear DNA replication. *J. Mol. Biol.* **116**: 249.

McKnight, S.L., M. Bustin, and O.L. Miller, Jr. 1978. Electron microscopic analysis of chromosome metabolism in the *Drosophila melanogaster* embryo. *Cold Spring Harbor Symp. Quant. Biol.* **42**: 741.

Nawotka, K.A. and J.A. Huberman. 1988. Two dimensional gel electrophoretic method for mapping DNA replicons. *Mol. Cell. Biol.* **8**: (in press).

Nelson, R.G. and W.L. Fangman. 1979. Nucleosome organization of the yeast 2-μm DNA plasmid: A eukaryotic minichromosome. *Proc. Natl. Acad. Sci.* **76**: 6515.

Newlon, C.S., R.J. Devenish, P.A. Suci, and C.J. Roffis. 1981. Replication origins used in vivo in yeast. In *The initiation of DNA replication* (ed. D.S. Ray), p. 501. Academic Press, New York.

Razin, S.V., M.G. Kekelidze, E.M. Lukanidin, K. Scherrer, and G.P. Georgiev. 1986. Replication origins are attached to the nuclear skeleton. *Nucleic Acids Res.* **14**: 8189.

Spotila, L.D. and J.A. Huberman. 1985. Method for mapping DNA replication origins. *Mol. Cell. Biol.* **5**: 85.

Struhl, K., D.T. Stinchcomb, S. Sherer, and R.W. Davis. 1979. High frequency transformation of yeast: Autonomous replication of hybrid molecules. *Proc. Natl. Acad. Sci.* **76**: 1035.

Tapper, D.P. and M.L. DePamphilis. 1978. Discontinuous DNA replication: Accumulation of simian virus 40 DNA at specific stages in its replication. *J. Mol. Biol.* **120**: 401.

Zakian, V.A., B.J. Brewer, and W.L. Fangman. 1979. Replication of each copy of the yeast 2 micron DNA plasmid occurs during the S phase. *Cell* **17**: 923.

Zannis-Hadjopoulos, M., G. Kaufmann, S.-S. Wang, R.L. Lechner, E. Karawya, J. Hesse, and R.G. Martin. 1985. Properties of some monkey DNA sequences obtained by a procedure that enriches for DNA replication origins. *Mol. Cell. Biol.* **5**: 1621.

Analysis of Replication Intermediates by Two-dimensional Agarose Gel Electrophoresis

B.J. Brewer, E.P. Sena,* and W.L. Fangman

Department of Genetics SK-50, University of Washington, Seattle, Washington 98195

The replication of duplex DNA proceeds through branched intermediates. Because of their distinct topological properties, these branched forms can exhibit slower migration in agarose gels relative to unbranched, linear DNA molecules of equivalent mass. We have modified the two-dimensional (2-D) agarose gel technique of Bell and Byers (1983) to generate conditions where branched DNA fragments migrate in one dimension in proportion to their mass but are retarded in the second dimension in a manner that depends on the number, length, and topology of their branches. Increased retardation in the second dimension is obtained by using higher agarose concentration and higher voltage, and by including ethidium bromide. Southern hybridization permits the detection of rare branched forms so that purification of replication intermediates is not required. Electron microscopy was used to confirm the gel pattern predicted for Y-shaped replication intermediates. Replication intermediates consisting of simple Ys, bubbles, and double Ys can be distinguished on 2-D gels; their gel patterns allow replication origins to be mapped.

DNA replication begins at many locations along eukaryotic chromosomes. A fundamental question regarding eukaryotic replication is whether these origins of replication occur at specific sites on a chromosome in each cell cycle or at randomly chosen sites. The extreme view that there is no specificity for initiation is supported by the findings of Harland and Laskey (1980) that any DNA molecule injected into *Xenopus* eggs is capable of cell-cycle-regulated replication. The other extreme view, that sites of replication initiation are dictated by specific sequences, is most strongly supported by the properties of autonomously replicating sequence (ARS) plasmids in yeast (Williamson 1985; Kearsey 1986). In prokaryotic, viral, and mitochondrial genomes origins are specified by local DNA sequence. However, the results with ARS plasmids could be the consequence of a sequence that is responsible for establishing some architectural feature of the eukaryotic chromosome such as folding, chromatin structure, or matrix or scaffold binding.

The common technique for determining the location of an origin is to map the position of eye-forms (bubbles) relative to a restriction enzyme cleavage site by examining a collection of purified, homogeneous replication intermediates (RIs) in the electron microscope. This procedure has been used successfully with viral and prokaryotic plasmid molecules but has not been feasible for analyzing the larger eukaryotic chromosome. Even when a chromosomal segment has been cloned and reintroduced into cells as an autonomously replicating plasmid, quantities of RIs adequate for the physical

mapping of origins have been impossible to obtain. We have, therefore, investigated the possibility of using 2-D gel electrophoresis of total DNA combined with Southern analysis to characterize RIs. The 2-D gel technique of Bell and Byers (1983) was modified to allow visualization of θ-shaped plasmid replication intermediates, catenated circular daughter duplexes, and the linear branched forms created by restriction endonuclease digestion of replicating circular molecules. In this paper, we illustrate the approach with RIs and catenanes of the yeast 2-μm plasmid. We establish by electron microscopy the 2-D gel pattern of Y-shaped RIs and X-shaped recombination intermediates derived from purified yeast mitochondrial DNA. Finally, we discuss how the technique can be used to map replication origins and termini, and to determine the direction of replication fork movement. The use of this technique to map the origins of the 2-μm plasmid and an *ARS1* recombinant plasmid in yeast has been published elsewhere (Brewer and Fangman 1987).

Methods

2-D agarose gel electrophoresis is adapted from the procedure of Bell and Byers (1983). The first-dimension gel is run at low voltage in low percentage agarose to separate DNA molecules in proportion to their mass. The second dimension is run at high voltage in higher agarose concentrations in the presence of ethidium bromide, so that the mobility of a nonlinear molecule is drastically influenced by its shape.

First dimension

A horizontal slab gel consisting of 0.4% agarose in TBE (Maniatis et al. 1982) is cast using a support plate 13 cm

---

*Present address: Molecular Biology Department, SRI International, LA153, 333 Ravenswood Avenue, Menlo Park, California 94025-3493.

CANCER CELLS 6 / Eukaryotic DNA Replication. © 1988 by Cold Spring Harbor Laboratory 0-87969-308-8/88 $1.00

wide by 20 cm long by 0.6 cm high. The comb with teeth 4 mm wide by 1.2 mm thick is placed ∼ 1 mm from the support plate surface. Electrophoresis of the submerged gel is carried out in TBE at 0.7–1.0 V/cm for 18–30 hours; the exact conditions used depend on the size of the molecule to be analyzed. The fragment of interest and one of twice its mass are separated by 4–5 cm during the first-dimension electrophoresis. After staining with ethidium bromide (0.3 μg/ml in TBE) for ∼ 20 minutes, the gel is photographed with UV illumination and the lanes to be run in the second dimension are marked. (Care is taken to limit the amount of UV exposure, since nicking can reduce the recovery of branched structures.) The lane of interest is excised with a clean razor blade. One cut edge must be straight and perpendicular, removing all excess agarose, since it will be through this edge that the molecules will pass in the second dimension.

Second dimension
The relevant portion of the 0.4% gel lane is placed on a clean gel support at 90° to the initial direction of electrophoresis. A 1.0–1.2% agarose solution in TBE with 0.3 μg/ml ethidium bromide is cooled to 60°C and then poured around the 0.4% gel lane to a final depth that just covers the 0.4% slab. Electrophoresis in TBE with 0.3 μg/ml ethidium bromide is performed submerged, at 5 V/cm in a 4°C room for 4–8 hours. An apparatus with a large buffer reservoir (2–3 l of TBE) is used and buffer is circulated from anode to cathode at 50–100 ml/minute during electrophoresis. The progress of the second dimension is monitored by illumination with a hand-held UV lamp until the smallest linears are near the end of the second-dimension gel. Under these conditions the largest linear molecules will have migrated ∼ 1/3 of the length of the gel. The gel is then photographed and treated as any agarose gel for Southern analysis. To facilitate the transfer of large molecules, the HCl treatment is included (see Maniatis et al. 1982).

Strains, culture conditions, and DNA techniques are described in Brewer and Fangman (1987), Sena et al. (1986), and Jacquier and Dujon (1983).

Results

2-μm plasmid replication intermediates
The 2-μm plasmid is a 6.32-kb nuclear episome of yeast present in 50–100 copies per cell. Its replication mimics that of chromosomal DNA in that each copy replicates exactly once each S phase (Zakian et al. 1979). Replication begins from a single site on each molecule, but the site of initiation has not been physically determined. An attempt to map the origin by electron microscopy (EM) and to correlate it with the ARS element was not conclusive (Newlon et al. 1981).

Since 2-μm replicates as a circular Cairns (θ) form (Petes and Williamson 1975), we reasoned that its RIs would migrate among the circular forms of DNA on 2-D gels. Furthermore, the replicating forms would be present only in yeast DNA isolated from S-phase cells. To explore the utility of 2-D gel electrophoresis, DNA was isolated from synchronized cultures of *MAT*a *cdc7* cells: one sample was isolated from cells arrested in the G₁ phase of the cell cycle by the mating pheromone α factor, and the other sample was harvested 10 minutes after the culture was released from the *cdc7* temperature-sensitive arrest point at the beginning of S phase (see Brewer and Fangman 1987, for details of the synchronization procedure). Equivalent amounts of total yeast DNA were run on parallel 2-D gels, and the Southern blots were hybridized with a probe from the 2-μm *FLP* gene to detect all forms of the 2-μm plasmid. These autoradiograms are shown in the top half of Figure 1. A cartoon of the S-phase sample is included for clarification.

2-μm DNA isolated from G₁ phase cells is present in a series of circular forms of monomer, dimer, trimer, and larger multimers. As a consequence of breakage during isolation, a variable amount of each of these multimers is converted from the covalently closed circular class to nicked circular forms and linears of 6.32 kb, 12.6 kb, 18.9 kb, etc. The linear 2-μm DNA molecules migrate across the 2-D gel in a diagonal arc that coincides with the arc of linear fragments of chromosomal DNA that is visible in the ethidium-bromide-stained gel (data not shown). All of the circular forms are retarded in their mobilities in the second dimension with respect to this arc of linears. The relationship between the closed and nicked forms of each multimer can be deduced by the horizontal and vertical streaks that connect the two forms of each multimer. These streaks are the consequence of random nicking during the course of electrophoresis that converts a covalently closed molecule to its nicked counterpart. When the sample is nicked with DNase I (Shortle and Nathans 1978) prior to electrophoresis, the pattern is simplified in that there are no streaks and each multimer is present in only the nicked circular form (see Brewer and Fangman 1987).

2-μm DNA isolated from the S-phase culture has additional classes of circular molecules that generate overlapping arcs. These forms migrate in the first dimension between covalently closed monomer 2-μm molecules and nicked dimer 2-μm molecules. In the second dimension their mobility is retarded to a greater extent than any of the simple circular forms, suggesting a more complex topology. There are two major types of arcs: One type is made up of discrete dots and the other is continuous. From the migration in the first dimension the two arcs of discrete dots are likely to be the catenated products of replication where the two parental strands are still interlocked by a discrete but variable number of turns (Sundin and Varshavsky 1980; DiNardo et al. 1984). The upper arc is composed of catenanes in which both circular members are nicked or gapped (the A-form catenanes of Sundin and Varshavsky 1980); the lower arc is composed of catenanes in which one circular member is nicked or gapped and the other is covalently closed (the B-form catenanes, ibid.). These assignments were confirmed by examining DNase-I-nicked S-phase DNA samples (see Fig. 2 in Brewer and Fang-

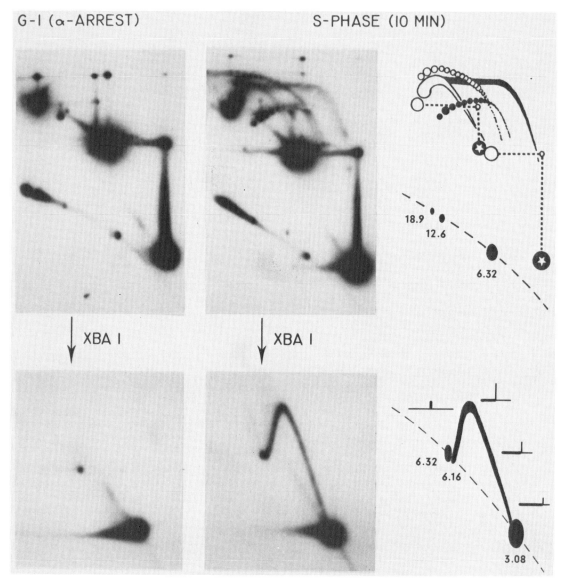

Figure 1 2-D agarose gel electrophoresis of 2-μm DNA. Total DNA isolated from G₁ and S-phase cultures was analyzed on 2-D gels. The first dimension (from left to right) was carried out for 15 hr at 1 V/cm in 0.4% agarose. The second dimension (from top to bottom) was carried out in a 4°C room for 8 hr at 5 V/cm in 1% agarose with 0.3 μg/ml ethidium bromide. 2-μm DNA was detected by hybridization with a 1500-bp probe from the 2-μm *FLP* gene. DNA in the lower autoradiograms was cut with *Xba*I before electrophoresis. The cartoons to the right illustrate the forms found in the S-phase samples. (*Upper cartoon*) Linear fragments, diagonal dashed line; covalently closed circular monomer and dimer molecules, closed circles with stars; nicked circular monomer and dimer molecules, large open circles; nicking during electrophoresis, horizontal and vertical dotted lines; A-form catenanes, arc of open dots; B-form catenanes, arc of solid dots; Cairns form RIs: nicked, open arc; covalently closed, solid arc. (*Lower cartoon*) Linear fragments, diagonal dashed line; simple Y RIs, continuous solid arc. The branched stick figures represent different extents of replicated (thin line) and unreplicated (thick line) DNA among the simple Y RIs.

man 1987); after nicking only the upper arc of dots remained. Also by analogy with the work of Sundin and Varshavsky (1980), the first-dimension mobility of the continuous arcs suggests that they are composed of Cairns forms that range in their extent of replication. The fact that there are two continuous arcs again reflects the presence of both nicked and covalently closed forms among the replicating plasmid molecules. One arc contains circular RIs that have an interruption in one of the parental strands, and the other arc consists of circular RIs in which both parental strands are intact (see Fig. 1,

upper right cartoon). DNase-I-nicking of the S-phase sample confirms the assignment of nicked and covalently closed RIs (see Fig. 2 in Brewer and Fangman 1987).

Simple Y replication intermediates from the 2-μm plasmid

The 2-μm plasmid has two *Xba*I sites that divide the molecule into fragments of 3.08 and 3.24 kb. 2-D gel analysis of *Xba*I-digested G₁ DNA hybridized with the *FLP* probe is shown in the lower left panel of Figure 1.

The probe detects the linear 3.08-kb fragment and a linear 6.32-kb fragment that results from partial digestion. In addition to these linear fragments, *Xba*I digestion of the Cairns forms from the S-phase DNA sample should yield branched molecules of various sizes that will not migrate with the diagonal arc of linear fragments. Although the major hybridization is to linear 3.08- and 6.32-kb fragments, the probe detects a prominent arc of nonlinear molecules that range in size (based on their mobility in the first dimension) from 3.08 to 6.16 kb (Fig. 1, lower right autoradiogram). Their size range, nonlinear structure, and presence during S phase are compatible with the hypothesis that the arc consists of RIs of the 3.08-kb 2-μm fragment. This arc of molecules experiences a minimum mobility in the second dimension at a size equivalent to ~5.0 kb, whereas molecules that have just begun replication (slightly >3.08 kb) and molecules that are almost finished with replication (slightly <6.16 kb) are nearly linear in their topology. The simplest structure that can explain this mobility pattern is a series of molecules with a single replication fork that we call simple Ys. As a replication fork appears at one end of the *Xba*I fragment, one of the replicated arms produces a side branch on an otherwise linear 3.08-kb fragment (Fig. 1, lower right cartoon). As replication proceeds, both the mass of the fragment and the length of the side branch increase. The longer the side branch, the more retarded the mobility in the second dimension. When the molecule is half replicated it contains three branches of equal length. As the fork passes the center of the 3.08-kb fragment, the molecule can undergo a simple isomerization to create a linear composed of the two replicated arms with the unreplicated portion as a smaller side branch at its center (see Fig. 1). The greater the extent of replication, the longer the apparent linear (up to 6.16 kb) and the shorter the unreplicated branch. If this interpretation of the 2-D gel pattern is correct, these results indicate that there is neither an origin nor a terminus of replication in this half of the 2-μm plasmid.

Confirmation of simple Y migration on 2-D gels

The mitochondrial deletion genome 8-3 is a 4.6-kb reiterated sequence that retains the *rep1* region of the wild-type mitochondrial genome. EM analysis of purified 8-3 mitochondrial DNA linearized with the restriction enzyme *Hha*I revealed a low percentage of branched replication and recombination intermediates (Sena et al. 1986). When *Hha*I-cleaved DNA is subjected to 2-D gel electrophoresis, a pattern very similar to the *Xba*I 2-μm gel pattern is seen (Fig. 2), suggesting that replication of the 8-3 mitochondrial DNA repeat occurs primarily through simple Y intermediates. A second prominent form of nonlinear molecules is also observed. It varies little in apparent mass (9.2–9.7 kb) but varies considerably in mobility in the second dimension, as if shape were the only variable among this second class of branched molecules. Based on the earlier EM analysis (Sena et al. 1986), we hypothesized that this latter spike arising from the 9.2-kb dimer spot consists of X-shaped

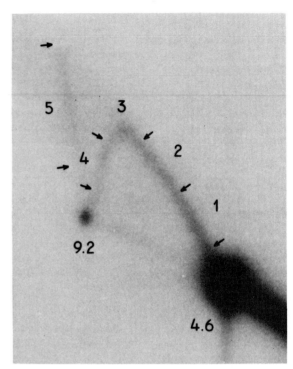

Figure 2 2-D agarose gel electrophoresis of *Hha*I-cleaved 8-3 mitochondrial DNA. 50 ng of purified 8-3 mitochondrial DNA was digested with *Hha*I and analyzed on a 2-D gel. Electrophoresis in the first dimension (from left to right) was carried out for 18 hr at 1 V/cm in 0.4% agarose. The second dimension (from top to bottom) was carried out at room temperature for 3 hr at 6.5 V/cm in 1% agarose with 0.04 μg/ml ethidium bromide. The DNA was detected by hybridization with nick translated 8-3 mitochondrial DNA. The segments of the branched arcs labeled 1–5 refer to regions of a parallel gel that were subsequently removed for EM analysis.

molecules that are intermediates in recombination between two 4.6-kb units. Molecules along the spike would differ in the position of their crossover points, with the slowest migrating forms having their crossover points near the centers of the 4.6-kb units and the faster migrating forms having their crossover points near one of the *Hha*I ends. The overall topology of the latter molecule would be very nearly linear, whereas the topology of the former would deviate most significantly from a simple linear.

Electron microscopy was used to confirm the expected structures of the various forms of *Hha*I-cut 8-3 mitochondrial DNA resolved on the 2-D gel. The portion of the gel containing the arc of simple Ys was subdivided into segments (1–4, Fig. 2); DNA was extracted from each gel segment (Thuring et al. 1975) and examined in the electron microscope. Simple Ys were the major class in each segment (except for sample 1, which was contaminated by 4.6-kb linears). The majority of these simple Ys had the properties that two of their arms were of equal length and the sum of the third arm plus one of the equal arms was 4.6 kb. If we assume that the equal arms result from replication, then the length of one of these arms divided by the unit length of 4.6 kb is the fraction of the molecule that has been replicated. Among the 83 molecules examined, the average replication for gel segments 1–4 is 0.19, 0.33, 0.48, and 0.75, respectively. The average length of the replicated arms increases along the arc with the inflection point (segment 3) containing simple Ys with three equal arms. This analysis clearly establishes the 2-D gel migration behavior of simple Ys. DNA from the spike (segment 5, Fig. 2) was examined and was found to contain the expected X-shaped molecules.

Discussion

We have established how simple Y-shaped RIs migrate on 2-D agarose gels. However, simple Ys are not the only topologically distinct form of RIs. If initiation or termination of replication were to occur within a defined stretch of DNA, the RIs would contain bubbles or double Ys, respectively. Because of their distinct topologies, they would be expected to behave differently from one another and from simple Ys on 2-D gels.

Consider a hypothetical restriction fragment of 1 kb. If it were replicated by a fork that proceeds from one end to the other, its 2-D gel pattern would have the characteristic shape for simple Ys that is shown in Figure 3A. However, if this fragment contains an origin for bidirectional replication, then its RIs would produce a series of bubble-shaped molecules. RIs would begin as 1-kb

linear molecules with a small internal bubble that would increasingly take on the characteristics of circular molecules approaching the properties of a nicked circle of 2 kb. As the forks pass the restriction sites, the RI instantaneously falls apart into two 1-kb linears so that the arc would end abruptly at the position of 2-kb nicked circles. We cannot predict a priori the exact trajectory of such bubbled molecules, but data presented in Brewer and Fangman (1987) reveal that bubbled RIs generate a 2-D gel pattern with the shape shown in Figure 3B.

If the 1-kb fragment were to be replicated by two forks that enter from each end simultaneously and meet at its center, then the RIs produced would consist of double Y-shaped molecules. As double Ys emerge from the 1-kb spot of linears, they would be retarded in their mobility in proportion to the length of their branches. At a mass of 1.2 kb, for example, the two branches would be 100 bp each. In comparison, however, a simple Y of 1.2 kb would have a single branch of 200 bp. Thus, a double Y might be expected to migrate faster than a simple Y of equivalent mass. As replication of the fragment approaches completion, a structure very similar to a recombination intermediate with the crossover point at its center is produced. Double Y RIs would produce a simple line on 2-D gels that begins at the position of 1-kb linears and terminates at the position expected for 2-kb X-shaped recombination intermediates (Fig. 3C).

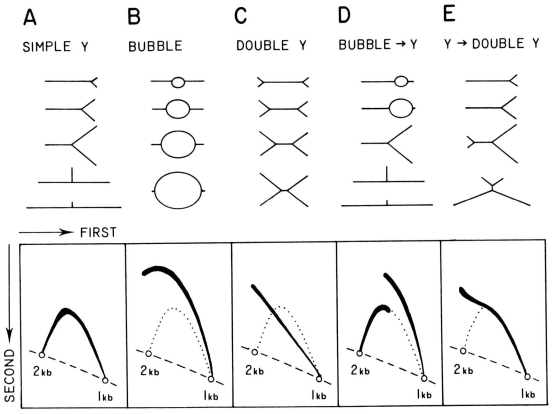

Figure 3 The effect of structure of RIs on the 2-D gel pattern: predictions for an arbitrary 1-kb fragment. The lower panels depict the expected migration in 2-D agarose gels of the five types of RIs shown above. The dashed lines mark the locations of linear molecules of various sizes; the dotted lines mark the location of simple Y RIs.

Neither initiation nor termination need occur in the exact center of a fragment to yield useful information. If an origin is asymmetrically located, then the RIs from this fragment will contain bubbles until the fork nearest an end passes the restriction site. The fragment will then complete replication as simple Ys. The 2-D gel pattern produced by these RIs will contain a discontinuity (Fig. 3D). Such a discontinuous pattern is informative in two ways. First, it allows the migration behavior of bubbled RIs to be established, and second, information about the position of the origin can be obtained. For example, if the arc of bubbles disappears at a mass equivalent to 1.5 kb, then the remaining active fork must have been at the center of the molecule when the other fork passed its restriction site. Assuming equal synthesis rates for the two forks, the origin can be mapped to 0.25 kb from one end of the fragment. If, on the other hand, the 1-kb fragment is replicated by two forks that meet at an asymmetric location within it, then the RIs arising from the position of 1-kb linears will follow the trajectory of simple Ys until the second fork appears at the other end of the fragment, creating a double Y. Since the second branch will only gradually have an influence on the fragment's mobility, a gradual transition between the arc of simple Ys and the line of double Ys will be seen (Fig. 3E).

In theory, the patterns observed for different RIs on 2-D gels should permit the accurate localization of replication origins and termination sites and permit the estimation of relative fork rates. In practice, there is the complicating factor that even at very low voltages and agarose concentrations the migration of DNA is not directly proportional to mass. This effect of topology on migration in the first dimension can be seen in the pattern produced by the X-shaped recombination intermediates of the 8-3 mitochondrial DNA (Fig. 2) and in the apparent size of simple Ys at the inflection point. For example, from the size estimated by migration in the first dimension, a simple Y at the inflection point would appear to be more than 60% replicated, yet the EM data on purified simple Ys support our assumption that these molecules are exactly 50% replicated. The size of a molecule at an inflection point or discontinuity is thus overestimated by this small amount. As a consequence, the location of an origin or terminus can be similarly affected.

Qualitatively, the results predicted for various RI forms are striking. These forms have been observed with different restriction fragments of the 2-μm plasmid and an *ARS1* recombinant plasmid (Brewer and Fangman 1987). For example, linearizing the plasmids in a position opposite the ARS element produces RIs with the 2-D gel pattern expected for bubbles and linearizing them at or near the ARS produces the expected double-Y forms (Brewer and Fangman 1987). Thus, this technique has been an extraordinarily powerful tool in settling the debate regarding the role of ARS elements in plasmid maintenance. We feel that it holds great promise for the study of replication origins in chromosomes.

Acknowledgments

This work was supported by U.S. Public Health Service grant GM-18926 and National Science Foundation grant PCM-8408712.

References

Bell, L. and B. Byers. 1983. Separation of branched from linear DNA by two-dimensional gel electrophoresis. *Anal. Biochem.* **130:** 527.

Brewer, B.J. and W.L. Fangman. 1987. The localization of replication origins on ARS plasmids in *S. cerevisiae*. *Cell* **51:** 463.

DiNardo, S., K. Voelkel, and R. Sternglanz. 1984. DNA topoisomerase II mutant of *Saccharomyces cerevisiae*: Topoisomerase II is required for segregation of daughter molecules at the termination of DNA replication. *Proc. Natl. Acad. Sci.* **81:** 2616.

Harland, R.M. and R.A. Laskey. 1980. Regulated replication of DNA microinjected into eggs of *X. laevis*. *Cell* **21:** 761.

Jacquier, A. and B. Dujon. 1983. The intron of the mitochondrial 21s rRNA gene: Distribution in different yeast species and sequence comparison between *Kluyveromyces thermotolerans* and *Saccharomyces cerevisiae*. *Mol. Gen. Genet.* **192:** 487.

Kearsey, S. 1986. Replication origins in yeast chromosomes. *Bioessays* **4:** 157.

Maniatis, T., E.F. Fritsch, and J. Sambrook. 1982. *Molecular cloning: A laboratory manual*. Cold Spring Harbor Laboratory, Cold Spring Harbor, New York.

Newlon, C.S., R.J. Devenish, P.A. Suci, and C.J. Roffis. 1981. Replication origins used in vivo in yeast. *ICN-UCLA Symp. Mol. Cell. Biol.* **22:** 501.

Petes, T.D. and D. Williamson. 1975. Replicating circular DNA molecules in yeast. *Cell* **4:** 249.

Sena, E.P., B. Revet, and E. Moustacchi. 1986. In vivo homologous recombination intermediates of yeast mitochondrial DNA analyzed by electron microscopy. *Mol. Gen. Genet.* **202:** 421.

Shortle, D. and D. Nathans. 1978. Local mutagenesis: A method for generating viral mutants with base substitutions in preselected regions of the viral genome. *Proc. Natl. Acad. Sci.* **75:** 2170.

Sundin, O. and A. Varshavsky. 1980. Terminal stages of SV40 DNA replication proceed via multiply intertwined catenated dimers. *Cell* **21:** 103.

Thuring, R.W.J., J.P.M. Sanders, and P. Borst. 1975. A freeze-squeeze method for recovering long DNA from agarose gels. *Anal. Biochem.* **66:** 213.

Williamson, D.H. 1985. The yeast ARS element, six years on: A progress report. *Yeast* **1:** 1.

Zakian, V.A., B.J. Brewer, and W.L. Fangman. 1979. Replication of each copy of the yeast 2 micron DNA plasmid occurs during the S phase. *Cell* **17:** 923.

Interactions between Purified Cellular Proteins and Yeast Origins of DNA Replication

J.F.X. Diffley and B. Stillman

Cold Spring Harbor Laboratory, Cold Spring Harbor, New York 11724

Autonomously replicating sequences (ARS) in the yeast *Saccharomyces cerevisiae* function in vivo as origins of DNA replication. Characterization of proteins that interact specifically with these sequences will be important in understanding how eukaryotic DNA replication initiates. Two such proteins, ARS binding factors I and II (ABFI and ABFII) are described in this report. ABFI was purified to homogeneity as a 135-kD polypeptide. This protein binds specifically to a subset of all ARSs, which includes ARS1 and HMRE at sites that are important, although not essential, for ARS function. (HMRE is the transcriptional silencer sequence located at the HMR silent mating type cassette locus.) In addition to functioning as an ARS, HMRE is also required for transcriptional repression at the silent mating type locus, and the ABFI binding site within HMRE is important for transcriptional silencing as well as ARS function.

ABFII was purified to homogeneity as a 21-kD polypeptide. Although ABFII binds with equal affinity to both ARS and control (vector) DNA, its binding to these two DNAs is qualitatively quite different. The binding of ABFII at ARS1 induces a complex series of changes in the pattern of DNA bending. Furthermore, DNase I footprinting demonstrates that binding to ARS1 and the histone H4 ARS occurs at multiple discrete locations within domains important for ARS function. In contrast, ABFII binding to pBR322 DNA does not induce DNA bending and occurs randomly along the fragment.

In most eukaryotes DNA synthesis is the first major landmark in the cell cycle after the cell becomes committed to divide. Understanding the molecular mechanism by which the initiation of DNA replication occurs will likely lead to new insights into how the process of DNA replication and ultimately how the cell cycle is regulated.

Cell-free systems that faithfully replicate virus DNA have been extremely useful in yielding a deeper understanding of the enzymology and mechanism of eukaryotic DNA replication. In comparing viral and chromosomal DNA replication, however, one must ultimately consider the critical role played by virus-encoded proteins, especially in the initiation reactions. The identity of cellular proteins with functions and biochemical activities analogous to the virus-encoded initiator proteins can at present only be inferred.

The identification of ARSs as origins of DNA replication in the yeast *S. cerevisiae* allows us to approach the mechanism of initiation of chromosomal DNA replication more directly. That ARSs are, in fact, origins of DNA replication is based on many different lines of evidence (for review, see Williamson 1985). ARSs allow any colinear DNA to be maintained episomally, replicating once per cell cycle under control of the same genes required for chromosomal DNA synthesis. The number of ARSs is approximately equal to the number of origins of replication. Mutations within ARS1 that reduce ARS function increase the frequency of aberrant 1:0 and not 2:0 segregation events, consistent with a defect in replication rather than in segregation of daughters after

replication (Koshland et al. 1985). Finally, replication has been directly shown to initiate at or near ARS sequences in vivo (Saffer and Miller 1986; Brewer and Fangman 1987; Huberman et al. 1987).

From analysis of several ARSs, two important generalizations have emerged concerning the sequences required for efficient ARS function (Broach et al. 1983; Celniker et al. 1984; Kearsey 1984; Bouton and Smith 1986; Mills et al. 1986). First, all known ARSs contain and apparently require the ARS core consensus sequence ($^A/_T$TTTATPuTTT$^A/_T$). Second, this sequence alone is not capable of efficient ARS function. Sequences flanking the ARS core consensus sequence, which apparently exhibit little homology and can range from as little as 14 bp on only one side of the consensus sequence in the case of the HO ARS (Kearsey 1984) to several hundred bp including sequences on both sides of the consensus sequences in the case of ARS1 (Celniker et al. 1984), are important for ARS function.

ARS1 is located at the 3′ end of the *TRP1* gene and has been shown to consist of three functional domains, A, B, and C (Kingsman et al. 1979; Struhl et al. 1979; Celniker et al. 1984; Srienc et al. 1985). Domain A contains the ARS core consensus sequence, and domains B and C flank domain A on either side. Domain B has the greatest influence on ARS function and has recently been shown to contain a binding site for a protein identified in crude extracts (Shore et al. 1987) that overlaps both a region of bent DNA (Snyder et al.

235

1986) and a sequence found 3′ to the consensus sequence in many but not all ARSs (Palzkill et al. 1986).

Origins of DNA replication from sources as diverse as the *Escherichia coli* chromosome, *E. coli* episomes such as F, P1, R1, and pSC101, bacteriophage λ, and eukaryotic viruses like the adenoviruses and the papovaviruses all contain binding sites for sequence-specific initiator proteins (Tsurimoto and Matsubara 1981; Nagata et al. 1983; Rigby and Lane 1983; Vocke and Bastia 1983; Fuller et al. 1984; Abeles 1986; Tokino et al. 1986; Masai and Arai 1987). Since yeast origins require specific sequences, our approach to studying the mechanism of ARS function has been based on the prediction that eukaryotic replication origins will also contain binding sites for initiator proteins. The identification, characterization, and purification of such ARS binding proteins will likely lead to a better understanding of ARS function. In this paper, we summarize our studies on two ARS1-specific DNA binding proteins that we identified in crude extracts: ABFI and ABFII.

Materials and Methods

Strains and DNAs
The protease-deficient strain BJ 1991 (Matα leu2 ura3 trp1 prb1 pep4) used in the identification and purification of ABFI and ABFII was kindly provided by Rich Kostriken. The plasmids pARS1.2 and pARS1.4.1, which both contain domains A and B of ARS1 (nt 616–927 and nt 734–927, respectively) cloned into pUC19 were described (Diffley and Stillman 1988).

Purification of ABFI and ABFII
The preparation of extracts from late log phase yeast and the purification of ABFI have been described elsewhere (Diffley and Stillman 1988). Blue Sepharose fractions containing ABFII activity were combined and dialyzed against buffer X (50 mM piperazine-N,N'-bis[2 ethanesulfonic acid]) (PIPES), 10 mM sodium metabisulfite, 1 mM phenylmethylsulfonyl fluoride (PMSF), 10 mM dithiothreitol (DTT), 1 mM EDTA, and 20% glycerol). To remove Triton X-100, this fraction was applied to a 10-ml column of heparin agarose in buffer X, washed with 20 ml buffer X, and ABFII was eluted with buffer X containing 1 M $(NH_4)_2SO_4$. This fraction was applied directly to a phenyl-Sepharose column (1.4 × 2.5 cm) equilibrated in buffer X containing 1 M $(NH_4)_2SO_4$. The column was washed extensively with buffer X and ABFII was eluted with buffer X containing 5% Triton X-100. This fraction was applied directly to a Mono S 5/5 column (Pharmacia) in buffer X adjusted to pH 7.0. The column was washed with this buffer and developed with a 20-ml gradient from 0 to 700 mM NaCl in buffer X at pH 7.0. Active fractions were combined, aliquoted, and stored at −70°C.

Supercoiling by ABFII
Covalently closed circular relaxed and ^{32}P-labeled pARS1.2 was prepared by nicking 5 μg of unlabeled DNA with 25 ng DNase I in 50 μl for 2 minutes in 50 mM Tris-HCl (pH 7.2) and 10 mM $MgCl_2$. These conditions converted more than 70% of the form I DNA to nicked circles. ^{32}P was incorporated into these nicked molecules by chewing back and filling in with labeled nucleotides and T4 DNA polymerase. Nicks were religated with DNA ligase, and labeled unligated molecules were removed by digesting exhaustively with exonuclease III. Approximately 10 ng of this DNA was incubated with ABFII and 1 unit of calf thymus topoisomerase I (BRL) for 1 hour at 37°C in 50 μl containing 50 mM Tris-HCl (pH 7.5), 0.5 mM DTT, 10 mM $MgCl_2$, 2.5 mM EDTA, and 15 μg bovine serum albumin. Reactions were stopped, DNA was purified by extraction with phenol and chloroform-isoamyl alcohol (24:1) and precipitated with ethanol. Samples were subjected to electrophoresis in 0.7% agarose gels, and labeled DNA was visualized by autoradiography.

DNA binding assays
DNA binding reactions were formulated as described by Diffley and Stillman (1986) and either filtered through nitrocellulose (Riggs et al. 1970) or subjected to electrophoresis through low ionic strength gels (Fried and Crothers 1981). DNase I footprinting was done by the method of Galas and Schmitz (1978) as modified by Diffley and Stillman (1986).

Results

Identification of ARS binding factors
The previously described DNA binding reaction conditions (Diffley and Stillman 1986) were used to identify ARS1-specific DNA-protein interactions. In this assay, nonspecific DNA-protein interactions are reduced by preincubating protein fractions with a competitor DNA made from a defined mixture of homopolymers prior to the addition of either a specific or nonspecific labeled probe. DNA-protein complexes can be identified after either filtration through nitrocellulose (Riggs et al. 1970) or electrophoresis through low ionic strength polyacrylamide gels (Fried and Crothers 1981). In Figure 1A, a whole-cell extract made from late log phase yeast was titrated into reactions containing competitor DNA and labeled probe, either a fragment containing ARS1 domains A and/or B or a fragment from pBR322 of approximately the same size, and reactions were filtered through nitrocellulose. Fragments containing domain B but not domain A from ARS1 were specifically retained when compared to the pBR322 control. When electrophoresis was used (Fig. 1B), two complexes that form with DNA containing domains A and B of ARS1 could be identified, but were not observed when an equal-sized fragment from pBR322 was used. The proteins forming these complexes were different, since they could be separated from each other by a number of chromatographic techniques (not shown), and these proteins were therefore designated ABFI and ABFII.

A

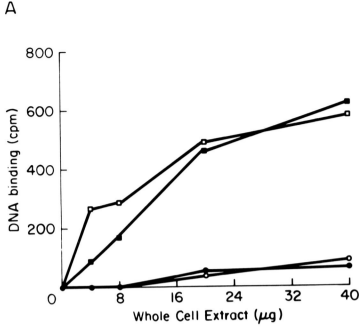

B

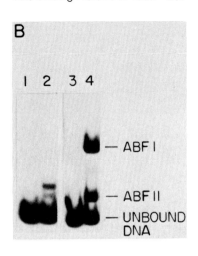

Figure 1 Detection of ARS binding factors in crude yeast extracts. (*A*) Filtration through nitrocellulose was used to detect ARS1-specific DNA protein complexes. DNA binding reactions were formulated as described (Diffley and Stillman 1986) and contained the amounts of whole cell yeast extract indicated in the figure. Labeled DNA (1000 cpm total) used in this experiment were the 276-bp *Bam*HI-*Sal*I fragment from pBR322 (●—●), the 326-bp *Eco*RI-*Hin*dIII fragment from pARS1.2 containing both domains A and B of ARS1 (□—□), the 211-bp *Hin*dIII-*Pst*I fragment from pARS1.2 containing domain B alone (■—■) and the 145-bp *Pst*I-*Eco*RI fragment from pARS1.2 containing domain A alone (○—○). Amounts of bound DNA were quantitated in a liquid scintillation counter.(*B*) Electrophoresis through low ionic strength polyacrylamide gels (Fried and Crothers 1981) was used to identify ARS1-specific DNA protein complexes. Reactions were formulated as described containing either no yeast extract (lanes *1* and *3*) or 100 ng of whole cell yeast extract (lanes *2* and *4*) and 10,000 cpm of either the 276-bp *Bam*HI-*Sal*I fragment from pBR322 or the 242-bp fragment from pARS1.4.1, which contains both domains A and B of ARS1. The positions of ABFI, ABFII, and unbound DNA are indicated.

Purification of ARS binding factors

A procedure for the purification of ABFI and ABFII was developed and is outlined in Figure 2A. ABFI and ABFII eluted together from heparin agarose, which resulted in a 50–100-fold purification, and the two activities were subsequently separated by chromatography on Blue Sepharose. ABFI was then purified by chromatography on phenyl-Sepharose, denatured DNA cellulose, Sephacryl S-300, and FPLC Mono Q. The final fraction of ABFI contained only a single polypeptide of 135 kD (Fig. 2B), which coeluted exactly with DNA binding activity from the Mono Q column and which, when isolated from a preparative SDS-polyacrylamide gel and renatured (Hager and Burgess 1980), exhibited ABFI binding activity (Diffley and Stillman 1988). From these results, we conclude that the 135-kD polypeptide is ABFI. ABFII was purified by chromatography on phenyl-Sepharose and FPLC Mono S. The final fraction of ABFII contained only a single polypeptide of 21 kD (Fig. 2C), which coeluted with the DNA binding activity from the Mono S column and which, when isolated from a preparative SDS-polyacrylamide gel and renatured, exhibited ABFII binding activity (not shown). This 21-kD polypeptide, then, is ABFII.

Initial characterization of ABFII binding

ABFI is a sequence-specific DNA binding protein that can be shown by either nitrocellulose filter binding or gel retention to bind ARS1 DNA but not nonspecific pBR322 DNA (data not shown). Further analysis of ABFI binding is presented below. In contrast, ABFII binds to fragments containing either ARS1 DNA or pBR322 DNA with roughly equal affinity. This protein is of interest, however, because its binding to these two DNA fragments is qualitatively quite different. ABFII was titrated into reactions containing unlabeled competitor DNA and the same labeled probes as described in Figure 1B. Addition of increasing amounts of ABFII into reactions containing either fragment resulted in the formation of multiple DNA-protein complexes of decreasing mobility, arguing that multiple ABFII promoters could bind to each fragment (Fig. 3,A and B). Since both gel filtration chromatography and glycerol gradient sedimentation (data not shown) suggested that ABFII exists as a monomer in solution, the basic unit of ABFII binding is probably a monomer. The appearance of each successive DNA–ABFII complex occurred at about the same ABFII concentration for both fragments, showing that under these conditions, the affinity of ABFII for ARS1

A

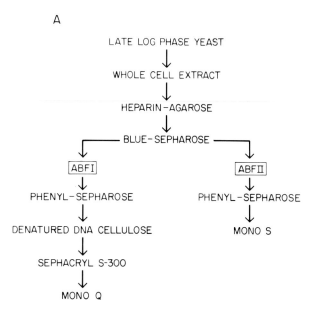

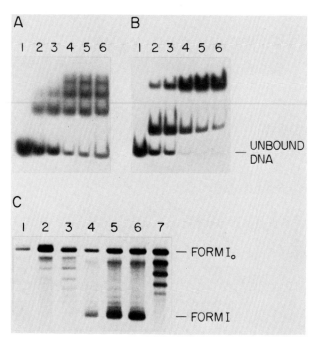

Figure 3 Characterization of ABFII binding. (*A*) and (*B*) Gel retention analysis of ABFII binding. From left to right DNA binding reactions contained 0, 4, 8, 16, 32, and 64 ng of a partially purified fraction of ABFII and either (*A*) the *Bam*HI-*Sal*I fragment from pBR322 or (*B*) the *Eco*RI-*Hin*dIII fragment from pARS1.4.1.(*C*) ABFII-induced supercoiling. The ability of ABFII to supercoil relaxed, labeled pARS1.2 in the presence of calf thymus topoisomerase I was tested as described in Methods. Reactions contained 0, 20, 60, 200, 250, 300, and 600 ng of purified ABFII, respectively. After deproteinization, DNA was subjected to electrophoresis through 0.7% agarose gels, dried, and autoradiographed.

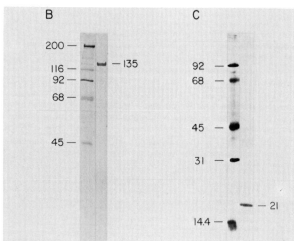

Figure 2 Purification of ARS binding factors I and II. (*A*) The scheme for the purification of ABFI and ABFII is indicated and described in Diffley and Stillman (1988 and this paper). (*B*) A 10-μl aliquot from the peak fraction of the final Mono Q column in the ABFI purification (*right*) was subjected to SDS poly-acrylamide gel electrophoresis (Laemmli 1970) and stained with silver (Oakley et al. 1980). The left lane contains molecular weight markers of 200 kD (myosin), 116 kD (β-galactosidase), 92 kD (phosphorylase b), 68 kD (bovine serum albumin), and 45 kD (ovalbumin). The position of the 135-kD ABFI poly-peptide is indicated.(*C*) A 10 μl aliquot from the peak fraction of the final Mono S column in the ABFII purification (*right*) was subjected to SDS polyacrylamide gel electrophoresis and stained with silver. The left lane contains molecular weight markers of 92 kD (phosphorylase b), 68 kD (bovine serum albumin), 45 kD (ovalbumin), 31 kD (carbonic anhydrase), and 14 kD (lysozyme). The position of the 21-kD ABFII polypeptide is indicated.

and pBR322 DNA is approximately equal, a result that is supported by competition experiments (not shown). Interestingly, however, the electrophoretic mobilities of DNA–ABFII complexes with pBR322 or ARS1 fragments of approximately equal size are drastically differ-

ent. ABFII binding to pBR322 DNA fragments (Fig. 3A) yielded an ordered pattern reminiscent of the binding of the *E. coli* lac repressor to its operator (Fried and Crothers 1981). By analogy, this suggests that the binding of ABFII does not bend DNA fragments containing these pBR322 sequences. The irregular pattern of ABFII binding to ARS1 DNA (Fig. 3B), however, is highly reminiscent of the *E. coli* CAP protein that, on interacting with its recognition sequences in the lac promoter, induces DNA bending (Crothers and Fried 1983). The irregular pattern of ABFII binding is dependent on the position of the ARS on the fragment (not shown) and suggests that ABFII induces a specific bending pattern at ARS1.

A characteristic of many small DNA binding proteins like the prokaryotic HU and IHF proteins (for review, see Drlica and Rouviere-Yaniv 1987) and the eukaryotic HMG1 and 2 proteins (Javaherian et al. 1978) is the ability to alter the linking number of a relaxed, covalently closed circular plasmid in the presence of a nicking-closing enzyme like topoisomerase I, and the results shown in Figure 3C demonstrate that ABFII shares this ability. ABFII was titrated into reactions containing constant amounts of labeled, relaxed plasmid and purified topoisomerase I. After incubation, DNA was deproteinized, subjected to agarose gel electrophoresis, and autoradiographed. The ability of ABFII to alter the linking number of this plasmid was demonstrated by the appearance of form I DNA in lanes 3, 4, and 5 (Fig. 3C). The disappearance of form I DNA at higher concentrations of ABFII as in lane 6 was not due to the exclusion of topoisomerase I from the plasmid by simple competition with ABFII, since increasing the amount of topoisomerase I in these reactions fivefold did not affect the appearance or disappearance of form I DNA in this titration.

Characterization of ABFI and ABFII binding by DNase I footprinting

ABFI was shown by competition experiments to bind to a subset of all ARSs that included ARS1, but interestingly also included the ARS sequence at the HMRE locus (Diffley and Stillman 1988), which is also required for the silencing of transcription from the HMR silent mating type cassette (Abraham et al. 1984; Brand et al. 1985, 1987). The ABFI binding sites at these two ARSs could be localized by DNase I footprinting (Galas and Schmitz 1978) as shown in Figure 4A and B, to single sites in domains shown to be important for full ARS function (Celniker et al. 1984; Snyder et al. 1986; Brand et al. 1987; Diffley and Stillman 1988).

The ability of ABFII to induce a specific bending pattern with ARS1 DNA argued that ABFII did not bind randomly along this fragment but must, in fact, bind at specific locations. DNase I footprinting was used to investigate this possibility. If ABFII bound randomly along a fragment of DNA with no preference for location, then every DNase I cleavage site should be protected to the same extent at high amounts of ABFII. This, in fact, best describes the protection pattern of ABFII on pBR322 DNA (Fig. 4C); essentially all DNase I cleavage sites were protected at least to some extent by ABFII. The protection pattern of ABFII on ARS1 DNA, however, is strikingly different. ABFII bound at multiple, discrete, and roughly contiguous sites across ARS1. The binding sites were separated by DNase I cleavage sites that were not protected by saturating amounts of ABFII, arguing that these ABFII binding sites are not just preferred, but are absolute. A similar pattern was also seen at the histone H4 ARS (not shown). Therefore, although ABFII binds to all DNA with roughly equal affinity, the binding to at least two different ARSs occurs at discrete sites, whereas the binding to nonspecific pBR322 DNA occurs randomly along the fragment. Furthermore, binding to at least one ARS, ARS1, induces a complex pattern of DNA bending.

Discussion

Prokaryotes and eukaryotes appear to have met the challenges of regulating DNA synthesis in different ways (for review, see Kornberg 1980). In prokaryotes, both chromosomal and episomal DNA replication is controlled at the level of initiation, and initiation is controlled, at least in part, by the levels of initiator proteins.

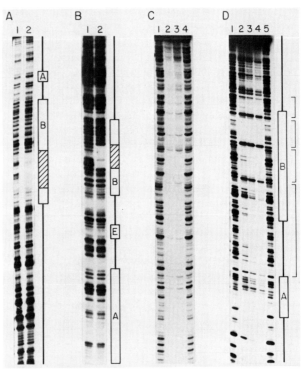

Figure 4 DNase I footprinting. The DNase I footprinting pattern of ABFI on ARS1 and HMRE (*A* and *B*) and ABFII on pBR322 and ARS1 (*C* and *D*) is shown. In *A* the HindIII-EcoRI fragment from pARS1.2 containing domains A and B was labeled at the 5′ end of the HindIII site. In *B* the XhoI site of pJA82.6Δ173 was labeled at the 5′ end. In both *A* and *B* lane 1 contains no added ABFI, and lane 2 contains 10 ng of purified ABFI. In *C* the BamHI-SalI fragment from pBR322 was labeled at the 5′ end of the BamHI site. Lanes 1 and 4 contain no added ABFII. Lanes 3 and 4 contain 50 and 100 ng of purified ABFII, respectively. In *D* the HindIII-EcoRI fragment from pARS1.2 was labeled at the 5′ end of the EcoRI site. Lanes 1 and 5 contain no added ABFII. Lanes 2, 3, and 4 contain 10, 30, and 100 ng of purified ABFII, respectively. Schematic drawings alongside the footprints in *A*, *B*, and *D* indicate the position of functional domains, ABFI binding sites (hatched regions in *A* and *B*), and ABFII binding sites (brackets in *D*).

Levels of these proteins, in turn, are often carefully controlled both by feedback inhibition of initiator protein biosynthesis and sequestration of free initiator protein by multiple protein binding sites known as incompatibility loci (Hansen and Rasmussen 1977; Tsutsui et al. 1983; Abeles et al. 1984; Sølgaard-Andersen et al. 1984; Chattoraj et al. 1985; Kelley and Bastia 1985). In addition, other sequences, for example, dam methylation sequences, are also important in regulating origin function (Russell and Zinder 1987). Perhaps because the prokaryotic chromosome (or episome) is a single replicon, prokaryotic replication origins are complex sequence elements that have evolved as cardinal loci for the control of cell growth.

Although much less is known about the molecular mechanisms governing eukaryotic DNA replication, it is likely that control of cell growth and DNA replication are effected on multiple levels prior to S phase. In yeast, for example, S phase is dependent on the execution of a number of genetically defined events during G₁ (for review, see Pringle and Hartwell 1981). Moreover, a number of proteins apparently required for DNA replication are expressed in a cell-cycle-dependent fashion just prior to S phase (Storms et al. 1984; Barker et al. 1985; Farnham and Schimke 1985; Jenh et al. 1985; Stuart et al. 1985; Prelich et al. 1987a,b; Plevani et al.; Budd et al.; both this volume). The complexity of eukaryotic DNA replication with respect to the number of origins and the temporal regulation of origin function during S phase (Blumenthal et al. 1974; Callan 1974) makes it unlikely that replication is controlled solely by controlling the level of some initiator protein. Thus, although each eukaryotic origin of replication may have complex and subtle roles during S phase, the sequences required for origin function may be simpler sequences than their prokaryotic counterparts and may not serve as central loci for the control of S phase and, consequently, cell growth. This notion is supported experimentally by the fact that any sequence can be replicated in a controlled fashion when injected into a *Xenopus* oocyte (Harland and Laskey 1980). Additionally, there is some evidence that the yeast ARS core consensus sequence, which is, in fact, a very simple sequence expected to arise randomly once every 10,000 bp in the yeast genome, is capable of functioning alone as an ARS, albeit very weakly (Srienc et al. 1985). The sequences that normally flank the core and increase mitotic stability may function to make origins more efficient and may not actually be mechanistically required for origin function. It is within this context that the roles of ABFI and ABFII in ARS function must be considered, since both proteins appear to interact specifically with sequences that flank the ARS core consensus sequence, and neither protein appears to interact specifically with the essential core consensus.

ABFI was purified as a 135-kD sequence-specific DNA binding protein that bound to a single site at both ARS1 and HMRE, but did not bind to all ARSs. Deletion of this binding site at both ARS1 and HMRE reduced the mitotic stability of these plasmids but did not affect the ability of these ARSs to transform yeast at high frequency (Snyder et al. 1986; Brand et al. 1987; Diffley and Stillman 1988). Deletion of these binding sites, therefore, did not inactivate either ARS, although it did reduce the apparent efficiency of these sequences to serve as replication origins. HMRE, in addition to being an ARS, also functions in *cis* to completely repress transcription of the mating type information contained within HMR in a position- and orientation-independent manner (Abraham et al. 1984; Brand et al. 1985, 1987). HMRE contains three functional elements designated A, E, and B that are required for repression. Element A is the ARS core consensus sequence, element E is a binding site for the cellular protein SBF-E, and element B is a binding site for ABFI. These three elements exhibit some functional redundancy, since any one can be deleted without drastically reducing silencer function. Deletion of any two elements, however, completely inactivates the silencer. Since one of these three elements is

an ABFI binding site, ABFI can apparently function in transcriptional repression. Characterization of the gene encoding the ABFI polypeptide and mutations therein will allow an analysis of these possibilities and yield an understanding of the in vivo role of ABFI. The availability of the purified ABFI protein provides approaches that will allow the identification of this gene.

A role for ABFII in ARS function is more difficult to assign on the basis of biochemistry and sequence analysis, due primarily to the fact that this 21-kD protein can bind any DNA with roughly equal affinity, although its binding to ARS containing DNA is qualitatively different from its binding to nonspecific pBR322 DNA. As shown by DNase I footprinting, ABFII binding to pBR322 DNA appears to occur randomly across the entire fragment, whereas binding to ARS1 and the histone H4 ARS (not shown) occurs at multiple discrete sites within sequence elements that flank the ARS core consensus sequence and are required for full ARS function. A summary of the ABFI and ABFII binding sites at ARS1 is shown in Figure 5. ABFII, furthermore, can alter the conformation of at least one ARS, ARS1, apparently by DNA bending. It is interesting that both of these biochemical characteristics, the ABFII ARS binding pattern and the ABFII induced ARS bending, are reminiscent of initiator protein binding at many origins of DNA replication. dnaA binds at the *E. coli oriC* both to specific sequences and nonspecifically in a cooperative fashion until 20–40 dnaA monomers are bound at *oriC* (Fuller et al. 1984). A number of episome and bacteriophage-encoded initiator proteins also bind at multiple contiguous sites within their respective origins of replication, and some of these proteins have been shown to bend origin DNA upon binding (Germino and Bastia 1983; Mukherjee et al. 1985; Koepsel and Khan 1986; Zahn and Blattner 1987). Finally, the SV40-encoded large T antigen (TAg) exhibits both specific and nonspecific DNA binding activity and binds at multiple sites within the SV40 origin of DNA replication and, upon binding, alters the structure of the origin DNA (Dean et al.; Tegtmeyer et al.; Stahl et al.; all this volume). The pattern of ABFII binding at both ARS1 and the histone H4 ARS is such that the ARS core consensus sequence is at least partially exposed to DNase I digestion, which is interesting since both the dnaA binding sites at *oriC* and the TAg binding sites at the SV40 *ori* lie adjacent to conserved sequences required for DNA replication. dnaA binds adjacent to the 13-mer sequences required to interact with the dnaB helicase (Baker et al., this volume) and TAg binds adjacent to an essential 17-bp AT-rich sequence (Dean et al.; Tegtmeyer et al.; both this volume).

The involvement of low-molecular-weight, nonspecific or moderately specific DNA binding proteins like ABFII in DNA replication is not without precedent. The specific initiation of DNA replication at *oriC* in vitro requires the histone-like HU protein (for review, see Drlica and Rouviere-Yaniv 1987). HU, although appearing to be a nonspecific DNA binding protein, was shown to be specifically localized at *oriC* during the early stages of replication in vitro (Funnell et al. 1987), indicating that

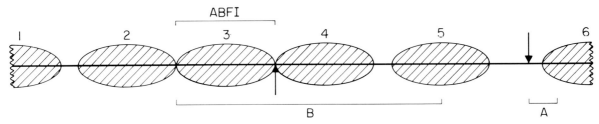

Figure 5 Summary of ABFI and ABFII binding at ARS1. Positions of ABFII (hatched ovals) and ABFI (bracket) binding sites as derived from DNase I footprints with respect to the location of domains A and B of ARS1 are indicated. Arrows indicate the position of DNase I hypersensitive sites induced by ABFII.

HU must interact specifically with *oriC* sequences and/or proteins in the initiation complex. The in vivo replication of the *E. coli* plasmid pSC101, in addition to requiring the host dnaA protein and the plasmid-encoded sequence-specific repA protein, also requires the host-encoded IHF protein. IHF, like HU, is a low-molecular-weight, histone-like protein that appears to be homologous to HU. Unlike HU, however, IHF appears to be at least a moderately sequence-specific DNA binding protein (Craig and Nash 1984). The replication of pSC101 requires IHF (Gamas et al. 1986) to bind at a site within an AT-rich region between essential dnaA and repA binding sites (Stenzel et al. 1987). IHF binding further bends the already bent AT-rich region, and it has been suggested that IHF functions by bringing the dnaA and repA proteins, bound at their cognate sequences, together. Interestingly, both IHF and HU, like ABFII, appear to bind DNA by wrapping the DNA around the protein core (Fig. 3C).

The possible involvement of ABFII, a nonspecific DNA binding protein, in DNA replication is consistent with mutational analysis at both ARS1 and the histone H4 ARS. The discrete ABFII binding sites at both ARSs lie within and around regions important for ARS function (Celniker et al. 1984; Srienc et al. 1985; Bouton and Smith 1986). Many of the ABFII binding sites at ARS1 lie within domain B (Fig. 5), known to be important for ARS function. It is interesting that ABFII binding site 3 (see Fig. 5) exactly overlaps the ABFI binding site. The presence of ABFI does not affect the affinity or pattern of ABFII binding, and so it is possible that these proteins may cooperate in the establishment of a functional origin. Footprinting analysis on ARS1 deletion mutants indicates that the ABFII binding sites are at least somewhat independent of each other since deletion of sites 1,2, and 3 did not affect sites 4,5, and 6 and deletion of sites 4 and 5 did not affect sites 1,2,3, and 6 (not shown). The sequences required for function of the histone H4 ARS were shown to be dependent on the orientation of this ARS with respect to the vector DNA, which implicates a potential role for nonspecific vector sequences in ARS function. Furthermore, although sequences that flank the histone H4 ARS core consensus sequence were essential, as determined by deletion analysis, linker scanning mutations within this flanking sequence had no effect on ARS function. Interestingly, to explain this, Bouton and Smith (1986) proposed that

these flanking sequences contain multiple binding sites for a moderately specific DNA binding protein. Again, in order to understand the in vivo role of ABFII, the gene encoding it must be identified and characterized, and the availability of purified ABFII will allow this.

Acknowledgments

This work was supported by grants from the National Institutes of Health (AI-20460) and the Rita Allen Foundation.

References

Abeles, A.L. 1986. P1 plasmid replication: Purification and DNA binding activity of the replication protein RepA. *J. Biol. Chem.* **261:** 3548.

Abeles, A.L., K.M. Snyder, and D.K. Chattoraj. 1984. P1 plasmid replication: Replicon structure. *J. Mol. Biol.* **173:** 307.

Abraham, J., K.A. Nasmyth, J.N. Strathern, A.J.S. Klar, and J.B. Hicks. 1984. Regulation of mating type information in yeast: Negative control requiring sequences both 5' and 3' to the regulated region. *J. Mol. Biol.* **176:** 307.

Barker, D.G., J.H.M. White, and L.H. Johnston. 1985. The nucleotide sequence of the DNA ligase gene (CDC 9) from *Saccharomyces cerevisiae*: A gene which is cell cycle regulated and induced in response to DNA damage. *Nucleic Acids Res.* **13:** 8323.

Blumenthal, A.B., H.J. Kriegstein, and D.S. Hogness. 1974. The units of DNA replication in *Drosophila melanogaster* chromosomes. *Cold Spring Harbor Symp. Quant. Biol.* **38:** 205.

Bouton, A.H. and M.M. Smith. 1986. Fine structure analysis of the DNA sequence requirements for autonomous replication of *Saccharomyces cerevisiae* plasmids. *Mol. Cell. Biol.* **6:** 2354.

Brand, A.H., G. Micklem, and K. Nasmyth. 1987. A yeast silencer is composed of DNA replication and transcriptional activation sequences. *Cell* **51:** 709.

Brand, A.H., L. Breeden, J. Abraham, R. Sternglanz, and K. Nasmyth. 1985. Characterization of a "Silencer" in yeast: A sequence with properties opposite to those of a transcriptional enhancer. *Cell* **41:** 41.

Brewer, B.J. and W.L. Fangman. 1987. The localization of replication origins on ARS plasmids in *Saccharomyces cerevisiae*. *Cell* **51:** 463.

Broach, J.R., Y.-Y. Li, J. Feldman, M. Jayaram, J. Abraham, K.A. Nasmyth, and J.B. Hicks. 1983. Localization and sequence analysis of yeast origins of DNA replication. *Cold Spring Harbor Symp. Quant. Biol.* **47:** 1165.

Callan, H.G. 1974. DNA replication in the chromosomes of eukaryotes. *Cold Spring Harbor Symp. Quant. Biol.* **38:** 195.

Celniker, S.E., K. Sweder, F. Srienc, J.E. Bailey, and J.L. Campbell. 1984. Deletion mutations affecting autonomously replicating sequence ARS I of *Saccharomyces cerevisiae*. *Mol. Cell. Biol.* **4:** 2455.

Chattoraj, D.K., K.M. Snyder, and A.L. Abeles. 1985. P1 plasmid replication: Multiple functions of repA protein at the origin. *Proc. Natl. Acad. Sci.* **82:** 2588.

Craig, N.L. and H.A. Nash. 1984. *E.coli* integration host factor binds to specific sites in DNA. *Cell* **39:** 707.

Crothers, D.M. and M. Fried. 1983. Transmission of long-range effects in DNA. *Cold Spring Harbor Symp. Quant. Biol.* **47:** 263.

Diffley, J.F.X. and B. Stillman. 1986. Purification of a cellular double-stranded DNA binding protein required for initiation of adenovirus DNA replication by using a rapid filter binding assay. *Mol. Cell. Biol.* **6:** 1363.

———. 1988. Purification of a yeast protein that binds to origins of DNA replication and the transcriptional silencer. *Proc. Natl. Acad. Sci.* (in press).

Drlica, K. and J. Rouviere-Yaniv. 1987. Histonelike proteins of bacteria. *Microbiol. Rev.* **51:** 301.

Farnham, P.J. and R.T. Schimke. 1985. Transcriptional regulation of mouse dihydrofolate reductase in the cell cycle. *J. Biol. Chem.* **260:** 7675.

Fried, M. and D.M. Crothers. 1981. Equilibria and kinetics of lac repressor-operator interactions by polyacrylamide gel electrophoresis. *Nucleic Acids Res.* **9:** 6505.

Fuller, R.S., B.E. Funnell, and A. Kornberg. 1984. The dnaA protein complex with the *E.coli* chromosomal replication origin (oriC) and other DNA sites. *Cell* **38:** 889.

Funnell, B.E., T.A. Baker, and A. Kornberg. 1987. *In vitro* assembly of a prepriming complex at the origin of the *Escherichia coli* chromosome. *J. Biol. Chem.* **262:** 10327.

Galas, D.J. and A. Schmitz. 1978. DNase footprinting: A simple method for the detection of protein-DNA binding specificity. *Nucleic Acids Res.* **5:** 3157.

Gamas, P., A.C. Burger, G. Churchward, L. Caro, D. Galas, and M. Chandler. 1986. Replication of pSC101: Effects of mutations in the *E.coli* DNA binding protein IHF. *Mol. Gen. Genet.* **204:** 85.

Germino, J. and D. Bastia. 1983. Interaction of the plasmid R6K-encoded replication initiator protein with its binding sites on DNA. *Cell* **34:** 125.

Hager, D.A. and R.R. Burgess. 1980. Elution of proteins from sodium dodecyl sulfate-polyacrylamide gels, removal of sodium dodecyl sulfate and renaturation of enzymatic activity: Results with sigma subunit of *E.coli* RNA polymerase, wheat germ topoisomerase and other enzymes. *Anal. Biochem.* **109:** 76.

Hansen, F.G. and K.V. Rasmussen. 1977. Regulation of the dnaA product in *E.coli*. *Mol. Gen. Genet.* **155:** 219.

Harland, R.M. and R.A. Laskey. 1980. Regulated replication of DNA microinjected into eggs of *Xenopus laevis*. *Cell* **21:** 761.

Huberman, J.A., L.D. Spotila, K.A. Nawotka, S.M. El-Assouli, and L.R. Davis. 1987. The *in vivo* replication origin of the yeast 2 micron plasmid. *Cell* **51:** 473.

Javaherian, K., L.F. Liu, and J.C. Wang. 1978. Nonhistone proteins HMG1 and HMG2 change the DNA helical structure. *Science* **199:** 1345.

Jenh, C., P.K. Geyer, and L.F. Johnson. 1985. The control of thymidylate synthetase mRNA content and gene expression in an overproducing mouse cell line. *Mol. Cell. Biol.* **5:** 2527.

Kearsey, S. 1984. Structural requirements for the function of a yeast chromosomal replicator. *Cell* **37:** 299.

Kelley, W. and D. Bastia. 1985. Replication initiator protein of plasmid R6K autoregulates its own synthesis at the transcriptional step. *Proc. Natl. Acad. Sci.* **82:** 2574.

Kingsman, A.J., L. Clarke, R.K. Mortimer, and J. Carbon. 1979. Replication in *Saccharomyces cerevisiae* of plasmid pBR313 carrying DNA from the yeast TRP1 region. *Gene* **7:** 141.

Koepsel, R.R. and S.A. Khan. 1986. Static and initiator protein-enhanced bending of DNA at a replication origin. *Science* **233:** 1316.

Kornberg, A. 1980. Regulation of replication. *DNA replication*, p. 443. W.H. Freeman, San Francisco.

Koshland, D., J.C. Kent, and L.H. Hartwell. 1985. Genetic analysis of the mitotic transmission of minichromosomes. *Cell* **40:** 393.

Laemmli, U.K. 1970. Cleavage of structural proteins during the assembly of the head of bacteriophage T4. *Nature* **227:** 680.

Masai, H. and K.-I. Arai. 1987. RepA and DnaA proteins are required for initiation of R1 plasmid replication *in vitro* and interact with the ori R sequence. *Proc. Natl. Acad. Sci.* **84:** 4781.

Mills, J.S., A.J. Kingsman, and S.M. Kingsman. 1986. *Drosophila* ARSs contain a yeast ARS consensus sequence and a replication enhancer. *Nucleic Acids Res.* **14:** 6633.

Mukherjee, S., I. Patel, and D. Bastia. 1985. Conformational changes in a replication origin induced by an initiator protein. *Cell* **43:** 189.

Nagata, K., R.A. Guggenheimer, and J. Hurwitz. 1983. Specific binding of a cellular DNA replication protein to the origin of replication of adenovirus DNA. *Proc. Natl. Acad. Sci.* **80:** 6177.

Oakley, B.R., D.R. Kirsch, and N.R. Morris. 1980. A simplified ultrasensitive silver stain for detecting proteins in polyacrylamide gels. *Anal. Biochem.* **105:** 361.

Palzkill, T.G., S.G. Oliver, and C.S. Newlon. 1986. DNA sequence analysis of ARS elements from chromosome III of *Saccharomyces cerevisiae*: Identification of a new conserved sequence. *Nucleic Acids Res.* **14:** 6247.

Prelich, G., M. Kostura, D.R. Marshak, M.B. Mathews, and B. Stillman. 1987a. The cell-cycle regulated proliferating cell nuclear antigen is required for SV40 replication *in vitro*. *Nature* **326:** 471.

Prelich, G., C.-T. Tan, M. Kostura, M.B. Mathews, A.G. So, K.M. Downey, and B. Stillman. 1987b. Functional identity of proliferating cell nuclear antigen and a DNA polymerase-δ auxiliary protein. *Nature* **326:** 517.

Pringle, J.R. and L.H. Hartwell. 1981. The *Saccharomyces cerevisiae* cell cycle. In *The molecular biology of the yeast Saccharomyces: Life cycle and inheritance* (ed. J.N. Strathern et al.), p. 97. Cold Spring Harbor Laboratory, Cold Spring Harbor, New York.

Rigby, P.J. and D.P. Lane. 1983. Structure and function of simian virus 40 large T-antigen. *Adv. Viral Oncol.* **3:** 31.

Riggs, A.D., H. Suzuki, and S. Bourgeois. 1970. *lac* repressor-operator interaction. I. Equilibrium studies. *J. Mol. Biol.* **48:** 67.

Russell, D.W. and N.D. Zinder. 1987. Hemimethylation prevents DNA replication in *E.coli*. *Cell* **50:** 1071.

Saffer, L.D. and O.L. Miller, Jr. 1986. Electron microscopic study of *Saccharomyces cerevisiae* rDNA chromatin replication. *Mol. Cell. Biol.* **6:** 1148.

Shore, D., D.J. Stillman, A.H. Brand, and K.A. Nasmyth. 1987. Identification of silencer binding proteins from yeast: Possible roles in SIR control and DNA replication. *EMBO J.* **6:** 461.

Snyder, M., A.R. Buchman, and R.W. Davis. 1986. Bent DNA at a yeast autonomously replicating sequence. *Nature* **324:** 87.

Sølgaard-Andersen, L., L.A. Rokeach, and S. Molin. 1984. Regulated expression of a gene important for replication of plasmid F in *E.coli*. *EMBO J.* **3:** 257.

Srienc, F., J.E. Bailey, and J.L. Campbell. 1985. Effect of ARS1 mutations on chromosome stability in *Saccharomyces cerevisiae*. *Mol. Cell. Biol.* **5:** 1676.

Stenzel, T.T., P. Patel, and D. Bastia. 1987. The integration host factor of *Escherichia coli* binds to bent DNA at the origin of replication of the plasmid pSC101. *Cell* **49:** 709.

Storms, R.K., R.W. Ord, M.T. Greenwood, B. Mirdamadi, F.K. Chu, and M. Belfort. 1984. Cell cycle-dependent expression of thymidylate synthetase in *Saccharomyces cerevisiae*. *Mol. Cell. Biol.* **4:** 2858.

Struhl, K., D.T. Stinchcomb, S. Scherer, and R.W. Davis. 1979. Autonomous replication of hybrid DNA molecules. *Proc. Natl. Acad. Sci.* **76:** 1035.

Stuart, P., M. Ito, C. Stewart, and S.E. Conrad. 1985. Induction of cellular thymidine kinase occurs at the mRNA level. *Mol. Cell. Biol.* **5:** 1490.

Tokino, T., T. Murotsu, and K. Matsubara. 1986. Purification and properties of the mini-F plasmid-encoded E protein needed for autonomous replication control of the plasmid. *Proc. Natl. Acad. Sci.* **83:** 4109.

Tsurimoto, T. and K. Matsubara. 1981. Purified bacteriophage λ O protein binds to four repeating sequences at the λ replication origin. *Nucleic Acids Res.* **9:** 1789.

Tsutsui, H., A. Fujiyama, T. Murotsu, and K. Matsubara. 1983.

Role of nine repeating sequences of the mini-F genome for expression of F-specific incompatibility phenotype and copy number control. *J. Bacteriol.* **155:** 337.

Vocke, K. and D. Bastia. 1983. DNA-protein interactions at the origin of DNA replication of the plasmid pSC101. *Cell* **35:** 495.

Williamson, D.H. 1985. The yeast ARS element, six years on: A progress report. *Yeast* **1:** 1.

Zahn, K. and F.R. Blattner. 1987. Direct evidence for DNA bending at the lambda replication origin. *Science* **236:** 416.

Control of S Phase in Fission Yeast

P. Nurse, J. Hayles, M. Lee, P. Russell, and V. Simanis
Cell Cycle Control Laboratory, Imperial Cancer Research Fund,
London, WC2A 3PX, United Kingdom

A review is made of the controls operative in G_1 that regulate the initiation of S phase in the fission yeast *Schizosaccharomyces pombe*. Two gene functions encoded by $cdc2^+$ and $cdc10^+$ are required at start, a control point located late in G_1, where the program of events leading to S phase is initiated. The $cdc2^+$ gene product is a 34-kD protein kinase that loses its activity in cells arrested before start by nutrient depletion. The $cdc2^+$ gene function is also required for the initiation of mitosis where it is controlled by a network of several other genes, including two further potential protein kinases. A human homolog of $cdc2^+$ has been cloned using a human cDNA library to complement a $cdc2^{ts}$ mutant. The homolog has 63% identity in protein sequence to $cdc2^+$. This suggests that elements of S-phase control are likely to be the same in all eukaryotic organisms.

The two events common to all eukaryotic cell cycles are S phase and mitosis. During S phase the chromosomes become replicated, and in mitosis they are segregated into the two daughter cells. The controls operative over these events have been extensively studied in the fission yeast *S. pombe*, exploiting the good classic and molecular genetic methodologies available for this organism. In this paper, we will review the controls operative in G_1 that regulate the initiation of S phase in *S. pombe*.

Genes required for S phase and its initiation
Around 45 genes have been identified in *S. pombe* that are necessary for successful completion of the cell cycle (Nurse et al. 1976; Nasmyth and Nurse 1981; Yanagida et al. 1986). Ten of these have been implicated in DNA replication. The four gene products encoded by *cdc2, 10, 20,* and *22* function in G_1 before S phase (Nasmyth and Nurse 1981; Nurse and Bissett 1981). Temperature-sensitive mutants in these genes arrest in G_1 and fail to initiate DNA replication when incubated at the restrictive temperature. The $cdc2^+$ gene is also required again later in the cycle for the initiation of mitosis (Nurse and Thuriaux 1980a). Six other gene products are thought to be required for the process of DNA replication. These are encoded by *cdc17, 18, 19, 21, 23,* and *24* (Nasmyth and Nurse 1981). When temperature-sensitive mutants of these genes are arrested in S phase using hydroxyurea, and are then shifted to the restrictive temperature in the absence of hydroxyurea, they fail to complete the cell cycle. These experiments indicate that the genes function during the process of DNA replication, rather than during its initiation.

Four of the genes, *cdc2, 10, 17,* and *22*, have been cloned (Beach et al. 1982; Aves et al. 1985; Johnston et al. 1986; Gordon and Fantes 1986). The $cdc17^+$ gene encodes DNA ligase (Nasmyth 1977), and the $cdc2^+$ gene encodes a protein kinase (Simanis and Nurse 1986). The biochemical functions of $cdc10^+$ and $cdc22^+$ remain unknown. The genes encoding the four

core histones H2A, H2B, H3, and H4 have also been cloned and are presumably also necessary for successful DNA synthesis (Matsumoto and Yanagida 1985).

Start control over S phase
The control determining the cell cycle timing of S phase has been called "start," after a similar control described in the budding yeast (Nurse and Bissett 1981). The start control point is located in G_1 and is the earliest identified gene-controlled event of the cell cycle. Haploid cells that have passed start are committed to the cell cycle in the sense that they are unable to undergo the alternative cell fate of conjugation until the cell cycle in progress has been completed. Mutants of $cdc2^+$ and $cdc10^+$ arrest cells before start in a state that still allows cells to conjugate if challenged to do so, establishing that the $cdc2^+$ and 10^+ gene functions are required for commitment to the cell cycle.

Once past start, cells rapidly complete the other functions required in G_1. Normally about 0.1 of a cell cycle elapses between start and the onset of DNA synthesis (Nasmyth et al. 1979). In nitrogen-depleted medium, the total length of G_1 becomes considerably extended. This extension takes place almost entirely during the G_1 period prior to start (Nasmyth 1979). Once start has been completed, the cell rapidly proceeds to S phase, indicating that traverse of start acts as a major rate-limiting step for the initiation of DNA replication. Passage of start begins the program of events that lead to S phase; these events include the execution of the functions encoded by $cdc20^+$ and $cdc22^+$, and the accumulation of histone transcripts (Matsumoto et al. 1987). Histone transcripts peak in level at the time of the G_1 to S-phase transition. Arresting cells at start prevents this accumulation of histone transcripts, but arresting cells later in G_1 after start leads to the normal rise in histone transcript levels.

The expansion of G_1 in nitrogen-starved cells described above is due to the need for cells to attain a

245

critical mass before they can pass start. This was revealed initially by the study of wee mutants that undergo mitosis and cell division at a reduced cell size compared with normal (Nurse 1975). In these cells the G_1 period is extended by 0.3 of a cell cycle. The smaller dividing cells are too small at the beginning of their cell cycle to pass start, and have to grow for a further 0.3 of a cell cycle before they attain the necessary cell mass. A similar situation was revealed in cells made small by other means: by nitrogen depletion, by forming spores, or by growth in a nitrogen-limited chemostat (Nurse and Thuriaux 1977; Nasmyth 1979). The requirement for cells to attain a critical cell mass before passing start may mean that cells need to acquire sufficient cytoplasmic resources before they can begin the program of events leading to DNA replication and the rest of the cell cycle.

Given the important role of start in the control of S phase and the cell cycle, it is necessary to understand what happens at start in molecular terms. We have begun this investigation by cloning the $cdc10^+$ and $cdc2^+$ genes and using the cloned genes as probes to characterize their molecular mechanisms of action.

Molecular characterization of the $cdc10^+$ gene

The $cdc10^+$ gene has been cloned from a genomic bank of *S. pombe* by complementation of a $cdc10^{ts}$ mutant (Aves et al. 1985). It encodes a low abundance 2.7-kb polyadenylated RNA, which does not change significantly in level during synchronous cultures or during entry into stationary phase. Therefore, transcriptional control does not play any role in regulating $cdc10^+$ function during the cell cycle.

The sequence of the gene reveals a long open reading frame potentially able to encode a protein of molecular mass 85 kD. The protein sequence does not contain any extensive hydrophobic regions, and is thus unlikely to be a membrane protein. Secondary structure predictions suggest the presence of substantial regions of surface α-helix, indicative of a globular water soluble protein. Recently $cdc10^+$ has been shown to share around 25% homology with *SWI6*, a gene required for mating-type switching in the budding yeast *Saccharomyces cerevisiae* (Breedon and Nasmyth 1987). This gene product has been shown to be necessary for activation of *HO* gene transcription during the G_1 phase of the cell cycle. The regions of homology may represent structural features that are associated with similarities in the two gene functions. One possibility would be the activation of transcription during G_1, since *SWI6* is required for *HO* transcription in G_1 and $cdc10^+$ for histone transcription in G_1.

Molecular characterization of the $cdc2^+$ gene

The $cdc2^+$ gene was cloned by complementation of a $cdc2^{ts}$ mutant (Beach et al. 1982). It encodes a 1.6-kb polyadenylated transcript derived from the $cdc2^+$ precursor RNA by splicing out four introns. The transcript

level does not change during synchronous culture or during entry into stationary phase (Durkacz et al. 1986).

The sequence of the gene indicated that it potentially encodes a protein of 297 amino acid residues in length with about 20% homology to a number of protein kinases (Hindley and Phear 1984). We have raised antibodies against this protein using peptides corresponding to the predicted carboxy-terminal region of the amino acid sequence (Simanis and Nurse 1986). A 34-kD protein was detected in *S. pombe* cell extracts by Western blotting. The level of this protein was greatly increased in cells containing $cdc2^+$ fused to a strong promoter, showing that the $cdc2^+$ gene product is indeed a 34-kD protein. Immunoprecipitation from cells labeled with ^{32}P has shown that this protein, called p34, is phosphorylated in vivo. Assays of the p34 immune complex have shown that it possesses protein kinase activity capable of phosphorylating casein in vitro. This is associated with the $cdc2^+$ gene product because the protein kinase activity is thermolabile in vitro when assayed from certain $cdc2^{ts}$ alleles temperature sensitive for $cdc2$ function in vivo. These data indicate that protein phosphorylation must play an important role in committing cells to the mitotic cell cycle and regulating the onset of S phase. The p34 protein kinase presumably phosphorylates one or more protein substrates that are required to begin the program of events leading to DNA replication.

No significant changes in p34 level or phosphorylation state were observed in synchronous cultures. However, when cells ceased proliferation and accumulated in G_1 as a consequence of nitrogen starvation, p34 rapidly became dephosphorylated (Simanis and Nurse 1986). The dephosphorylation was paralleled by a decrease of in vitro $cdc2^+$ protein kinase activity. On shifting the starved cells back into complete medium, p34 became rephosphorylated and regained protein kinase activity. These findings are consistent with the idea that the p34 protein kinase activity could play an important role in regulating entry into the cell cycle. Upon nitrogen deprivation, p34 loses its protein kinase activity, and as a consequence, cells are unable to pass start. Because p34 also becomes dephosphorylated, the loss of protein kinase activity could be due to p34 dephosphorylation. However, the causal relationship between p34 phosphorylation and protein kinase activity has yet to be established, and it could be that the in vivo phosphorylation of p34 is the consequence rather than the cause of the increase in p34 protein kinase activity.

Genes interacting with $cdc2^+$

Three genes have been found to be important in regulating the $cdc2^+$ gene function at the initiation of mitosis. We shall only briefly mention these here as they fall outside the main focus of this review. The gene functions encoded by $cdc25^+$ (Russell and Nurse 1986) and $nim1^+$ (Russell and Nurse 1987a) act as positive effectors of $cdc2^+$ activity, and the gene function encoded by the $wee1^+$ acts as a negative effector (Russell and Nurse 1987b). The sequences of the $nim1^+$ and $wee1^+$

genes indicate that they could both potentially encode proteins that have homologies to protein kinases. These data suggest that the $cdc2^+$ mitotic initiation function is controlled by a regulatory network that includes several protein kinases.

A further gene $suc1$ is also thought to interact with the $cdc2$ gene function (Hayles et al. 1985). Mutants in this gene or overexpression of its transcripts leads to the suppression of certain $cdc2^{ts}$ alleles (Hayles et al. 1986). It appears that the reduced $cdc2$ gene product activity in these $cdc2^{ts}$ alleles, which leads to cell cycle arrest at both the $cdc2$ points of action in G_1 and in G_2, can be compensated by changes in $suc1$ activity. Because the effects are $cdc2$ allele specific, it has been argued that there may be a direct physical interaction between the $cdc2^+$ and $suc1^+$ gene products. Sequencing of the $suc1^+$ gene suggests that it encodes a small polypeptide less than 13 kD in molecular mass (Hindley et al. 1987). There are no homologies with published sequences of other proteins and so no suggestions can be made concerning its biochemical function. However, since a deletion of the $suc1^+$ gene from the chromosome leads to defects in cell growth as well as in cell cycle progress, it is likely that its product interacts with other proteins in the cell as well as p34 (Hayles et al. 1986).

Start in other eukaryotic organisms

An analogous start control also exists in the G_1 phase of the cell cycle of the budding yeast *S. cerevisiae* (for review, see Hartwell 1974). As in *S. pombe*, cells before start are uncommitted to the cell cycle, and once past start, the cells begin the program of events that leads to S phase. Traverse of start also acts as a major rate-limiting step in the budding yeast cell cycle. An homologous gene to $cdc2^+$ called $CDC28$ functions at start. $CDC28$ has 62% amino acid identity with $cdc2^+$ and is of very similar molecular weight (Hindley and Phear 1984). The two genes are also functionally interchangeable; $CDC28$ can complement a $cdc2^{ts}$ mutant (Beach et al. 1982), and $cdc2^+$ can complement a $cdc28^{ts}$ mutant (Booher and Beach 1986). Biochemical studies have revealed that CDC28 encodes a protein kinase that can become phosphorylated. These similarities in start and the $cdc2^+/CDC28$ genes are highly suggestive that the basic mechanisms regulating traverse of G_1 and the initiation of DNA synthesis will be identical or very similar in the two organisms.

Recently, it has been shown that a gene function homologous with $cdc2^+/CDC28$ also exists in human cells (Lee and Nurse 1987). Mutant *S. pombe* $cdc2^{ts}$ cells were transformed with a human cDNA library expressed behind the early SV40 promoter, which works well in *S. pombe*. Clones were selected that could grow at the restrictive temperature. These clones were found to contain a human cDNA that complemented the defective $cdc2^{ts}$ gene function. Sequencing of this cDNA revealed that it could potentially encode a protein of identical molecular weight to $cdc2^+$ and with 63% identity in amino acid sequence. This degree of homolo-gy is very similar to the 62% seen with $CDC28$. The gene encoding the human cDNA has been called $CDC2$ with the suffix Hs to denote its *Homo sapiens* origin. The $CDC2$Hs gene appears to be able to provide all the functions encoded by the fission yeast $cdc2^+$ gene, since a yeast strain deleted for $cdc2$ grows and undergoes its cell cycle normally if it contains $CDC2$Hs. Antibodies raised against a peptide corresponding to part of the $CDC2$Hs sequence have detected a 34-kD protein in human fibroblast cells (Lee and Nurse 1987).

A separate study has also come to a similar conclusion that human cells contain a protein homologous with p34 (Draetta et al. 1987). Antibodies that could detect the proteins encoded by both fission yeast $cdc2^+$ and budding yeast $CDC28$ also detected a 34-kD protein in human HeLa cells. This protein has similarly spaced tryptophan residues to the $cdc2$ and $CDC28$ gene products. These antibodies appear to be detecting the protein encoded by $CDC2$Hs; biochemical studies are suggestive that this protein is phosphorylated and has protein kinase activity.

These data strongly support the notion that mammalian cells contain a homolog to $cdc2^+$. It is likely that $CDC2$Hs will have a similar role to that of $cdc2$ in regulating the human cell cycle, although it cannot be excluded that the $CDC2$Hs function may have been recruited into some other regulatory network and has no role to play in the cell cycle. However, we think this is unlikely, given the functional and molecular similarities of the two gene products.

Conclusions and Prospects

The major control over the initiation of S phase in *S. pombe* occurs at start located in the G_1 phase of the cell cycle. Once start is passed, cells become committed to the cell cycle and begin the program of events that leads to S phase. Two gene functions have been shown to be required to traverse start, one encoded by $cdc10^+$ and the other by $cdc2^+$. Little is known about the molecular properties of $cdc10^+$, but sequence homologies have raised the possibility that it may have a role in regulating transcription during G_1. The $cdc2^+$ gene product has been shown to be a protein kinase of 34 kD molecular mass, suggesting that phosphorylation of one or more protein substrates is required to begin the program of events leading to the onset of DNA replication. The p34 protein kinase loses its activity in cells that have ceased proliferating and have accumulated in G_1 before start. This modulation of protein kinase activity could be implemented by changes in the overall phosphorylation state of p34 and may have an important role in regulating entry into the cell cycle and the initiation of DNA synthesis. The $cdc2^+$ gene function is also important for regulating the initiation of mitosis, a function controlled by a network involving several other protein kinases.

The identification of a human homolog $CDC2$Hs to $cdc2$ is suggestive that similar cell cycle controls may be operative also in human cells. If this is the case, then at least some of the basic elements of cell cycle control can be expected to be common to all eukaryotic cells. As a consequence, a new approach to the study of cell cycle control will be possible in multicellular eukaryotic cells. Cell cycle genes can be isolated from these organisms using expression cDNA libraries by complementation of appropriate cell cycle mutants in genetically amenable organisms such as *S. pombe*, *S. cerevisiae*, or *Aspergillus nidulans*. Over 100 cell cycle genes have now been identified in these three simple eukaryotes, and it is likely that many of these genes will also be represented in multicellular organisms such as *H. sapiens*. Because of the very considerable evolutionary divergence between the organisms, protein sequence identities are likely to be significant and useful for focusing attention on particular regions of the protein structure. Therefore, comparisons of the sequences of these functionally equivalent genes will be useful for identifying those parts of the protein that will have been conserved, and thus can be expected to be particularly important for the gene function.

One of the major problems with investigating the cell cycle in multicellular organisms is the difficulty in establishing the functional significance of particular genes and of mutants in those genes. In organisms such as the yeasts, a cell cycle gene can be specifically engineered in vitro and then used to replace the normal wild-type gene in the genome. Using these methodologies, precise causal relations can be established between particular gene functions and the cellular phenotype. Two new approaches to this problem are now possible. First, detailed functional studies can be carried out in the simpler organisms and the relevant biochemical properties identified and then investigated in the multicellular organism. For example, a change in phosphorylation state of p34 in fission yeast during entry into the cell cycle would suggest that a similar change may occur with the human *CDC2*Hs p34. Second, it will also be possible to carry out functional studies in cells of the multicellular organism exploiting the use of dominant mutants. The human genes can be used to replace the functionally equivalent yeast homologs. Further plasmid-borne human gene equivalents can be mutagenized in vitro and introduced into the yeast cells to look for interesting dominant mutants. For example, *CDC2*Hs would replace *cdc2*[+] in *S. pombe*, and after mutagenizing plasmid-borne copies of *CDC2*Hs, dominant mutants that affect the cell cycle in specific ways would be isolated in the yeast. Once such mutants have been isolated, then the mutated *CDC2*Hs gene can be shifted into human cells to determine if it has similar effects on the cell cycle in this organism as well. Because the mutants are dominant, their effects will be expressed in the human diploid cells. If there are similar effects, this suggests that the yeast and mammalian cells are responding functionally in a similar way to the *cdc2* gene, and thus this aspect of the behavior can be legitimately studied in yeast. In this way rapid progress can be expected in our understanding of how the cell cycle and the initiation of S phase are regulated in cells of multicellular organisms.

References

Aves, S., B. Durkacz, A. Carr, and P. Nurse. 1985. Cloning, sequencing and transcriptional control of the *Schizosaccharomyces pombe cdc10* "start" gene. *EMBO J.* **4:** 457.

Beach, D., B. Durkacz, and P. Nurse. 1982. Functionally homologous cell cycle control genes in budding and fission yeast. *Nature* **300:** 682.

Booher, R. and D. Beach. 1986. Site specific mutagenesis of *cdc2*[+]; a cell cycle control gene of the fission yeast *Schizosaccharomyces pombe. Mol. Cell. Biol.* **6:** 3523.

Breedon, L. and K. Nasmyth. 1987. Similarity between cell cycle genes of budding yeast and fission yeast and the *Notch* gene of *Drosophila. Nature* **329:** 651.

Draetta, G., L. Brizuela, J. Potashkin, and D. Beach. 1987. Identification of p34 and p13; human homologs of the cell cycle regulators of fission yeast encoded by *cdc2*[+] and *suc1*[+]. *Cell* **50:** 319.

Durkacz, B., A. Carr, and P. Nurse. 1986. Transcription of the *cdc2* cell cycle control gene of fission yeast *Schizosaccharomyces pombe. EMBO J.* **5:** 369.

Gordon, C.B. and P.A. Fantes. 1986. The *cdc22* gene of *Schizosaccharomyces pombe* encodes a cell cycle regulated transcript. *EMBO J.* **5:** 2981.

Hartwell, L. 1974. *Saccharomyces cerevisiae* cell cycle. *Bacteriol. Rev.* **38:** 164.

Hayles, J., S. Aves, and P. Nurse. 1986. *suc1* is an essential gene involved in both the cell cycle and growth in fission yeast. *EMBO J.* **5:** 3373.

Hayles, J., D. Beach, B. Durkacz, and P. Nurse. 1985. The fission yeast cell cycle control gene *cdc2*: Isolation of a sequence *suc1* that suppresses *cdc2* mutant function. *Mol. Gen. Genet.* **202:** 291.

Hindley, J. and G.A. Phear. 1984. Sequence of the cell cycle division gene *CDC2* from *Schizosaccharomyces pombe*; patterns of splicing and homology to protein kinases. *Gene* **31:** 129.

Hindley, J., G. Phear, M. Stein, and D. Beach. 1987. *Suc1*[+] encodes a predicted 13 kilodalton protein that is essential for cell viability and is directly involved in the division cycle of *Schizosaccharomyces pombe. Mol. Cell. Biol.* **7:** 504.

Johnston, L.H., D.G. Barker, and P. Nurse. 1986. Cloning and characterisation of the *Schizosaccharomyces pombe* DNA ligase gene *CDC17. Gene* **41:** 321.

Lee, M.G. and P. Nurse. 1987. Complementation used to clone a human homologue of the fission yeast cell cycle control gene *cdc2. Nature* **327:** 31.

Matsumoto, S. and M. Yanagida. 1985. Histone gene organisation in fission yeast: A common upstream sequence. *EMBO J.* **4:** 3531.

Matsumoto, S., M. Yanagida, and P. Nurse. 1987. Histone transcription in cell cycle mutants in fission yeast. *EMBO J.* **6:** 1093.

Nasmyth, K.A. 1977. Temperature-sensitive lethal mutants in the structural gene for DNA ligase in the yeast *Schizosaccharomyces pombe. Cell* **12:** 1109.

———. 1979, A control acting over the initiation of DNA replication in the yeast *Schizosaccharomyces pombe. J. Cell Sci.* **36:** 215.

Nasmyth, K. and P. Nurse. 1981. Cell division cycle mutants altered in DNA replication and mitosis in the fission yeast *Schizosaccharomyces pombe. Mol. Gen. Genet.* **182:** 119.

Nasmyth, K., P. Nurse, and R.S.S. Fraser. 1979. The effect of cell mass on the cell cycle timing and duration of S-phase in fission yeast. *J. Cell Sci.* **39:** 215.

Nurse, P. 1975. Genetic control of cell size at cell division in yeast. *Nature* **256:** 547.

Nurse, P. and Y. Bissett. 1981. Gene required in G1 for commitment to the cell cycle and in G2 for control of mitosis in fission yeast. *Nature* **292:** 558.

Nurse, P. and P. Thuriaux. 1977. Controls over the timing of DNA replication during the cell cycle of fission yeast. *Exp. Cell. Res.* **107:** 365

————. 1980. Regulatory gene controlling mitosis in the fission yeast *Schizosaccharomyces pombe*. *Genetics* **96:** 627.

Nurse, P., P. Thuriaux, and K. Nasmyth. 1976. Genetic control of the cell division cycle in the fission yeast *Schizosaccharomyces pombe*. *Mol. Gen. Genet.* **146:** 167.

Russell, P. and P. Nurse. 1986. *cdc25*$^+$ functions as an inducer in the mitotic control of fission yeast. *Cell* **45:** 145.

————. 1987a. The mitotic inducer *nim1*$^+$ functions in a regulatory network of protein kinase homologs controlling the initiation of mitosis. *Cell* **49:** 569.

————. 1987b. Negative regulation of mitosis by *wee1*$^+$, a gene encoding a protein kinase homolog. *Cell* **49:** 559.

Simanis, V. and P. Nurse. 1986. The cell cycle control gene *cdc2*$^+$ of fission yeast encodes a protein kinase potentially regulated by phosphorylation. *Cell* **45:** 261.

Yanagida, M., K. Hiraoka, T. Uemura, S. Miyake, and T. Hirano. 1986. Control mechanisms of chromosome movement in mitosis of fission yeast. *UCLA Symp. Mol. Cell. Biol.* **33:** 279.

Regulation of Cell Division in Yeast by the Cdc28 Protein Kinase

S.I. Reed, J.A. Hadwiger, M.D. Mendenhall, and C. Wittenberg
Department of Molecular Biology, MB-7, Research Institute of Scripps Clinic,
La Jolla, California 92037

The protein kinase encoded by the *Saccharomyces cerevisiae* gene *CDC28* is thought to be involved in control of cell division. We have found that under conditions of nutrient limitation and treatment with mating pheromones, Cdc28 protein kinase activity, as measured in vitro, is lost. In addition, using synchronized cell cultures, we have determined that active protein kinase complexes can be prepared from G_1 cells but that activity in non-G_1 complexes can be restored by adding a factor from asynchronous, starved, or pheromone-treated cells. Further experiments along these lines have allowed us to conclude that starved and pheromone-responsive cells have an inactive Cdc28 protein kinase, whereas non-G_1 cycling cells contain an active Cdc28 protein kinase but are deficient in an exchangeable factor required for activity. We have also concluded that changes in activity observed under any of these conditions do not result from fluctuations in the steady-state level of the Cdc28 protein or from changes in its phosphorylation state. Using chromatographic techniques, we have found that the active form of the Cdc28 protein kinase is a 140-kD complex. This complex is present in non-G_1 cycling cells but is inactive, whereas it is absent from cells that have been starved or treated with mating pheromone. We propose that Cdc28 protein kinase activity is controlled by external conditions at the level of assembly of this high-molecular-weight complex.

In *S. cerevisiae*, cell division is controlled in response to nutrient limitation and by the action of mating pheromones (for reviews, see Pringle and Hartwell 1981; Thorner 1981). Both types of environmental stimuli act by regulating a yeast cell's progression through the G_1 interval of the cell division cycle. Thus, under conditions where proliferation is to be restrained, cells are prevented from exiting from G_1 and becoming committed to a new round of division. It has been proposed that both forms of control may be mediated by controlling a single G_1 event, given the operational designation "start" (Hartwell et al. 1974). To test this hypothesis and to characterize the signaling pathways that are operational in division control, mutants defective in this process have been isolated, the genes so defined cloned, and their encoded products characterized (Nasmyth and Reed 1980; Reed 1980, 1982; Reed et al. 1982; Breter et al. 1983; Ferguson et al. 1986). Temperature-sensitive mutations in the gene *CDC28* confer a conditional inability to exit from G_1 (Hartwell et al. 1974; Reed 1980). Mutant cells, therefore, complete current division cycles and become arrested in the G_1 interval. Analysis of the *CDC28* gene and subsequent analysis of the Cdc28 protein using immune sera prepared against synthetic antigens indicated that the Cdc28 product is a protein kinase (Lörincz and Reed 1984; Reed et al. 1985). This designated activity and the phenotype of *cdc28* mutants suggest that Cdc28-specific phosphorylation of target proteins may be crucial for the initiation of new cell cycles. Furthermore, control of cell division by external stimuli could, in principle, be achieved by regulating the activity of the Cdc28

protein kinase. Therefore, we have sought to determine whether conditions known to restrain cell division in yeast affect the activity and structure of the Cdc28 protein kinase. In this paper, we demonstrate that both nutrient limitation and activity of mating pheromones cause loss of activity of the Cdc28 protein kinase and a drastic alteration of its structure. We also present suggestive evidence that regulation of the Cdc28 protein kinase occurs through other subunits of an active protein kinase complex.

Materials and Methods

Strains and media

For experiments analyzing the effect of growth conditions and cell cycle parameters on the activity of Cdc28 protein kinase complexes, strains were as described in Mendenhall et al. (1987). For experiments analyzing the phosphorylation state of the Cdc28 protein under conditions of treatment with the mating pheromone, α-factor, the *bar1* strain 4202-15-3 (Jenness et al. 1983) was used. For analysis of Cdc28 high-molecular-weight complexes, the following strains were used: for exponential and stationary cultures the *pep4* (vacuolar protease deficient) strain PEP4D, for hydroxyurea-treated cultures, A364a (Hartwell 1976), for α-factor-treated cultures, 4202-15-3. Studies of the dominant lethal *CDC28* mutations were performed on a derivative of J16D (*MATa, cir⁰, trp1, ura3, leu2, his3*; M. Jayaram, pers. comm.) into which an integrative plasmid containing a *pGAL1::CDC28-dl1* chimeric gene (*GAL1* promoter and upstream untranslated region and *CDC28-*

CANCER CELLS 6 / *Eukaryotic DNA Replication*. © 1988 by Cold Spring Harbor Laboratory 0-87969-308-8/88 $1.00

dl1 coding region) had been integrated at the *ura3* locus, J16D(*CDC28-dl1*.int). All media, as well as drug and pheromone treatments, have been described elsewhere (Mendenhall et al. 1987).

Cdc28 protein kinase assays
Cdc28 protein kinase assays were performed as originally described by Reed et al. (1985) and as modified in Mendenhall et al. (1987). The antiserum used to prepare immune complexes was raised by injecting a rabbit with a synthetic peptide corresponding to the amino-terminal ten residues of the predicted Cdc28 protein coupled to keyhole limpet hemacyanin (Green et al. 1982). Before use in assays, serum was incubated at 56°C for 30 minutes to inactivate endogenous protein kinases.

Two-dimensional gel electrophoresis
Cells were harvested by centrifugation and lysed in 33 μl of isoelectric focusing sample buffer (Lörincz et al. 1982) at 25°C by mixing in a Vortex mixer with 0.5-mm glass beads (Braun). Glass beads were then removed as described by Wittenberg et al. (1987) and lysates cleared by centrifugation for 30 seconds in an Eppendorf microfuge before loading on isoelectric focusing tube gels. Proteins were separated by two-dimensional gel electrophoresis essentially as described by O'Farrell et al. (1977) except for the following. The sample buffer was modified as described by Lörincz et al. (1982), and the isoelectric focusing dimension was run at 1000 V for 2.5 hours. Proteins were blotted to nitrocellulose as described in the Trans-Blot manual (Bio-Rad). Cdc28 protein was detected by the procedure described in the Immunoblot Manual (Promega-Biotec) using serum raised against an 18-residue peptide corresponding to the carboxyl terminus of the predicted Cdc28 protein (anti-CDC28$_{281-298}$) as described by Wittenberg et al. (1987).

Determination of high-molecular-weight Cdc28 complexes
Total protein was prepared from PEP4D cells in exponential growth (approximately 4×10^7 cells per ml) or at stationary phase (budding index of <3%) or from A364a cells arrested with hydroxyurea or 4204-15-3 (*bar1*) cells arrested with α factor (Mendenhall et al. 1987) as follows. Cells were harvested and washed once in ice cold water. Cells were lysed in an equal volume of buffer A (50 mM Tris-HCl [pH 7.0], 0.1 mM EDTA, 0.5 mM dithiothreitol, containing 1 mM phenylmethylsulfonyl fluoride and 1 μg/ml each Aprotinin, leupeptin, and pepstatin A) by vortexing with glass beads. The lysate was cleared by centrifugation at 35,000g for 30 minutes. Polymin P was added to 0.25% with stirring and the precipitate removed by centrifugation for 15 min at 5000g. The resulting supernatant was adjusted to 70% ammonium sulfate and the precipitate collected by centrifugation at 20,000g. The pellet was resuspended in a minimal volume of buffer A and dialyzed in buffer B (buffer A containing 10% glycerol and

50 mM ammonium sulfate). This material was used for gel filtration chromatography.

Gel filtration chromatography was performed on a Superose 12 10/30 column (Pharmacia) driven by a Pharmacia fast performance liquid chromatography (FPLC) system. One-tenth ml of protein sample containing either three A$_{280}$ units (hydroxyurea and α-factor-arrested cells) or seven A$_{280}$ units (exponential and stationary cells) was loaded and eluted at 0.15 ml/min with 30 ml of buffer B, collecting 0.5-ml fractions. Fractions were subjected to SDS polyacrylamide gel electrophoresis followed by immunoblotting using anti-Cdc28$_{281-298}$ (Wittenberg et al. 1987) and an alkaline phosphatase-based enzyme-linked immunosorbent assay (Promega-Biotec). The 34-kD Cdc28 product was quantitated by scanning immunoblots with an Ultroscan XL laser densitometer (LKB). Cdc28 protein kinase activity in column fractions was quantitated as described above.

Nutritional shifts for induction of dominant lethal CDC28 allele
J16D(*CDC28-dl1*.int) cells were grown at 30°C to mid-logarithmic phase (10^7 cells per ml) in minimal medium (6.7 g/l yeast nitrogen base without amino acids [Difco]) supplemented with 40 μg/ml each of histidine, tryptophan, and leucine and 10 ml/l each of glycerol and ethanol. Induction was by addition of galactose to 2%. Cells were mounted and photographed before addition of galactose and 6 hours after induction using a Leitz SM-Lux microscope with a 100× objective and fitted with an Olympus polaroid camera.

Results

Cdc28 protein kinase activity is regulated in response to nutrient limitation and the action of mating pheromones

Using an immune complex assay described previously (Reed et al. 1985), we sought to determine whether changes in Cdc28 protein kinase activity correlated with the imposition of conditions known to lead to G$_1$ arrest of yeast cells. This assay relies on an endogenous basic substrate of 40 kD (p40) that coprecipitates with the Cdc28 protein kinase under the conditions employed. The Cdc28 specificity of the assay is based on the demonstration of temperature-sensitive or labile protein kinase activity when immune complexes are prepared from temperature-sensitive *cdc28* mutant cells (Reed et al. 1985). Although, technically, this assay is a measure of Cdc28 protein kinase–p40 complex activity, it will henceforth in this text be referred to simply as Cdc28 protein kinase activity. A comparison of activity precipitable from log phase cells and stationary cells is shown in Figure 1. No protein kinase activity is detectable in lysates from the nutrient-limited culture, although Cdc28 protein is present at approximately the same level in both lysates. Similar results were obtained upon subjecting logarithmic phase cells to nitrogen starvation. In addition, temperature-sensitive mutations in the gene

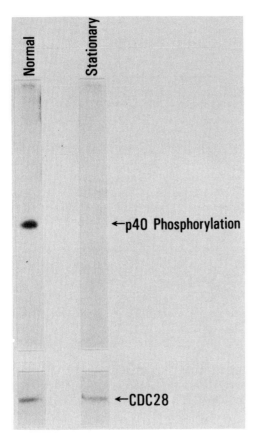

Figure 1 Cdc28 protein kinase assays were performed on lysates of asynchronous growing and stationary yeast cells as described in Materials and Methods. After separation by electrophoresis on SDS gels, reactions were analyzed by autoradiography. The lane labeled "normal" is an autoradiograph of a reaction from a typical growing culture and that labeled "stationary" is from a culture maintained in stationary phase for several days. The arrow indicates the position where the endogenous substrate p40 migrates. The panels below each lane are immunoblots of Cdc28 protein prepared from the same lysates assayed, demonstrating that the steady state-level of Cdc28 protein is invariant.

CDC35 that encodes adenylate cyclase confer a rapid temperature-dependent loss of Cdc28 protein kinase activity (Mendenhall et al. 1987). The phenotype conferred by such mutations resembles, both morphologically and physiologically, the nutrient-limited state and, as a result, cAMP has been suggested as a likely second messenger for the starvation response (Matsumoto et al. 1983; Tripp et al. 1986). Thus, loss of Cdc28 activity accompanies starvation, as well as perturbation of intracellular signals implicated in the starvation response. Mating pheromones, as part of their pleiotropic activity on responsive cells, cause arrest in G₁ (Bücking-Throm et al. 1973). As is the case with nutritional limitation, Cdc28 protein kinase activity is lost in response to treatment with mating pheromones (Mendenhall et al. 1987). Thus, both known forms of restraint on cell division encountered in nature, nutritional and pheromonal, lead to inactivation of the Cdc28 protein kinase, consistent with the latter having a key regulatory role.

Cdc28 protein kinase activity is only detectable in G₁

We sought to determine whether the Cdc28 protein kinase is active throughout the cell division cycle during unrestrained growth. When asynchronous cultures were treated with agents that cause specific cell cycle blocks outside of the G₁ interval, Cdc28 protein kinase activity was observed to decline and eventually disappear (Fig. 2A). Hydroxyurea, which blocks in S phase (Slater 1973), and nocodazole, which blocks in mitosis (Thomas et al. 1985; Pillus and Solomon 1986), each gave different kinetics of Cdc28 protein kinase inactivation, consistent with the Cdc28 protein kinase being active only during G₁ (Fig. 2B). Experiments using synchronized cells obtained either by induction (mating pheromone block followed by release) or by selection (elutriation rotor; Elliott and McLaughlin 1978) gave a similar result. Cdc28 protein kinase was most active immediately after the completion of mitosis, with activity declining gradually during G₁. Thus, it appears that

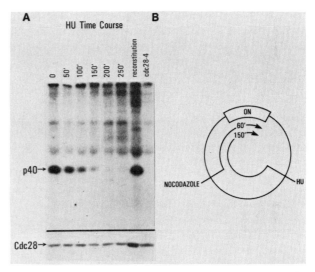

Figure 2 Analysis of Cdc28 protein kinase activity during the mitotic cycle and reconstitution by *cdc28* mutant extracts. (*A*) Autoradiographs of Cdc28 protein kinase assays as a function of synchronization in S phase using hydroxyurea. The time after addition of the drug is given above each lane. The position of phosphorylated substrate p40 is indicated by the arrow. The signal becomes undetectable after 150 min. The signal at 250 min after the addition of the drug can be reconstituted (lane marked "reconstitution") by addition of lysate prepared from the mutant *cdc28-4*, which has no detectable activity in vitro by itself (lane marked "*cdc28-4*"; Reed et al. 1985). A Cdc28 immunoblot assay is presented below each lane for the corresponding lysate, indicating that the steady-state level of the Cdc28 protein is invariant. (*B*) Schematic interpretation of hydroxyurea time course shown in *A* and nocodazole time course (not shown). The kinetics of loss of the p40 phosphorylation signal when asynchronous cultures are treated with these drugs are consistent with a relatively limited window of the cell cycle where phosphorylation is active. The signal is lost as cells that have just passed the respective block points at the time of drug addition (S phase for hydroxyurea and mitosis for nocodazole) have finally passed through this window of activity. Known kinetic parameters of the *S. cerevisiae* cell cycle place this window approximately at G₁.

during the normal cell division cycle, Cdc28 protein kinase, as defined by our assay, is active only during G_1.

In vitro complementation studies

It was of interest to determine whether inactivation of the Cdc28 protein kinase by conditions or agents that restrain cell division, such as nutritional limitation and mating pheromone, respectively, was analogous to inactivation during the mitotic cell cycle. Extracts prepared from cells were mixed pairwise prior to immunoprecipitation and assay. The rationale for this experiment was that different factors required for protein kinase function might be limiting under the various physiological conditions where activity was not detected. If such factors are exchangeable, reconstitution of activity would occur upon mixing of the appropriate extracts. Included in this series of experiments were extracts prepared from cells bearing the mutant allele *cdc28-4*. It has been demonstrated that complexes prepared from this mutant show no protein kinase activity in vitro (Reed et al. 1985). Thus, such extracts define a defect of the Cdc28 polypeptide itself. A reconstitution, or in vitro complementation, experiment using extracts from cells arrested by hydroxyurea and *cdc28-4* mutants is shown in Figure 2A. Although neither of the extracts alone shows protein kinase activity, the mixture of the two gives a strong signal (Fig. 2A). Based on the experimental rationale, whereas the mutant extract is deficient in protein kinase activity, the hydroxyurea-treated extract must be limited for a factor other than Cdc28 activity, which can be provided by the mutant extracts. The results of a large number of pairwise complementation assays are compiled in the grid shown in Figure 3. The extracts fall into

two in vitro complementation groups. One group consists of the *cdc28-4* mutant and all conditions that lead to G_1 arrest of the cell cycle. Included in this group is the *cdc35* mutant, which contains a defective adenylate cyclase. The other group consists of extracts from cells arrested within in the cell cycle but not in G_1. Included in this group, but not shown in Figure 3, are non-G_1 extracts prepared from synchronous cycling cultures. The former group, based on inability to complement *cdc28-4* mutant extracts, is characterized by an inactivation of the Cdc28 protein kinase, whereas the latter group must be limited for another component that is designated "exchangeable factor" because the latter can be supplied by complementing extracts to reconstitute activity in vitro.

Cdc28 protein kinase is not inactivated by dephosphorylation

The Cdc28 polypeptide is a phosphoprotein (Reed et al. 1985), suggesting that regulation of protein kinase activity may occur by altering its phosphorylation state. This hypothesis is rendered more credible by the correlation of activity, described above, with cAMP (Mendenhall et al. 1987) and, presumably, the cAMP-dependent protein kinase cascade (Toda et al. 1987), where the Cdc28 protein might be a downstream target, resulting in its activation. The phosphorylation state of the Cdc28 protein was analyzed by immunoprecipitation of ^{35}S- and ^{32}P-labeled lysates followed by two-dimensional gel analysis (O'Farrell et al. 1977) to identify phosphorylated and nonphosphorylated species. Extracts prepared under G_1-arresting conditions, demonstrated to inactivate the Cdc28 protein kinase, were then analyzed by two-dimensional gel electrophoresis followed by immunoblot analysis of the Cdc28 protein. Figure 4 shows immunoblots of extracts from cells immediately prior to and after 6 hours of incubation with the mating pheromone α factor, at which time all cells are arrested in G_1. There is no significant difference in the ratio of the two principal species corresponding to unphosphorylated (right; −P) and singly phosphorylated (left; +P). All other conditions leading to inactivation of Cdc28 activity give a similar result, with no significant change detected (J. Hadwiger and S. Reed, in prep.).

Inactivation of Cdc28 protein kinase activity correlates with loss of a high-molecular-weight complex

Since the Cdc28 protein kinase coprecipitates with a 40-kD polypeptide that can serve as a substrate in vitro, the nature of intracellular associations with other proteins was investigated. Extracts were fractionated by gel filtration to identify different size classes of Cdc28 complexes. Figure 5A shows a typical profile of Cdc28 immunological activity when extracts from asynchronous cultures are subjected to this analysis. Two size classes of Cdc28 protein are apparent, one at the expected free monomer molecular weight of 30–40 kD and another at 130–150 kD, containing approximately 10–20% of the

	Nocodazole	Hydroxyurea	*cdc28-4*	Stationary	*cdc35*	α Factor
Nocodazole	−	−	+	++	++	++
Hydroxyurea	−	−	+	++	++	++
cdc28-4	+	+	−	−	−	−
Stationary	++	++	−	−	−	−
cdc35	++	++	−	−	−	−
α Factor	++	++	−	−	−	−

Figure 3 In vitro complementation results of Cdc28 protein kinase assays of pairwise mixtures of lysates are summarized. (−) Indicates no signal; (+) indicates a signal at the wild-type level for asynchronous cells; (++) indicates a signal significantly above the wild-type asynchronous level. Note that two distinct in vitro complementation groups exist.

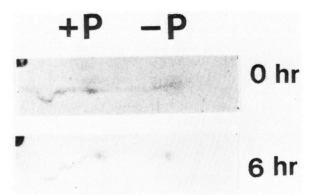

Figure 4 Two-dimensional gel analysis of Cdc28 protein from cells responding to mating pheromone. Lysates from cultures of strain 4204-15-3 were prepared prior to the addition of α-factor (500 ng/ml) and after 6 hr at 23°C and subjected to two-dimensional gel analysis as described in Materials and Methods. Cdc28 protein as detected by immunoblotting resolves primarily into two species, one of which is unphosphorylated (−P) and one of which contains a single phosphoryl group (+P). Several minor more acidic species are obscured because they comigrate with major yeast proteins. Note that the ratio of phosphorylated to unphosphorylated species does not change after 6 hr of treatment with α factor. By this time virtually all of the cells are unbudded and have gone through the morphogenetic transitions associated with the mating pheromone response (data not shown).

total. When each of the two peaks is pooled, immunoprecipitated, and assayed for Cdc28 protein kinase activity, only the high-molecular-weight pool is active. Thus, the majority of Cdc28 protein in cell lysates is in an inactive monomeric form, and activation, at least with respect to the criteria of the immune complex assay, depends on assembly of a complex. Further analysis of the high-molecular-weight species suggests that it is stable to a large number of chromatographic procedures, showing little, if any, dissociation, and that the 40-kD substrate is included in the complex (C. Wittenberg and S. Reed, in prep.).

Extracts were then prepared from cultures subjected to treatments known to result in loss of Cdc28 protein kinase activity and analyzed by gel filtration. The results are summarized in Figure 5, B–D. Treatment with hydroxyurea, shown to produce a cell-cycle-specific loss of activity that can be reconstituted, did not lead to loss of the high-molecular-weight Cdc28 complex (Fig. 5B). In fact, under conditions of synchronization using hydroxyurea, the fraction of Cdc28 protein in a high-molecular-weight form appears to increase (Fig. 5B). However, starvation and treatment with mating pheromone each lead to loss of the high-molecular-weight complex (Fig. 5, C and D, respectively). Thus, regulation of Cdc28 protein kinase activity may be at the level of assembly of the active complex.

Evidence for a positive regulatory factor

The observation that only a minority of the Cdc28 protein is in an active form suggests that a factor required for activity may be limiting. This idea is supported by the observation that engineered intracellular overproduction

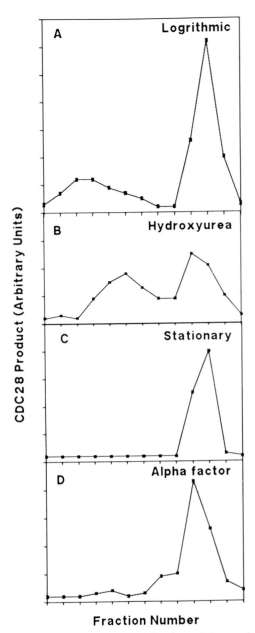

Fraction Number

Figure 5 Analysis of Cdc28 high-molecular-weight complexes. Lysates of yeast cultures from different growth conditions were subjected to Superose 12 gel filtration FPLC. The order of fraction collection is from left to right. (A) Cells in logarithmic growth; (B) cells synchronized using hydroxyurea; (C) cells in stationary phase; (D) cells synchronized using the mating pheromone α factor. The high-molecular-weight peaks seen in A and B have been calibrated using molecular weight standards to correspond to 130–150 kD, whereas the low-molecular-weight peaks seen in all samples correspond to 30–40 kD, the Cdc28 monomer size.

of the Cdc28 protein does not result in a significant increase in Cdc28 protein kinase activity (M. Mendenhall and S. Reed, unpubl.). The behavior of recently isolated *CDC28* mutants also supports a positive regulatory motif. In vitro mutagenesis of a plasmid-borne chimeric gene composed of the regulable but highly active *GAL1* promoter (Johnston and Davis 1984) and the *CDC28* coding region yielded alleles that were lethal when overexpressed in a *CDC28* wild-type strain (M. Mendenhall et al., in prep.). Interestingly, the phenotype conferred was that previously associated with loss of *CDC28* function, as typified by conditional temperature-sensitive alleles (Fig. 6B). Cells, upon a nutritional shift to galactose, the inducer of the *GAL1* promoter, completed current cell cycles but arrested in G₁. The G₁ arrest phenotype was reversed when the wild-type *CDC28* allele was concomitantly overexpressed with the dominant lethal allele. This observation, along with the finding that the mutant-encoded protein has no intrinsic protein kinase activity (M. Mendenhall et al., in prep.), suggests that the dominant loss of function phenotype occurs as a result of competition for a limiting positive factor. Such a limiting factor would be strategically situated to receive and convey information from upstream in the proposed regulatory cascades involving Cdc28 activity.

Discussion

Interpretation of the experiments reported here remains somewhat ambiguous since little is known about the 40-kD polypeptide on which the protein kinase assay relies, except that it has a basic isoelectric point and most likely is complexed to the Cdc28 protein in vivo. As of yet, we cannot conclude whether p40 is an important biological substrate. On the other hand, the overwhelming correlation of Cdc28 protein kinase activity on p40 with the growth state of cells and expectations based on the genetics of *CDC28* suggest that the assay is pertinent to the regulatory state of the Cdc28 protein kinase.

The identity of the exchangeable factor that promotes reconstitution of inactive complexes from non-G₁ cells remains to be established. A good circumstantial case can be made for p40, the 40-kD substrate in its unphosphorylated state, being this factor. The best sources of exchangeable factor are cells in which Cdc28

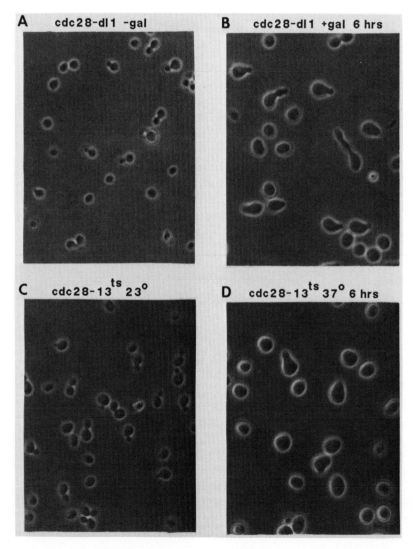

Figure 6 Comparison of *CDC28*^dl and *cdc28*^ts mutants. (*A*) and (*B*) are phase contrast micrographs of J16D(*CDC28-dl1*.int) in neutral (glycerol ethanol) medium and after 6 hr of induction initiated by the addition of galactose, respectively. Note that the cells have become unbudded, significantly larger, and assumed the shmoo morphology characteristic of many G₁ arrest mutants as well as cells responding to mating pheromone. For comparison, the *cdc28*^ts strain D13 (bearing the allele *cdc28-13*) is shown in *C* and *D* at permissive temperature and after 6 hr at restrictive temperature, respectively.

protein kinase is inactive, a situation that would lead to the accumulation of unphosphorylated substrate. The cells deficient in exchangeable factor are those that have traversed G_1, and presumably have phosphorylated all available substrate molecules. The decline in complex activity observed as cells progress through G_1 (Mendenhall et al. 1987) is consistent with this concept. If one makes the assumption, not yet proven, that p40 is the relevant biological substrate and that after the G_1 to S transition all of p40 has been phosphorylated, based on the assays described, then the model shown in Figure 7 accommodates most of the experimental and biological observations to date. Key features of the model are the fact that the regulatory system must be "reset" following mitosis by regenerating unphosphorylated p40 and the fact that all known environmental signals that control cell division can operate, in principle, by regulating Cdc28 protein kinase activity. The in vitro studies described support such an integrational role for the Cdc28 protein kinase.

The basis for control of Cdc28 protein kinase activity remains to be established. Our results are in conflict with those reported for the homologous protein kinase, Cdc2, in the distantly related fungus *S. pombe*. Simanis and Nurse (1986) report a correlation with dephosphorylation of the Cdc2 protein kinase and loss of activity upon starvation. We observe no dephosphoryla-

tion of the Cdc28 protein kinase. On the other hand, phosphorylation of the Cdc2 protein kinase is assayed using ^{32}P incorporation followed by immunoprecipitation rather than by immunoblotting two-dimensional gels of whole cell lysates, possibly accounting for the differences observed. In addition, the assays used to measure activity are different in that the Cdc2 assay depends on the exogenous substrate casein, with no endogenous activity detected (Simanis and Nurse 1986), whereas the Cdc28 protein kinase is not active on casein but has an endogenous activity. Clearly the in vitro behavior of these systems is different. It remains to be determined whether these dissimilarities are superficial or whether they reflect fundamental regulatory differences. Our data are consistent with a positive regulatory subunit being the mediator of activity rather than modification of the Cdc28 polypeptide itself. Both genetic and biochemical means are being utilized to identify this protein and the gene that encodes it.

Acknowledgments

This work was supported by National Institutes of Health grants GM-28005 and GM-38328 and National Science Foundation grant PCM-84-02344 to S.I.R. S.I.R. also acknowledges the support provided by American Cancer Society Faculty Research Award FRA-248. M.D.M. is a fellow of the Jane Coffin Childs Memorial Fund for Medical Research.

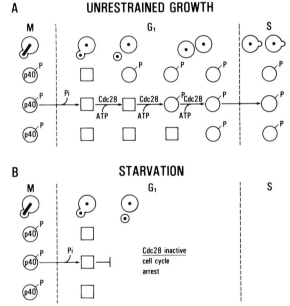

Figure 7 Hypothetical model describing control of passage through G_1 by Cdc28 phosphorylation of p40. In growing cells, the substrate p40 is found in either a phosphorylated ($\bigcirc$) or an unphosphorylated ($\square$) form. p40 is specifically dephosphorylated at mitosis and is then rephosphorylated by the Cdc28 protein kinase. DNA synthesis is initiated only when p40 is completely converted to the phosphorylated form. Under normal growth conditions, the Cdc28 protein kinase is constitutively active, but it is inactivated when the cell is exposed to mating pheromone or starved for essential nutrients. Under the latter conditions, p40 cannot be phosphorylated and the cell remains in G_1.

References

Breter, H.-J., J. Ferguson, T.A. Peterson, and S.I. Reed. 1983. The isolation and transcriptional characterization of three genes which function at start, the controlling event of the *S. cerevisiae* cell division cycle: *CDC36*, *CDC37* and *CDC39*. *Mol. Cell. Biol.* **3**: 881.

Bücking-Throm, E., W. Duntze, L.H. Hartwell, and T.R. Manney. 1973. Reversible arrest of haploid yeast cells at the initiation of DNA synthesis by a diffusible sex factor. *Exp. Cell Res.* **76**: 99.

Elliott, S.C. and C.S. McLaughlin. 1978. Rate of macromolecular synthesis through the cell cycle of the yeast *Saccharomyces cerevisiae*. *Proc. Natl. Acad. Sci.* **75**: 4384.

Ferguson, J., J.-Y. Ho, T.A. Peterson, and S.I. Reed. 1986. Nucleotide sequence of the yeast cell division cycle start genes *CDC28*, *CDC36*, *CDC37*, and *CDC39*, and structural analysis of the predicted products. *Nucleic Acids Res.* **14**: 6681.

Green, N., H. Alexander, A. Olson, A. Alexander., T.M. Shinnick, J.G. Sutcliffe, and R.A. Lerner. 1982. Immunogenic structure of the influenza virus hemagglutinin. *Cell* **28**: 477.

Hartwell, L.H. 1976. Sequential function of gene products relative to DNA synthesis in the yeast cell cycle. *J. Mol. Biol.* **104**: 803.

Hartwell, L.H., J. Culotti, J.R. Pringle, and B.J. Reid. 1974. Genetic control of the cell division cycle in yeast. *Science* **183**: 46.

Jenness, D.D., A.C. Burkholder, and L.H. Hartwell. 1983. Binding of α-factor pheromone to yeast *a* cells: Chemical and genetic evidence for an α-factor receptor. *Cell* **35**:521.

Johnston, M. and R.W. Davis. 1984. Sequences that regulate the divergent *GAL1-GAL10* promoter in *Saccharomyces cerevisiae*. *Mol. Cell. Biol.* **4**: 1440.

Lörincz, A.T. and S.I. Reed. 1984. Primary structure homology between the product of yeast division control gene *CDC28* and vertebrate oncogenes. *Nature* **307:** 183.

Lörincz, A.T., M.J. Miller, N. Xuong, and E.P Geiduschek. 1982. Identification of proteins whose synthesis is modulated during the cell cycle of *Saccharomyces cerevisiae. Mol. Cell. Biol.* **2:** 1532.

Matsumoto, K., I. Uno, and T. Ishikawa. 1983. Control of cell division in *Saccharomyces cerevisiae.* Mutants defective in adenylate cyclase and cAMP-dependent protein kinase. *Exp. Cell Res.* **141:** 151.

Mendenhall, M.D., C.A. Jones, and S.I. Reed. 1987. Dual regulation of the yeast Cdc28-p40 protein kinase complex: Cell cycle, pheromone, and nutrient limitation effects. *Cell* **50:** 927.

Nasmyth, K.A. and S.I. Reed. 1980. Isolation of genes by complementation in yeast: Molecular cloning of a cell-cycle gene. *Proc. Natl. Acad. Sci.* **77:** 2119.

O'Farrell, P.Z., H.M. Goodman, and P.H. O'Farrell. 1977. High resolution two dimensional electrophoresis of basic as well as acidic proteins. *Cell* **12:** 1133.

Pillus, L. and F. Solomon. 1986. Components of microtubular structures in *Saccharomyces cerevisiae. Proc. Natl. Acad. Sci.* **83:** 2468.

Pringle, J.R. and L.H. Hartwell. 1981. The *Saccharomyces cerevisiae* cell cycle. In *The molecular biology of the yeast* Saccharomyces: *Life cycle and inheritance* (ed. J.N. Strathern et al.), p.97. Cold Spring Harbor Laboratory, Cold Spring Harbor, New York.

Reed, S.I. 1980. The selection of *S. cerevisiae* mutants defective in the start event of cell division. *Genetics* **95:** 561.

———. 1982. Preparation of product-specific antisera by gene fusion: Antibodies specific for the product of the yeast cell cycle gene *CDC28. Gene* **20:** 253.

Reed, S.I., J. Ferguson, and J.C. Groppe. 1982. Preliminary

characterization of the transcriptional and translational products of the *Saccharomyces cerevisiae* cell division cycle gene *CDC28. Mol. Cell. Biol.* **2:** 412.

Reed, S.I., J.A. Hadwiger, and A.T. Lörincz. 1985. Protein kinase activity associated with the product of the yeast cell division cycle gene *CDC28. Proc. Natl. Acad. Sci.* **82:** 4055.

Simanis, V. and P. Nurse. 1986. The cell cycle control gene cdc2$^+$ of fission yeast encodes a protein kinase potentially regulated by phosphorylation. *Cell* **45:** 261.

Slater, M.L. 1973. Effect of reversible inhibition of deoxyribonucleic acid synthesis on the yeast cell cycle. *J. Bacteriol.* **113:** 263.

Thomas, J.H., N.F. Neff, and D. Botstein. 1985. Isolation and characterization of mutations in the β-tubulin gene of *Saccharomyces cerevisiae. Genetics* **112:** 715.

Thorner, J. 1981. Pheromonal control of development in *Saccharomyces cerevisiae.* In *Molecular biology of the yeast* Saccharomyces: *Life cycle and inheritance* (ed. J.N. Strathern et al.), p.143. Cold Spring Harbor Laboratory, Cold Spring Harbor, New York.

Toda, T., S. Cameron, P. Sass, M. Zoller, and M. Wigler. 1987. Three different genes in *S. cerevisiae* encode the catalytic subunits of the cAMP-dependent protein kinase. *Cell* **50:** 277.

Tripp, M.L., R. Pinon, J. Meisenhelder, and T. Hunter. 1986. Identification of phosphoproteins correlated with proliferation and cell cycle arrest in *Saccharomyces cerevisiae*: Positive and negative regulation by cAMP-dependent protein kinase. *Proc. Natl. Acad. Sci.* **83:** 5973.

Wittenberg, C., S.L. Richardson, and S.I. Reed. 1987. Subcellular localization of a protein kinase required for cell cycle initiation in *Saccharomyces cerevisiae*: Evidence for an association between the *CDC28* gene product and the insoluble cytoplasmic matrix. *J. Cell Biol.* **105:** 1527.

p34 Protein Kinase, a Human Homolog of the Yeast Cell Cycle Control Proteins Encoded by cdc2$^+$ and CDC28

G. Draetta, L. Brizuela, and D. Beach
Cold Spring Harbor Laboratory, Cold Spring Harbor, New York 11724

The cdc2$^+$ gene of *Schizosaccharomyces pombe* plays a central role in cell cycle regulation. It is the only identified cdc gene required for progression through both the G$_1$ and G$_2$ phases of the cell cycle, and it regulates the rate of entry into both S phase and nuclear division. The gene product of cdc2$^+$ (p34^{cdc2}) is 62% homologous to the product of the *CDC28* gene of *Saccharomyces cerevisiae* (p36^{CDC28}). Both have protein kinase activity in vitro.

We have identified (Draetta et al. 1987) a homologous protein in human cells. Monoclonal and polyclonal antibodies raised against the p34^{cdc2} protein recognize a 34-kD protein from human cells. Peptide mapping of p34^{cdc2}, p36^{CDC28}, and human p34 with N-chlorosuccinimide revealed complete conservation of four tryptophan residues among the three proteins. p34 is present in multiple phosphorylated forms within the cell. Using an antiserum raised against a seven-amino-acid peptide derived from the carboxyl terminus of the predicted human p34 sequence, we show the specific phosphorylation of a 62-kD band present in immunoprecipitates from human cells. In cells synchronized by centrifugal elutriation, the levels of p34 are constant throughout the cell cycle phases, whereas the 62-kD band phosphorylation peaks in fractions enriched in G$_2$/M cells.

Elucidation of the pathways that underlie the control of cell division in eukaryotes is a major objective in efforts to understand abnormal cell proliferation. Much attention has been devoted to the study of the transition from quiescence to active growth (for review, see Bishop 1985). Many growth factors, their receptors, and their oncogenic counterparts have been identified that are capable of inducing cell proliferation and, in some cases, immortalization and transformation. To date, however, little or nothing is known about the ultimate targets of growth factors and oncogenes. Through direct or indirect interaction, cell cycle mechanisms must be activated. Attempts are being made to identify cell cycle control functions in mammalian cells: These involve both isolation of temperature-sensitive mutants defective in cell cycle progression and identification and characterization of gene functions that are induced in specific cell cycle phases (Ferrari and Baserga 1987). However, the interconnection between the pathways of growth control and cell cycle control remain obscure.

The yeasts *S. pombe* and *S. cerevisiae* have been used as model organisms for cell cycle studies (Mitchison 1957; Hartwell 1974; for review, see Hayles and Nurse 1986). A number of genes have been isolated that are needed for cell cycle progression. Among these genes the cdc2$^+$ gene of *S. pombe* and the *CDC28* of *S. cerevisiae* have been characterized in detail because of their role in controlling cell cycle progression. In particular, the cdc2$^+$ gene has been shown to be required at both the G$_1$ and G$_2$ phases of the cell cycle

(Nurse and Bissett 1981) and to act at rate-limiting steps. There exist activated alleles of cdc2 that cause cells to progress through mitosis prematurely (Nurse and Thuriaux 1980). cdc2^{ts} mutant cells arrested in G$_1$ at the restrictive temperature can still undergo sexual conjugation (Nurse and Bissett 1981). Therefore, the cdc2$^+$ gene has been described as a "start" gene. *CDC28*, a start gene of *S. cerevisiae*, is functionally equivalent to the cdc2$^+$ gene. *CDC28* is capable of rescuing temperature-sensitive cdc2 *S. pombe* mutants (Beach et al. 1982), and the cdc2$^+$ gene, after removal of its four introns, can rescue temperature-sensitive cdc28 strains (Booher and Beach 1986).

The cdc2$^+$ and *CDC28* gene products have a molecular weight of 34,000 and share 62% amino acid sequence identity (Hindley and Phear 1984; Lorincz and Reed 1984). Both proteins have been shown to have protein kinase activity in vitro (Reed et al. 1985; Simanis and Nurse 1986), but at present no physiologically relevant substrate(s) has been biochemically identified.

Since *S. cerevisiae* and *S. pombe* are evolutionarily very distantly related, as judged by the sequences of other functionally homologous genes (Russell 1983; Nadin-Davis et al. 1986), the strong homology between the cdc2$^+$ and *CDC28* gene products suggested that a search for a related protein in higher eukaryotes might be productive. Using monoclonal antibodies raised against the p34^{cdc2} protein that cross-reacted with the CDC28 gene product, we have identified a human homolog (called p34) of the two yeast proteins (Draetta

259

et al. 1987). The structural similarity between yeast and human p34 was shown by peptide mapping, protein kinase activity, and the association of p34 with p13, the human homolog of the *suc1*⁺ gene product of *S. pombe* (Brizuela et al. 1987). Lee and Nurse (1987), using complementation of a temperature-sensitive defect in the *cdc2* gene of *S. pombe*, have isolated a gene (*cdc2*Hs) from a human cDNA library that rescues the strain at the restrictive temperature and whose translated sequence has approximately 60% amino acid homology with the yeast proteins.

In this paper, we describe an analysis of the p34 protein kinase in an initial attempt to relate its behavior to the cell cycle.

Experimental Procedures

Cell culture
Human diploid fibroblasts (Hs68, ATCC, Rockville, MD) were grown in Dulbecco's modified Eagle's medium (DMEM) supplemented with 10% fetal bovine serum, at 37°C, 5% CO_2. The cells were used at passage 14–18 for all the experiments. HeLa cells were grown in suspension culture in F13 medium supplemented with 5% calf serum.

Centrifugal elutriation of HeLa cells
Two liters of HeLa cells (~4–8 × 10¹⁰ cells) were loaded onto a Beckman elutriator rotor (model JE10X) as described (G. Morris and M. Mathews, in prep.). Eleven fractions were collected. From each fraction, 5 × 10⁶ cells were washed twice with PBS and then processed for either immunoblot or immunoprecipitation.

Flow cytometry using a fluorescence-activated cell sorter, EPICS (Coulter), was performed as described (G. Morris and M. Mathews, in prep.). 1 × 10⁶ cells were analyzed taken from each elutriated fraction and from the starting culture.

Cell labeling
To label proteins, 1–5 × 10⁶ HeLa cells or one 10-cm plate (~50% confluence) of Hs68 cells were used for each experimental point. Cells were incubated for 1–2 hours with 0.1–0.5 mCi Tran ³⁵S-label (ICN) in methionine-free DMEM, or with 0.5–1 mCi ³²P-inorganic phosphate (ICN) in phosphate-free DMEM.

Antibody production and immunochemical assays
The preparation of affinity-purified anti-p34^cdc2 polyclonal antibodies has been described (Draetta et al. 1987). For the anti-p34 carboxy-terminal peptide antibodies, the peptide CDNQIKKM was synthesized according to the sequence of p34 deduced from its cDNA sequence (Lee and Nurse 1987). The cysteine residue was added to the amino terminus to couple the peptide to keyhole limpet hemocyanin according to the procedure described by Green et al. (1982). 100 μg of protein in

complete Freund's adjuvant were injected every 2 weeks until anti-p34 immunoreactivity could be detected by immunoprecipitation.

For preparation of extracts, cells were lysed by the addition of 100 μl of buffer A (PBS, containing 1% Triton-X100, 0.5% deoxycholate, 0.1% SDS, 50 mM NaF, 5 mM EDTA, 1 mM dithiothreitol [DTT]). The following were used as protease inhibitors: phenylmethylsulfonyl fluoride, 50 mg/l; leupeptin, 1 mg/l; soybean trypsin inhibitor, 10 mg/l; aprotinin, 1 mg/l; tosyl phenylalanine chloromethyl ketone, 10 mg/l. After 30 minutes on ice, the cell extracts were centrifuged at 13,000g for 5 minutes. Aliquots were taken for protein quantitation, using the method of Bradford (1976) or radioactivity counting. Equal amounts of precipitable cpm (³²P- or ³⁵S-labeled extracts) or equal amounts of total protein (nonlabeled extracts) were used. Samples were precleared with 40 μl of a 50% protein-A-agarose suspension (Pierce) for 30 minutes at 4°C. Bovine serum albumin was then added to 1% (w/v) final concentration and 3–10 μl of antipeptide serum or 25 μg of affinity-purified antibodies were added. After a 1-hour incubation at 0°C and a 5-minute centrifugation at 13,000g, supernatants were added to Eppendorf tubes containing 40 μl of protein-A-agarose. After incubation on rotator for 20 minutes, pellets were washed three times in buffer A. 30 μl of 2X Laemmli sample buffer (2XLSB) (Laemmli 1970) were then added and the samples boiled for 5 minutes. Samples were run on 7.5–15% gradient SDS-polyacrylamide gel electrophoresis. Gels were stained with Coomassie blue, dried, and autoradiographed.

For protein kinase assays, after the third Buffer-A wash, protein-A agarose pellets were washed once with 50 mM Tris-HCl (pH 7.4), containing 10 mM MgCl₂, 1 mM DTT, 1 μM ATP, 5 μCi[γ-³²P]ATP (NEN, NEG-002A), in the presence or absence of 1 mg/ml casein. After 5 minutes preincubation at 37°C, the reaction was started by addition of the ATP and continued for 5 more minutes. 30 μl of 2X LSB were then added, and samples were boiled as above.

Immunoprecipitates from in vivo ³²P-labeled samples were treated with 5 μg of deoxyribonuclease I (Worthington) and 2.5 μg of boiled ribonuclease A (Sigma) in 20 μl 50 mM Tris-HCl (pH 7.4), 10 mM MgCl₂, for 5 minutes on ice before addition of 2XLSB.

For alkaline phosphatase treatment, pellets were added with 25 μl of 100 mM Tris-HCl (pH 9.5), 5 mM MgCl₂, 100 mM NaCl. 1 μl of a purified alkaline phosphatase preparation (Sigma P0780) was added to each sample. Control and treated samples were incubated for 5 minutes at 37°C. In some samples, 100 mM p-nitrophenyl phosphate (final concentration) was added together with the enzyme, to act as a competitive inhibitor of the protein dephosphorylation.

Transfer of the protein from gels and immunoblotting were performed as described (Towbin et al. 1979; Draetta et al. 1987). ¹²⁵I-labeled protein-A (ICN) was used for detection.

Results and Discussion

Characterization of p34, the human homolog of p34^{cdc2} and p36^{cdc28}

In Figure 1, we show a site-specific peptide mapping of the human p34 compared to p34^{cdc2} of fission yeast and p36^{CDC28} of budding yeast. Using N-chlorosuccinimide (NCS), a chemical agent that can specifically cleave polypeptides at tryptophan residues (Schecter et al. 1976; Lischwe and Sung 1977), we demonstrated (Draetta et al. 1987) that a distinct proteolytic pattern can be obtained upon hydrolysis of the three proteins. Both p34^{cdc2} and p36^{CDC28} have four tryptophan residues, each in a position that is conserved within the sequence of the two proteins (Hindley and Phear 1984; Lorincz and Reed 1984). As seen in the figure, human p34 yields a pattern of partial NCS degradation products that is almost identical to that of p34^{cdc2} and p36^{CDC28}. Therefore, and in consideration of the fact that tryptophan position within homologous proteins tends to be conserved (Potter et al. 1982), we conclude that p34^{cdc2}, p36^{CDC28}, and human p34 have the same number and relative distribution of tryptophan residues. The translated sequence of cdc2Hs (Lee and Nurse 1987) does in fact show the presence of four tryp-

tophans in exactly the same positions as in p34^{cdc2} and p36^{CDC28}. Similarity of molecular weight, immunological cross-reactivity with both mono- and polyclonal antibodies, kinase activity in immunoprecipitates, and physical association with p13, the human homolog of p13^{suc1} of fission yeast (see Draetta et al. 1987) are other independent types of evidence for a structural homology between the three proteins.

We have described the occurrence of different forms of p34 by two-dimensional gel electrophoresis (Draetta et al. 1987). These forms could represent posttranslational modifications of p34 (i.e., phosphorylation). In Figure 2 we present the results of an experiment performed using Hs68 and HeLa cells. In both cell lines by in vivo [^{35}S]methionine labeling and immunoprecipitation with anti-p34^{cdc2} affinity-purified polyclonal antibodies, we could detect a major protein band that exactly migrated on SDS-PAGE with the bacterially synthesized p34^{cdc2} marker. Two additional bands were immunoprecipitated; they both migrated slightly more slowly than the marker. These bands were not due to proteins that cross-react with the affinity-purified antibodies, since they were also immunoprecipitated by an anti-p34 carboxy-terminal peptide polyclonal serum (see Fig. 3), and they were effectively displaced in the presence of excess peptide. Using in vivo ^{32}P-inorganic phosphate labeling of HeLa and Hs68 cells, we found phosphor-

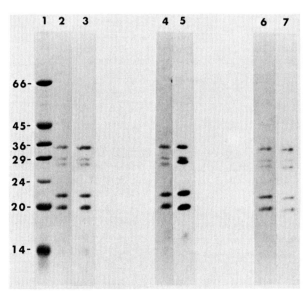

Figure 1 Proteolytic cleavage patterns of p34^{cdc2}, p36^{CDC28}, and human p34. (Lane *1*) Standard markers with molecular masses indicated in kD. (Lanes *2–7*) Proteins cleaved by N-chlorosuccinimide in the presence of urea. (Lane *2*) Coomassie-stained p34^{cdc2}; (lane *3*) ^{35}S-labeled p34^{cdc2}; (lane *4*) Coomassie-stained p34^{cdc2}; (lane *5*) ^{35}S-labeled p36^{CDC28}; (lane *6*) Coomassie-stained p34^{cdc2}; (lane *7*) ^{35}S-labeled human p34. Lanes *2* and *3*, *4* and *5*, and *6* and *7*, respectively, are different visualizations (Coomassie-blue staining or autoradiography) of single gel lanes. In each lane the uppermost band represents undegraded protein and the smallest (20 kD) the entire amino-terminal two-thirds of the polypeptide. The intervening three bands are, in each case, partial cleavage products. (Reprinted, with permission, from Draetta et al. 1987.)

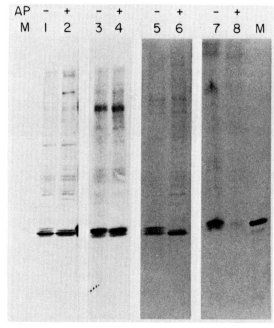

Figure 2 Multiple phosphorylated forms of p34. Immunoprecipitation of [^{35}S]methionine and [^{32}P]phosphate in in vivo labeled Hs68 and HeLa cells were performed as described in Experimental Procedures. Samples were incubated at 37°C for 5 min, in the presence or absence of purified alkaline phosphatase (AP). The marker (M) is [^{35}S]methionine-labeled p34^{cdc2} from *Escherichia coli*. (Lanes *1–4*) HeLa cells; (lanes *5–8*) Hs68 cells. Lanes *1,2,5,* and *6* are ^{35}S-labeled cells, and lanes *3,4,7,* and *8* are from ^{32}P-labeled samples.

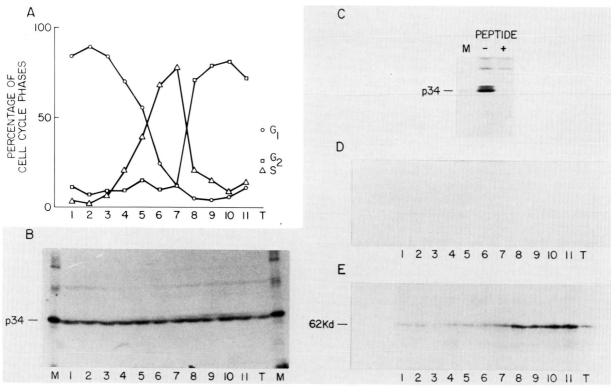

Figure 3 p34 protein kinase during the cell cycle. (Panel *A*) Percentage of the cell cycle phases determined by flow cytometry in the various fractions after centrifugal elutriation of cells. T = cell sample before elutriation. (Panel *B*) Immunoblot with anti-p34 antibodies from cell extracts made at each time point. (M = 200 ng bacterially synthetized p34^{cdc2}). Equal amounts of total protein were loaded per each lane. (Panel *C*) Results from ^{35}S-labeled HeLa cells. Immunoprecipitations performed in the presence of excess peptide show the disappearance of the 34-kD bands. (Panels *D* and *E*) Kinase activity of immunoprecipitates from each time point. Kinase activity was measured as endogenous phosphorylation. Immunoprecipitations were performed using the anti-p34 carboxy-terminal peptide polyclonal serum.

ylated bands of approximately 34 kD by immunoprecipitation with both the anti-p34^{cdc2} (Fig. 2) and anti-peptide antibodies (not shown). In both cases the most prominent phosphorylated band is the slowest migrating on SDS-PAGE.

A treatment with alkaline phosphatase of the labeled immunoprecipitates was therefore performed to confirm that the slower migrating bands occurred as a result of phosphorylation. We found that the upper two bands from the [^{35}S]methionine-labeled immunoprecipitate disappeared or were of decreased intensity, but the lower band stayed intact and even increased in intensity (Fig. 1). A parallel treatment of the ^{32}P-labeled immunocomplex caused the disappearance of the phosphorylated bands. The changes in the band profile were caused by phosphatase treatment and not by some contaminating proteolytic activity, since p34 dephosphorylation was inhibited by the addition of 100 mM *p*-nitrophenyl phosphate (data not shown).

Cell cycle regulation of p34 kinase activity
Since the p34 protein is a homolog of the cell cycle control proteins p34^{cdc2} and p36^{CDC28}, it was of interest to establish whether the levels of the protein in human cells might fluctuate during the cycle. As a method of

cell synchronization, centrifugal elutriation was chosen. In Figure 3 we present the results of such an experiment. The degree of synchrony was assessed by FACS analysis and expressed as percentage of cell cycle phases for each fraction (panel A). Cell populations at ~ 90% in G$_1$, 80% in S, and 80% in G$_2$/M were obtained. An immunoblot of extracts from the different cell fractions revealed that the total level of p34 did not change in the different cell cycle phases (panel B).

As in the case of p34^{cdc2} and p36^{CDC28}, p34 from human cells has kinase activity in immunoprecipitates (Draetta et al. 1987). We found that immunocomplexes of human p34 have the ability to phosphorylate casein in vitro. To substantiate this finding, a newly developed anti-p34 carboxy-terminal peptide antibody was used to confirm that the kinase activity measured in immunoprecipitates is due to p34 and not to a contaminating kinase recognized by the affinity-purified polyclonal antibodies. In panel C the specific displacement of the p34 band from a ^{35}S-labeled immunoprecipitate from HeLa cells is illustrated.

Cell fractions taken before and throughout the elutriation were immunoprecipitated with anti-p34 carboxy-terminal peptide polyclonal serum and incubated with 1 μM [γ-^{32}P]ATP for 5 minutes at 37°C. The phosphorylation of a 62-kD band was evident. This band was phosphorylated more heavily in the immunoprecipitates from fractions enriched in G_2/M cells (see panel E). In each fraction, no phosphorylation of a 62-kD band was observed following addition of excess free peptide to the immunoprecipitation reactions (panel D). In our experimental conditions there is no evidence of auto-phosphorylating activity of the p34 protein.

The identification in mammalian cells of p34, a protein homologous to the p34^{cdc2} and p36^{CDC28} of yeast, might bring some insight in the understanding of cell cycle control in higher eukaryotes. We have demonstrated that p34 exists in multiple phosphorylated forms. We have addressed the question of cell cycle regulation of the protein kinase. In actively growing cells synchronized by centrifugal elutriation, the total levels of p34 are constant, but the ability of p34 to phosphorylate a 62-kD protein peaks in the G_2/M-enriched fractions. We are presently investigating the possibility that changes in the state of phosphorylation of p34 might be related to this phenomenon.

Acknowledgments

Monika Stein is thanked for her valuable technical assistance. We thank Linda Rodgers for performing FACS analysis and Georgia Binns for the peptide synthesis. Gilbert Morris is thanked for his suggestions on the use of the elutriation centrifuge.

References

Beach, D.H., B. Durkacz, and P.M. Nurse. 1982. Functionally homologous cell cycle control genes in budding and fission yeast. *Nature* **300**: 706.

Bishop, J.M. 1985. Viral oncogenes. *Cell* **42**: 23.

Booher, R. and D.H. Beach. 1986. Site-specific mutagenesis of *cdc2*+, a cell cycle control gene of the fission yeast *Schizosaccharomyces pombe*. *Mol. Cell. Biol.* **6**: 3523.

Bradford, M.M. 1976. A rapid and sensitive method for the quantitation of microgram quantities of protein utilizing the principle of protein-dye binding. *Anal. Biochem.* **72**: 248.

Brizuela, L., G. Draetta, and D. Beach. 1987. p13^{suc1} acts in the fisson yeast cell division cycle as a component of the p34^{cdc2} protein kinase. *EMBO J.* **6**: 3507.

Draetta, G., L. Brizuela, J. Potashkin, and D. Beach. 1987. Identification of p34 and p13, human homologs of the cell cycle regulators of fission yeast encoded by *cdc2*+ and *suc1*+. *Cell* **50**: 319.

Ferrari, S. and R. Baserga. 1987. Oncogenes and cell cycle genes. *Bioessays* **7**: 9.

Green, N., H. Alexander, A. Olson, S. Alexander, J.M. Shinnick, J.G. Sutcliffe, and R.A. Lerner. 1982. Immunogenic structure of the influenza virus hemagglutinin. *Cell* **28**: 477.

Hartwell, L.H. 1974. *Saccharomyces cerevisiae* cell cycle. *Bacteriol. Rev.* **38**: 164.

Hayles, J. and P. Nurse. 1986. Cell cycle regulation in yeast. *J. Cell Sci.* **4**: 155.

Hindley, J. and G.A. Phear. 1984. Sequence of the cell division gene *cdc2* from *Schizosaccharomyces pombe*; patterns of splicing and homology to protein kinases. *Gene* **31**: 129.

Laemmli, U.K. 1970. Cleavage of the structural proteins of the head of bacteriophage T4. *Nature* **227**: 680.

Lee, M. and P. Nurse. 1987. Complementation used to clone a human homologue of the fission yeast cell cycle control gene *cdc2*+. *Nature* **327**: 31.

Lischwe, M.A. and M.A. Sung. 1977. Use of *N*-chlorosuccinimide/urea for the selective cleavage of tryptophenyl peptide bonds in proteins. *J. Biol. Chem.* **152**: 4976.

Lorincz, A.T. and S.I. Reed. 1984. Primary structure homology between the product of yeast cell division control gene CDC28 and vertebrate oncogenes. *Nature* **307**: 183.

Mitchison, J.M. 1957. The growth of single cells. I. *Schizosaccharomyces pombe*. *Exp. Cell Res.* **13**: 244.

Nadin-Davis, S.A., R.C.A. Yang, S.A. Narang, and A. Nasim. 1986. The cloning and characterization of a *ras* gene from *Schizosaccharomyces pombe*. *J. Mol. Evol.* **23**: 41.

Nurse, P.M. and Y. Bissett. 1981. Gene required in G1 for commitment to cell cycle and in G2 for control of mitosis in fission yeast. *Nature* **292**: 558.

Nurse, P. and P. Thuriaux. 1980. Regulatory genes controlling mitosis in the fission yeast *Schizosaccharomyces pombe*. *Genetics* **96**: 627.

Potter, M., J.B. Newell, S. Rudikoff, and E. Haber. 1982. Classification of the mouse VK groups based on the partial amino acid sequence to the first invariant tryptophan: Impact of the 14 new sequences from IgG myeloma proteins. *Mol. Immunol.* **19**: 1619.

Reed, S.I., J.A. Hadwiger, and A. Lorincz. 1985. Protein kinase activity associated with the product of the yeast cell cycle gene CDC28. *Proc. Natl. Acad. Sci.* **82**: 4055.

Russell, P.R. 1983. Evolutionary divergence of the mRNA transcription initiation mechanism in yeast. *Nature* **301**: 167.

Schecter, Y., A. Patchornik, and Y. Burstein. 1976. Selective chemical cleavage of tryptophenyl peptide bonds by oxidative chlorination with *N*-chlorosuccinimide. *Biochemistry* **15**: 5071.

Simanis, V. and P.M. Nurse. 1986. The cell cycle control gene *cdc2*+ of yeast encodes a protein kinase potentially regulated by phosphorylation. *Cell* **45**: 261.

Towbin, H., T. Staehelin, and J. Gordon. 1979. Electrophoretic transfer of proteins from polyacrylamide gels to nitrocellulose sheets: Procedure and some applications. *Proc. Natl. Acad. Sci.* **76**: 4350.

Factors Regulating Histone Gene Transcription during the Cell Cycle

N. Heintz

Howard Hughes Medical Institute, The Rockefeller University, New York, New York 10021

Upon entry into the S phase of the eukaryotic cell cycle, there is a rapid and coordinate induction in the transcription of genes encoding each of the histone subtypes. Detailed analysis of both DNA sequences and protein molecules important for the expression of the histone H4, H2b, and H1 genes has revealed that the elements controlling expression of each of these histone gene subtypes are distinct. Identification of the histone H2b subtype-specific consensus element as the single sequence necessary and sufficient for its transcriptional activation upon entry into S phase and identification of a 90-kD transcription factor whose differential activity during the cell cycle is dependent on this regulatory element suggest a simple model for the coordinate regulation of histone gene expression during the cell cycle.

The transition from the G_1 to the S phase of the eukaryotic cell cycle ultimately results in the activation of chromosomal DNA synthesis and chromatin replication. It is now well established that the expression of all five subtypes of histone genes is increased coincidentally with the increased rate of cellular DNA synthesis. This tight coupling of the rates of histone protein synthesis and DNA synthesis (see Bonner et al., this volume) suggests that the cascade of events leading to entry into the S phase may be revealed by the detailed biochemical analysis of the molecular mechanisms for activation of either of these processes. Furthermore, it is quite probable that the molecular signals that result in the activation of these mechanisms, and perhaps some of their components, may be identical. Therefore, the approach we have taken toward an understanding of the transition from the G_1 to the S phase of the mammalian cell cycle is to define the molecular mechanisms regulating S-phase-specific histone gene expression.

The experiments I discuss herein focus on two related questions dealing with the induction of replication variant histone gene transcription upon entry into S phase. First, what are the DNA sequences and protein factors involved in the expression of the individual histone gene subtypes? Second, how is the coordinate activation of all of the five histone gene subtypes achieved? Although in-depth answers to these queries must await further analysis, our present knowledge of histone H4, H2b, and H1 transcription suggests a very useful model for further consideration of these issues.

Results and Discussion

In the past several years, in vitro (Heintz and Roeder 1984; Hanly et al. 1985; Dailey et al. 1986; Sive et al. 1986) and in vivo studies (Artishevsky et al. 1984; Capasso and Heintz 1985; Seiler-Tuyns and Paterson 1987) have established that histone gene transcription is regulated by *trans*-acting factors that act through promoter proximal DNA sequences. In particular, the detailed in vitro analysis of the histone H4 and H2b promoters first revealed the complexity and distinct properties of mammalian histone gene promoters. Thus, maximal transcription of each of these genes in vitro requires multiple promoter proximal DNA sequence elements. In no case, however, did these studies pinpoint the precise sequence elements responsible for the S phase induction of histone gene transcription. To further consider this issue, and as a focus for the present discussion of histone gene regulation, a schematic representation of the histone H4, H2b, and H1 promoters is given in Figure 1.

Promoter sequences and protein factors important for histone H4 transcription

Our initial study of DNA sequences important for in vitro transcription of a human histone H4 gene (Hanly et al. 1985) has recently been considerably refined by in vitro and in vivo analysis of additional mutations within the H4 promoter. To date, at least three upstream sequence elements have been demonstrated to be important for histone H4 transcription. The most distal of these elements is located between 82 and 105 bp upstream of the H4 cap site and is the binding site for the transcription factor H4tf-1 (Dailey et al. 1986). 5' deletion mutants that remove this site or point mutations that destroy H4tf-1 binding are at least twofold less active both in vivo and in vitro. This sequence is conserved at approximately the same position in four of the six human histone H4 genes we have sequenced in the laboratory. A second sequence element that has been demonstrated to function in H4 transcription is defined by a cluster of point mutations introduced into the H4 promoter at positions −84 to −86. These mutations also cause an approximate twofold drop in transcription in vitro and in vivo. However, changes in this region of the promoter simultaneously alter sequences closely matching the consensus elements for either the SP-1 (Dynan and

265

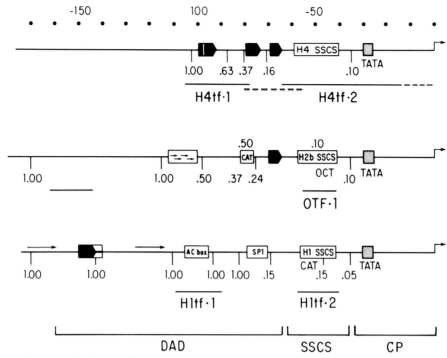

Figure 1 Schematic diagram of the human histone H4, H2b, and H1 promoters. General domain structure of the three promoters is indicated as follows: (DAD) distal activating domain; (SSCS) subtype-specific consensus domain; (CP) core promoter. Abbreviated names of selected protein factors interacting with these domains are indicated below each promoter diagram and are explained in the text.

Tjian 1983) or NFκB (Sen and Baltimore 1986). This region of the H4 promoter is not highly conserved, and the involvement of these general factors in S-phase-specific expression of the H4 gene is probably less likely. The third element that we believe to be important for H4 gene transcription is extremely highly conserved in position, orientation, and DNA sequence. It comprises the binding site for H4tf-2 between positions −35 and −65 in the promoter. This has been termed the subtype-specific consensus sequence because of its high conservation in histone H4 genes from a variety of organisms (see Wells 1986). Neither in vitro nor in vivo transient expression assays have convincingly demonstrated a function for this sequence. However, this region of a *Xenopus laevis* H4 promoter is known to function as a positive element for expression in oocyte injection experiments (Clerc et al. 1983). As discussed below, we believe that our failure to observe function of this element in mammalian systems results from the nature of the assays so far employed, and that the biological activity of this element will become apparent upon further experimentation. Although evidence indicating that the H4 promoter is required for transcriptional regulation upon entry into S phase in stably transfected cell lines has been presented (Capasso and Heintz 1985; Seiler-Tuyns and Paterson 1987), it remains to be proven which (if any) of these events is directly responsible for cell cycle regulation in vivo.

Our initial study of the factors interacting with the H4 promoter elements (Dailey et al. 1986) resulted in the identification of the H4tf-1 and H4tf-2 activities, and

showed that neither factor can efficiently bind to any of the other histone gene subtypes. Subsequent biochemical studies have yielded several interesting facts concerning these proteins. The first interesting point to be made concerns the relative abundance of these proteins in the cell. It is quite clear from quantitative DNA-binding assays that the H4tf-1 factor, which binds to the distal promoter element, is very much more abundant than the H4tf-2 protein. The very limiting amounts of the H4tf-2 in the cell, or in extracts prepared from isolated nuclei, provide a reasonable explanation for the difficulty of detecting this protein's activity in transient expression assays in vivo or in transcription experiments in vitro. Since each of these assays is done in DNA excess, the stoichiometry of the various factors important for expression of the gene becomes the critical issue for detection of their independent activity. Thus, the very great excess of the transcription factors interacting with the two distal elements in the H4 promoter relative to H4tf-2, which interacts with the subtype-specific consensus element, suggests that most of the molecules transcribed in these assays do not contain bound H4tf-2. Therefore, we cannot expect to detect changes in transcription due to mutations in the H4tf-2 binding site. In the normal cell, however, all of the transcription factors are in excess over the small number of histone H4 genes, and we expect that under these conditions H4tf-2 plays a critical role in transcription.

During the course of purification of the H4tf-1 and H4tf-2 factors, it became evident that the DNA-binding activity of each of these proteins is sensitive to dialysis against EDTA-containing buffers. Further studies of this phenomenon (Dailey et al. 1987) led to the discovery that both of these factors require bound metal ions for DNA binding and transcription activity. Thus, inactivation of these proteins by treatment with 1,10 phenanthroline could be reversed by excess Zn^{++}. In the case of H4tf-2, activity could also be restored by excess Fe^{++}. This last result is quite provocative because cells deprived of Fe^{++} arrest in S phase (Trowbridge and Lopez 1982). The metal dependence of H4tf-1 and H4tf-2 is reminiscent of the properties of the 5S gene-specific RNA polymerase III transcription factor TFIIIA, and suggests that these proteins may contain the "zinc finger" DNA-binding motif first noted in that molecule (Miller et al. 1985).

Identification of the histone H2b cell cycle specific regulatory sequence and transcription factor

Analysis of a variety of 5' deletion, substitution, and point mutations in the H2b promoter first indicated that this histone gene also possesses a complex promoter (Sive et al. 1986). In this case, however, all of the H2b upstream sequence elements were active in vitro, including the subtype-specific consensus sequence. To identify which of these elements is responsible for the S phase induction of histone H2b transcription, each of these mutant promoters was fused to the bacterial chloramphenicol acetyltransferase gene and assayed for its transcriptional phenotype in vivo (LaBella et al. 1988). The general protocol for these experiments was to cotransfect the histone H2b fusion genes and an unregulated internal control gene into human cultured cells, to synchronize the cells using a single aphidicolin block, and to measure the expression of fusion mRNAs pre-S phase and after release into S phase by nuclease S1 mapping using a single DNA probe. In this way, we could accurately quantitate both the level of expression and the S phase induction of each construct relative to the unchanging level of expression of the cotransfected internal control gene. The results of these experiments can be summarized as follows. Deletion of any sequences upstream of the subtype-specific consensus sequence has no effect on the inducibility of the gene upon entry into S phase, but can severely reduce the absolute level of transcription. Thus, deletion of sequences upstream of -77 results in only 5% of the wild-type level of expression, but this residual transcription is still induced approximately fivefold upon entry into S phase. Point mutations that inactivate the H2b subtype-specific consensus element retain wild-type levels of expression prior to S phase, but are not induced after release into S phase. These results demonstrate that the subtype-specific consensus element is responsible for transcriptional regulation of the H2b gene upon entry into S phase. They further suggest that the upstream sequence elements in this promoter act independently to increase the rate of transcription initiation.

DNA-binding studies by Sive and Roeder (1987) employed probes prepared from the H2b promoter to detect a protein in crude nuclear extracts from unsynchronized HeLa cells that specifically interacts with this region of the H2b promoter. We have recently purified and characterized this activity (Fletcher et al. 1987) and identified it as a 90-kD protein (OTF-1) that is quite abundant in HeLa cells. The purified factor can stimulate H2b transcription greater than 20-fold when reconstituted with general transcription initiation factors in an H2b subtype-specific manner. In vitro transcription experiments in extracts from synchronized HeLa cells demonstrate that OTF-1 is preferentially active for histone H2b transcription in S phase. Our in vitro analysis, therefore, confirms the in vivo result cited above and strongly argues that this protein is the transcriptional regulator for S phase induction of H2b transcription. Our present efforts involve the use of specific antibodies to characterize the mechanism for activation of this factor at the G_1/S phase boundary of the cell cycle.

Promoter sequences and protein factors involved in histone H1 transcription

As is evident from Figure 1, the general structure of the histone H1 promoter is quite similar to those for H4 and H2b. Thus, the H1 promoter contains a subtype-specific consensus element immediately upstream of the TATA box that is very highly conserved in sequence, position, and orientation. Mutations within this region of the H1 promoter cause an approximately twofold decrease in the in vitro transcription efficiency, and a greater than fivefold drop in expression in transient assays in vivo. However, interpretation of these results is complicated by the fact that a CCAAT box is present within the very highly conserved 17-bp sequence in the H1 promoter. Since it seems quite likely that there are several proteins within HeLa cells that can interact with this core sequence, we do not know which of these is responsible for the activity we see in these assays, and whether that activity is appropriate to normal histone H1 gene expression and cell cycle regulation. The fact that the sequences flanking the CCAAT homology in the H1 promoter are very highly conserved, whereas those flanking CCAAT box in histone H2b genes, thymidine kinase genes, and a variety of other cellular genes are not, supports the idea that an H1-specific protein may exist. Present data from these types of in vivo and in vitro assays are not, therefore, sufficient to definitively identify the role of this element in histone H1 transcription.

Two additional transcription elements are found distal to the subtype-specific element described above. The first of these is a factor SP1 site that, as discussed above for the H4 gene, is essential for efficient transcription in vivo and in vitro but probably does not play a regulatory role in this promoter. A second very highly conserved histone H1-specific sequence is present approximately 90 nucleotides upstream of the H1 cap site. This sequence was first noted by Coles and Wells (1985) and is found in all histone H1 promoters so far analyzed from higher eukaryotes. This very strong conservation suggests that this site is important for histone H1 function, but functional tests in this and other (Younghusband et al. 1986) laboratories have failed to reveal its function.

Despite the difficulties that we have encountered in deciphering the roles of the H1 sequence elements in transcriptional regulation in vivo, we have proceeded with the analysis of proteins binding to both of the H1-specific promoter elements. Conventional and affinity chromatography have resulted in extensive purification of these factors and have revealed several interesting properties. It is apparent that the factor interacting with the H1 AC box is very limiting in cells, which may explain our difficulties in establishing a role for its binding site in vivo. The factor binding to the H1 proximal subtype-specific sequence is quite abundant, and our provisional molecular weight for this protein does not match published values for other CCAAT binding proteins. Both of these preparations are sufficiently pure for preparation of specific antibodies, and it will be useful to generate these tools for further analysis of these activities.

A model for histone gene regulation during the cell cycle

The definitive identification of the histone H2b subtype-specific consensus element as responsible for the S phase induction H2b transcription, and the structural similarity of the three histone promoters described herein, suggest a very simple model for cell cycle control of histone gene transcription. We propose that these histone promoters comprise two constitutive domains: the core promoter, including the CAP site and TATA box, which functions to assemble the general transcription initiation complex and to position the start site of transcription; and the distal activating domain, which is essential for efficient transcription independent of position in the cell cycle. It is quite possible that this distal activating domain is also responsible for setting the relative level of transcription of the various members of a given histone gene subtype in a cell-specific manner. We suggest that, as observed for the H2b gene, the regulatory domain of the H4 and H1 promoters is located immediately upstream of the TATA box and is subtype specific. Thus, the transcription factors responsible for regulation of genes encoding these three histone gene subtypes are distinct. In this case, the mechanism responsible for activation of these factors is pleiotropic, and could be responsible for modifying proteins involved in other S-phase-specific events. One interesting possibility, for example, is that the machinery responsible for activating histone gene transcription factors at the G_1/S phase boundary could also activate proteins involved in the transcription of other S-phase-regulated genes or the initiation of chromosomal DNA synthesis. Our present studies are aimed at identifying this mechanism and determining whether it is fundamental to a wide range of S-phase-specific functions.

Acknowledgments

I would like to acknowledge R.G. Roeder for his involvement in aspects of this work. I further acknowledge the members of both my own and the Roeder laboratories who have participated in these studies for their efforts to understand histone gene regulation. I am grateful to the Pew Scholars Program for their support during the course of these studies.

References

Artishevsky, A., A. Grafsky, and A. Lee. 1984. Isolation of a sequence capable of conferring cell cycle regulation to a heterologous gene. *Science* **230**: 1061.

Capasso, O. and N. Heintz. 1985. Regulated expression of mammalian histone H4 genes in vivo requires a *trans*-acting transcription factor. *Proc. Natl. Acad. Sci.* **82**: 5622.

Clerc, R.G., P. Bucher, K. Strub, and M.L. Birnstiel. 1983. Transcription of a cloned *Xenopus laevis* H4 histone gene in the homologous frog oocyte system depends on an evolutionary conserved sequence motif in the −50 region. *Nucleic Acids Res.* **11**: 8641.

Coles, L.S. and J.R.E. Wells. 1985. An H1 histone gene-specific 5′ element and evolution of H1 and H5 genes. *Nucleic Acids Res.* **13**: 585.

Dailey, L., S.B. Roberts, and N. Heintz. 1987. RNA polymerase II transcription factors H4tf-1 and H4tf-2 require metal to bind specific DNA sequences. *Mol. Cell. Biol.* **7**: 4582.

Dailey, L., S.H. Hanly, R.G. Roeder, and N. Heintz. 1986. Distinct transcription factors bind to two regions of the histone H4 promoter. *Proc. Natl. Acad. Sci.* **83**: 7241.

Dynan, W.S. and R. Tjian. 1983. The promoter specific transcription factor Sp1 binds to upstream sequences in the SV40 early promoter. *Cell* **35**: 79.

Fletcher, C., N. Heintz, and R.G. Roeder. 1987. Purification and characterization of OTF-1, a transcription factor regulating cell cycle expression of a human histone H2b gene. *Cell* **51**: 773.

Hanly, S.M., G.C. Bleecker, and N. Heintz. 1985. Identification of promoter elements necessary for transcription regulation of a human histone H4 gene in vitro. *Mol. Cell. Biol.* **5**: 380.

Heintz, N. and R.G. Roeder. 1984. Transcription of histone genes in extracts from synchronized HeLa cells. *Proc. Natl. Acad. Sci.* **81**: 1713.

LaBella, F., H.L. Sive, R.G. Roeder, and N. Heintz. 1988. Cell-cycle regulation of a human histone H2b gene is mediated by the H2b subtype-specific consensus element. *Genes Dev.* **2**: 32.

Miller, J., A.D. McLachlan, and A. Klug. 1985. Repetitive zinc-binding domains in the protein transcription factor TFIIIA from *Xenopus* oocytes. *EMBO J.* **4**: 1609.

Seiler-Tuyns, A. and B.M. Paterson. 1987. Cell cycle regulation of a mouse histone H4 gene requires the H4 promoter. *Mol. Cell. Biol.* **7**: 1048.

Sen, R. and D. Baltimore. 1986. Multiple nuclear factors interact with the immunoglobulin enhancer sequences. *Cell* **46**: 705.

Sive, H.L. and R.G. Roeder. 1987. Interaction of a common factor with conserved promoter and enhancer sequences in histone H2b, immunoglobulin and U2 small nuclear RNA genes. *Proc. Natl. Acad. Sci.* **83**: 6382.

Sive, H.L., N. Heintz, and R.G. Roeder. 1987. Multiple sequence elements are required for maximal in vitro transcription of a human histone H2b gene. *Mol. Cell. Biol.* 3329.

Trowbridge, I.S. and F. Lopez. 1982. Monoclonal antibodies to transferrin receptor blocks transferrin binding and inhibits tumor cell growth in vitro. *Proc. Natl. Acad. Sci.* **79**: 1175.

Wells, D.E. 1986. Compilation analysis of histones and histone genes. *Nucleic Acids Res.* **14**: r119.

Younghusband, H.B., R. Sturm, and J.R.E. Wells. 1986. Mutagenesis of conserved 5′ elements and transcription of a chicken H1 histone gene. *Nucleic Acids Res.* **14**: 635.

Qualitative and Kinetic Characterization of Soluble Histone Pools: Linkage between Protein and DNA Synthesis during the Cell Cycle

W.M. Bonner, R.S. Wu,* H.T. Panusz,[†] and C. Muneses

Laboratory of Molecular Pharmacology, Developmental Therapeutics Program, Division of Cancer Treatment, National Cancer Institute, National Institutes of Health, Bethesda, Maryland 20892

During chromosome replication, the synthesis of DNA in the nucleus and histone proteins in the cytoplasm are closely balanced. To investigate whether or not the soluble pools of uncomplexed histones may be involved in this balance, we have partially characterized these pools from Chinese hamster ovary (CHO) cells in several different metabolic states. Pool histones can be distinguished from those incorporated into chromatin by the different pattern of histone H4 modification and the lack of ubiquitinated adducts of histones H2A and H2B.

Kinetic studies using short-term labeling indicate that there are at least two histone pools, a fast pool with a turnover half-time in the order of 1 minute and a slow pool with a much longer turnover half-time. These biphasic chase kinetics are not altered when protein synthesis is inhibited. Quick measurements of the rate of DNA synthesis just after protein synthesis is inhibited show that the rate also decelerates with biphasic kinetics similar to the depletion kinetics of the histone pools under the same conditions. These results show that the inhibition of DNA synthesis by inhibitors of protein synthesis may be mediated solely by the availability of histones for chromatin formation. In contrast, when DNA synthesis is directly inhibited, the nascent histones accumulate in the pool. However, some histone continues to enter chromatin with about three molecules of nascent H2B/H2A incorporated for each molecule of H4/H3. These results suggest that nascent histone molecules may be displacing preexisting histone molecules from the chromatin. When cells are labeled long-term, the labeled pool contains predominantly H2B/H2A, a finding consistent with some displacement of histones from chromatin. Cells synchronized in the G_1 phase show very similar histone pool kinetics to those in S-phase cells with DNA synthesis inhibited. This similarity also includes the predominant incorporation of nascent H2B/H2A into the chromatin of G_1 cells. These results indicate that histone synthesis in G_1-phase cells may be balanced to the amount of available DNA in the same manner as that found in S-phase cells. Furthermore, the results suggest that the histone concentration in the fast pool could regulate the stability of the histone mRNAs, not only when DNA synthesis is limiting but also when protein synthesis is limiting.

Histones are known to be synthesized on cytoplasmic ribosomes, to migrate into the nucleus, and then to become incorporated into chromatin; however, the mechanisms underlying these processes are poorly understood. In the *Xenopus* oocyte, which contains a large store of nonchromatin histone, two different acidic proteins have been found in histone complexes (Kleinschmidt and Franke 1982; Kleinschmidt et al. 1985; Dillworth et al. 1987). Whether or not the same types of complexes exist in somatic cells remains to be established, but various investigators have presented evidence that there exists a small pool of soluble histone in somatic cells (Butler and Mueller 1973; Oliver et al. 1974).

Present addresses: *Clinical Investigations Branch, Cancer Therapy Evaluation Program, Division of Cancer Treatment, National Cancer Institute, National Institutes of Health, Bethesda, Maryland 20892. [†]Sloan-Kettering Institute for Cancer Research, New York, New York 10021.

In addition, this pool of histone may be involved in regulating the intricate balance between the synthesis of histone and DNA during the cell cycle as well as in S phase (for review, see Wu et al. 1986). Butler and Mueller (1973) showed that when DNA synthesis was inhibited, translatable histone mRNA levels decreased to a few percent of control levels over a period of 30 minutes. These authors presented evidence to indicate that there was an elevation of histone in the soluble fraction immediately after inhibition of DNA synthesis and suggested that the increased concentration of soluble histone led to the decrease of histone mRNA levels. More recently, Stimac et al. (1983) showed that inhibition of protein synthesis led to a stabilization of histone mRNAs. Investigators in several laboratories using cloned histone genes substantiated and extended these results (DeLisle et al. 1983; Heintz et al. 1983; Plumb et al. 1983; Sittman et al. 1983; Baumbach et al. 1984; Graves and Marzluff 1984; Helms et al. 1984; Sive et al.

269

1984; Stimac et al. 1984; Sariban et al. 1985). Sariban et al. (1985), after analyzing several classes of inhibitors, suggested a unified model in which histone protein and DNA synthesis are balanced by a combination of histone availability and histone mRNA stability. The absence of DNA synthesis in G_1/G_2 or the inhibition of the same in S phase would lead to an accumulation of soluble histone resulting in decreased stability and amounts of replication-linked histone mRNA. Inhibiting protein synthesis would lead to a depletion of soluble histone, resulting in increased stability and amounts of replication-linked histone mRNA. Wu and Bonner (1985) extended this model to include cells growing under conditions of limited protein synthesis. Under these conditions, S-phase cells compensate for the limited protein synthesis by increasing the amount of the replication-linked histone mRNAs to enable the chromosome cycle to proceed at close to control rates. However, soluble histone has been difficult to isolate from somatic cells, and it has not been possible to test whether the concentrations and rates of flux of pool histones are consistent with this unified model. In this paper, we investigate the characteristics and kinetics of the soluble histone pools in CHO cells. We conclude that the results obtained support the unified model as originally presented by Sariban et al. (1985). In addition, we present evidence that there are several histone pools, including one that may contain histone displaced from chromatin.

Experimental Procedures

Cell growth
CHO cells were grown in Ham's F-10 with 10% fetal calf serum (FCS), and were tested periodically for mycoplasma contamination. For a typical experiment, cells were seeded in T-75 tissue culture flasks with 3×10^6 cells or in a T-150 flask with 7×10^6 cells, and were allowed to grow overnight until approximately doubled. Synchronized cells in G_1 were obtained and labeled as described previously (Wu et al. 1982).

Preparation of pool histone
Experiments were performed in a warm room at 37°C, and all components were equilibrated to that temperature. Cells were labeled with $[^{14}C]$lysine (10 µCi/ml) in lysine-free HF-10 media with undialyzed 10% FCS. Five ml was used for a T-150 and 2.5 ml for a T-75 flask.

In continuous labeling experiments, stock solutions of inhibitors were added directly to the flasks and mixed gently but quickly with the labeled media. Flasks were incubated with gentle rocking. The cycloheximide stock solution was 1 mg/ml in PBS; hydroxyurea was 1 M in PBS; aphidicolin was 1 mg/ml in DMSO; the control was PBS.

In pulse-chase experiments, the inhibitors were added to the chase media (HF-10 with 10% FCS and tenfold-increased lysine). The labeling medium was removed and the chase media added (20 ml for a T-150 and 10 ml for a T-75).

To terminate the incubation, the media were aspirated, and ice cold PBS with 0.2 mg/ml of lysine added. The flasks were quickly transferred to a cold room for the preparation of pool histone. Care was taken to perform all the following steps in ice or at 4°C. The PBS was aspirated and the cells trypsinized (5 ml of Gibco trypsin for a T-150). After about 10 minutes, the flasks were tapped firmly to loosen the cells and about 8 ml of HF-10 medium with 10% FCS was added. The cells, after being titrated to a single cell suspension, were transferred to a 15-ml centrifuge tube. The cells were pelleted at 300g for 5 minutes and washed once more with PBS. The washed pellet was suspended in 0.5 ml of TM (10 mM Tris-HCl [pH 7.5], 1 mM MgSO$_4$), the suspension transferred to a microfuge tube, and the cells pelleted for 1–2 seconds. The pellet was resuspended well in 0.5 ml of TM. An aliquot of 10 µl was removed for cell counting with either a Coulter Counter or Hemocytometer. To lyse the cells, Triton-N101 was added to a final concentration of 0.3% to the suspension. After a 5–10 minute incubation, randomly chosen samples were checked in the microscope for complete lysis. Nuclei were pelleted for 10 minutes in a microfuge with a horizontal rotor. The supernatant was carefully removed to another microfuge tube, leaving about 20 µl covering the undisturbed nuclear pellet. The nuclear pellet was resuspended in 0.5 ml of TE (10 mM Tris HCl [pH 7.5], 1 mM EDTA). Histones were extracted from both the soluble and nuclear fractions by adding HCl and 2-mercaptoethanol to final concentrations of 0.5 M and 1%, respectively. After a 1-hour extraction with occasional vortexing, the samples were spun in a microfuge for 10 minutes. The supernatants were removed and freeze dried.

One technical problem was whether or not the altered soluble histone concentrations would be maintained in the absence of inhibitors at 4°C. This was tested in an experiment in which the appropriate inhibitors were added to all the solutions used to prepare soluble histone. These additions did not affect the results, and it was concluded that the inhibitors were not necessary to maintain the altered histone pool concentrations after the cells were cooled.

Two-dimensional gel electrophoresis
The freeze-dried samples were resuspended in AUT sample buffer (1 M acetic acid, 50 mM ammonia, 5 M urea). Typical loadings were 5×10^6 cell equivalents for the soluble fraction and 1×10^6 for the nuclear. Gels were prepared, run, and stained as described previously (Wu and Bonner 1981; Wu et al. 1982). Gels were stained for 15–30 minutes, soaked directly in Fluoro-Hance (Research Products International Corp.) for 30 minutes, then dried and fluorographed (Bonner and Lasky 1974; Laskey and Mills 1975). To quantitate radioactivity in histone species, the relevant spots were first located by superimposing the film over the dried gel, then cut out and digested overnight in a scintillation vial

with 1 ml of a solution of 95 parts of 30% hydrogen peroxide and 5 parts of concentrated ammonia. The solubilized gel was taken up in water-soluble scintillation cocktail and the radioactivity determined.

Quick determination of DNA protein synthesis
Cells were grown overnight in T-25 flasks. The following steps were performed in a warm room at 37°C with all solutions equilibrated to that temperature. The growth medium was replaced with 1 ml of HF-10 with 10% FCS. Inhibitors were added from a 10 × stock solution and rapidly but gently mixed with the growth medium. At the noted time, [^{3}H]thymidine or [^{3}H]lysine was added from a 10 × stock and also mixed rapidly but gently. Final concentrations were 100 μCi/ml for both labels. HF-10 contains 3 μM thymidine, which floods the thymidine pool, ensuring that the rate of [^{3}H]thymidine incorporation is proportional to the rate of DNA synthesis (Cleaver 1967). After 1 minute, 10 ml of ice-cold PBS containing 10 × thymidine and 10 × lysine was added to the flask and mixed quickly with the labeling media. The contents of the flask were aspirated and 10 ml of ice-cold 20% perchloric acid containing 10 × thymidine and lysine (PCA-TK) was added. Flasks were accumulated in the cold until the time course was finished. All flasks were then washed three times with 10 ml of the PCA-TK, being careful to rinse all the surfaces. The flasks were then washed twice with 10 ml of 100% ethanol and left to dry at room temperature. The attached cell layers were solubilized by covering the layer with 1 ml of TM containing 5 μg/ml of DNase I and incubating with slow rocking at 37°C for 30 minutes.

NaOH (0.1 ml of 5 M) and SDS (0.1 ml of 10%) were then added, and the incubation was continued for another hour. The flasks were tilted upright to collect the extract, and 0.1-ml aliquots were taken for scintillation counting. In some cases, OD_{260} was determined to normalize the samples, but this was not necessary; duplicates generally agreed within 20%.

Results

Characterization of soluble histone

Figure 1 shows the results obtained when the supernatant and nuclear fractions from cells labeled with [^{14}C]-lysine for 15 minutes were separated and analyzed by two-dimensional electrophoresis. The terms soluble or pool histone are used throughout this report to denote those histones isolated from the supernatant fraction.

There are several qualitative differences between the patterns of the pool and chromosomal histone that eliminate the possibility that the former is contaminated with the latter to any significant extent. The most easily discernible difference is in the pattern of H4 modification. Chromosomal H4 exists primarily in the unmodified or b_0 form (Fig. 1B), whereas pool H4 exists primarily in the dimodified or b_2 form (Ruiz-Carrillo et al. 1975) with some in the b_0 and b_1 forms (Fig. 1A). The H4 in these latter two forms does not seem to be indicative of chromosomal contamination, but rather normal pool forms, at least in CHO cells, since these two forms are always present in approximately the same proportion relative to the b_2 form in a wide variety of conditions that have been studied. Typically in pool H4 of CHO cells,

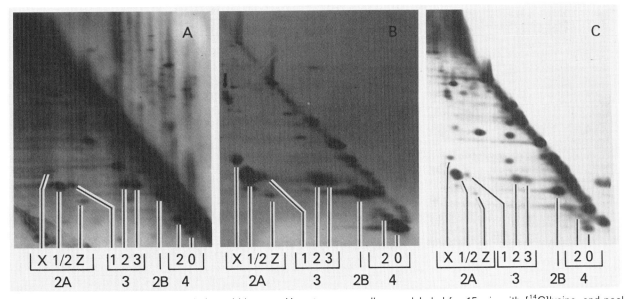

Figure 1 Patterns of pool and chromatin-bound histones. Hamster ovary cells were labeled for 15 min with [^{14}C]lysine, and pool histones were prepared as described in Experimental Procedures. The nuclear pellet was extracted with 0.15 M NaCl in 10 mM Tris-HCl (pH 7.5), 1 mM $MgSO_4$ to yield the salt wash fraction. The washed nuclear pellet was then extracted with 1 M HCl to yield chromatin-bound histone. The three fractions were analyzed by two-dimensional electrophoresis as described in Experimental Procedures. (*A*) Pool histones from 8.7×10^6 cells; (*B*) chromatin-bound histones from 10^6 cells; (*C*) salt wash fraction from 8.7×10^6 cells.

the b_2 form may account for 60% of the total with the b_1 and b_0 forms accounting for 20% each; in chromosomal H4, the respective percentages are 10, 25, and 65.

Two other differences are also apparent. One is the relative lack of ubiquitinated derivatives of H2B and H2A in the pool. (The arrow in Fig. 1B notes the position of the ubiquitin adducts of chromosomal H2A.) The other is the relative amounts of the H3 variants in the pool and in the chromatin. The pool seems to be enriched in the H3.3 variant relative to the chromatin. This difference is discussed below, as it is at least partly due to the contribution from the histone pools of G_1 cells (see Fig. 4E).

Soluble histone could be prepared with 0.15 M NaCl in the TM solution with no significant difference either in the pattern or in the amount of material recovered. When the nuclear pellet left after the supernatant fraction was removed was further extracted with 0.15 M NaCl, only material with the same pattern as the chromosomal histone was extracted, probably resulting from some breakage of the nuclei during resuspension. These results indicated that virtually all the histone that was not bound to chromatin had been recovered in the supernatant fraction during the initial extraction.

Kinetics of labeling histone pools

Two kinds of labeling protocols were used to study the changes in the pools of the various histone species. In the continuous labeling protocol, cells were incubated in growth media containing $[^{14}C]$lysine for 10 minutes, then for various times in the same labeling media containing inhibitors of DNA or protein synthesis (Fig. 2, A–D). In the pulse-chase protocol, cells were incubated in growth media containing $[^{14}C]$lysine for 20 minutes, and then in media lacking label but containing inhibitors (Fig. 2, E and F). Chromosomal histones (Fig. 2, A and B, circles) incorporated label at a linear rate for the duration of the continuous labeling protocol, indicating that the experimental manipulations did not disrupt cellular metabolism in general and chromosome replication in particular.

The curves showing the kinetic data of label incorporation into pool histones are noted by open circles in panels C–F of Figure 2. In the continuous labeling protocol (panels C and D), pool histones continued to be labeled after the initial period at decreasing rates but also at rates that do not show equilibrium labeling of the pools within 40 minutes. The explanation for this lack of equilibrium labeling of the pool is seen in the pulse-chase protocol (panels E and F). Label in pool histones clearly displayed biphasic chase kinetics, a rapid decrease to about 50% of the initial value in three minutes, followed by a much slower decrease. These data indicate that there are at least two components to the nascent histone pool, a fast component (fast pool) with a half-turnover time of about 1 minute and a slow component (slow pool) with a much longer half-turnover time. The continuous labeling data (Fig. 2, C and D) are consistent with two components, assuming that the fast pool is already labeled almost to equilibrium during the initial 10-minute labeling period.

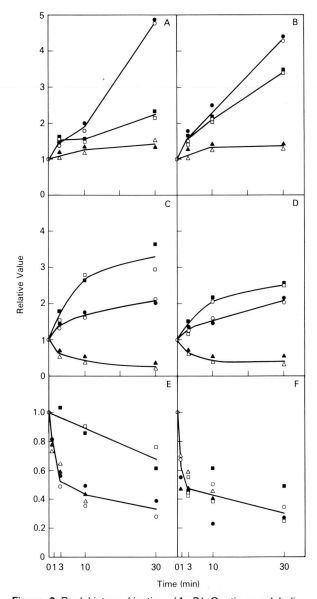

Figure 2 Pool histone kinetics. (*A–D*) Continuous labeling protocol: Hamster ovary cells were labeled for 10 min with $[^{14}C]$lysine as described in Experimental Procedures. Hydroxyurea was added to some flasks (final concentration of 10 mM) and cycloheximide to others (final concentration of 10 μg/ml). Controls received PBS. At the times indicated, the cells were harvested. Pool and chromatin-bound histones were prepared, analyzed, and quantitated as described in Experimental Procedures. (*A,B*) Chromatin-bound histones; (*C,D*) pool histones; (*A,C*) H4 (open symbols)/H3 (closed symbols); (*B,D*) H2B (open symbols)/H2A (closed symbols); (circles) control; (squares) hydroxyurea treated; (triangles) cycloheximide treated. (*E,F*) Pulse-chase labeling kinetics: Hamster ovary cells were labeled for 20 min with $[^{14}C]$lysine as described in Experimental Procedures. Labeled media were then replaced with complete media (with ten times the normal concentration of lysine) containing PBS (control), aphidicolin (10 μg/ml), or cycloheximide (10 μg/ml). Incubation continued for the times indicated, at which time the cells were harvested and the pool and chromatin-bound histones were prepared, analyzed, and quantitated as described in Experimental Procedures. Only pool histone data are shown. (*E*) H4 (open symbols)/H3 (closed symbols); (*F*) H2B (open symbols)/H2A (closed symbols); (circles) controls; (squares) aphidicolin treated; (triangles) cycloheximide treated.

Since these experiments use exponential cell cultures, G_1 and G_2 cells are present in the population and might be the source of the slow pool. As shown below (Fig. 4, E and F), G_1 and G_2 cells exhibit a nascent histone pattern qualitatively different from that exhibited by S-phase cells in both the pool and the chromatin. Since the slow pool after the 30-minute chase exhibits the same histone variant pattern as the control (data not shown), the possibility that the slow pool is solely from G_1/G_2 cells can be eliminated.

Histone pool when protein synthesis is inhibited

Inhibition of protein synthesis is known to lead to the inhibition of DNA synthesis (Gautschi and Kern 1973; Venkatesan 1977). The mechanism of the linkage between these two processes has not been elucidated, but Sariban et al. (1985) proposed that the rate of DNA synthesis could be limited in such cases by the availability of histone from the pool. The data in Figure 2 show that when protein synthesis was inhibited, both the continuous label and pulse-chase protocols resulted in a rapid decline in the amount of labeled pool histone. This is reasonable since both protocols result in a chase in this case, and in fact, the data curves from the two protocols are almost superimposable.

The data from the pulse-chase protocol (Fig. 2, E and F) show that the labeled histones exited the pool at similar rates whether or not protein synthesis was inhibited. However, in the former case, bulk level of the pool was presumably falling at the same rate as the label, since histone synthesis was insignificant, whereas in the control the bulk pool was remaining constant. The similarity of these two rates suggests that DNA synthesis continues in the absence of protein synthesis at a rate sufficient to complex with the remaining pool histone. If so, then the rate of DNA synthesis should decrease at a rate similar to that of the concentration of the pool histone when protein synthesis is inhibited.

The experiments presented in Figure 3 were designed to test this supposition. The inset of Figure 3 shows a semilogarithmic plot of the rate of DNA synthesis at various times after the addition of the protein synthesis inhibitor. The plot is biphasic with a break at 5 minutes. During the fast phase of inhibition, DNA synthesis decelerates with a half-time of about 1 minute after a lag of 0.5–1 minute. This and other data (not shown) show that during the slower phase, DNA synthesis decelerates with first-order kinetics with a half-time of about 40 minutes, decreasing to 1% of the control after 3 hours. Figure 3 (main panel) presents data comparing the initial deceleration of DNA synthesis with the decreasing concentration of the pool histone; the two are very similar. The level of the total histone pool decreased more quickly than did the rate of DNA synthesis. Note that if the total values plotted in Figure 3 were separated into fast and slow components, the fast histone pool would be seen to decrease faster than the fast deceleration component of DNA synthesis. The finding that cycloheximide inhibited protein synthesis (triangles, Fig. 3) and hydroxyurea inhibited DNA synthesis (squares, Fig. 3) more quickly than cycloheximide led to the inhibition of

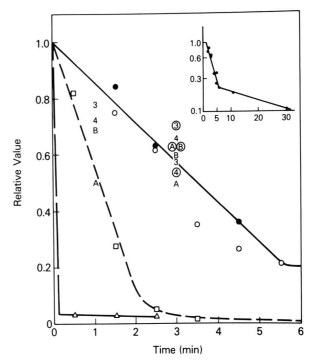

Figure 3 Histone pool levels and the rates of protein and DNA synthesis: Rates of DNA and protein synthesis in the presence of inhibitors were measured as described in Experimental Procedures. Pool levels of various histone species were taken from the cycloheximide-treated cultures in the experiments shown in Figs. 2 and 3. (Circles) 1-min rates of DNA synthesis after the addition of cycloheximide (10 μg/ml). Open and closed circles represent two experiments. (Inset) The same data presented on a semilog graph. (Squares) 1-min rates of DNA synthesis after the addition of hydroxyurea; (triangles) 1-min rates of protein synthesis after the addition of cycloheximide. Histone pool levels. (4) H4; (3) H3; (B) H2B; (A) H2A. (Circled symbols) Data from Fig. 2,C and D. (Uncircled symbols) Data from Fig. 2,E and F.

DNA synthesis indicated that the last is not due to a slow rate of entry of these inhibitors or label into the cells. These findings support the suggestion (Sariban et al. 1985) that the rate of DNA synthesis may be limited by the amount of histone available from the pool for chromatin formation.

In these cells, the slow deceleration phase of DNA synthesis begins at 25% of the control rate, whereas the fast and slow histone pools seem to contain about equal amounts of labeled material. This difference is not a discrepancy, because it is the flux of histone from these two pools rather than the size of the pools that would limit the rate of DNA synthesis. In addition, the relative amount of label in the two histone pools should vary until both pools are labeled to equilibrium. Another consideration is that the DNA synthesized in the absence of protein synthesis may be partly deficient of histones (Seale and Simpson 1975; Annunziato and Seale 1982). Putting these complicating factors aside for later resolution, we conclude that in the absence of protein synthesis, the fast phase of decelerating DNA synthesis is due to the depletion of the fast histone pool, and the slow phase of decelerating DNA synthesis could be supported by the slow histone pool.

Histone pool when DNA synthesis is inhibited

The kinetic behavior of labeled histone when DNA synthesis was inhibited is shown by the square symbols in Figure 2. With continuous labeling, all the histones accumulated in the pool to a certain extent over the control when DNA synthesis was inhibited, but H4 and H3 showed quicker and greater accumulation than did H2B and H2A (Fig. 2,C and D). This difference in behavior between the two histone pairs was also noticeable when chromatin was analyzed (Fig. 2A and B). Nascent H4 and H3 accumulated in the chromatin at a much slower rate than did H2B and H2A. More quantitative interpretation of the results from this protocol is complicated because the histones are labeled both before and after inhibition. In addition, in the absence of DNA synthesis, the rate and variant pattern of histone synthesis is changing as replication-linked histone mRNAs are being degraded (Butler and Mueller 1973; for review, see Wu et al. 1986).

With the pulse-chase protocol, the histones are labeled only before the addition of inhibitor. (The particular experiment presented in Fig. 2, E and F, used aphidicolin rather than hydroxyurea to inhibit DNA synthesis, but comparable results were also obtained with the latter.) Figure 2,E and F, shows that when DNA synthesis was inhibited, labeled H4 and H3 chased out of the pool with much slower kinetics than did labeled H2B and H2A, particularly at times shorter than 3 minutes when the fast pool was being depleted of labeled histone. These results indicate that H4/H3 and the H2A/H2B pairs in the fast pool partition independently from each other.

To investigate this phenomenon further, cells were labeled either simultaneously with the addition of inhibitor, or 30 minutes after the addition of inhibitor (Fig. 4). During the first 15 minutes after addition of inhibitor (Fig. 4, A and B), the nascent forms of all four histone species accumulated in the pool to 25–60% over their respective amounts found in the control for this experiment (Fig. 1). Particularly noticeable was the selective accumulation of the S-phase variants H3.2 and .1 relative to H3.3 in the pool of the inhibited sample. (H3.3 is mostly from G_1 cells that do not respond to inhibitors of DNA synthesis.) Although the pool concentrations of the labeled histones all increased during this period, other quantitative parameters were considerably different for the two pairs. For H4/H3, total synthesis was decreased to 19% of the control, but exit from the pool was greatly decreased, so that 25–30% of the nascent H4/H3 remained in the pool, compared to 3–5% for the control. For H2B/H2A, on the other hand, total synthesis was decreased to 45–50%, and exit from the pool was slightly decreased, so that only 4–8% of the H2B/H2A remained in the pool, only slightly more than the 2–3% in the control.

The mRNA levels for the S-phase histones are known to decrease rapidly when DNA synthesis is inhibited, and by 30 minutes of inhibition, there is very little S-phase mRNA left (for review, see Wu et al. 1986). Thus, when DNA synthesis was inhibited 30 minutes

before labeling (Fig. 4, C and D), variant synthesis has changed toward the G_1 pattern with primarily basal variants H3.3, H2A.Z, and .X being synthesized and deposited in the chromatin. With H2A, very little of the nascent S-phase variants H2A.1 and .2 are found in the pool either, but with H3 there do seem to be small amounts of nascent S-phase variants H3.2 and .1 in the pool that are not detectable in the chromatin. Although the synthesis of all four histones has been decreased to 6–15% of the control, 34–42% of the nascent H4/H3 remains in the pool, whereas only 5–9% of the nascent H2B/H2A remains in the pool. This imbalance is apparent in Figure 4,C and D.

These results extend the findings of other investigators that H4/H3 and H2B/H2A can enter chromatin by different pathways. Worcel et al. (1978) showed that in *Drosophila* tissue culture cells, H2B/H2A are deposited in chromatin 2–10 minutes after H4/H3 had been. Louters and Chalkley (1985) have presented evidence, confirmed in Figure 4,C and D, that H2B/H2A continues to enter chromatin when DNA synthesis has been inhibited for longer periods of time. Both these mechanisms could be functioning in this experiment. If H4/H3 entry into chromatin (and exit from the pool) stops immediately when the inhibitor of DNA synthesis is added (Fig. 2E), H2B/H2A could continue its entry into chromatin (Fig. 2F), complexing with the last H4/H3 tetramers to be incorporated. This kind of mechanism could also explain the relatively high rate of H2B/H2A synthesis (45–50% of the uninhibited control) during the first 15 minutes after DNA synthesis was inhibited. Some sort of exchange or displacement of preexisting histone from the chromatin could then explain the continued entry of all the histones, but preferentially the H2B/H2A, into chromatin during long-term inhibition of DNA synthesis.

If displacement of histone from chromatin occurs under uninhibited conditions of growth, then it may be possible to detect displaced histone with a long-term labeling protocol that labels most of the chromosomal histone. When such an experiment was carried out and pool histone was isolated from cells labeled for one generation, the pool contained predominantly H2B/H2A, about three molecules of H2B/H2A for each H4/H3 (Fig. 5). In addition, this pool seems to be even further enriched for H2A.Z. Consistent with the long-term labeling is that the histone pool detected by silver stain is also predominantly H2B/H2A (data not shown). The relationship of this pool, detected by long-term label or silver stain, to the fast and slow pools detected by short-term label is currently being investigated. However, if some of the displaced histone enters the fast pool, then the concentrations of the histones in this pool may be underestimated by the short-term labeling experiments, particularly in the H2B/H2A pool when DNA synthesis is inhibited.

Thus, the results of these experiments in which DNA synthesis was inhibited support the original suggestion of Butler and Mueller (1973) that histones accumulate in the pool when DNA synthesis is inhibited, but with significant differences for the H4/H3 and the H2B/H2A pairs. These differences apply not only to the S-phase variants that dominate the pattern during the first 15 minutes of inhibition, but also for the basal variants that dominate the pattern after 30 minutes of inhibition.

Histone pool in G_1 cells

During G_1 and G_2 there is no DNA synthesis, and histone synthesis is at a much lower level. Wu and Bonner (1981) reported that the pattern of histone synthesis in G_1 is similar to that in S phase when DNA synthesis is inhibited; namely, that there is little or no synthesis of the major H2A and H3 variants. Wu et al. (1983) showed that these histones synthesized in G_1 were incorporated into nucleosomes. Jackson and Chalkley (1985) confirmed these results and extended them to show that there were differential rates of deposition of the H4/H3 and H2B/H2A pairs into the G_1 chromatin. Figure 4,E and F, shows the pattern of labeled histone in the pool and chromatin of synchronized G_1 cells. In the G_1 pool, H4 and H3 are clearly visible; H2B and H2A, although detectable, are at much lower levels. In the chromatin, all the histone species are detectable, but the relative amounts differ. The results are strikingly similar to those in Figure 4,C and D, in which DNA synthesis has been inhibited for 30 minutes. First, histone synthesis has been inhibited to similar extents. Second, much of the H4/H3 remains in the pool and most of the H2B/H2A enters the G_1 chromatin. In the chromatin there are again about three molecules of labeled H2B and H2A for each H4 and H3 molecule. These results indicate that the histone pools and histone accumulation in chromatin respond similarly qualitatively and quantitatively in G_1 cells and in S-phase cells with inhibited DNA synthesis. This finding suggests that the regulation of histone synthesis in G_1 cells may be based on the amount of free DNA in the same way as it is in S-phase cells. Since there is presumably no free DNA in G_1 cells, the histone pool parameters mimic those of S-phase cells when DNA synthesis is inhibited.

Discussion

The results presented above can be conveniently summarized by means of a model incorporating the following features.

1. There are several histone pools. With short labeling times, a fast pool and a slow pool can be detected. There are two fast pools, one for H4/H3 and another for H2B/H2A. Both of the fast pools and the slow pool are present in all phases of cycling cells. The fast pool is linked to replication, and the concentration of histone in this pool regulates the transcriptional and posttranscriptional mechanisms that determine the concentration of replication-linked mRNAs. In addition, there is a pool of displaced chromosomal histone detected with long labeling times, which may contain histone displaced from chromatin. The relationship of this last pool to the others is currently under study.

2. The nascent histone variant pattern is the same in the fast and slow pools, with both basal and replication-linked histone variants found in both pools. The nascent histone variant pattern is determined by the phase and state of the cell, as described below in feature 5.

3. When there is no DNA replication, there is little if any flux into chromatin from the fast H4/H3 pool, whether it contains primarily H3.3 as in G_1 cells, or whether it contains all the H3 variants as when DNA replication has just been inhibited in S-phase cells. Under the same conditions, there is flux from the fast H2B/H2A pool into chromatin, whether it contains primarily H2A.X and .Z as in G_1 cells, or whether it contains all the H2A variants as when DNA synthesis has just been inhibited in S-phase cells. However, the flux from the fast H2B/H2A pool is somewhat decreased since these histones do also accumulate in the pool when DNA synthesis is inhibited.

4. When protein synthesis is inhibited, the fast pool is quickly depleted, the extent of depletion limiting the rate of DNA synthesis. When the fast pool is depleted, the rate of DNA synthesis continues to decline at a reduced rate, relying at least in part on the slow histone pool.

5. The level of the fast histone pool directly or indirectly determines the concentration of the replication-linked histone mRNAs through changes in the stability and the rate of transcription. When the fast pool is depleted as when protein synthesis is inhibited, replication-linked histone mRNA becomes indefinitely stable. When the level of histone in the fast pool increases as when DNA synthesis is inhibited or stopped at the end of S phase, replication-linked histone mRNA becomes extremely labile. The intermediate lability of replication-linked histone mRNA during S phase is due to the momentary level of the fast histone pool, which in turn reflects the balance between protein and DNA synthesis. The nascent histone variant pattern depends on the relative stability of the replication-linked and the basal histone mRNAs, which in turn depends on the state of the cell and the balance between protein and DNA synthesis.

The histones have kinetically separable pools. Although there are several possible mechanisms to achieve this, one attractive possibility would be the presence of several types of histone carriers. Although none have been described for somatic cells, two kinds of soluble histone complexes have been isolated from *Xenopus* oocytes (Kleinschmidt and Franke 1982; Kleinschmidt et al. 1985), one of which contains H3 and H4 bound to protein N1/N2 and a second which contains H2A and H2B bound to nucleoplasmin (Dillworth et al. 1987). Such multiple carriers in somatic cells would satisfy the requirement for independently acting pools as well as the requirement for different conditions for incorporation into chromatin.

The mechanism behind the specific lability of replica-

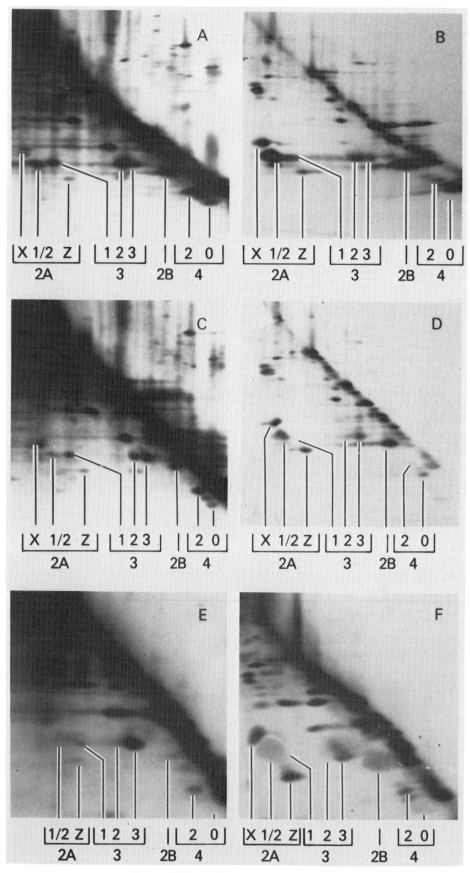

Figure 4 (*See facing page for legend.*)

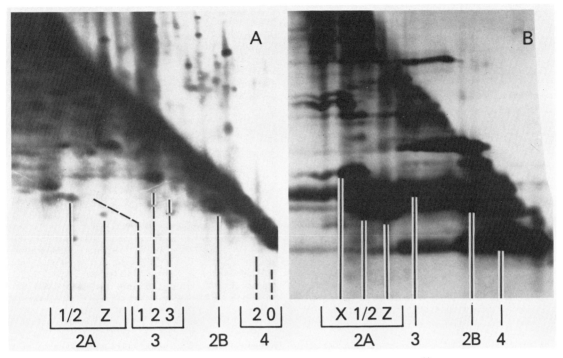

Figure 5 Histone pool detected by long-term label. Cells were labeled overnight with 1 μCi [^{14}C]lysine in lysine-free HF-10 media with undialyzed 10% FCS. Soluble pool histones and nuclei were prepared as described in Experimental Procedures. (*A*) Pool histones; (*B*) chromatin-bound histones.

tion-linked histone mRNA has not been elucidated. Ross and Kobs (1986) have studied the decay of histone H4 mRNA in cell-free extracts and shown that it initiates at or near the 3' terminus and proceeds toward the 5' end. If the rate of decay is regulated by fast pool histone levels, other molecules involved with the fast pool histones, such as the carriers, might be involved in the mRNA stability. For example, free carrier molecules could inhibit a specific nuclease for replication-linked histone mRNAs. Then as fast pool histone levels arose, nuclease would become activated. Testing such hypotheses will require isolating the soluble histone complexes in somatic cells.

A diploid cell (6 pg DNA) can be calculated to require about 5×10^7 molecules of each nucleosomal histone per S phase, or an average of $0.8-1.0 \times 10^5$ per minute in an 8–10-hour S phase. With a calculated flux of 60–120% per minute in an S-phase cell, a fast pool would contain about 1×10^5 molecules of each histone. Measuring the specific activity of the lysine pool and making several other assumptions, we have estimated the size of the H4 fast pool to be approximately 1×10^5 molecules. Thus, there seems to be agreement between independent estimates of the demand for and the supply of histones during replication.

The results presented here as summarized above support and extend the model of Butler and Mueller (1973) as modified by Sariban et al. (1985). The relative rates of histone and DNA synthesis determine the concentration of histone in the fast pool, which regulates the amount of the replication-linked histone mRNA, not only when DNA synthesis is limiting but also when protein synthesis is limiting. Histone synthesis in G_1 seems to be regulated in the same manner as it is in S phase. Presently, this model does not include regulation of histone synthesis in quiescent cells, but the relation of histone pools in quiescent cells to those in cycling cells is currently under investigation. In addition, these results show the existence of other histone pools that may be involved in some less well understood roles of histones in chromatin.

References

Annunziato, A.T. and R.L. Seale. 1982. Maturation of nucleosomal and non-nucleosomal components of nascent chromatin: Differential requirements for concurrent protein synthesis. *Biochemistry* **21**: 5431.

Baumbach, L.L., F. Marashi, M. Plumb, G. Stein, and J. Stein. 1984. Inhibition of DNA replication coordinately reduces

Figure 4 Patterns of pool and chromatin-bound histone synthesis after inhibition of DNA synthesis and in G_1; (*A–D*) Hamster ovary cells were labeled for 15 min with [^{14}C]lysine either coincident with the addition of hydroxyurea (10 mM) or 30 min after the addition of hydroxyurea. Pool and chromatin histones were prepared, and analyzed as described in Experimental Procedures. (*A* and *C*) Pool histones; (*B* and *D*) chromatin-bound histones; (*A* and *B*) labeled coincident with inhibition; (*C* and *D*) labeled 30 min after inhibition. (*E* and *F*) Hamster ovary cells in G_1 were obtained as described in Wu et al. (1982). The cells were labeled for 1 hr starting 1 hr after mitotic shake-off with [^{14}C]arginine (G_1) or 7 hr after (S phase). Pool and chromatin-bound histones were prepared and analyzed as described in Experimental Procedures. (*E*) Pool histones; (*F*) chromatin-bound histones.

cellular levels of core and H1 histone mRNAs: Requirement for protein synthesis. *Biochemistry* **23**: 1618.

Bonner, W.M. and R.A. Laskey. 1974. A film detection method for tritium-labelled proteins and nucleic acids in polyacrylamide gels. *Eur. J. Biochem.* **46**: 83.

Butler, M.B. and G.C. Mueller. 1973. Control of histone synthesis in HeLa cells. *Biochim. Biophys. Acta* **294**: 481.

Cleaver, J.E. 1967. *Thymidine metabolism and cell kinetics.* Elsevier/North-Holland, Amsterdam.

DeLisle, A.J., R.A. Graves,. W.F. Marzluff, and L.F. Johnson. 1983. Regulation of histone mRNA production and stability in serum-stimulated mouse 3T6 fibroblasts. *Mol. Cell. Biol.* **3**: 1920.

Dilworth, S.M., S.J. Black, and R.A. Laskey. 1987. Two complexes that contain histones are required for nucleosome assembly *in vitro*: Role of nucleoplasmin and N1 in *Xenopus* egg extracts. *Cell* **51**: 1009.

Gautschi, J.K. and R. M. Kern. 1973. DNA replication in mammalian cells in the presence of cycloheximide. *Exp. Cell Res.* **80**: 15.

Graves, R.A. and W.F. Marzulff. 1984. Rapid reversible changes in the rate of histone gene transcription and histone mRNA levels in mouse myeloma cells. *Mol. Cell. Biol.* **4**: 351.

Heintz, N., H.L. Sive, and R.G. Roeder. 1983. Regulation of human histone gene expression: Kinetics of accumulation and changes in the rate of synthesis and in the half-lives of individual histone mRNAs during the HeLa cell cycle. *Mol. Cell. Biol.* **3**: 539.

Helms, S., L. Baumbach, G. Stein, and J. Stein. 1984. Requirements of protein synthesis for the coupling of histone mRNA levels and DNA replication. *FEBS Lett.* **168**: 65.

Jackson, V. and R. Chalkley. 1985. Histone synthesis and deposition in the G$_1$ and S phases of hepatoma tissue culture cells. *Biochemistry* **24**: 6921.

Kleinschmidt, J.A. and W.W. Franke. 1982. Soluble acidic complexes containing histones H3 and H4 in nuclei of *Xenopus laevis* oocytes. *Cell* **29**: 799.

Kleinschmidt, J.A., E. Fortkamp, G. Krohnet, H. Zentgraf, and W. Werner. 1985. Co-existence of two different types of soluble histone complex in nuclei of *Xenopus laevis* oocytes. *J. Biol Chem.* **260**: 1166.

Laskey, R.A. and A.D. Mills. 1975. Quantitative film detection of ^{3}H and ^{14}C in polyacrylamide gels by fluorography. *Eur. J. Biochem.* **56**: 335.

Louters, L. and R. Chalkley. 1985. Exchange of histones H1, H2A, and H2B in vivo. *Biochemistry* **24**: 3080.

Oliver, D., D. Granner, and R. Chalkley. 1974. Identification of a distinction between cytoplasmic histone synthesis and subsequent histone deposition within the nucleus. *Biochemistry* **13**: 746.

Plumb, M., J. Stein, and G. Stein. 1983. Influence of DNA synthesis inhibitor on the coordinate expression of core human histone genes during S phase. *Nucleic Acids Res.* **11**: 7927.

Ross, J. and G. Kobs. 1986. H4 histone messenger RNA decay in cell-free extracts initiates at or near the 3′ terminus and proceeds 3′ to 5′. *J. Mol. Biol.* **188**: 579.

Ruiz-Carrillo, A., L.J. Wangh, and V.G. Allfrey. 1975. Processing of newly synthesized histone molecules. *Science* **190**: 117.

Sariban, E.R., R.S. Wu, L.C. Erickson, and W.M. Bonner. 1985. Interrelationships of protein and DNA synthesis during replication in mammalian cells. *Mol. Cell. Biol.* **5**: 1279.

Seale, R.L. and R.T. Simpson. 1975. Effects of cycloheximide on chromatin biosynthesis. *J. Mol. Biol.* **94**: 479.

Sittman, D.B., R.A. Graves, and W.F. Marzluff. 1983. Histone mRNA concentrations are regulated at the level of transcription and mRNA degradation. *Proc. Natl. Acad. Sci.* **80**: 1949.

Sive, H.L., N. Heintz, and R.G Roeder. 1984. Regulation of human histone gene expression during the HeLa cell cycle requires protein synthesis. *Mol. Cell. Biol.* **4**: 2723.

Stimac, E., V.E. Groppi, Jr., and P. Coffino. 1983. Increased histone mRNA levels during inhibition of protein synthesis. *Biochem. Biophys. Res. Commun.* **114**: 131.

———. 1984. Inhibition of protein synthesis stabilizes histone mRNA. *Mol. Cell. Biol.* **4**: 2082.

Venkatesan, N. 1977. Mechanism of inhibition of DNA synthesis by cycloheximide in balb/3T3 cells. *Biochim. Biophys. Acta* **478**: 437.

Worcel, A., S. Han, and M.L. Wong. 1978. Assembly of newly replicated chromatin. *Cell* **15**: 969.

Wu, R.S. and W.M. Bonner. 1981. Separation of basal histone synthesis from S-phase histone synthesis in dividing cells. *Cell* **27**: 321.

———. 1985. Mechanism for differential sensitivity of the chromosome and growth cycles of mammalian cells to the rate of protein synthesis. *Mol. Cell. Biol.* **5**: 2959.

Wu, R.S., L.J. Perry, and W.M. Bonner. 1983. Fate of newly synthesized histone in G$_1$ and G$_0$ cells. *FEBS Lett.* **162**: 161.

Wu, R.S., S. Tsai, and W.M. Bonner. 1982. Patterns of histone variant synthesis can distinguish G$_0$ from G$_1$ cells. *Cell* **31**: 367.

Wu, R.S., H.T. Panusz, C.L. Hatch, and W.M. Bonner. 1986. Histones and their modifications. *CRC Crit. Rev. Biochem.* **20**: 201.

Cell Biology of Topoisomerase II

W.C. Earnshaw and M.M.S. Heck

Department of Cell Biology and Anatomy, Johns Hopkins University School of Medicine,
Baltimore, Maryland 21205

The expression of topoisomerase II is tightly regulated, both as a function of cell cycle position and as a function of proliferative state. When cells cease proliferating, they rapidly lose all detectable antigen. When they commence proliferating, cells acquire the enzyme coordinate with the onset of replication. In exponentially growing cell cultures, the protein is synthesized throughout S and G_2 phases. During mitosis, topoisomerase II is a major component of the chromosomes, where it appears concentrated in anchoring complexes at the base of the chromatin loop domains. The finding that the enzyme is also a major component of the mitotic chromosome scaffold suggests that it may have a dual structural/catalytic role. Chromosome decondensation following mitosis is accompanied by a dramatic decrease in the stability of topoisomerase II. This suggests that the cycle of chromosome condensation/decondensation may depend on a parallel cycle of synthesis/degradation of topoisomerase II.

There are two principal DNA topoisomerases in eukaryotic cells: type I enzymes, which induce transient protein-linked breaks in one strand of the double helix, and type II enzymes, in which both strands of the double helix are cleaved. Eukaryotic type II DNA topoisomerases use ATP to relax superhelical twist in DNA molecules, to catenate and decatenate covalently closed double-stranded circular DNA molecules, and to knot and unknot DNA (Wang 1985). Under ordinary circumstances, type I enzymes (which do not use ATP) perform only the relaxation of superhelical twist (Wang 1985).

Despite extensive characterization in vitro, the role of these enzymes in vivo remains largely undefined. This is probably because the major function of the topoisomerases during interphase is relaxation of superhelical twist, and either enzyme can perform this task. Thus, even though defective mutants have recently been isolated in *Saccharomyces* and *Schizosaccharomyces*, the phenotypes they exhibit under restrictive conditions are complex. For example, mutants defective in topoisomerase I function are viable in both yeasts (Thrash et al. 1984; Uemura and Yanagida 1984). In contrast, topoisomerase II is an essential gene (DiNardo et al. 1984; Uemura and Yanagida 1984). In its absence, cells die in anaphase of mitosis (Holm et al. 1985; Uemura and Yanagida 1986), implying that sister chromatid segregation involves the decatenation of topologically interlocked DNA domains (an activity that cannot be performed by type I topoisomerases). Analysis of double mutants (Brill et al. 1987) indicates that one or both enzymes are essential for DNA replication and polymerase I transcription; however, the identity of the specific topoisomerases involved in these activities remains unclear, since both proceed apparently normally in single mutant strains.

Earlier experiments from this laboratory suggested that topoisomerase II might perform additional nonenzymatic functions in vivo. We showed that the protein is one of the major components of the mitotic chromosome scaffold fraction (Earnshaw et al. 1985), a biochemical fraction containing the most insoluble polypeptides of chromosomes (Adolph et al. 1977). (In contrast, topoisomerase I is not found in the scaffold fraction, and is quantitatively extracted by 1 M NaCl [McConaughy et al. 1981].) Components of the scaffold fraction have been proposed by Laemmli and co-workers to be structural proteins involved in chromosome condensation and in maintenance of the loop domain architecture of the chromosomes (Laemmli et al. 1978). This suggested to us that topoisomerase II might fulfill a dual catalytic/structural role, much like myosin and dynein.

The finding that topoisomerase II is one of the major components of the nuclear matrix fraction in *Drosophila melanogaster* (Berrios et al. 1985) suggested that this dual role for type II DNA topoisomerases might be important throughout interphase as well. This may explain the association of newly replicated DNA with the nuclear matrix fraction (Pardoll et al. 1980; van der Velden et al. 1984), since topoisomerase II is intimately associated with newly replicated DNA molecules (Nelson et al. 1986). Previous evidence for involvement of topoisomerase II in replication had come from analysis of terminal stages of SV40 replication (Sundin and Varshavsky 1981), where it was shown that the termination of viral replication involves the separation of multiply intertwined catenated dimers.

Whether topoisomerase II is involved in transcription is uncertain. Several laboratories have independently identified sequences that are apparently responsible for association of DNA loop domains with the nuclear matrix. These sequences often include, or are adjacent to, elements with enhancer activity. In addition, they are often associated with the presence of a consensus sequence (Sander and Hsieh 1985) for sites of preferred cleavage by *Drosophila* topoisomerase II (Cockerill and Garrard 1986; Gasser and Laemmli 1986). Thus, enhancers may be sites of interaction with the nuclear matrix mediated by topoisomerase II binding.

279

CANCER CELLS 6 / *Eukaryotic DNA Replication.* © 1988 by Cold Spring Harbor Laboratory 0-87969-308-8/88 $1.00

On the other hand, topoisomerase II is not concentrated at transcriptionally active loci (puffs) on *Drosophila* polytene chromosomes (Heller et al. 1986). (In contrast, topoisomerase I *is* concentrated at puffs.) Furthermore, when both topoisomerases are inactivated simultaneously in *Saccharomyces*, transcription by RNA polymerase II continues, albeit at a decreased rate (Brill et al. 1987).

In recent years, the type I and II enzymes have been shown to have little in common other than their ability to introduce transient protein-linked breaks in DNA. The type I topoisomerase appears to be a fairly ubiquitous soluble enzyme, whereas the type II enzyme is a largely insoluble structural protein that varies significantly in abundance from cell type to cell type. In this paper, we will summarize our findings concerning the location, expression, and cell cycle dynamics of the two topoisomerases in eukaryotic cells. In these experiments, the two topoisomerases will be shown to exhibit significant differences at nearly every level.

Materials and Methods

Immunocytochemical methods

These procedures have been described previously as follows: immunoblotting (Earnshaw and Rothfield 1985); indirect immunofluorescence (Earnshaw and Migeon 1985); and immunoelectron microscopy (Earnshaw and Heck 1985).

Proliferation studies

Isolation and immunocytochemical analysis of cells involved in chicken erythropoiesis and myogenesis and lymphoid activation were described previously (Heck and Earnshaw 1986).

Cell cycle analyses

Methods for analysis of the accumulation and stability of topoisomerases I and II across the cell cycle are described elsewhere (M.M.S. Heck et al., in prep.). Analysis of the expression of topoisomerase II across the cell cycle was performed as follows. An exponentially growing culture of MSB-1 lymphoblastoid cells (growing in RPMI +5% fetal calf serum) was pulse labeled with [^{35}S]methionine for 2 hours, after which the population was fractionated according to size by centrifugal elutriation. This separates the population into ~ 15 fractions, according to position in the cell cycle (confirmed by flow cytometry). Equal numbers of cells from each fraction were then disrupted by boiling in SDS-containing buffer and processed for immunoprecipitation with anti-topoisomerase II as described previously (Heck and Earnshaw 1986). The immunoprecipitates were subjected to SDS-PAGE, and the amount of newly synthesized antigen determined by fluorography (Laskey and Mills 1975) and densitometry.

Results

Topoisomerase II: Specific marker for cell proliferation

When complex tissues are stained with antibodies against topoisomerase II, the levels of antigen are seen to vary dramatically from cell to cell. For example, in the germinal epithelium from testis virtually all cells lack detectable antigen (Fig. 1). The only immunopositive cells are isolated clusters of primary and secondary spermatocytes. Similarly, when unsynchronized populations of cells growing in culture were examined by indirect immunofluorescence, many were found to express significantly reduced levels of topoisomerase II antigen. The antigen-negative cells were far more abundant in primary cultures than in transformed lines.

These variations in antigen content could be due to differences in cell cycle position or growth status between cells. Alternatively, the variations in staining could be an artifact of the fluorescence staining procedure.

To examine the relationship between cell cycle position and topoisomerase II content, an exponentially growing population of MSB-1 lymphoblastoid cells was sorted in a fluorescence-activated cell sorter according to DNA content (position in the cell cycle). Populations characteristic of G_1, S, and $G_2 + M$ were collected and processed for indirect immunofluorescence. Topoisomerase II content was found to show a strong correlation with cell cycle position (Table 1). Virtually all cells that lacked detectable topoisomerase II antigen had a G_1 DNA content. This suggested to us that either the antigen is degraded (or masked) during a portion of the G_1 period, or that nondividing cells lack topoisomerase II.

We first examined the possibility that the antigen-negative cells were no longer proliferating. To do this, we examined antigen levels in two developmental systems where cells undergo programmed changes in proliferative activity.

The first of these, erythropoiesis, involves a transition from transcriptionally active proliferating blast cells to quiescent mature erythrocytes (which retain their nuclei, but are completely inactive in both replication and in transcription). For the first 8–10 days of development of the chicken, erythropoiesis occurs in the circulating blood. At early times, the population of cells in the blood is composed of various cohorts of primitive and later, definitive erythroblasts. These cells are actively proliferating, and mitotic figures are commonly seen in blood smears (data not shown).

Table 1 Correlation between Cell Cycle Position and Content of Topoisomerase II Antigen in MSB-1 Cells

Cell cycle phase	Negative cells	Total cells counted	Negative cells (%)
G_1	71	494	14
S	13	488	2
$G_2 + M$	0	297	0

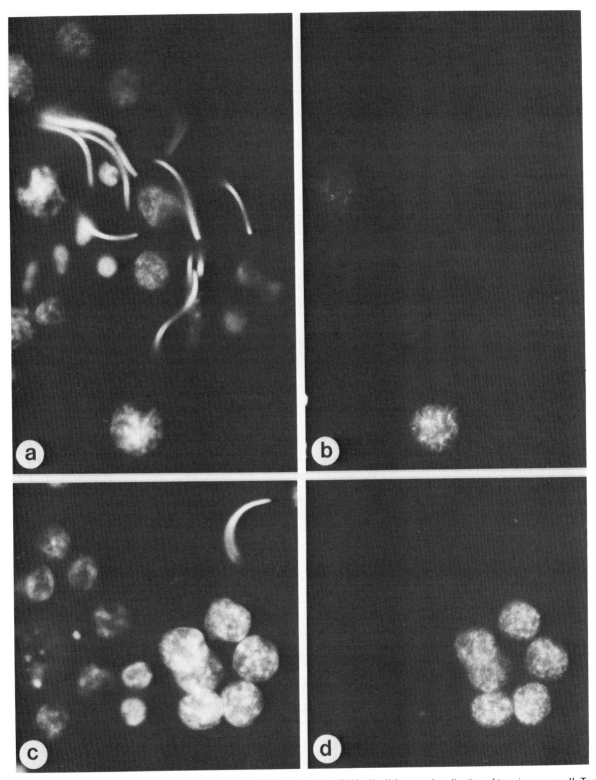

Figure 1 Localization of topoisomerase II in testis. (*a,c*) DAPI stain of the DNA. (*b,d*) Immunolocalization of topoisomerase II. Testes were surgically removed from roosters, the capsule removed, and the seminiferous tubules gently diced with a razor blade. Subsequently, the cell suspension was centrifuged onto a cover slip and processed as described previously for detection of topoisomerase II using antibody 2B2. The great majority of cells, including the elongated spermatozoa, lack detectable antigen. Immunopositive cells appear to contain condensed chromatin, and are probably spermatocytes in meiotic prophase.

When erythroblasts are examined for the presence of topoisomerase II by either indirect immunofluorescence or immunoblotting, the antigen is found to be present in significant amounts (Heck and Earnshaw 1986). However, this situation is dramatically altered after 8–10 days, when erythropoiesis shifts to the marrow compartment. Now, mitotic figures are no longer seen in the circulating blood, which is composed primarily of primitive and definitive erythrocytes. These terminally differentiated cells lack detectable topoisomerase II, as determined by both indirect immunofluorescence (Fig. 2) and immunoblotting (Heck and Earnshaw 1986). The drop in antigen levels is dramatic: from $\sim 1.5 \times 10^5$ copies of the enzyme in a 4-day erythroblast to < 300 copies in a mature erythrocyte (Heck and Earnshaw 1986). Thus, when cells make the transition from the growing state to a quiescent, terminally differentiated state, they cease to express topoisomerase II antigen.

It was important to assess whether the drop in topoisomerase II levels was associated with the cessation of transcription or with the cessation of proliferation, or both. This was done by monitoring the changes in

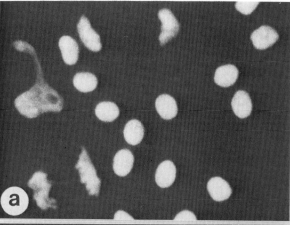
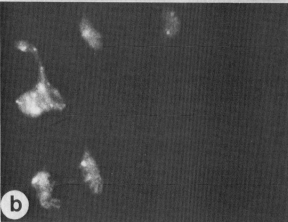

Figure 2 Immunofluorescence analysis of a mixture of chicken erythrocytes and MSB-1 lymphoblastoid cells using an antibody specific for topoisomerase II. (*a*) DAPI stain of the DNA. (*b*) Localization of topoisomerase II. Only the MSB-1 cells (from bottom to top; anaphase, interphase, and telophase) contain detectable antigen.

topoisomerase II content during the early stages of myogenesis. Explanted embryonic myoblasts proliferate rapidly for several days in culture. During this time, these cells have readily detectable levels of topoisomerase II antigen (Heck and Earnshaw 1986). The onset of myogenesis occurs when adjacent myoblasts fuse to form syncitial myotubes. Myotubes are committed to terminal differentiation: They have ceased division and synthesize large amounts of the mRNAs and proteins of the contractile apparatus.

Immunocytochemical analysis revealed that early myotubes lack detectable topoisomerase II (Heck and Earnshaw 1986). At the same time, these cells continue to actively transcribe the genes encoding components of the contractile apparatus (Hayward and Schwartz 1986). Thus, the normal levels of topoisomerase II found in the dividing nucleus are not required for ongoing transcription of these genes.

The above experiments indicate that topoisomerase II is a sensitive and specific marker for cell proliferation. Topoisomerase I is *not* such a marker. When mature chicken erythrocytes are examined by immunoblotting, they are found to contain about 40% of the level of topoisomerase I antigen that occurs in erythroblasts (Heck and Earnshaw 1986). Topoisomerase I is present in adult liver, whereas topoisomerase II is not (data not shown).

Stability of topoisomerase II in transformed and normal cells

The disappearance of topoisomerase II from nonproliferating cells could occur in two ways: (1) A specific signal to degrade topoisomerase II could be sent as a consequence of the decision to cease proliferation. That is, topoisomerase II could be less stable in nongrowing than growing cells. (2) Alternatively, topoisomerase II might normally be degraded at one point of the cell cycle (for example, upon exit from mitosis) and then synthesized de novo as part of the program of initiation of the next division cycle. In this case, when cells cease proliferating they no longer express the antigen because they no longer send the signal to initiate the next division.

One of the most obvious differences between normal and transformed cells is that in the latter, the mechanisms governing the decision of whether to initiate another round of replication and division appear to be constitutively locked in the "on" mode. Thus, if possibility (1) above were true, then one might expect to observe elevated levels of topoisomerase II in transformed cells as compared to nontransformed proliferating populations.

We have measured total antigen levels in several cell types by immunoprecipitation (Table 2). These data show clearly that there are about five- to tenfold more copies of the enzyme in transformed cells than in their normal counterparts.

Such a difference in amount of topoisomerase II antigen could reflect a change in either the synthesis or stability of the enzyme (or both). We have therefore

Table 2 Numbers of Topoisomerase II Monomers in Normal and Transformed Cells

Cell type	Number of copies	Number of determinations
5-Day erythroblasts	$7.8 \pm 1.6 \times 10^4$	6
Chick embryo fibroblasts	1×10^5	5
MSB-1 lymphoblastoid	$4.3 \pm 1.3 \times 10^5$	36
249 hepatoma	$4.9 \pm 2.9 \times 10^5$	9

measured the stability of topoisomerases I and II in normal (embryo fibroblasts) and transformed (249 hepatoma) cells as follows. Cells were pulse labeled with [^{35}S]methionine and chased for various times. Labeled antigen was measured by solubilization of the cells in SDS-containing buffer followed by immunoprecipitation, SDS-PAGE, and quantitative autoradiography (M.M.S. Heck et al., in prep.).

The half-life of topoisomerase II in an exponential population of the transformed cell line 249 was found to be 12 ± 3 hours (M.M.S. Heck et al., in prep.). The enzyme is about fourfold less stable in the primary culture, with a half-life of 3.3 ± 0.5 hours. Assuming equivalent biosynthetic rates, the difference in stability of the enzyme could account for the difference in copy number between the normal and transformed cells.

These determinations highlight yet another difference between the two topoisomerases. In contrast to the values obtained with topoisomerase II, topoisomerase I is, if anything, slightly *more* stable in nontransformed cells. Its half-life in the transformed cells was 16 ± 1 hours, whereas the value determined in embryo fibroblast was 23 ± 1 hours (M.M.S. Heck et al., in prep.).

Expression of topoisomerase II across the cell cycle

We have also examined whether the cellular content of topoisomerase II varies significantly across the cell cycle. Because of the apparent involvement of topoisomerase II in mitotic chromosome structure, we placed particular emphasis on the period of time surrounding mitosis. For these studies, we have used selection rather than induction synchrony methods to avoid subjecting the cells to drugs that might alter cellular physiology in unexpected ways.

Our first experiments involved analysis of the reentry of a nondividing population of peripheral blood lymphocytes into the cell cycle. These cells circulate in the blood in a quiescent state (G_0) awaiting stimulation by an appropriate antigen. Peripheral blood lymphocytes lack topoisomerase II detectable by either immunoblotting or indirect immunofluorescence, as predicted by our experiments with erythropoiesis and myogenesis (Heck and Earnshaw 1986).

When T lymphocytes from such a population are stimulated with concanavalin A, a fraction of the cells becomes activated and reenters the proliferative cycle. These cells are seen on pulse label to incorporate ^{3}H-thymidine, and to coordinately express topoisomerase II antigen (Heck and Earnshaw 1986). Because the

background level of DNA replication in an unstimulated culture of these cells is zero, it was possible to use this experiment to ask at what point (relative to replication) topoisomerase II antigen was expressed, by correlating the appearance of antigen with the *first* incorporation of ^{3}H-thymidine into DNA.

The coupling between the onset of S phase and the expression of topoisomerase II antigen was extremely tight under these conditions. Of 300 cells in which replication had occurred, 295 also expressed topoisomerase II antigen (Heck and Earnshaw 1986). No cells were observed in which topoisomerase II expression had occurred in the absence of replication. These results imply that topoisomerase II does not accumulate in late G_1, but rather, that its synthesis is temporally coupled to that of the DNA.

This expression of antigen consists of de novo protein synthesis and not unmasking of a previously existing pool of latent antigenic determinants. In immunoblotting experiments, the antigen was seen to appear coincident with its detection by immunofluorescence.

A similar link between the onset of replication and the expression of topoisomerase II also occurs in exponentially growing cells. A random poulation of MSB-1 cells was pulse labeled for 2 hours with [^{35}S]methionine prior to separation according to size by centrifugal elutriation. This enabled us to look at approximately 15 segments of the cell cycle without having to resort to induction synchrony procedures. An aliquot of each fraction was analyzed by flow cytometry to determine its average cell cycle position. The rest of the fraction was then processed for immunoprecipitation of topoisomerase II (Materials and Methods). Newly synthesized molecules were detected by autoradiography. Note that this protocol avoids the possible effects that synchronization procedures might have on the expression topoisomerase II, since the pulse label occurred while the cells were growing in exponential culture, prior to fractionation by centrifugal elutriation.

The results of such an experiment are summarized in Figure 3. Topoisomerase II is synthesized across the

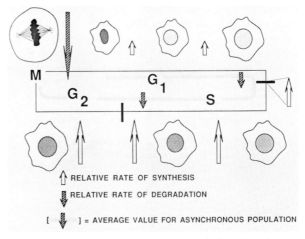

Figure 3 Patterns of synthesis and degradation of topoisomerase II across the cell cycle in chicken cells.

entire cell cycle in these cells; however, the level of expression is low in G_1. This changes substantially at the onset of S phase, when the synthetic rate jumps about twofold. The rate continues to increase, reaching a maximum of about three times the G_1 value by late S. Even though the major increase in expression of topoisomerase II occurs at the G_1–S transition, synthesis of protein remains high throughout S and on through G_2.

Thus, experiments with both normal and transformed cultures agree that the level of expression of topoisomerase II is markedly stimulated at the onset of S-phase, implying that topoisomerase II is likely to participate in DNA replication. An alternative explanation is that the enzyme functions only during mitosis, but that the period of DNA replication (when the chromatin is maximally decondensed) is used to correctly position the enzyme where it will act in the subsequent mitosis.

The continued high synthetic rate throughout G_2 was unexpected. This is not what would be predicted if the function of the protein were only to participate directly in the events of DNA metabolism. However, such a pattern of synthesis would be predicted for a protein with a dual function both during replication and during mitosis.

Accumulation and stability of topoisomerase II across the cell cycle

Further differences in the expression of topoisomerases I and II are revealed by analysis of the accumulation and stability of the two proteins across the cell cycle, and particularly in the period around mitosis.

The levels of both proteins were measured in cells that had been fractionated by centrifugal elutriation. An aliquot from each elutriation fraction was characterized by flow cytometry to determine the predominant cell cycle phase, and the bulk of fraction was then solubilized by boiling in SDS-PAGE buffer (M.M.S. Heck et al., in prep.). Thus, this procedure examines total cellular protein and does not depend on selective solubilization of the antigens.

The amount of protein in each successive elutriation fraction increases as the total protein mass increases across the cell cycle. To compare the amounts of specific antigens between fractions and between experiments, the amount of antigen in each fraction was divided by the total amount of protein in that fraction (determined either by densitometric scanning, or by eluting the Coomassie blue from the entire lane and reading the OD_{605}). This value of SA_{ag} (specific antigenicity) gives a measure of whether a given antigen accumulates preferentially during a given segment of the cell cycle.

Topoisomerase I does not accumulate preferentially across the cell cycle. The value of SA_{topoI} remains close to 1.0 for all elutriation fractions examined (M.M.S. Heck et al., in prep). This means that topoisomerase I accumulation follows that of the bulk of cellular proteins.

Topoisomerase II shows a significantly different pattern of accumulation (Heck et al., in prep.). This enzyme is preferentially expressed beginning in early S phase, with SA_{topoII} reaching a maximum of ~1.7 in late G_2.

Thus, topoisomerase II accumulates in significantly greater amounts than do the bulk of the cellular proteins. Assuming that the content of topoisomerase II is relatively constant from generation to generation in growing cells, this implies that the "excess" topoisomerase II must be degraded at some point during the cycle.

The obvious time to look for such degradation is at the M–G_1 transition. We therefore obtained populations of mitotic cells by selective detachment. Serial shakeoffs were performed at 15-minute intervals, with the cells being retained in mitosis by resuspension in cold medium (M.M.S.Heck et al., in prep.). When sufficient cells were accumulated (6 shakeoffs), they were resuspended in warm medium and allowed to complete mitosis and reenter the next cell cycle. Aliquots were taken at time 0 (addition of the warm medium) and at various time points thereafter; the mitotic index determined; and the bulk of the cells solubilized by boiling in SDS-PAGE buffer.

In such an experiment, it is expected that the level of any protein should drop to 50% as a consequence of cell division, and this was essentially what was observed for topoisomerase I. The levels of this antigen dropped to 58% of the mitotic value at 90 minutes after resumption of mitosis and then began to steadily increase as the cells continued to grow (M.M.S. Heck, in prep.).

The behavior of topoisomerase II was significantly different. By 90 minutes the level of the protein had fallen to 36% of the mitotic value. This level continued to decrease gradually, reaching 31% at 3 hours post-release (Fig. 3; M.M.S. Heck et al., in prep.). Therefore, topoisomerase II is selectively degraded as cells exit from mitosis and proceed into the subsequent G_1.

This change in topoisomerase II content is due to a dramatic decrease in the stability of the protein. As described above, the half-life of topoisomerase II in an exponential population of the transformed cell line 249 was found to be 12 ± 3 hours. In marked contrast, during the transition from mitosis to the first 3 hours of G_1, the half-life decreased about sevenfold to < 2 hours (M.M.S. Heck et al., in prep.). Thus, the process of chromosome decondensation is accompanied by a programmed degradation of topoisomerase II.

Differential distribution of topoisomerases I and II in mitotic chromosomes

We have used both light and electron microscopy to map the location of topoisomerases I and II in mitotic chromosomes. The two enzymes exhibit very different distributions. As shown by indirect immunofluorescence, both topoisomerases are abundant components of mitotic chromosomes (Fig. 2; data not shown for topoisomerase I). In these images, it is difficult to determine whether the antigens are distributed throughout the chromosome or whether they are restricted to discrete subdomains. However, in previous studies we have been able to use immunofluorescence procedures to demonstrate that topoisomerase II occupies a limited subdomain within the chromosome (Earnshaw and Heck 1985).

A more conclusive experiment involves the use of antibody to cross-link the antigens of swollen chromosomes in solution. In these experiments, if an antigen is distributed on the chromatin loop domains, addition of antibody results in collapse of the loops and a condensation of the overall structure (Fig. 4). If, on the other hand, the antigen is not bound to the chromatin along the loop domains, addition of the antibody does not cause the loops to collapse, and there is no change in the width of the swollen chromosome (Fig. 4). As Figure 4c shows, topoisomerase I is distributed along the loop chromatin, and topoisomerase II is not.

Where is the topoisomerase II? The combination of antibody cross-linking and immunofluorescence data (Earnshaw and Heck 1985) suggests that topoisomerase II is concentrated at the base of the chromatin loops. This interpretation is also supported by data such as shown in Figure 5,a and b. In this experiment, chromosomes were centrifuged onto carbon films and then stained with anti-topoisomerase II. In some cases the antibody appeared to stain the axial regions of the chromosomes, whereas in others (Fig. 5) the antibody was localized in many discrete foci. The most likely interpretation of these foci is that they are anchoring

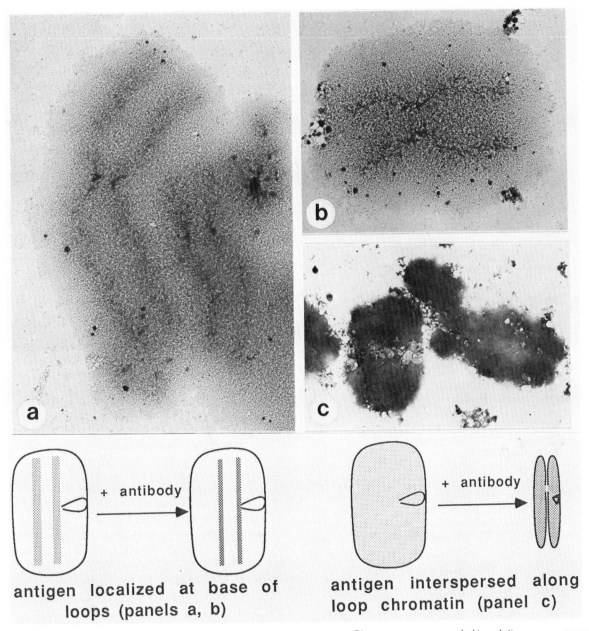

antigen localized at base of loops (panels a, b)

antigen interspersed along loop chromatin (panel c)

Figure 4 In situ precipitation of topoisomerases I and II within chromosomes. Chromosomes suspended in solution were exposed to anti-topoisomerase II (2B2 diluted 1:62.5, *a,b*) or anti-topoisomerase I (autoantibody SC diluted 1:50) as described previously (Earnshaw and Heck 1985). Treatment of chromosomes with anti-topoisomerase I causes collapse of the loop domains, but treatment with anti-topoisomerase II does not.

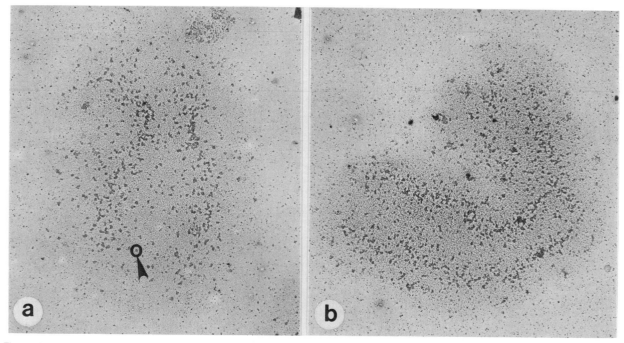

Figure 5 Immunocytochemical localization of topoisomerase II in mitotic chromosomes in the electron microscope. The antigen is localized in discrete foci (termed here *anchoring complexes*) that in some cases are concentrated along the chromosome axis (*b*), and in others are more dispersed (*a*). One of the anchoring complexes is indicated in *a*. Note that the actual size of the anchoring complexes is likely to be substantially smaller than it appears in these images, since in these experiments, the complexes were coated with three successive layers of antibody (Earnshaw and Heck 1985).

complexes at the bases of rosettes of loop domains. Each chromosome may be composed of many such rosettes, as proposed by Comings (1977) and Pienta and Coffey (1984).

Our current experiments focus on the identification of other components in these anchoring complexes.

Discussion

The two topoisomerases

The studies reported above present a number of significant differences between topoisomerases I and II.

1. The two enzymes show different solubility properties, and therefore must interact differently with other chromosomal proteins and DNA. Topoisomerase I is readily solubilized by 1 M NaCl (McConaughy et al. 1981) and is not a component of the mitotic chromosome scaffold fraction. Topoisomerase II is largely insoluble, even in the presence of 2 M NaCl, unless β-mercaptoethanol or dithiothreitol is present (Earnshaw et al. 1985). β-Mercaptoethanol has been shown previously to specifically destabilize the chromosome scaffold (Lewis and Laemmli 1982).
2. Topoisomerase II is encoded by an essential gene in yeasts, but topoisomerase I is not (DiNardo et al. 1984; Thrash et al. 1984; Uemura and Yanagida 1984).
3. Topoisomerase I is associated with sites of active

transcription, but topoisomerase II is not (Heller et al. 1986).
4. Topoisomerase II is only present in actively proliferating cells (Duguet et al. 1983; Heck and Earnshaw 1986; Sullivan et al. 1986). Topoisomerase I is present also in quiescent cells (Heck and Earnshaw 1986).
5. Topoisomerase II is significantly less stable in normal cells than in transformed cells. Topoisomerase I is, if anything, more stable in normal cells.
6. As cells traverse the cycle, topoisomerase II increases in mass threefold, whereas topoisomerase I and the bulk of cellular proteins double.
7. As cells exit from mitosis, the half-life of topoisomerase II is dramatically decreased, probably in conjunction with chromosome decondensation. The stability of topoisomerase I appears unaltered during this time period.
8. Topoisomerase I appears to be randomly distributed along the loop domain chromatin in mitotic chromosomes. Topoisomerase II is not present in significant amounts on the loop chromatin, being instead concentrated in what appear to be anchoring complexes at the base of the loop domains.

Taking into account the above observations, it appears that the only significant attribute shared by the two topoisomerases is their ability to act enzymatically on DNA. Topoisomerase I is apparently a classic soluble enzyme, whereas topoisomerase II appears to have a dual catalytic/structural role.

Expression of topoisomerase II across the cell cycle

The patterns of synthesis and degradation of topoisomerase II around the cell cycle are summarized in Figure 3. Two aspects of these observations appear particularly significant.

1. A significant increase in synthetic rate accompanies entry of the cells into S phase. This implies that the enzyme functions during DNA replication. In addition, the rate of synthesis remains high during G_2. This synthesis presumably represents the production of *structural* topoisomerase II, which, as a component of the chromosome scaffold, is likely to participate in the process of mitotic chromosome condensation.
2. The stability of the enzyme varies significantly across the cell cycle. During the transition from mitosis to G_1, the half-life decreases about sevenfold to < 2 hours. Thus, chromosome condensation is accompanied by synthesis of topoisomerase II, and chromosome decondensation is accompanied by degradation of the enzyme.

These observations suggest a new aspect of the cellular control of the dramatic structural alterations that occur at the onset of mitosis. Until now, thought in the field has centered on the role of posttranslational modifications (principally phosphorylation) of preexisting proteins in triggering the onset of mitosis in general (Adlakha and Rao 1986), and nuclear envelope breakdown in particular (Gerace and Blobel 1980). These arguments have been much strengthened by recent successes in development of cell-free systems in which nuclear envelope breakdown and assembly are achieved (Burke and Gerace 1986; Suprynowicz and Gerace 1986; Newport and Spann 1987). However, chromosome condensation, although it does occur to a limited extent, is never as dramatic in the former systems as it is in vivo. We suggest that this may be because the chromosome condensation/decondensation cycle is accompanied by (and may require) a parallel cycle of synthesis/degradation of topoisomerase II.

Topoisomerase II, the chromosome scaffold, and mitotic chromosome structure

Figure 6 summarizes our current understanding of the distribution of topoisomerases I and II in mitotic chromosomes. Topoisomerase I appears distributed widely along the chromatin, and does not appear to be a significant structural protein.

Topoisomerase II appears to be concentrated in a number of discrete *anchoring complexes*, which probably form the bases of the chromatin loops. As indicated in the figure, these anchoring complexes are likely to contain other structural components of the chromosome scaffold. There is no evidence to suggest whether or not topoisomerase II is an integral or peripheral component of these complexes.

We currently assume that the only significant nonhistone substructure in mitotic chromosomes is the anchoring complex. Some aspect of the procedures developed for the isolation of chromosome scaffolds apparently causes an aggregation of these complexes, thus generating the rapidly sedimenting aggregate that Laemmli termed the chromosome scaffold fraction (Adolph et al. 1977). It is unlikely that the scaffold exists in mitotic chromosomes as a discrete substructure. Regardless of its role in chromosome structure, the scaffold fraction has proven to be a reproducible source of important nonhistone proteins, including topoisomerase II, centromere proteins (Earnshaw et al. 1984), and proteins apparently involved in sister chromatin pairing (Cooke et al. 1987).

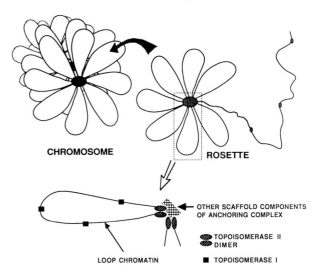

Figure 6 Diagram showing the relative locations of topoisomerases I and II in chromosome loop domains.

Acknowledgments

We gratefully acknowledge the excellent technical assistance of Carol A. Cooke, without whom this work would not have been possible. We also acknowledge our collaborators in various stages of the project, including Walter Hittelman, Leroy Liu, and Brian Halligan. We thank P. Fisher, M. Soloski, L. Gerace, and J. Glass for helpful discussions. These studies were supported by National Institutes of Health grant GM-30985 to W.C.E. M.M.S.H. was a predoctoral fellow of the National Science Foundation.

References

Adlakha, R.C. and P.N. Rao. 1986. Molecular mechanisms of the chromosome condensation and decondensation cycle in mammalian cells. *Bioessays* **5:** 100.

Adolph, K.W., S.M. Cheng, J.R. Paulson, and U.K. Laemmli. 1977. Isolation of a protein scaffold from mitotic Hela cell chromosomes. *Proc. Natl. Acad. Sci.* **11:** 4937.

Berrios, M., N. Osheroff, and P.A. Fisher. 1985. In situ localization of DNA topoisomerase II, a major polypeptide component of the *Drosophila* nuclear matrix fraction. *Proc. Natl. Acad. Sci.* **82:** 4142.

Brill, S.J., S. DiNardo, K. Voelkel-Meiman, and R. Sternglanz. 1987. Need for DNA topoisomerase activity as a swivel for DNA replication for transcription of ribosomal RNA. *Nature* **326:** 414.

Burke, B. and L. Gerace. 1986. A cell free system to study reassembly of the nuclear envelope at the end of mitosis. *Cell* **44:** 639.

Cockerill, P.N. and W.T. Garrard. 1986. Chromosomal loop anchorage of the kappa immunoglobulin gene occurs next to the enhancer in a region containing topoisomerase II sites. *Cell* **44:** 273.

Comings, D.E. 1977. Mammalian chromosome structure. *Chromosomes Today* **6:** 19.

Cooke, C.A., M.M.S. Heck, and W.C. Earnshaw. 1987. The INCENP antigens: Movement from the inner centromere to the midbody during mitosis. *J. Cell Biol.* (in press).

DiNardo, S., K. Voelkel, and R. Sternglanz. 1984. DNA topoisomerase II mutant of *Saccharomyces cerevisiae*: Topoisomerase II is required for segregation of daughter molecules at the termination of DNA replication. *Proc. Natl. Acad. Sci.* **81:** 2616.

Duguet, M., C. Lavenot, F. Harper, G. Mirambeau, and A.-M. De Recondo. 1983. DNA topoisomerases from rat liver: Physiological variations. *Nucleic Acids Res.* **11:** 1059.

Earnshaw, W.C. and M.M.S. Heck. 1985. Localization of topoisomerase II in mitotic chromosomes. *J. Cell Biol.* **100:** 1716.

Earnshaw, W.C. and B.R. Migeon. 1985. Three related centromere proteins are absent from the inactive centromere of a stable isodicentric chromosome. *Chromosoma* **92:** 290.

Earnshaw, W.C. and N.F. Rothfield. 1985. Identification of a family of human centromere proteins using autoimmune sera from patients with scleroderma. *Chromosoma* **91:** 313.

Earnshaw, W.C., N. Halligan, C. Cooke, and N. Rothfield. 1984. The kinetochore is part of the metaphase chromosome scaffold. *J. Cell Biol.* **98:** 352.

Earnshaw, W.C., B. Halligan, C.A. Cooke, M.M.S. Heck, and L.F. Liu. 1985. Topoisomerase II is a structural component of mitotic chromosome scaffolds. *J. Cell Biol.* **100:** 1706.

Gasser, S.M. and U.K. Laemmli. 1986. Cohabitation of scaffold binding regions with upstream/enhancer elements of three developmentally regulated genes of *D. melanogaster*. *Cell* **46:** 521.

Gerace, L. and G. Blobel. 1980. The nuclear envelope lamina is reversibly depolymerized during mitosis. *Cell* **19:** 277.

Hayward, L.J. and R.J. Schwartz. 1986. Sequential expression of chicken actin genes during myogenesis. *J. Cell Biol.* **102:** 1485.

Heck, M.M.S. and W.C. Earnshaw. 1986. Topoisomerase II: A specific marker for cell proliferation. *J. Cell Biol.* **103:** 2569.

Heller, R.A., E.R. Shelton, V. Dietrich, S.C.R. Elgin, and D.L. Brutlag. 1986. Multiple forms and cellular localization of *Drosophila* DNA topoisomerase II. *J. Biol. Chem.* **261:** 8063.

Holm, C., T. Goto, J.C. Wang, and D. Botstein. 1985. DNA topoisomerase II is required at the time of mitosis in yeast. *Cell* **41:** 553.

Laemmli, U.K., S.M. Cheng, K.W. Adolph, J.R. Paulson, J.A. Brown, and W.R. Baumbach. 1978. Metaphase chromosome structure: The role of nonhistone proteins. *Cold Spring Harbor Symp. Quant. Biol.* **42:** 351.

Laskey, R.A. and A.D. Mills. 1975. Quantitative film detection of ^{3}H and ^{14}C in polyacrylamide gels by fluorography. *Eur. J. Biochem.* **56:** 335.

Lewis, C.D. and U.K. Laemmli. 1982. Higher order metaphase chromosome structure: Evidence for metalloprotein interactions. *Cell* **17:** 849.

McConaughy, B.L., L.S. Young, and J.J. Champoux. 1981. The effect of salt on the binding of the eukaryotic DNA nicking-closing enzyme to DNA and chromatin. *Biochim. Biophys. Acta* **655:** 1.

Nelson, W.G., L.F. Liu, and D.S. Coffey. 1986. Newly replicated DNA is associated with DNA topoisomerase II in cultured rat prostatic adenocarcinoma cells. *Nature* **322:** 187.

Newport, J. and T. Spann. 1987. Disassembly of the nucleus in mitotic extracts: Membrane vesicularization, lamina disassembly, and chromosome condensation are independent processes. *Cell* **48:** 219.

Pardoll, D.M., B. Vogelstein, and D.S. Coffey. 1980. A fixed site of replication in eukaryotic cells. *Cell* **19:** 527.

Pienta, K.J. and D.S. Coffey. 1984. A structural analysis of the role of nuclear matrix and DNA loops in the organization of the nucleus and chromosome. *J. Cell Sci.* (suppl.)**1:** 123.

Sander, M. and T.-S. Hsieh. 1985. *Drosophila* topoisomerase II double-strand DNA cleavage: Analysis of DNA sequence homology at the cleavage site. *Nucleic Acids Res.* **13:** 1057.

Sullivan, D.M., B.S. Glisson, P.K. Hodges, S. Smallwood-Kentro, and W.E. Ross. 1986. Proliferation dependence of topoisomerase II mediated drug action. *Biochemistry* **25:** 2248.

Sundin, O. and A. Varshavsky. 1981. Arrest of segregation leads to accumulation of highly intertwined catenated dimers: Dissection of the final stages of SV40 DNA replication. *Cell* **25:** 659.

Suprynowicz, F.A. and L. Gerace. 1986. A fractionated cell-free system for analysis of prophase nuclear disassembly. *J. Cell Biol.* **103:** 2073.

Thrash, C., K. Voelkl, S. DiNardo, and R. Sternglanz. 1984. Identification of *Saccharomyces cerevisiae* mutants deficient in DNA topoisomerase I activity. *J. Biol. Chem.* **259:** 1375.

Uemura, T. and M. Yanagida. 1984. Isolation of type I and II DNA topoisomerase mutants from fission yeast: Single and double mutants show different phenotypes in cell growth and chromatin organization. *EMBO J.* **3:** 1737.

———. 1986. Mitotic spindle pulls but fails to separate chromosomes in type II DNA topoisomerase mutants: Uncoordinated mitosis. *EMBO J.* **5:** 1003.

van der Velden, H.M.W., G. van Willigen, R.H.W. Wetzels, and F. Wanka. 1984. Attachment of origins of replication to the nuclear matrix and the chromosomal scaffold. *FEBS Lett.* **171:** 13.

Wang, J.C. 1985. DNA topoisomerases. *Annu. Rev. Biochem.* **54:** 665.

Cyclin (PCNA, Auxiliary Protein of DNA Polymerase δ), Dividin, and Progressin Are Likely Components of the Common Pathway Leading to DNA Replication and Cell Division in Human Cells

J.E. Celis, P. Madsen, S.U. Nielsen, B. Gesser, H.V. Nielsen, G. Petersen Ratz, J.B. Lauridsen, and A. Celis

Department of Medical Biochemistry, University Park, Aarhus University, DK-8000 Aarhus C, Denmark

Cyclin ($M_r = 36,000$), also known as PCNA or the auxiliary protein of mammalian DNA polymerase δ, dividin (nuclear phosphoprotein, $M_r = 54,000$), and progressin ($M_r = 33,000$) are proliferation-sensitive and cell-cycle-specific proteins (synthesized mainly in S phase) whose rate of synthesis increases at or near the G_1/S transition border of the cell cycle of human cells. The synthesis of these proteins, unlike that of histones, is independent of DNA replication. In vivo replicative DNA synthesis, on the other hand, has not been observed in the absence of synthesis of these proteins. As expected for S-phase-specific proteins, the levels of synthesis of these polypeptides correlate directly with the proliferative state of human cells. Nondividing cultured cells synthesize little of these proteins, whereas proliferating cells (of both normal and transformed origin) make elevated but variable amounts of all three proteins. At present, only the function of cyclin (PCNA) is known (involved in some step in DNA replication); all available information, however, indicates that these proteins are common components of the pathway leading to DNA replication and cell division. The role of these proteins in the initiation of DNA replication and cell cycle progression is discussed.

Cell proliferation in normal cultured cells is controlled by growth factors present in the serum (Hayashi and Sato 1976). When actively proliferating normal cells are deprived of such factors, for example, by lowering the serum content in the media, they cease to cycle and enter a quiescent state termed G_0 (Baserga 1978; Pardee et al. 1978). Control mechanisms involved in this decision are thought to operate mainly in G_1, as resting cells exhibit a G_1 content of DNA (Pardee et al. 1978, and references therein). Addition of serum or defined mitogens to quiescent cells triggers an orderly sequence of events (mitogenic response) that culminate in replicative DNA synthesis and ultimately in cell division (Holley 1975; Pardee et al. 1978). There is at present mounting evidence suggesting that defined mitogens such as polypeptide growth factors, hormones, and pharmacological agents (alone or in various combinations depending on the cell type) act synergistically to stimulate a sequence of multimolecular events that converge into a central pathway leading to DNA replication (for references, see Rozengurt 1986; Celis et al. 1987b). Proteins that are components of this common pathway are thought to be present in all proliferating cell types and to be synthesized (increased synthesis) at or near the G_1/S transi-

tion border of the cell cycle (Celis et al. 1984b, 1987b, and references therein).

Encouraged by the high resolving power of two-dimensional gel electrophoresis, we in this laboratory (Bravo and Celis 1980; Celis et al. 1984a,b, and references therein) undertook the task of searching for components of the pathway(s) that control cell proliferation in human cells by comparing the overall polypeptide patterns of normal cells grown under various conditions, and between normal and transformed cells, tumors included. Specifically, we looked for proteins whose rate of synthesis increased substantially in proliferating cells of both normal and transformed origin and that were modulated during the cell cycle. Moreover, we required these proteins to be present in all human cell types studied, as we surmised that these may correspond to components of the common pathway leading to DNA replication and cell division (Celis et al. 1984b, 1987b, and references therein). In this paper we review and present new data concerning three proliferation-sensitive and cell-cycle-specific human proteins (cyclin, Bravo et al. 1981; Celis et al. 1984a,b, 1987b, Fig. 1; dividin, Celis and Nielsen 1986, Fig. 2; and progressin, Celis et al. 1987a, Fig. 2) that are likely components of

CANCER CELLS 6 / *Eukaryotic DNA Replication.* © 1988 by Cold Spring Harbor Laboratory 0-87969-308-8/88 $1.00

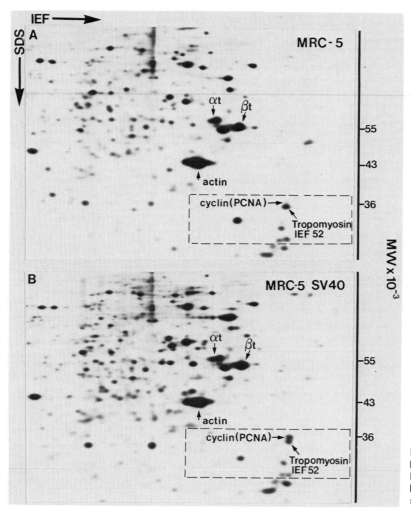

Figure 1 Cyclin (PCNA) synthesis in (*A*) slowly proliferating human MRC-5 fibroblasts and (*B*) SV40-transformed human MRC-5 fibroblasts. Protein IEF 52 corresponds to a tropomyosin (Bravo et al. 1981).

this pathway. The role of these proteins in cell cycle progression is discussed.

Results

Novel proteins that are putative components of the common pathway leading to DNA replication and cell division

Cyclin (PCNA): A role in chromosomal DNA replication
Bravo and Celis, using high-resolution two-dimensional gel electrophoresis (1980), were among the first to search for cell cycle phase-specific proteins in mammalian cells. Their studies, which analyzed global patterns of gene expression throughout the cell cycle of HeLa cells, identified an acidic nuclear protein of apparent $M_r = 36,000$ (isoelectric focusing [IEF] 49 in the HeLa protein catalog, Bravo and Celis 1984), later termed cyclin (Bravo et al. 1981), which was preferentially synthesized during S phase (see also Fig. 3B). Increased synthesis of this ubiquitous protein starts late in G_1 near the G_1/S transition border and reaches a maximum in mid to late S phase (Celis et al. 1987b, and references therein, Fig. 3B). Independently, E. Tan and

co-workers characterized autoantibodies found in the sera from a small percentage of patients with systemic lupus erythematosus (SLE) (Miyachi et al. 1978). These autoantibodies were shown to stain the nucleus of proliferating cells and to react with an acidic polypeptide of $M_r = 36,000$ (Takasaki et al. 1981) that was termed proliferating cell nuclear antigen (PCNA). In 1984, Mathews and colleagues (Mathews et al. 1984) showed that cyclin and PCNA were identical.

As expected for an S-phase-specific protein, the rate of synthesis of cyclin (PCNA) has been shown to correlate directly with the proliferative state of normal cultured cells and tissues of various species (Celis et al. 1984a,b; Bravo 1986; J.I. Garrels and B.R. Franza, in prep., and references therein). Cyclin (PCNA) is absent or present in very low amounts in normal nondividing cultured cells of various origins, but it is synthesized in elevated but variable amounts by proliferating cells of both normal (slowly proliferating human MRC-5 fibroblasts, Fig. 1A) and transformed origin (MRC-5 SV40, Fig. 1B). Cyclin (PCNA) synthesis is regulated at the level of transcription, as suggested by in vitro translation experiments (see references in Celis et al. 1987b) and dot hybridization studies using the cloned gene (Almendral et al. 1987).

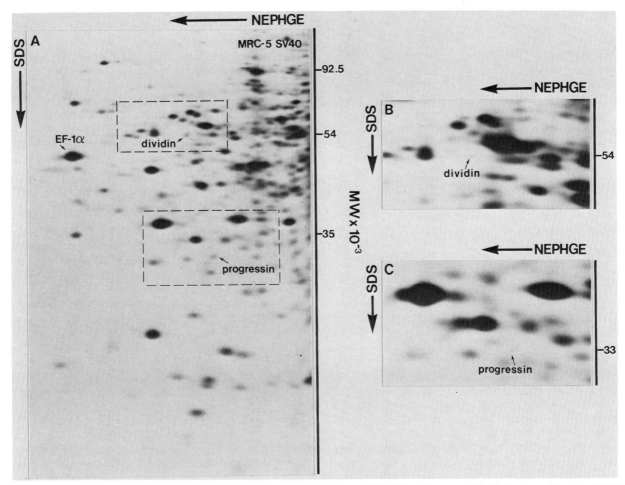

Figure 2 Dividin and progressin synthesis in (*A*) SV40-transformed human MRC-5 fibroblasts and (*B,C*) slowly proliferating MRC-5 fibroblasts. Only the relevant area of the gels is shown in *B* and *C*. Areas shown in Figs. 3D and E are enclosed in *A*.

Immunofluorescence studies of methanol-fixed cells using PCNA autoantibodies specific for cyclin showed that only S-phase cells reacted with these antibodies (Takasaki et al. 1981; Bravo 1986; Celis et al. 1986, 1987b, and references therein) (Fig. 3), and that various patterns of cyclin (PCNA) antigen distribution subdivided S phase (Takasaki et al. 1981; Bravo 1986; Celis et al. 1986, 1987, and references therein) (Fig. 3). Moreover, many of the cyclin (PCNA) patterns were shown to mimic topographical patterns of DNA synthesis (for references, see Celis et al. 1986, 1987b). In particular, late patterns of nucleolar DNA replication as determined by [³H]thymidine autoradiography could be superimposed with immunofluorescence patterns of cyclin (PCNA) antigen distribution (Celis and Celis 1985; Madsen and Celis 1985). These, as well as other observations argued strongly for a role of this protein in chromosomal DNA replication (Celis and Celis 1985; Madsen and Celis 1985; Bravo 1986; Celis et al. 1986, 1987b). A role for cyclin (PCNA) in nucleotide excission DNA repair has also been proposed (Celis and Madsen 1986). Interestingly, repair-deficient *Xeroderma pigmentosum* cells (XP8LO, group A; XP126LO, group F; XPITE, group C) synthesize normal levels of cyclin

(PCNA), suggesting that the defect(s) is unrelated to this protein (results not shown).

Recently, immunofluorescence and biochemical data have firmly established a role for cyclin (PCNA) in DNA replication. First, Nakamura and colleagues (H. Nakamura et al., in prep.) have shown complete colocalization of cyclin (PCNA) antigen and DNA polymerase α with replicating replicon clusters as visualized with BrdU antibodies, and second, work in two laboratories identified cyclin (PCNA) as the auxiliary protein of mammalian DNA polymerase δ (Tan et al. 1986; Bravo et al. 1987; Prelich et al. 1987a,b). Cyclin (PCNA) has no detectable DNA polymerase, primase, ATPase, or nuclease activity, but it is able to stimulate the activity of the DNA polymerase δ core enzyme up to a few hundred-fold when using templates with low template/primer ratio (Tan et al. 1986). Cyclin (PCNA) has no effect on the activity of calf thymus DNA polymerase α when using similar template/primers having long stretches of single-stranded DNA (Tan et al. 1986). Recent studies by Prelich et al. (1987a) have further shown that cyclin (PCNA) may function in the elongation stage of SV40 DNA replication in vitro. Cyclin (PCNA) synthesis is activated by the adenovirus E1A gene concomitant with induction of cellular DNA replication (Zerler et al. 1987).

Interestingly, many of the properties of cyclin (PCNA) resemble those of the β subunit of *Escherichia coli* DNA polymerase III holoenzyme (Kornberg 1980, and references therein). Both proteins are required to replicate templates with low template/primers ratio and exist as dimers of identical subunits. These observations, as well as the fact that cyclin (PCNA) is found at the sites of DNA replication throughout S phase (Celis and Celis 1985; Madsen and Celis 1985; Celis et al. 1986; H. Nakamura et al., in prep.), argue strongly for a role of this protein in chromosomal DNA replication. A role for DNA polymerase δ in replicative DNA synthesis is also evident, implying that DNA polymerase α is not the sole polymerase involved in eukaryotic DNA replication. Analysis of the rate of synthesis of core polymerase δ throughout the cell cycle should reveal whether this protein is regulated in a similar fashion as cyclin (PCNA). Nevertheless, a re-evaluation of the polymerases involved in eukaryotic DNA replication seems necessary in view of the above observations.

Further evidence suggesting that cyclin (PCNA) may be a central component of the common pathway leading to DNA replication and cell division comes from our studies of adult and newborn human and mouse tissues, respectively. Most normal human adult tissues analyzed by two-dimensional gel electrophoresis and silver staining exhibit very low or undetectable levels of cyclin (PCNA). Tissues so far analyzed include aorta, bladder, cavum oris, cerebellar cortex, cerebral cortex, cornea, ductus deferens, epididymis, fat tissue, heart muscle, kidney cortex, kidney medulla, larynx, lung, mammary gland, medulla oblongata, mesencephalon, palate, pharynx, posterior eye polus, prostata, rectum, skeletal muscle, skin, submaxillary glands, thyroid gland, trachea, ureter, uterus, veins, and vesicula seminalis. The fraction of dividing cells present in some of these tissues is too low to be detected by silver staining. Many newborn mouse tissues (gut, spleen, kidney, liver, lung), on the other hand, exhibit high levels of cyclin (PCNA), suggesting that this protein has a central role in cell proliferation in all cell types. So far, DNA replication in vivo has never been observed in the absence of cyclin (PCNA) synthesis, suggesting that expression of this protein is an obligatory event in G_1 to S transition of the cell cycle. Cyclin (PCNA) synthesis, however, can take place in vivo in the presence of DNA synthesis inhibitors (Bravo 1986, and references therein).

Nuclear phosphoprotein dividin
Dividin (nonequilibrium pH gradient electrophoresis [NEPHGE] 10a in the HeLa protein catalog; Bravo and Celis 1984) is a stable human proliferation-sensitive nuclear phosphoprotein ($M_r = 54,000$) that is synthesized almost exclusively during the S phase of the cell cycle of AMA cells (Fig. 3D) (Celis and Nielsen 1986; Nielsen et al. 1987). Dividin synthesis is first detected late in G_1 near the G_1/S transition border, reaches a maximum in mid to late S phase, and declines thereafter

(Fig. 3D). No detectable synthesis of this protein has been observed in growth-arrested normal cells, but its synthesis is stimulated late (G_1/S transition border) after addition of serum to quiescent human MRC-5 fibroblasts (Celis and Nielsen 1986). Dividin is a minor component of human cells (less than 0.01%), suggesting that it may not perform a structural role. Dividin is tightly bound to chromatin and can only be extracted by treatment with buffers containing high salt (0.6 M or higher).

At present there is no information as to the function of dividin. Whether this protein is involved in the control of DNA replication and cell proliferation or merely functions in some specific aspect of DNA replication is currently unknown. As far as we can judge from molecular size estimates, isoelectric point, cell type specificity, and cellular distribution, dividin is different from the oncogene products known to be expressed in a cell-cycle-specific manner (fos, myc, c-myb, ras, and p53) (for references, see Celis and Nielsen 1986; Denhardt et al. 1986), or to other cell-cycle-specific proteins such as thymidine kinase, histones, p68, dihydrofolate reductase, p55, statin, and thymidine synthetase (Denhardt et al. 1986, and references therein). In particular, dividin differs from p53 in its isoelectric point (p53 is more acidic), cell-type specificity (p53 is not present in HeLa cells), and stage of the cell cycle at which it is synthesized (p53 is synthesized in S and part of G_1; for references, see Celis and Nielsen 1986; Denhardt et al. 1986). Interestingly, Song and Adolph (1983) have identified a 55,000 molecular weight nonhistone protein in HeLa cells that is preferentially phosphorylated during S phase. The relation between this protein and dividin is at present unknown.

Currently, we do not know whether dividin is present in other species besides humans. So far, dividin has been observed in all transformed human cultured cells of epithelial, fibroblast, and lymphoid origin (Celis and Nielsen 1986; Nielsen et al. 1987). Synthesis of DNA has not been observed in the absence of dividin synthesis, suggesting that expression of this protein is an obligatory late event in the mitogenic response. Dividin synthesis, on the other hand, is not affected by inhibitors of DNA replication (results not shown).

Progressin
Recent studies in our laboratory (Celis et al. 1987a) have identified a proliferation-sensitive and cell-cycle-specific protein (Fig. 3E) that has been termed progressin. This basic protein, which has an apparent M_r of 33,000, is synthesized by proliferating cells of both normal and transformed origin (Fig. 2), but could not be detected in quiescent cells. Increased synthesis of this protein starts at or near the G_1/S transition border of the cell cycle (Fig. 3E). Low but detectable levels of this protein can be observed in mitotic and G_1 cells (Fig. 3E) (Celis et al. 1987a).

As in the case of cyclin (PCNA) and dividin, the synthesis of progressin is independent of DNA replication (Celis et al. 1987a). So far, DNA replication has

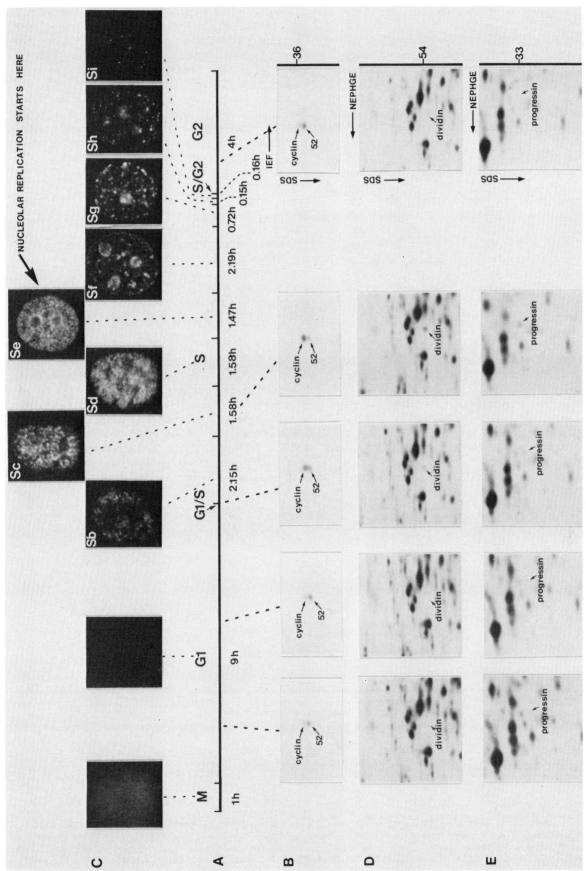

Figure 3 Synthesis of cyclin (PCNA), dividin, and progressin during the cell cycle of transformed human amnion cells (AMA). (*A*) Duration of the cell cycle phases (duration of sub-S-phases is also included; see Celis and Celis 1985). (*B*) Synthesis of cyclin (PCNA) at various stages of the cell cycle. Protein IEF 52 corresponds to a tropomyosin (Bravo et al. 1981). (*C*) Sequence of cyclin (PCNA) antigen distribution as deduced by indirect immunofluorescence using PCNA autoantibodies specific for cyclin. Patterns of cyclin (PCNA) antigen distribution are known to represent actual patterns of DNA replication (Celis et al. 1986). Mitotic, G₁, and G₂ cells contain cyclin (PCNA) (Celis et al. 1986), but this form is not recognized by the autoantibodies in methanol-fixed cells. (*D,E*) Synthesis of dividin (*D*) and progressin (*E*) at various stages of the cell cycle.

never been observed in the absence of progressin synthesis.

As far as we can judge from silver-stained gels of transformed human cells, progressin is a minor component of these cells. Progressin is most likely not phosphorylated, and there is no information as to whether it is present in proliferating cells of species other than humans. Progressin has been identified in transformed human cell lines of fibroblast, epithelial, and lymphoid origin (Celis et al. 1987a).

Discussion

Studies in our laboratory have identified three proliferation-sensitive and cell-cycle-specific proteins (cyclin [PCNA], dividin, and progressin) whose rate of synthesis is modulated during the cell cycle of human cells. The synthesis of these proteins starts at or near the G_1/S transition border of the cell cycle, reaches a maximum in mid to late S phase, and decreases thereafter. Besides exhibiting a similar pattern of synthesis throughout the cell cycle, all three proteins are stable, and unlike histones (for a review, see Denhardt et al. 1986), their synthesis is not coupled to DNA replication (Bravo 1986, and references therein; this paper). DNA replication, on the other hand, has so far not been observed in the absence of synthesis of these proteins, implying that they are essential components of the common pathway leading to DNA replication and cell division. All three proteins are synthesized only by proliferating cells (epithelial, fibroblast, and lymphoid origin), a fact that underlines a key role in cell cycle progression.

What is the role of cyclin (PCNA), progressin, and dividin in the initiation of DNA-replication and cell cycle progression in human cells? Our studies concerning

distribution of cyclin (PCNA) and DNA replication in binucleated homokaryons produced by polyethylene glycol-induced fusion of mitotic AMA cells have shed some light onto this question (Celis and Celis 1985). A small percentage of asynchronous S-phase homokaryons was observed in these fusions, suggesting that an intranuclear event(s) was required for cyclin (PCNA) distribution and DNA replication, irrespective of the fact that these nuclei shared common cytoplasmic factors (Celis and Celis 1985; see also Blow and Watson 1987). The nature of this intranuclear event(s) is at present unknown, although it may correspond to the formation of prereplicative complexes. Here, we would like to propose that newly synthesized cyclin (PCNA) (and perhaps progressin and dividin) may be one of the factors that trigger initiation of DNA replication once prereplicative complexes are formed. Taken together, our studies also imply that cell cycle progression is most likely not controlled by a single labile protein as suggested by Rossov et al. (1979), but rather by a set of events (a few are indicated in Fig. 4; see also Denhardt et al. 1986), some of which seem to be independent of each other.

Acknowledgments

We thank S. Himmelstrup Jørgensen for typing the manuscript and O. Sønderskov for photography. We also thank H.H. Rasmussen and B. Basse for helpful discussion and for reading the manuscript. P. Madsen and S.U. Nielsen were recipients of fellowships from the Medical Research Council. H.V. Nielsen was supported by a fellowship from the Fund for Laegevidenskabens Fremme. B. Gesser was a recipient of a fellowship from Forskning Teknologisk Udvikling. This work was support-

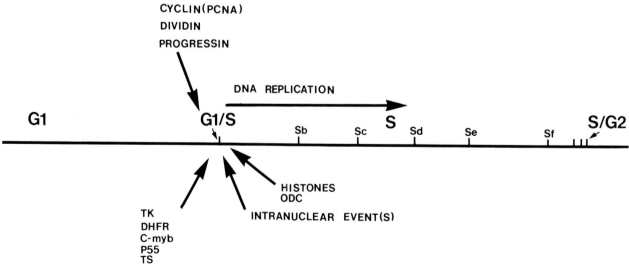

Figure 4 Some events at the G_1/S transition border of the cell cycle of human AMA cells. Increased synthesis of histones, ODC (ornithine decarboxylase), TK (thymidine kinase), DHFR (dihydrofolate reductase), c-myb, p55, and TS (thymidine synthetase) during S phase has been observed in various cell types (Denhardt et al. 1986, and references therein), but has not been investigated in AMA cells. The synthesis of histones and ODC is dependent on DNA replication, whereas synthesis of cyclin (PCNA), dividin, progressin, TK, and DHFR is unaffected by inhibitors of DNA replication (Bravo 1986; Denhardt et al. 1986, and references therein; this paper).

ed by grants from the Danish Cancer Society, the Danish biotechnology program, the Medical and Natural Science Research Councils, the Danish Rheumatoid Society, NOVO, the King Christian the Tenth Fund, and the Fund for Laegevidenskabens Fremme.

References

Almendral, J., D. Hübsch, P. Blundell, H. Macdonald-Bravo, and R. Bravo. 1987. Cloning and sequence of the human nuclear protein cyclin: Homology with DNA-binding proteins. *Proc. Natl. Acad. Sci.* **84**: 1575.

Baserga, R. 1978. Resting cells and the G1 phase of the cell cycle. *J. Cell. Physiol.* **95**: 377.

Blow, J.J. and J.V. Watson. 1987. Nuclei act as independent and integrated units of replication in a *Xenopus* cell-free DNA replication system. *EMBO J.* **6**: 1997.

Bravo, R. 1986. Synthesis of the nuclear protein cyclin (PCNA) and its relationship to DNA replication. *Exp. Cell. Res.* **163**: 287.

Bravo, R. and J.E. Celis. 1980. A search for differential polypeptide synthesis throughout the cell cycle of HeLa cells. *J. Cell Biol.* **84**: 795.

———. 1984. Catalogue of HeLa proteins. In *Two dimensional gel electrophoresis of proteins: Methods and applications* (ed. J.E. Celis and R. Bravo), p. 445. Academic Press, New York.

Bravo, R., R. Frank, P.A. Blundell, and H. Macdonald-Bravo. 1987. Cyclin (PCNA) is the auxiliary protein of DNA polymerase δ. *Nature* **326**: 515.

Bravo, R., S.J. Fey, J. Bellatin, P. Mose Larsen, J. Arevalo, and J.E. Celis. 1981. Identification of a nuclear and of a cytoplasmic polypeptide whose relative proportions are sensitive to changes in the rate of cell proliferation. *Exp. Cell Res.* **136**: 311.

Celis, J.E. and A. Celis. 1985. Individual nuclei in polykaryons can control cyclin distribution and DNA synthesis. *EMBO J.* **4**: 1187.

Celis, J.E. and P. Madsen. 1986. Increased nuclear cyclin PCNA antigen staining of non S-phase transformed human amnion cells engaged in nucleotide excission DNA repair. *FEBS Lett.* **209**: 277.

Celis, J.E. and S. Nielsen. 1986. Proliferation sensitive nuclear phosphoprotein "dividin" is synthesized almost exclusively during the S-phase of the cell cycle in AMA cells. *Proc. Natl. Acad. Sci.* **83**: 8187.

Celis, J.E., G. Petersen Ratz, and A. Celis. 1987a. Progressin: A novel proliferation-sensitive and cell cycle-regulated human protein whose rate of synthesis increases at or near the G₁/S transition border of the cell cycle. *FEBS Lett.* **223**: 237.

Celis, J.E., R. Bravo, P. Mose Larsen, and S.J. Fey. 1984a. A nuclear protein whose level correlates directly with the proliferative state of normal as well as transformed cells. *Leuk. Res.* **8**: 143.

Celis, J.E., P. Madsen, S. Nielsen, and A. Celis. 1986. Nuclear patterns of cyclin (PCNA) antigen distribution subdivide S-phase in cultured cells: Some application of PCNA antibodies. *Leuk. Res.* **10**: 237.

Celis, J.E., P. Madsen, A. Celis, H.V. Nielsen, and B. Gesser. 1987b. Cyclin (PCNA, auxiliary protein of DNA polymerase δ) is a central component of the pathway(s) leading to DNA replication and cell division. *FEBS Lett.* **220**: 1.

Celis, J.E., R. Bravo, P. Mose Larsen, S.J. Fey, J. Bellatin, and A. Celis. 1984b. Expression of cellular proteins in normal and transformed human cultured cells and tumours: Two dimensional gel electrophoresis as a tool to study neoplastic transformation and cancer. In *Two dimensional gel electrophoresis of proteins: Methods and applications* (ed. J.E. Celis and R. Bravo), p. 308. Academic Press, New York.

Denhardt, D.T., D.R. Edwards, and C.L. Parfett. 1986. Gene expression during the mammalian cell cycle. *Biochim. Biophys. Acta* **865**: 83.

Hayashi, I. and G.H. Sato. 1976. Replacement of serum by hormones permits growth of cells in a defined medium. *Nature* **259**: 132.

Holley, R.W. 1975. Growth control of mammalian cells in cell culture. *Nature* **258**: 487.

Kornberg, A. 1980. *DNA replication.* W.H. Freeman, San Francisco.

Madsen, P. and J.E. Celis. 1985. S-phase patterns of cyclin (PCNA) antigen staining resemble topographical patterns of DNA synthesis. A role of cyclin in DNA replication. *FEBS Lett.* **193**: 5.

Mathews, M.B., R.M. Bernstein, R. Franza, and J.I. Garrels. 1984. The identity of the "proliferating cell nuclear antigen" and "cyclin". *Nature* **309**: 374.

Miyachi, K., M.L. Fritzler, and E.M. Tan. 1978. Autoantibodies to a nuclear antigen in proliferating cells. *J. Immunol.* **121**: 2228.

Nielsen, S., A. Celis, G. Petersen Ratz, and J.E. Celis. 1987. Identification of two human phosphoproteins (dividin and IEF 59dl) that are first detected late in G1 near the G₁/S border of the cell cycle. *Leukemia* **1**: 69.

Pardee, A.B., R. Dubraw, J.L. Hamlin, and R.F. Kletzien. 1978. Animal cell cycle. *Annu. Rev. Biochem.* **47**: 715.

Prelich, G., M. Kostura, D.R. Marshak, M.B. Mathews, and B. Stillman. 1987a. The cell-cycle regulated proliferating cell nuclear antigen is required for SV40 DNA replication *in vitro*. *Nature* **326**: 471.

Prelich, G., C.-K. Tan, M. Kostura, M.B. Mathews, A.G. So, K.M. Downey, and B. Stillman. 1987b. Functional identity of proliferating cell nuclear antigen and a DNA polymerase-δ auxiliary protein. *Nature* **326**: 517.

Rossov, P.W., V.G.H. Riddle, and A.B. Pardee. 1979. Synthesis of labile, serum-dependent protein in early G₁ control animal cell growth. *Proc. Natl. Acad. Sci.* **76**: 4446.

Rozengurt, E. 1986. Early signals in the mitogenic response. *Science* **234**: 161.

Song, M.K.H. and K.W. Adolph. 1983. Phosphorylation of nonhistone proteins during the HeLa cell cycle. *J. Biol. Chem.* **258**: 3309.

Tan, C.K., C. Castillo, A.G. So, and K.M. Downey. 1986. An auxiliary protein for DNA polymerase from fetal calf thymus. *J. Biol. Chem.* **261**: 12310.

Takasaki, Y., J.S. Deng, and E.M. Tan. 1981. A nuclear antigen associated with cell proliferation and blast transformation. Its distribution in synchronized cells. *J. Exp. Med.* **154**: 1899.

Zerler, B., R.J. Roberts, M.B. Mathews, and E. Moran. 1987. Different functional domains of the adenovirus E1A gene are involved in regulation of host cell cycle products. *Mol. Cell. Biol.* **7**: 821.

Regulated DNA Replication in Cell-free Extracts of *Xenopus* Eggs

J.J. Blow,* M.A. Sheehan,* J.V. Watson,[†] and R.A. Laskey*

*Cancer Research Campaign Molecular Embryology Group, Department of Zoology, Cambridge CB2 3EJ; [†]MRC Clinical Oncology Unit, MRC Centre, Cambridge CB2 2QH, England

We have developed a cell-free extract of *Xenopus* eggs that efficiently initiates and completes DNA replication in vitro. Full semiconservative replication is demonstrated by density substitution. The efficiency of replication is similar to that in the intact egg: 70–100% of nuclei and up to 38% of naked DNA molecules replicate completely in vitro. Nuclear templates are strictly restricted to a single round of replication per incubation. Haploid sperm nuclei replicate fully to achieve a diploid DNA content, after which further DNA synthesis stops. However, the individual nuclei replicate asynchronously and fast within the same extract. This suggests that the nucleus is a fundamental unit of replication in vitro. Furthermore, the extract assembles purified DNA into nucleus-like structures, and replication occurs within these synthetic nuclei. The ability of the extract to initiate replication is dependent on its ability to assemble the template DNA into the nucleus-like structures. Re-replication can be induced by introducing replicated nuclei to fresh extract.

One of the major drawbacks to studying the control of eukaryotic DNA replication has been the lack of nonviral systems that initiate DNA replication in vitro. Recent advances in our understanding of eukaryotic DNA replication have arisen from the development of in vitro systems for adenovirus and SV40 replication. However, eukaryotic genomic DNA replication differs from viral replication in a number of important ways.

First, initiation occurs at many sites throughout the large eukaryotic genome, so that it can be replicated in a reasonably short period of time. Second, different initiation sites are used in different cell types and at different stages of development. In *Drosophila*, for example, S phase varies from 3.4 minutes in the early embryo to more than 10 hours in Schneider's cell line, due to differences in replicon size (Blumenthal et al. 1974). Third, the eukaryotic genome is strictly limited to a single round of semiconservative replication in each cell cycle. Viral DNA, in contrast, can replicate many times in a cell cycle, so that it multiplies with respect to the host DNA.

To study some of these unique features of eukaryotic DNA replication, we have developed a cell-free DNA replication system from eggs of the South African clawed toad, *Xenopus laevis*. There are a number of features of the *Xenopus* egg that make it a promising source of material for such a cell-free system. After fertilization, the *Xenopus* egg undergoes 11 synchronous rounds of DNA replication in less than 8 hours, in the absence of significant transcription (Newport and Kirschner 1982). Protein synthesis is required for the early embryo to progress from interphase to mitosis, whereas DNA replication can occur throughout interphase (Graham 1966; Gurdon 1967; Harland and Laskey 1980). However, progression into mitosis and the subsequent interphase can occur in the absence of protein synthesis on microinjection of MPF (Newport and

Kirschner 1984). Therefore, most of the components required for the first 11 rounds of DNA replication must already be present in the egg. Histones, for example, are stored in the egg complexed to two proteins, nucleoplasmin and N1 (Laskey et al. 1978; Kleinschmidt et al. 1985; Dilworth et al. 1987). Accordingly, egg extracts have a large capacity to assemble chromatin and perform complementary strand DNA synthesis (Méchali and Harland 1982). Furthermore, the *Xenopus* egg will replicate any DNA template microinjected into it (Harland and Laskey 1980; Méchali and Kearsey 1984). Replication of exogenous DNA occurs in step with the cell cycle of the early embryo and is irrespective of DNA sequence (Harland and Laskey 1980; Méchali and Kearsey 1984).

In this paper, we describe a cell-free system from *Xenopus* eggs that efficiently initiates and completes DNA replication in vitro (Blow and Laskey 1986). Replication of nuclear DNA is strictly limited to one complete round of semiconservative replication, as though the egg extract were blocked in a single cell cycle. The system is based on one described previously by Lohka and Masui (1983, 1984) that assembles apparently normal interphase nuclei from highly condensed sperm chromatin. Naked DNA is also assembled into nucleus-like structures in the cell-free system (Blow and Laskey 1986; Newmeyer et al. 1986; Newport 1987), as it is in vivo (Forbes et al. 1983). Considerable evidence now exists (Blow and Watson 1987a; Newport 1987; Sheehan et al. 1988) that nuclear assembly plays an important role in the initiation process.

Experimental Procedures

Preparation of extracts

Extracts of *X. laevis* eggs were prepared as described by Blow and Laskey (1986). Unfertilized eggs were laid in high-salt Barth (110 mM NaCl, 2 mM KCl, 1 mM MgSO$_4$, 0.5 mM Na$_2$HPO$_4$, 2 mM NaHCO$_3$, 15 mM Tris-Cl [pH 7.4]), dejellied in 2% cysteine (pH 7.4), and washed several times in 20% modified Barth solution (20% MBS; 18 mM NaCl, 0.2 mM KCl, 0.5 mM NaHCO$_3$, 2 mM HEPES NaOH [pH 7.4], 0.15 mM MgSO$_4$, 0.05 mM Ca[NO$_3$]$_2$, 0.1 mM CaCl$_2$). They were then activated in 0.5 µg/ml calcium ionophore A23187 and 20% MBS for 5 minutes. The eggs were washed in 20% MBS and incubated for a further 15 minutes at room temperature, while all eggs showing degenerative changes were removed. The eggs were then washed, first in 20% MBS and then in ice-cold extraction buffer (50 mM HEPES KOH [pH 7.4], 50 mM KCl, 5 mM MgCl$_2$, 2 mM β-mercaptoethanol, 3 µg/ml leupeptin 10 µg/ml cytochalasin B). Eggs were placed in cooled 4-ml tubes, excess buffer was removed, and the eggs were centrifuged in a Beckman SW50Ti rotor, 9000 rpm at 4°C for 15 minutes. This produced four major fractions: a dense plug of yolk platelets and pigment, a golden-brown cytoplasmic layer, a translucent cytoplasmic layer, and a yellow plug of lipid. The golden-colored cytoplasm was removed and recentrifuged as above to remove residual debris. 10% glycerol and 2 mM ATP was then added, and the extract was frozen by dropping 15-µl aliquots directly into liquid nitrogen.

The extract was fractionated into soluble and vesicular components as described by Sheehan et al. (1988). Before freezing, the extract was centrifuged in an SW60Ti rotor (Beckman) at 100,000*g* for 1 hour at 4°C. The extract separates into a clear supernatant (the soluble fraction), a loose membranous pellet, and a dense golden gel-like pellet. The soluble fraction was removed, glycerol added to 7%, and the mixture frozen as above. The membranous pellet was washed in 5 ml extraction buffer containing 5% glycerol, and pelleted in a SW60Ti rotor at 100,000*g* for 10 minutes. The pellet formed the vesicular fraction and was frozen in liquid nitrogen in 5-µl aliquots.

In vitro reaction conditions

Beads containing frozen extract were thawed at 20°C immediately before use, and supplemented with 60 mM phosphocreatine and 150 µg/ml creatine phosphokinase (Sigma). Aliquots (20 µl) were incubated at 23°C with DNA, [α-^{32}P]dATP, [^{3}H]dATP (Amersham International), bromodeoxyuridine triphosphate (BrdUTP, Sigma), and biotin-11-dUTP (BRL) as appropriate. DNA template preparation, TCA precipitation, and CsCl density substitution were as described by Blow and Laskey (1986).

Preparation of nuclei for microscopy and flow cytometry

Nuclei were prepared for microscopy and flow cytometry as described by Blow and Watson (1987a). For flow cytometry, incubations were resuspended in 3 ml of fixation buffer (60 mM KCl, 15 mM HEPES KOH [pH 7.4], 1 mM β-mercaptoethanol) at room temperature.

Nuclei were fixed with 10 mM ethylene bis(succinimidylsuccinate) for 10 minutes, stopped with 30 mM Tris-HCl (pH 7.4). The solution was underlayered with two sucrose cushions: 200 µl 15% sucrose in Buffer A (60 mM KCl, 15 mM Tris-HCl [pH 7.4], 15 mM NaCl, 1 mM β-mercaptoethanol, 0.5 mM spermidine 3HCl, 0.15 mM spermine 4HCl) and 200 µl 70% sucrose in Buffer A. Nuclei were spun into the sucrose by centrifugation in a Beckman SW60Ti rotor at 6000 rpm for 10 minutes at 4°C. Both sucrose cushions, containing the isolated nuclei, were pooled. Nuclei were then stained with 25 µg/ml propidium iodide, 25 µg/ml RNase, and 4 µl fluorescent-conjugated streptavidin (fluorescein or Texas red; Amersham International). Flow cytometry was performed as described (Blow and Watson 1987a).

Nuclei were prepared for microscopy as for flow cytometry, with all volumes scaled down by a factor of 3, and centrifugation in an MSE Centaur 2 at 3500 rpm. Hoechst 33258 was used instead of propidium iodide to stain total DNA. Nuclei were then viewed wet.

Results

Semiconservative DNA replication in sperm nuclei

On fertilization of the *Xenopus* egg, the highly condensed sperm chromatin decondenses and is assembled into the male pronucleus, after which its DNA is replicated (Graham 1966). Lohka and Masui (1983, 1984) have described a cell-free extract of frog eggs that will assemble condensed, demembranated sperm nuclei into structures closely resembling normal nuclei, surrounded by a double membrane and studded with nuclear pores. Lohka and Masui also noted that such nuclei incorporate [^{3}H]thymidine and suggested that DNA replication occurs after pronuclear formation in vitro, as it would in vivo. We have developed extracts similar to those of Lohka and Masui, but which can be frozen and thawed, and have investigated their value as a model system for studying the process and control of cellular DNA replication (Blow and Laskey 1986).

Initial experiments showed that the amount of DNA synthesized on addition of sperm nuclei to the *Xenopus* egg extract is extensive. After a 4–6-hour incubation, the amount of DNA synthesized is comparable to that originally added in the sperm nuclei. Figure 1A (closed circles) shows a time course of DNA synthesis after addition of sperm nuclei to the egg extract. There is an initial lag of about 1 hour before DNA synthesis starts. This corresponds to the time taken for the first nuclei to acquire a complete surrounding membrane, as judged by phase contrast optics (Fig. 1A, open circles). This is longer than the presynthesis lag in vivo (10–20 min; Graham 1966), but represents the same sequence of events. The egg extract can be separated into soluble and vesicular fractions by centrifugation at 100,000*g* (Lohka and Masui 1984). Neither fraction alone will support nuclear formation, which can be restored by recombining the two fractions. Figure 1B shows that, similarly, neither fraction alone supports DNA synthesis, which can also be restored by recombination (Sheehan

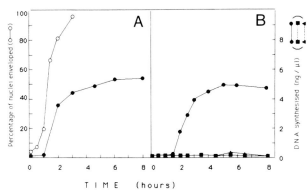

Figure 1 Time course of replication and nuclear formation in the cell-free system. Demembranated sperm nuclei were incubated in the *Xenopus* egg extract at 5 ng DNA/µl (*A*) or 6 ng DNA/µl (*B*). (Closed symbols) The quantity of DNA synthesized was determined from the proportion of [α-³²P]dATP incorporated into acid insoluble material. (Open circles) The proportion of fully enveloped nuclei was determined by phase contrast microscopy. (*A*) Incubation was performed in the extract as described by Blow and Laskey (1986). (*B*) The extract in *A* was assayed after division into soluble (▲—▲) and vesicular (■—■) components, or after recombination of these at a 10:1 ratio (●—●) (Sheehan et al. 1988). (Fig. 1A reprinted, with permission, from Blow and Laskey 1986.)

et al. 1988). Similar results have been reported by Newport (1987). This suggests that the ability of the egg extract to replicate DNA may be related to its ability to assemble the DNA into nucleus-like structures.

To demonstrate that the DNA synthesis occurring in vitro represents semiconservative replication, we performed density substitution experiments similar to those originally described by Meselson and Stahl (1958). This involves labeling nascent DNA with BrdUTP (a dense analog of thymidine) and [α-³²P]dATP; DNA is then isolated and fractionated on CsCl density equilibrium gradients. The results of such an experiment are shown in Figure 2. Unsubstituted *Xenopus* DNA has a density of about 1.71, whereas *Xenopus* DNA with all its thymidine residues substituted with BrdU has a density of about 1.78. However, Figure 2 shows that over a 6-hour time course, all of the labeled DNA has a density of 1.75, as expected of DNA substituted at exactly half its thymidine residues by a single round of semiconservative replication. None of the observed synthesis is due to partial strand repair, which would label largely unsubstituted DNA.

Comparison of Figure 2, A, B, and C, shows that, although replication continues over a period of more than 2 hours, few replicative intermediates can be seen. The initiation of new forks on different DNA molecules must therefore occur over a period of 2 hours or more. This means that individual DNA molecules (> 50 kb, as demonstrated in the inset to Fig. 2C) replicate relatively fast, so that the overall rate of replication is largely dependent on the rate of initiation on different DNA molecules. This conclusion is directly demonstrated by flow cytometry (see below). The inset to Figure 2C shows that replication is sensitive to aphidicolin, a specific inhibitor of eukaryotic polymerases α and δ.

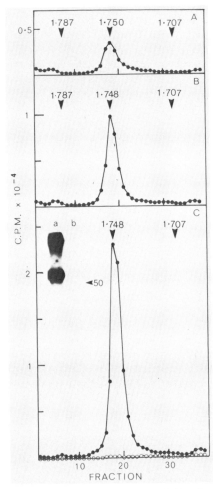

Figure 2 Density substitution of sperm nuclei incubated in the extract for 2, 4, and 6 hr. (●—●) Sperm nuclei were incubated at 10 ng DNA/µl in egg extract with 0.25 mM BrdUTP and [α-³²P]dATP for 2 (*A*), 4 (*B*), or 6 (*C*) hr; the DNA was extracted and fractionated on CsCl density gradients. Arrows show the CsCl density as determined from the refractive index. (*C*) (○—○) 6-hr incubation as above, but without addition of sperm nuclei (minus DNA control). (Inset to *C*) Autoradiograph of 0.4% agarose gel of 6-hr incubation. (Lane *a*) Conditions as for density gradient; (lane *b*) as for density gradient but with 10 µl/ml aphidicolin. Horizontal arrow shows position of 50-kb marker. (Reprinted, with permission, from Blow and Laskey 1986.)

Figure 2 also shows that no re-replication, producing fully substituted DNA, occurs in a single incubation. This is particularly surprising as virtually all the added DNA is replicated, and initiation on new DNA molecules occurs over at least 2 hours. This means that the extract is able to distinguish replicated from unreplicated DNA, and permits initiation only on the latter. This resembles the way that eukaryotic cells limit nonviral replication to a single round per cell cycle.

Independent control of replication within individual nuclei

On introduction into *Xenopus* egg cytoplasm, both in vivo and in vitro, there is a correlation between the time taken for sperm nuclei to be assembled into mature pronuclei and the lag period before they start to replicate (Graham 1966; Blow and Laskey 1986). To investigate whether nuclear organization plays an important role in controlling DNA replication, we have developed a technique for quantifying the extent of replication within individual nuclei (Blow and Watson 1987a,b). This involves labeling DNA replicated in vitro with the thymidine analog biotin-11-dUTP (Langer et al. 1981). Nuclei can then be probed with fluorescent streptavidin, which binds tightly and specifically to biotin. Control experiments demonstrated that the extent of DNA replication within individual nuclei is proportional to their streptavidin fluorescence, as quantified by flow cytometry. In this technique, nuclei are introduced one at a time into a flow chamber where they are excited by laser light; the fluorescent emission from each nucleus is then measured. Using fluoresceinated streptavidin to label biotin, and propidium iodide to label DNA, we could therefore measure the total DNA content and the quantity of nascent DNA within each nucleus.

Figure 3 shows a population of sperm nuclei after 1.5 hours in the *Xenopus* cell-free extract with biotin-11-dUTP. Figure 3, A and B, shows a sample of this population stained separately for DNA and biotin, respectively. Some nuclei stain strongly with biotin, and some hardly stain at all. Incorporation of $[\alpha\text{-}^{32}P]dATP$

showed that just over half of the template DNA had been replicated in this population. When these nuclei are analyzed by flow cytometry, a clear relationship emerges between the DNA content and the biotin signal (Fig. 3C). The data are presented as a contour plot, showing the number of nuclei in any given area determined by both their biotin and total DNA contents. 1N and 2N show the haploid and diploid contents, respectively. On both sides the contour plot is flanked by standard frequency plots for the numbers of nuclei in that dimension. All the nuclei fall on a straight line between the haploid DNA content with background biotin signal and the diploid DNA content with high biotin signal. This shows that the biotin-streptavidin signal is an accurate measure of the extent of in vitro replication.

Figure 3C shows a number of key features about the way nuclei replicate in vitro. First, most nuclei are either haploid or diploid, with few nuclei in "S phase" in between (shown clearly in the cross-sectional view along the DNA axis). When nuclei are analyzed at different times during an incubation, nuclei can be seen to leave the haploid population and enter S phase over a period of about 2 hours (Blow and Watson 1987a). They progress relatively rapidly through S phase, replicating fully in about 1 hour on average. Some nuclei replicate fully in less than 0.5 hour, approaching the time taken in

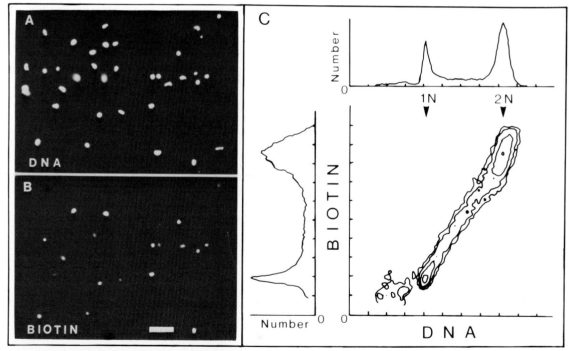

Figure 3 Relationship between biotin incorporation and DNA content of nuclei labeled in vitro with biotin-11-dUTP. Sperm nuclei were incubated at 7 ng DNA/µl for 1.5 hr in extract with 8 µM biotin-11-dUTP. Nuclei were isolated and stained with fluorescent streptavidin and a DNA-binding fluorochrome. (*A*) Nuclei stained with Hoechst 33258 for total DNA. (*B*) The same field as *A* but stained with Texas-red streptavidin for biotin. Scale bar 50 µm (also for *A*). (*C*) Nuclei were analyzed by flow cytometry to measure the biotin and DNA content of each nucleus. This locates each nucleus on a graph with axes representing biotin and DNA content. The distribution of all nuclei is shown as a contour plot, representing the density of nuclei in a given area. Contour levels are 3, 8, 30, and 100 in arbitrary units. Standard two-dimensional frequency plots of numbers of nuclei against DNA and against biotin flank the contour plot. 1N and 2N show the haploid and diploid DNA contents. Nuclei with DNA contents less than haploid largely represent highly condensed sperm nuclei. (Reprinted, with permission, from Blow and Watson 1987a.)

vivo. Therefore, some nuclei have replicated fully before others have even entered S phase. This is consistent with BrdUTP density substitution experiments, such as Figure 2, which show that initiation on different molecules occurs over a period of 2 hours or more. Second, there are no nuclei with DNA or biotin contents greater than diploid; neither are there haploid nuclei with biotin contents greater than background. This means that once nuclei have undergone one complete round of replication, they stop. This is again consistent with BrdUTP density substitution experiments, such as Figure 2, which show that nuclear DNA is not re-replicated in a single incubation. This highlights the ability of the extract to distinguish replicated from unreplicated DNA, initiating only on the latter.

Further experiments (Blow and Watson 1987a) involved pulse-labeling nascent DNA with biotin-11-dUTP to measure the replication rates of nuclei at different stages through S phase. Nuclei enter S phase at high initial replication rates, representing 70–120% of the haploid genome per hour. At all later stages of replication, nuclei replicate at lower average rates. This suggests that most, if not all, initiation events occur in a burst on entry of the nucleus into S phase. It also shows that individual nuclei are fundamental units of replication in the cell-free system, as initiation events are coordinately controlled within each nucleus, but different nuclei enter S phase at different times during an incubation.

Naked DNA is replicated in nucleus-like structures in vitro

When naked DNA is microinjected into *Xenopus* eggs, it is replicated in step with the cell cycle of the early embryo, and without apparent regard to DNA sequence (Harland and Laskey 1980; Méchali and Kearsey 1984). The egg extract has a similar capacity. Naked DNA templates, including those without any eukaryotic sequences, undergo complete semiconservative replication in vitro (Blow and Laskey 1986; Blow et al. 1987). There is considerable variability in the efficiency of replication of naked DNA. This is partly due to an effect of the size of the template DNA. Larger DNA templates are replicated more efficiently in vitro, as they are in the intact egg (Méchali and Kearsey 1984).

Purified DNA microinjected into *Xenopus* eggs is also assembled into nucleus-like structures, as judged by light microscopy (Forbes et al. 1983). The *Xenopus* egg extract also assembles naked DNA into nuclei (Blow and Laskey 1986; Newmeyer et al. 1986; Newport 1987). Such nuclei are surrounded by a double membrane, studded with structures resembling nuclear pores, and they accumulate nuclear proteins (Newmeyer et al. 1986). The efficiency of nuclear formation is dependent on the size of the DNA molecules, larger DNAs being more efficiently assembled. Figure 4 shows some structures formed after incubating *Xenopus* genomic DNA in the extract. Figure 4A shows two typical structures, which are smaller than the nuclei formed from sperm chromatin. However, the size of nuclei formed from

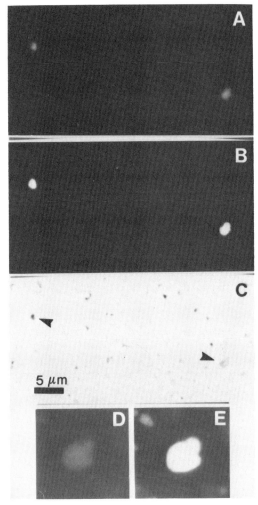

Figure 4 DNA synthesis in nuclei assembled from purified DNA. 8 ng/µl purified sperm DNA was incubated in extract with 40 µM biotin-11-dUTP for 4 hr. Nuclei were fixed and stained with Hoechst 33258 for DNA (*A* and *D*) and Texas-red streptavidin for biotin (*B* and *E*). Fields viewed under fluorescence (*A, B, D, E*) or phase contrast optics (*C*). Two fields (*A, B, C*) and (*D, E*) are shown, both at the same magnification.

naked DNA is variable, and a larger structure is shown in Figure 4D.

In view of the strong correlation between nuclear formation and DNA replication in the *Xenopus* egg, we investigated whether the DNA replication observed with naked DNA takes place within nuclei. Genomic DNA was therefore incubated in the egg extract with biotin-11-dUTP. Nuclei were then isolated and stained with Texas-red streptavidin. Figure 4, B and E, shows that the DNA assembled into nucleus-like structures has also replicated and incorporated biotin-11-dUTP. The nuclei formed from naked DNA in vitro are functionally active.

Re-replication of DNA in vitro

Replication in the egg extract is normally limited to a single round of semiconservative replication. However, in certain circumstances, re-replication of DNA is observed. This provides very good evidence that genuine initiation occurs in vitro. It also provides some insight into the way that re-replication is prevented within a single cell cycle. Although re-replication of naked DNA occasionally occurs in a single incubation, this never happens to DNA added in the form of nuclei (Blow and Laskey 1986). As discussed above, the extract must have a way of distinguishing replicated from unreplicated DNA, in order to permit initiation only on the latter.

However, efficient re-replication can occur when DNA replicated in one incubation is isolated and added to fresh extract (Blow and Laskey 1986). Such an experiment is presented in Figure 5. Sperm nuclei were incubated for 5 hours in extract supplemented with [³H]dATP and BrdUTP. DNA was prepared from one aliquot of the incubation and fractionated on a CsCl gradient (Fig. 5A). This shows, as above (Figs. 2 and 3), that all DNA synthesis represents a single round of semiconservative replication, with no re-replication. A second aliquot from this incubation was resuspended in buffer, and nuclei were then pelleted by gentle centrifugation. These nuclei were then incubated in a fresh aliquot of extract, containing [α-³²P]dATP and BrdUTP, for a further 5 hours. The CsCl density gradient profile of DNA isolated from this incubation is shown in Figure 5B. The DNA replicated in the first incubation has been efficiently transferred to the second incubation, as the total amount of ³H is the same in Figure 5, A and B. However, half of the tritiated DNA is now in the heavy/heavy peak, demonstrating that half of the DNA replicated in the first incubation has been replicated again in the second incubation. The ³²P pattern is also consistent with this. Just under half the DNA labeled with ³²P is in the heavy/heavy peak. This means that virtually all the replication that occurred in the second incubation represented replication of DNA that had already been replicated in the first incubation.

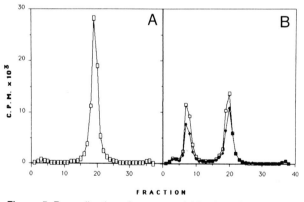

FRACTION

Figure 5 Re-replication of sperm nuclei in vitro. Sperm nuclei were incubated at 4 ng DNA/μl in extract with 0.3 mM BrdUTP and [³H]dATP for 5 hr. DNA was isolated from one aliquot and fractionated on a CsCl gradient (*A*). Nuclei in a second aliquot were resuspended in buffer, pelleted, and incubated in fresh extract containing 0.3 mM BrdUTP and [α-³²P]dATP for a further 5 hr. DNA was isolated and fractionated on a CsCl gradient (*B*). (□—□) ³H; (◆—◆) ³²P. Heavy/light DNA in fraction 19 has a density of 1.75, and heavy/heavy DNA in fraction 7 has a density of 1.79.

Discussion

The initiation of DNA replication in vitro

In this paper, we describe a cell-free system derived from *Xenopus* eggs that efficiently initiates and completes DNA replication in vitro (Blow and Laskey 1986). Semiconservative DNA replication is demonstrated by BrdUTP density substitution, whereas net DNA synthesis is directly demonstrated by flow cytometry. DNA added in the form of nuclei is replicated at high efficiency (70–100%), but naked DNA is more variable. This variability is partly due to differences in template size and mimics the behavior of the intact egg (Méchali and Kearsey 1984). When haploid sperm nuclei are added to the egg extract, they are replicated fully until they have reached the diploid DNA content. They then stop taking up DNA precursors and remain diploid. This shows that not only is the cell-free system capable of efficient replication, but that this replication is strictly controlled and resembles a cell limited to a single S phase.

Complete semiconservative replication of template DNA is good evidence for the *initiation* of replication in vitro. However, previous attempts to achieve initiation in vitro have underestimated the potential contamination of DNA templates by preformed primers (for review, see Jong and Scott 1985). A number of features eliminate a role for preformed primers in our results (Blow and Laskey 1986): (1) Our DNA templates were prepared as suggested by Jong and Scott to minimize contamination with preformed primers. (2) The kinetics of replication seen in our system are very different from those of primer-dependent synthesis. (3) None of our templates showed activity in a polymerase-primase assay similar to the one used by Jong and Scott. (4) All of the templates we used could be re-replicated by the extract. If DNA is replicated in one incubation and then added to fresh extract, a significant amount of re-replication occurs. In addition, naked DNA templates sometimes re-replicate during a single incubation (Blow and Laskey 1986). Hutchison et al. (1987) have also reported protein synthesis-dependent re-replication in a single incubation of a similar extract. Re-replication in vitro provides strong evidence for genuine initiation of replication. The implications of these results for the mechanism preventing re-replication in a single cell cycle are discussed elsewhere (Blow et al. 1987).

Nuclear assembly is required for replication in vitro

One unique feature of this cell-free extract is that it will assemble apparently normal interphase nuclei from highly condensed sperm chromatin (Lohka and Masui 1983, 1984) and from naked DNA (Blow and Laskey 1986; Newmeyer et al. 1986; Newport 1987). These nuclei will accumulate nuclear proteins in vitro (Newmeyer et al. 1986). Several different results indicate that the ability to initiate replication in vitro is dependent on the ability to assemble the template DNA into such nucleus-like structures: (1) Only those extracts that can assemble nuclei can initiate replication in vitro. If the extract is divided into soluble and vesicular components, neither fraction alone can support nuclear formation or DNA replication (Lohka and Masui 1984; Newport 1987; Sheehan et al. 1988). On recombination of the two fractions, both activities are restored. (2) With different forms of template DNA, there is a correlation between the efficiency of nuclear formation and the efficiency of replication (Blow and Laskey 1986; Blow et al. 1987). (3) The lag that occurs before replication starts in vitro is similar to the time required for nuclei to acquire a complete surrounding membrane (Blow and Laskey 1986). (4) Abnormal or immature nuclei do not replicate in vitro (Blow and Watson 1987a; Sheehan et al. 1988). (5) With both naked and nuclear DNA as template, replication occurs within the synthetic nuclei (Blow and Watson 1987a; this paper). (6) Nuclei behave as fundamental units of replication in the cell-free system (Blow and Watson 1987a; see below).

Nuclei as fundamental units of replication

Analysis of how initiation is organized within individual nuclei has been possible with the use of biotin-11-dUTP to label nascent DNA in intact nuclei, and flow cytometry (Blow and Watson 1987a,b). Different nuclei in the same extract start to replicate ("enter S phase") at different times over a period of about 1.5 hours. Individual nuclei replicate relatively fast, doubling their DNA content in about 1 hour on average. This means that the overall rate of replication in vitro is largely dependent on the rate at which individual nuclei enter S phase. Individual nuclei reach their maximum rates of replication soon after entering S phase. These high initial rates ($>80\%$ haploid genome per hour) require $>40,000$ synchronous initiations within each nucleus. At later stages of S phase, nuclei replicate at average rates lower than the initial rates. This means that most, if not all, initiation events within a nucleus occur in an essentially synchronous burst on entry into S phase.

These results suggest how initiation could be controlled in the cell-free system. First, initiations are *coordinated* within individual nuclei, giving the observed high initial rates of replication. Second, individual nuclei enter S phase at different times, so that the coordinated initiations are activated *independently* by different nuclei. This means that there must be a signal activating initiation that acts throughout the nucleus, but does not spread outside it. Such a signal could explain why nuclear formation is required for initiation in vitro.

Acknowledgments

We thank the Cancer Research Campaign for funding this work and for providing a studentship for J.B.

References

Blow, J.J. and R.A. Laskey. 1986. Initiation of DNA replication in nuclei and naked DNA by a cell-free extract of *Xenopus* eggs. *Cell* **47**: 577.

Blow, J.J. and J.V. Watson. 1987a. Nuclei act as independent and integrated units of DNA replication in a *Xenopus* cell-free DNA replication system. *EMBO J.* **6**: 1997.

———. 1987b. A probe for nascent DNA in intact nuclei. *Trends Genet.* **3**: 233.

Blow, J.J., S.M. Dilworth, C. Dingwall, A.D. Mills, and R.A. Laskey. 1987. Chromosome replication in cell-free systems from *Xenopus* eggs. *Philos. Trans. R. Soc. Lond. B* **317**: 483.

Blumenthal, A.B., H.J. Kreigstein, and D.S. Hogness. 1974. The units of DNA replication in *Drosophila melanogaster* chromosomes. *Cold Spring Harbor Symp. Quant. Biol.* **38**: 205.

Dilworth, S.M., S.J. Black, and R.A. Laskey. 1987. Two complexes that contain histones are required for nucleosome assembly in vitro: Role of nucleoplasmin and N1 in *Xenopus* egg extracts. *Cell* **51**: 1009.

Forbes, D.J., M.W. Kirschner, and J.W. Newport. 1983. Spontaneous formation of nucleus-like structures around bacteriophage DNA microinjected into *Xenopus* eggs. *Cell* **34**: 13.

Graham, C.F. 1966. The regulation of DNA synthesis and mitosis in multinucleate frog eggs. *J. Cell Sci.* **1**: 363.

Gurdon, J.B. 1967. On the origin and persistence of a cytoplasmic state inducing nuclear DNA synthesis in frogs' eggs. *Proc. Natl. Acad. Sci.* **58**: 545.

Harland, R.M. and R.A. Laskey. 1980. Regulated replication of DNA microinjected into eggs of *Xenopus laevis*. *Cell* **21**: 761.

Hutchison, C.J., R. Cox, R.S. Drepaul, M. Gomperts, and C.C. Ford. 1987. Periodic DNA synthesis in cell-free extracts of *Xenopus* eggs. *EMBO J.* **6**: 2003.

Jong, A.Y.S. and J.F. Scott. 1985. DNA synthesis in yeast cell-free extracts dependent on recombinant plasmids purified from *Escherichia coli*. *Nucleic Acids Res.* **13**: 2943.

Kleinschmidt, J.A., E. Fortkamp, G. Krohne, H. Zentgraf, and W.W. Franke. 1985. Co-existence of two different types of soluble histone complexes in nuclei of *Xenopus laevis* oocytes. *J. Biol. Chem.* **260**: 1166.

Langer, P.R., A.A. Waldrop, and D.C. Ward. 1981. Enzymatic synthesis of biotin-labelled polynucleotides: Novel nucleic acid affinity probes. *Proc. Natl. Acad. Sci.* **78**: 6633.

Laskey, R.A., B.M. Honda, A.D. Mills, and J.T. Finch. 1978. Nucleosomes are assembled by an acidic protein which binds histones and transfers them to DNA. *Nature* **275**: 416.

Lohka, M.J. and Y. Masui. 1983. Formation *in vitro* of sperm pronuclei and mitotic chromosomes induced by amphibian ooplasmic contents. *Science* **220**: 719.

———. 1984. Roles of cytosol and cytoplasmic particles in nuclear envelope assembly and sperm pronuclear formation in cell-free preparations from amphibian eggs. *J. Cell Biol.* **98**: 1222.

Méchali, M. and R. Harland. 1982. DNA synthesis in a cell-free system from *Xenopus* eggs: Priming and elongation on single stranded DNA *in vitro*. *Cell* **30**: 93.

Méchali, M. and S. Kearsey. 1984. Lack of specific sequence requirement for DNA replication in *Xenopus* eggs compared with high sequence specificity in yeast. *Cell* **38**: 55.

Meselson, M. and F. Stahl. 1958. The replication of DNA in *Escherichia coli*. *Proc. Natl. Acad. Sci.* **44**: 671.

Newmeyer, D.D., J.J. Lucocq, T.R. Burglin, and E.M. De-Robertis. 1986. Assembly *in vitro* of nuclei active in nuclear protein transport: ATP is required for nucleoplasmin accumulation. *EMBO J.* **5**: 501.

Newport, J. 1987. Nuclear reconstitution *in vitro*: Stages of assembly around protein-free DNA. *Cell* **48**: 205.

Newport, J. and M. Kirschner. 1982. A major developmental transition in early *Xenopus* embryos. I. Characterization and timing of cellular changes at the midblastula stage. *Cell* **30**: 675.

———. 1984. Regulation of the cell cycle during early *Xenopus* development. *Cell* **37**: 731.

Sheehan, M.A., A.D. Mills, A.M. Sleeman, R.A. Laskey, and J.J. Blow. 1988. Steps in the assembly of replication-competent nuclei in a cell-free system from *Xenopus* eggs. *J. Cell Biol.* **106**: 1.

Slow Replication Fork Movement during *Drosophila* Chorion Gene Amplification

A.C. Spradling and E. Leys

Department of Embryology, Carnegie Institution of Washington, Baltimore, Maryland 21210

During oogenesis, chromosomal domains surrounding the two major chorion gene clusters extensively amplify in follicle cells. Replication forks initiate near the center of each domain and elongate bidirectionally for varying distances, producing gradients of decreasing amplification. The average rate of replication fork elongation during amplification of the third chromosomal domain was found to be only 50–100 bp/min. This is 25–50 times slower than elongation rates reported for diploid cleavage nuclei or tissue culture cells, but similar to rates in polytene salivary glands. Our measurements suggest that slow replication fork elongation, rather than termination, is responsible for the chorion gene amplification gradients.

Higher organisms appear to scrupulously control the replication of their chromosomes (for review, see Hand 1978). Genomic regions within a differentiated cell replicate at the same time during each S phase. These tissue-specific patterns of DNA synthesis arise during development, although their functional significance for differentiation remains a matter of conjecture. Dipterans such as *Drosophila melanogaster* exhibit some of the most widespread and dramatic examples of developmentally regulated replication, including the differential reduplication of specific chromosome regions in polytene cells that no longer have to segregate daughter chromosomes (for review, see Spradling and Orr-Weaver 1987). Eggshell (chorion) protein gene amplification during *Drosophila* oogenesis provides a special example of developmentally regulated replication that is experimentally accessible (for review, see Kafatos et al. 1985; Kalfayan et al. 1985).

Chorion gene amplification facilitates rapid egg production by *Drosophila* females. During the final 6 hours of oogenesis, follicle cells surrounding each developing oocyte must synthesize and secrete the protein-rich eggshell (see Mahowald and Kambysellis 1980; Margaritis 1985). Unique genes encoding all six major chorion proteins (s15, s16, s18, s19, s36, s38) lie in two chromosomal domains on the X or third chromosome whose copy number increases 16- or 60-fold in follicle cells just prior to gene transcription. DNA sequences adjacent to the chorion genes also overreplicate; the level of amplification decreases gradually over regions of 40–50 kb on both sides of the gene clusters, producing a bell-shaped amplification profile (see Fig. 1). This follicle-cell-specific increase in chorion gene copy number is essential for eggshell synthesis, since mutant females that cannot amplify are sterile; they underproduce chorion proteins and construct abnormal, thin eggshells (Spradling and Mahowald 1981; Orr et al. 1984; R. Kelley and A. Spradling, unpubl.).

The two amplified domains constitute developmentally regulated chromosomal replicons. Replication forks initiate at a site (or sites) within the gene clusters and elongate bidirectionally along the chromosome. Approximately four rounds of initiation would be required to produce the observed amplification of the X chromosome genes, and on the third chromosome six rounds would be necessary. Successive replication forks travel decreasing distances along the chromosome, giving rise to the observed gradients of amplification. Nested replication forks with the expected structure have been observed in chromatin from amplifying follicle cells (Osheim and Miller 1983).

cis-Regulatory "amplification control elements" within each gene cluster control amplification. Following P element-mediated transformation, transposons containing certain chorion region sequences induce locally a normal program of follicle cell-specific differential replication (deCicco and Spradling 1984; Orr-Weaver and Spradling 1986; Delidakis and Kafatos 1987; Spradling et al. 1987). The level, but not the tissue-specificity, of transposon-induced amplification is subject to position effects. Transformation experiments have permitted elements both necessary and sufficient for amplification to be mapped (for review, see Orr-Weaver and Spradling 1987; Spradling and Orr-Weaver 1987). These studies strongly suggest that amplification is regulated at the level of replication fork initiation.

Much less is known about the fate of replication forks induced during the process of amplification after they leave the vicinity of the replication origin(s). Do the first replication forks terminate at specific termination sites that define the ends of the amplified domain? The existence and structure of such sites would be of considerable interest. Termination sites might correspond to junctions between adjacent chromosomal replicons or to a structural constraint such as the bases of chromosome loops. Subsequent forks might be unable to pass the forks ahead of them, leading to a backup of forks that would create the observed gradient. It is uncertain to what extent topological constraints would limit one replication fork from approaching a second fork that was

305

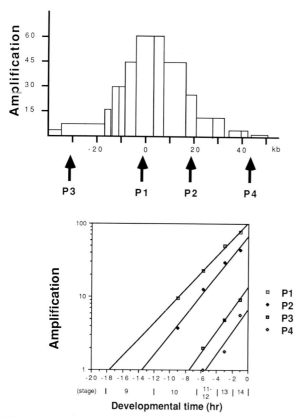

Figure 1 Amplification rates of sequences within the chromosome 3 domain. At the top of the figure, the amplification level of sequences surrounding the third chromosome chorion gene cluster is shown (data from Spradling 1981). The locations of DNA sequences used as probes to measure the rate of amplification of specific subregions are shown by arrows. P1 (1 kb) is centered 1 kb upstream of the s18 5′ end. P2 (3 kb) is centered 20 kb downstream from P1. P3, a 12-kb λ genomic clone (2101) is centered 30 kb upstream of P1; the 15-kb genomic clone P4 (1704) is centered 44 kb downstream of P1. Each probe was labeled with ³²P by nick translation and hybridized to egg chamber DNA from the indicated stages immobilized by slot-blotting on nitrocellulose. As explained in the text, the level of probe sequence amplification was determined by scanning autoradiograms of the filters. Normalization was carried out by hybridization with a *Drosophila* rDNA probe (pDMcY22), followed by excision of individual slots for scintillation counting. The duration of oogenetic stages is discussed in Mahowald and Kambysellis (1980).

moving in the same direction within a follicle cell chromosome. During SV40 replication, oppositely oriented replication forks cannot elongate normally during the final 100–200 bp prior to fusion (Sundin and Varshavsky 1981). However, since only about six forks are expected along any amplified third chromosome strand within a distance of 40–50 kb, fork-fork interactions spanning a much longer distance, about 6–8 kb, must be postulated to explain the shape of the gradient.

For this reason, we suspected that slow elongation, rather than fork termination, might be responsible for the chromosomal amplification pattern. Replication forks would initiate in the gene cluster and progress outward at a slow and steady rate, without terminating. The

shape of the amplification gradient would thus be determined by the rate of initiation and the amount of time elapsed since the first initiation events. According to this model, if the time of amplification could somehow be extended, the total size of the amplified regions would increase proportionally. In this report, we describe experiments that strongly support this model of chorion gene amplification.

Materials and Methods

Isolation of DNA

To maximize ovarian development, 2–4-day-old adult females were cultured in the presence of fresh live yeast for 24–36 hours prior to egg chamber isolation. Most experiments utilized wild-type strain Oregon R. However, the data in Figure 1 are taken from an experiment where phenotypically wild-type flies heterozygous for the mutation *fs(3)293* were used (see Spradling and Orr-Weaver 1987). For each filter, approximately 100 egg chambers of stages 10, 11 + 12, 13, or 14 were isolated by manual dissection using morphological criteria given in Mahowald and Kambysellis (1980). Stage 10–14 egg chambers were used because the durations of egg chamber stages earlier than stage 10 are known with less certainty, and adequate amounts of accurately staged material were difficult to obtain. Egg chamber DNA was extracted as described previously (Spradling 1981).

Amplification measurements

DNA resuspended in TE (10 mM Tris [pH 8], 1 mM EDTA) was denatured by addition of denaturing buffer (5 × = 3 M NaOH, 1.5 M NaCl). After 5 minutes, each sample was neutralized by addition of an equal volume of neutralization buffer (2 M Tris [pH 7.5], 4 M NaCl), and filtered through nitrocellulose paper on a slot blot apparatus (Schleicher and Schuell, Inc.). Hybridization of filters, labeling of probes with ³²P by nick translation, scanning of autoradiographs, and calculation of amplification levels were as described previously (deCicco and Spradling 1984; Orr-Weaver and Spradling 1986). As before, the *rosy* gene was used as an indicator of single copy DNA in determining absolute amplification values. The amount of DNA retained in each slot was controlled by rehybridizing each filter with a probe specific for rDNA, excising each slot with a razor blade, and measuring the signal in a scintillation counter.

Results

Kinetics of amplification

The ''termination'' and ''slow elongation'' models can be distinguished by measuring the amplification kinetics of specific regions spaced along the length of the amplified domain. Both models predict an exponential rise in the copy number of a central fragment located near the site of the presumptive replication origin. However, the expected behavior of a distal probe is very different in the two cases. In the termination model, the distal regions would amplify very early, following the arrival of the first replication fork. The progress of subsequent forks is blocked; consequently, no further increase in the amplification level of terminal fragments is expected. In contrast, the slow elongation model predicts that in the early stages of amplification, the copy number of distal probes will not increase. After a time lag (corresponding to the total distance between the origin and the probe divided by the elongation rate), amplification will begin and will continue at the same rate as seen initially near the center. Amplification of distal sequences occurs following the arrival of the same replication forks whose effects were mapped centrally near the onset of amplification.

The third chromosome amplified region was selected for a test of these ideas. In Figure 1, the distribution of amplified sequences in stage 13 and 14 egg chambers is illustrated. The location within the amplified domain of four DNA probes, P1–P4, is also shown. Quantitative hybridization to egg chamber DNA immobilized on nitrocellulose filters was used to determine the amplification kinetics of sequences recognized by the probes. Egg chambers were isolated from well-fed, phenotypically wild-type adults, heterozygous for the mutation *fs(3)293*, and separated by morphological criteria into groups of increasing developmental age. Because of the limited material that could be obtained by manual isolation, egg chambers of stage 10, stages 11 and 12, stage 13, and stage 14 were used. The durations of these stages are shown on the time scale in Figure 1, where time zero is taken as the end of oogenesis.

To determine the level of amplification of P1–P4 sequences at these times, DNA was extracted from whole egg chambers, denatured, and immobilized on nitrocellulose membranes by "slot blotting." As a control, DNA from embryos and from adult males (which lack ovaries and therefore do not amplify sequences surrounding the chorion genes) was also included. After exposure of the filters to X-ray film, the signals were quantitated by densitometry. The same filters were rehybridized with a probe specific for rDNA to correct for small differences in the amount of DNA retained on the filters. The results of one such experiment are plotted in Figure 1.

Replication forks elongate slowly during amplification

The onset of amplification of a given sequence is clearly related to its position within the domain. Sequences near the center (P1) begin amplification about 17 hours prior to the completion of oogenesis, a time corresponding to stage 9. This is in agreement with previous measurements (Spradling and Mahowald 1980; Orr et al. 1984). Sequences more distant from the center of the amplification gradient do not begin to amplify until later times in egg chamber development. In the case of P2, a probe lying about 20 kb downstream from P1, amplification begins only about 13 hours prior to completion of oogenesis, near the beginning of stage 10. Once amplification of P2 has started, the rate of amplifi-

cation is similar to that of P1 sequences. P3 and P4 sequences, which lie about 30 kb upstream and 44 kb downstream from P1, respectively, do not begin to amplify until the onset of stage 11 or stage 13. These are the results expected from the slow elongation model. No evidence for a plateau in amplification toward the end of oogenesis was observed, even in the case of sequences located some distance from the presumed replication origin. Dividing the distance between P1 and P2, 20 kb, by the lag in the onset of amplification, 4 hours, yields an average rate of elongation of $20 \text{ kb}/4 \times 60 \text{ min} = 83$ bp/min. The average elongation rate between P1 and P3 was somewhat slower, $30 \text{ kb}/10 \times 60 = 50 \text{ bp/min}$. Forks moved between P1 and P4 at about 61 bp/min = $44 \text{ kb}/12 \times 60$.

Further experiments will be required to determine if the small differences in the rate of leftward elongation (P1 to P3: 50 bp/min) and rightward elongation (P1 to P2: 83 bp/min) are significant. It is intriguing that the shape of the amplification gradient is slightly steeper on the left compared to the right sides (Fig. 1), the expected result if such a difference existed. However, at present these differences lie within the experimental error of our measurements. It also remains uncertain whether replication forks slow down as they approach the ends of the amplified regions, as suggested by the slower elongation rate between P2 and P4, compared to P1 and P2. Measurements of amplification kinetics using an Oregon R wild-type strain were similar to the results of Figure 1 (not shown). The elongation rate was 108 ± 35 bp/min.

The kinetics of the P1 probe amplification is similar to the measurements reported previously by Spradling and Mahowald (1980) and by Orr et al. (1984). However, the latter authors reported a slower rate of amplification during stages 9 and 10 than during stages 11–14. This distinction depends on accurate measurement of amplification in stage 8 and 9 egg chambers, a technically difficult task since the levels of amplification are low, and morphological criteria do not allow a high degree of resolution among egg chambers of different ages during this 11-hour period (see Mahowald and Kambysellis 1980).

The kinetics of P1–P4 amplification conforms closely to the results expected from the slow elongation model. These results also provide further support for the reinitiation model of amplification. Furthermore, if secondary origins exist within DNA flanking the gene clusters, these results suggest that their contribution to total DNA accumulation must be minor. Our measurements cannot distinguish between a single origin and closely spaced multiple origins within the gene clusters themselves, however.

Discussion

Significance of slow elongation

The rates of elongation measured during amplification are much slower than those found in most eukaryotic cells. Replication forks in *Drosophila* embryos and tissue culture cells travel at about 2.6 kb/min (at 25°C), a value similar to that of other higher organisms (Blumenthal et al. 1974). However, very slow rates of replication fork elongation were reported previously in insect polytene salivary gland cells (Cordeiro and Menghenini 1975; Steinemann 1981). The elongation rate within *Drosophila* follicle cells has not been measured directly. If they elongate like other polytene cells, replication forks within the amplified regions may move at rates that are simply characteristic of follicle cell replicons. The association of slow elongation with polyteny may not be fortuitous. Perhaps the difficulty of separating the multiple strands held together by somatic pairing represents a slow step in the process of fork movement. However, the individual chromatids in many polytene cells, including ovarian follicle cells, are not aligned sufficiently to produce visible polytene chromosomes. Thus, it may be some other aspect of the polytene replication cycle that is responsible for the slow rate of fork movement.

The developmentally synchronized progression of replication forks outward from the chorion gene clusters provides several experimental advantages for studies of *Drosophila* replication. Because the forks move so slowly, it is relatively easy to measure changes in the rates of initiation or elongation using the simple hybridization tests shown in Figure 1. Such measurements may provide insight into several conditions that alter the process of amplification. For example, it may be possible to determine whether genes involved in amplification and/or general replication act at the level of initiation or elongation. At least four genes mapping outside the two gene clusters are required for normal levels of amplification (Orr et al. 1984; Snyder et al. 1986; R. Kelley and A.C. Spradling, unpubl.). The amplification kinetics of one of these, *fs(3)293*, revealed that the approximately eightfold reduction in third chromosome amplification in homozygotes resulted from an approximately twofold decrease in the rate of initiation, rather than an effect on elongation (data not shown). Amplification in the mutant does not simply "start late," but occurs more slowly throughout the period of choriogenesis. Finally, comparison of kinetic measurements of X and third chromosome amplification may reveal the reason for the lower level of X cluster amplification.

Similar studies may also reveal more about the molecular basis of the position effects that reduce the amplification levels of transposons containing amplification control sequences. Two classes of models for such position effects have been proposed (see Orr-Weaver and Spradling 1986). If replication fork termination inhibited the progression of nearby replication forks, as discussed above, then transposon insertion near a terminator might limit the ability of a chromosome region to amplify. Kinetic measurements similar to those described here could be used to identify such putative terminator sequences in cloned DNA surrounding position-effected insertions. However, the finding that terminators do not appear to be present in the third chromosome gene cluster favors an alternative interpretation. Some aspect of the local sequence or chromatin

structure at the site of insertion may decrease the rate of initiation.

Are the amplified chorion domains normal replicons?

The finding that replication forks proceed within the amplified chorion domains at rates similar to those in other polytene *Drosophila* cells is consistent with the idea that amplification represents normal replication under tissue-specific control. Presumably, most of the same enzymatic machinery is used during amplification as was used in follicle cells previously during cellular proliferation. Genetic analysis of amplification is consistent with this idea. At least two of the genes that disrupt amplification also mutate to lethality, indicating that their products probably function outside the developing egg chamber (for review, see Spradling and Orr-Weaver 1987). However, the amplified domains may not correspond exactly to chromosomal replicons used during the replication of the follicle cell genome prior to amplification. If our interpretation is correct, the total length of the amplified domain (80–100 kb) is a property of the slow elongation rate and the total time since the onset of initiation. During normal replication, forks initiating at the origin within the gene cluster would be expected to fuse with a fork progressing from an adjacent replicon. Thus, although 80–100 kb is well within the size of replicons measured previously in *Drosophila* cells (see Spradling and Orr-Weaver 1987), the replicons in these chromosome regions may be quite different in size at other times during follicle cell development. This could be true even if the same origin is used during amplification and normal follicle cell replication. At present, there is no way to map individual replication origins in *Drosophila* chromosomes, precluding a direct test of this possibility.

Polytene cells normally undergo a cell cycle similar to that in diploid cells. DNA synthesis is not continuous; S phases alternate with periods where [^{3}H]thymidine is not incorporated. If a cell cycle continues to control replication initiation during amplification, then a major change in that cycle must occur at the time amplification begins. Measurements of increases in the total DNA content of follicle cell nuclei (for review, see Bohrmann et al. 1986) suggest that 3 or 4 rounds of follicle cell genomic replication occur between stage 5 and stage 9 (before the onset of amplification), a period of approximately 24 hours. Since most of the follicle cell euchromatin appears to be equally replicated, this corresponds to a doubling every 6–8 hours. The slopes of the lines in Figure 1 indicate that the rate of cell cycle oscillation must increase very substantially during stage 9 when the chorion domains begin to differentially replicate. The average rate of doubling of central probe sequences was about 2.6 hours beginning at this time.

Alternatively, chorion domain replication may not occur according to a cell cycle. Each DNA molecule containing the appropriate *cis*-regulatory sequences may be equally likely to initiate a succeeding round of replication. At present, it is not technically feasible to determine if the chorion domains replicate once and only once per cell cycle during the late stages of oogenesis. However, further study of the process of amplification should continue to provide insight into the developmental regulation of DNA replication in *Drosophila*.

Acknowledgments

This work was supported by a grant from the National Institutes of Health to A.C.S. G.L. was a National Institutes of Health postdoctoral fellow.

References

Blumenthal, A., H. Kriegstein, and D.S. Hogness. 1974. The units of replication in *Drosophila melanogaster* chromosomes. *Cold Spring Harbor Symp. Quant. Biol.* **38:** 205.

Bohrmann, J., G. Kiefer, and K. Sander. 1986. Inverse correlation between mean nuclear DNA content and cell number in nurse cell clusters of *Drosophila*. *Chromosoma* **94:** 36.

Cordeiro, M. and R. Menghenini. 1975. The rate of DNA replication in the polytene chromosomes of *Rhynchosciara angelae*. *J. Mol. Biol.* **78:** 261.

deCicco, D. and A. Spradling. 1984. Localization of a *cis*-acting element responsible for the developmentally regulated amplification of *Drosophila* chorion genes. *Cell* **38:** 45.

Delidakis, C. and F.C. Kafatos. 1987. Amplification of a chorion gene cluster in *Drosophila* is subject to multiple *cis*-regulatory elements and to long range position effects. *J. Mol. Biol.* **197:** 11.

Hand, R. 1978. Eucaryotic DNA: Organization of the genome for replication. *Cell* **15:** 317.

Kafatos, F.C., S.A. Mitsialis, N. Spoerel, B. Mariani, J.R. Lingappa, and C. Delidakis. 1985. Studies on the developmentally regulated expression and amplification of insect chorion genes. *Cold Spring Harbor Symp. Quant. Biol.* **50:** 537.

Kalfayan, L., J. Levine, T. Orr-Weaver, S. Parks, B. Wakimoto, D. deCicco, and A. Spradling. 1985. Localization of sequences regulating *Drosophila* chorion gene amplification and expression. *Cold Spring Harbor Symp. Quant. Biol.* **50:** 527.

Mahowald, A.P. and M.P. Kambysellis. 1980. Oogenesis. In *The genetics and biology of* Drosophila (ed. M. Ashburner and T.R.F. Wright), p. 141. Academic Press, New York.

Margaritis, L.H. 1985. Structure and physiology of the eggshell. In *Comprehensive insect physiology, biochemistry and pharmacology* (ed. G.A. Kerkut and L.I. Gilbert), vol. 1, p. 113. Pergamon Press, Elmsford, New York.

Orr, W., K. Komitopoulou, and F.C. Kafatos. 1984. Mutants suppressing in *trans* chorion gene amplification in *Drosophila*. *Proc. Natl. Acad. Sci.* **81:** 3773.

Orr-Weaver, T. and A.C. Spradling. 1986. *Drosophila* chorion gene amplification requires an upstream region regulating s18 transcription. *Mol. Cell. Biol.* **6:** 4624.

———. 1987. Regulation of *Drosophila* chorion gene amplification. *Stadler Genet. Symp.* (in press).

Osheim, Y.N. and O.L. Miller. 1983. Novel amplification and transcriptional activity of chorion genes in *Drosophila melanogaster* follicle cells. *Cell* **33:** 543.

Snyder, P.B., V.K. Galanopoulos, and F.C. Kafatos. 1986. *Trans*-acting amplification mutants and other eggshell mutants of the third chromosome in *Drosophila melanogaster*. *Proc. Natl. Acad. Sci.* **83:** 3341.

Spradling, A.C. 1981. The organization and amplification of two clusters of *Drosophila* chorion genes. *Cell* **27:** 193.

Spradling, A.C. and A.P. Mahowald. 1980. Amplification of chorion genes during oogenesis in *Drosophila melanogaster*. *Proc. Natl. Acad. Sci.* **77:** 1096.

———. 1981. A chromosome inversion alters the pattern of specific DNA replication in *Drosophila* follicle cells. *Cell* **27:** 203.

Spradling, A. and T. Orr-Weaver. 1987. Regulation of DNA replication during *Drosophila* development. *Annu. Rev. Genet.* **21:** 373.

Spradling, A.C., D.V. deCicco, B.T. Wakimoto, J.F. Levine, L.J. Kalfayan, and L. Cooley. 1987. Amplification of the X-linked chorion gene cluster requires a region upstream from the *s38* chorion gene. *EMBO J.* **6:** 1045.

Steinemann, M. 1981. Chromosomal replication in *Drosophila virilis*. III. Organization of active origins in the highly polytene salivary gland cells. *Chromosoma* **82:** 289.

Sundin, O. and A. Varshavsky. 1981. Arrest of segregation leads to accumulation of highly intertwined catenated dimers: Dissection of the final stages of SV40 DNA replication. *Cell* **25:** 659.

Deletion Analysis of *cis*-Acting Elements for Chorion Gene Amplification in *Drosophila melanogaster*

C. Delidakis* and F.C. Kafatos*[†]

*Department of Cellular and Developmental Biology, Harvard University, Cambridge, Massachusetts 02138; [†]Institute of Molecular Biology and Biotechnology and Department of Biology, University of Crete, Heraclio, Crete 71110, Greece

The developmentally regulated chorion gene amplification in *Drosophila* is a model system of a eukaryotic chromosomal replicon. Using P-element transformation, we have attempted to define *cis*-acting elements involved in the control of amplification. Constructs containing the entire third chromosome chorion locus can amplify at most chromosomal positions, although the extent of amplification is very sensitive to chromosomal location. In vitro deletion analysis has pointed to the existence of multiple elements needed in concert for the attainment of high amplification levels. To overcome the problem of position effects, we also induced in vivo deletions on an established, highly amplifying transformed line. Their preliminary analysis confirms the findings of the in vitro constructed deletions and suggests that a region ~1.5 kb long in the vicinity of s15 and s19 chorion genes might include a particularly important element for the attainment of high copy levels. The in vivo deletions also define a separate and as yet minimal fragment that can amplify at a low level: a 1.6- to 2.25-kb fragment in the vicinity of gene s18, including the amplification control element (ACE) previously recognized by subtraction (Orr-Weaver and Spradling 1986).

The two major chorion gene clusters of *Drosophila melanogaster* undergo amplification in the follicle cells of the ovary (Spradling and Mahowald 1980). This tissue-specific amplification is also temporally regulated, starting before the onset of chorion gene transcription and continuing until the end of oogenesis, whereupon follicle cells degenerate. Analysis of the amplified DNA has revealed a gradient of amplification over a ~100-kb domain, within which the 10-kb chorion gene cluster is centrally located and maximally amplified. The gradient apparently results from multiple initiation rounds from a single origin (or closely spaced origins) within the chorion cluster followed by bidirectional fork movement, creating a multiforked structure (Spradling 1981; Spradling and Mahowald 1981; Osheim and Miller 1983). Thus, chorion gene amplification is an attractive model system, as it involves a single chromosomal replicon whose controlling elements are amenable to analysis. Furthermore, as amplification escapes the normal cell-cycle control of replication, it can be used to study the signals involved in this control and the way they are bypassed in a temporally specific manner during oogenesis. We are studying the *cis*-acting requirements for amplification of the third chromosome chorion cluster, hoping to gain insight in both the above processes.

Using P-element transformation (Rubin and Spradling 1982), it has been shown (de Cicco and Spradling 1984; Orr-Weaver and Spradling 1986; Delidakis and Kafatos 1987) that certain fragments of the third chromosome chorion cluster can autonomously amplify with correct developmental specificity when inserted in various chromosomal positions. Furthermore, these fragments induce amplification of their neighboring se-

quences at the new chromosomal locations, in agreement with the idea that replication is initiated within the cluster and extends into the flanking DNA. Although it was originally thought that a single origin would be sufficient for amplification control, it now seems that multiple *cis*-acting elements are needed in concert for the attainment of full amplification levels. As these accessory elements are probably spread over an area of more than 5 kb, it is not feasible to analyze the total *cis* regulation of amplification by using small DNA fragments. The analysis is further complicated by the inhibitory effects exerted at many chromosomal positions: Constructs competent for amplification yield some transformed lines that fail to amplify or show severely reduced copy levels. Thus, to identify amplification-controlling elements, large amplification-competent constructs have been established, and their deletion analysis has been undertaken. Using this approach, Orr-Weaver and Spradling (1986) have identified an essential 510-bp-long region upstream of chorion gene s18, henceforth called the ACE3 region, whose deletion apparently prevents amplification. We have further identified two broad regions (each about 2.3 kb) that apparently contain amplification-enhancing elements: Deletion of either region causes a significant drop in the attainable amplification levels (Delidakis and Kafatos 1987). Here we report experiments that attempt to localize these enhancing elements more closely.

Methods

Fly transformation and quantitative analysis of amplification are described in Delidakis and Kafatos (1987).

311

Construction of small deletions

Deletions were created in a Ctcp background, a chorion construct identical to CtcS1R3 (Delidakis and Kafatos 1987) except for the in-frame insertion of a 288-bp fragment of an *Antheraea polyphemus* chorion gene coding sequence in the s15 gene (B.D. Mariani et al., in prep.). Deletion CtcΔBgXb was a gift of J. Lingappa. To construct CtcΔRSm, Ctcp was partially digested with

*Eco*RI, and a 16.8-kb fragment lacking the 4.35-kb *Eco*RI fragment that encompasses s16 was isolated; to this was ligated a *Sma*I (*Eco*RI linkered)-*Eco*RI subfragment of the 4.35-kb *Eco*RI fragment. CtcΔ³ was isolated among the ligation products of the following reaction: CtcΔRSm was digested with *Sal*I and partially with *Eco*RI, and the vector fragment lacking fragment S1R2 (see Fig. 1) was isolated and ligated with a mixture of the

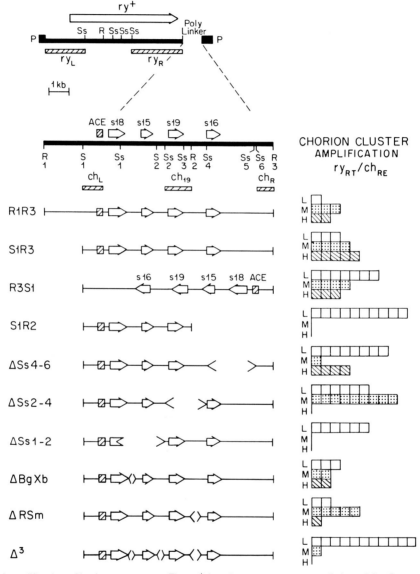

Figure 1 Summary of amplification of in vitro constructs. The *ry*⁺-bearing transposons consisting of the Carnegie 20 vector and third chromosome chorion DNA are shown. Restriction sites are indicated and are numbered sequentially in chorion DNA (R) *Eco*RI, (S) *Sal*I, (Ss) *Sst*I. The positions of the transcription units as well as ACE and the P-element ends (P) have been marked. The hatched bars under the restriction maps indicate DNA fragments used as probes in amplification assays. Fragments of the chorion cluster incorporated in different transposons are shown under the chorion map, blank areas signifying deletions. The histogram next to each construct indicates the distribution of amplification levels in independent transformed lines (each square corresponds to one line). Amplification levels have been arbitrarily grouped into three categories: *Low* (L) includes lines showing from no amplification up to 20% of endogenous amplification; *moderate* (M) includes lines ranging from 21% to 50% of endogenous amplification; *high* (H) includes lines amplifying to more than 50% of endogenous. Amplification levels of the transposon were measured using the ry_R probe and compared to endogenous levels determined by the ch_R probe. Individual amplification levels for the last three constructs are shown in Table 1.

3.7-kb s18/s15-containing *Sal*I fragment (S1S2) from Ctc∆BgXb and the 1.4-kb *Xho*I-*Eco*RI fragment containing s19.

Generation of in vivo deletions
To generate deletions on a pre-existing highly amplifying transformed line of construct R3S1, line R3S1-*L2*, we utilized the ability of P transposons to undergo internal deletions when placed in a dysgenic background (Daniels et al. 1985). For convenience, we used the transposase-producing but inefficient in transposition P element *P(tpse*⁺) (F. Spencer and G.M. Rubin, pers. comm.) inserted singly in the third chromosome. The scheme used for generating deletions will be described in detail elsewhere. Briefly, the chromosome bearing the *L2* transposon was placed in the presence of the *P(tpse*⁺) chromosome for one generation. In the next generation we removed the *P(tpse*⁺) bearing flies and screened the rest for a *rosy*⁻ phenotype resulting from excision or partial deletion of the transposon. Individual *ry*⁻ flies were used to establish lines, and deletions were subsequently mapped by Southern blotting.

Results

All constructs used in this study are based on the Carnegie 20 vector (Rubin and Spradling 1983), which is shown in Figure 1, along with a restriction map of the chorion cluster. The behavior of the first seven constructs as well as a detailed description of the method used to measure amplification are given in Delidakis and Kafatos (1987). Briefly, for amplification measurements we perform a Southern blot with DNA samples from males (nonamplifying sample) and late stage follicles (usually mixed stages 13 and 14, amplifying sample). The blot is simultaneously probed with two probes: (1) a single-copy sequence to provide an internal control for the amount of DNA loaded (this probe is usually ry_R, which detects the endogenous *ry* gene and an additional, construct-specific fragment that may be amplified in the follicular sample) and (2) a chorion-specific probe (this is usually ch_R, which detects amplification of distinct restriction fragments from both the endogenous cluster and the transformed chorion DNA). As seen in Figure 1, the first three constructs, which contain the entire chorion cluster and varying amounts of flanking DNA, as well as deletion ∆Ss4-6, can all amplify to high levels. The amplification levels vary widely in independent lines (position effect), but pairwise statistical comparisons of the distributions of values obtained with these constructs showed no significant differences. On the other hand, the truncated or internally deleted constructs S1R2, ∆Ss2-4, and ∆Ss1-2 yield significantly reduced amplification levels, suggesting the existence of enhancing elements within the missing DNA (Delidakis and Kafatos 1987).

Analysis of small deletions

We have made three additional deletion constructs in an attempt to delimit further the amplification-enhancing elements. The deletions made are shown in Figure 1 (constructs ∆BgXb, ∆RSm, and ∆³). We were guided in their construction by the results of the large-scale deletions, as well as by the observation of clustered repeated elements within the chorion DNA (Delidakis and Kafatos 1987). These deletions were made on Ctcp, a construct identical to CtcS1R3 except for the marking of the s15 gene by insertion of a 288-bp fragment of silkmoth chorion DNA. From the analysis of amplification in ten lines carrying undeleted Ctcp inserts, no significant effects were seen relative to S1R3 (data not shown).

The amplification levels of all lines tested from each of these constructs are shown in Table 1 and are summarized in Figure 1. From 7 and 8 lines of ∆BgXb and ∆RSm, respectively, we obtained a distribution of amplification levels ranging from single-copy to high levels. The two-sample Kolmogorov-Smirnov test (Sokal and Rohlf 1981) showed no significant differences between S1R3 and each of these two deletions. ∆RSm may have a small quantitative effect, similar to that of ∆Ss2-4, since only one of its lines exceeded 50% of the endogenous amplification levels, and only reached 64%. However, our sample size was not sufficiently large to allow detection of such small effects.

Contrary to ∆BgXb and ∆Rsm, ∆³ results in a significant drop in amplification levels ($p ≤ 0.05$ using the Kolmogorov-Smirnov test) with 11/12 lines exhibiting low levels and only one line showing amplification at 31% of the endogenous level (see Table 1). The total amount of DNA deleted in this construct is 1.5 kb, less than the 2.55 kb deleted in ∆Ss4-6, a fully amplification-competent construct; this eliminates the trivial explanation of increased position effects on the centrally located ACE element as the explanation for reduced amplification. In conjunction with the results of the larger deletions summarized above, the data suggest that either (1) there are redundant amplification-enhancing elements within the cluster so that only a multiple deletion can

Table 1 Amplification Levels of Small Deletion Constructs

∆BgXb	∆RSm	∆³
7	11	3
16	17	4
21	23	7
34	29	9
43	37	11
90	43	14
125	44	14
	64	15
		16
		17
		18
		31

The amplification levels of each transformant line of constructs ∆BgXb, ∆RSm, and ∆³ are given. They were measured using probe ry_R and are shown as percentages of the endogenous amplification levels at ch_R. A value of 3% corresponds to a nonamplifying transformant (cf. Delidakis and Kafatos 1987).

affect amplification levels significantly, or (2) there is an especially effective enhancing element between −611 and −197 of s19, the area deleted by Δ³ but unaffected by either ΔBgXb or ΔRSm. The data are not sufficient to test whether minor elements are present in the DNA regions removed by the large but not by the small deletions.

Analysis of in vivo deletions

The analysis of in vitro constructs is complicated by the randomness of chromosomal insertion sites that strongly affect amplification, thus necessitating the analysis of many lines per construct and the use of statistics for comparisons between constructs. Position effects may mask subtle quantitative effects of a deletion, a possible example being the case of ΔRSm, where a much larger sample size would be needed to safely decide whether there is an effect or not. To overcome these position effects, we have used a feature of P-element transposition described by Daniels et al. (1985): In a dysgenic germ line, where P elements are stimulated to transpose and excise, they frequently become internally deleted. In fact, internal P-element deletions can be recovered without concomitant transposition, making it possible to generate deletions in a pre-existing transposon while maintaining it at the same chromosomal site and thus overcoming the complication of position effects. To avoid generating deletion lines in a P genetic background, we mated flies from a transformed line with flies carrying in the *P(tpse⁺)* chromosome, a single P element that is capable of transposase production but very inefficient in its own transposition. Subsequently, we recovered in the second generation flies that had undergone internal deletions in the transposon (*ry⁻*), while also removing the *P(tpse⁺)* chromosome to avoid further transpositions/deletions (see Methods).

As our starting line, we used the most highly amplifying R3S1 line, R3S1-*L2*, which bears a third chromosome insert reaching 91% of the endogenous chorion amplification level. Among the 29 *ry⁻* derivative lines isolated, 21 were found to be internal deletions extending into the chorion region of the R3S1 construct. Of these, 7 were analyzed by blot hybridization for amplification and for the extent of the deletion. As seen in Figure 2, deletions ΔD, ΔH, ΔK, and ΔR have a relatively minor effect on amplification, dropping the levels from 91% to 51%, 35%, 45%, and 40%, respectively; the last three deletions remove at least 4.35 kb of chorion DNA, which may include minor amplification-enhancing element(s). The alternative interpretation, that the deletions bring inhibitory sequences from the left closer to ACE, cannot be excluded but is unlikely, since *ry* DNA is not inhibitory (cf. the S1R3 construct in Fig. 1), and the chromosomal insertion site of R3S1-*L2* appears to be especially favorable for amplification. A more severe drop is seen in deletions that extend 0.7–3 kb further into chorion DNA: deletions ΔP and ΔS result in amplification levels of 15% and 14%, respectively. The larger deletion ΔJ removes an additional 0.3–2.3 kb of chorion DNA and only drops the level slightly further, to 10%.

These results as a minimum suggest that an important element for amplification is found in the vicinity of the s15 gene between the deletion ΔH, ΔK, ΔR, and ΔP, ΔS endpoints. Part of that region is also included in the Δ³ deletion as well as in ΔSs1-2, the two in vitro deletion constructs that strongly affect amplification. We suggest that an amplification-enhancing element may be found between −611 and −197 of s19.

Another important conclusion from this analysis is that the ΔJ deletion still amplifies, albeit at a low level. This defines a 1.6- to 2.25-kb chorion fragment as sufficient for amplification—the smallest fragment reported as yet to have that capacity. This fragment contains the entire ACE, as well as the s18 upstream region and the 5′ end of the s18 gene itself.

Concluding Remarks

Although chorion gene amplification is subject to control from multiple *cis*-acting elements, to date only ACE has been defined unequivocally by deletion analysis (Orr-Weaver and Spradling 1986). This has been largely due to the fact that quantitative effects on amplification have to be dramatic before they can be detected above the background of position effects. Although deletions of ACE abolish amplification, deletion of any one of the putative enhancing elements has substantially less dramatic effects; only large or multiple deletions show obvious decreases in amplification levels. The combination of in vitro and in vivo deletion analysis has greatly enhanced our ability to detect quantitative effects. Analysis of unidirectional in vivo deletions suggested that there are a few regions in chorion DNA, deletion of which results in a drop in amplification levels, the region encompassing the s15 and s19 genes having the most dramatic effect. We are in the process of analyzing additional deletion endpoints to define this enhancing element more closely.

It is still not known what the precise function of each of the *cis*-acting elements is. ACE seems to be responsible for the developmentally regulated uncoupling of replication from cell-cycle control, as amplification does not take place in its absence. However, it is not certain yet whether the replication origin is included within ACE. Interestingly, interspersed through the chorion cluster DNA there are seven sequence repeats that show strong homology (10/11 to 11/11 identity) to the yeast ARS core consensus sequence (Broach et al. 1983; Kearsey 1984). One of these repeats is included within the enhancing region defined by the deletion ΔH, ΔK, ΔR, and ΔP, ΔS endpoints. Directed mutagenesis will be needed to show whether this repeat or any other sequence feature has functional significance.

Acknowledgments

We thank J.R. Lingappa for providing the CtcΔBgXb construct and C. Swimmer for helpful discussions. We also thank B. Klumpar for photography, M. Youk-See for artwork, and E. Fenerjian for secretarial assistance. The

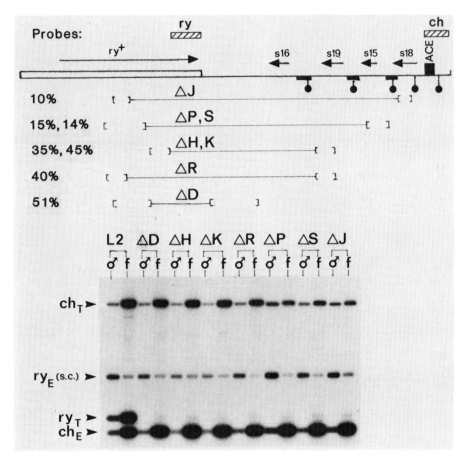

Figure 2 Amplification of in vivo deletions. The R3S1 construct contained in line R3S1-*L2* is shown, which was subjected to P-transposase-induced deletions (see text). The positions of the *ry* and chorion transcription units as well as the ACE are indicated. The DNA removed in the triple deletion Δ^3 is indicated by three black boxes under the chorion map. (●) Elements homologous to the yeast ARS core sequence. The extent of the seven in vivo deletions analyzed is shown below the map, brackets indicating uncertainty in the exact position of the endpoints. The percentage next to each deletion indicates the amplification levels reached relative to endogenous amplification; the undeleted line amplified to the 91% level. The actual Southern analysis of amplification is also shown: Male (♂) and late stage follicular (f) DNAs from each line were simultaneously probed with a *rosy* and a chorion probe (shown as hatched bars above the map). Bands corresponding to endogenous fragments are marked as ry_E and ch_E, and transformant-specific bands are marked ry_T and ch_T. Note the absence of a ry_T band in the deleted lines; all deletions remove the area homologous to the *ry* probe.

work has been supported by a National Institutes of Health grant. C.D. is a Schlumberger fellow supported by Fondation Les Treilles.

References

Broach, J.R., Y.Y. Li, J. Feldman, M. Jayaram, J. Abraham, K.A. Nasmyth, and J.B. Hicks. 1983. Localization and sequence analysis of yeast origins of DNA replication. *Cold Spring Harbor Symp. Quant. Biol.* **47**: 1165.

Daniels, S.B., M. McCarron, C. Love, and A. Chovnick. 1985. Dysgenesis-induced instability of *rosy* locus transformation in *Drosophila melanogaster*: Analysis of excision events and the selective recovery of control element deletions. *Genetics* **109**: 95.

de Cicco, D.V. and A.C. Spradling. 1984. Localization of a *cis*-acting element responsible for the developmentally regulated amplification of *Drosophila* chorion genes. *Cell* **38**: 45.

Delidakis, C. and F.C. Kafatos. 1987. Amplification of a chorion gene cluster in *Drosophila* is subject to multiple *cis*-regulatory elements and to long-range position effects. *J. Mol. Biol.* **197**: 11.

Kearsey, S. 1984. Structural requirements for the function of a yeast chromosomal replicator. *Cell* **37**: 299.

Orr-Weaver, T.L. and A.C. Spradling. 1986. *Drosophila* chorion gene amplification requires an upstream region regulating s18 transcription. *Mol. Cell. Biol.* **6**: 4624.

Osheim, Y.N. and O.L. Miller, Jr. 1983. Novel amplification and transcriptional activity of chorion genes in *Drosophila melanogaster* follicle cells. *Cell* **33**: 543.

Rubin, G.M. and A.C. Spradling. 1982. Genetic transformation of *Drosophila* with transposable element vectors. *Science* **218**: 348.

————. 1983. Vector for P-element mediated gene transfer in *Drosophila*. *Nucleic Acids Res.* **11**: 6341.

Sokal, R.R. and F.J. Rohlf. 1981. *Biometry: The principles and practice of statistics in biological research.* W.R. Freeman, San Francisco.

Spradling, A.C. 1981. The organization and amplification of two chromosomal domains containing *Drosophila* chorion genes. *Cell* **27**: 193.

Spradling, A.C. and A.P. Mahowald. 1980. Amplification of genes for chorion proteins during oogenesis in *Drosophila melanogaster*. *Proc. Natl. Acad. Sci.* **77**: 1096.

————. 1981. A chromosome inversion alters the pattern of specific DNA replication in *Drosophila* follicle cells. *Cell* **27**: 203.

Enhancement of Gene Amplification by Perturbation of DNA Synthesis in Cultured Mammalian Cells

R.T. Schimke, C. Hoy, G. Rice, S.W. Sherwood, and R.I. Schumacher
Department of Biological Sciences, Stanford University, Stanford, California 94305

The frequency of amplification of the dihydrofolate reductase (DHFR) gene and methotrexate (MTX) resistance can be enhanced by a variety of agents that have in common the inhibition of DNA synthesis (hydroxyurea, aphidicolin, UV light, and hypoxia). Flow cytometric analysis indicates a complex series of effects of transient inhibition of DNA synthesis, depending on when in a cell cycle DNA synthesis is inhibited. In those cells whose DNA synthesis is inhibited in the middle of S phase, upon resumption of DNA synthesis, mitosis is delayed significantly, and prior to mitosis, they contain $>G_2/M$ DNA content. Concomitant inhibition of protein synthesis during inhibition of DNA synthesis abolishes the enhanced frequency of resistance and markedly reduces other consequences of transient DNA inhibition, including chromosome breaks and cell killing. The marked delay in M phase following restoration of DNA synthesis suggests that the "overreplication" of DNA may in part result from perturbations of the relationship between S and M, such that mitosis occurs variably in a second S phase.

One form of genomic fluidity observed in somatic cells is gene amplification, including oncogenes associated with tumor progression (Bishop 1987), drug resistances during cancer chemotherapy (Schimke 1984), and insecticide resistance (Mouches et al. 1986). Under laboratory conditions a number of examples of gene amplification have been reported employing step-wise drug-selection regimens (for review, see Hamlin et al. 1984; Schimke 1984; Stark and Wahl 1984). We, as well as others, have been interested in studying the mechanism of gene amplification. The basic question is: Where does the additional gene (DNA sequence) come from? Alternative sources include: (1) uptake of DNA from killed or fused cells, (2) unequal sister chromatid exchange, and (3) overreplication prior to mitosis.

An approach we have taken in our studies with MTX resistance and DHFR gene amplification is to study possible initial steps in the process, in the belief that the alternative approach, i.e., studying structure and recombinational sequences of amplified sequences, gives limited information, inasmuch as all mechanisms involve recombination events. Specifically, we have shown that a variety of treatments of cells prior to placement in MTX for selection can increase the frequency of DHFR gene amplification. These pretreatments include metabolic inhibitors of DNA synthesis, hydroxyurea (Brown et al. 1983) and aphidicolin (Hoy et al. 1987), agents that introduce adducts into DNA, UV light, N-acetoxy acetoaminofluorene (Tlsty et al. 1984), and anoxia (Rice et al. 1986). All such treatments have in common inhibition of DNA synthesis and an enhancement of MTX resistance only after restoration of DNA synthesis prior to selection. We have proposed that such perturbations of DNA synthesis patterns result in overreplication of DNA within a single cell cycle. Among the con-

sequences resulting from recombination of the additional DNA strands is the generation of amplified DNA sequences on which selection for expression-amplification of specific genes occurs (Schimke 1984; Schimke et al. 1986). This approach has significant drawbacks, as does the study of recombination structures, inasmuch as we deduce mechanisms by studying a heterogeneous population of cells (see below) from which eventually emerge clonal populations with amplified genes.

We here review certain of these results and certain aspects of mechanisms of amplification that result from perturbation of DNA synthesis and the resulting alterations in cell cycle kinetics.

Experimental Procedures

All of the experiments discussed employ MTX-sensitive Chinese hamster ovary (either CHOK or AA8) cells. Details of cell growth, clonal selection, and use of flow cytometric instrumentation are referenced or described in the figure legends.

Results

Enhancement of DHFR gene amplification by pretreatment with hypoxia

We summarize various experiments in which CHO AA8 cells were subjected to an atmosphere devoid of O_2. Figure 1 shows the effect of varying times of hypoxia pretreatment on the frequency of MTX resistance when cells are placed in MTX at the time of restoration of the normal atmosphere. Increasing times of exposure to hypoxia results in an increasing frequency of MTX resistance. Twenty-four hours of hypoxia enhances the fre-

317

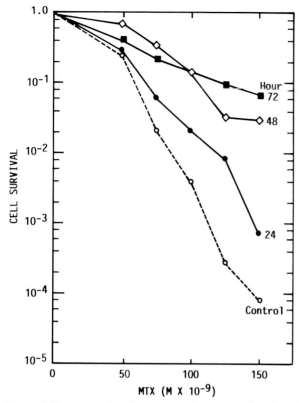

Figure 1 Frequency of methotrexate resistance as a function of time in hypoxia. Cells were placed under hypoxic conditions for the times specified and plated immediately into MTX-containing medium. Cell survival curves are normalized to relative plating efficiency in normal medium (plating efficiency was 100, 11, and 6% of control cells at 24, 48, and 72 hr of hypoxia, respectively. Details are given in Rice et al. (1986). (Reprinted, with permission, from Rice et al. 1986.)

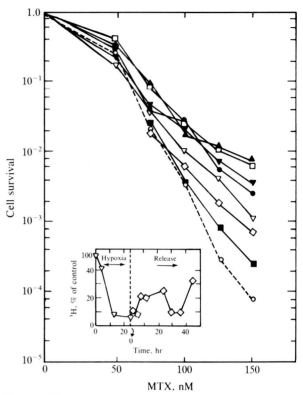

Figure 2 The effect of recovery time after pretreatment with hypoxia on the frequency of MTX resistance. Cells were subjected to hypoxia for 24 hr and placed under normal aeration conditions for the times specified before addition of MTX. Control is cells without hypoxia and 0 time is cells plated into MTX immediately after 24 hr of hypoxia. The inset indicates thymidine incorporation for 10 min at the times indicated. Details are given in Rice et al. (1986). (Reprinted, with permission, from Rice et al. 1986.)

quency approximately tenfold, whereas 72 hours of hypoxia increases the frequency approximately 1000-fold. Inasmuch as approximately 5% of cells survive such treatment, it is obvious that we have induced resistance in the cell population, rather than selecting for preexisting cells. Figure 2 shows that the time when cells are placed in MTX following restoration of the normal atmosphere has a profound effect on the frequency of MTX resistance. Following 24 hours of hypoxia, exposure to MTX for detecting high frequencies of MTX resistance is optimal approximately 12–24 hours after return to a normal atmosphere, and is approximately 100-fold over control cells at this time. At later time periods, the enhanced frequency diminishes. Figure 2 (inset) shows that hypoxia inhibits DNA synthesis, and following return to normal atmosphere, the incorporation of thymidine is restored in a complicated biphasic pattern. The finding that the enhanced frequency requires restoration of DNA synthesis is similar to that observed following treatment of cells with hydroxyurea (Brown et al. 1983) and UV light (Tlsty et al. 1984).

Figure 3 shows a flow cytometric analysis of the progression of cells through a cell cycle as it is per-

turbed by hypoxia. In this method an asynchronous cell population is "pulsed" for 20 minutes with bromodeoxy-uridine (BrdU). At any subsequent time, cells are fixed in ethanol and analyzed for DNA content (horizontal axis) and fluorescence derived from an antibody system that detects BrdU-substituted DNA. Panels A and B show an analysis immediately after a BrdU pulse and display G_1, S, and G_2/M populations based on DNA content. Inasmuch as only S-phase cells have incorporated BrdU, these cells form an "arc" of fluorescence of cells with DNA content intermediate between G_1 and G_2/M cells. Panel C shows this population 4 hours later. The G_2/M cells have progressed into G_1; the G_1 cells are now progressing into S; and some of the original S-phase cells have completed a cell cycle and are in G_1 (G_1 DNA content with anti-BrdU fluorescence). Panel D shows the cells 8 hours after the BrdU pulse: The initial G_1 cells are now in S, and some of the original S cells (BrdU containing) are beginning to enter S ($> G_1$ DNA content). Thus, this method can be employed to follow the cell cycle progression of cells, in particular those previously in S phase. Panel E shows cells labeled immediately prior to treatment with 24 hours of hypoxia

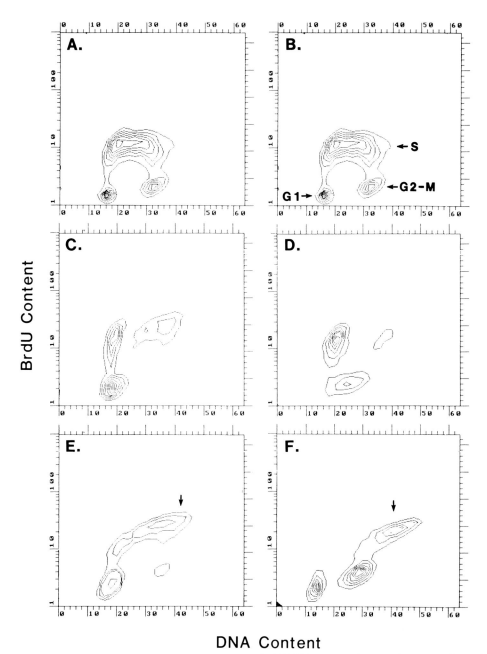

BrdU Content

DNA Content

Figure 3 Hypoxia results in the generation of cells with greater than G_2/M DNA content. An asynchronous cell population is labeled for 20 min with BrdU. Cells are subsequently grown in normal medium and at any time are fixed in ethanol, treated with HCl, heated, and treated with ribonuclease. They are then reacted with an anti-BrdU antibody and a fluorescent secondary antibody. In addition, they are stained with propidium iodide (DNA quantitation). Details of the method are given in Rice et al. (1986). See text for explanation of results. (A and B) Control cells analyzed immediately. (C and D) Control cells analyzed 4 and 8 hr after a 20-min BrdU pulse. (E and F) Cells subjected to hypoxia for 24 hr after BrdU labeling, analyzed at 0 and 12 hr after return to aeration. (Reprinted, with permission, from Rice et al. 1986.)

(compare with Fig. 3A). The G_2/M cells have progressed into G_1; however, hypoxia prevents G_1 cells from progressing into S. Those cells in S phase at the time of treatment remain in S, and their DNA content is progressing slightly beyond the G_2/M border. Panel F shows these same cells 12 hours after return to normal atmosphere (see insert of Fig. 2 for overall DNA synthesis). By this time the prior G_1 cells have been cycling. However,

the cells previously in S at the time of hypoxia treatment have not yet divided, but their DNA content/cell has continued to increase. In fact, such cells do not begin to undergo mitosis until approximately 36 hours after restoration to a normal atmosphere.

Figure 4 shows the profile of cells 24 hours after being subjected to 24 hours of hypoxia as stained with Hoechsts 33342. Approximately 60% of the cells con-

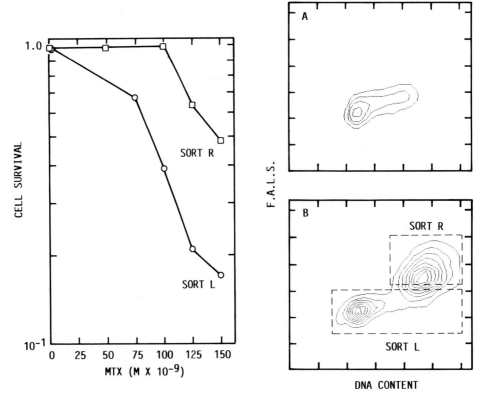

Figure 4 Hypoxia-induced enhancement of methotrexate resistance comes from the subset of a cell population with $> G_2/M$ DNA content per cell. Cells were subjected to hypoxia for 24 hr. Cells were returned to normal aeration, stained with Hoechsts 33342, and sorted into the indicated R and L populations, which constitute larger cells (forward angle light scatter-FALS) and in which a proportion of the cells display greater than 4C DNA content. (*A*) Control "contour" plot, (*B*) hypoxia-treated cells. Following sorting, cells were plated into the indicated MTX concentrations and colonies (>50 cells) counted 1–3 weeks later. Cell survival is corrected for the reduced plating efficient resulting from sorting. Details are provided in Rice et al. (1986). (Reprinted, with permission, from Rice et al. 1986.)

tain $> G_2/M$ DNA per cell. When these cells are sorted as indicated, the enhanced resistance to MTX is derived from that subset of the population with $> G_2/M$ DNA content/cell. The finding that the enhanced resistance comes from the subset of cells with $> G_2/M$ DNA content is in keeping with prior studies from our laboratory employing metabolic inhibitors of DNA synthesis (Hill and Schimke 1985; Johnston et al. 1986; Hoy et al. 1987).

These results show that only the cells that were in S at the time of inhibition of DNA synthesis respond by the subsequent generation of $> G_2/M$ DNA content/cell. Furthermore, they show that hypoxia has a profound effect in delaying M beyond the time expected *if* cell cycle events simply continued to progress at a normal time interval following restoration of DNA synthesis. Other results (S. Sherwood, in prep.) indicate that the delay-arrest is in G_2 and is not the result of a prolonged M phase. Hoy et al. (1987) have employed this same technique to analyze cell cycle kinetics subsequent to treatment with UV light, hydroxyurea, or aphidicolin. Table 1 summarizes some of the results with hydroxyurea and aphidicolin. As with the case of hypoxia, those cells in an asynchronous population in S at the time DNA inhibition was imposed have a greatly delayed entry into

M (varying from 24 to 60 hours). Equally interesting is the effect of inhibition of DNA synthesis on cells in G_1 at the time of imposition of DNA synthesis inhibition.

Table 1 Comparison of Cell Cycle Transit Times for Control, Hydroxyurea-, or Aphidicolin-treated Animals

	G_1-G_1	S–S	4C DNA
Control	15 hr	14 hr	none
Hydroxyurea[1]	6–8 hr	>20 hr	6–8 hr
Aphidicolin[2]	6 hr	>22 hr	4–12 hr

The cells used in these studies are CHO AA8 cells. Details are given in Hoy et al. (1987). The G_1-G_1 and S–S are the times when cells in either G_1 or S at the time of the initial analysis have progressed to a second G_1 or a second S, i.e., when drug-treated, the G_1 cells were those in G_1 at the time of drug treatment and the S cells were in S at the time of treatment. The cell cycle time starts with the time after cells begin to cycle once the drug has been removed from the cultures. Cells rapidly become heterogeneous, and a 20% cell population was used as the criterion for timing, i.e., at least 20% of cells had to be in a cell cycle phase to record the time.
[1]Cells were exposed to 2 mM hydroxyurea for 18 hr. Thymidine incorporation was 5% of control during and at the time of removal of hydroxyurea.
[2]Cells were exposed to 6 μM aphidicolin for 18 hr and thymidine incorporation was reduced to 5% of normal incorporation.

Whereas control cells progress from G_1 to the next G_1 in 15 hours, upon release from DNA synthesis inhibition, those cells in G_1 return to a second G_1 in 6–8 hours, i.e., their transit through the cell cycle is markedly accelerated. Furthermore, when these cells return to the second G_1, their progression into the next S phase is markedly retarded (data not shown). Table 1 also shows that following restoration of DNA synthesis, the time before a measurable proportion of the cells has $> G_2/M$ DNA/cell varies from 4 to 12 hours (variable from experiment to experiment). The data with hydroxyurea and aphidicolin are in keeping with the hypoxia data in showing a marked delay entering M in those cells whose DNA synthesis is inhibited when they are in S phase. Hoy et al. (1987) have shown that the enhanced frequency of MTX resistance comes from the cell population with G_2/M DNA content/cell (see Fig. 4 for hypoxia treatment).

Effects of concomitant inhibition of protein and DNA synthesis on subsequent properties of cells

The agents we have employed to inhibit DNA synthesis have small or no effects on protein synthesis. Indeed, during the period of inhibition of DNA synthesis and subsequent to its restoration, there is a progressive increase in cell size-volume and a comparable ($\sim$ twofold) increase in protein content/cell. We have proposed that during the time of inhibition of DNA synthesis, proteins accumulate that result in the overreplication of DNA prior to mitosis, and we have provided evidence that DHFR, as well as at least five other proteins, is synthesized at a higher rate during the period of inhibition of DNA synthesis (Johnston et al. 1986). We also reported that inhibition of protein synthesis by cycloheximide when DNA synthesis was inhibited markedly retarded the appearance of cells with $> G_2/M$ DNA/cell. We have examined the effect of concomitant inhibition of

protein (cycloheximide) and DNA synthesis (aphidicolin and hydroxyurea) on various of the consequences of inhibition-restoration of DNA synthesis, including cell killing, generation of chromosomal aberrations, as well as enhancement of MTX resistance. Table 2 summarizes certain of these results.

Inhibition of protein synthesis itself decreases plating efficiency of cells to 66% of normal. However, when combined with either aphidicolin or hydroxyurea, cell killing is reduced markedly relative to the effects of the DNA synthesis inhibitor alone. Others have reported comparable findings (Lieberman et al. 1970; Bhuyan and Fraser 1971; Ayusawa et al. 1983). Cycloheximide treatment of cells has minimal effect on chromosomal aberrations, whereas treatment with aphidicolin or hydroxyurea generates a high frequency of chromosomal aberrations, of which we here record the most striking (breakage-fragmentation of chromosomes). Inhibition of protein synthesis during the period of inhibition of DNA synthesis markedly reduces the frequency and severity of chromosomal aberrations (damage). Lastly, concomitant inhibition of protein and DNA synthesis markedly reduces the enhanced resistance that occurs when cells are treated with inhibitors of DNA synthesis only. These results are consistent with the proposal that protein synthesis in the absence of DNA synthesis (i.e., unbalanced growth) is required for the generation of $> G_2/M$ DNA content/cell, the generation of broken chromosomes and its attendant cell killing, as well as the enhancement of gene amplification.

Discussion

The studies for this laboratory have been consistent with the concept that a major mechanism resulting in gene amplification is an overreplication of DNA in a single cell cycle, generating additional DNA strands that can un-

Table 2 Effects of Cycloheximide (CHX) Inhibition of Protein Synthesis on Aphidicolin- and Hydroxyurea-induced Generation of MTX Resistance, Cell Killing, and Chromosomal Aberrations

	HU	HU + CHX	APC	APC + CHX	CHX
Cell survival	1×10^{-2}	4×10^{-1}	3×10^{-2}	2×10^{-1}	0.6
MTX resistance	5×10^{-1}	4×10^{-3}	5×10^{-2}	1.7×10^{-3}	7×10^{-3}
Chromosome aberrations	% of cells with grade 3 aberrations 8 and 24 hr after restoration of DNA synthesis by removal of drug				
4 hr	33.3	2.6	0	0	0
24 hr	17.9	6.0	66.4	1.0	0

CHO K1 cells (American Tissue Culture Collection) were grown in Hamm's F12. Cytotoxicity was measured by a clonogenic assay and MTX was added at various concentrations. Colonies (>50 cells) were counted 1–3 weeks later after staining with crystal violet. Resistance frequencies are given as the ratio of MTX-resistant colonies compared to surviving colonies, taking into account the effects of CHX on cell killing. Chromosome damage was graded on a level of 1 to 3 as reported previously (Sherwood et al. 1987). We here report only the % metaphases with the most severe damage (>10 chromatid breaks plus pulverized chromosomes) and only in cells at 8 and 24 hr after resumption of DNA synthesis. CHX, 10 μg/ml, inhibited protein synthesis to 5% of control as measured by labeled amino acid uptake. For the studies on chromosome aberrations, cells were subjected to hydroxyurea (HU), 1 mM, and aphidicolin (APC), 1 μg/ml, for 18 hr and then placed in normal growth media in the presence of colcemid for studying metaphase spreads. For the studies on cell killing and MTX resistance the concentrations of HU and APC were 3 mM and 5 μg/ml, respectively.

dergo various types of recombination events, several of which result in either chromosomal or extrachromosomal amplifications of genes (Schimke 1984; Schimke et al. 1986). We have proposed that variable portions of the genome are replicated prior to mitosis as a result of an increased capacity for initiation of replication that accumulates during the period when DNA, but not protein, synthesis is inhibited. However, our recent results employing flow cytometric analyses indicate that various of the agents that enhance gene amplification frequencies markedly delay the entry into mitosis of that subset of cells treated in S. These observations raise questions as to whether the control process(es) perturbed by inhibition of DNA synthesis is at the G_1/S boundary, i.e., initiation of DNA synthesis, or whether (alternatively or additionally) it is at the G_2/M boundary, i.e., whether cells progress into a second S phase without an intervening mitosis, a suggestion we made several years ago (Hill and Schimke 1985). Although the result is the same, i.e., overreplication of DNA in a *single* cell cycle, and the possible recombination events are similar (Schimke et al. 1986), concepts concerning the control of such events as they related to mechanisms of amplification would differ markedly between the two extreme alternatives. The finding in *Schizosaccharomyces pombe* that certain cdc mutations can affect both the G_1/S and G_2/M transitions (Nurse and Bissett 1981) suggests that alterations in both processes may be involved in amplification events.

That perturbation of DNA replication patterns can alter cell cycle kinetics has been studied by Merz and Schneider (1983). Using flow cytometric techniques different from those we employed, they reported that a 12-hour period of hypoxia in Ehrlich ascites tumor cells results in abrogation of the normally occurring M, and that prior to mitosis, cells accumulate twice the normal DNA content, i.e., they contain 8C DNA content in G_2. Furthermore, they reported that hypoxia-treated cells, on restoration of DNA synthesis, have a markedly foreshortened G_1 phase. Although their studies and ours use different cell types and different techniques, we confirm the concept that perturbations of DNA synthesis profoundly alter a variety of aspects of cell cycle kinetics, and the alterations are dependent on the prior history of cells; in particular, where they are in the cell cycle at the time the perturbation occurs. Our results are not necessarily consistent with those of Merz and Schneider (1983) with respect to DNA content/cell at the time M phase occurs. Although we have not measured DNA content in cells actually progressing through M, as their technique is specifically designed to do, chromosome spreads from cells recovering from transient inhibition of DNA synthesis show a spectrum of chromosomal aberrations. Our results are more consistent with the concept that the delayed mitosis can occur at variable times during a second S phase. In the study of chromosomal aberrations generated following hydroxyurea inhibition of mouse L5178Y cells, Hill and Schimke (1985) found that upon restoration of DNA synthesis, the first cells entering M contained normal

chromosomes. This finding is consistent with the finding (Table 1) that cells arrested in G_1 progress extremely rapidly through the cell cycle subsequently and divide before the cells arrested in S divide. These workers found that the cells with chromosomal aberrations entered M only at a later time, a finding consistent with a delay of entry into M. The chromosomal aberrations were limited to those cells that contained $> G_2/M$ DNA content and included normal chromosomes with extrachromosomal DNA, varying degrees of polyploidization with partially condensed chromosomes, as well as occasional complete endoreduplication, in addition to the above structures with varying degrees of chromosomal gaps-breaks. Such a spectrum of chromosomal aberrations would be consistent with a chromosome condensation-mitosis process superimposed at variable times in a second S phase.

Our results indicate that continued protein synthesis is required for the perturbations of cell cycle events as we have studied them. Our results, as well as those of many other laboratories, have shown that inhibition of protein synthesis with cycloheximide rapidly inhibits DNA synthesis, a finding interpreted to indicate that continued protein synthesis is required for DNA replication (presumably some proteins are turning over rapidly). Such a conclusion has been questioned by the results of Roufa (1978) employing a temperature-sensitive mutant in protein synthesis, which reported that DNA synthesis continued at restrictive temperatures in the absence of protein synthesis. In his studies, the cells were subjected to "synchronization" by succession of double thymidine block followed by hydroxyurea treatment prior to the temperature shift. Thus, it is possible that during the period of inhibition of DNA synthesis, an accumulation of the protein(s) consumed during DNA replication could have occurred such that DNA synthesis becomes independent of protein synthesis. This suggestion is consistent with the finding of an accelerated rate of DNA synthesis in *Escherichia coli* upon restoration of DNA synthesis following its inhibition in the presence of continued protein synthesis (Tipp-Schindler et al. 1979).

Our results, as well as those of Merz and Schneider (1983), showing alterations in timing of cell cycle processes indicate the complexities of events when cultured mammalian cells are perturbed by varying growth conditions. They raise the possibility that cell cycle kinetics are determined by an independent oscillatory program on which can be superimposed various cell cycle processes, some of which are independent and others dependent on cell cycle progression (Klevecz et al. 1986). Given the finding that cells whose DNA synthesis is inhibited during the S phase are delayed in progression into and through mitosis, our results raise the question as to what determines the decision to undergo chromosome condensation and mitosis and what proteins accumulate during inhibition of DNA synthesis that prevent decisions for mitosis. Lee and Nurse (1987) have found that the 34-kD protein kinase of *S. pombe*, i.e., cdc2, necessary for both initiation into S as well as progression from G_2 into mitosis, has a counterpart in human cells. Analysis of cell cycle mutants in systems amenable to genetic analysis will surely assist in understanding how the extremely complex regulatory circuits of cell cycle progression function in normal and perturbed conditions. To the extent that such regulatory circuits are altered in cells with a high frequency of amplification-rearrangement events, i.e., cancer cells, such information will be important in understanding the complexities of how replication is controlled.

References

Ayusawa, D., K. Shimizu, H. Koyama, K. Takeishi, and T. Seno. 1983. Accumulation of DNA strand breaks during thymineless death in thymidylate synthase-negative mutations of mouse FM3A cells. *J. Biol. Chem.* **258**: 12448.

Bhuyan, B.K. and T.J. Fraser. 1971. Antagonism between DNA synthesis inhibitors and protein synthesis inhibitors in mammalian cell cultures. *Cancer Res.* **34**: 778.

Bishop, J.M. 1987. The molecular genetics of cancer. *Science* **235**: 305.

Brown, P.C., T.D. Tlsty, and R.T. Schimke. 1983. Enhancement of methotrexate resistance and dihydrofolate reductase gene amplification by treatment of mouse 3T6 cells with hydroxyurea. *Mol. Cell. Biol.* **3**: 1097.

Hamlin, J.L., J.D. Milbrandt, N.H. Heintz, and J.C. Azizkhan. 1984. DNA sequence amplification in mammalian cells. *Int. Rev. Cytol.* **90**: 131.

Hill, A.B. and R.T. Schimke. 1985. Increased gene amplification in L5178Y mouse lymphoma cells with hydroxyurea-induced chromosomal aberrations. *Cancer Res.* **45**: 5050.

Hoy, C.A., G.C. Rice, M. Kovacs, and R.T. Schimke. 1987. Overreplication of DNA in S-phase CHO cells after DNA synthesis inhibition. *J. Biol. Chem.* **262**: 11927.

Johnston, R.N., J. Feder, A.B. Hill, S.W. Sherwood, and R.T. Schimke. 1986. Transient inhibition of DNA synthesis results in increased dihydrofolate reductase synthesis and subsequent increased DNA content per cell. *Mol. Cell. Biol.* **6**: 3373.

Klevecz, R.R., S.A. Kauffman, and R.M. Shyomko. 1986. Cellular clocks and oscillators. *Int. Rev. Cytol.* **86**: 97.

Lee, M.G. and P. Nurse. 1987. Complementation used to clone a human homologue of the fission yeast cell cycle control gene cdc2. *Nature* **327**: 31.

Lieberman, M.W., R.S. Verbin, N. Landay, H. Liang, E. Farber, T.-N. Lee, and R.A. Starr. 1970. A probable role for protein synthesis in intestinal epithelial cell damage induced in vivo by cytosine arabinoside, nitrogen mustard, or X-irradiation. *Cancer Res.* **30**: 942.

Merz, F. and F. Schneider. 1983. Growth characteristics of anaerobically treated early and late S-period of Ehrlich ascites tumor cells after reaeration. *Z. Naturforsch.* **38**: 313.

Mouches, C., N. Pasteur, J.B. Berg, O. Hyrien, M. Raymond, B.R. de Saint Vincent, M. de Silvestri, and G.P. Georghiou. 1986. Amplification of an esterase gene is responsible for insecticide resistance in a California *Culex* mosquito. *Science* **233**: 778.

Nurse, P. and Y. Bissett. 1981. Cell cycle genes required in G1 for commitment to cell division and in G2 for control of mitosis in fission yeast. *Nature* **292**: 558.

Rice, G.C., C. Hoy, and R.T. Schimke. 1986. Transient hypoxia enhances the frequency of dihydrofolate reductase gene amplification in Chinese hamster ovary cells. *Proc. Natl. Acad. Sci.* **83**: 5978.

Roufa, D.J. 1978. Replication of a mammalian genome: The role of de novo protein biosynthesis during S phase. *Cell* **13**: 129.

Schimke, R.T. 1984. Gene amplification in cultured animal cells. *Cell* **37**: 705.

Schimke, R.T., S.W. Sherwood, A.B. Hill, and R.N. Johnston. 1986. Overreplication and recombination of DNA in higher eukaryotes: Potential consequences and biological implications. *Proc. Natl. Acad. Sci.* **83**: 2157.

Sherwood, S.W., A.S. Daggett, and R.T. Schimke. 1987. Interaction of hyperthermia and metabolic inhibitors on the induction of chromosome damage in Chinese hamster ovary cells. *Cancer Res.* **47**: 3584.

Stark, G.R. and G.M. Wahl. 1984. Gene amplification. *Annu. Rev. Biochem.* **53**: 447.

Tipp-Schindler, R., G. Zahn, and W. Messer. 1979. Control of initiation of DNA replication in *Escherichia coli*. I. Negative control of initiation. *Mol. Gen. Genet.* **168**: 185.

Tlsty, T.D., P.C. Brown, and R.T. Schimke. 1984. UV radiation facilitated methotrexate resistance and amplification of the dihydrofolate reductase gene in cultured 3T6 mouse cells. *Mol. Cell. Biol.* **4**: 1050.

Somatic Cell Genetic Studies of Amplificator Cell Lines

M. Rolfe, C. Knights, and G.R. Stark

Molecular Biology Laboratory, Imperial Cancer Research Fund, London WC2A 3PX, United Kingdom

When Syrian hamster BHK cells are exposed to N-phosphonoacetyl-L-aspartate (PALA) or methotrexate (MTX) alone, resistant colonies appear with a frequency of about 10^{-4} as a result of amplification of the CAD or DHFR genes, respectively. However, if BHK cells are selected simultaneously with PALA and MTX, the expected frequency of doubly resistant colonies (10^{-8}) is exceeded by 20–200 ×. Four doubly resistant cell lines have recently been analyzed and have an amplificator phenotype (Giulotto et al. 1987): They can amplify a number of target genes at rates considerably higher than wild-type BHK cells. We are attempting to analyze the biochemical basis of the amplificator phenotype by somatic cell genetic techniques. The amplificator line MP1 was fused with 40.5, a monkey CV-1 line that carries a twofold amplification of the monkey CAD gene and is resistant to 150 μM PALA. The hybrid population (MP1 × 40.5) was grown for 3 days and then subjected to a stringent PALA selection (1 mM). Only those hybrids in which the amplificator function from the MP1 cells had successfully acted on and amplified the monkey CAD gene should be able to survive this stringent selection. This did occur; the appearance of resistant colonies in the hybrid populations was absolutely dependent on the presence of the amplificator phenotype in MP1 cells.

DNA amplification is a widespread phenomenon in continuous cell lines and in tumors. Cell lines selected to resist various metabolic inhibitors almost invariably achieve their resistance by amplification of the target gene for the protein with which the inhibitor interacts. In tumors, many cellular oncogenes have been found to be amplified and their corresponding mRNAs overexpressed. Both of these types of amplification appear to give cells a selective growth advantage within a large population (for recent reviews, see Cowell 1982; Hamlin et al. 1984; Schimke 1984; Stark and Wahl 1984).

DNA amplification has been studied using two main approaches: analysis of the structures of amplified regions of DNA and searching for agents that increase the frequency of amplification events in a cell population. Amplified regions of DNA are composed of nonidentical units linked through nonhomologous recombinations that can occur at many different locations (Ardeshir et al. 1983; Federspiel et al. 1984). The units are sometimes arranged as inverted repeats (Ford et al. 1985; Ford and Fried 1986; Saito and Stark 1986). The amount of coamplified DNA may be particularly large after the first step of amplification (Giulotto et al. 1986) but decreases with increasing gene copy number in later steps (I. Saito et al., unpubl.).

Frequencies of 10^{-4} to 10^{-6} are found for spontaneous amplification events in various cell lines. This relatively high spontaneous frequency can be increased by treatment with hydroxyurea, which interferes with DNA synthesis, or with other agents that damage DNA and produce stalled replication forks (Brown et al. 1983; Tlsty et al. 1984; Hill and Schimke 1985; Kleinberger et al. 1986). Transient hypoxia can also increase the frequency of amplification (Rice et al. 1986).

More recently, a new approach has been developed for studying the mechanism of DNA amplification. Cell lines have been isolated that have an increased rate of DNA amplification when compared to wild-type cells (Giulotto et al. 1987). Such "amplificator" cell lines were isolated from BHK cells that were simultaneously selected with PALA and MTX. When BHK cells are exposed to PALA or MTX alone, resistant colonies appear with a frequency of 10^{-4} as a result of amplification of the CAD or DHFR genes, respectively. When BHK cells are selected simultaneously with PALA and MTX, the expected frequency of doubly resistant colonies (10^{-8}) is exceeded by 10–200 ×. Cell lines derived from such doubly resistant colonies can amplify a number of target genes at rates considerably higher than wild-type cells.

We are now attempting to analyze the biochemical basis of the amplificator phenotype by somatic cell genetic techniques. We have used 40.5, a line derived from monkey CV-1 cells, as an indicator to assay the amplificator function in somatic cell hybrids formed between this line and the amplificator cell line, MP1. We have preliminary evidence that the amplificator function can act in *trans*, and therefore, is dominant.

Materials and Methods

Cell culture and fusions

All cells were grown in E4 Dulbecco's modified Eagle's medium supplemented with 10% fetal calf serum (FCS) (Gibco). Dialyzed serum used in PALA selections was prepared as described previously (Swyryd et al. 1974). PALA, NSC-224131, was from the National Cancer Institute (Bethesda, Maryland). Somatic cell hybrids

325

were formed as described by Hankinson (1983). In brief, 10^5 cells of each cell line were mixed, plated in 50-mm plates, and incubated in E4 + 10% FCS overnight. The cells were rinsed with phosphate-buffered saline, treated with 1 ml of 50% PEG 1000 5% DMSO for 1 minute, rinsed extensively with E4 + 10% FCS and incubated for 72 hours. At this point, each 50-mm plate was trypsinized, redispersed into a 90-mm plate and grown in E4 + 10% dialyzed serum + 1 mM PALA. After 10 weeks growth, colonies were counted and cells were collected for DNA analysis.

Whole cell alkaline slot blotting
Samples of about 10^4 cells were analyzed by whole cell alkaline slot blotting (P. McIntyre and G.R. Stark, in prep.). Cells were hydrolyzed in 0.4 M NaOH at 80°C for 30 minutes and loaded onto GeneScreenPlus nylon membranes by means of a slot blot apparatus. Monkey CAD sequences were visualized with a 2.2-kb genomic probe isolated from a monkey cell line that carries ~10 copies of the CAD gene (M. Rolfe and G.R. Stark, unpubl.). The probe is free of reiterated sequences and does not cross-hybridize with hamster DNA. Hamster CAD sequences were similarly visualized with a repeat-free 2.1-kb fragment of Syrian hamster genomic DNA (Brison et al. 1982). The total amount of DNA bound on a filter was visualized using total random primed genomic DNA as a probe. Amounts of DNA were quantified using a Joyce-Loebl densitometer.

Results

The CV-1 derivative 40.5, a single-step mutant that was selected in 40 μM PALA, contains a low-level amplification of the monkey CAD locus (M. Rolfe and G.R. Stark, unpubl.). This cell line can grow in 150 μM PALA and is considerably more resistant to this drug than the amplificator cell line MP1, which was selected in 15 μM PALA and 150 nM MTX (Giulotto et al. 1987). We have exploited this difference in sensitivity by forming somatic cell hybrids between these two lines and selecting them in high concentrations of PALA. Previously, it was shown that the level of amplification of the CAD gene in MP1 cells was greater than that in single-step PALA-resistant mutants. Our rationale was that if a hybrid cell were capable of growing in 1 mM PALA, it could only do so if the amplificator function from the MP1 cell had acted, in *trans*, upon the monkey CAD gene, amplifying it to a high enough level to allow the cell to survive such a stringent selection. In our first experiment, a series of different fusions were set up and selected in 1 mM PALA as described in Materials and Methods. As shown in Table 1, no colonies were seen in 40.5 × 40.5, BHK × BHK, or 40.5 × BHK fusions. In MP1 × MP1 fusions a low frequency of resistant colonies was detected; possible explanations for this observation are discussed below. In the MP1 × 40.5 fusion there were 30–50 times more resistant colonies than in MP1 × MP1 fusions. This was an encouraging result, but might have been explained if the amplified CAD gene in MP1 and

Table 1 Frequency of PALA-resistant Colonies in Various Hybrid Populations

Fusion	Number of cells fused	Colonies / 10^6 cells in 1 mM PALA
40.5 × 40.5	2 × 10^6	0
40.5 × MP1	2 × 10^6	38
MP1 × MP1	2 × 10^6	1
BHK × MP1	2 × 10^6	0
BHK × BHK	2 × 10^6	0
40.5 × BHK	2 × 10^6	0

the amplified CAD gene in 40.5 together would allow growth in 1 mM PALA, so that resistance was not related to the amplificator phenotype. To control for this possibility, a second series of fusions was set up with the additional control of an independent single-step PALA-resistant mutant fused to 40.5. This BHK cell line, 60.5, was selected in 60 μM PALA and has a CAD gene copy number equivalent to that in MP1 but without the amplificator phenotype (data not shown). There were no PALA-resistant colonies in the 40.5 × 60.5 control fusions (Table 2), thus discounting the possibility that a simple additive effect of amplified monkey and hamster CAD sequences could allow survival in 1 mM PALA. The 30- to 50-fold increase in colonies in the 40.5 × MP1 fusions compared with MP1 × MP1 fusions was again observed. Several colonies from 40.5 × MP1 fusions were collected and analyzed in whole cell slot blotting experiments for their content of monkey and hamster CAD genes. Figure 1 shows the result of one such analysis. Cells from the pooled fusion colonies (fusion population: FP) clearly contained monkey CAD sequences with a copy number equivalent to or greater than 40.5 cells and wild-type levels of hamster CAD sequences.

Discussion

We have described a series of somatic cell fusion experiments where an amplificator cell line has been fused with an indicator cell line in an attempt to determine whether the genetic or epigenetic alteration in amplificator cells was dominant or recessive. It is clear from the results presented here that survival of hybrid colonies in 1 mM PALA is absolutely dependent on the amplificator phenotype of the cell line MP1, and that this phenotype is dominant in somatic cell hybrids.

The low background level of colonies resistant to 1 mM PALA in MP1 × MP1 fusions can be explained by supposing that two doses of the amplificator function

Table 2 Frequency of PALA-resistant Colonies in Hybrids between 40.5 × MP1 and 40.5 × 60.5

Fusion	Number of cells fused	Colonies / 10^6 cells in 1 mM PALA
40.5 × MP1	2 × 10^6	56
MP1 × MP1	2 × 10^6	2
60.5 × 60.5	2 × 10^6	0
40.5 × 60.5	2 × 10^6	0

CELL TYPE

PROBE   CV-1   40.5   FP   MP1   60.5   BHK

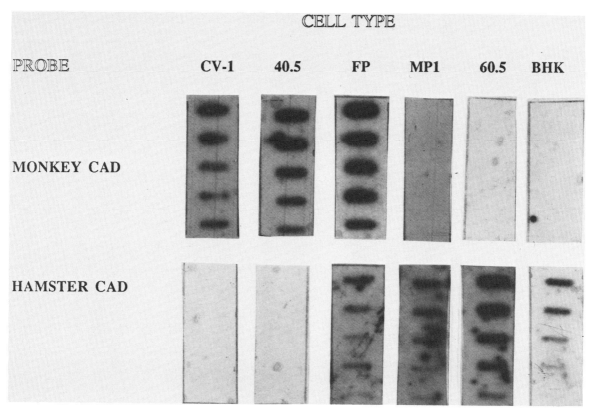

MONKEY CAD

HAMSTER CAD

Figure 1 Analysis of monkey and hamster CAD sequences in FP cells. 2×10^5 cells of the indicated type were hydrolyzed as described in Materials and Methods. The slots from the top to the bottom of each filter represent five aliquots of 10^5, 5×10^4, 2×10^4, 10^4, and 5×10^3 cells. Each filter was hybridized with a 2.2-kb genomic CAD DNA fragment from monkey cells, then stripped and rehybridized with a hamster-specific CAD fragment.

are present in such hybrid cells and that such an excess of this function can amplify the endogenous CAD gene to a level high enough to allow growth in 1 mM PALA.

Numerous attempts to ring clone individual resistant colonies have been unsuccessful. Resistant colonies grow very slowly. We estimate that a visible colony containing ∼1000 cells can be detected easily after 10 weeks of growth in 1 mM PALA. This suggests that the doubling time is ∼7 days, which is extremely slow and may contribute to the poor survival of picked clones. If selection pressure is removed when colonies are picked, the cells begin to grow more quickly, but when these cells are then analyzed in Southern blots they have lost the monkey CAD sequences they once had, and if they are re-exposed to 150 μM–1 mM PALA they no longer survive (data not shown). Such cells have a phenotype indistinguishable from the MP1 phenotype, using the above criteria. We presume that the monkey chromosome carrying the amplified CAD gene and allowing growth in PALA is the only monkey component in the hybrid cells because primate chromosomes are rapidly segregated in primate/rodent hybrids. Loss of the monkey chromosome upon removal of the selective pressure therefore results in restoration of the MP1 phenotype.

This slow growth and instability of the hybrid cells has hampered a more detailed molecular analysis of such

cells owing to insufficient material being available. However, using the sensitive whole-cell slot blotting procedure, we have been able to analyze gross sequence components in FP hybrid cells and have shown that FP cells do contain monkey and hamster CAD sequences. The hamster CAD component in FP cells is not present at a level significantly greater than that in wild-type cells. This may be explained by the fact that the MP1 cells were grown out of selection for several weeks prior to their fusion with 40.5 cells. It has been shown previously that the PALA-resistant phenotype in MP cells is unstable and lost following prolonged growth out of selection (Giulotto et al. 1987).

At present we do not have a detailed quantitative analysis of the monkey CAD gene copy number in the hybrid cells but from our preliminary experiments there does not seem to be a large overamplification of the monkey CAD locus in such cells. We are now analyzing the CAD gene copy number in FP cells in greater detail.

The results from the somatic cell fusion experiments have encouraged us to attempt to transfer the amplificator function from MP1 cells into 40.5 cells by chromosome-mediated gene transfer (Housman and Nelson 1986). Such experiments, if successful, will greatly contribute to our study of the molecular basis of the amplificator phenotype and give valuable insights into the mechanisms of DNA amplification in mammalian cells.

References

Ardeshir, F., E. Giulotto, J. Zieg, O. Brison, W.S.L. Liao, and G.R. Stark. 1983. Structure of amplified DNA in different Syrian hamster cell lines resistant to N-(phosphonoacetyl)-L-aspartate. *Mol. Cell. Biol.* **3:** 2076.

Brown, P.C., T.D. Tlsty, and R.T. Schimke. 1983. Enhancement of methotrexate resistance and dihydrofolate reductase gene amplification by treatment of mouse 3T6 cells with hydroxyurea. *Mol. Cell. Biol.* **3:** 1097.

Brison, O., F. Ardeshir, and G.R. Stark. 1982. General method for cloning amplified DNA by differential screening with genomic probes. *Mol. Cell. Biol.* **2:** 578.

Cowell, J.K. 1982. Double minutes and homogeneously staining regions: Gene amplification in mammalian cells. *Annu. Rev. Genet.* **16:** 21.

Federspiel, N.A., S.M. Beverly, J.W. Schilling, and R.T. Schimke. 1984. Novel DNA rearrangements are associated with dihydrofolate reductase gene amplification. *J. Biol. Chem.* **259:** 9127.

Ford, M. and M. Fried. 1986. Large inverted duplications are associated with gene amplification. *Cell* **45:** 425.

Ford, M., M. Griffiths, B. Davies, J. Wilson, and M. Fried. 1985. Isolation of a gene enhancer within an amplified inverted duplication after "expression selection". *Proc. Natl. Acad. Sci.* **82:** 3370.

Giulotto, E., C. Knights, and G.R. Stark. 1987. Hamster cells with an increased rate of DNA amplification, a new phenotype. *Cell* **48:** 837.

Giulotto, E., I. Saito, and G.R. Stark. 1986. Structure of DNA formed in the first step of CAD gene amplification. *EMBO. J.* **5:** 2115.

Hamlin, J.L., J.D. Milbrandt, N.H. Heintz, and J.C. Azizkhan. 1984. DNA sequence amplification in mammalian cells. *Int. Rev. Cytol.* **90:** 31.

Hankinson, O. 1983. Dominant and recessive aryl hydrocarbon hydroxylase deficient mutants of mouse hepatoma line, Hepa-1, and assignment of recessive mutants to three complementation groups. *Somatic Cell Genet.* **9:** 497.

Hill, A.B. and R.T. Schimke. 1985. Increased gene amplification in L5178Y mouse lymphoma cells with hydroxyurea-induced chromosomal aberrations. *Cancer Res.* **45:** 5050.

Housman, D.E. and D.L. Nelson. 1986. Use of metaphase chromosome transfer for mammalian gene mapping. In *Gene transfer* (ed. R. Kucherlapati), p. 95. Plenum Press, New York.

Kleinberger, T., S. Etkin, and S. Lavi. 1986. Carcinogen mediated methotrexate resistance and dihydrofolate reductase amplification in Chinese hamster cells. *Mol. Cell. Biol.* **6:** 1958.

Rice, G.C., C. Hoy, and R.T. Schimke. 1986. Transient hypoxia enhances the frequency of dihydrofolate reductase gene amplification in Chinese hamster ovary cells. *Proc. Natl. Acad. Sci.* **83:** 5978.

Saito, I. and G.R. Stark. 1986. Charomids: New cosmid vectors for efficient cloning and mapping of large or small restriction fragments. *Proc. Natl. Acad. Sci.* **83:** 8664.

Schimke, R.T. 1984. Gene amplification in cultured animal cells. *Cell* **37:** 705.

Stark, G.R. and G.M. Wahl. 1984. Gene amplification. *Annu. Rev. Biochem.* **53:** 447.

Swyryd, E.A., S.S. Seaver, and G.R. Stark. 1974. N-(phosphonoacetyl)-L-aspartate, a potent transition state analog of aspartate transcarbamylase, blocks proliferation of mammalian cells in culture. *J. Biol. Chem.* **249:** 6945.

Tlsty, T.D., P.C. Brown, and R.T. Schimke. 1984. UV radiation facilitates methotrexate resistance and amplification of the dihydrofolate reductase gene in cultured 3T6 mouse cells. *Mol. Cell. Biol.* **4:** 1050.

Analysis of the Initiation Locus of the Amplified Dihydrofolate Reductase Domain in CHO Cells

J.L. Hamlin,* T.-H. Leu,* P.K. Foreman,* C.A. Ma,* J.P. Vaughn,*
P.A. Dijkwel,* L. Creeper,[†] and H. Willard[†]

*Department of Biochemistry, University of Virginia, Charlottesville, Virginia 22908;
[†]Department of Medical Genetics, University of Toronto, Toronto, Ontario, M5S 1A8, Canada

Our laboratory has demonstrated previously that DNA replication initiates at a preferred locus in the amplified dihydrofolate reductase (DHFR) domain in a methotrexate-resistant CHO cell line (CHOC 400). The entire domain has been cloned, including the initiation locus itself. We have recently employed an in-gel renaturation method to analyze in vivo labeled DNA that allows a more precise localization of origins of replication in amplified DNA sequences. Utilizing this method on CHOC 400 cells, we have been able to localize the preferred initiation site to a sequence less than 5 kb in length. In other studies, analysis of the initiation locus by a variety of criteria suggests a complex arrangement of several sequence elements that may contribute to origin function. Among these are a 750-bp fragment that replicates autonomously in yeast, a preferred micrococcal nuclease cutting site in chromatin mapping upstream of this element, and a downstream matrix attachment site. To determine whether any of these sequences are common to other initiation sites, we have developed a strategy for cloning a second amplified CHO origin.

Our laboratory is interested in the structural and functional organization of mammalian chromosomal replicons. As a model system, we are studying the amplified DHFR domain in CHOC 400. The entire 260-kb amplicon has been cloned in overlapping cosmids (Looney and Hamlin 1987), and replication of the amplicon has been shown to initiate preferentially within a 20-kb region located 20–30 kb downstream from the DHFR gene (Heintz and Hamlin 1982). To determine the location of this and other amplified origins more precisely, we have utilized an in-gel renaturation technique to analyze in vivo labeled DNA that eliminates background labeling contributed by the early-firing single copy origins in the genome. The method allows the radioactivity of individual amplified restriction fragments to be quantitated, generating specific radioactivity plots that mark the origin more precisely. The initiation locus in the DHFR amplicon has been localized by this method within a 5-kb region that has been characterized by a variety of criteria.

Experimental Procedures

Cell lines, synchrony regimens, and labeling methods

The methotrexate-resistant CHOC 400 cell line was developed in our laboratory and contains approximately 1000 copies of the DHFR amplicon (Milbrandt et al. 1981). The methotrexate-resistant Chinese hamster lung fibroblast, A3, was developed by Biedler and Spengler (1976) and contains approximately 700 copies of the DHFR gene. Monolayer cultures were maintained as described previously (Milbrandt et al. 1981). Cultures were arrested in G_0 by isoleucine starvation for 45 hours and were then incubated for 12 hours in complete medium containing 10 µg aphidicolin/ml (NCI). Cultures were washed once with complete medium and were then pulse-labeled for various intervals in the early S period with 50 µCi/ml [³H]thymidine (80 Ci/mM; New England Nuclear Corp. [NEN]) in medium containing 0.2 µg FUdR/ml. The labeling was quenched by rapid washing in warm medium containing 10 µg unlabeled TdR/ml and 2 µg CdR/ml. Cells were then allowed to traverse the cell cycle for 12 hours in this medium, and were harvested by washing twice with phosphate-buffered saline followed by lysis at 37°C for 8 hours in 10 mM Tris, (pH 7.9)/10 mM EDTA/10 mM NaCl/1% SDS containing 100 µg Proteinase K/ml.

Preparation of DNA, restriction digestion, and in-gel renaturation

The DNA was purified by standard procedures being careful to avoid shear. After dialysis into 10 mM Tris, (pH 7.9)/0.1 mM EDTA, each sample was digested with the appropriate restriction enzyme in the buffer recommended by the supplier (Bethesda Research Laboratories), followed by separation on a 1.0% agarose gel (0.4 × 18 × 20 cm). The digests (6 µg/well) were then subjected to two cycles of in-gel renaturation exactly as described by Roninson (1983). The digests were transferred to GeneScreen Plus (NEN) by the alkaline method of Reed and Mann (1985); the transfer was sprayed with EN³HANCE (NEN) and exposed to Kodak X-Omat film at −85°C using a Dupont Cronex intensifying screen. As controls, a second portion of

329

each digest (1.2 μg) was separated on 1.0% agarose and was transferred directly to GeneScreen Plus.

Autonomous replication in yeast and nuclear matrix attachment
The *Hind*III fragments from the initiation locus depicted in Figure 2 were subcloned into the *Hind*III site of the yeast shuttle vector, pJZ14, which contains the *Leu2* gene (Hinnen et al. 1978). Methods for transfection of yeast and analysis of replication properties will be presented in detail elsewhere (L.A. Creeper et al., in prep.). Nuclear matrix structures were prepared by the LIS method of Mirkovitch et al. (1984); details of the analysis of specific sequence attachment to matrices will be presented in a forthcoming paper (P.A. Dijkwel and J.L. Hamlin, in prep.).

Results

Analysis of early replicating sequences in the CHOC 400 DHFR amplicon by in-gel renaturation
In Figure 1 (panel A) is shown an autoradiogram of *Eco*RI digests of CHOC 400 DNA labeled with [³H]thymidine for 30, 60, or 90 minutes in the early S

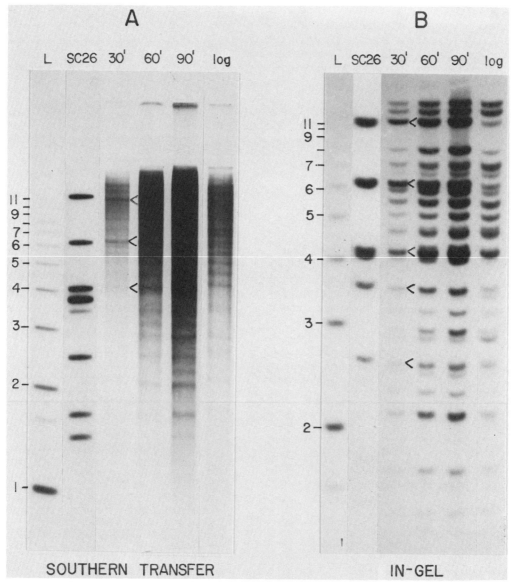

Figure 1 Detection of in vivo labeled early-replicating fragments in CHOC 400 by two methods. Cells were synchronized and pulse-labeled as described in Experimental Procedures. After separation of *Eco*RI digests on a 1% agarose gel, the digests were either transferred to GeneScreen Plus directly (*A*), or were first subjected to the in-gel renaturation procedure and then transferred (*B*). The transfers were sprayed with EN³HANCE and exposed to X-ray film. The 1-kb ladder (BRL; *A* and *B*) and the *Eco*RI digest of cosmid SC26 (*A*) were end-labeled with ³²P by the method of Roninson (1983). In *B*, the SC26 lane represents the hybridization signal obtained when the SC26 cosmid was used to probe the in-gel renaturation transfer after it was washed free of EN³HANCE with toluene. Note that the bands hybridizing to this cosmid correspond to the most intensely labeled fragments in the 30- and 60-minute samples.

period. In the 30-minute sample, three prominently labeled amplified bands (11, 6.0/6.1, and 4.2 kb) are detected against the background smear of single copy DNA. By comparison to the log-labeled sample in panel A, it is clear that initiation of DNA replication in the amplified DHFR domain occurs preferentially in the neighborhood of these bands (Heintz and Hamlin 1982). Because of background labeling, however, it is not possible to quantitate the specific radioactivity in each band by densitometry, and the resolution of this method is therefore limited. These *Eco*RI fragments (along with other flanking fragments) are completely contained in the cosmid SC26 (second lane, panel A; see Fig. 2 for map position of these bands).

To eliminate background labeling, we have subjected the same labeled digests to the in-gel renaturation procedure of Roninson (1983). In this method, digests of genomic DNA are separated on an agarose gel and are successively denatured with base, renatured to allow repetitive DNA fragments to anneal, and then treated with S1 nuclease to get rid of single copy sequences. After two cycles of in-gel renaturation, the DNA is transferred to a membrane, and the membrane is sprayed with EN³HANCE and exposed to X-ray film. The results of this analysis are shown in Figure 1, panel B. All of the background single copy sequences have been eliminated by this procedure, and the pattern of amplified, labeled bands is distinct and quantifiable by densitometry. A comparison of the 30-minute sample to the log-labeled DNA indicates that the same three *Eco*RI fragments (in addition to bands at 3.4 and 2.5 kb) detected in the previous experiment are the most highly labeled bands in the DHFR amplicon. When the filter is washed free of the scintillant and hybridized to cosmid SC26, these bands are seen to be totally contained within this cosmid (Fig. 1, panel B, lane 2).

By densitometric measurements of the relative intensities of the bands in this and several other digests, we have been able to localize the preferred initiation site to a 5-kb region centered approximately at the junction between the 6.0-kb and 6.1-kb *Eco*RI fragments depicted in the map in Figure 2 (T.-H. Leu and J.L. Hamlin, in prep.). We have analyzed this region by several

criteria to gain insight into the organization of a mammalian origin.

Properties of the DHFR initiation locus

All of the *Hin*dIII fragments as well as the 6.1-kb *Eco*RI fragment shown in Figure 2 have been subcloned into a yeast shuttle vector containing the *Leu2* selective marker, and each clone has been tested for autonomous replication in yeast. Our data indicate that a 1.54-kb *Hin*dIII fragment (which maps in the left half of the 6.0-kb *Eco*RI fragment; see Fig. 2) transforms yeast to the Leu2 phenotype with high frequency and can be detected as an autonomously replicating element in Hirt supernatants prepared from transformed yeast maintained under selection (L.A. Creeper et al., in prep.). By additional subcloning, the ARS element has been further narrowed down to the left half of the 1.54 *Hin*dIII fragment. However, when tested for autonomous replication in CHO or mouse cells, neither this fragment nor any other fragment from the 26-kb region defined by Sc26 was able to replicate autonomously by the criterion of persistent *Dpn*I-resistant episomal material (P.K. Foreman and J.L. Hamlin, unpubl.).

We have also analyzed the chromatin structure in this region by micrococcal nuclease and DNase I digestion. In preliminary experiments, we have detected a preferred micrococcal nuclease cutting zone located approximately 2 kb upstream of the yeast ARS element (Fig. 2; J.P. Vaughn and J.L. Hamlin, unpubl.). In addition, analysis of specific association of sequences in this region with the nuclear matrix (prepared by the LIS method of Mirkovitch et al. 1984) indicates that a matrix attachment site is located in the left half of the 6.75-kb *Hin*dIII fragment. This fragment overlaps the right end of the 6.0-kb early-replicating *Eco*RI fragment depicted in Figure 2. Thus, the 5-kb region in which replication initiates displays several properties that might be expected of chromosomal origins.

Approaches toward the isolation of other amplified origins

Just as with transcribed genes, several mammalian origins of replication will have to be analyzed to detect

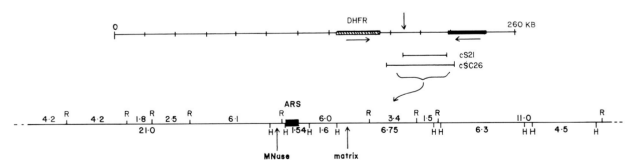

Figure 2 Map of the CHOC 400 initiation locus. A relative map of the position of the DHFR gene and the initiation locus (arrow) in the DHFR amplicon is shown. The position of a second unidentified gene is also indicated by the black box (P.K. Foreman and J.L. Hamlin, unpubl.). The region covered by the cosmid cSC26 is expanded in the lower half of the figure and shows the positions of the elements discussed in the text. R and H indicate *Eco*RI and *Hin*dIII sites, respectively.

conserved elements that may be important for function. In the absence of a viable assay for origin function at the present time, we are attempting to isolate other early-firing origins from amplified DNA sequences in CHO cells. We have recently cloned the entire 260-kb amplified DHFR domain from the CHOC 400 cell line in a series of overlapping recombinant cosmids (Looney and Hamlin 1987). We have utilized probes isolated from these cosmids in combination with pulse-field gradient electrophoresis to analyze *Sfi*I restriction fragments in other methotrexate-resistant Chinese hamster cell lines. By this method, we have been able to show that the amplified DHFR domains in two other independently isolated drug-resistant Chinese hamster lung fibroblasts (A3 and MK42; Biedler and Spengler 1976; Nunberg et al. 1978) are considerably larger than that observed in CHOC 400 (C.A. Ma et al., in prep.). Since these amplicons appear to be at least 450 kb in length, we reasoned that they must contain more than one origin of replication per repeating amplicon. To address this question directly and to determine whether the origin detected in the smaller CHOC 400 amplicon is also used by these cell lines, we utilized the in-gel renaturation method described above to analyze the DNA labeled in the early S period in synchronized cultures of A3, a cell line that contains approximately 700 copies of the DHFR gene. The results of this analysis are presented in Figure 3 .

The presence of additional fragments in log-labeled A3 DNA relative to the CHOC 400 pattern (Fig. 3) suggests that the amplicon in this cell line is larger than 260 kb, and confirms our results from pulse-field gradient electrophoretic studies on these cell lines. When the A3 cell line was labeled with [³H]thymidine for the first 30 minutes of the S period, the pattern of prominently labeled *Eco*RI fragments visualized after the in-gel renaturation procedure includes the 11-, 6.0/6.1-, 4.2-, 3.4-, and 2.5-kb early labeled fragments detected in the CHOC 400 genome (marked by dots between the 30- and 60-minute samples in Fig. 3; compare the 30-minute samples in Figs. 3 and 2, respectively). Thus, the initiation locus in the CHOC 400 DHFR amplicon also serves as an origin in the larger A3 amplicon. In addition, however, a 5.5-kb doublet and a 10-kb fragment are intensely labeled in the first 30 minutes of the S period in the A3 amplicon (arrows, Fig. 3), and these fragments are not observed in CHOC 400 digests. We know from mapping studies that these bands are not located in the 260-kb region common to the CHOC 400 and A3 amplicons. Hence, they must represent an additional initiation site or sites mapping in the 200-kb region unique to the A3 amplicon. This result indicates that more than one replicon has been amplified in this cell line, and that these replicons initiate DNA synthesis synchronously in early S.

Discussion

We have shown that the in-gel renaturation technique developed by Roninson (1983) can be used on in vivo

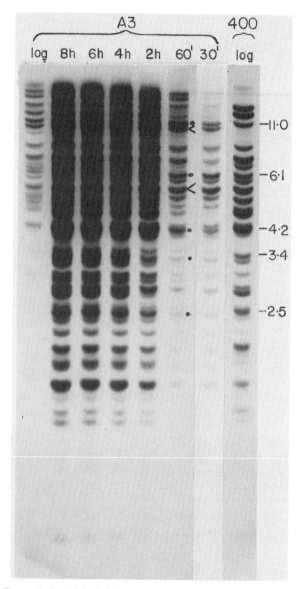

Figure 3 Early-labeled fragments in the A3 DHFR amplicon. A3 cells were synchronized, labeled for the indicated times in early S, and analyzed by in-gel renaturation as in Fig. 1. A log-labeled *Eco*RI digest of CHOC 400 is included as a control. Black dots indicate early-labeled fragments also detected in CHOC 400, and arrows indicate additional early-labeled bands unique to the A3 cell line.

labeled DNA to determine the earliest replicating restriction fragments in the amplified DHFR domain in CHOC 400 and in the A3 cell line. Because the background labeling of single copy DNA sequences is eliminated in this method, the specific radioactivity of labeled amplified bands can be quantitated by densitometry. The position of highest labeling can be determined with a resolution of approximately 5 kb in genomic DNA digested with restriction enzymes recognizing six bp sequences. Using this method, we have further localized the initiation locus in the CHOC 400 amplicon to a 5-kb region mapping approximately 25 kb downstream from the 3′ terminus of the DHFR gene (see Fig. 2). Additional studies on this initiation locus demonstrate several interesting elements that may be involved in the function of the origin. A 1.54-kb HindIII subclone located approximately in the center of the 5-kb region replicates autonomously in yeast. Interestingly, this fragment contains several short elements that are homologous to sequences contained in two human genomic fragments that were demonstrated to replicate autonomously in yeast (Monteil et al. 1984; L.A. Creeper et al., in prep.). However, until we have determined the exact location of the origin in the CHOC 400 DHFR amplicon, the significance of these observations (if any) will not be understood. The presence of a preferred micrococcal nuclease cutting zone upstream of this ARS element in combination with a downstream matrix attachment site suggests that this origin may have a complex structure with multiple functional elements spread over a considerable distance. The real importance of these elements to origin function will not be appreciated until a functional assay either in vivo or in vitro is developed.

The presence of at least one other early-firing initiation locus in the larger amplicon of the methotrexate-resistant A3 cell line suggests that a second Chinese hamster chromosomal origin can be cloned with relative ease. The early-labeled amplified bands can be excised from preparative agarose gels and used as probes on a small cosmid library to identify and isolate the region in question. We are presently developing a slightly different version of the in-gel renaturation procedure that will allow us to localize the origins of replication in the A3 amplicon with far more precision than we have achieved thus far. A comparison of the sequences of the two early-firing origins should indicate any homologies that could have functional significance.

Acknowledgments

We thank June Biedler and Larry Chasin for cell lines and Bill Pearson for helpful discussions. This work was supported by the American Cancer Society and the National Institutes of Health.

References

Bielder, J.L. and B.A. Spengler. 1976. A novel chromosome abnormality in human neuroblastoma and antifolate-resistant Chinese hamster cells in culture. *J. Natl. Cancer Inst.* **57:** 683.

Heintz, N.H. and J.L. Hamlin. 1982. An amplified chromosomal sequence that includes the gene for dihydrofolate reductase initiates replication within specific restriction fragments. *Proc. Natl. Acad. Sci.* **79:** 4083.

Hinnen, A., J.B. Hicks, and G.R. Fink. 1978. Transformation of yeast. *Proc. Natl. Acad. Sci.* **75:** 1929.

Looney, J.E. and J.L. Hamlin. 1987. Isolation of the amplified dihydrofolate reductase domain from methotrexate-resistant Chinese hamster ovary cells. *Mol. Cell. Biol.* **7:** 569.

Milbrandt, J.D., N.H. Heintz, W.C. White, S.M. Rothman, and J.L. Hamlin. 1981. Methotrexate-resistant CHO cells have amplified a 135 kb region that includes the gene for dihydrofolate reductase. *Proc. Natl. Acad. Sci.* **78:** 6043.

Mirkovitch, J., M.-E. Mirault, and U.K. Laemmli. 1984. Organization of the higher-order chromatin loop: Specific DNA attachment sites on nuclear scaffold. *Cell* **39:** 223.

Monteil, J.F., C.J. Norbury, M. Tuite, M.J. Dobson, J.S. Mills, A.J. Kingsman, and S.M. Kingsman. 1984. Characterization of human chromosomal sequences which replicate autonomously in *Saccharomyces cerevisiae*. *Nucleic Acids Res.* **12:** 1049.

Nunberg, J.H., R.J. Kaufman, R.T. Schimke, G. Urlaub, and L. Chasin. 1978. Amplified dihydrofolate reductase genes are localized to a homogeneously staining region of a single chromosome in a methotrexate-resistant Chinese hamster ovary cell line. *Proc. Natl. Acad. Sci.* **75:** 5553.

Reed, K.C. and D.A. Mann. 1985. Rapid transfer of DNA from agarose gels to nylon membranes. *Nucleic Acids Res.* **13:** 7207.

Roninson, I.B. 1983. Detection and mapping of homologous repeated and amplified DNA sequences by DNA renaturation in agarose gels. *Nucleic Acids Res.* **11:** 5413.

Temporal Order of Replication of Multigene Families Reflects Chromosomal Location and Transcriptional Activity

K.S. Hatton,* V. Dhar,* T.A. Gahn,* E.H. Brown,* D. Mager,[†] and C.L. Schildkraut*

*Department of Cell Biology, Albert Einstein College of Medicine, Bronx, New York 10461;
[†]British Columbia Cancer Research Centre, British Columbia, Canada

Mammalian genes replicate in a defined temporal order. Actively transcribed, tissue-specific genes usually replicate early (during the first quarter) in S. Genes and flanking sequences located within 250 kb of these actively transcribed genes also replicate early during S, even if they are not transcribed. Therefore, the timing of replication appears to depend on the chromosomal location of DNA sequences and on the transcriptional activity of the chromosomal domain in which they are located. Multiple copies of extrachromosomal bovine papillomavirus DNA do not appear to be constrained to replicate during a particular interval of the S phase.

The identification of DNA replication origins in mammalian cells has been hindered by the complexity of the mammalian genome. Evidence has been presented that a mammalian chromosomal origin of replication is present in the amplified dihydrofolate reductase gene domain in Chinese hamster cells (see e.g., Burhans et al. 1986). Studies in our laboratory have concentrated on measuring the temporal order of replication of mammalian DNA sequences with the aim of localizing an origin of replication as one of our goals.

We have used differential incorporation of 5-bromodeoxyuridine (BrdU) to measure the direction of replication in order to determine the sites of initiation of DNA replication in several well-mapped multigene families, including the murine immunoglobulin heavy chain constant region (IgC_H) gene cluster (Brown et al. 1987). By comparing the timing of replication of individual DNA segments spanning about 300 kb in this cluster, we showed that in the Friend-virus-transformed murine erythroleukemia (MEL) cell line the earliest segments to replicate are near the 3' end and that replication proceeds linearly with time toward the 5' end of the cluster. Assuming those segments that have not yet been studied also replicate at the same linear rate, the origin of replication should be less than 100 kb in the 3' direction from the $C\alpha$ gene. This would suggest that this cluster is part of a large replicon.

In the present study, we have measured the temporal order of replication along the length of the well-characterized β-like-globin gene cluster in the K562 human erythroleukemia cell line. In the K562 cell line the ϵ-globin gene is constitutively expressed and the fetal globin genes are transcribed at a low level. Although the adult β-like-globin genes (δ and β) remain transcriptionally inactive in the K562 cell line (Benz et al. 1980), they are also early replicating. All of the sequences that we have examined that flank these genes are also early replicating.

Our studies indicate that transcriptionally active and inactive gene loci exhibit a difference in the timing of their replication in various mouse cell lines. The actively transcribed gene as well as several hundred kb of surrounding nontranscribed genes and flanking sequences replicate early during S. Thus, the location of DNA sequences within a chromosomal domain determines the timing of their replication. We have recently begun to study extrachromosomal DNA sequences such as the bovine papillomavirus (BPV) to gain further information about the role of chromosomal location in determining the timing of DNA replication.

Materials and Methods

Cell lines, culture conditions, BrdU labeling, and centrifugal elutriation

The sources, culture conditions, BrdU labeling, and centrifugal elutriation were as described previously for the MEL, S107, MPC11, and L60T cell lines (Calza et al. 1984) and the RL♂11, 22D6, and 300-19P cell lines (Brown et al. 1987). The BALB/c 3T3, Hepa 1.6 (Darlington et al. 1980), BPV containing fibroblast mouse cell lines ID-13 (Law et al. 1981), and Clone B (provided by P. Howley) were grown in Dulbecco's modified Eagle's medium containing 10% fetal calf serum (FCS) and labeled with BrdU (20 μg/ml) for 2 hours prior to elutriation. The K562 cell line (provided by O. Smithies) was grown and subjected to elutriation as described previously (Iqbal et al. 1987).

Isolation of BU-DNA, DNA transfer, and hybridization

The preparation, restriction endonuclease digestion with *Eco*RI, and isolation of newly replicated DNA by Cs_2SO_4 centrifugation, fractionation by electrophoresis, transfer to diazobenzyloxymethyl (DBM) paper, and the quantitation of the results were performed as

335

described previously (Braunstein et al. 1982; Calza et al. 1984; Brown et al. 1987).

Results and Discussion

Our studies on the temporal order of replication of genes in mammalian cells use the technique of centrifugal elutriation in which cells are fractionated according to their position in the cell cycle. Appropriate fractions are pooled to produce cells representing four intervals of

the S phase. Since these cells have been previously labeled with BrdU, we can isolate bromouracil containing DNA (BU-DNA) that has replicated during four different intervals of S. This BU-DNA is cleaved with *Eco*RI and fractionated on agarose gels. We determine the interval of S during which a particular *Eco*RI segment replicates from the relative concentration of the segment in the BU-DNA.

Most of the *Eco*RI segments we have examined that contain or flank tissue-specific single-copy genes ap-

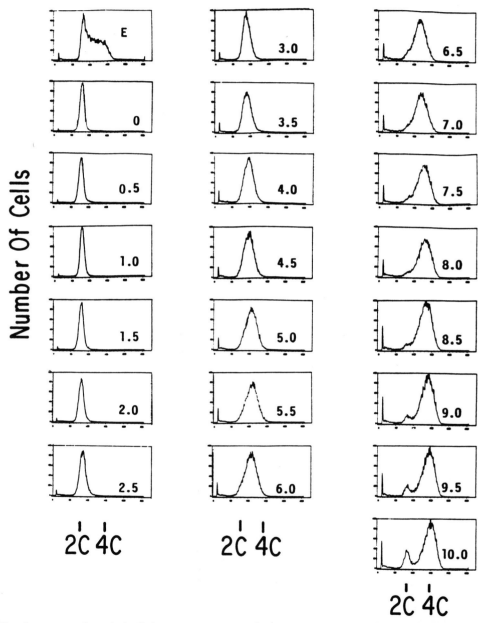

Figure 1 MEL cells progress through the S phase at a constant rate. A population of cells in G_1 was collected under sterile conditions by centrifugal elutriation and incubated at 37°C. Samples were taken at 30-min intervals (time after incubation in hours is shown in the lower right of each histogram) for flow microfluorometric (FMF) analysis. For each histogram, the ordinate gives the relative number of cells having DNA contents (shown on the abscissa) between 2.0 C (G_1) and 4.0 C (G_2). An FMF profile obtained from an exponentially growing culture of MEL cells is shown in the first histogram (E). In the samples taken after 8 hr, the small peak at the 2.0 C value indicates those cells that have traversed G_2 and have re-entered G_1. An aliquot of the G_1 cells incubated for 4 days showed no indication of bacterial contamination.

pear to replicate during a particular quarter of the S phase. If we assume that an *Eco*RI segment replicates at a unique time during S, we can calculate the DNA content (expressed as a C value where C is the haploid DNA content of a cell in G_1) of the nucleus at the time the segment replicates. This determination has been described previously (Brown et al. 1987) and is based in part on the kinetics of DNA replication through the S phase. We have measured the DNA content of a population of MEL cells as they progress through the S phase (Fig. 1) and have shown that their DNA content increases linearly with time (Brown et al. 1987). Thus for the MEL cell line, we have not observed any evidence of a bimodal S phase as has been reported previously for some Chinese hamster cell lines (for review, see Goldman et al. 1984). This allows us to determine the percentage of the cells in a particular population that incorporated BrdU when the nuclear DNA content was at a particular C value. From this percentage and the relative concentration of the *Eco*RI segment in the BU-DNA that replicated during each of the four intervals of S, we can determine the C value that most closely corresponds to the DNA content of the nucleus at the time the segment replicated.

Using this approach, we have been able to measure small differences in the timing of replication of genes and flanking sequences. This has allowed us to establish (see e.g., Furst et al. 1981; Calza et al. 1984; Brown et al. 1987; Hatton et al. 1988) a working set of rules (summarized below) that describe the temporal order of replication of tissue-specific mammalian DNA sequences that we have studied. (1) Nonrepetitive mammalian DNA sequences replicate during defined intervals of the S phase. The time at which these sequences replicate depends on the cell type examined. (2) Alleles of a particular sequence usually replicate at similar times during S. (3) Alleles can sometimes replicate at different times, even in the same cell, depending on the chromosomal position of that gene. Examples include the c-*myc* and the *Cγ2b* genes in the MPC11 cell line (Calza et al. 1984). (4) Actively transcribed genes usually replicate very early (first quarter) during S. We have compared the timing of replication of several genes and their flanking sequences in nine different murine cell lines expressing tissue-specific functions. As can be seen diagrammatically in Figure 2, a gene replicates earlier in a cell line in which it is transcribed than in a cell line in which it is transcriptionally silent (Hatton et al. 1988). Additional studies comparing the timing of replication of active and silent genes have been reported (see e.g., Goldman et al. 1984 and references therein). (5) Replication early during S is not limited to transcriptionally active genes. Some genes, such as those coding for the complement proteins (C2, C4, and factor B), replicate early during S in cell lines in which we have not detected steady-state transcripts from these genes (Hatton et al. 1988). (6) A pseudogene may replicate early or late during S. (7) The temporal order of replication of some genes and their flanking sequences corresponds to their linear order in the genome in cell lines in

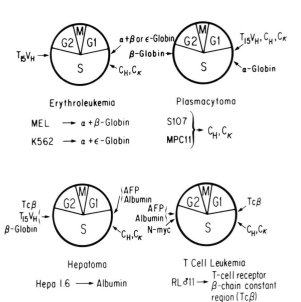

Figure 2 The differences in temporal order of replication of tissue-specific genes. Tissue-specific genes expressed in each cell line are indicated below the cell cycle diagrams. The arrows indicate the approximate time of replication during the S phase for the genes and multigene families shown: (AFP) α-fetoprotein; (Cκ) immunoglobulin κ chain constant region; ($T_{15}V_H$) T_{15} variable region gene family of the immunoglobulin heavy chain. (Reprinted, with permission from Hatton et al. 1988.)

which these genes are not transcribed. One example is the IgC$_H$ gene cluster (Brown et al. 1987). (8) Early replicating genes such as those coding for the κ constant region (Cκ), and their joining segments (Jκ), and those coding for the IgC$_H$ genes can replicate even earlier in cell lines in which they are expressed. (9) Contiguous regions of DNA spanning 15–250 kb replicate during the same quarter of the S phase. The replication of the human β-like-globin gene cluster is discussed in detail below.

Initially, most of these rules were determined from studies using cell lines derived from erythroid or lymphoid tissues. More recently, these studies have been extended to include the Hepa 1.6 cell line, which is derived from a mouse hepatoma. The Hepa 1.6 cell line grows attached to a substratum and thus had to be trypsinized before elutriation. After trypsinization, the cells tend to be present in clumps, resulting in the contamination of the late S-phase fractions by G_1 cells. To overcome this problem, we pass the cell suspension through a fine syringe needle to create a single-cell suspension before injection into the elutriation chamber. Figure 3 shows the FMF profiles obtained after elutriation of Hepa 1.6 cells.

Replication of the human β-like-globin gene region

To determine the temporal order of replication along the human β-like-globin gene locus, we have studied 16 *Eco*RI DNA segments using specific radioactive probes

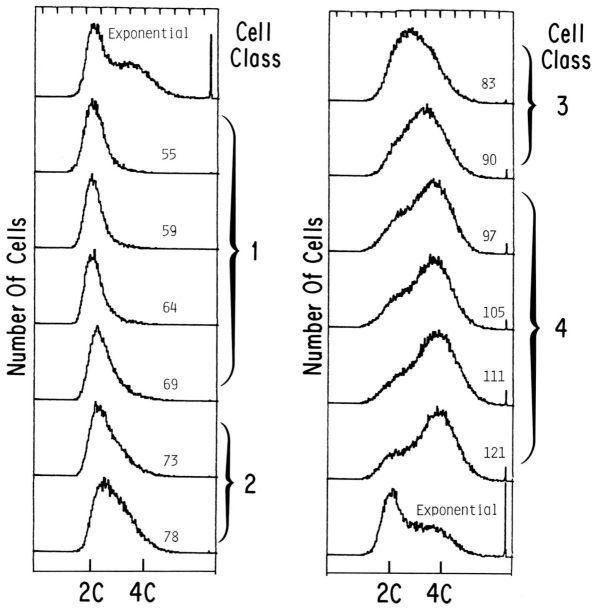

Figure 3 FMF histograms (see Fig. 1 for description) of cell-cycle populations obtained by centrifugal elutriation of Hepa 1.6 cells. The numbers in the lower right-hand corner of each profile indicate the flow rate (ml/min) of the elutriation medium used to collect the fraction. The fractions were pooled into four classes of cells representing different intervals of S phase, and BU-DNA was prepared from each of the four intervals.

and the elutriation technique described above. We performed four independent centrifugal elutriation experiments and found that the segments (encompassing approximately 140 kb) from the β-like-globin gene cluster replicate during the first half of the S phase (the results for four typical segments are shown in Fig. 4A) even though the transcriptionally active genes (ε, ^{G}γ, and ^{A}γ) in this cell line only encompass about 6 kb of the locus. We found that the transcriptionally inactive (δ and β) globin genes and other flanking sequences were also early replicating in this cell line. This supports our observations that a chromosomal domain as large as 250 kb can be early replicating if one or more transcribed genes are located in this region (Hatton et al. 1988).

By comparing the differences in the relative concentrations of each *Eco*RI segment relative to adjoining segments, the temporal direction of DNA replication was mapped in this locus. Two segments were found to replicate earlier than the others in this 140-kb region. This suggests that DNA replication in the β-like-globin locus may originate within or near these two earliest replicating segments, ~40–45 kb apart, and proceeds bidirectionally. One of these segments (detected by the pRK29 probe and shown in Fig. 4B) is located within 1 kb of a major DNase I hypersensitive site (V. Dhar et

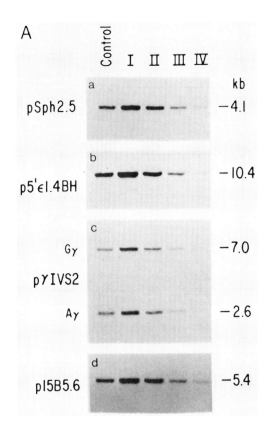

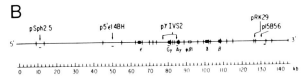

Figure 4 (*A*) Early replication of the human β-like-globin gene cluster and flanking sequences in K562 cells. An equal amount (5 μg) of *Eco*RI-digested DNA replicated during four intervals of the S phase (Lanes *I–IV*) was electrophoresed, transferred to DBM paper, and hybridized to nick-translated genomic fragments from the human β-like-globin region. (*a*) 2.5-kb *Sph*I fragment from pSph2.5 (Taramelli et al. 1986); (*b*) 1.4-kb *Bam*HI/*Hind*III fragment from p5′ε1.4BH (Li et al. 1985); (*c*) 1-kb *Eco*RI/*Bam*HI fragment from pγIVS2 provided by O. Smithies; and (*d*) 900-bp *Hind*III/*Eco*RI fragment from p15B5.6 provided by F. Grosveld. The control lane represents *Eco*RI-digested DNA from exponential K562 cells. (*B*) The *Eco*RI map of the human β-like-globin gene cluster and its flanking sequences. This cluster of genes and their flanking sequences (approximately 140 kb) consists of five β-like-globin genes, i.e., one embryonic (ε), two fetal (^Gγ and ^Aγ) and two adult (δ and β) globin genes. The arrows indicate the *Eco*RI segments that are detected by the probes listed above.

al., in prep.). Since the differences in the timing of replication between adjacent DNA fragments are small, we cannot completely rule out the possibility that they all replicate at the same time or in a random manner at an early time in the S phase.

Replication of extrachromosomal DNA sequences

One of the conclusions that has emerged from the studies described above is that the timing of replication of DNA sequences depends on their relative location within the genome. Recently we have asked whether extrachromosomal sequences behave differently from genomic sequences by examining the replication timing of two extrachromosomal viral DNA sequences, BPV and Epstein-Barr virus (EBV). BPV, which has an 8-kb double-stranded circular DNA genome, is capable of transforming rodent cells in culture. Each transformed line maintains a stable number of copies of BPV, usually between 30 and 150 (Law et al. 1981). EBV has a 172-kb double-stranded linear genome and can immortalize human B lymphocytes where the EBV genome circularizes via terminal direct repeats (Lindahl et al. 1976). Since in both cases the viral genomes do not integrate into the cellular DNA but remain extrachromosomal (Lindahl et al. 1976; Law et al. 1981), they provide the opportunity to study replication of DNA that is not part of the chromosome structure. If replication of BPV or EBV occurs at a defined time during S phase, then they would provide a model by which to study the temporal control of eukaryotic DNA replication. Thus, our first goal was to determine the time of replication of BPV in two virally transformed mouse C127 cell lines (ID-13, Clone B, Clone D) and the time of replication of EBV in a human lymphoblastoid cell line.

Our results (Table I) show that BPV does not replicate at a defined time but instead replicates throughout S phase. To demonstrate that the elutriation was effective, two controls are shown. The mouse complement gene C2, which is early replicating in all mouse cell lines examined (Hatton et al. 1988), replicates early in S in the BPV-transformed cells. In contrast, a DNA segment 5′ of the mouse salivary amylase (*Amy-1*) gene replicates late in S in the BPV-transformed cells. Our results on the timing of replication of BPV are in agreement with those of Gilbert and Cohen (1987). Those investigators found that, unlike chromosomal replicons, each molecule of BPV is not limited to one round of replication per cell cycle. Instead, the BPV genomes replicate randomly, so that in a given S phase some molecules replicate more than once and some do not replicate at all (Gilbert and Cohen 1987). Therefore, the replication of BPV does not appear to be subject to the same restraints as those that define the temporal order of eukaryotic DNA replication. We are actively pursuing the study of EBV replication with the hope that it will provide a model with which to study the mechanisms of temporal control of eukaryotic DNA replication.

Acknowledgments

These studies were supported by grants to C.L.S. from the National Institutes of Health (GM-22332), the American Cancer Society (CD-312), and the March of Dimes (1-1078). E.B. is a special fellow of the Leukemia Society of America. K.H. was supported by an NIH postdoctoral fellowship (F32-CA-07744). V.D. and T.A.G. were supported by an NIH training grant (5 T32-CA-09060). Support was also provided by Cancer Center Core grant (NIH/NCI P30-CA-13330).

Table 1 Temporal Replication of Bovine Papillomavirus DNA

DNA sequence detected	Cell line	Relative concentration of segments in BU-DNA isolated from cell class[a]			
		I	II	III	IV
BPV	ID 13	20.8	26.0	31.5	21.7
BPV	clone B	16.7	20.7	29.0	33.6
Controls					
C2	clone B	68.7	12.5	11.5	7.3
5′ of *Amy-1*	clone B	5.6	10.4	35.4	48.6

The 8-kb BPV genome, inserted into pML2, served as a probe (provided by P. Howley) for BPV. A 2.5-kb *Sac*I segment about 10 kb 5′ of the *Amy-1* gene was detected by probe 8D (provided by M. Meisler). A cDNA probe detected two *Sac*I segments containing the C2 gene (3.8 kb, for which the values in the table are shown, and 13 kb).

[a]Expressed as percentage of the total concentration in all four intervals.

References

Benz, E.J., M.J. Murnane, B.L. Tonkonow, B.W. Berman, E.M. Mazur, C. Cavallesco, T. Jenko, E.L. Snyder, B.G. Forget, and R. Hoffman. 1980. Embryonic-fetal erythroid characteristics of a human leukemic cell line. *Proc. Natl. Acad. Sci.* **78:** 348.

Braunstein, J.D., D. Schulze, T. DelGiudice, A. Furst, and C.L. Schildkraut. 1982. The temporal order of replication of murine immunoglobulin heavy chain constant region sequences corresponds to their linear order in the genome. *Nucleic Acids Res.* **10:** 6887.

Brown, E.H., M.A. Iqbal, S. Stuart, K.S. Hatton, and C.L. Schildkraut. 1987. Rate of replication of the murine immunoglobulin heavy chain locus: Evidence that the region is part of a single replicon. *Mol. Cell. Biol.* **7:** 450.

Burhans, W.C., J.E. Selegue, and N.H. Heintz. 1986. Isolation of the origin of replication associated with the amplified chinese hamster dihydrofolate reductase domain. *Proc. Natl. Acad. Sci.* **83:** 7790.

Calza, R.E., L. Eckhardt, T. DelGuidice, and C.L. Schildkraut. 1984. Changes in gene position are accompanied by a change in time of replication. *Cell* **36:** 689.

Darlington, G.J., H.P. Bernhard, R.A. Miller, and F.H. Ruddle. 1980. Expression of liver phenotypes in cultured mouse hepatoma cells. *J. Natl. Cancer Inst.* **64:** 809.

Furst, A., E.H. Brown, J.D. Braunstein, and C.L. Schildkraut. 1981. α-Globin sequences are located in a region of early-replicating DNA in murine erythroleukemia cells. *Proc. Natl. Acad. Sci.* **78:** 1023.

Gilbert, D.M. and S.N. Cohen. 1987. Bovine papilloma virus plasmids replicate randomly in mouse fibroblasts throughout the S phase of the cell cycle. *Cell* **50:** 59.

Goldman, M.A., G.P. Holmquist, M.C. Gray, L.A. Caston, and A. Nag. 1984. Replication timing of genes and middle repetitive sequences. *Science* **224:** 686.

Hatton, K.S., V. Dhar, E.H. Brown, S. Stuart, M.A. Iqbal, V. Didamo, and C.L. Schildkraut. 1988. The replication program of active and inactive multigene families in mammalian cells. *Mol. Cell. Biol.* (in press).

Iqbal, M.A., J. Chinsky, V. Didamo, and C.L. Schildkraut. 1987. Replication of proto-oncogenes early during the S phase in mammalian cell lines. *Nucleic Acids Res.* **15:** 87.

Law, M.-F., D.R. Lowy, I. Dvoretzky, and P.M. Howley. 1981. Mouse cells transformed by bovine papillomavirus contain only extrachromosomal viral DNA sequences. *Proc. Natl. Acad. Sci.* **78:** 2727.

Li, Q., P.A. Powers, and O. Smithies. 1985. Nucleotide sequence of 16-kilobase pairs of DNA 5′ to the human ε-globin gene. *J. Biol. Chem.* **260:** 14901.

Lindahl, T., A. Adams, G. Bjursell, G.W. Bornkamm, C. Kaschka-Dierich, and U. Jehn. 1976. Covalently closed circular duplex DNA of Epstein-Barr virus in a human lymphoid cell line. *J. Mol. Biol.* **102:** 511.

Taramelli, R., D. Kioussis, E. Vanin, K. Bartram, J. Groffen, J. Hurst, and F.G. Grosveld. 1986. γδβ-Thalassaemias 1 and 2 are the result of a 100 kbp deletion in the human β-globin cluster. *Nucleic Acids Res.* **14:** 7017.

Biochemical and Genetic Characterization of the Yeast DNA Polymerase–DNA Primase Complex

P. Plevani, M. Foiani, S. Francesconi, C. Mazza, A. Pizzagalli, P. Valsasnini, and G. Lucchini

Dipartimento di Genetica e di Biologia dei Microrganismi, Via Celoria 26, 20133, Milano, Italy

Yeast DNA polymerase I and DNA primase are purified as a multipeptide complex by immuno-affinity chromatography. The bifunctional complex is constituted of five polypeptides called p180, p140, p74, p58, and p48 according to their molecular weights. Biochemical and immunological analysis correlates DNA primase to p58 and p48, whereas DNA polymerase is associated with the two higher-molecular-weight polypeptides. Specific antisera have been raised against the isolated protein species of the yeast complex. These immunological reagents have been used to study the structural interrelations among the individual components of the protein complex and to isolate the genes encoding for the catalytic DNA polymerase (POL1) and one of the two polypeptides associated with DNA primase (PRI1). Both genes are unique in the yeast genome and essential for cell viability. POL1 and PRI1 are localized, on chromosome XIV and chromosome IX, respectively, of the yeast genome.

Our present understanding of the molecular events of DNA replication in prokaryotic cells is mostly due to the availability of DNA synthesis mutants and to the development of in vitro DNA replication systems that allowed the purification and characterization of a number of proteins involved in such a complex process (Kornberg 1980).

The replication of a eukaryotic genome raises significant problems that bacteria do not have. In fact, the DNA is condensed within the nucleus in many chromosomes, and the chromatin structure is likely to affect the activity of the enzymes involved in the DNA replication machinery. Moreover, chromosomal DNA synthesis proceeds in a temporally and spatially regulated order through the activation of many units of replication.

The yeast *Saccharomyces cerevisiae* is an ideal model system for studies on the molecular mechanisms of eukaryotic DNA replication. The yeast genome is only 1.35×10^4 kb and, although the small size of the 17 yeast chromosomes makes cytological studies difficult, it is packaged in a typical chromatin structure. Moreover, yeast is the only eukaryotic system where DNA sequences essential for chromosome replication and segregation (origins of replication, centromeres, and telomers) have been identified, and many strains of *S. cerevisiae* contain an endogenous multicopy plasmid, called 2-μm DNA, that can be considered a suitable model to study some features of nuclear replication. Finally, a number of proteins whose activities suggest a role in replication have been isolated from yeast, and a combination of modern and classic genetics has allowed the isolation of genes involved in cellular replication (Campbell 1986).

A long-standing goal of our laboratory is to gain a detailed understanding of the functions of a number of yeast replication proteins to reconstitute an in vitro DNA replication system with purified components. Lately, our efforts have been mainly addressed to the study of the structure and function of the yeast DNA polymerase I–DNA primase complex and to the isolation of the corresponding genes. DNA polymerase I (or α) is the most abundant DNA polymerase in yeast, and a body of circumstantial evidence suggests a major role for this enzyme in DNA replication. For instance, its association with a DNA primase activity able to synthesize RNA primers similar to those found at the 5′ end of the Okazaki fragments indicates that this protein complex can be involved in the discontinuous DNA synthesis on the lagging strand of the replication forks. Moreover, it has been suggested that the mechanism of priming on the leading strand at an origin of replication may be analogous to the initiation of DNA synthesis on the lagging strand, thus implying a critical role for the DNA polymerase–DNA primase complex, not only in the propagation of the replication forks, but also in the formation of specific DNA initiation complexes (Campbell 1986). In this paper, we will summarize our understanding of the structure of this protein complex and our results on the isolation of the POL1 and PRI1 genes, which encode two polypeptides, identified respectively as the core catalytic DNA polymerase I and one of the two subunits of yeast DNA primase.

Materials and Methods

Strains and plasmids
S. cerevisiae strains S288c, α, prototroph and TD28, *a*, *ura 3.52*, *inos 1*, *can 1* were from Dr. G.R. Fink of MIT. Strain DES5 *a*/α, *ura 3.52*/*ura 3.52* was constructed in our laboratory. The yeast genomic libraries in λgt11 and YEp24 were provided by Drs. R. Yuong and R. Davis of Stanford University and Dr. D. Botstein of MIT, respectively.

341

Enzyme and antibody preparation

Isolation of the DNA polymerase I–DNA primase complex by immunoaffinity chromatography, separation of the two enzymatic activities, and production of polyvalent rabbit antisera against the p140, p74, p58, and p48 polypeptides have been described in detail elsewhere (Plevani et al. 1985; Lucchini et al. 1987). DNA polymerase and DNA primase activities have been assayed as described previously (Plevani et al. 1985).

Isolation of the POL1 and PRI1 genes

Positive recombinant phages containing portions of the POL1 and PRI1 genes were identified by immunoscreening of a yeast genomic library constructed in the λgt11 expression vector (Young and Davis 1983; Lucchini et al. 1985, 1987). The entire POL1 and PRI1 genes were isolated from the YEp24 library as described previously (Lucchini et al. 1987; Plevani et al. 1987b).

Disruption of the POL1 and PRI1 genes

To verify whether the POL1 and PRI1 genes are performing essential functions for cell viability, we disrupted the two genes using the method of Shortle et al. (1982). Plasmids containing deletions of both 5′ and 3′ ends of the POL1 (pE12) or PRI1 (pSF48) genes were constructed by inserting the EcoRI-XhoI fragment of POL1 and the EcoRI-BglII fragment of PRI1 into the integrating vector YIp5 (Botstein et al. 1979). Plasmids were cut with HindIII to direct the integration at the POL1 or PRI1 loci and used to transform the diploid yeast strain DES5 to uracil prototrophy. Integration of a single copy of the plasmid at the appropriate loci was verified by Southern analysis. After sporulation, 20 tetrads from each transformed diploid were dissected and analyzed for colony formation and uracil requirement.

Other techniques

DNA preparation, DNA restriction analysis, and agarose gel electrophoresis were carried out as described by Maniatis et al. (1982). SDS-polyacrylamide gel electrophoresis was performed as described by Laemmli (1970). Total yeast DNA and total yeast RNA were prepared as described by Winston et al. (1983) and by Hinnebusch and Fink (1983). Poly(A)$^+$ RNA was isolated by a two-step purification with oligo(dT) cellulose. The filter carrying the DNA from separated yeast chromosomes was a kind gift from Dr. P. Philippsen (Biozentrum, Basel, Switzerland).

Results

The structure of the yeast DNA polymerase–DNA primase complex

Earlier studies identified two antigenically unrelated extramitochondrial DNA polymerases in yeast cells (Chang 1977). The most abundant enzyme, called DNA polymerase I, shows biochemical and structural properties similar to those of DNA polymerase α purified from

higher eukaryotic cells (Chang 1977; Badaracco et al. 1983). We also found that a priming activity, which allows in vitro DNA replication of unprimed DNA templates, could be isolated in association with DNA polymerase I by traditional protein purification procedures that require several chromatographic steps (Plevani et al. 1984). The use of a specific immunological reagent has been extremely useful in isolating this protein complex in a highly purified form. In fact, by using a mouse monoclonal antibody to yeast DNA polymerase I covalently linked to protein-A Sepharose, it is possible to purify the DNA polymerase–DNA primase complex in a single step starting from yeast crude extract (Plevani et al. 1985, 1987b). The polypeptide composition of this complex analyzed by SDS-polyacrylamide gel electrophoresis (PAGE) is shown in Figure 1. A series of polypeptides ranging in size from 180 to 140 kD can be detected in the high-molecular-weight range, together with three other major polypeptides, called p74, p58, and p48 according to their molecular weights. Four antisera have been prepared by excising the protein

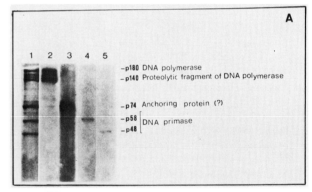

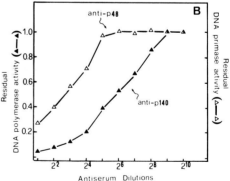

Figure 1 Immunological characterization of the DNA polymerase–DNA primase complex. (A) The immunopurified DNA polymerase–DNA primase complex, after electrophoresis in 10% SDS-polyacrylamide gel, was stained with Coomassie blue (lane 1) or transferred to nitrocellulose filters, which were probed with antisera raised against p140 (lane 2), p74 (lane 3), p58 (lane 4), and p48 (lane 5). Immunocomplexes were visualized after incubation with ^{125}I-Protein A and autoradiography. The putative functions of the major polypeptides found in the yeast DNA polymerase–DNA primase complex are indicated. (B) 3 units of DNA polymerase and DNA primase were incubated with serial dilutions of anti-p140 and anti-p48 sera as described (Chang 1977) and assayed for residual enzymatic activity.

bands corresponding to polypeptides p140, p74, p58, and p48 from a preparative SDS-polyacrylamide gel (Lucchini et al. 1987). These specific immunological reagents have been used to analyze the antigenic relationships among the different polypeptides of the yeast complex. As shown in Figure 1, the antiserum raised against p140 recognized, on Western blots of the total complex, not only the p140 itself, but also the p180 polypeptide, as well as the ladder of protein bands of intermediate molecular weight. These data indicate that all these protein species are immunologically related, and they confirm our previous finding that the p140 polypeptide is a proteolytic derivative of p180, whereas the ladder of bands in between likely represent intermediate degradation products (Plevani et al. 1985). On the contrary, all the three remaining antisera only react with the specific polypeptide used as antigen, thus clearly indicating that p74, p58, and p48 are not immunologically related to each other or to DNA polymerase I.

Functions of the yeast DNA polymerase–DNA primase polypeptides

The functions of the five major polypeptides found in the bifunctional yeast complex are summarized in Figure 1. These conclusions derive from several biochemical, immunological, and genetic evidences: (1) Polypeptides p180 and p140 are immunologically related, and as shown in Figure 1, the anti-p140 antiserum strongly inhibits DNA polymerase activity. (2) We have been able to directly correlate the DNA polymerase activity with p180, p140, and the ladder of bands in between by assaying enzymatic activity in situ on SDS-PAGE gels after renaturation of the separated polypeptides (Plevani et al. 1985). (3) Cloning and characterization of the POL 1 gene has definitely confirmed the identification of the p180 polypeptide with the native core catalytic DNA polymerase subunit (Johnson et al. 1985; Lucchini et al. 1985; Plevani et al. 1987b). (4) The two polypeptides p58 and p48 are associated with the DNA primase activity on MAb immunochromatography and on Bio-Rex 70 chromatography (Plevani et al. 1987b). Moreover, native yeast DNA primase has an estimated molecular weight of 110,000, which is consistent with a two-peptide structure (Plevani et al. 1985). (5) Isolated DNA primase, where only the p58 and p48 polypeptides are detectable, synthesizes oligoribonucleotides of a discrete length on natural and synthetic DNA templates (Badaracco et al. 1985, 1986). (6) Although, at present, we do not know whether only one or both of the p58 and p48 polypeptides are necessary for complete DNA primase activity, the p48 polypeptide is certainly related to this activity, as demonstrated by DNA primase inhibition with anti-p48 antiserum (Fig. 1B) and by cloning of the corresponding gene (Lucchini et al. 1987). (7) The function of the p74 polypeptide is still unknown, because we failed in trying to associate any enzymatic activity to this polypeptide. We simply speculate that it may represent an anchoring protein necessary for the stability of the DNA polymerase–DNA primase complex, but definitive conclusions about the structure and func-

tion of the p74 polypeptide await cloning and characterization of the corresponding gene.

Isolation and characterization of the POL1 and PRI1 yeast genes

The antisera prepared against the p140, p74, p58, and p48 protein species of the DNA polymerase–DNA primase complex have been used to identify recombinant phages containing part of the corresponding genes by immunoscreening of a λgt11 expression library (Lucchini et al. 1985, 1987). Because the anti-p140 and anti-p48 antisera inhibit, respectively, DNA polymerase and DNA primase activities, we focused our work on the isolation of the genes encoding these polypeptides. We used the yeast DNA fragments isolated from positive recombinant phages to identify the complete genes by screening of a yeast genomic library constructed in the high copy number vector YEp24 (Lucchini et al. 1987; Plevani et al. 1987b).

The restriction maps of the POL1 and the PRI1 genes encoding DNA polymerase I and the p48 subunit of DNA primase are shown in Figure 2. The complete POL1 gene is contained within the 7.2-kb BstEII-BamHI fragment. In fact, yeast cells containing a high copy number recombinant plasmid carrying the BstEII-BamHI insert show an approximately fivefold increase in DNA polymerase activity compared with yeast cells containing the control vector lacking the POL1 insert (Plevani et al. 1987b). Moreover, as shown in Figure 3, Northern blot analysis on poly(A)+ mRNA isolated from the above-described yeast transformants showed an even higher increase of the 5.2-kb mRNA that we previously identified as the DNA polymerase I mRNA (Lucchini et al. 1985).

The PRI1 gene is included within the NruI-SstI yeast fragment shown in Figure 2. In fact, the 1.45-kb mRNA species encoding the p48 polypeptide is overproduced in yeast cells transformed with a high copy number recombinant plasmid carrying the NruI-SstI fragment

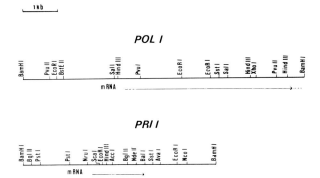

Figure 2 Restriction maps of the POL1 and PRI1 loci. The maps were determined by restriction analysis of plasmids containing the BamHI fragments spanning the POL1 and PRI1 loci and confirmed by Southern blot analysis of total yeast DNA digested with the appropriate enzymes. The direction of transcription is indicated. The exact 5′ and 3′ endpoints of the PRI1 mRNA have been determined by S1 mapping. The 5′ and 3′ termini of POL1 mRNA are only approximate.

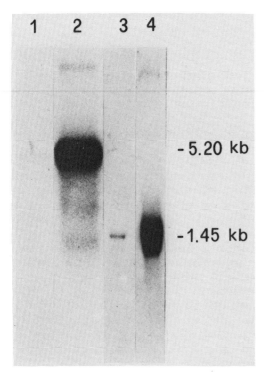

Figure 3 Overexpression of *POL1* and *PRI1* mRNAs. Poly(A)⁺ RNA was prepared from cells of yeast strain TD28 transformed with the vector YEp24 (lanes *1* and *3*), its derivative plasmids pGL7-4, and YEpβ2 containing, respectively, the *Bst*EII-*Bam*HI *POL1* insert (lane *2*) and the *Bam*HI *PRI1* region (lane *4*). Northern blots were probed with the 2.6-kb *Pvu*I-*Sal*I fragment or the 0.7-kb *Eco*RI-*Bgl*II fragment to detect, respectively, the *POL1* and *PRI1* mRNAs.

(Figs. 2 and 3). It has been impossible to assay for any increase in DNA primase activity in extracts prepared from the above yeast transformants because DNA primase cannot be easily assayed in crude extracts, due to interfering enzymatic activities or to the presence of oligonucleotides that can mimic the action of true DNA primase. However, the identity of the cloned *PRI1* gene has been proved by cloning the *Nru*I-*Sst*I fragment under the control of the phage T7 promoter and by subsequent in vitro transcription and translation (Lucchini et al. 1987).

The *PRI1* gene has now been completely sequenced and the 5′ and 3′ endpoints of the PRI1 mRNA have been mapped (Plevani et al. 1987a). An open reading frame coding for a protein of 409 amino acids with a calculated molecular weight of 47,623 has been found in the *PRI1* region. The complete sequence of the *POL1* gene and exact mapping of the corresponding transcript are under way in our laboratory. The use of appropriate probes in Northern analysis allowed us to locate the 5′ endpoint of the *POL1* mRNA inside the *Hind*III-*Pvu*I fragment and the 3′ endpoint within the *Hind*III-*Bam*HI region (Fig. 2).

Southern blots and hybridization of total yeast DNA digests with internal fragments of the *POL1* and *PRI1* genes showed that these two genes are present in single copy in the haploid genome (Lucchini et al. 1985,

1987). We carried out gene-disruption experiments, using the method of Shortle et al. (1982) to determine whether *POL1* and *PRI1* functions are essential for yeast cell viability. This method required the subcloning of an internal fragment of *POL1* and *PRI1* into the yeast integrating plasmid YIp5, which contains the *URA 3* selectable marker (Botstein et al. 1979). Integration of a single copy of the appropriate plasmid at the *POL1* or *PRI1* locus by transformation of a *ura3.52* homozygous diploid strain results in the disruption of one copy of the corresponding gene. In both cases, sporulation of these heterozygous transformants gave rise to tetrads exhibiting a 2:2 spore lethality, which was linked to the disrupted copy of the gene. As shown in Figure 4, only two spores in each of a number of dissected tetrads deriving from strains heterozygous for the *POL1* or the *PRI1* gene disruption are viable and can form colonies. As expected, all the viable spores were ura⁻. Therefore, both *POL1* and *PRI1* genes are unique in the yeast genome, and their protein products perform essential functions in yeast cells that cannot be substituted by other proteins with analogous enzymatic activity.

As mentioned previously, yeast chromosomes are small, and they have never been observed during the mitotic cell cycle by classic cytogenetic analysis. However, their size presents at least one major advantage. It is possible to separate most of the yeast chromosomes by orthogonal pulsed-field gel electrophoresis (OFAGE), so that the location of a cloned gene can be easily mapped by direct Southern transfer and hybridization with the appropriate probes (Carle and Olson 1985). As shown in Figure 5, blot hybridization of intact

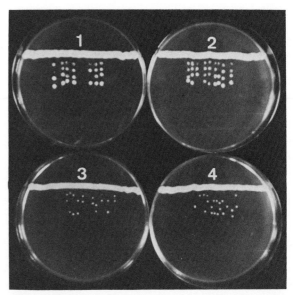

Figure 4 *POL1* and *PRI1* genes are essential for yeast cell viability. Spores from single tetrads derived from the untransformed yeast diploid strain DES5 (plates 1 and 2) and from the same strain made heterozygous for the gene disruption of *POL1* (plate 3) or *PRI1* (plate 4) were isolated on YEPD and incubated for 3 days at 28°C. The four spores from each tetrad are vertically aligned.

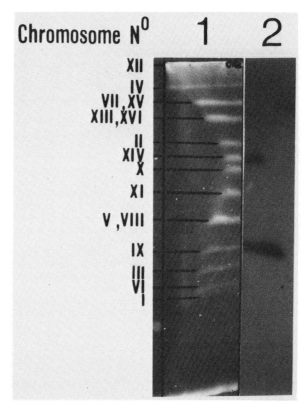

Figure 5 Chromosomal mapping of the *POL1* and *PRI1* genes. (*1*) Ethidium-bromide-stained gel of the yeast chromosomal DNA separated by OFAGE (Carle and Olson 1985). (*2*) DNA from the gel shown in panel *1* was transferred to nitrocellulose filter and probed with the 0.8-kb *Eco*RI fragment of *POL 1*. A single band corresponding to chromosome XIV was detected. The same filter was then probed with the 0.7-kb *Eco*RI-*Bgl*II fragment of *PRI 1* that hybridized with chromosome IX DNA.

yeast chromosomes with internal fragments of the *POL1* and *PRI1* genes allowed us to localize these two genes on chromosomes XIV and IX, respectively.

Discussion and Future Perspectives

DNA polymerase–DNA primase complex has been purified during the last few years from a variety of eukaryotic organisms (for a recent review, see Campbell 1986). A comparative analysis suggests a consensus structure conserved from yeast to mammalian cells: a large catalytic core DNA polymerase present as a polypeptide ranging from 125 to 200 kD, a set of intermediate polypeptides of 68–77 kD, and two small subunits of approximately 58 and 48 kD, generally associated with DNA primase activity. However, by comparison with a number of well-defined prokaryotic DNA replication systems, it is likely that the DNA polymerase–DNA primase complex represents a minimal core around which the replisome will be assembled. Indeed, only unprimed single-stranded DNA templates can be efficiently replicated in vitro by the concerted action of polymerase and primase. Replication of a double-stranded DNA molecule will likely require other

proteins such as DNA helicases, DNA-binding proteins, DNA topoisomerases, and other accessory proteins. Moreover, recognition of a eukaryotic origin of replication will eventually need transcriptional activation and/or recognition by specific prepriming proteins.

Some of these proteins have already been purified from eukaryotic cells through the availability of specific biochemical assays suitable to classic enzyme purification. Although such a pure enzymological approach does not immediately define the physiological role of the isolated proteins, extensive analysis of their biochemical properties might give some insight on their putative in vivo functions and should facilitate reconstitution studies in more complete replication systems. Moreover, the availability of highly purified proteins allows the production of specific immunological reagents. These are important probes both in assessing the function of individual components of protein complexes active in in vitro replication systems and in isolating the corresponding gene by immunoscreening of genomic or cDNA expression libraries.

Cloning of genes involved in DNA metabolism is particularly useful in yeast cells, due to the peculiarity of this biological system and to the development of sophisticated molecular techniques. By disrupting one copy of the gene in a diploid yeast strain, it is possible to verify whether the gene, when it is present in single copy in the haploid genome, is performing an essential function. Even more interestingly, the availability of the cloned gene allows the production of conditional lethal mutants through in vitro mutagenesis, and the mutated copy can be used to replace the wild-type allele at its chromosomal locus. The production of *ts* mutants in genes involved in DNA replication is certainly a challenging goal. In fact, although there are a number of mutants that affect yeast cell cycle or incorporation of precursors into DNA in vivo (Campbell 1986), only *CDC 9*, encoding DNA ligase, can be related to a function directly involved in the DNA replication process. Recently, we and others (Budd and Campbell 1987; G. Lucchini et al. in prep.) succeeded in producing in vitro thermosensitive mutants in the *POL1* gene. The availability of these mutants will be extremely useful in assessing the role of DNA polymerase I in DNA replication, repair, and recombination and in analyzing the remaining polymerases in yeast. Moreover, we believe that by searching for external suppressors of these *ts* mutations, it will be possible to identify genes encoding other proteins interacting with DNA polymerase, for which a specific biochemical assay is not immediately available. The cloned *POL1* gene has also been used to gain some information about the cell-cycle regulation of this essential enzyme and its induction in response to DNA-damaging agents. These studies demonstrated that the DNA polymerase I transcript is regulated in both the mitotic cell cycle and in meiosis and is also induced after UV irradiation of yeast cells (Johnston et al. 1987). The *POL1* transcript peaks around the G_1/S boundary at exactly the same time as an increase of the *CDC 8*, *CDC 9*, *CDC 21*, and *PRI1* mRNAs was also observed. It will be very interesting to evaluate whether the regulatory pathways of all these five genes involved in DNA metabolism (Campbell 1986) are in some way related.

Furthermore, subcloning of the *POL1* and *PRI1* genes into appropriate expression vectors will allow over-production of DNA polymerase and p48 in both homologous and heterologous systems. The availability of large amounts of the purified proteins will be essential to identify functional domains governing protein-protein interactions and binding to the template DNA.

Acknowledgments

This work was partially supported by a grant from Progetto Finalizzato Ingegneria Genetica e Basi Molecolari delle Malattie Ereditarie, CNR, Roma, Italy. P.V. was supported by a fellowship from Fondazione Anna Villa Rusconi.

References

Badaracco, G., L. Capucci, P. Plevani, and L.M.S. Chang. 1983. Polypeptide structure of DNA polymerase I from *Saccharomyces cerevisiae. J. Biol. Chem.* **258:** 10720.

Badaracco, G., M. Bianchi, P. Valsasnini, G. Magni, and P. Plevani. 1985. Initiation, elongation and pausing of in vitro DNA synthesis catalyzed by immunopurified yeast DNA primase-DNA polymerase complex. *EMBO J.* **4:** 1313.

Badaracco, G., P. Valsasnini, M. Foiani, R. Benfante, G. Lucchini, and P. Plevani. 1986. Mechanism of initiation of in vitro DNA synthesis by the immunopurified complex between yeast DNA polymerase I and DNA primase. *Eur. J. Biochem.* **161:** 435.

Botstein, D., S.C. Falco, S.E. Stewart, M. Brennan, S. Scherer, D.T. Stinchomb, K. Struhl, and R.W. Davis. 1979. Sterile host yeast (SHY): An eukaryotic system of biological containment for recombinant DNA experiment. *Gene* **8:** 17.

Budd, M. and J.L. Campbell. 1987. Temperature-sensitive mutations in the yeast DNA polymerase I gene. *Proc. Natl. Acad. Sci.* **84:** 2838.

Campbell, J.L. 1986. Eukaryotic DNA replication. *Annu. Rev. Biochem.* **55:** 733.

Carle, G.F. and M.V. Olson. 1985. An electrophoretic karyotype for yeast. *Proc. Natl. Acad. Sci.* **82:** 3756.

Chang, L.M.S. 1977. DNA polymerase from baker yeast. *J. Biol. Chem.* **252:** 1873.

Hinnebusch, A.G. and G.R. Fink. 1983. Repeated DNA sequences upstream from *HIS 1* also occur at several other co-regulated genes in *Saccharomyces cerevisiae. J. Biol. Chem.* **258:** 5238.

Johnson, L.M., M. Snyder, L.M.S. Chang, R.W. Davis, and J.L. Campbell. 1985. Isolation of the gene encoding yeast DNA polymerase I. *Cell* **43:** 369.

Johnston, L.H., J.H.M. White, A.L. Johnson, G. Lucchini, and P. Plevani. 1987. The DNA polymerase I transcript is regulated in both the mitotic cell cycle and in meiosis and is also induced after DNA damage. *Nucleic Acids Res.* **15:** 5017.

Kornberg, A. 1980. *DNA replication.* W.H. Freeman, San Francisco.

Laemmli, U.K. 1970. Cleavage of structural proteins during the assembly of the head of bacteriophage T4. *Nature* **227:** 680.

Lucchini, G., A. Brandazza, G. Badaracco, M. Bianchi, and P. Plevani. 1985. Identification of the yeast DNA polymerase I gene with antibody probes. *Curr. Genet.* **10:** 245.

Lucchini, G., S. Francesconi, M. Foiani, G. Badaracco, and P. Plevani. 1987. Yeast DNA polymerase-DNA primase complex: Cloning of *PRI1* a single essential gene related to DNA primase activity. *EMBO J.* **6:** 737.

Maniatis, T., E. Fritsch, and J. Sambrook. 1982. *Molecular cloning: A laboratory manual.* Cold Spring Harbor Laboratory, Cold Spring Harbor, New York.

Plevani, P., S. Francesconi, and G. Lucchini. 1987a. The nucleotide sequence of the *PRI1* gene related to DNA primase in *Saccharomyces cerevisiae. Nucleic Acids Res.* **15:** 7975.

Plevani, P., G. Badaracco, C. Augl, and L.M.S. Chang. 1984. DNA polymerase and DNA primase complex in yeast. *J. Biol. Chem.* **259:** 7532.

Plevani, P., M. Foiani, P. Valsasnini, G. Badaracco, E. Cheriathundam, and L.M.S. Chang. 1985. Polypeptide structure of DNA primase from a yeast DNA polymerase-primase complex. *J. Biol. Chem.* **260:** 7102.

Plevani, P., G. Lucchini, M. Foiani, P. Valsasnini, A. Brandazza, M. Bianchi, G. Magni, and G. Badaracco. 1987b. Structure and function of the yeast DNA polymerase I-DNA primase complex. *Life Sci. Adv.* **6:** 53.

Shortle, D., J.E. Haber, and D. Botstein. 1982. Lethal disruption of the yeast actin gene by integrative DNA transformation. *Science* **217:** 371.

Winston, F., F. Chumley, and G.R. Fink. 1983. Eviction and transplacement of mutant genes in yeast. *Methods Enzymol.* **101:** 211.

Young, R.A. and R.W. Davis. 1983. Yeast RNA polymerase II genes: Isolation with antibody probes. *Science* **222:** 778.

Yeast DNA Polymerases and ARS-binding Proteins

M. Budd, C. Gordon, K. Sitney, K. Sweder, and J.L. Campbell

Divisions of Chemistry and Biology, 147-75, California Institute of Technology, Pasadena, California 91125

Recent characterization of eukaryotic polymerases suggests that yeast DNA polymerases I and II correspond to higher cell DNA polymerases α and δ, respectively. We have used temperature-sensitive mutants in the POL1 gene to differentiate the functions of polymerases I and II of yeast. First, the pol1-17 mutation completely inactivates DNA polymerase I, but does not affect polymerase II, suggesting that polymerase I and II are different entities. DNA polymerase I is essential for mitotic replication and sporulation but is not essential for X-ray repair. Some meiotic DNA synthesis occurs in $pol1_{ts}$ mutants, but no mitotic DNA synthesis occurs; thus polymerase II cannot compensate for loss of polymerase I in mitosis but may be able to do so in meiosis and repair. Loss of pol1 function leads to nondisjunction in some cases. As expected for a replicative polymerase, POL1 expression is periodic in the cell cycle.

At least three proteins that bind to yeast ARS DNA have been purified using conventional and oligonucleotide affinity chromatography. ARS1-specific binding activity was monitored during purification by gel retardation and competition binding experiments using synthetic oligonucleotides containing two sequences, element A and element B, that are conserved at other ARS elements. Two of the purified proteins bind specifically to element B of ARS1 and to no other region in any non-ARS DNA. As expected for proteins that are involved in ARS function, however, the proteins do bind to other ARSs as well as to ARS1. DNase I footprinting shows a single binding site at the HMRE-ARS. Since the proteins bind to all ARSs tested, and not just ARS1, and since analysis of deletion mutants suggests that element B is required for the autonomous replication of ARS1, we propose that these proteins are required for replication. A third protein is also discussed.

At the moment, the most interesting intellectual problem in eukaryotic DNA replication is without doubt how the multiple initiations within eukaryotic chromosomes are temporally and spatially regulated within the cell cycle and how reinitiation within activated replicons is prevented in a single S phase. To understand this type of regulation, we must know what gene products are involved and how they are regulated. At the moment, we know so little about the proteins involved in eukaryotic DNA replication that we are not even sure what cellular DNA polymerases are required for replication. Developments during the past year, although reconfirming the participation of DNA polymerase α in replication, have indirectly suggested that a second DNA polymerase, namely, DNA polymerase δ, is also required (Dresler and Frattini 1986; Bravo et al. 1987; Prelich et al. 1987a,b). Furthermore, new information links progression into S phase with cell-cycle-regulated synthesis of the cellular DNA polymerases and their cofactors (for review, see Blow 1987).

Yeast contains apparent analogs of both DNA polymerases α and δ, and therefore is an ideal system in which to explore the contributions of each polymerase to replication and its regulation using the powerful combination of biochemistry and genetic approaches possible in yeast. DNA polymerase I of yeast seems to be the analog of DNA polymerase α (for review, see Campbell 1986). It has an identical subunit structure, including a 180-kD catalytic core subunit, a 70-kD subunit of un-

known function, and 55- and 45-kD subunits that together comprise the primase activity. DNA polymerase I is sensitive to aphidicolin and to 1 μM butylphenyl-deoxyguanosine triphosphate (BuPdGTP), like polymerase α, and is free of 3' to 5' exonuclease activity. We have cloned the POL1 gene and derived mutants that show that polymerase I is essential for growth (Johnson et al. 1985). The question is whether it is the sole polymerase.

Yeast contains a second high-molecular-weight DNA polymerase, called polymerase II, that during initial purification steps makes up 50% of the polymerase in the cell (Wintersberger and Wintersberger 1970; Wintersberger 1974; Chang 1977). Like δ, it contains a 3' to 5' exonuclease, is sensitive to aphidicolin, and is relatively insensitive to BuPdGTP. It has always seemed reasonable that it is a direct analog of higher cell polymerase δ, although only recently have DNA polymerases II and δ been well enough characterized to warrant a strong statement on the subject (Johnson et al. 1985; Campbell 1986; Crute et al. 1986; Wahl et al. 1986; Lee and Toomey 1987; M. Budd and J.L. Campbell, unpubl.). DNA polymerase II may have a role in replication in addition to DNA polymerase I, and this possibility is addressed in the studies reported here.

Initiation of DNA replication within eukaryotic chromosomes is thought to occur at multiple origins of replication spaced at 30–100-kb intervals along the DNA. Selection of these sites is likely to involve specific protein-DNA interactions, as inferred from recent

347

studies of *Escherichia coli*, bacteriophage λ, and simian virus 40 DNA replication. In these three systems, the binding of multiple copies of an origin-specific protein nucleates a series of protein-protein and protein-DNA interactions that lead to unwinding of the DNA by a DNA helicase and synthesis by DNA primase and DNA polymerase (Dodson et al. 1985, 1987; Baker et al. 1986, 1987; Wold et al. 1987). In *E. coli* the initiator protein is the dnaA protein, in bacteriophage λ it is the O protein, and in SV40 it is T antigen. We would like to identify proteins with similar functions that interact with yeast chromosomal origins of replication or ARSs.

Yeast ARSs are genomic sequences that allow autonomous replication of colinear DNA when cloned into a plasmid containing a yeast selectable marker (Struhl et al. 1979). Physical mapping of replication intermediates formed in vivo or in vitro suggests ARSs are chromosomal origins of replication (Celniker and Campbell 1982; Brewer and Fangman 1987; J.A. Huberman, pers. comm.). Since it is now possible to purify proteins by direct binding assays, we have begun to characterize proteins that may interact with ARSs in the cell. In this paper, we report on two proteins that bind specifically to an element within domain B of ARS1 and to another site at the HMRE-ARS (defined in Shore et al. 1987) that was not previously recognized to be conserved between ARSs. We describe a third protein that binds to ARS DNA but does not specifically recognize any sequence within the ARS and that binds to other DNAs as well.

Methods

Strains and plasmids
These are described in the text.

Growth of cells and preparation of DNA-free extracts
Strain PEP4D was grown to A_{590} = 6 in YPD medium. Cells were harvested in a Sharples centrifuge, frozen in liquid N_2, and stored at −70°C. Thirty grams of cells were thawed and resuspended in 80 ml of buffer A (20 mM HEPES [pH 7.4], 1 mM EDTA, 1 mM β-mercaptoethanol) containing 1.0 M KCl and protease inhibitors (0.5 mM phenylmethylsulfonyl fluoride, 2 μg/ml pepstatin A/1 mM EGTA/1 μg/ml soybean trypsin inhibitor/1 mM benzamidine, 1 μg/ml leupeptin) at 4°C. Cells were disrupted by three passages through a Dynomill cell disrupter at 4°C; the final volume recovered was 500 ml. After centrifugation at 19,000g for 45 minutes, 130 ml of a 30% (w/v) solution of polyethylene glycol 6000 containing 2.0 M KCl was added. The mixture was stirred for 45 minutes at 4°C, and the resulting precipitate was removed by centrifugation at 8500g for 30 minutes. The supernatant (620 ml) was dialyzed against 3.5 l of buffer A containing 0.05 M KCl and then against buffer A containing 0.1 M KCl for 17 hours. During this dialysis a precipitate forms, which is removed by centrifugation at 8000g for 10 minutes. The supernatant was designated fraction I (Jong et al. 1985).

Sporulation and recombination
To obtain the data (see Table 1 in Jong et al. 1985), cells were inoculated into YPD medium and grown to a density of 1.5×10^7 cells/ml. Cells were resuspended in presporulation medium at a density of 2×10^6 and grown to a cell density of 1×10^7. Cells were then washed in sporulation medium (1% potassium acetate), resuspended in sporulation medium at a cell density of 1×10^7, and incubated at 23°C and 36°C.

DNA repair
Cells were grown in YPD medium to a cell density of 7×10^7, collected onto nitrocellulose filters, irradiated with 30 krads of X-ray (50 keV, 20 m amp, unfiltered) and resuspended in YPD medium in the presence of [³H]uracil at 36°C. After 0, 1, 2, or 3 hours, cells were harvested, converted to spheroplasts, and lysed on the bottom of a nitrocellulose tube. A 15–30% alkaline sucrose gradient was pumped into the tube, and lysed spheroplasts were spun at 12,000 rpm for 16 hours. Fractions were collected, acid-precipitated, and counted.

All other procedures are as described in the text.

Results

DNA polymerases

Characterization of polymerase mutants in Saccharomyces cerevisiae
We have recently described the isolation and characterization of seven temperature-sensitive mutations in the gene for DNA polymerase I, *POL1* (Johnson et al. 1985; Budd and Campbell 1987). The mutants have been used to show that *POL1* maps to chromosome XIV (Budd and Campbell 1987). We have also determined the site of the individual mutations within the *POL1* gene by marker rescue. Marker rescue was carried out by cloning a set of restriction fragments spanning the whole 5.4-kb gene in plasmid pSEY8 and transforming strains *pol1-11, -12, -13, -14, -15, -16,* and *-17*. (See Johnson et al. [1985], for restriction map of *POL1*.) Colonies were replicated to medium lacking uracil and placed at 36°C. Appearance of papillation indicated recombination and hence marker rescue. Only plasmid pSEY8-C, carrying the internal *Eco*RI-*Xho*I fragment of *POL1*, allowed papillation. The finding that plasmid pSEY8-D, which carries the internal *Hin*dIII-*Xho*I-*Hin*dIII fragment and which overlaps fragment C, does not allow papillation, placed the mutation in an 1100-bp *Eco*RI-*Hin*dIII fragment. Similar experiments were carried out using restriction sites within this subregion of the gene, and all the mutations fall in a 500-bp region. Interestingly, the mutations seem to cluster in a central portion of the gene, suggesting that this region is important in the folding or stability of DNA polymerase. T. Wang (Stanford University) has recently sequenced the *Eco*RI-*Bam* fragment of our clone, and we will soon know where the mutations map at the DNA sequence level, since she has made the sequence available to us.

Residual DNA synthesis in vivo

The availability of *pol1*_{ts} mutants has allowed us to address the question of whether polymerases I and II have overlapping functions. The first thing we investigated was whether there was any residual DNA synthesis in a *pol1*_{ts} mutant after shift of an asynchronous, proliferating population to the nonpermissive temperature. If polymerase II is essential for replication in addition to polymerase I, it was possible that polymerase II could continue synthesis in the absence of polymerase I, which would be observed as considerable residual synthesis in the mutant. Incorporation of [³H]uridine into DNA during a 3-hour pulse at the nonpermissive temperature was reduced in all mutants (see Table 1 in Budd and Campbell 1987). The extent of synthesis was 25–50% relative to wild type, greater than the amount expected from mutants that by other criteria appear to stop replication immediately on shift to the nonpermissive temperature. For instance, the mutants show first cycle arrest and do not divide after shift-up but arrest homogeneously with a single, large bud with no increase in cell number (Budd and Campbell 1987).

One problem with quantitating DNA synthesis in vivo in yeast is the fact that yeast lacks a scavenger pathway for synthesizing dTMP, since the organism lacks thymidine kinase. Thus, DNA must be labeled indirectly by introduction of [³H]uridine, which is incorporated into both DNA and RNA. To measure the radioactivity in DNA specifically, cells must be incubated in alkali to hydrolyze RNA. If this

treatment is not efficient, aberrantly high levels of DNA synthesis are recorded. Residual DNA synthesized in the mutants was therefore further analyzed by sucrose gradient analysis and flow cytometry. Sucrose gradients were informative because they showed clearly that in strain *pol1-17* there was no detectable high-molecular-weight DNA synthesized after shift to the nonpermissive temperature. All synthesis observed could be accounted for as mitochondrial DNA (Fig. 1). Apparently, when DNA polymerase I is defective, no nuclear DNA synthesis can occur, and if polymerase II has a role, it is not independent of polymerase I. These studies also tell us that polymerase I functions at the stage of elongation, since replication of chromosomal DNA ceases immediately upon shift to the nonpermissive temperature. These studies will be extended using synchronized cells to determine if this polymerase is also essential for initiation or entry into S phase.

Another method of determining DNA synthesis that does not involve radioactive pulse labeling is flow cytometry. For flow cytometry, cultures were grown to logarithmic phase, harvested, and fixed. They were submitted to acid hydrolysis of RNA and stained for cytometry with acriflavin. Stained cells were then introduced one by one into a flow chamber, excited by a laser, and ensuing fluorescence, which is proportional to DNA content per cell, was measured. Data on the light scatter (size) for each cell was also obtained. In wild-type

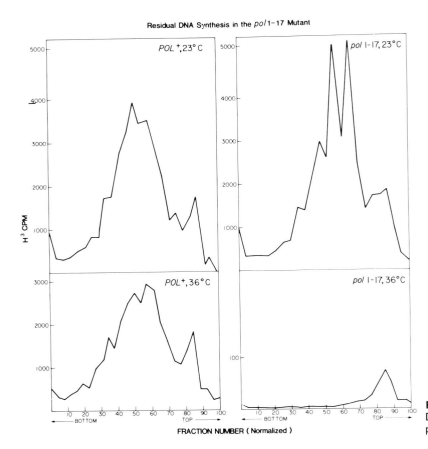

Residual DNA Synthesis in the *pol1-17* Mutant

Figure 1 Velocity sedimentation analysis of DNA synthesized at the permissive and nonpermissive temperatures in a *pol1*_{ts} mutant.

proliferating cells, two peaks of fluorescence, corresponding to unreplicated (haploid, 1N) and replicated (diploid, 2N) cells are seen. The 1N peak contains cells in G_1, the region between the peaks contains the cells in S phase, and the 2N peak represents G_2 cells. When the temperature is shifted up in the replication mutant, the G_2 cells that have completed DNA replication should divide and join the 1N population. If the mutant is deficient in initiation, the G_1 population should not enter S phase. Cells in S phase at the shift-up should arrest there and so, ideally, one would expect a pattern that shows only the 1N peak, with a small percentage of the cells remaining in S phase.

Flow cytometric results divided the mutants into three separate groups (data not shown). First, one mutant, *pol1-17*, shows a pattern very like that expected for an elongation mutant. The 2N peak disappears completely. There is one peak corresponding to 1N and a slight increase in the number of cells that have a DNA content between 1N and 2N, which could either be due to leakiness or to mitochondrial DNA synthesis. The latter is probably the case, since comparison shows that the amounts of mitochondrial DNA synthesis by sucrose gradient analysis and the DNA increase in flow cytometry agree fairly well. We are currently repeating the flow cytometry with *rho*^{0} (no mitochondrial DNA) derivatives of the *pol1-17* mutant.

In a second class of mutants, represented by *pol1-11*, there was a larger population with a greater increase in DNA content after temperature shift-up, but no complete conversion to 2N chromosomes. We consider these mutants to be leaky, although one could also argue that they are more temperature sensitive for assembly into a replication complex or holoenzyme than for actual polymerization. This behavior is similar to that observed in the mouse polymerase α temperature-sensitive mutant (Eki et al. 1986).

The third class, represented by *pol1-14*, yielded an unexpected pattern. Although pulse labeling shows that even at 23°C the *pol1-14* mutants are defective in DNA synthesis, there is a much higher DNA content in these supposedly "haploid" isolates. Even at the permissive temperature, cells contained approximately 5N chromosomes. As in the *pol1-11* strain, synthesis was somewhat leaky. The interesting point is that it seems as if these mutants have either undergone endoreduplication or nondisjunction to increase their ploidy. We have not investigated this further, but this could be due to the fact that the particular *pol* mutation affects interactions with other proteins involved in initiation or modifies polymerase so that the normal block to reinitiation in a single S phase is not operative. These alleles will be particularly interesting for reversion studies.

Meiosis — sporulation and meiotic recombination

The ability of the *pol1-17* mutant to sporulate was tested at 23°C and 36°C. Since some steps in sporulation are inherently temperature sensitive in many yeast strains, the *pol1-17* mutation was crossed into a strain derived from strain SK-1. The SK-1 background allows for high-frequency, synchronous sporulation at temperatures up to 36°C. The strains also contain the *his1-1/his1-7* heteroalleles, allowing one to follow recombination during the course of sporulation by removing cells from sporulation medium, plating onto media lacking histidine, and assaying for *HIS* prototrophs. After 24 hours at 23°C, both mutant and isogenic wild type sporulated with a frequency of 95%. There was a 200-fold increase in the number of *HIS1* prototrophs. At 36°C, wild type sporulated at a frequency of 82% and there was a 200-fold increase in the number of *HIS1* prototrophs. The *pol1-17/pol1-17* diploid, however, sporulated at a frequency of less than 0.1% with an increase in the number of *HIS1* prototrophs of only about 20-fold. Thus, although the formation of tetrads is blocked in the *pol1-17* mutant at 36°C, commitment to meiotic recombination is reduced but not blocked.

Experiments to determine if the defect in meiosis is due to a block in DNA synthesis are now underway. Preliminary results suggest that the chromosomes do undergo extensive premeiotic DNA synthesis. However, this result is so surprising that artifacts must be ruled out. For instance, was 36°C a high enough temperature to entirely block synthesis? Did our acid hydrolysis treatment of labeled cells entirely eliminate RNA? If the results hold true, however, there may be a major role for DNA polymerase II in meiosis, or at least polymerase II may be able to compensate for loss of polymerase I.

Role of DNA polymerase I in DNA repair

The role of DNA polymerase I in repair of X-ray-induced single-strand breaks was investigated with alkaline sucrose gradients. The strains used in the experiment were two isogenic haploid strains, SS111 POL$^+$ and SS111 *pol1-17*, called SS111-17 (see Budd and Campbell 1987). Protocols are described in Methods. The results showed, again surprisingly, that after postirradiation incubation of 1, 2, or 3 hours, there is no significant difference between the *POL1* and the *pol1-17* cells in the number of single-strand breaks repaired (Fig. 2). Analysis by orthogonal-field-alternation gel electrophoresis gels of double-strand break repair in isogenic diploids showed that double-strand break repair occurred, although with slightly delayed kinetics (data not shown).

Cell cycle regulation of POL1

Many genes involved in replication are expressed periodically in the cell cycle, and we have investigated whether DNA polymerase I is such a gene. Cells were synchronized by centrifugal elutriation. Elutriated cells were allowed to grow, and cells were harvested at 15-minute intervals. Total RNA was prepared and analyzed by blot hybridization using a probe carrying both the *POL1* gene and the constitutively expressed *URA3* gene. As shown in Figure 3, there is a sixfold variation in the level of the RNA during the cell cycle. To see at which point in the cell cycle this increased RNA accumulation was occurring, the same blot was probed with the histidine H2A gene. This is one of the best studied

SINGLE-STRAND BREAK REPAIR
in a *pol1*$_{ts}$ MUTANT

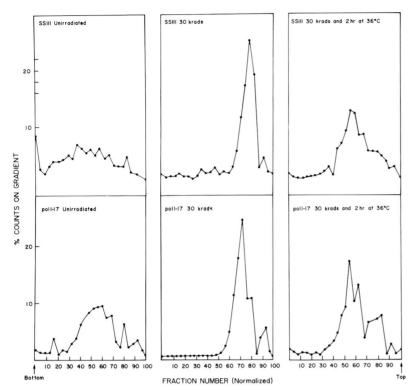

Figure 2 Sedimentation velocity analysis of DNA repair in *pol1-17* after irradiation with X-rays.

cell-cycle-regulated genes in yeast, and it is clear that *POL1* is expressed 15–30 minutes before the peak in histone mRNA, late in G$_1$. Similar results have been obtained by Johnston et al. (1987).

Does this pattern of expression have anything to do with progression into S phase? We have not yet explicitly tested this. We have, however, expressed the *POL1* gene under the control of the yeast *GAL1,10* promoter, which is not cell-cycle regulated. Cells grow normally when polymerase is expressed from this promoter on plasmid pBM150 (*Gal1-POL*$^+$). The current caveat in these experiments is that we do not know whether we have removed the upstream cell-cycle-control sequences of *POL1* in the *GAL* constructions. If not, they may function normally in the presence of the *GAL1,10* components, as has been observed in GAL-HO constructions (K. Nasmyth, pers. comm.).

DNA polymerase I and DNA polymerase II are distinct enzymes
We have begun to characterize the residual DNA polymerase activity in extracts of the *pol1-17* mutant, since it was the least leaky mutant in vivo. Polymerase "activity" in extracts was reduced to less than 10–20% of wild-type levels at both 23°C and 36°C, consistent with previous proposals that polymerase I makes up the largest fraction of polymerase in extracts. To determine

what combination of polymerase I, polymerase II, and mitochondrial polymerase was remaining, we have fractionated the activity in extracts. In summary, there is no detectable DNA polymerase I in this strain. All residual polymerase is thermostable and has the drug sensitivity, template requirements, and nucleolytic properties usually ascribed to DNA polymerase II (data not shown). This suggests that polymerase II is either the product of a different gene from *POL1*, or that the specific base pair change due to the *pol1-17* mutation does not affect polymerase II activity as strongly as it does polymerase I activity. This is unlikely, since the *pol1-17* mutation lies in the middle of the coding sequence and polymerase II is almost the same size as polymerase I.

When yeast strains containing pBM150 (*Gal1-POL1*$^+$) are grown on galactose as the sole carbon source, the amount of DNA polymerase I protein is increased by at least 100-fold compared to wild-type levels, as determined by DNA polymerase activity and Western blot analysis. During extensive purification of the overproduced polymerase I, however, we have found no evidence for overproduction of polymerase II, again suggesting that polymerases I and II are different.

There is, however, one interesting difference between the DNA polymerase II purified from the *pol1-17* mutant and that purified from wild type. During the final purification steps, the polymerase II from the mutant is less stable than polymerase II from the wild type.

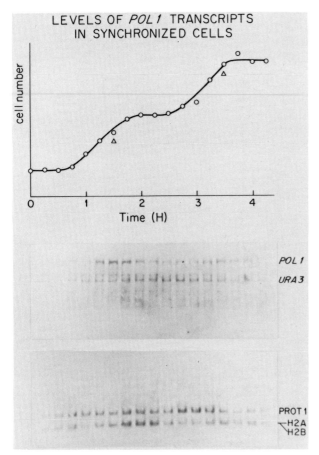

LEVELS OF *POL1* TRANSCRIPTS IN SYNCHRONIZED CELLS

Figure 3 Cell-cycle regulation of *POL1* mRNA levels.

ARS-binding proteins

Purification of ARS-binding proteins

For several years, we have been studying proteins that bind to yeast ARS1 (Campbell et al. 1986a,b). In addition, Shore et al. (1987) have described an activity in crude preparations that binds to both HMRE and to element B of ARS1 and have suggested that binding is due to a single protein species, which they called SBF-B. In this report, we describe extensive purification of several proteins that bind to ARS1. One of these purified proteins binds to both ARS1 and to the identical sequence at the HMRE ARS reported by Shore et al. (1987) and is likely to be identical to SBF-B.

Native DNA cellulose chromatography

A native DNA cellulose column was equilibrated with buffer A containing 0.1 M KCl. A DNA-free extract prepared as described in Methods was loaded onto the column, and the column was washed with 550 ml of the same buffer. A 450-ml linear gradient from 0.1 to 1.0 M KCl in buffer A was used to elute bound proteins. Gel retardation was used to monitor binding to a labeled DNA fragment containing both domains A and B. As shown in Figure 4, two different complexes were observed. Proteins eluting between 0.27 and 0.32 M KCl

gave rise to complex 1, and proteins eluting between 0.33 and 0.40 M gave rise to complex 2. Fractions giving rise to complex 1 were pooled and the protein purified through heptylagarose, phosphocellulose, and oligonucleotide chromatography (K. Sweder et al., in prep.). Similarly, fractions giving rise to the more rapidly migrating complex 2 were pooled and purified as above.

Analysis of the purified proteins by gel electrophoresis

The preparations giving rise to complex 1 and complex 2 proteins were subjected to gel electrophoresis in the presence of SDS. As can be seen in Figure 4B, they correspond to predominant 55-kD and 88-kD species, respectively. Assignment of active species has been accomplished by renaturation of the activity from an SDS gel. By this procedure, activity has been recovered only for the 88-kD species. The 55-kD protein is either a contaminant or is more difficult to renature. For simplicity, in this work, we will refer to the two preparations as the 55- and 88-kD proteins.

Specificity of binding

Initial attempts to locate the recognition and binding sequence for each protein within the ARS1 fragment employed competition binding assays using three oligonucleotides. Two oligonucleotides correspond to element A and one to element B. The sequences of element A oligonucleotides are:

GAATTCCAGATTTTATGTTTAGATC

and

TTTTACAGATTTTATGTTTAGATCTTTTATCTTG.

The sequence of the element B oligonucleotide is

CAATTCATTTCTTAGCATTTTTGACGAAATTTG.

Competition experiments were carried out so that the total amount of competitor, both oligonucleotide and neutral DNA, was equivalent in each reaction mixture. Neutral DNA used was either salmon sperm DNA or poly(dIdC), and the results obtained were identical with each. Both the 55-kD and 88-kD proteins apparently recognize element B, since the element B oligonucleotide efficiently competed for the labeled DNA but the element A oligonucleotide acted like nonspecific DNA (Fig. 5A).

To ensure that binding was only to domain B, a fragment was constructed that contained only element A. Neither purified protein bound to this fragment (Fig. 5B). Furthermore, neither protein bound to a labeled fragment that contained the yeast heat shock transcription factor recognition sequence, which contains no recognizable homology to ARS elements and which cannot function as an ARS (Wiederrecht et al. 1987). In these experiments with more purified fractions, a third complex was observed that migrated just slightly more slowly than the free DNA (Fig. 5A). We will discuss the protein responsible for this complex further below.

Binding to other ARSs

One of the best studied ARSs, outside of ARS1, is that found at the silent mating type locus, HMRE. This ARS is

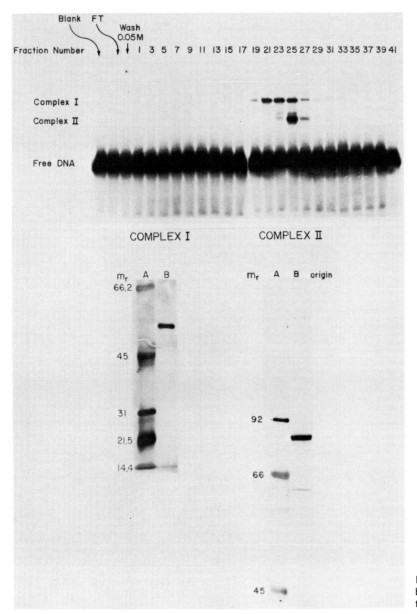

Figure 4 DNA cellulose elution profile of ARS binding proteins and SDS gel analysis of proteins found in complex I and complex II.

of particular interest because the sequences required for replication seem to overlap those required to regulate expression of the *mat* gene at HMR. The functional elements within the HMRE-ARS have been defined by sequence comparison with other ARSs and by extensive mutagenesis (e.g., Abraham et al. 1984; Shore et al. 1987). Like ARS1, the HMRE-ARS contains at least two elements. Element A is defined as nucleotides 358–346 in Shore et al. (1987). The second element, B, defined by mutagenesis and footprinting with crude protein fractions, lies between nucleotides 282 and 250. The labeled fragments used in our studies contained both these domains. Both the 55- and 88-kD proteins bind to this fragment. Elements A and B are not, however, identical to their counterparts at ARS1, and the flanking DNA also differs.

DNase I footprinting of binding at HMRE
Standard footprinting procedures were used, and the results are shown in Figure 5C. The 55-kD preparation protects between 281 and 256 bp in the HMRE fragment element B. There is also some protection in the region adjacent to domain B. The bases protected suggest that this is due to the presence of contaminating GRF1 (SBF-E) as reported by Shore et al. (1987), although it is not clear why these two proteins should have copurified when assaying with the ARS1 fragments. The 88-kD protein, which we have shown to be an active binding species as described above, protects on the region from 281 and 256 bp, exactly the same region as SBF-B (Shore et al. 1987). When both proteins are present, the pattern is the sum of the two individual patterns (Fig. 5C).

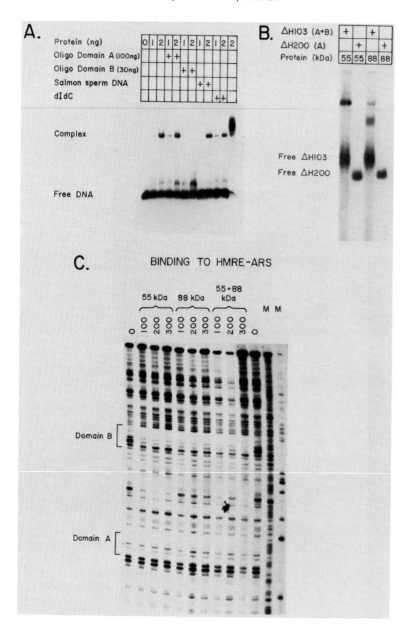

Figure 5 (*A*) Oligonucleotide competition binding assay to determine specificities. (*B*) Exclusive binding of domain B by ARS1 binding proteins. (*C*) DNase I footprinting of HMRE-ARS.

Factor X

In the fractions eluting from phosphocellulose, a new complex was observed (see Fig. 5A). This complex migrated faster than the other two, suggesting that the protein was smaller than 55 kD. Furthermore, on enrichment, a ladder of bands was seen representative of multimers of a single species binding to DNA (Fig. 6).

The specificity of binding was determined, as for complex 1 and complex 2, by competition binding experiments (data not shown). Binding could be efficiently competed out by equimolar amounts of either the domain A oligonucleotide, the domain B oligonucleotide, or salmon sperm DNA, suggesting that the factor responsible for the new complex was a nonspecific DNA binding protein and not ARS specific. Since the protein copurifies with the 88-kD ARS binding protein, it was important to investigate the question of specificity fur-

ther. We have characterized the binding to the heat shock transcription factor recognition sequence, the control fragment used in the foregoing studies. The pattern of binding to this fragment on gel retardation looks identical to that on the ARS fragments (Fig. 6). The molecular weight of this protein is below 20 kD, but we have not purified it to homogeneity.

Discussion

An important question in eukaryotic replication is whether polymerase α is the sole polymerase required for DNA replication. We have used temperature-sensitive mutants affecting DNA polymerase I of yeast to assess directly the role of DNA polymerase I (α) in replication and indirectly the role of polymerase II (δ). Our results suggest that polymerase I, which is the

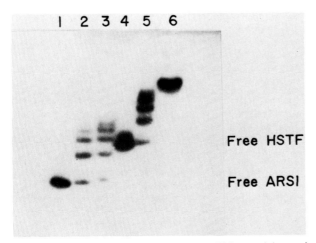

Figure 6 Multimeric binding of factor X to ARS-containing and non-ARS DNAs. (Lanes *1–3*) ARS1 fragment from ΔH103; (lanes *4–6*) heat-shock transcription factor fragment (Wiederrecht et al. 1987). (Lanes *1* and *4*) No protein; (lanes *2* and *5*) 12 ng factor X; (lanes *3* and *6*) 24 ng factor X.

accepted analog of higher cell DNA polymerase α, is essential for mitotic replication, there being no chromosomal synthesis without it. Therefore, polymerase II cannot compensate for a loss of DNA polymerase I for replication. Polymerase I is also essential for sporulation, but residual levels of DNA synthesis are higher in meiosis than in mitosis. X-ray repair is nearly normal in the mutants. As expected for the replicative polymerase, the *POL1* gene is expressed periodically in the cell cycle. The only detectable polymerase in the *pol1$_{ts}$* mutant is DNA polymerase II, suggesting that polymerase I and II are different entities. On the basis of our studies, we propose that DNA polymerase II of yeast is an analog of DNA polymerase δ.

We have also found that multiple proteins bind to ARS elements. We and others have carried out extensive mutational analysis of ARS1 (Celniker et al. 1984; Srienc et al. 1985; Palzkill et al. 1986), the 2 μm ARS (Broach et al. 1983), the HO ARS (Kearsey 1984), the ARS at the HMRE locus, and ARSs from *Drosophila* and human DNA. This work has identified three domains within each ARS, which have been designated A, B, and C. Domain C is the region where replication bubbles form during in vitro replication of ARS1 (Celniker and Campbell 1982), but although deletions of this domain cause a measurable defect in replication of plasmids carrying them, the effect is small. Domain A is a short stretch of nucleotides 11–19 bp, located 3′ to domain C and containing a conserved 11-bp element, element A. Point mutations in element A cause complete loss of ARS function, defining this as an essential sequence. Furthermore, a 19-bp segment of ARS1 containing only element A allows autonomous replication, albeit inefficiently, suggesting that element is both necessary and partially sufficient for ARS function. Domain B, which extends 50–100 bp 3′ to element A, also contains a conserved element, element B. Deletion of element B at ARS1 leads to severe defects in replication; element B⁻

plasmids transform at high frequency, but the doubling time of transformants is seven times that of wild type. The two conserved elements, A and B, suggest that at least two proteins may bind to ARS DNA. Finally, deletions of increasing size in domain B result in defects in increasing magnitude, suggesting that there may be more than two proteins. Thus, a eukaryotic chromosomal origin may be more complex than the prokaryotic or viral counterparts. In addition to analogs of dnaA or T antigen, other sequence-specific proteins may also bind to essential regions of eukaryotic chromosomal origins.

In the current work, we have described the identification of two proteins that bind sequence specifically within domain B of ARS1, suggesting they may be involved in replication. Both proteins bind to a sequence 3′ to the 11-bp conserved sequence, element A, based on binding competition experiments using synthetic oligonucleotides containing an ARS1 element B sequence or element A sequence. Both proteins also bind to the HMRE ARS at a sequence 3′ to element A. Further delineation of the protein binding site was achieved by DNase I footprinting. Both proteins protect a 24-bp region that is 66 bp 5′ to the T-rich strand of the ARS core sequence HMRE. This is the same region that is protected from DNase I cleavage by partially purified extracts as described by Shore et al. (1987). There is limited homology between the sequence bound 5′ to the HMRE ARS and element B of ARS1. It is therefore possible that the protein is recognizing some DNA structure that is shared by the different DNA sequences, or that the recognition sequence is not a continuous sequence of base pairs.

The fact that both the 55- and 88-kD proteins bind to the same sequence suggests they may be related; the 55-kD protein may be a proteolytic fragment of the 88-kD protein. It is also possible that they are both proteolytic fragments of a larger protein. For instance, another protein, apparently 135 kD in size, has been isolated that recognizes element B of ARS1 (J.F.X. Diffley and B. Stillman, pers. comm.).

It is tempting to speculate what role proteins that bind element B serve in yeast DNA replication. Possibly the protein is a positive regulatory factor that selects the ARS sequence for replication initiation. Once bound, the protein could act as a contact site for other replication proteins via protein-protein interactions. This would be similar to λO protein or large T antigen. λO protein binds sequence specifically and then associates with other replication proteins, such as P protein, dnaB, dnaJ, and dnaK. This protein complex is recognized by primase and can synthesize multiple primers on DNA. The large T antigen of SV40 binds to DNA polymerase α via another protein and recognizes a specific sequence of DNA (Smale and Tjian 1986). Similarly, *E. coli* or *oriC* replication initiates through the binding of dnaA to *oriC* and directly interacts with RNA polymerase.

Another attractive model is that the protein acts as a transcriptional regulator. By binding to sequences 80 ±30 bp away from the core sequence, element A, these proteins could prevent transcription through the ARS region that would interfere with DNA replication. This could be the case for the silent mating type locus HMRE, since mutations in the binding site for this protein interfere with both replication and repression of the silent *mat* locus. Furthermore, the termination of the mRNA of the *TRP* gene occurs very near element B of ARS1, and the effects on replication may be due to interference with transcription termination. Alternatively, the proteins could participate in transcriptional activation of the origin.

Another possibility is that the proteins binding to element B act as regulators of replication by preventing reinitiation at an origin that has already replicated. This would require the protein to somehow distinguish a newly replicated origin from an unreplicated origin.

The third ARS binding factor, factor X, may prove interesting when we have functional assays for ARS binding proteins. In *E. coli,* the histone-like protein HU binds to DNA without appreciable sequence specificity, yet HU can functionally complement the role of a sequence-specific DNA binding protein called IHF in λ site-specific recombination (Gardner and Nash 1986) and in recombination mediated by the bacterial insertion sequence in TN10 (Morisato and Kleckner 1987). HU and IHF show significant structural homology and therefore may have a similar local effect on the structure of DNA to which they bind, accounting for the ability of HU to carry out IHF function. More specifically, it has been proposed that HU, while apparently binding nonspecifically to DNA, may bind productively only at a limited subset of sites. That is, HU may produce different effects on DNA structure at the λatt sites and at the IS10 sites than in random DNA sequences. Factor X may be like HU protein; future studies will be aimed at investigating potential differences in the local structural effects of binding of factor X at ARSs versus binding at random loci.

References

Abraham, J., K.A. Nasmyth, J.N. Strathern, A.J.S. Klar, and J.B. Hicks. 1984. Regulation of mating-type information in yeast. *J. Mol. Biol.* **176:** 307.

Baker, T.A., B.E. Funnell, and A. Kornberg. 1987. Helicase action of dnaB protein during replication from the *Escherichia coli* chromosomal origin of replication. *J. Biol. Chem.* **262:** 6877.

Baker, T.A., K. Sekimizu, B.E. Funnell, and A. Kornberg. 1986. Extensive unwinding of the plasmid template during staged enzymatic initiation of DNA replication from the origin of the *Escherichia coli* chromosome. *Cell* **45:** 53.

Blow, J. 1987. Many strands converge. *Nature* **326:** 441.

Bravo, R., R. Frank, P.A. Blundell, and H. MacDonald-Bravo. 1987. Cyclin/PCNA is the auxiliary protein of DNA polymerase-delta. *Nature* **326:** 515.

Brewer, B. and W.L. Fangman. 1987. The localization of replication origins on ARS plasmids in *S. cerevisiae. Cell* **51:** 463.

Broach, J.R., Y. Li, J. Feldman, M. Jayaram, J. Abraham, K.A. Nasmyth, and J.B. Hicks. 1983. Localization and sequence analysis of yeast origins of DNA replication. *Cold Spring Harbor Symp. Quant. Biol.* **47:** 1165.

Budd, M. and J.L. Campbell. 1987. Temperature sensitive

mutants of yeast DNA polymerase I. *Proc. Natl. Acad. Sci.* **84:** 2838.

Campbell, J.L. 1986. Eukaryotic DNA replication. *Annu. Rev. Biochem.* **55:** 733.

Campbell, J.L., M. Budd, C. Gordon, A.Y.S. Jong, K. Sweder, A. Oehm, and M. Gilbert. 1986a. Yeast DNA replication. In *Extrachromosomal elements in lower eukaryotes* (ed. G. Fink et al.), p. 463. Plenum Press, New York.

―――. 1986b. Yeast DNA replication. *UCLA Symp. Mol. Cell. Biol. New Ser.* **47:** 265.

Celniker, S.E. and J.L. Campbell. 1982. Yeast DNA replication *in vitro:* Initiation and elongation events mimic *in vivo* processes. *Cell* **31:** 563.

Celniker, S.E., K.S. Sweder, F. Srienc, J.E. Bailey, and J.L. Campbell. 1984. Deletion mutations affecting autonomously replicating sequence ARS1 of *Saccharomyces cerevisiae. Mol. Cell. Biol.* **4:** 2455.

Chang, L.M.S. 1977. DNA polymerases from baker's yeast. *J. Biol. Chem.* **252:** 1873.

Crute, J.J., A.F. Wahl, and R.A. Bambara. 1986. Purification and characterization of two new high molecular weight forms of DNA polymerase delta. *Biochemistry* **25:** 26.

Dodson, M., J. Roberts, R. McMacken, and H. Echols. 1985. Specialized nucleoprotein structures at the origin of replication of bacteriophage lambda: Complexes with lambda-O protein and with lambda-O, lambda-P, and *Escherichia coli* dnaB proteins. *Proc. Natl. Acad. Sci.* **82:** 4678.

Dodson, M., F.B. Dean, P. Bullock, H. Echols, and J. Hurwitz. 1987. Bidirectional unwinding of duplex DNA from the SV40 origin of replication mediated by T antigen: Visualization of the reaction by electron microscopy. *Science* **238:** 964.

Dresler, S.L. and M.G. Frattini. 1986. DNA replication and UV-induced repair synthesis in human fibroblasts are much less sensitive than DNA polymerase alpha to inhibition by butylphenyl-deoxyguanosine triphosphate. *Nucleic Acids Res.* **14:** 7093.

Eki, T., Y. Murakami, T. Enomoto, F. Hanaoka, and M. Yamada. 1986. Characterization of DNA replication at a restrictive temperature in a mouse DNA temperature-sensitive mutant ts FT20 strain, containing heat-labile DNA polymerase λ activity. *J. Biol. Chem.* **261:** 8888.

Gardner, J. and H. Nash. 1986. Role of *E. coli* 1H F protein in lambda site-specific recombination: A mutational analysis of binding sites. *J. Mol. Biol.* **191:** 181.

Jong, A.Y.S., R. Aebersold, and J.L. Campbell. 1985. Multiple species of single-stranded DNA binding proteins in *Saccharomyces cerevisiae. J. Biol. Chem.* **260:** 16367.

Johnson, L.M., M. Snyder, L.M.S. Chang, R.W. Davis, and J.L. Campbell. 1985. Isolation of the gene encoding yeast DNA polymerase I. *Cell* **43:** 369.

Johnston, L.H., J.H.M. White, L. Johnson, G. Lucchini, and P. Plevani. 1987. The yeast DNA polymerase I transcript is regulated in both the mitotic cell cycle and in meiosis and is also induced after DNA damage. *Nucleic Acids Res.* **15:** 5017.

Kearsey, S. 1984. Structural requirements for the function of a yeast chromosomal replicator. *Cell* **37:** 299.

Lee, M.Y.W.T. and N.L. Toomey. 1987. Human placental DNA polymerase delta: Identification of a 170-kilodalton polypeptide by activity staining and immunoblotting. *Biochemistry* **26:** 1076.

Morisato, D. and N. Kleckner. 1987. Tn 10 transposition and circle formation *in vitro. Cell* **51:** 101.

Palzkill, T.G., S.G. Oliver, and C.S. Newlon. 1986. DNA sequence analysis of ARS elements from chromosome III of *Saccharomyces cerevisiae:* Identification of a new conserved sequence. *Nucleic Acids Res.* **14:** 6247.

Prelich, G., M. Kostura, D.R. Marshak, M.B. Mathews, and B. Stillman. 1987a. The cell-cycle regulated proliferating cell nuclear antigen is regulated for SV40 DNA replication *in vitro. Nature* **326:** 471.

Prelich, G., C.-K. Tan, M. Kostura, M.B. Mathews, A.G. So, K.M. Downey, and B. Stillman. 1987b. Functional identity of proliferating cell nuclear antigen and a DNA polymerase-delta auxiliary protein. *Nature* **326:** 517.

Shore, D., D.J. Stillman, A.H. Brand, and K.A. Nasmyth. 1987. Identification of silencer binding proteins from yeast: Possible roles in S1R control and DNA replication. *EMBO J.* **6:** 461.

Smale, S.T. and R. Tjian. 1986. T antigen-DNA polymerase alpha complex implicated in simian virus 40 DNA replication. *Mol. Cell. Biol.* **6:** 4077.

Srienc, F., J.E. Bailey, and J.L. Campbell. 1985. Effect of ARS1 mutations on chromosome stability in yeast. *Mol. Cell. Biol.* **5:** 1676.

Struhl, K., D. Stinchcomb, S. Scherer, and R.W. Davis. 1979. High frequency transformation of yeast: Autonomous replication of hybrid DNA molecules. *Proc. Natl. Acad. Sci.* **76:** 1035.

Wahl, A.F., J.J. Crute, R.D. Sabatino, J.B. Bodner, R.L. Marraccino, L.W. Harwell, E.M. Lord, and R.A. Bambara. 1986.

Properties of two forms of DNA polymerase delta from calf thymus. *Biochemistry* **25:** 7821.

Wiederrecht, G., D.J. Shuey, W.A. Kibbe, and C.S. Parker. 1987. The *Saccharomyces* and *Drosophila* heat shock transcription factors are identical in size and DNA binding properties. *Cell* **48:** 507.

Wintersberger, E. 1974. Deoxyribonucleic acid polymerases from yeast. Further purification and characterization of DNA dependent DNA polymerases A and B. *Eur. J. Biochem.* **50:** 41.

Wintersberger, U. and E. Wintersberger. 1970. Studies on deoxyribonucleic acid polymerase from yeast. *Eur. J. Biochem.* **13:** 11.

Wold, M.S., J.J. Li, and T.J. Kelly. 1987. Initiation of simian virus 40 DNA replication *in vitro*: Large tumor-, antigen-, and origin-dependent unwinding of the template. *Proc. Natl. Acad. Sci.* **84:** 3643.

Immunoaffinity Purification and Structural Characterization of the Yeast DNA Primase–DNA Polymerase Complex

M.H. Pausch, B.C. Peterson,* and L.B. Dumas
Department of Biochemistry, Molecular Biology, and Cell Biology,
Northwestern University, Evanston, Illinois 60208

Four classes of monoclonal antibodies were generated that interact with polypeptides associated with yeast DNA polymerase and DNA primase activities. All four classes immunoprecipitated both enzymes, suggesting that the enzyme activities exist as a complex. One monoclonal antibody, 24D9, was used to immunoaffinity-purify a stable enzyme fraction in higher yield and greater purity than conventionally purified preparations. The fraction contained major polypeptides of 180, 86, 70, 58, 49, and 47 kD, which were partially resolved by selective elution. DNA primase activity was primarily associated with a subfraction enriched for the 58-, 49-, and 47-kD polypeptides, suggesting that the DNA primase catalytic site is carried on these polypeptides. A subfraction containing the 180-, 86-, and 70-kD polypeptides had substantial DNA polymerase activity and nearly undetectable amounts of DNA primase activity. DNA polymerase activity was associated with the 180-kD subunit that remained bound to the immunoaffinity column, demonstrating that it is the DNA polymerase catalytic subunit. Peptide mapping analysis demonstrated that the 49- and 47-kD DNA-primase-associated polypeptides are structurally related, and analysis with antibodies showed that the 86- and 70-kD polypeptides have epitopes in common. In both cases, the smaller polypeptide is likely to be a proteolytic product of the larger. These data suggest that the yeast DNA primase–DNA polymerase complex is composed of four gene products: a 180-kD DNA polymerase polypeptide, an 86-kD polypeptide of unknown function, and 58- and 49-kD DNA-primase-associated polypeptides.

A detailed understanding of chromosome duplication in the eukaryotic cell requires an in-depth examination of the DNA primase–DNA polymerase complex. Its subunit structure and catalytic functions must be defined, and the regulation of its enzymatic activities and of the expression of its structural genes must be examined with reference to the cell's position in the cell cycle. The purified intact complex, isolated subunits, subunit-specific antibody probes, and cloned structural genes are all essential for such studies.

Several laboratories are pursuing well-focused aspects of this broad study of the DNA primase–DNA polymerase enzyme complex from baker's yeast, where the regulatory, genetic, and cell cycle studies may be easier than with more complex organisms. Our laboratory has prepared *Saccharomyces cerevisiae* protein fractions that contain this enzyme complex (Singh and Dumas 1984) and has studied RNA primer synthesis and its coupling to DNA chain extension (Singh et al. 1986). We have learned that the yeast enzyme preparation catalyzes the synthesis of discrete length RNA oligomers (8–12 nucleotides) and, in the absence of substrates for the DNA polymerase, multimers of a modal length of 11–12 nucleotides. In the presence of DNA precursors, RNA primer synthesis is tightly coupled to DNA chain extension. These studies have not yet provided a detailed understanding of this transition from RNA to DNA synthesis. Progress has been limited by the complexity and heterogeneity of the conventionally purified yeast enzyme complex and by the lack of separated catalytic activities.

We sought a better scheme to obtain a highly pure, more intact, stable enzyme complex as well as its individual, separated enzyme activities and subunits. Such a scheme is necessary for more detailed structural and functional studies. We chose to produce monoclonal antibodies against the components present in our conventionally purified protein preparations, with the intention of employing these antibodies both in immunoaffinity purification of the enzyme complex and in the characterization of its individual subunits. Immunoaffinity purification of the yeast enzyme complex has been reported (Plevani et al. 1985), but with yields below that for conventional schemes and with poor stability of the DNA primase. We have achieved improved yields of the enzyme complex relative to the conventional procedure. The enzyme activities are very stable, and the polypeptide composition reflects a more intact subunit structure. Through selective elution we have partially resolved the catalytic activities. We report here the characteristics of our monoclonal antibodies, the immunoaffinity purification protocol, and some structural features of the enzyme complex.

*Present address: Abbott Laboratories, Abbott Park, Illinois 60064.

359

Experimental Procedures

General immunological methods

Anti-mouse-IgG serum was elicited by repeated dorsal subcutaneous immunization of a rabbit with BALB/c mouse serum antibody purified by protein-A affinity (Ey et al. 1978). Each injection consisted of 100 μg of antibody in an equal volume of Freund's complete adjuvant (initial injection) or Freund's incomplete adjuvant (subsequent injections) until a high serum titer was detected by radioimmunoassay (Pierce and Klinman 1976). Blood obtained was processed by allowing clotting to occur at 37°C for 1 hour. The clot was removed by centrifugation and the serum stored at −20°C.

Ascites fluid antibodies were produced by intraperitoneal injection of 10^7 hybridoma cells into 6−12-week-old BALB/c mice (Jackson Labs or Cumberland Labs) that had been primed at least 3 days earlier by intraperitoneal injection of 0.5 ml of 2,6,10,14-tetramethylpentadecane. Ascites fluid was subsequently collected; the fluid was clarified by centrifugation and stored at −20°C in a solution of 0.2 M triethanolamine containing 50% glycerol.

Purification of DNA primase−DNA polymerase

Conventional chromatographic purification of DNA primase−DNA polymerase was carried out using a modification of the described procedure (Singh and Dumas 1984). Proteins in the S-100 fraction were selectively precipitated with $(NH_4)_2SO_4$ (29.1 g/100 ml) prior to the phosphocellulose column. The specific activities of DNA polymerase and DNA primase in the purest fraction (fraction V) were 4000 units/mg and 1000 units/mg, respectively.

Production of hybridoma cell lines

Female BALB/c mice (Jackson Labs) were immunized intraperitoneally with protein from fraction V (40 μg/mouse) emulsified with an equal volume of Freund's complete adjuvant (0.8 μl total volume per mouse). Two booster immunizations of fraction V emulsified in an equal volume of Freund's incomplete adjuvant were administered at 2-week intervals (24 μg each, 0.6 ml). Serum antibody levels were examined by radioimmunoassay 3 days after the final intraperitoneal immunization (Pierce and Klinman 1976). Mice exhibiting high serum titers were boosted intravenously with 32 μg of fraction V in 0.4 ml of 20 mM sodium phosphate, 0.1 M NaCl (pH 7.2). Immune mice were sacrificed 3 days later and spleen lymphocytes were purified by centrifugation through Ficoll gradients (Mishell et al. 1980). Enriched lymphocytes (10^8) were plated with 10^7 SP2/0 mouse myeloma cells (Schulman et al. 1978) and fused by overlaying with 50% polyethylene glycol 1450. Hybridoma colonies were selected by growth in 96-well microtiter dishes containing HAT medium (Littlefield 1964).

Polyclonal ascites fluid production

Two additional immunizations of fraction V protein emulsified in Freund's complete adjuvant (24 μg, 0.6 ml each) were administered intraperitoneally to an immune mouse prepared as described above. Ascites fluid was drained when the intraperitoneal cavity became full.

Screening hybridoma culture supernatants

We screened our hybridoma collection for the presence of antibodies that promote the immunoprecipitation of DNA primase and DNA polymerase activities by a modification of the method of Tanaka et al. (1982). Incubations were carried out at 4°C with gentle rocking. Protein-A-agarose beads (PAA) were prebound in bulk with 0.5 μl of rabbit anti-mouse antibodies (RaM) per μl of packed beads, washed with 50 mM Tris-HCl, 0.15 M KCl (pH 7.6) (TBS), and resuspended in a volume of TBS equal to the packed beads. Forty μl of RaM-PAA suspension was incubated for 2 hours with 200 μl of culture supernatant from each hybridoma colony. The beads were pelleted by centrifugation and the supernatant was removed. Fetal bovine serum (0.5 ml) was added and rocking continued for an additional hour at 4°C. The washed beads were then incubated with DNA primase−DNA polymerase fraction V (0.1 units of DNA primase and 0.4 units of DNA polymerase) in 50 μl of TBS containing 5 mg/ml bovine serum albumin. Bound DNA polymerase and DNA primase activities were swept out of solution by pelleting the DNA primase−DNA polymerase−Ab−RaM−PAA complexes. Five μl of the resulting supernatant were assayed for residual DNA polymerase or DNA primase activities as described previously (Singh and Dumas 1984). A positive result was defined as greater than 50% reduction in DNA polymerase or DNA primase activities remaining in the supernatant, as compared to control immunoprecipitations using SP2/0 culture supernatant. DNA polymerase and DNA primase activities bound to the pellet were assayed after washing as above. Hybridoma colonies yielding positive culture supernatants were cloned by limiting dilution, expanded and stored at −140°C in culture medium containing 10% (v/v) dimethylsulfoxide. The hybridoma cell lines described have been stable to repeated passages, and selected cell lines secrete antibody after storage for more than 1 year.

Immunoaffinity purification of the DNA primase−DNA polymerase complex

Yeast cell culture, cell lysis, formation of 100,000g supernatant, and phosphocellulose chromatography were performed essentially as described (Singh and Dumas 1984). Reducing agent (2-mercaptoethanol) was omitted from the phosphocellulose elution buffers to avoid damaging the immunoaffinity column. The pooled DNA primase and DNA polymerase activities eluted from phosphocellulose were applied directly to a 0.8 cm^2 × 5 cm 24D9 affinity column equilibrated in buffer A (50 mM Tris-HCl, 10% [v/v] ethylene glycol, 10 mM $Na_2S_2O_5$, 10 mM benzamidine, 2 μg/ml pepstatin A [pH 7.6]) containing 0.1 M NaCl at a linear flow rate of 40 cm/hr. The column was constructed by covalently coupling 8 mg of purified 24D9 monoclonal antibody to 4 ml of packed protein-A-Sepharose beads (Plevani et al. 1984). The column was washed at 80 cm/hr with 10-

column volumes of each of the following: buffer A containing 0.1 M NaCl, buffer A containing 1 M NaCl, and buffer A containing 0.1 M NaCl. Protein was eluted at 25 cm/hr with 10-column volumes of 50 mM Tris-HCl, 1.0 M MgCl$_2$, 10 mM benzamidine, 2 μg/ml pepstatin A (pH 7.6) followed by 10-column volumes of a solution of 3.5 M MgCl$_2$ buffered to pH 7.0 by addition of solid Tris base. MgCl$_2$ was removed by dialysis of the fractions against buffer B (buffer A containing 0.1% [v/v] Nonidet P-40, 1.0% [v/v] Triton X-100, and 5 mM 2-mercaptoethanol). The fractions were stored at −20°C after dialysis against buffer C (buffer B lacking 2-mercaptoethanol and ethylene glycol but containing 1 mM dithioerythritol and 50% [v/v] glycerol). Samples of each fraction were assayed for DNA primase and DNA polymerase activity as described (Singh and Dumas 1984).

Electrophoresis
SDS-containing denaturing polyacrylamide gels were formulated as described by Dreyfuss et al. (1984) and stained with silver (Merrill et al. 1980).

Western blot analysis of polypeptides recognized by monoclonal antibodies
Protein from the immunoaffinity-purified DNA primase–DNA polymerase fraction (250 ng per lane) was resolved in a denaturing 10% polyacrylamide gel (5 hr at 150 V) and electrophoretically transferred to nitrocellulose by application of 0.25 A for 14 hours (Towbin et al. 1979). The nitrocellulose was dissected and individual strips probed with protein-A affinity-purified monoclonal antibody preparations obtained from ascites fluid raised by injection of each positive hybridoma cell line. Bound antibodies were detected by subsequent binding of ^{125}I-goat anti-mouse IgG and autoradiography. High-molecular-weight standards resolved in the same gel, transferred to nitrocellulose, and detected by amido black staining were myosin (200 kD), β-galactosidase (116 kD), phosphorylase (92.5 kD), bovine serum albumin (66 kD), and ovalbumin (45 kD).

Partial chemical cleavage of the 58-, 49-, and 47-kD polypeptides
The 58-, 49-, and 47-kD polypeptides (1 μg of each) were applied to a denaturing 15% polyacrylamide gel and resolved by electrophoresis (100 V for 1.5 hr, then 150 V for 4 hr). The gel was stained with Coomassie blue for 30 minutes and destained. The p58, p49, and p47 bands were individually excised, transferred to separate glass test tubes, and cleaved in situ with N-chlorosuccinimide as described (Lischwe and Ochs 1982). The gel slices were forced into separate wells of a second denaturing 15% polyacrylamide gel. The peptide fragments were resolved by electrophoresis (1.5 hr at 100 V, then 17 hr at 40 V) and stained with silver. Low-molecular-weight standards electrophoresed in the same gel were ovalbumin (45 kD), carbonic anhydrase (31 kD), soybean trypsin inhibitor (21.5 kD), and lysozyme (14.4 kD).

Immunological analysis of the 180-, 86-, and 70-kD polypeptides
A sample including the 180-, 86-, and 70-kD polypeptides was applied to a denaturing 10% polyacrylamide gel and resolved by electrophoresis at 150 V for 5 hours. After 10 minutes of Coomassie-blue staining followed by brief destaining, bands containing approximately 100 ng of each polypeptide were excised and loaded into separate wells of a denaturing 10% polyacrylamide gel. After electrophoresis (5 hr at 150 V), proteins in the gel were electrophoretically transferred to nitrocellulose using 0.25 A for 12 hours (Towbin et al. 1979). The blot was first blocked with nonfat dry milk (Johnson et al. 1984), then incubated for 4 hours with anti-fraction V ascites fluid diluted 100-fold in TBS containing 5 mg/ml BSA and 0.02% NaN$_2$. Unbound antibodies were washed away. The individual lanes were dissected apart, antibodies bound to each strip were eluted with 50 mM glycine-HCl, 0.15 M NaCl (pH 2.3), and the pH of the eluate was adjusted to neutrality. The affinity-purified antibodies were then used to probe a second set of nitrocellulose strips. Each strip contained approximately 100 ng of each of the six major DNA primase–DNA polymerase polypeptide species. The strips were prepared by electrophoretic transfer (0.25 A for 12 hr) of the immunoaffinity-purified preparation resolved in a denaturing 10% polyacrylamide gel for 5 hours at 150 V. The presence of bound antibody was detected after washing by subsequent binding of ^{125}I-labeled goat anti-mouse IgG and autoradiography.

Results and Discussion

Monoclonal antibodies that immunoprecipitate DNA primase and DNA polymerase activities
Mouse hybridoma cell lines producing antibodies against yeast DNA primase–DNA polymerase fraction V (Singh and Dumas 1984) were obtained by fusion of SP2/0 mouse myeloma cells to splenic lymphocytes from immune animals. We directly screened 606 hybridoma culture supernatants for the presence of antibodies able to promote immunoprecipitation of both enzyme activities. Of the 17 cell lines which appeared to secrete appropriate antibodies, eight have been characterized in some detail. A summary of our immunoprecipitation, enzyme inhibition, and Western blot analyses is presented in Table 1.

Four classes of hybridomas were identified. All eight culture supernatants contained antibodies capable of immunoprecipitating both enzymes. Class I antibodies did not appear to inhibit either enzyme and specifically recognized a polypeptide of molecular weight approximately 180,000 (see Fig. 1). Class II antibodies similarly showed no apparent enzyme inhibition, and specifically recognized an 86-kD polypeptide (Fig. 1). Both class III and class IV antibodies were unable to recognize denatured polypeptides on Western blots. However, the class IV antibody specifically inhibited the DNA primase activity in the enzyme complex. Inhibition was dose dependent, and the extent of inhibition in solution was

Table 1 Properties of Antibodies Secreted by Hybridoma Cell Lines

Class	Hybridoma cell line	Ability of supernatant fluid to precipitate[a]		Activities detected in immune complex[b]		Polypeptides recognized on Western blots (kD)[c]
		DNA polymerase	DNA primase	DNA polymerase	DNA primase	
I	24D9,24E9	+++	+++	+	+	180
II	21D8,23E7	++	++	+	+	86
III	21G4,22E2 6H5	++	+	+	+	n.d.[d]
IV	21A6	+	+++	+	−	n.d.

[a]Measurements using culture supernatant fluids are considered to be semiquantitative. Supernatant fluid from SP2/0 cultures was used as a negative control. All culture supernatants listed were capable of immunoprecipitating at least 50% of the activity associated with one of the enzymes.

[b]The number of units of enzyme detected in the immune complex pellets usually represented a large fraction of the activity removed from the supernatant, but never all of it. Enzyme assays where activity is bound to large particles are considered semiquantitative. (−) indicates no activity detected.

[c]See Figure 1.

[d]n.d. = none detected.

approximately equivalent to the degree of immune precipitation achieved with antibody coupled to agarose beads (Fig. 2). Thus, inhibition by this antibody was due to its direct binding to the enzyme complex.

These data corroborate previous observations from our laboratory (Singh and Dumas 1984) and from

Plevani et al. (1984, 1985) demonstrating that these two yeast enzymes are part of a multisubunit complex. The 180- and 86-kD polypeptides are constituents of this enzyme complex. The class IV antibody, 21A6, recognized an antigen essential for DNA primase activity. Although this antibody did not recognize denatured polypeptides on Western blots, studies of antibody binding to separated subunits of the enzyme complex demonstrate that 21A6 antibody recognizes a component dif-

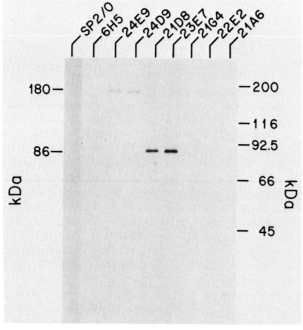

Figure 1 Recognition of immobilized DNA primase–DNA polymerase polypeptides by immunoprecipitation-positive monoclonal antibodies. Immunoaffinity-purified DNA primase–DNA polymerase was resolved by electrophoresis in a denaturing polyacrylamide gel and electrophoretically transferred to nitrocellulose. The blot was probed with monoclonal antibody preparations designated at the top. The positions of high-molecular-weight standards resolved in the same gel and transferred to nitrocellulose are presented to the right. The apparent molecular weight of each polypeptide recognized is indicated to the left.

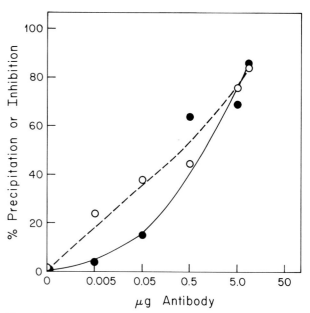

Figure 2 Immunoprecipitation and inhibition of DNA primase by the 21A6 monoclonal antibody. Inhibition was determined by assaying fraction V enzyme activity in reaction mixtures to which protein-A-affinity-purified 21A6 antibody had been added. Immunoprecipitation was measured using assays of enzyme activity in supernatants derived after pelleting antibody-antigen complexes adsorbed to protein-A-agarose beads. Addition of control antibody had no detectable effect on DNA primase activity. (●) Precipitation; (○) inhibition.

ferent from the 180- and 86-kD polypeptides (M. Brooks and L. Dumas, in prep.). Thus, the monoclonal antibody collection includes reagents recognizing at least three different components of the DNA primase–DNA polymerase complex.

Immunoaffinity purification of the DNA primase–DNA polymerase complex

A monoclonal antibody suitable for the construction of an immunoaffinity purification matrix should recognize a known, specific antigen in the enzyme complex. Its interaction with the antigen should be strong enough to provide a matrix with large capacity. Finally, the interaction should be reversible under conditions that permit the recovery of catalytic activity. The 24D9 monoclonal antibody meets these criteria. It specifically recognizes the 180-kD subunit of the enzyme complex, the DNA polymerase subunit (Plevani et al. 1985; see below). This antibody is capable of immune precipitation of most of the DNA polymerase and DNA primase from a solution of enzyme fraction V. Both enzyme activities can be recovered in acceptable yields following selective elution from the antibody matrix. The anti-DNA polymerase antibody has the additional feature of binding only those DNA priming activities physically associated with the DNA polymerase, thereby minimizing the problems associated with extraneous priming activities.

Table 2 provides a summary of the results of such an immunoaffinity purification. A high-speed supernatant of a crude yeast cell extract was chromatographed on phosphocellulose to increase the relative concentration of the DNA primase–DNA polymerase complex and reduce the level of protease contamination. This step also resulted in a substantial purification of the complex. These first two steps were similar to those in the more conventional purification scheme used earlier. The enzyme complex was efficiently adsorbed to an affinity matrix consisting of the 24D9 monoclonal antibody covalently coupled to protein-A-Sepharose. Approximately 80% of the DNA polymerase activity was routinely adsorbed to the matrix. Enzyme activities were eluted with solutions containing high concentrations of $MgCl_2$, a mildly chaotropic agent used by Plevani et al. (1984). The amount of DNA polymerase activity recovered was

approximately equivalent to that obtained in the conventional fraction V, and the specific activity was 3-fold greater. The yield of DNA primase activity was 6.5-fold greater, with a 22-fold specific activity increase compared to fraction V. In addition, whereas the ratio of DNA primase activity to that of DNA polymerase was 1/2.8 in fraction V (Singh and Dumas 1984), the immunoaffinity-purified material had a ratio of 2.6/1. This suggests loss of DNA primase during the conventional purification due to dissociation from the enzyme complex and/or proteolysis.

The DNA primase and DNA polymerase activities were partially resolved by elution with $MgCl_2$. Nearly all (97%) of the recovered DNA primase activity was eluted with 1 M $MgCl_2$; only 41% of the recovered DNA polymerase eluted under these conditions. Most of the recovered DNA polymerase activity (59%) was eluted with 3.5 M $MgCl_2$. In some experiments, the resolution of DNA primase activity from DNA polymerase by this differential elution has been even greater (M. Brooks and L. Dumas, in prep.).

Electrophoresis of the protein fractions in SDS-containing polyacrylamide gels allowed a comparison of the polypeptide compositions (see Fig. 3). The 1 M $MgCl_2$ eluate was enriched for polypeptides of 58, 49, and 47 kD, and the 3.5 M $MgCl_2$ eluate was enriched for polypeptides of 180, 86, and 70 kD. Some DNA polymerase activity and 180-kD polypeptide remained associated with the antibody matrix (data not shown). This and earlier observations (Plevani et al. 1985) demonstrate that the largest polypeptide carries the DNA polymerase catalytic site.

The DNA primase activity appears to be associated with the smaller polypeptides from the enzyme complex, as had been reported earlier by Plevani et al. (1985). Additional observations from this laboratory (M. Brooks and L. Dumas, in prep.) demonstrate that protein fractions containing only the 58-, 49-, and 47-kD polypeptides account for all of the DNA primase activity, that the 21A6 monoclonal antibody still inhibits the DNA primase activity in this subfraction, and that the same antibody immunoprecipitates these same three polypeptides. This demonstrates that these polypeptides are sufficient for the observed DNA primase activity.

Table 2 Immunoaffinity Purification of the Yeast DNA Primase–DNA Polymerase Complex

| Fraction | Protein (mg) | Priming activity | | DNA Polymerase | | Primase/ polymerase activity |
		activity (units)	specific activity (units/mg)	activity (units)	specific activity (units/mg)	
Phosphocellulose	58	13,600	230	6,300	110	2.2
Antibody column						
1.0 M $MgCl_2$ eluate		5,500		900		6.1
3.5 M $MgCl_2$ eluate		200		1,300		0.15
Pooled fraction	0.15[a]	5,700	38,000	2,200	15,000	2.6

Purification was from 400 g of yeast cells.
[a]Protein content in this fraction was estimated by comparison to known amounts of BSA after denaturing polyacrylamide gel electrophoresis and staining with silver.

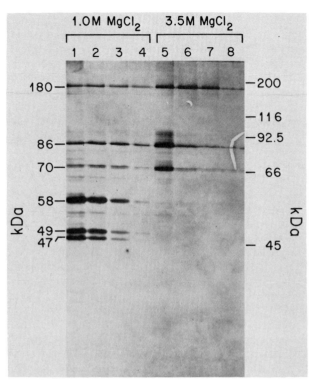

Figure 3 Analysis of polypeptides found in fractions eluted from the 24D9-immunoaffinity column. 40 μl of each fraction eluted from the 24D9-immunoaffinity column were resolved by electrophoresis in a denaturing 15% polyacrylamide gel at 100 V for 16 hr and then stained with silver. (Lanes *1–4*) Fractions eluted with 1 M MgCl$_2$; (lanes *5–8*) fractions eluted with 3.5 M MgCl$_2$. The positions of high-molecular-weight marker proteins are found on the left. The apparent molecular weights of the major proteins are displayed to the right.

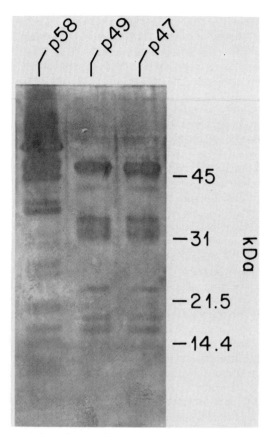

Figure 4 Peptide mapping analysis of the 58-, 49-, and 47-kD DNA primase associated polypeptides. Partial *N*-chlorosuccinimide cleavage products of the 58-, 49-, and 47-kD polypeptides were resolved by electrophoresis in a denaturing polyacrylamide gel and stained with silver. The positions of low-molecular-weight markers resolved in the same gel are displayed to the right.

Relatedness of polypeptides associated with the enzyme complex

Although six major polypeptides were identified in the highly purified DNA primase–DNA polymerase preparation, the enzyme complex might be composed of fewer than six gene products. Some of these polypeptides could be posttranslationally modified products of others; for example, proteolytic cleavage products. We employed partial chemical cleavage analysis of individual polypeptide and antibodies purified by binding to individual polypeptides to test this possibility.

The 58-, 49-, and 47-kD polypeptides were subjected to partial chemical cleavage analysis using *N*-chlorosuccinimide, which cleaves specifically at tryptophan residues (Lischwe and Sung 1977). Each was individually excised from polyacrylamide gels following electrophoresis under denaturing conditions and brief Coomassie-blue staining. Chemical cleavage restrictions were carried out in the gel slices (Lischwe and Ochs 1982). Each slice then served as the sample for a second electrophoretic separation under denaturing conditions. The final gel was stained with silver (see Fig. 4).

The partial chemical cleavage products of the 49- and 47-kD polypeptides were nearly identical, but the prod-

ucts of cleavage of the 58-kD species were different from the other two. The 58-kD species is clearly unrelated to the two smaller polypeptides, whereas the 49- and 47-kD polypeptides are structurally related. The results suggest that the 47-kD species arose from the 49-kD subunit as a result of proteolytic modification of the single gene product. Other forms of modification of the original translation product cannot be excluded by these observations.

The relatedness of the larger components associated with the enzyme complex was examined using antibodies. With enzyme fraction V as antigen we prepared mouse ascites fluid in which we detected polyclonal antibodies against the 180-, 86-, and 70-kD polypeptides and other less abundant species, but not the 58-, 49-, and 47-kD DNA-primase-associated polypeptides. Three different antibody fractions were derived from this ascites fluid based on their ability to bind to the 180-, 86-, or 70-kD polypeptides. This was accomplished by electrophoretic blotting each of the three polypeptides to nitrocellulose, adsorbing specific antibodies from the ascites fluid mixture, then separately eluting the three sets of antibodies. Each antibody subfraction was subsequently used to probe Western blots of the immuno-affinity-purified DNA primase–DNA polymerase complex. The results are displayed in Figure 5.

Antibodies purified by binding to the 86-kD polypeptide and antibodies purified by binding to the 70-kD polypeptide both recognized the 86- and 70-kD species on Western blots, but failed to recognize the 180-, 58-, or 47-kD polypeptides. The antibodies purified on the basis of their binding to the 180-kD polypeptide recognized only that species and minor degradation products on the Western blot; no recognition of the 86-kD, 70-kD, or DNA primase-associated polypeptides was detected. These results demonstrate that the 86- and 70-kD polypeptides have epitopes in common and suggest that the 70-kD species arose by proteolytic degradation of the 86-kD subunit. Neither appears to be related to the DNA primase subunits. The 180-kD polypeptide appears to be unrelated to either the 86-kD subunit or the DNA primase subunits.

Comparison with the enzyme complex from other sources

These studies suggest that the yeast DNA primase–DNA polymerase complex consists of four different subunits with molecular masses of 180, 86, 58, and 49 kD. The 180-kD subunit is the catalytic DNA polymerase, whereas the 58- and 49-kD subunits are sufficient for DNA primase activity. Neither the DNA primase catalytic polypeptide nor the antigen recognized by the 21A6 inhibitory monoclonal antibody has yet been determined. Plevani et al. (1985) found polypeptides of 180, 140, 74, 58, and 48 kD associated with a similar yeast enzyme complex; the 140-kD polypeptide appears to be a proteolytic product of the 180-kD subunit. Our studies suggest that their 74-kD species arose from the 86-kD subunit. Our ability to detect the structurally related 49- and 47-kD polypeptides, in contrast to the 48-kD species detected by Plevani et al., is most easily explained by our use of prolonged electrophoresis in 15% polyacrylamide gels. We observe a somewhat broad band of approximately 48 kD when the more conventional 10% acrylamide gel separation is used (M. Brooks and L. Dumas, unpubl.).

The protein complex isolated from yeast cells shares similarities with those isolated from other eukaryotic cells. The DNA primase–DNA polymerase complex from *Drosophila melanogaster* embryos consists of polypeptides of 182, 73, 60, and 50 kD. The largest subunit plays an essential role in DNA polymerase activity, and the DNA primase activity is associated with one or both of the two smallest subunits (Kaguni et al. 1983). Human KB cells yield a complex including a 180-kD DNA polymerase α subunit and polypeptides of 77, 55, and 49 kD (Wong et al. 1986). Partial degradation products of the 180-kD subunit are also associated with the purified fraction. The complex isolated from calf thymus includes 185-, 160-, 68-, 55-, and 48-kD polypeptides (Chang et al. 1984). Immunoblot analysis indicates that the 160-kD species is derived from the 185-kD subunit, whereas the 48-kD species appears to be derived from

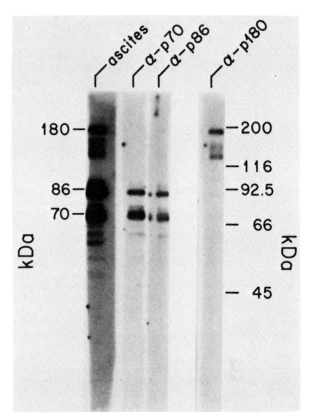

Figure 5 Immunological analysis of the 180-, 86-, and 70-kD polypeptides. Immunoaffinity-purified protein resolved in a denaturing polyacrylamide gel was blotted onto nitrocellulose, which was then cut into individual strips. Individual strips were probed with the polyclonal ascites fluid (anti-fraction V) and the subunit-specific antibody preparations (anti-p70, anti-p86, anti-p180). The positions of high-molecular-weight standards resolved in the same gel and transferred to nitrocellulose are displayed to the right. The apparent molecular weight of each polypeptide recognized is found to the left.

the 68-kD polypeptide. These studies suggest that the yeast complex will serve as a useful model for the enzymes from other eukaryotes.

We now have a well-defined, enzymatically active DNA primase–DNA polymerase complex from yeast, as well as antibodies directed against individual components of this complex. Isolation of the individual subunits can be pursued, as can detailed studies of the structure of the complex and the functions of the individual polypeptides. Studies of the regulation of enzyme activities and the control of expression of subunit structural genes will be facilitated by the cloned genes for the 180-kD subunit (Johnson et al. 1985; Lucchini et al. 1985), the 86-kD subunit (D. Hinkle, pers. comm.), and the smaller of the two DNA-primase-associated subunits (Lucchini et al. 1987).

Acknowledgments

We thank Susan K. Pierce for advice and assistance with immunological techniques and Mindy Brooks for advice with immunoaffinity purification. Soo Chang and

Kris Goltry provided technical assistance. This investigation was supported by United States Public Health Service Research grant GM-23443 (to L.B.D.) and National Research Service award GM-10579 (to B.C.P.), both from the National Institute of General Medical Sciences.

References

Chang, L.M.S., E. Rafter, C. Augl, and F.J. Bollum. 1984. Purification of a DNA polymerase-DNA primase complex from calf thymus glands. *J. Biol. Chem.* **259:** 14679.

Dreyfuss, G., S.A. Adam, and Y.D. Choi. 1984. Physical change in cytoplasmic messenger ribonucleoproteins in cells treated with inhibitors of mRNA transcription. *Mol. Cell. Biol.* **4:** 415.

Ey, P.L., S.J. Prowse, and C.R. Jenkin. 1978. Isolation of pure IgG_1, IgG_{2a} and IgG_{2b} immunoglobulins from mouse serum using protein A-Sepharose. *Immunochemistry* **15:** 429.

Johnson, D.A., J.W. Gautsch, J.R. Sportsman, and J.H. Elder. 1984. Improved technique utilizing nonfat dry milk for analysis of proteins and nucleic acids transferred to nitrocellulose. *Gene Anal. Tech.* **1:** 3.

Johnson, L.M., M. Snyder, L.M.S. Chang, R.W. Davis, and J.C. Campbell. 1985. Isolation of the gene encoding yeast DNA polymerase I. *Cell* **43:** 369.

Kaguni, L.S., J.M. Rossignol, R.C. Conaway, G.R. Banks, and I.R. Lehman. 1983. Association of DNA primase with β/γ subunits of DNA polymerase α from *Drosophila melanogaster* embryos. *J. Biol. Chem.* **258:** 9037.

Lischwe, M.A. and D. Ochs. 1982. A new method for partial peptide mapping using N-chlorosuccinimide/urea and peptide silver staining in sodium dodecyl sulfate-polyacrylamide gels. *Anal. Biochem.* **127:** 453.

Lischwe, M.A. and M.T. Sung. 1977. Use of N-chlorosuccinimide/urea for the selective cleavage of tryptophanyl peptide bonds in proteins. *J. Biol. Chem.* **252:** 4976.

Littlefield, J.W. 1964. Selection of hybrids from matings of fibroblasts in vitro and their presumed recombinants. *Science* **145:** 709.

Lucchini, G., A. Brandazza, G. Badaracco, M. Bianchi, and P. Plevani. 1985. Identification of the yeast DNA polymerase I gene with antibody probes. *Curr. Genet.* **10:** 245.

Lucchini, G., S. Francesconi, M. Foiani, G. Badaracco, and P. Plevani. 1987. Yeast DNA polymerase-DNA primase complex: Cloning of PRI 1, a single essential gene related to DNA primase activity. *EMBO J.* **6:** 737.

Merrill, C.R., D. Goldman, S.A. Sedman, and M.H. Ebert. 1980. Ultrasensitive stain for proteins in polyacrylamide gels shows regional variation in cerebrospinal fluid proteins. *Science* **211:** 1437.

Mishell, B.B., S.M. Shiigi, C. Henry, E.L. Chan, J. North, R. Gollily, M. Slomich, K. Miller, J. Marbrook, D. Parks, and A.H. Good. 1980. Centrifugation through ficoll-hypaque. In *Selected methods in cellular immunology* (ed. B.B. Mishell and S.M. Shiigi), p. 24. W.H. Freeman, San Francisco.

Pierce, S.K. and N.R. Klinman. 1976. Allogenic carrier-specific enhancement of hapten-specific secondary B-cell responses. *J. Exp. Med.* **144:** 1254.

Plevani, P., G. Badaracco, C. Augl, and L.M.S. Chang. 1984. DNA polymerase I and DNA primase complex in yeast. *J. Biol. Chem.* **259:** 7532.

Plevani, P., M. Foiani, P. Valsasnini, G. Badaracco, C. Cheriathundam, and L.M.S. Chang. 1985. Polypeptide structure of DNA primase from a yeast DNA polymerase-primase complex. *J. Biol. Chem.* **260:** 7102.

Schulman, M., C.D. Wilde, and G. Kohler. 1978. A better cell line for making hybridomas secreting specific antibodies. *Nature* **276:** 269.

Singh, H. and L.B. Dumas. 1984. A DNA primase that copurifies with the major DNA polymerase from the yeast *Saccharomyces cerevisiae*. *J. Biol. Chem.* **259:** 7936.

Singh, H., R.G. Brooke, M.H. Pausch, G.T. Williams, C. Trainor, and L.B. Dumas. 1986. Yeast DNA primase and DNA polymerase activities. An analysis of RNA priming and its coupling to DNA synthesis. *J. Biol. Chem.* **261:** 8564.

Tanaka, S., S.Z. Hu, T.S.F. Wang, and D. Korn. 1982. Preparation and preliminary characterization of monoclonal antibodies against human DNA polymerase α. *J. Biol. Chem.* **257:** 8386.

Towbin, H., T. Staehelin, and J. Gordon. 1979. Electrophoretic transfer of proteins from polyacrylamide gels to nitrocellulose sheets: Procedure and some applications. *Proc. Natl. Acad. Sci.* **76:** 4350.

Wong, S.W., L.R. Paborsky, P.A. Fisher, T.S.F. Wang, and D. Korn. 1986. Structural and enzymological characterization of immunoaffinity-purified DNA polymerase α-DNA primase complex from KB cells. *J. Biol. Chem.* **261:** 7958.

Enzymatic Activities Associated with the Polymerase Subunit of the DNA Polymerase–Primase of *Drosophila melanogaster*

S.M. Cotterill,*‡ M.E. Reyland,†§ L.A. Loeb,† and I.R. Lehman*

*Department of Biochemistry, Stanford University, Stanford, California 94305; †The Joseph Gottstein Memorial Cancer Research Laboratory, Department of Pathology SM-30, University of Washington, Seattle, Washington 98195

The 182-kD polymerase subunit of the *Drosophila* polymerase–primase can be dissociated from its other three subunits (73, 60, and 50 kD) by glycerol gradient sedimentation in the presence of 50% ethylene glycol. In contrast to the intact polymerase–primase, the isolated 182-kD subunit possesses a potent $3' \rightarrow 5'$ exonuclease activity. The $3' \rightarrow 5'$ exonuclease excises mismatched nucleotides at the 3' termini of primed synthetic and natural DNA templates. Excision of a mismatched nucleotide at the 3' terminus occurs at a tenfold greater rate than the correctly paired nucleotide. When replication fidelity is measured by the φX174 *am*3 reversion assay, the isolated polymerase subunit is at least 100-fold more accurate than either the intact polymerase–primase or a complex of the 182- and 73-kD subunits. These results suggest that the $3' \rightarrow 5'$ exonuclease serves a proofreading function during DNA replication.

The processivity of replication of primed M13 single-stranded DNA by the intact polymerase–primase is relatively low (15–30) both in the presence and absence of *Escherichia coli* single-stranded DNA binding protein (SSB). In contrast, the isolated 182-kD subunit is highly processive in the presence of SSB. Thus, DNA replication by the 182-kD polymerase subunit of the *Drosophila* polymerase–primase shows a higher fidelity and greater processivity than the intact four-subunit enzyme.

The DNA polymerase–primase of *Drosophila melanogaster* consists of four subunits with molecular weights of 182,000, 73,000, 60,000, and 50,000 (Kaguni et al. 1983a). Polymerase activity is associated with the 182-kD subunit and primase with the 60- and/or 50-kD subunits (Kaguni et al. 1983b). No activity has been identified with the 73-kD subunit. This subunit composition is very similar to that found in other eukaryotes. In fact, there is a remarkable conservation of structure between species as diverse as yeast and man, suggesting that this particular arrangement of polypeptides may be of significance in polymerase–primase function (Campbell 1986; Lehman et al. 1987).

We have recently developed a method for the dissociation of the *Drosophila* polymerase–primase into its constituent subunits to give a good yield of both polymerase and primase activities (Cotterill et al. 1987a). The availability of the separated subunits has permitted us to examine the activity of the isolated 182-kD polymerase subunit and to investigate the effect on the 182-kD subunit of its association with the other three subunits of the polymerase–primase. This report summarizes our findings.

Present addresses: ‡Department of Biochemistry, Imperial College of Science and Technology, South Kensington, London SW7 2AV, England; §Department of Pharmacological Sciences, SUNY, Stony Brook, New York 11794.

Results

Processivity and fidelity of DNA replication by polymerase–primase

The intact *Drosophila* polymerase–primase replicates DNA templates with long single-stranded stretches (≥5000 nucleotides) less efficiently than it replicates templates with relatively short single-stranded regions. For example, the polymerization rate with singly primed φX174 DNA is approximately 120 nucleotides/min/ enzyme molecule. When the single-stranded regions are of intermediate length (500–1000 nucleotides) as is the case when multi-primed φX174 DNA is used (an average of 5 primers per molecule), the polymerization rate increases to 1100 nucleotides/min/enzyme molecule (Kaguni et al. 1984). This value approaches the rate of replication fork movement in vivo (2600/min) in early cleavage embryos of *Drosophila* (Blumenthal et al. 1974). The relatively low rate of nucleotide polymerization over long single-stranded stretches may, in part, be a consequence of the relatively low degree of processivity (15–30 nucleotides polymerized/binding event) of the *Drosophila* enzyme (Villani et al. 1981).

The *Drosophila* polymerase–primase lacks a proofreading $3' \rightarrow 5'$ exonuclease activity, which in prokaryotic DNA polymerases contributes significantly to the fidelity of DNA replication (Brutlag and Kornberg 1972). Despite the absence of a $3' \rightarrow 5'$ exonuclease,

367

Table 1 Comparison of Fidelity of *Drosophila* Polymerase–Primase with *E. coli* DNA Polymerase III Holoenzyme

	Reversion frequency	
Reaction condition	polymerase–primase	Pol III holoenzyme
Unbiased pool	2.6×10^{-6} [a]	1.9×10^{-6}
A > T	1.1×10^{-4}	1.9×10^{-4}
G > A	4.1×10^{-6}	1.4×10^{-5}
G > C	3.1×10^{-6}	8.3×10^{-7}

In the unbiased pool determinations, the concentration of all four deoxynucleoside triphosphates was 40 μM. In the biased pool experiments the concentrations of the indicated nucleotides were 1000 and 10 μM, respectively. (Reprinted, with permission, from Kaguni et al. 1984.)
[a] Reversion frequency of uncopied DNA was 1.0×10^{-6}.

the *Drosophila* polymerase–primase shows a fidelity of deoxynucleotide polymerization that is nearly identical to that of *E. coli* DNA polymerase III holoenzyme (Table 1) (Kaguni et al. 1984). In these experiments, replication of singly-primed φX174 DNA was used to determine the reversion frequency of the φX174 *am3* mutation to wild type and pseudo-wild type as a result of nucleotide misincorporation during synthesis of the φX174 complement (Weymouth and Loeb 1978). To increase the sensitivity of measurement, the deoxynucleoside triphosphate pool was biased to favor misincorporation (Fersht 1979).

A similar high fidelity of DNA replication has recently been observed with the calf thymus DNA polymerase–primase purified by antibody affinity chromatography (Reyland and Loeb 1987). The earlier reports of a 10- to 100-fold lower fidelity for the calf thymus enzyme may have resulted from degradation of the enzyme during the earlier procedures used in its purification (Brosius et al. 1983; Reyland and Loeb 1987).

Fidelity of 182-kD polymerase subunit

The replication fidelity of the isolated 182-kD polymerase subunit as measured by the φX174 *am3* reversion assay is approximately 100-fold greater than that of the intact enzyme (Table 2). It is also 100-fold greater than a complex of the 182- and 73-kD subunits, suggesting that it is the interaction of the 73-kD subunit with the polymerase that reduces the fidelity of DNA replication (Cotterill et al. 1987b).

The 182-kD polymerase subunit is an exceptionally accurate enzyme. Thus, the *am3* reversion frequency is not more than twofold above background, even under conditions in which the deoxynucleoside triphosphate pool is biased 50:1 in favor of the incorrect nucleotide. This finding suggests an approximate error rate of 10^{-7}, which approaches the limits of detection in this system. This high fidelity of replication is not a consequence of a lack of extension of the primer by the polymerase. In all cases, the number of nucleotides incorporated was sufficient to copy well past the position of the *amber* codon on the template (Cotterill et al. 1987b).

Association of a $3' \rightarrow 5'$ exonuclease activity with the 182-kD polymerase subunit

Although, as noted above, the intact polymerase–primase lacks a $3' \rightarrow 5'$ exonuclease, the isolated polymerase subunit has a potent $3' \rightarrow 5'$ exonuclease activity (Table 3). The ratio of $3' \rightarrow 5'$ exonuclease to polymerase in the isolated 182-kD subunit is up to 200-fold greater than in the intact enzyme and 7- to 15-fold higher than in *E. coli* DNA polymerase I (Table 3). The absence

Table 2 Fidelity of *Drosophila* DNA Polymerase–Primase and Isolated Subunits

	Nucleotides incorporated per template molecule	Phage titer		Reversion frequency ($\times 10^{6}$)
		am3 ($\times 10^{-6}$)	wild type ($\times 10^{-2}$)	
Experiment 1				
Polymerase–primase	20	39.5	20.1	49.4
182-kD subunit	10	170	3.4	0.5
182-kD/73-kD complex	22	171.5	158.3	90.8
Experiment 2				
Polymerase–primase	n.d.[a]	32	36	110
182-kD subunit	n.d.	180	3	0.8
182-kD/73-kD complex	n.d.	95	106	109

The deoxynucleoside triphosphate pool was biased to promote misincorporation; dATP was added at 1000 μM; dCTP, dGTP, and [^{32}P]dTTP were at 20 μM. (Reprinted, with permission, from Cotterill et al. 1987.)
[a] n.d. indicates not determined.

Table 3 Exonuclease Activity of *Drosophila* DNA Polymerase–Primase and the Isolated 182-kD Subunit

Enzyme	DNA polymerase activity units	3′-Terminal nucleotide rendered acid-soluble (pmol)		
		mismatched		matched
		[³H]dC	[³H]dA	[³H]dT
Preparation 1				
Polymerase–primase	0.03	<0.5	<0.5	1.0
182-kD subunit	0.009	14.2	40.0	3.8
Preparation 2				
Polymerase–primase	0.06	0.9	1.2	n.d.[a]
182-kD subunit	0.009	11.1	34.5	4.5
E. coli DNA polymerase I	0.20	36.9	31.9	n.d.

The substrates used were: Mismatched, $(dA)_{3000}(dT)_{46}[^3H]dC_1$, and $(dA)_{3000}(dT)_{46}[^3H]dA_1$. Matched: $(dA)_{3000}(dT)_{46}[^3H]dT_1$. The 182-kD subunit was isolated as described in Cotterill et al. (1987). (Reprinted, with permission, from Cotterill et al. 1987.)

[a]n.d. indicates not determined.

of exonuclease activity in the intact enzyme is not the result of a dissociable inhibitor, since addition of a 100-fold excess of polymerase–primase to the 182-kD subunit had no effect on its exonuclease activity.

DNA polymerase and $3' \rightarrow 5'$ exonuclease activities comigrate perfectly with the 182-kD subunit during glycerol gradient sedimentation, indicating that the two activities reside in the same 182-kD polypeptide (Cotterill et al. 1987b).

The $3' \rightarrow 5'$ exonuclease activity associated with the polymerase subunit shows all the hallmarks of a proofreading exonuclease. Thus, the rate of excision of a mismatched 3′ terminal nucleotide is 3- to 10-fold greater than a correctly matched nucleotide. Moreover, a mismatched A is excised at a 3-fold greater rate than a mismatched C residue. *E. coli* DNA polymerase I does not show this preference.

The template-dependent conversion of a deoxynucleoside triphosphate to the monophosphate (deoxynucleoside triphosphate turnover) is a manifestation of coupled $5' \rightarrow 3'$ polymerization and $3' \rightarrow 5'$ exonuclease action by a DNA polymerase (Kornberg 1980). In agreement with an earlier report, the *Drosophila* polymerase–primase showed no detectable turnover of dTTP (Kaguni et al. 1984). In contrast, the isolated 182-kD subunit shows substantial dTTP turnover (Table 4). The level of turnover is approximately 5-fold greater than *E. coli* DNA polymerase I, a value that is consistent with the 5- to 7-fold higher $3' \rightarrow 5'$ exonuclease activity of the 182-kD polymerase subunit (see Table 3).

These findings strongly suggest that the 100-fold increase in replication fidelity of the 182-kD subunit is a consequence of a cryptic $3' \rightarrow 5'$ proofreading exonuclease that is activated upon dissociation from the polymerase–primase. Inasmuch as a complex of the 182- and 73-kD subunits shows the same replication fidelity as the intact four-subunit enzyme, the 73-kD subunit may serve to mask the $3' \rightarrow 5'$ exonuclease activity.

Increased processivity of the 182-kD subunit

As noted above, the *Drosophila* DNA polymerase–primase, like comparable eukaryotic enzymes, shows a relatively low degree of processivity when replicating singly primed circular single-stranded DNA templates. Coating of the DNA with the *E. coli* SSB has little if any effect on the rate or processivity of polymerization (Cotterill et al. 1987a). The processivity of the 182-kD polymerase subunit is also low; however, addition of *E. coli* SSB to the single-stranded DNA converts the 182-kD subunit into a highly processive form of the enzyme. As shown in Figure 1, nearly full-length products are synthesized even at early time points. A more detailed analysis of the products revealed that almost all of the pause sites had been abolished under these conditions. Furthermore, the rate of DNA synthesis is significantly increased (Cotterill et al. 1987a). The stimulation in the rate and processivity of replication by the 182-kD subunit reaches saturation at a ratio of nucleotide:SSB of

Table 4 dTTP Turnover by Intact *Drosophila* DNA Polymerase–Primase and 182-kD Subunit

Enzyme	dTMP incorporated (pmol)	dTMP released (pmol)	dTTP turnover[a] (%)
Polymerase–primase	2.6	<0.1	<0.1
	5.0	<0.1	<0.1
	9.6	<0.1	<0.1
182-kD subunit	1.9	0.9	32.1
	4.2	2.1	33.0
	8.9	5.4	37.8
E. coli DNA polymerase I	53.3	3.8	6.6

The 182-kD subunit was isolated as described in Cotterill et al. (1987a).

[a]Measurements of dTTP turnover were performed as described in Kaguni et al. (1984).

$$\frac{\text{dTMP released}}{\text{dTMP incorporated} + \text{dTMP released}} \times 100$$

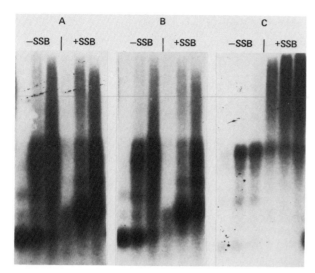

Figure 1 Processivity of 182-kD polymerase subunit in the presence of *E. coli* SSB. (*A*) The intact polymerase–primase, (*B*) the complex of 182-kD and 73-kD subunits, and (*C*) the isolated 182-kD subunit. The template used was M13mp8 single-stranded DNA primed with a synthetic 15-mer that extended from map position 1361–1376. SSB was present at a ratio of 8 nucleotides:SSB monomer. Samples were taken at 5, 15, and 60 minutes and subjected to alkaline agarose gel electrophoresis. (Reprinted, with permission, from Cotterill et al. 1987a.)

8–10:1, an amount sufficient to saturate the φX174 single-stranded DNA template with SSB (Lohman and Overman 1985).

Discussion

The isolated 182-kD polymerase subunit of the *Drosophila* polymerase–primase has a potent proofreading 3′ → 5′ exonuclease and shows a high fidelity of DNA replication. Furthermore, its replication of primed single-stranded DNA templates coated with SSB is highly processive. None of these features, which are very desirable in an enzyme that must quickly and faithfully replicate the *Drosophila* genome, are found in the intact four-subunit enzyme. The finding that the fidelity and processivity of a complex of the 182-kD polymerase and 73-kD subunits are indistinguishable from the intact enzyme suggests that it is the 73-kD polypeptide that masks the 3′ → 5′ exonuclease activity and lowers the fidelity and processivity of deoxynucleotide polymerization. Possibly the 73-kD polypeptide performs a regulatory function during DNA replication in vivo.

A novel eukaryotic DNA polymerase, DNA polymerase δ, has recently been implicated in SV40 and chromosomal DNA replication (Bravo et al. 1987; Prelich et al. 1987). An important feature of the DNA polymerase δ purified from rabbit bone marrow and calf thymus, and that which distinguishes it from the α polymerase, is the presence of a 3′ → 5′ exonuclease (Byrnes et al. 1976; Lee et al. 1984; Crute et al. 1986). Our finding that the α polymerase of *Drosophila*, the DNA polymerase–primase, contains a potent, albeit cryptic, 3′ → 5′ exonu-

clease indicates that the existence of this activity can no longer be a distinguishing characteristic of DNA polymerase δ.

Acknowledgments

This work was supported by grants from the National Institutes of Health (GM-06196 and AGO-2908 to I.R.L. and R35-CA39903 to L.A.L.). M.E.R. was supported by postdoctoral fellowships from the National Institutes of Health (CA-07658, CA-09437) and S.M.C. was supported by a SERC NATO Fellowship.

References

Blumenthal, A.B., H.J. Kreigstein, and D.S. Hogness. 1974. The units of DNA replication in *Drosophila melanogaster* chromosomes. *Cold Spring Harbor Symp. Quant. Biol.* **38:** 205.

Bravo, R., R. Frank, P.A. Blundell, and H. Macdonald-Bravo. 1987. Cyclin/PCNA is the auxiliary protein of DNA polymerase-δ. *Nature* **326:** 515.

Brosius, S., F. Grosse, and G. Krauss. 1983. Subspecies of DNA polymerase α from calf thymus with different fidelity in copying synthetic template primers. *Nucleic Acids Res.* **11:** 193.

Brutlag, D. and A. Kornberg. 1972. Enzymatic synthesis of deoxyribonucleic acid. XXXVI. A proofreading function for the 3′ → 5′ exonuclease in deoxyribonucleic acid polymerase. *J. Biol. Chem.* **247:** 241.

Byrnes, J.J., K.M. Downey, V.L. Blank, and A.G. So. 1976. A new mammalian DNA polymerase with 3′ to 5′ exonuclease activity: DNA polymerase δ. *Biochemistry* **15:** 2817.

Campbell, J.L. 1986. Eukaryotic DNA replication. *Annu. Rev. Biochem.* **55:** 733.

Cotterill, S.M., G. Chui, and I.R. Lehman. 1987a. DNA polymerase-primase from embryos of *Drosophila melanogaster*. The DNA polymerase subunit. *J. Biol. Chem.* **262:** 16100.

Cotterill, S.M., M.E. Reyland, L.A. Loeb, and I.R. Lehman. 1987b. A cryptic proofreading of 3′ → 5′ exonuclease associated with the polymerase subunit of the DNA polymerase-primase from *Drosophila melanogaster*. *Proc. Natl. Acad. Sci.* **84:** 5635.

Crute, J.J., A.F. Wahl, and R.A. Bambara. 1986. Purification and characterization of two new high molecular weight forms of DNA polymerase delta. *Biochemistry* **25:** 26.

Fersht, A. 1979. Fidelity of replication of phage φX174 DNA by DNA polymerase III holoenzyme: Spontaneous mutation by misincorporation. *Proc. Natl. Acad. Sci.* **76:** 4946.

Kaguni, L.S., R.A. DiFrancesco, and I.R. Lehman. 1984. The DNA polymerase-primase from *Drosophila melanogaster* embryos. Rate and fidelity of polymerization on single-stranded DNA templates. *J. Biol. Chem.* **259:** 9314.

Kaguni, L.S., J.-M. Rossignol, R.C. Conaway, and I.R. Lehman. 1983a. Isolation of an intact polymerase-primase from embryos of *Drosophila melanogaster*. *Proc. Natl. Acad. Sci.* **80:** 2221.

Kaguni, L.S., J.-M. Rossignol, R.C. Conaway, G.R. Banks, and I.R. Lehman. 1983b. Association of DNA primase with β/γ subunits of DNA polymerase α from *Drosophila melanogaster* embryos. *J. Biol. Chem.* **258:** 9037.

Kornberg, A. 1980. *DNA replication.* W.H. Freeman, San Francisco.

Lee, M.Y.W.T., C.-K. Tan, K.M. Downey, and A.G. So. 1984. Further studies on calf thymus DNA polymerase δ purified to homogeneity by a new procedure. *Biochemistry* **23:** 1906.

Lehman, I.R., R.A. DiFrancesco, L.S. Kaguni, and S. Cotterill. 1987. Assembly of a DNA replication complex from *Drosophila melanogaster* embryos. *UCLA Symp. Mol. Cell. Biol. New Ser.* **47:** 89.

Lohman, T. and L.B. Overman. 1985. Two binding modes in *Escherichia coli* single strand binding protein-single-stranded DNA complexes. Modulation by NaCl concentration. *J. Biol. Chem.* **260:** 3194.

Prelich, G., C.-K. Tan, M. Kostura, M.B. Mathews, A.G. So, K.M. Downey, and B. Stillman. 1987. Functional identity of proliferating cell nuclear antigen and a DNA polymerase δ auxiliary protein. *Nature* **326:** 517.

Reyland, M.E. and L.A. Loeb. 1987. On the fidelity of DNA replication. Isolation of high fidelity DNA polymerase-primase complexes by immunoaffinity chromatography. *J. Biol. Chem.* **262:** 10824.

Villani, G., P.J. Fay, R.A. Bambara, and I.R. Lehman. 1981. Elongation of RNA-primed DNA templates by DNA polymerase α from *Drosophila melanogaster* embryos. *J. Biol. Chem.* **256:** 8202.

Weymouth, L.A. and L.A. Loeb. 1978. Mutagenesis during *in vitro* DNA synthesis. *Proc. Natl. Acad. Sci.* **75:** 1924.

A Multiprotein DNA Polymerase α Complex from HeLa Cells: Interaction with Other Proteins in DNA Replication

E.F. Baril, L.H. Malkas, R. Hickey, C.J. Li, J.K. Vishwanatha,*
and S. Coughlin[†]

Cell Biology Group, Worcester Foundation for Experimental Biology,
Shrewsbury, Massachusetts 10545

DNA polymerase α from HeLa cells was previously isolated as a 10S multiprotein complex (Vishwanatha et al. 1986a). The complex purified to near homogeneity has a molecular mass of 640 kD and is formed by at least eight proteins. The catalytic or modulating functions of five of the proteins have been defined. The multiprotein DNA polymerase α complex from the combined low salt (0.15 M KCl) nuclear extract-postmicrosomal supernatant (NE-PMS) of HeLa cells sediments as a 16S multienzyme complex with associated topoisomerase I, RNase H, and DNA-dependent ATPase activities. The multienzyme complex is separated from a nonsedimentable fraction of these enzymes in which the polymerase α is 8S. All of the T-antigen-dependent activity for the in vitro replication of SV40 DNA resides with the 16S multienzyme complex. The 16S multienzyme complex may have physiological relevance, therefore, in DNA replication in vivo.

DNA polymerase α is the major DNA polymerase in proliferating animal cells and is considered to be the primary polymerase involved in chromosome replication (DePamphilis and Wassarman 1980; Kornberg 1980, 1982; Campbell 1986; Fry and Loeb 1986). During the past few years it has become more apparent that this enzyme exists as a multiprotein complex analogous to the elegantly characterized DNA replicase (pol III) holoenzyme of *Escherichia coli* (Kornberg 1980, 1982). Through the development of improved purification procedures, multiprotein forms of DNA polymerase α have been purified to near homogeneity from *Drosophila melanogaster* embryos (Kaguni et al. 1983a), HeLa cells (Vishwanatha et al. 1986a), and calf thymus (Ottiger et al. 1987) by conventional purification procedures. Multiprotein forms of DNA polymerase α have also been isolated from KB cells (Wang et al. 1984), as well as DNA polymerase I (the polymerase α counterpart) from yeast (Plevani et al. 1984) by immunoaffinity chromatography. Although the structure-function relationships of the subunits of the DNA polymerase α complexes in eukaryotes is not yet as thoroughly characterized as for the prototype DNA polymerase III holoenzyme in *E. coli*, there are some similarities, as well as variations on the theme. There is now general agreement that the DNA polymerase α catalytic subunit is a single polypeptide of 160,000 to 200,000 daltons in molecular size (Fry and Loeb 1986). The previous low-molecular-weight forms of multiple polypeptides were apparently a result of proteolysis. For a number of years it was considered

that DNA polymerase α, unlike the prokaryotic DNA polymerases, lacked an associated 3′ → 5′ exonuclease activity (DePamphilis and Wassarman 1980; Kornberg et al. 1980; Campbell 1986; Fry and Loeb 1986). However, a 3′ → 5′ exonuclease activity has been demonstrated recently with highly purified, multiprotein forms of DNA polymerase α from HeLa cells (Skarnes et al. 1986), calf thymus (Ottiger et al. 1987), and *Drosophila* embryos (Cotterill et al. 1987). The discovery of the association of DNA primase with DNA polymerase α in *Drosophila* embryos (Conway and Lehman 1982) and mouse cells (Tseng and Ahlem 1983; Yagura et al. 1983) was a departure from the paradigm DNA polymerase holoenzymes in prokaryotes (Kornberg 1980). The association of DNA primase with DNA polymerase α from a variety of eukaryotic cell types has now been reported (Kaguni et al. 1983a,b; Chang et al.1984; Gronostajski et al. 1984; Plevani et al. 1984; Wang et al. 1984; Vishwanatha and Baril 1986; Ottiger et al. 1987).

We have isolated a 640-kD multiprotein form of DNA polymerase α from HeLa cells that has been purified to near homogeneity (Lamothe et al. 1981; Vishwanatha et al. 1986a). In addition to DNA polymerase α, this complex has associated DNA primase and 3′ → 5′ exonuclease activities plus accessory proteins that function with the polymerase α subunit for synthesis on primed single-stranded DNA templates. The multiprotein complex is composed of at least eight subunits and the functions of five of these have been identified and partially characterized over the past few years (Lamothe et al. 1981; Pritchard et al. 1983; Skarnes et al. 1986; Vishwanatha et al. 1986a). In addition to characterizing the 640-kD DNA polymerase α complex, we have been investigating the possible interaction of this complex with other proteins involved in DNA replication. In this

Present addresses: *Department of Biochemistry, University of Nebraska Medical Center, Omaha, Nebraska 68105; [†]Department of Microbiology, Sterling-Winthrop Research Institute, Rensselaer, New York 12144.

373

paper, after a brief summary of the published evidence for the structure of the 640-kD multiprotein DNA polymerase α complex, we present our studies on the isolation of this complex as a 16S multienzyme complex for DNA replication from HeLa cell extracts. This higher order multienzyme complex is competent in the in vitro replication of SV40 DNA in the presence of T antigen and, therefore, may have relevance to the DNA synthesizing machinery in vivo.

Methods

Enzyme purifications

The purification of the multiprotein form of DNA polymerase α from the combined NE-PMS of exponentially growing HeLa cells in culture was by modification (L.H. Malkas et al., in prep.) of a previously published procedure (Vishwanatha et al. 1986a). For most of the experiments that are described here, the NE-PMS was further subfractionated according to the scheme outlined in Figure 2. The NE-PMS fraction was adjusted to 2 M in KCl concentration and polyethylene glycol 8000 was added to a concentration of 5% (w/v) with constant stirring at 4°C. The suspension was centrifuged at 16,000g (Sorvall, SS-34 rotor) for 30 minutes, and the resulting supernatant was dialyzed against 50 mM Tris-HCl (pH 7.5)/0.15 M KCl/1 mM dithiothreitol (DTT)/1 mM EDTA/1 mM EGTA/1 mM aminoacetonitrilehemisulfate (AAN)/1 mM phenylmethyl sulfonyl fluoride (PMSF) (buffer A) containing 0.25 M sucrose. The dialyzed fraction was clarified by centrifugation (13,000g for 10 min), overlayered onto a cushion of 2 M sucrose in buffer A and subjected to discontinuous gradient centrifugation at 241,200g (VTi 50 rotor) for 4.75 hours at 4°C. Following the centrifugation, the supernatant solution (S-4 fraction) and the 2 M sucrose interphase (P-4 fraction) were successively removed by aspiration. The P-4 fraction was equilibrated with 50 mM Tris-HCl (pH 7.5)/50 mM KCl/1 mM DTT/1 mM EDTA/1 mM AAN/ 1mM PMSF/10% glycerol (buffer B) by dialysis and was loaded onto a DEAE (DE-52)-cellulose column that was coupled in descending order to native and denatured DNA-cellulose columns equilibrated with buffer B as described previously (Vishwanatha et al. 1986a). The columns were successively eluted with 2-column volumes of buffer A containing 10% glycerol. The effluent from the denatured DNA-cellulose column was dialyzed against buffer A and chromatographed on DEAE-BioGel as described previously (Vishwanatha et al. 1986a).

For chromatography of the P-4 and S-4 fractions on Q-Sepharose, the respective fractions were first equilibrated with buffer B by dialysis, loaded onto columns of Q-Sepharose that were equilibrated with buffer B and the columns were washed with 8-column volumes of the equilibration buffer. Following the wash, the columns were eluted by a continuous gradient of increasing KCl concentration from 0.05 to 0.5 M in buffer A.

The DNA polymerase-α₂-associated AT-specific binding protein was isolated by chromatography on oligo(dT)-cellulose (L. Malkas and E. Baril, in prep.).

The matrix was pre-equilibrated with 50 mM Tris-HCl (pH 7.5)/1 mM DTT/1 mM EDTA/10% glycerol (buffer C). After loading of the DNA polymerase-α₂-containing fraction from DEAE-BioGel (Vishwanatha et al. 1986a), the column was washed with 10-column volumes of the equilibration buffer and eluted by a continuous gradient of increasing KCl concentration from 0.2 M to 0.5 M in buffer C.

Enzyme assays

DNA polymerase α activity with activated and primed single-stranded DNA templates (Lamothe et al. 1981), DNA primase (Vishwanatha and Baril 1986), and DNA polymerase-α-associated 3′ → 5′ exonuclease activity were assayed according to published procedures (Skarnes et al. 1986). The AT sequence binding protein was routinely assayed by retention of [³H]poly(dT) or [³H]poly(dA) on nitrocellulose filters (L. Malkas and E. Baril, in prep.). DNA-dependent ATPase activity was assayed by measurement of the conversion of [γ-³²P]ATP to charcoal nonadsorbable form in the presence of heat-denatured DNA (J.K. Vishwanatha and E.F. Baril, in prep.). Ribonuclease H activity was assayed by the conversion of [³H]poly(A) to acid-soluble material using [³H]poly(A)·poly(dT) as substrate (S. Coughlin and E. Baril, unpubl.). Type I and type II DNA topoisomerase activities were assayed according to published procedures (Liu and Miller 1981; Miller et al. 1981).

DNA replication assay

T antigen and SV40 *ori*-dependent DNA replication in vitro was carried out according to the procedure of Li and Kelly (1984) using pJL0 or pSV01 DNAs and subfractions of HeLa cell extracts as discussed with the individual experiments. SV40 large T antigen was purified from CV-1 cells infected with SV40 cs1085. The purification was by immunoaffinity chromatography according to the procedure of Simanis and Lane (1985) using the PAb 419 monoclonal antibody against SV40 T antigen.

Results

Multiprotein DNA polymerase α complex from HeLa cell

The procedure for the isolation and purification of the multiprotein DNA polymerase α complex from HeLa cells was designed to isolate the majority of the polymerase α from cells in a multiprotomeric form by minimizing proteolysis and to select for proteins that have a higher affinity among themselves than for native or denatured DNA. A low-salt (0.15 M KCl) extract of isolated nuclei plus the postmicrosomal supernatant solution of a cell homogenate was used as the starting material for the isolation, since we had established that most of the DNA polymerase activity that functions with primed single-strand DNA templates and DNA primase activities is extracted under these conditions (Vishwanatha et al. 1986a).

The initial steps in the purification, therefore, involved chromatography of the combined NE-PMS solution on a DEAE-cellulose column (Vishwanatha et al. 1986a). After loading and washing with the equilibration buffer (50 mM Tris-HCl [pH 7.5] / 1 mM EDTA / 1 mM DTT / 10% glycerol), the column was coupled in series to columns of native and denatured DNA-cellulose and eluted with the equilibration buffer containing 0.15 M KCl. The effluent from the denatured DNA-cellulose column contained the majority of the DNA polymerase α and DNA primase activities (more than 70%) that were applied to the DEAE-cellulose column. When the eluted fraction was chromatographed on DEAE-BioGel, most of the DNA polymerase activity was eluted by 0.15 M KCl, whereas a minor fraction (about 10%) of DNA polymerase activity eluted at 0.3 M KCl. These polymerases were designated DNA polymerase α_2 and α_3, respectively, based on their order of elution (Lamothe et al. 1981). DNA polymerase α_2 functions with equal efficiency with primed single-stranded DNA templates and activated DNA and has associated DNA primase and an exonuclease activity that is specific for single-stranded DNA substrates. DNA polymerase α_3 lacks these associated activities and functions only with activated DNA as a template. Preparative gel electrophoresis of DNA polymerase α_2 under nondenaturing conditions followed by gel transfer experiments under nondenaturing conditions showed that the DNA polymerase α activities with primed single-stranded and activated DNA templates, DNA primase, and exonuclease activities all reside with a single protein band of 640 kD (Lamothe et al. 1981; Vishwanatha et al. 1986a). It is noteworthy that activity gel analysis of crude HeLa cell extracts under nondenaturing conditions has also recently shown that the DNA polymerase α activity resides with a 640-kD protein band (Holler et al. 1985). Also, immunoblot analysis of the P-4 subfraction of the NE-PMS (Fig. 2) under nondenaturing conditions using the monoclonal antibody (SJK 132-20) to human DNA polymerase α showed a single, strong 500-kD band (N. Pedersen et al., unpubl.).

Gel transfer experiments under denaturing conditions of the 640-kD protein from nondenaturing gel electrophoresis showed a complex polypeptide subunit structure (Table 1). This consists of 10 polypeptides in the molecular size range of 183, 70, 69, 52, 47, 35, 25, and 15 kD (Vishwanatha et al. 1986a). This complex subunit structure has also been recently observed for the holoenzyme form of DNA polymerase α from calf thymus (Ottiger et al. 1987) and is in general agreement with the subunit structures of DNA polymerase α–primase complexes purified from KB cells (Wang et al. 1984) and calf thymus (Chang et al. 1984) by immunoaffinity chromatography.

Resolution and purification of the subunits of the multiprotein DNA polymerase α complex

An analysis of the dissociation of the subunits and the activities associated with the multiprotein DNA polymerase α complex under conditions that disrupt electrostatic and hydrophobic interactions indicated that the association was predominantly due to hydrophobic interactions (Vishwanatha et al. 1986a). Thus, we utilized hydrophobic affinity chromatography as an initial step to resolve the components of the multiprotein DNA polymerase α complex (Lamothe et al. 1981; Baril et al. 1983; Vishwanatha and Baril 1986; Vishwanatha et al. 1986a). The separated subunits were further purified to homogeneity in some cases by conventional enzyme purification procedures.

Chromatography of the 640-kD multiprotein complex on butylagarose separates the hydrophobic 94-kD subunit (Baril et al. 1983) and the exonuclease activity (Skarnes et al. 1986) that appears in the column wash from a DNA polymerase α–primase-C1,C2 accessory protein complex that is eluted by 0.1% Triton X-100 (Lamothe et al. 1981; Vishwanatha et al. 1986a). The 94-kD subunit was shown to specifically bind the unique dinucleotide, diadenosine-5′·5′′′ P_1,P_4-tetraphosphate (Ap$_4$A), (Zamecnik 1983) and through photoaffinity labeling was shown to be composed of two identical 47-kD subunits (Table 1) (Baril et al. 1983). The binding of Ap$_4$A, however, has no significant effect on the catalytic activity of the DNA polymerase, primase, or

Table 1 Subunits of the 640-kD DNA Polymerase α Complex from HeLa Cells

Native molecular size (kD)	Subunits	Function	Reference
183	1	DNA polymerase α catalytic subunit	Vishwanatha et al. (1986a); SenGupta et al. (1987)
92	1	unknown	
70	1	primase	Vishwanatha and Baril (1986)
69	1	3′ → 5′ exonuclease	Skarnes et al. (1986)
52	1	accessory protein (C2), primer recognition	Lamothe et al. (1981); Pritchard et al. (1983); Vishwanatha et al. (1986a)
94	2	unknown (binds Ap$_4$A)	Baril et al. (1983)
96	4	accessory protein (C1), primer recognition	Lamothe et al. (1981); Pritchard et al. (1983); Vishwanatha et al. (1986a)

exonuclease activities in vitro. Thus, the actual physiological function of the 94-kD subunit remains unknown. The single-stranded DNA-specific exonuclease activity was purified to homogeneity and this activity was shown to reside with the 69-kD subunit (Skarnes et al. 1986) (Table 1). The enzyme specifically hydrolyzes single-stranded DNA substrates by a nonprocessive mechanism, and hydrolysis proceeds predominantly from the $3' \rightarrow 5'$ direction but with a low activity from $5' \rightarrow 3'$ direction. The exonuclease can remove single-mismatched bases in an elongating DNA strand and is a candidate for a proofreading activity associated with the multiprotein DNA polymerase α complex (Skarnes et al. 1986).

The DNA primase activity of the 640-kD multiprotein DNA polymerase α complex can be resolved from polymerase α by successive steps in chromatography on phenylSepharose and hexylagarose (Vishwanatha and Baril 1986). The DNA primase activity appears in the low-salt eluate of the column, whereas polymerase α binds tightly and requires 0.05% taurodeoxycholate for its elution. Further purification of the DNA primase by chromatography on columns of phosphocellulose and Cibacron blue agarose followed by glycerol gradient centrifugation results in primase activity that is more than 90% pure. Analysis of the peak of primase activity from the glycerol gradient by SDS-polyacrylamide gel electrophoresis showed a major protein band of 70 kD (Vishwanatha and Baril 1986). The assignment of DNA primase to the 70-kD polypeptide (Table 1), however, must remain tentative at this time since the labile nature of free primase did not permit the analysis of its activity by nondenaturing gel electrophoresis.

The 183-kD polypeptide of the multiprotein DNA polymerase α complex represents the polymerase α catalytic subunit (Table 1). Polyclonal antibody to the 183-kD polypeptide that had been isolated by preparative SDS-polyacrylamide gel electrophoresis was prepared in rabbits (Vishwanatha et al. 1986a). The antibody specifically reacts with the 183-kD polypeptide in immunoblot analysis of the multiprotein complex (Vishwanatha et al. 1986a; SenGupta et al. 1987) and specifically neutralizes DNA polymerase α activity (SenGupta et al. 1987). The antibody also reacted strongly and specifically with a 183-kD polypeptide during immunoblot analysis of crude HeLa cell extracts, although a second much weaker bank of 230 kD was observed at higher levels of the extract (SenGupta et al. 1987).

The 24-kD and 52-kD polypeptides of the 640-kD multiprotein polymerase α complex represent the C1 and C2 accessory proteins, respectively (Table 1), that were previously reported for HeLa (Lamothe et al. 1981) and CV-1 cells (Pritchard and DePamphilis 1983). In the native state, the C1 protein exists as a tetramer of identical 24-kD subunits, whereas the C2 protein is a single 52-kD subunit (Lamothe et al. 1981; Vishwanatha et al. 1986a). We had shown that both the C1 and C2 proteins are required for DNA polymerase α to function with primed single-stranded DNA templates. This activity could be reconstituted in vitro using the isolated DNA

polymerase α and C1 and C2 proteins (Lamothe et al. 1981). These accessory proteins were also shown to exist in association with DNA polymerase α from CV-1 cells (Pritchard and DePamphilis et al. 1983). In that case also, a functionally active DNA polymerase α–C1,C2 protein complex could be reconstituted from the isolated proteins. It was shown that the CV-1 and HeLa cell C1,C2 proteins in the presence of DNA templates having a high ratio of single-stranded DNA template to DNA or RNA primers increased the rate of DNA synthesis by decreasing the K_m for the primer about 50- to 100-fold (Pritchard et al. 1983). Thus, it was proposed that the C1,C2 accessory proteins function as primer recognition proteins by preventing nonproductive binding of DNA polymerase to single-stranded DNA templates.

Proteins other than the 640-kD DNA polymerase α complex in the DNA polymerase α_2 fraction

The DNA polymerase α_2 fraction that is eluted from DEAE-BioGel contains several proteins in addition to the 640-kD multiprotein DNA polymerase α complex. These proteins do not comigrate with the 640-kD DNA polymerase α complex during its purification by preparative gel electrophoresis under nondenaturing conditions. Whether some of these proteins interact specifically with the multiprotein polymerase α complex as part of a loosely associated DNA replication complex, as has been elegantly demonstrated for prokaryotes (Kornberg 1980, 1982; Alberts 1985), remains to be seen. Most of the proteins are separated from the DNA polymerase α complex during further stages of purification using conventional purification procedures. RNase H and protein kinase (casein type II) activities (Table 2) cofractionate with the DNA polymerase α–primase complex that is

Table 2 Enzyme Activities Associated with the DNA Polymerase α_2 Chromatographic Fraction

Activity	Total units[a]
DNA polymerase α with	
activated DNA	3620
primed single-stranded DNA	2715
DNA primase	937
DNase	
$3' \rightarrow 5'$ exonuclease	230
endonuclease	<1
ATPase	<1
RNase H	4645
Topoisomerase	
type I	not detectable
type II	not detectable
Protein kinase (casein)	321
AT sequence recognition protein	1230

[a]Quantities are per 20 g of HeLa cells. Units of DNA polymerase, primase, and exonuclease activities are as described previously (Vishwanatha et al. 1986a). One unit of RNase H activity equals 1 nmole of [³H]poly(A) converted to acid-soluble form per hour at 30°C. One unit of AT-sequence-binding protein equals 10,000 cpm of [³H]poly(dA) or [³H]poly(dT) bound to nitrocellulose filters after a 30-min incubation period at 25°C.

resolved from the DNA polymerase α multiprotein complex during subsequent chromatographic steps on phenylSepharose and phosphocellulose (S. Coughlin and E. Baril, unpubl.). We have not been able to show any significant effect of phosphorylation by the protein kinase, however, on the catalytic properties of the polymerase α or DNA primase.

An AT sequence recognition protein also cofractionates with the multiprotein DNA polymerase α complex during its early stages of purification (Table 2). The sequence recognition protein is separated from the DNA polymerase α complex by chromatography on oligo-(dT)-cellulose (L. Malkas and E. Baril, in prep.). The DNA polymerase α complex appears in the column flow-through fraction and the AT sequence recognition protein is eluted by 0.35–0.40 M KCl. Further analysis of the protein binding by gel mobility shift and nitrocellulose filter binding assays with SV40 DNA containing the replication origin revealed a binding preference by the protein for a sequence within the origin region for DNA replication. The binding occurs in the presence of excess noncompetitor DNA and in a protein-concentration-dependent manner. In the presence of unlabeled SV40 DNA, a competition for binding for a DNA fragment containing the *ori* region was observed in the gel mobility shift assay. This binding was markedly decreased when DNA from SV40 deletion mutants having deletions in the 17-bp contiguous AT-rich tract of the SV40 replication origin (Stillman et al. 1985; Ryder et al. 1986) was used in the assays. DNA from SV40 deletion mutants having deletions in other domains of the SV40 replication origin, that in some cases also contained AT tracts, showed similar levels of binding by the protein as with wild-type SV40 DNA. The 17-bp AT tract has been reported to be essential for initiation of SV40 DNA replication (Gerard and Gluzman 1986: Hertz et al. 1987) and for high affinity binding of SV40 large T antigen to the T-antigen-binding site I (Ryder et al. 1986). Thus, the AT sequence recognition protein may have significance to the initiation step in DNA replication.

In vitro replication of SV40 DNA with the low-salt nuclear extract and postnuclear supernatant from HeLa cells

The recently developed cell-free system for the in vitro replication of SV40 DNA containing the origin for replication in the presence of large T antigen (Li and Kelly 1984, 1985) provides an excellent means to assess the involvement of multiprotein DNA polymerase α complex and other proteins in DNA replication. The DNA polymerase α₂ fraction that is eluted from DEAE-BioGel and contains the partially purified multiprotein DNA polymerase α complex, as well as other proteins, proved incompetent in the in vitro assay for replication of SV40 DNA in the presence of T antigen. This is understandable since chromatography of the combined NE-PMS on the coupled columns of DEAE-cellulose, native or denatured DNA-cellulose most probably remove essential proteins for DNA replication that are not tightly associated with

the multiprotein DNA polymerase α complex. For example, DNA topoisomerase I and a DNA-dependent ATPase bind to the native DNA-cellulose and require 0.3 M KCl for their elution (J.K. Vishwanatha and E. Baril, in prep.).

As a first step to the investigation of proteins that interact with the multiprotein DNA polymerase α complex in DNA replication, we assessed the low-salt nuclear extract and postnuclear supernatant solution, which are the starting materials for the enzyme isolation, for their competence in the in vitro SV40 DNA replication assay. Since the levels of catalytic or modulating activities associated with the DNA polymerase α complex increase during the transition of cells from G₁ to mid-S phase of the cell cycle (Vishwanatha et al. 1986a), we used the nuclear extract and postnuclear supernatant isolated from synchronized cells in mid-S phase as described previously (Chiu and Baril 1975).

The 0.15 M KCl nuclear extract showed a low level of activity for replication of SV40 DNA in vitro when assayed in the presence of immunoaffinity-purified T antigen by a published procedure (Fig. 1, lanes A and E) (Li and Kelly 1985). This activity was increased when the postnuclear supernatant solution was used in the assay (Fig. 1, lanes B and F) and was not enhanced to any apparent degree when the nuclear extract was combined with the postnuclear supernatant solution (Fig. 1, lanes C and G). The activity with the postnuclear supernatant or the combined fractions also appears similar to that observed with the crude cell lysate (Fig. 1, lanes D and H). These results indicate that the low-salt NE-PMS fraction used for the enzyme purification does contain the essential proteins for SV40 DNA replication.

Subfractionation of NE-PMS

The combined NE-PMS solution contains the multiprotein DNA polymerase α complex (Lamothe et al. 1981; Vishwanatha et al. 1986a) plus other essential proteins for the replication of SV40 DNA in vitro (Fig. 1). These subcellular fractions also contain numerous proteins that do not function in DNA replication. To partially purify a complex of enzymes that may be involved in the replication of SV40 DNA in vitro in the presence of T antigen, the purification scheme outlined in Figure 2 was developed (L. Malkas and E. Baril, in prep.). The polyethylene glycol precipitation step in the presence of 2 M KCl is a key step in the purification since it removes 50% of the protein in the combined NE-PMS, but the in vitro replication activity for SV40 DNA and the DNA polymerase α-complex-associated enzymatic activities are retained in the supernatant. The differential gradient centrifugation step onto a 2 M sucrose cushion was utilized, since this was shown previously to be effective in the separation of an aggregate of enzymes involved in DNA replication from their soluble counterparts.

As shown in Table 3, the majority of the DNA polymerase activity that functions with primed single-stranded DNA templates, DNA primase, DNA-dependent ATPase, and the T-antigen-dependent in vitro replication of SV40 DNA activities was recovered at the interphase above

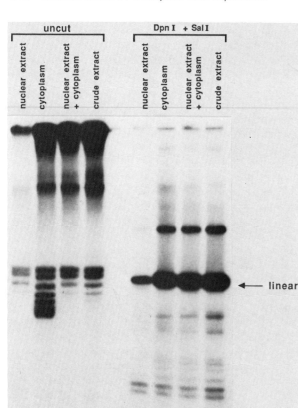

Figure 1 In vitro replication of pJL0 plasmid DNA containing *ori*⁺ SV40 DNA by extracts of HeLa cells. The in vitro replication assays were performed according to a published procedure (Li and Kelly 1985) with plasmid DNA (60 ng), purified T antigen, and various cell extracts. Incubation was at 35°C for 4 hrs. The radioactive products were either electrophoresed as such (uncut) or digested with *Dpn*I and *Sal*I prior to electrophoresis on agarose gels and autoradiography. The arrow marks the position of full-length plasmid DNA. The fractions from synchronized HeLa cells in mid-S phase that were used were low-salt (0.15 M KCl) nuclear extract; postnuclear supernatant; combined nuclear extract and postnuclear supernatant; combined nuclear extract–postmicrosomal supernatant; and crude lysate of HeLa cells.

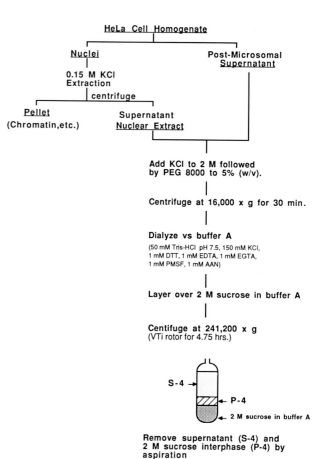

Figure 2 Flow diagram of the fractionation procedure used to isolate the postmicrosomal P-4 and S-4 fractions from HeLa cells.

DNA. Metabolic labeling experiments with radioactively labeled thymidine and uridine indicated the absence of DNA and RNA in the P-4 fraction (L. Malkas and E. Baril, in prep.).

Table 3 Enzyme Activities Recovered in the P-4 and S-4 Fractions

	Subcellular fraction	
	P-4	S-4
Activity	(total units)	
DNA polymerase with		
activated DNA	5,648	3,365
primed single-stranded DNA	2,916	1,320
DNA primase	1,224	29
ATPase		
plus denatured DNA	16,000	14,380
minus denatured DNA	1,468	18,725
Topoisomerase[a]		
type I	+	+
type II	−	−
RNAse H	1,530	346
T-antigen dependent		
in vitro synthesis of SV40 DNA[b]	75	<1

[a]Topoisomerase activity was not quantitated but equal activities appear to be present in these subcellular fractions (Fig. 3).

[b]One unit is equal to the incorporation of 2 pmoles of dNMP into SV40 DNA/hr/60 ng of PJLO DNA.

the 2 M sucrose cushion (P-4 fraction). It is assuring that all of these activities were not recovered exclusively with the P-4 fraction, however. DNA polymerase α activity using activated DNA as a template, some RNase H, DNA-independent ATPase, and topoisomerase I (Fig. 3) activities are also recovered in the nonsedimentable supernatant solution (S-4). We do not observe any detectable topoisomerase II activity in the P-4 or S-4 fractions. The P-4 fraction, however, contains nearly all of the DNA polymerase α activity that functions with primed single-stranded DNA templates and DNA primase activity that resides with the multiprotein DNA polymerase α complex (Vishwanatha et al. 1986a). In addition to topoisomerase I activity, this fraction also contains all of the DNA-dependent ATPase and the T-antigen-dependent in vitro replication activity for SV40

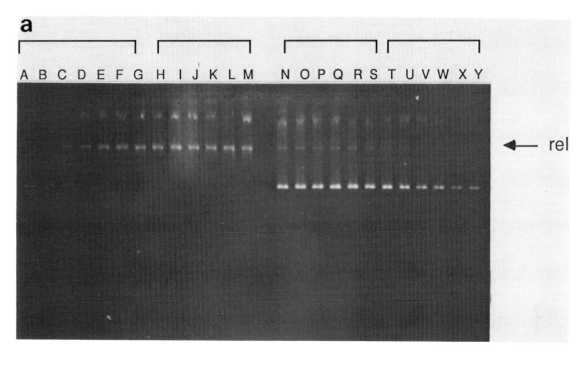

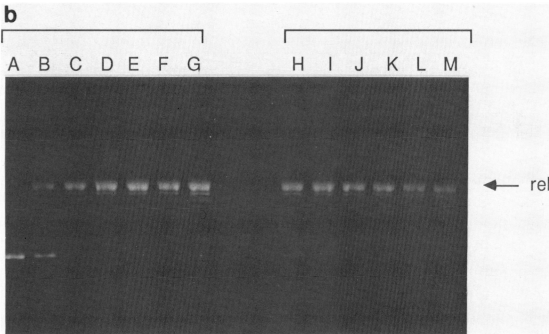

Figure 3 Agarose gel electrophoresis of the products from assay of topoisomerase I activity in the P-4 and S-4 fractions. The assay of topoisomerase I activity was performed according to a published procedure (Liu and Miller 1981) using pUC8-14 DNA and various amounts of protein from the respective cell fractions. Incubation was at 35°C for 10 min. (a) Assay of the S-4 fractions at 0, 0.19, 0.48, 0.95, 1.9, 4.8, and 9.5 μg protein/assay (lanes A–G); assay of the 0.3 M KCl eluate from chromatography of S-4 on native DNA-cellulose at 0.15, 0.38, 0.75, 1.5, 3.8, and 7.5 μg of protein/assay (lanes H–M); assay of the denatured DNA-cellulose column of 0.3 M KCl eluate from chromatography of the S-4 fraction at 0.2, 0.5, 1, 2, 5, and 10 μg protein/assay (lanes N–S) and assay of the 0.15 M KCl eluate from chromatography of the S-4 fraction on coupled columns of DEAE-cellulose, native and denatured DNA-cellulose, and DEAE-BioGel (Vishwanatha et al. 1986a) at 0.2, 0.5, 1, 2, 5, and 10 μg protein/assay (lanes T–Y). (b) Assay of the P-4 fraction at 0, 0.26, 0.65, 1.3, 2.6, 6.5, and 13 μg protein/assay (A–G); assay of the 0.3 M KCl eluate from chromatography of the P-4 fraction on a native DNA-cellulose column at 0.09, 0.23, 0.46, 0.9, 2.3, 4.6, and 9 μg protein/assay (lanes H–M).

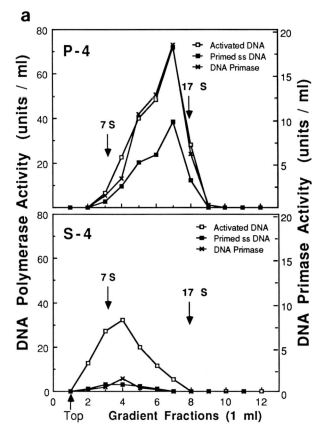

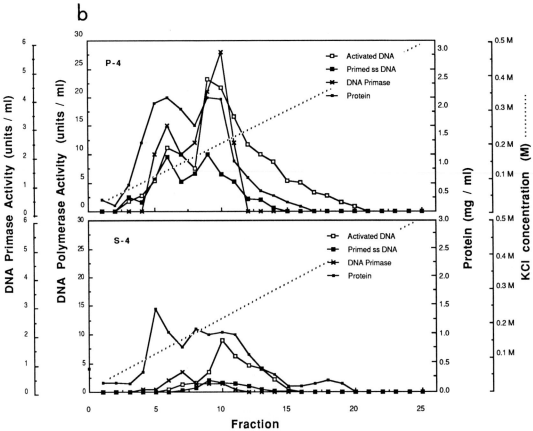

Figure 4 (*See facing page for legend.*)

Multiprotein DNA polymerase α complex from P-4 fraction exists as a larger 16S form

The 640-kD multiprotein DNA polymerase α complex and the polymerase α catalytic subunit from HeLa cells were shown by glycerol gradient centrifugation to have an $S^0_{20,w}$ of 10S and 6S, respectively (Vishwanatha et al. 1986a). The separation of the DNA polymerase α complex along with other enzymes for DNA synthesis (i.e., RNase H, DNA-dependent ATPase, topoisomerase I, etc.) in the P-4 fraction from the nonsedimentable forms of these enzymes in the S-4 fraction (Table 3) is suggestive that the P-4 fraction may contain higher molecular weight forms of the enzymes, possibly in association as a multienzyme complex. To investigate this possibility, the isolated P-4 and S-4 fractions were further fractionated on a 5–30% sucrose gradient in the presence of 0.5 KCl. As shown in Figure 4, the DNA polymerase α activity with activated and primed single-stranded DNA templates and the DNA primase activity in the P-4 fraction co-sedimented as a major 16S peak with a shoulder of about 13S. In contrast, the DNA polymerase α activity in the isolated S-4 fraction sedimented at 8S (Fig. 4a), and there was little to no DNA polymerase α activity using primed single-stranded DNA as template or DNA primase activity with the 8S fraction or throughout the gradient.

The DNA polymerase activities in the isolated P-4 and S-4 fractions also showed different profiles during chromatography on columns of Q-Sepharose (Fig. 4b). For the P-4 fraction, about 30% of the protein that was applied to the column appeared in the column flow-through. There is no DNA polymerase or primase activity with this fraction. The flow-through fraction also did not contain DNA-dependent ATPases or RNase H activities (data not shown). DNA polymerase α activity using activated and primed single-stranded DNA templates and DNA primase activity were co-eluted by the continuous gradient of increasing KCl concentration with two incompletely separated peaks of protein (Fig. 4). All of the activities coincided with the peaks of protein, although the levels of activity were higher with the peak eluting at the higher concentration KCl.

For the S-4 fraction, about 50% of the protein and 60% of the DNA polymerase activity that were applied to the Q-Sepharose column were recovered in the column flow-through fraction (data not shown). A broad peak of protein and a single peak of DNA polymerase activity were eluted by a continuous gradient of increasing KCl concentrations. In contrast to the results obtained with the P-4 fraction, the peaks of eluted protein and DNA polymerase activity peaks were not coincidental. Also, low levels of DNA polymerase activity with primed

single-stranded DNA template and DNA primase activity were present with this fraction. The peak of DNA primase activity also did not coincide with the peak of DNA polymerase activity (Fig. 4).

DNA polymerase activity in the P-4 and S-4 fractions belongs to the α-class DNA polymerase

The DNA polymerase activity in the low-salt NE-PMS supernatant solution of HeLa cells was shown previously (Vishwanatha et al. 1986a) to be inhibited by aphidicolin (Ikegami et al. 1978) and butylphenylguanine (Wright et al. 1982). These were both considered specific inhibitors of DNA synthesis and of the α-class DNA polymerase activity. However, it has recently been reported that a DNA polymerase δ isolated from rabbit bone marrow (Byrnes 1985) and calf thymus (Lee et al. 1985; Crute et al. 1986) is also sensitive to aphidicolin and to BuPdGTP (Khan et al. 1984), the ribosyltriphosphate form of butylphenylguanine. DNA polymerase δ, however, is reportedly about 100-fold less sensitive to BuPdGTP than is DNA polymerase α (Byrnes 1985).

To assure ourselves that the different forms of DNA polymerase in the P-4 and S-4 fractions are indeed α-class DNA polymerases, we checked the activities for their sensitivities to BuPdGTP and to a neutralizing monoclonal antibody (SJK132-20) prepared by Korn and co-workers to human DNA polymerase α (Tanaka et al. 1982). The DNA polymerase activities in the P-4 and S-4 fractions and the enzymes partially purified from these fractions were all inhibited by the neutralizing antibody to DNA polymerase α (Fig. 5). Although the activities in the crude fractions are neutralized less by the antibody, this may be attributable to lack of availability of a fraction of the enzymes for interaction with the antibody, since the activity of the partially purified enzymes from these fractions was completely neutralized by the antibody (Fig. 5). The DNA polymerase activities partially purified from the P-4 and S-4 fractions were also inhibited by BuPdGTP at concentrations of 0.5–10 μM (Fig. 5). The sensitivity of the DNA polymerase activities to this agent is 50- to 100-fold greater than that reported for DNA polymerase δ activity (Byrnes 1985; Lee et al. 1985; Crute et al. 1986). Thus, the DNA polymerase α activities that are subfractionated from HeLa cell homogenates into the P-4 and S-4 fractions all belong to the α-class DNA polymerases.

Discussion

One of the major conclusions of this work is that the 640-kD multiprotein DNA polymerase α complex from

Figure 4 Velocity centrifugation on a 10–30% sucrose gradient and Q-Sepharose chromatography of the P-4 and S-4 fractions from HeLa cells. (a) 1 ml of the P-4 (6.6 mg protein) and S-4 (6 mg protein) fractions were loaded onto 5–30% sucrose gradients in buffer B plus 0.5 M KCl prepared in polyallomer tubes for the SW41 rotor and layered over a 2 M sucrose cushion. After centrifugation at 36,000 RPM for 16 hr, 1-ml fractions were collected by tube puncture and assayed as described in Methods. Horse spleen apoferritin (17S) and yeast alcohol dehydrogenase (7S) were used as markers. (b) The P-4 (30 mg protein) and S-4 (25 mg protein) fractions were chromatographed on 1-ml columns of Q-Sepharose by the procedure described in Methods. The units of enzyme activity are as described previously (Vishwanatha et al. 1986a). Units 1 ml of DNA polymerase activity with activated (□) and primed single-stranded (■) DNA templates, DNA primase activity (×), mg protein per ml (●) and (M) KCl concentration (. . . .).

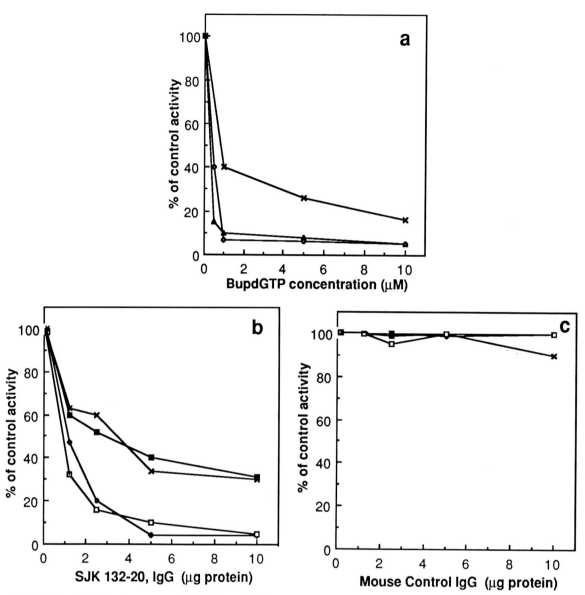

Figure 5 Inhibition of DNA polymerase activity in P-4 and S-4 fractions by BuPdGTP and monoclonal antibody (SJK132-20) to human DNA polymerase α. (*a*) The inhibition by BuPdGTP was carried out according to a published procedure (Byrnes 1985). The units/assay of DNA polymerase control activity for the respective fractions were; P-4 Q-Sepharose peaks A (▲) 0.30 and B (○) 0.46, and S-4 (×) 0.30. (*b*) The neutralization assays on the respective fractions of DNA polymerase by SJK132-20 IgG were performed according to a published procedure (Vishwanatha and Baril 1986). The units/assay of DNA polymerase for the 100% control activities for the respective fractions were P-4, 0.10 (■); DEAE-Bio, 0.15 M KCl eluate of P-4, 0.06 (●); S-4, 0.04 (×); DEAE-Bio, 0.15 M KCl eluate of S-4, 0.07 (□). (*c*) The neutralization assays were performed as in Fig. 5b, except that the designated amounts of purified mouse (control) IgG were used. The symbols are the same as in Fig. 4b.

HeLa cells interacts with other enzymes in DNA synthesis to form a higher order, sedimentable, multienzyme complex that may be involved in DNA replication in vivo. There are several lines of evidence to suggest that the association of these enzymes is not fortuitous. First, the multiprotein DNA polymerase α complex from the low-salt (0.15 M KCl) NE-PMS sediments onto a 2 M sucrose cushion as a discrete fraction (P-4). In addition to polymerase α, the P-4 fraction has topoisomerase I, RNase H, and most of the DNA-dependent ATPase activity present in the NE-PMS. The enzyme activities in the P-4 fraction were sedimentable and are separated by this procedure from nonsedimentable forms of the enzymes that are recovered in the supernatant (S-4) fraction. Immunoblot analysis of the P-4 and S-4 fractions under nondenaturing conditions using monoclonal antibody (SJK132-20) to human DNA polymerase α (Tanaka et al. 1982) showed that all of the 640-kD DNA polymerase α complex resides with the sedimentable P-4 fraction. Also, all of the activity for T-antigen-dependent replication of SV40 DNA in vitro is recovered with the P-4 fraction. This strongly suggests that the complex of enzymes in the P-4 fraction can function together in the replication of a double-stranded DNA that is dependent on specific initiation events in the *ori* region.

The purified 640-kD DNA polymerase α complex by velocity sedimentation analysis in a glycerol gradient in the presence of 0.5 M KCl was shown to be 10S (Vishwanatha et al. 1986a). This is similar to what has been reported for purified multiprotein forms of DNA polymerase α from Ehrlich ascites cells (Faust et al. 1984) and calf thymus (Ottiger et al. 1987). The analysis of the P-4 and S-4 fractions by velocity centrifugation in a sucrose gradient in the presence of 0.5 M KCl showed that the polymerase α activity in the P-4 fraction sedimented at 16S with a shoulder at 13S, whereas that in the S-4 fraction was 8S. This accounts for the sedimentable nature of the DNA polymerase α in the P-4 fraction. This is considerably larger than the 10S multiprotein DNA polymerase α complex and is probably attributable to the association of the other enzymes and proteins for DNA replication with the complex in the P-4 but not the S-4 fraction. This is also supported by the differences in the chromatographic profiles obtained during chromatography of the P-4 and S-4 fractions on Q-Sepharose, a strong anion exchange resin. For the P-4 fraction most of the DNA polymerase α and other enzyme activities and protein did bind to matrix and co-eluted as two incompletely resolved peaks of protein and enzymatic activities. This was not the case for the S-4 fraction, in which 50% of the protein and DNA polymerase activity did not bind to Q-Sepharose and the eluted DNA polymerase activity was not coincidental with the peak of eluted proteins.

Taken together, these results suggest that the interaction of DNA polymerase α with the other enzymes, and probably other proteins, in DNA synthesis has physiological relevance. The elegant studies of the DNA-synthesizing machinery in prokaryotes have shown that the prokaryotic DNA replicase interacts in a concerted fashion with other enzymes and proteins to form a loosely associated multienzyme complex for DNA replication (Kornberg 1980; Alberts 1985). It is most probable that similar interactions occur in the DNA-synthesizing machinery in animal cells. The partially resolved peaks of enzyme activities and protein that are observed during anion exchange chromatography and velocity against gradient centrifugation of the P-4 fraction suggest to us a reversible association of the enzyme activities.

Although the P-4 fraction was shown to have associated topoisomerase I, RNase H, and DNA-dependent ATPase activities in addition to the multiprotein DNA polymerase α complex, there are probably other essential proteins for DNA replication in the P-4 fractions. Among these is an AT sequence recognition protein that binds with high specificity to the AT-rich tract within the replication origin domain of SV40 DNA. Further enzymatic and physical analysis of this fraction will be required to define other essential proteins for DNA replication. The ability to separate this fraction of associated enzymes and proteins that function in SV40

DNA replication from the nonassociated components should now permit a meaningful analysis of the components by complementation assays and by the analysis of the initiation of synthesis of RNA primers as was performed previously with SV40 DNA in vitro (Vishwanatha et al. 1986b).

Acknowledgments

We are grateful to Bruce Stillman for the generous gift of SV40 origin deletion mutants, to George Wright for his kind gift of BuPdGTP, and to I. Robert Lehman for communicating results to us prior to publication. Our sincere appreciation goes to Dr. Nina Pedersen for her assistance in certain aspects of this work and for helpful discussions. We thank Ms. Sandra Johnson and Carol Savage for their expert technical assistance in preparation of the manuscript. This research was supported by grants P-30-12708 and CA-15187 from the National Institutes of Health. L.H.M. is the recipient of a postdoctoral fellowship from the National Institutes of Health. J.K.V. was a fellow of the Leukemia Society of America.

References

Alberts, B.M. 1985. Protein machines mediate the basic genetic processes. *Trends Genet.* 1: 26.

Baril, E.F., P. Bonin, D. Burstein, K. Mara, and P. Zamecnik. 1983. Resolution of the diadenosine 5′,5‴-P¹,P⁴-tetraphosphate binding subunit from a multiprotein form of HeLa cell DNA polymerase α. *Proc. Natl. Acad. Sci.* 80: 4931.

Byrnes, J.J. 1985. Differential inhibitors of DNA polymerases alpha and delta. *Biochem. Biophys. Res. Commun.* 132: 628.

Campbell, J.L. 1986. Eukaryotic DNA replication. *Annu. Rev. Biochem.* 55: 733.

Chang, L.M.S., E. Rafter, C. Augl, and F.J. Bollum. 1984. Purification of DNA polymerase-DNA primase complex from calf thymus glands. *J. Biol. Chem.* 259: 14679.

Chiu, R.C. and E.F. Baril. 1975. Nuclear DNA polymerases and the HeLa cell cycle. *J. Biol. Chem.* 250: 7951.

Conaway, R.C. and I.R. Lehman. 1982. A DNA primase activity associated with DNA polymerase α from *Drosophila melanogaster* embryos. *Proc. Natl. Acad. Sci.* 79: 2523.

Cotterill, S.M., M.E. Reyland, L.A. Loeb, and I.R. Lehman. 1987. A cryptic proofreading 3′→5′ exonuclease associated with the polymerase subunit of the DNA polymerase-primase from *Drosophila melanogaster. Proc. Natl. Acad. Sci.* 84: 5635.

Crute, J.J., A.F. Wahl, and R.A. Bambara. 1986. Purification and characterization of two new high molecular weight forms of DNA polymerase δ. *Biochemistry* 25: 26.

DePamphilis, M.L. and P.M. Wassarman. 1980. Replication of eukaryotic chromosomes: A close-up of the replication fork. *Annu. Rev. Biochem.* 49: 627.

Faust, E.A., G. Gloor, M.F. MacIntyre, and R. Nagy. 1984. ATP(GTP)-dependent conversion of MVM parvovirus single-stranded DNA to its replicative form by a purified 10S species of mouse DNA polymerase α. *Biochim. Biophys. Acta* 781: 216.

Fry, M. and L.A. Loeb. 1986. *Animal cell DNA polymerases.* CRC Press, Boca Raton, Florida.

Gerard, R. and Y. Gluzman. 1986. Functional analysis of the role of the A + T-rich region and upstream flanking sequences in simian virus 40 DNA replication. *Mol. Cell. Biol.* 6: 4570.

Gronostajski, R.M., J. Field, and J. Hurwitz. 1984. Purification of a primase activity associated with DNA polymerase α from HeLa cells. *J. Biol. Chem.* **259:** 9479.

Hertz, G.Z., M.R. Young, and J.E. Mertz. 1987. The A + T-rich sequence of the simian virus 40 origin is essential for replication and is involved in bending of the viral DNA. *J. Virol.* **61:** 2322.

Holler, E., H. Fischer, and S. Helmut. 1985. Non-disruptive detection of DNA polymerases in nondenaturing polyacrylamide gels. *Eur. J. Biochem.* **151:** 311.

Ikegami, S., T. Toguchi, M. Ohashi, M. Oguro, H. Nagano, and Y. Mano. 1978. Aphidicolin prevents mitotic cell division by interfering with the activities of DNA polymerase α. *Nature* **275:** 458.

Kaguni, L.S., J.M. Rossignol, R.C. Conaway, and I.R. Lehman. 1983a. Isolation of an intact DNA polymerase-primase from embryos of *Drosophila melanogaster*. *Proc. Natl. Acad. Sci.* **80:** 2221.

Kaguni, L.S., J.M. Rossignol, R.C. Conaway, G.R. Banks, and I.R. Lehman. 1983b. Association of DNA primase with the β/γ subunits of DNA polymerase α from *Drosophila melanogaster* embryos. *J. Biol. Chem.* **288:** 9037.

Khan, N.N., G.E. Wright, L.W. Dudycz, and N.C. Brown. 1984. Butylphenyl dGTP: A selective and potent inhibitor of mammalian DNA polymerase alpha. *Nucleic Acids Res.* **12:** 3695.

Kornberg, A. 1980. *DNA replication.* W.H. Freeman, San Francisco.

———. 1982. *Supplement to DNA replication.* W.H. Freeman, San Francisco.

Lamothe, P., B. Baril, A. Chi, L. Lee, and E. Baril. 1981. Accessory proteins for DNA polymerase α activity with single-stranded DNA templates. *Proc. Natl. Acad. Sci.* **78:** 4723.

Lee, M.Y.W.T., N.L. Toomey, and G.E. Wright. 1985. Differential inhibition of human placental DNA polymerases δ and α by BuPdGTP and BuAdATP. *Nucleic Acids Res.* **13:** 8623.

Li, J.J. and T.J. Kelly, Jr. 1984. Simian virus 40 DNA replication *in vitro*. *Proc. Natl. Acad. Sci.* **81:** 6973.

———. 1985. SV40 DNA replication *in vitro*: Specificity of initiation and evidence for bidirectional replication. *Mol. Cell. Biol.* **5:** 1238.

Liu, L.F. and K.G. Miller. 1981. Eukaryotic DNA topoisomerases. Two forms of type I DNA topoisomerases from HeLa cell nuclei. *Proc. Natl. Acad. Sci.* **78:** 3487.

Miller, K.G., L.F. Liu, and P.T. Englund. 1981. A homogeneous type II DNA topoisomerase from HeLa cell nuclei. *J. Biol. Chem.* **256:** 9334.

Ottiger, H., P. Frei, M. Hassig, and U. Hubscher. 1987. Mammalian DNA polymerase α: A replication competent holoenzyme form from calf thymus. *Nucleic Acids Res.* **15:** 4789.

Plevani, P., G. Badaracco, C. Aool, and L.M.S. Chang. 1984. DNA polymerase I and DNA primase complex in yeast. *J. Biol. Chem.* **259:** 7532.

Pritchard, C.G. and M.L. DePamphilis. 1983. Preparation of DNA polymerase α. C_1C_2 by reconstituting DNA polymerase α with its specific stimulatory cofactors C_1C_2. *J. Biol. Chem.* **258:** 9801.

Pritchard, C.G., D.T. Weaver, E.F. Baril, and M.L. DePamphilis. 1983. DNA polymerase α cofactors C_1C_2 function as primer recognition proteins. *J. Biol. Chem.* **258:** 9810.

Ryder, K., S. Silver, A.L. DeLucia, E. Fanning, and P. Tegtmeyer. 1986. An altered DNA conformation in origin region I is a determinant for the binding of SV40 large T antigen. *Cell* **44:** 719.

SenGupta, D.N., P. Kumar, B.Z. Zmudzka, S. Coughlin, J.K. Vishwanatha, F.A. Robey, C. Parrott, and S.H. Wilson. 1987. Mammalian α-polymerase: Cloning of partial complementary DNA and immunobinding of catalytic subunit in crude homogenate protein blots. *Biochemistry* **26:** 956.

Simanis, V. and D.P. Lane. 1985. An immunoaffinity purification procedure for SV40 large T antigen. *Virology* **144:** 88.

Skarnes, W., P. Bonin, and E. Baril. 1986. Exonuclease activity associated with a multiprotein form of HeLa cell DNA polymerase α. Purification and properties of the exonuclease. *J. Biol. Chem.* **261:** 6629.

Stillman, B., R.D. Gerard, R.A. Gugenheimer, and Y. Gluzman. 1985. T antigen and template requirements for SV40 DNA replication *in vitro*. *EMBO J.* **4:** 2933.

Tanaka, S., S.-Z. Hu, T.S.-F. Wang, and D. Korn. 1982. Preparation and preliminary characterization of monoclonal antibodies against human polymerase α. *J. Biol. Chem.* **257:** 8386.

Tseng, B.Y. and C.N. Ahlem. 1983. A DNA primase from mouse cells. Purification and partial characterization. *J. Biol. Chem.* **258:** 9845.

Vishwanatha, J.K. and E.F. Baril. 1986. Resolution and purification of free primase activity from the DNA primase-polymerase α complex of HeLa cells. *Nucleic Acids Res.* **14:** 8467.

Vishwanatha, J.K., S.A. Coughlin, M. Wesolowski-Owen, and E.F. Baril. 1986a. A multiprotein form of DNA polymerase α from HeLa cells. Resolution of its associated catalytic activities. *J. Biol. Chem.* **261:** 6619.

Vishwanatha, J.K., M. Yamaguchi, M.L. DePamphilis, and E.F. Baril. 1986b. Selection of template initiation sites and the lengths of RNA primers synthesized by DNA primase are strongly affected by its organization in a multiprotein DNA polymerase alpha complex. *Nucleic Acids Res.* **14:** 7305.

Wang, T.S.-F., S.-Z. Hu, and D. Korn. 1984. DNA primase from KB cells: Characterization of a primase tightly associated with immunoaffinity-purified DNA polymerase α. *J. Biol. Chem.* **259:** 1854.

Wright, G.E., E.F. Baril, V.M. Brown, and N.C. Brown. 1982. Design and characterization of N^2-arylaminopurines which selectively inhibit replicative DNA synthesis and replication-specific DNA polymerases: Guanine derivatives active on mammalian DNA polymerase alpha and bacterial DNA polymerase III. *Nucleic Acids Res.* **10:** 4431.

Yagura, T., T. Kozu, T. Seno, M. Saneyoshi, S. Hiraga, and H. Nagano. 1983. Novel form of DNA polymerase α associated with DNA primase activity of vertebrates. *J. Biol. Chem.* **258:** 13070.

Zamecnik, P.C. 1983. Diadenosine 5′,5′′′-P¹,-P⁴-tetraphosphate (AP_4A): Its role in cellular metabolism. *Anal. Biochem.* **134:** 1.

Human DNA Polymerase α: Protein Structure and Molecular Genetic Characterization

T.S.-F. Wang, D. Korn, and S.W. Wong

Laboratory of Experimental Oncology, Department of Pathology,
Stanford University School of Medicine,
Stanford, California 94305-5324

The protein structure and subunit components of human DNA polymerase α were defined by immunoaffinity methodology with monoclonal antibodies specific to DNA polymerase α. The structural gene and the locus required for expression of polymerase α were both mapped to the short arm of the X chromosome at Xp21.3 to Xp22.1. With reverse genetic approach, a 5433 bp near-full-length cDNA encoding a 165-kD, 1462-amino-acid, catalytic polypeptide of human DNA polymerase α was isolated.

Eukaryotic DNA replication is a tightly regulated mechanism involving the orderly coordination of many protein–protein and protein–DNA interactions (Kornberg 1980, 1982). One essential component of the replicative apparatus is DNA polymerase α, which has been accepted as the principal polymerase of chromosomal DNA replication (Fry and Loeb 1986). A thorough study of a key component of DNA polymerization is prerequisite to the understanding of the complex eukaryotic DNA replication mechanism. There is a current lack of understanding about the mechanism that regulates the expression of this essential gene and the structure-function relation to this enzyme. In an attempt to investigate these questions, we formulated a strategy to thoroughly analyze the protein and genetic structure of human DNA polymerase α. We first established a panel of murine hybridomas that produce monoclonal antibodies specific to DNA polymerase α (Tanaka et al. 1982). Utilizing these monoclonal antibodies, we developed two independent immunoaffinity purification protocols and analyzed the protein structure of polymerase α in detail (Wang et al. 1984; Wong et al. 1986). Based on the epitope specificity of one of the monoclonal antibodies, the expression of the gene of human DNA polymerase α was mapped to a specific region on the short arm of the human X chromosome (Wang et al. 1985). To gain further insight into the questions described above, we have determined amino acid sequences of several portions of polymerase α catalytic polypeptide, isolated a near-full-length cDNA clone via reverse-genetic approach, and deduced the complete amino acid sequence of the human DNA polymerase α. In addition, we have determined the chromosomal position of the structural gene of DNA polymerase α in the human genome.

Methods

Monoclonal antibody methodology
Immunization and somatic cell hybridization protocol, screening assay for polymerase-α-specific hybridomas, purification of monoclonal antibodies, and neutralization and binding assays of DNA polymerase-α-specific antibodies were exactly as described (Tanaka et al. 1982); solid-phase competitive radioimmunoassay was performed as described (Wong et al. 1986).

Immunoaffinitiy purification of human DNA polymerase α enzyme activity, antigen protein, and immunoprecipitation of polymerase α antigen from in vivo-labeled human KB cells were performed as described (Wong et al. 1984; Wong et al. 1986).

Immunoblot and peptide mapping
Identification of DNA polymerase α antigen by immunoblot and tryptic peptide mapping and partial chemical cleavage by N-chlorosuccinimide of polymerase polypeptides were performed as described (Wong et al. 1986).

Rodent–human somatic cell hybrids
All rodent–human somatic hybrid cells used in this study and their properties are described in detail (Wang et al. 1985).

Protein sequence analysis
High-sensitivity automated Edman degradation was performed on a model 470A gas phase sequencer with on-line phenylthiohydantoin (PTH) amino acid analysis (Model 120A) as described (Hunkapiller et al. 1983; Wong et al. 1988).

cDNA cloning procedure
Oligonucleotide probe design and hybridization/washing conditions are according to Lathe (1985). Construction of size-selected human KB cell cDNA library, a screening of polymerase α cDNA clones, and verification of the cDNA clone are described (Wong et al. 1988).

Nucleotide sequence analysis
DNA sequencing procedure was performed as described (Dale et al. 1985).

385

CANCER CELLS 6 / *Eukaryotic DNA Replication.* © 1988 by Cold Spring Harbor Laboratory 0-87969-308-8/88 $1.00

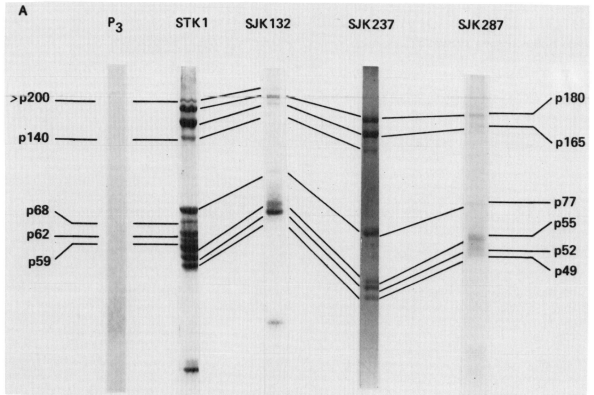

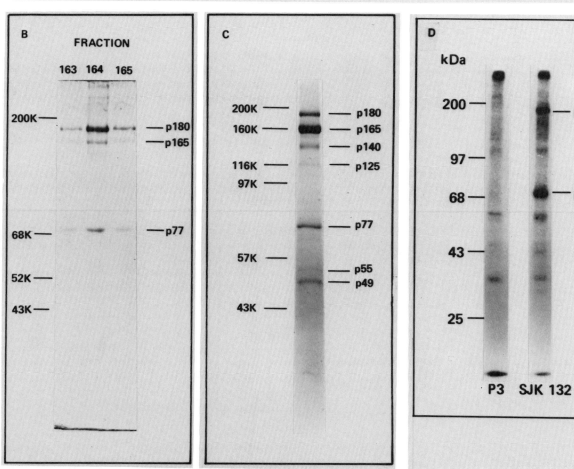

Figure 1 (*See facing page for legend.*)

Results

Properties of monoclonal antibodies against DNA polymerase α

A panel of 16 stable murine hybridomas that produce homogeneous IgG molecules was established (Tanaka et al. 1982). These murine monoclonal antibodies specifically recognize DNA polymerase α and show no cross-reactivity with DNA polymerase β and γ. Three of these 16 monoclonal antibodies exhibit neutralizing activity against polymerase α. Quantitative binding studies have been performed on five of the antibodies. The results generate the theoretically predicted linear Scatchard plots and demonstrate high binding affinities, with K_d values of 3.2×10^{-9} to 3.4×10^{-10} M.

The epitope specificities of three neutralizing antibodies, SJK132-20, SJK211-14, and SJK287-38, and two non-neutralizing antibodies, STK1 and SJK237-71, were evaluated by solid-phase competitive radioimmunoassay as described in Methods. The results demonstrate that, in general, the antigenic epitope recognized by each of the five antibodies appears to be unique and independent, except STK1 and SJK211-14. Notwithstanding this single abnormality, we have used four of these five monoclonal antibodies to pursue a detailed structural analysis of human DNA polymerase α.

Structural characterization of human DNA polymerase α

Two independent immunoaffinity protocols were developed to document the protein structure and subunit components of human DNA polymerase α. One protocol is designed to obtain enzymatically active polymerase α. Four of the monoclonal antibodies, STK1, SJK132-20, SJK237-71, SJK287-38, and nonimmune control monoclonal IgG P_3, were used independently in this immunoaffinity purification protocol. SJK237-71 has been the most useful antibody to obtain maximum yield of polymerase α from human KB cells. A detailed description of the protocol was reported (Wang et al. 1984; Wong et al. 1986). With SJK237-71 IgG as purification reagent, polymerase α is obtained in a simple four-step protocol as an immunocomplex in about 25–30% yield, with a specific activity of $1-2 \times 10^5$ units per mg of non-IgG protein and a tightly associated DNA primase activity (Wang et al. 1984). With either of the non-neutralizing antibodies, SJK237-71 or STK1, the yield of polymerase α activity is comparable. The yield of polymerase α purified from neutralizing antibodies such as with

SJK132-20 and SJK287-38 is less than 10% of those from non-neutralizing antibodies. Three groups of polypeptides are reproducibly obtained by SJK237-71: (1) a group of large polypeptides, size range from p180 to p125; (2) a p77 polypeptide; and (3) two polypeptides of p55 and p49 reported to be associated with primase activity. The same polypeptide components were obtained with the two neutralizing monoclonal antibodies as with SJK237-71. STK1 reproducibly yields three extra-small polypeptides of p68, p62, and p59. Polypeptides obtained from this protocol with four monoclonal antibodies and a nonimmune control antibody P_3 are demonstrated in Figure 1A.

Another immunoaffinity protocol utilizes covalently linked antibody-Sepharose resins that allow more stringent washing and harsher elution solvents to recover solely the pertinent antigen but without significant enzyme activity. The antigen polypeptide composition recovered by this protocol with SJK132-20 is shown in Figure 1B in three elution fractions detected by Coomassie blue stain as p180, p165, and p77. With SJK287-38, faint bands of p55 and p49 could be discerned by silver stain (Fig. 1C). The results indicate that the principal protein species recovered from this antigen isolation method comprise a family of large polypeptides predominantly of p180 and p165, with small and variable amounts of p140 and p125, and the invariant presence of p77. In contrast to the immunoaffinity purification protocol designed to recover maximum enzyme activity, the recovery of the smaller proteins, p55 and p49, was inconsistent, and when present at all, they were in minor quantity and detectable only by silver stain.

To examine this protein structure in vivo, another immunoprotocol was developed to identify DNA polymerase α antigen by direct immunoprecipitation from lysates of labeled human KB cells (see Methods). From [^{35}S]methionine-labeled human KB cells, the immunoprecipitate yields the principal polymerase α antigen p180, a small amount of p165, and a detectable p77. Pulse-chase experiments demonstrated no evident intracellular degradation of the principal labeled polymerase species, p180, to smaller species. The half-life of p180 is estimated to be > 15 hours in actively growing KB cells. Immunoprecipitation of extracts from KB cells labeled with [^{32}P]orthophosphate demonstrated that both principal protein species of polymerase α were phosphoproteins and, in each instance, the phosphoamino acids are phosphothreonine and phosphoserine (Fig. 1D).

Figure 1 (A) Sodium dodecyl sulfate-polyacrylamide gel analysis for human KB cell DNA polymerase α immunoaffinity-purified with monoclonal antibodies. Immunoaffinity-purification with monoclonal antibodies STK1, SJK132, SJK237, SJK287, and nonimmune control P_3 IgG was performed as described in Methods. The enzyme fraction isolated from each monoclonal antibody affinity column is an immunocomplex. Heavy and light chains for each antibody are p52 and p25 and p23, respectively. The nonimmune control, P_3, is from P_3/X63/Ag8, which secretes an IgG (γ1,K). (B) and (C) Purification of DNA polymerase α antigens by chromatography on covalently linked monoclonal IgG-Sepharose 4B columns. The antigen polypeptides were purified from SJK132-Sepharose and SJK287-Sepharose columns in B and C, respectively. Antigen polypeptides were analyzed on denatured polyacrylamide gel and stained with Coomassie blue in B and silver in C. (D) Immunoprecipitation of DNA polymerase α antigens from crude lysates of [^{32}P]orthophosphate. Experiments were performed as described in Methods with nonimmune IgG P_3 as control. (B,C, and D are reprinted, with permission, from Wong et al. 1986.)

Identification of catalytic polypeptide and peptide mapping analyses

To assess which of these polypeptides contains the antigenic epitope and catalytic function of DNA polymerization, an immunoblot with 12 of the monoclonal antibodies including the three potent neutralizing antibodies and a nonimmune control P₃ IgG were used. As demonstrated in Figure 2, all 12 monoclonal antibodies recognized an antigenic epitope on the polypeptide of 180 kD in this particular enzyme preparation. This result, in corroboration with the results of renaturing gels, indicates that p180 (and p165) are the principal protein species in these human cell extracts that contain or are required for the catalytic activity of DNA polymerase α.

To further evaluate the possible structural relationships among the several protein components described above, two independent peptide mapping analyses were performed. Each of the protein components of the immunoaffinity-purified enzyme fraction was subjected to tryptic peptide mapping and partial chemical cleavage by N-chlorosuccinimide, which specifically cleaves tryptophanyl peptide bonds (Lischwe and Ochs 1982). The results of tryptic peptide mapping are demonstrated in Figure 3; the two predominant large polypeptide species, p180 and p165, have apparently identical two-dimensional peptide maps, whereas the p77, p55, and p49 species have unique and distinct peptide maps that are unrelated to the large polypeptides and to each other. Furthermore, the minor species of the large polypeptides such as p140, p125, and the occasionally observed >p200 also demonstrate tryptic maps apparently identical to p180 and p165 (data not shown). This finding is further supported by N-chlorosuccinimide partial chemical cleavage data, which again demonstrate similar if not identical cleavage patterns of the family of large polypeptides and unique, distinct, and unrelated patterns of p77, p55, and p49 polypeptides (Wong et al. 1986).

Assignment of the gene for human DNA polymerase α to the X chromosome

Further assessment of the ability of four anti-human DNA polymerase α monoclonal antibodies to recognize a phylogenetically broad array of eukaryotic DNA polymerases indicates that whereas the three neutralizing antibodies exhibit variable extent of cross-reactivity among vertebrate species, the non-neutralizing antibody, SJK237-71, recognizes an epitope found in higher mammals only (human, simian, canine, and bovine). This lack of cross-reactivity with lower mammals, such as rodent DNA polymerase α, provides a convenient immunoassay to map the gene for human DNA polymerase α to a specific chromosome (Wang et al. 1985; M.A. Miller et al., in prep.).

A solid-phase immunoassay is established with proper controls and defined background values. Three sets of experiments were performed (Wang et al. 1985). Initially, seven hybrid clones from four independent rodent–human somatic cell hybridizations were screened. Only two hybrid clones containing human X chromosome are positive for the expression of human DNA polymerase α. To confirm this correlation, two hybrid clones, one containing human X chromosome only, another containing X but not Y and several other human chromosomes were sorted by an antibody against a cell surface antigen, 12E7, encoded on X or Y chromosomes (Levy et al. 1979; Goodfellow et al. 1984). In both cases, cell fractions that were positive for the presence of human X chromosome were positive for the expression of human polymerase α. The correlation was further confirmed by counterselection of the X chromosome. Three hybrid clones were subjected to medium selection and counterselection in hypoxanthine/aminopterin/thymidine (HAT) or in 6-thioguanine (6TG). When these three hybrid clones were maintained in HAT medium, which requires the presence of hypoxanthine phosphoribosyltransferase (HPRT) encoded on the X

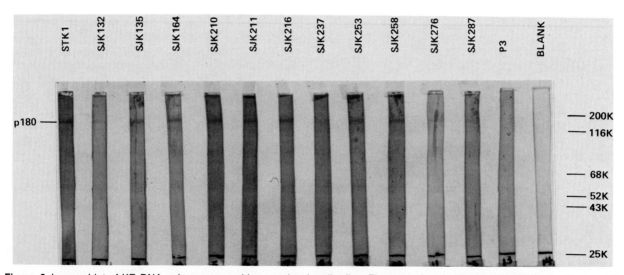

Figure 2 Immunoblot of KB DNA polymerase α with monoclonal antibodies. The procedure is described in Methods. The specific monoclonal antibody is shown above each nitrocellulose strip. The control strips were probed with nonimmune IgG (P₃) or with no primary antibody (blank). (Reprinted, with permission, from Wong et al. 1986.)

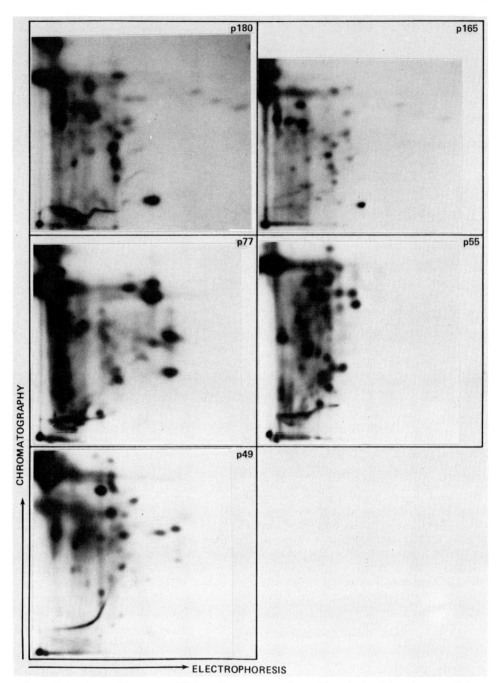

CHROMATOGRAPHY

ELECTROPHORESIS

Figure 3 Comparison of tryptic peptide maps of DNA polymerase α polypeptides obtained from immunoaffinity purification. The procedure is described in Methods. No peptide spots are detected in control experiments handled identically except without trypsin. (Reprinted, with permission, from Wong et al. 1986.)

chromosome, human DNA polymerase α expression, and antigen protein, as well as two X chromosome marker enzymes HPRT and glucose-6-phosphate dehydrogenase, activities were positive. In contrast, when propagated in 6TG medium, which excludes the cells containing HPRT gene, all these functions were negative. These data clearly indicate there is an absolute correlation between the presence of the human X chromosome and the expression of human DNA polymerase α. The genetic locus for polymerase α can thus be assigned to X chromosome (Wang et al. 1985).

Precise localization of the polymerase α gene on the X chromosome was accomplished by analysis of a panel of human–rodent hybrids containing either X/autosome translocation with well-defined breakpoints or interstitial deletion of the human X chromosome. These hybrid clones were assayed for expression of human polymerase α and X chromosome marker enzyme activities. Results indicate the expression of polymerase α can be precisely localized at the junctional region of Xp21.3 to Xp22.1 on the short arm of the X chromosome (Fig. 4). To determine whether this locus might be one of those

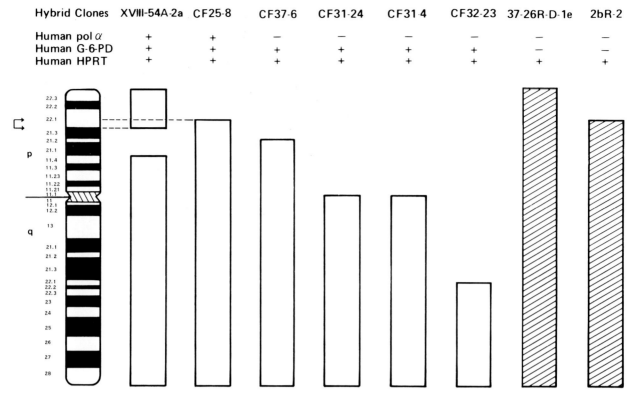

Figure 4 Assignment of the genetic locus of DNA polymerase α to the short arm of chromosome X near the junction of Xp21.3 and Xp22.1. The idiogram of trypsin-Giemsa banding pattern of the human X chromosome is presented at the left. The hatch pattern designates an inactivated X or der(X) chromosome. All hybrid clones were analyzed for human DNA polymerase α expression by SJK237-71 binding assays and for the presence of human glucose-6-phosphate dehydrogenase (G-6-PD) or HPRT activities as described in Methods. The arrows and the broken lines indicate the region of the X chromosome where the gene for DNA polymerase α is assigned. (Reprinted, with permission, from Wang et al. 1985.)

that escape X inactivation, two hybrid clones were assayed, one containing an intact inactivated X chromosome and another containing a translocated inactivated X chromosome with the same breakpoint as the positive clone CF25-8 at Xp22.1. Both of these hybrid clones containing inactivated X chromosome were negative for the expression of human DNA polymerase α. Thus, the DNA polymerase α expression locus does not escape the X inactivation (Wang et al. 1985).

Molecular and genetic characterization of human DNA polymerase α

In an attempt to investigate the structure-function relationship of DNA polymerase α and the regulation of the expression of this important DNA replication enzyme, a near-full-length cDNA clone of human DNA polymerase α was isolated. The strategy used to isolate this cDNA clone and to verify the authenticity of the cDNA clone is outlined in Figure 5. The catalytic polypeptide of human DNA polymerase α was separated from the associated subunits by gel permeation high performance liquid chromatography (HPLC), digested with trypsin, and resulting peptides separated by reverse-phase HPLC. Amino acid sequences of seven tryptic peptides were determined. In all, 85 amino acids were established and used to design oligonucleotide probes (Lathe 1985). A

cDNA library was constructed from >4-kb poly(A)$^+$ mRNA of early midlog human KB cells. A single positive cDNA clone was isolated after screening 1×10^5 colonies. This initial isolated cDNA clone was proven to be X-chromosome-linked by comparative analysis of genomic Southern hybridization with normal male (46,XY) and 4X cell line karyotyped (49,XXXXY). Northern blot hybridization yielded a single signal of 5.8 kb, which is large enough to encode a polypeptide of 180 kD. A restriction fragment of this initially isolated cDNA clone was used to further verify the chromosomal localization of the structural gene. Southern hybridization of *Eco*RI-digested genomic DNA samples from the panel of human–rodent somatic hybrid cells used previously to map the DNA polymerase α gene by expression indicates that the structural gene of human DNA polymerase α was mapped precisely at the same locus as expression at the junctional region of Xp21.3 to Xp22.1 (Wang et al. 1985; Wong et al. 1988). Sequence analysis of this cDNA clone indicates that this clone contains the 3′ end of the human polymerase α cDNA. The very 5′ end of this truncated initial cDNA clone was used to further screen a human pre-B cell cDNA library where five overlapping cDNA clones were obtained. The entire set of overlapping clones was sequenced and reassembled. The entire nucleotide sequence of the cDNA contains 5433 bp with a single open reading frame coding for

Isolation of human DNA polymerase α catalytic polypeptide by immunoaffinity protocol

Trypsin digestion of polymerase α catalytic polypeptide and separate
tryptic peptides by reverse phase HPLC

Amino acid sequence determination of tryptic peptides

Select seven peptides to design oligodeoxynucleotide probes

Make cDNA library from size-selected KB cell mRNA (>4 Kb)

Screen library at stringency of >85% probe-target homology

Confirmation of positive clones:

(1) Southern blot analysis with genomic DNA from 1X and 4X
     chromosome cell lines

(2) Northern blot analysis

(3) Nucleotide sequence analysis to match the sequence of probe used
     and correlated with previous determined amino acid sequence.

Figure 5 Strategy of human DNA polymerase α cDNA cloning.

1462 amino acids. A potential ATG initiation codon flanked by nucleotide sequences matching Kozak's criteria for translation initiation site was identified. The deduced amino acid sequence identifies all seven previously determined peptide sequences and derives a minimum molecular weight of 165,000. Primer extension identifies a transcription initiation site 295 nucleotides upstream of the putative translation start site. These results indicate a near-full-length cDNA has been isolated.

Discussion

Prerequisite to understanding of eukaryotic DNA replication is a thorough study of the key DNA replicative proteins. In an attempt to achieve this objective, a strategy was formulated as described above to study the principal chromosomal replicative enzyme, DNA polymerase α.

The immunoaffinity-purified enzyme fraction indicates the catalytic polypeptide is a family of proteins from 180 to 125 kD, with all being derivatives of the same primary structure. The polymerase protein deduced from cDNA is of minimum M_r 165,000. The discrepancy between the observed 180,000 and the derived 165,000 molecular weight could mean either there is an additional 15 kD of coding sequence upstream of the putative translation start site or it is due to posttranslation modification.

Another question is whether DNA polymerase α is the sole polymerizing enzyme for eukaryotic chromosome replication or whether DNA polymerase δ is also required; if so, what is the relationship between polymerase α and δ? One report described the requirement of a cellular protein, proliferating cell nuclear antigen (PCNA), for efficient viral DNA chain elongation in vitro (Prelich et al. 1987a) and the discovery that this protein is the accessory factor for polymerase δ, not α (Bravo et al. 1987; Prelich et al. 1987b), implying polymerase δ plays a role in eukaryotic DNA replication. Another report demonstrated that DNA polymerase α catalytic polypeptide of *Drosophila* contains a cryptic proofreading 3′–5′ exonuclease when separated from other associated subunits (Cotterill et al. 1987). Characterization of the enzymological properties of the recombinant polymerase α will definitely provide an answer to this interesting problem.

Acknowledgments

This research is supported by grant CA-14835 from the National Cancer Institute and by a gift from the D. Baxter Fund. S.W.W. is a predoctoral fellow supported by National Institutes of Health training grant CA-09302.

References

Bravo, R., R. Frank, P.A. Blundell, and H. Macdonald-Bravo. 1987. Cyclin/PCNA is the auxiliary protein of DNA polymerase δ. *Nature* **326:** 515.

Cotterill, S.M., M.E. Reyland, L.A. Loeb, and I.R. Lehman. 1987. A cryptic proofreading 3′-5′ exonuclease associated with the polymerase subunit of the DNA polymerase-primase from *Drosophila melanogaster. Proc. Natl. Acad. Sci.* **84:** 5635.

Dale, R.M.K., B.A. McClure, and J.P. Houchins. 1985. A rapid single-stranded cloning strategy for producing a sequential series of overlapping clones for use in DNA sequencing: Application to sequencing the corn mitochondrial 18S rDNA. *Plasmid* **13:** 31.

Fry, M. and L.A. Loeb, eds. 1986. DNA polymerase α. In *Animal cell DNA polymerase*, p. 13. CRC Press, Boca Raton, Florida.

Goodfellow, P., B. Ryan, T. Mohandas, and L.J. Shapiro. 1984. The cell surface antigen locus, M1C2X, is escaped X-inactivation. *Am. J. Hum. Genet.* **36:** 777.

Hunkapiller, M.W., R.M. Hewick, W.J. Dreyer, and L.E. Hood. 1983. High-sensitivity sequencing with a gas-phase sequenator. *Methods Enzymol.* **91:** 399.

Kornberg, A. 1980. *DNA replication.* W.H. Freeman, San Francisco.

———. 1982. *Supplement to DNA replication.* W.H. Freeman, San Francisco.

Lathe, R. 1985. Synthetic oligonucleotide probes deduce from amino acid sequence data. Theoretical and practical considerations. *J. Mol. Biol.* **183:** 1.

Levy, R., J. Dilley, R.I. Fox, and R. Warnke. 1979. A human thymus-leukemia antigen defined by hybridoma monoclonal antibodies. *Proc. Natl. Acad. Sci.* **76:** 6552.

Lischwe, M.A. and D. Ochs. 1982. A new method for partial peptide mapping using *N*-chlorosuccinimide/urea and peptide silver staining in sodium dodecyl-sulfate-polyacrylamide gels. *Anal. Biochem.* **127:** 453.

Prelich, G., M. Kostura, D.R. Marshak, M.B. Mathews, and B. Stillman. 1987a. The cell-cycle regulated proliferating cell nuclear antigen is required for SV40 DNA replication in vitro. *Nature* **326:** 471.

Prelich, G., C.-K. Tan, M. Kostura, M.B. Mathews, A.G. So, K.M. Downey, and B. Stillman. 1987b. Functional identity of proliferating cell nuclear antigen and a DNA polymerase δ auxiliary protein. *Nature* **326:** 517.

Tanaka, S., S.-Z. Hu, T.S.-F. Wang, and D. Korn. 1982. Preparation and preliminary characterization of monoclonal antibodies against human DNA polymerase α. *J. Biol. Chem.* **257:** 8386.

Wang, T.S.-F., S.-Z. Hu, and D. Korn. 1984. DNA primase from KB cells. Characterization of a primase activity tightly associated with immunoaffinity-purified DNA polymerase α. *J. Biol. Chem.* **259:** 1854.

Wang, T.S.-F., B.E. Pearson, H.A. Suomalainen, T. Mohandas, L.J. Shapiro, J. Schroder, and D. Korn. 1985. Assignment of the gene for human DNA polymerase α to the X chromosome. *Proc. Natl. Acad. Sci.* **82:** 5270.

Wong, S.W., L.R. Paborsky, P.A. Fisher, T.S.-F. Wang, and D. Korn. 1986. Structural and enzymological characterization of immunoaffinity-purified DNA polymerase α · DNA primase complex from KB cells. *J. Biol. Chem.* **261:** 7958.

Wong, S.W., A.F. Wahl, P.M. Yuan, N. Arai, B.E. Pearson, K. Arai, D. Korn, M.W. Hunkapiller, and T.S.-F. Wang. 1988. Human DNA polymerase α gene expression is cell proliferation dependent and its primary structure is similar to both prokaryotic and eukaryotic replicative DNA polymerases. *EMBO J.* **7:** 37.

Discontinuous DNA Synthesis by Purified Proteins from Mammalian Cells

M. Goulian, C. Carton, L. DeGrandpre, C. Heard, B. Olinger, and S. Richards

University of California, San Diego, Department of Medicine (M-013-G) and Center for Molecular Genetics, La Jolla, California 92093

We have purified five proteins from cultured mouse cells which, when incubated with a single-stranded circular DNA (in presence of rNTPs and dNTPs), convert it to a duplex covalent circle by a discontinuous mechanism. The five proteins are polymerase α−primase, RNase H-1, DNA ligase I, and two "accessory" factors (AF). One of the accessory proteins (AF-1) stimulates polymerase α−primase under conditions that require coordinate activity of the polymerase and primase, and appears to convert the mechanism from distributive to processive. Polymerase α−primase plus AF-1 together convert the single-stranded DNA circle to a duplex in which the new strand consists of many RNA-primed DNA fragments, ranging in size from 100 to 1500 nucleotides. When RNase H-1, DNA ligase I, and an additional accessory protein (AF-2) are also present during the incubation along with polymerase α−primase and AF-1 (or are added subsequently), the discontinuous product is converted to continuous strand. AF-2 is a 5′-3′ exonuclease and is probably required to excise residual ribonucleotide(s) remaining after partial removal of the oligoribonucleotide primer by RNase H-1, allowing ligation of the fragments. No additional gap-filling polymerase is required other than the polymerase α−primase that is already present.

From what is known about discontinuous DNA synthesis at the "lagging strand" of replication forks, it is assumed that at least four different enzymatic activities take part: primase, DNA polymerase, RNase H, and DNA ligase (Kornberg 1980, 1982). The studies described here represent an effort to reproduce a discontinuous synthesis mechanism in vitro with purified mammalian cell proteins that provide these functions.

Methods

Reactions were ordinarily carried out in 20-μl volume containing buffer, salts, dithiothreitol, dNTPs, rNTPs, and varying amounts of template single-strand circles (ssc) DNA (fd). Polymerase α assay was as described previously (Kollek and Goulian 1981), and assays using unprimed poly(dT) contained 20 μg/ml poly(dT), labeled dATP, and unlabeled rATP. The RNase H assay measured solubilization of the ^{32}P-labeled RNA strand of a RNA-DNA hybrid that had been synthesized with *Escherichia coli* RNA polymerase using a ssc DNA (fd) as template. Ligase was assayed by the formation of dAT circles, determined by inaccessibility of the [^{3}H]dAT to exonuclease (Modrich and Lehman 1970).

DNA polymerase α−primase was purified from a mouse lymphoid cell line (L1210) using five steps (phosphocellulose, DEAE-cellulose, DNA-cellulose, gel filtration, and hydroxylapatite [M. Goulian et al., in prep.]). AF-1 was purified by the same five steps using the stimulation of polymerase α−primase on unprimed poly-(dT) as an assay (M. Goulian et al., in prep.). RNase H and DNA ligase were purified with the same procedure as for polymerase α−primase and AF-1. AF-2 was purified with six steps (phosphocellulose, hydroxylapatite, Bio-Rex 70, DNA-cellulose, DEAE-cellulose, glycerol gradient) using an assay described below (M. Goulian et al., in prep.).

Results and Discussion

DNA polymerase α−primase (Yagura et al. 1982; Conaway and Lehman 1982) was purified ~200-fold with 20–40% recovery and a final specific activity of ~20,000 units/mg. No endo- or exonuclease activity could be detected in the most purified enzyme.

During the course of the purification of polymerase α−primase there appeared to be a partial dissociation of the activity in the standard polymerase α assay (with activated DNA) from the activity with unprimed poly(dT). Mixing experiments showed that this resulted from a stimulatory activity (with poly[dT]) that partially overlapped the peak of polymerase α−primase. Using the stimulation of polymerase α−primase on unprimed poly-(dT) as an assay, the stimulatory activity (AF-1) was purified from the same cultured mouse cells that were used as a source of polymerase α−primase.

AF-1 does not have an effect on polymerase α in the standard assay with activated DNA; however, it does stimulate polymerase α−primase on unprimed single-stranded DNA templates. Depending on the conditions used, the stimulation can vary between three- to fourfold on up to greater than 20-fold (Goulian et al. 1987 and in prep.).

393

In addition to stimulating incorporation, AF-1 had a profound effect on the nature of the product. When template ssc was in excess, the products (analyzed by neutral gel electrophoresis) were found in a dual distribution: molecules with incorporated radioactivity at or near the position of fully replicated circles (corresponding to the marker for "open" or relaxed duplex circles) and nonradioactive ssc template (Goulian et al. 1987 and in prep.). The same reaction mixture without AF-1 resulted in a small amount of replication on *all* of the template molecules, the typical product of distributive synthesis seen with most highly purified DNA polymerases in the absence of their processivity factors (Kornberg 1980, 1982). In all cases, the product strand consisted of many fragments, ranging in size from 100 to 1500 nucleotides, each bearing a short RNA primer at the 5′ end.

These results suggested features of processivity in the reaction of polymerase α–primase in the presence of AF-1. We have three kinds of information concerning the question of processivity (M. Goulian et al., in prep.).

1. Dilution experiments during the first round of replication; there appeared to be a slight effect at the highest dilutions (which were up to 50-fold); however, the effect was much less than expected from the effect of dilution before addition of polymerase α–primase and AF-1.
2. Competition experiments; no effect was detected when an excess of circles carrying multiple primers were added during the first round of replication.
3. When the circles with multiple primers were used as template, the presence of AF-1 again resulted in "preferential" completion of a subset of the primed circles, similar to what was seen with unprimed circles.

From the results thus far, we would postulate that AF-1 remains associated with a template ssc until synthesis is largely completed, before detaching and resuming the process with another molecule.

It is less clear whether polymerase α–primase also remains on a template along with AF-1 through each cycle, as opposed to detaching many times but usually reassociating with the subset of template molecules on which AF-1 is present.

AF-1 has no detectable NTPase (with or without DNA); no polymerase, nuclease, ligase, or topoisomerase. With current preparations of AF-1, we have not been able to show an effect on chain propagation by polymerase α, nor on synthesis of primers by primase, when these functions are measured separately. The effects of AF-1 are seen only with the coordinate activity of polymerase α and primase. The relationship of AF-1 to stimulatory proteins described by others (Yagura et al. 1982; Pritchard et al. 1983; Fry et al. 1985) remains to be defined.

Using the synthesis by polymerase α–primase + AF-1 of a complementary strand consisting of multiple independently primed fragments as a model for the initial

steps in synthesis of the lagging strand, we attempted to carry the reaction further.

A concentrated crude cell extract readily converted some of the discontinuous product to covalently closed circles (Fig. 1). Attempts to purify directly the activities required for this by such an assay were not successful, at least in part because of interfering nuclease activities, which were much more prominent in fractions than in concentrated whole crude extract. We therefore purified activities that are expected to be required for formation of continuous strand from the fragments, i.e., RNAse H and DNA ligase. The RNase H that we purified has been designated H-1 (Cathala et al. 1979) or the large-molecular-weight RNase H (Crouch and Dirksen 1985), and the ligase was ligase I (Söderhäll and Lindahl 1976).

When highly purified RNase H-1 and ligase-I were added to the reaction mixture of polymerase α–primase, AF-1, and fd ssc (either before incubation or after conversion of the ssc to duplex circles), there was no effect observed on the product, in either neutral or alkaline gels. However, crude extracts, now even at high dilutions, added in addition to the RNase H and ligase, resulted in prompt and efficient conversion of the fragments to continuous strand. Although initially we used neutral gels containing ethidium bromide to detect this (as in Fig. 1), we found alkaline gels provide much more information. With alkaline gels, partial joining can be seen, as well (Fig. 2), whereas neutral/ethidium bromide gels detected only covalently closed circular product.

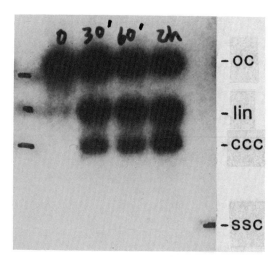

Figure 1 Conversion of product of polymerase α–primase (+ AF-1) with single-strand DNA circles to duplex covalent circles by crude cell extracts. Duplex circles with discontinuous synthetic strands were prepared by incubation of polymerase α–primase + AF-1 for 30 min with a limiting amount of fd ssc (see above, Results and Discussion; Goulian et al. 1987). Portions were re-incubated with concentrated crude cell extract for 30 min, 60 min, and 2 hr, after which they were electrophoresed in neutral agarose gel containing ethidium bromide. The first lane shows the product after the first incubation only. (oc) open "relaxed" duplex circles; (lin) linear duplex; (ccc) covalently closed duplex circles; (ssc) single-stranded circles.

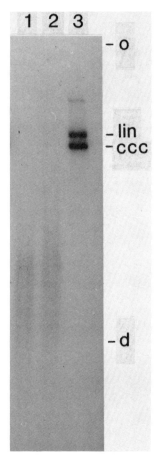

1 2 3

- o

- lin
- ccc

- d

Figure 2 Formation of continuous high-molecular-weight DNA strands via discontinuous intermediate by purified proteins. Polymerase α–primase, AF-1, RNase H-1, and ligase I were incubated 30 min with a limiting amount of fd ssc to form duplex circles with discontinuous synthetic strands. Portions were re-incubated with excess AF-2 (lane *3*), limiting AF-2 (1/30 the amount in lane *3*; lane *2*), and enzyme dilution buffer (lane *1*), following which they were analyzed in alkaline agarose gel. (o) Sample wells; (lin) linear; (ccc) covalently closed circles; (d) dye.

Using alkaline gel analysis of the product resulting from incubation with the four proteins (+ ssc) as an assay, we have purified the "circle closing activity" or accessory factor-2 (AF-2). The purified AF-2 is associated with a 44–46-kD exonuclease. It has no detectable polymerase, NTPase, RNase H, or ligase activity, nor does it stimulate these. The exonuclease attacks single- and double-stranded deoxypolymers, exclusively from the 5′ terminus, and produces primarily mononucleotides, except for poly(dAT), for which most of the product is dinucleotides. The relationship to previously described mammalian 5′-3′ exonucleases DNase IV and VIII is not yet certain. It differs from DNase VII in several respects (Pedrini and Grossman 1983), whereas it shows some but not all of the reported properties of DNase IV (Lindahl et al. 1969).

We think that the exonuclease probably functions in our system by excising one or a few ribonucleotides that remain after removal of most of the primer by RNase H-1, which is an endonuclease and known to be ineffi-

cient in removing the last 1 or 2 ribonucleotides at an RNA-DNA junction (Crouch and Dirksen 1985). From results of experiments with model substrates, the exonuclease does appear to have this ability (M. Goulian et al., in prep.). Thus, we are suggesting that the combined action of RNase H-1 and the exonuclease completely removes primer ribonucleotides, allowing ligation to occur.

It has been reported in the past that polymerase α is deficient in, or incapable of, gap filling (DePamphilis and Wassarman 1980). At least under the conditions of these experiments, polymerase α–primase, the only DNA polymerase present, is capable of completely filling gaps.

In summary, we have purified five mouse cell proteins, polymerase α–primase, an accessory factor for polymerase α–primase, RNase H-1, ligase I, and an exonuclease, which, acting together, convert a single strand to a double strand by a discontinuous mechanism, reproducing some of the essential features of DNA synthesis that are believed to take place at the lagging strand of replication forks. It remains to be shown that, aside from polymerase α–primase, these particular proteins are actually participants in DNA replication in the intact cell.

Acknowledgment

This work was supported by United States Public Health Service grant CA-11705.

References

Cathala, G., J. Rech, J. Huet, and P. Jeanteur. 1979. Isolation and characterization of two types of ribonuclease H in Krebs II ascites cells. *J. Biol. Chem.* **254:** 7353.

Conaway, R.C. and I.R. Lehman. 1982. A DNA primase activity associated with DNA polymerase α from *Drosophila melanogaster* embryos. *Proc. Natl. Acad. Sci.* **79:** 2523.

Crouch, R.J. and M.-L. Dirksen. 1985. Ribonuclease H. In *Nucleases* (ed. S.M. Linn and R.J. Roberts), p. 211. Cold Spring Harbor Laboratory, Cold Spring Harbor, New York.

DePamphilis, M.L. and P.M. Wassarman. 1980. Replication of eukaryotic chromosomes: A close-up of the replication fork. *Annu. Rev. Biochem.* **49:** 627.

Fry, M., J. Lapidot, and P. Weisman-Shomer. 1985. A DNA template recognition protein: Partial purification from mouse liver and stimulation of DNA polymerase α. *Biochemistry* **24:** 7549.

Goulian, M., C. Carton, L. De Grandpre, B. Olinger, and S. Richards. 1987. Processive discontinuous DNA synthesis by mammalian DNA polymerase α primase. *UCLA Symp. Mol. Cell. Biol. New Ser.* **47:** 101.

Kollek, R. and M. Goulian. 1981. Synthesis of parvovirus H-1 replicative form from viral DNA by DNA polymerase γ. *Proc. Natl. Acad. Sci.* **78:** 6206.

Kornberg, A. 1980. *DNA replication.* W.H. Freeman, San Francisco.

———. 1982. *Supplement to DNA replication.* W.H. Freeman, San Francisco.

Lindahl, T., J.A. Gally, and G.M. Edelman. 1969. Deoxyribonuclease IV: A new exonuclease from mammalian tissues. *Proc. Natl. Acad. Sci.* **62:** 597.

Modrich, P. and I.R. Lehman. 1970. Enzymatic joining of poly-nucleotides. IX. A simple and rapid assay of polynucleotide joining (ligase) activity by measurement of circle formation from linear deoxyadenylate-deoxythymidylate polymer. *J. Biol. Chem.* **245:** 3626.

Pedrini, A.M. and L. Grossman. 1983. Purification and charac-terization of DNase VIII. A 5'-3' directed exonuclease from human placental nuclei. *J. Biol. Chem.* **258:** 1536,

Pritchard, C.G., D.T. Weaver, E.F. Baril, and M.L. DePam-philis. 1983. DNA polymerase α cofactors C_1C_2 function as primer recognition proteins. *J. Biol. Chem.* **258:** 9810.

Söderhäll, S. and T. Lindahl. 1976. DNA ligases of eukaryotes. *FEBS Lett.* **67:** 1.

Yagura, T., T. Kozu, and T. Seno. 1982. Mouse DNA primase accompanied by a novel RNA polymerase activity: Purifica-tion and partial characterization. *J. Biochem.* **91:** 607.

Structure and Properties of the Immunoaffinity-purified DNA Polymerase α–Primase Complex

F. Grosse and H.-P. Nasheuer

Max-Planck-Institute for Experimental Medicine, Department of Chemistry, D-3400 Goettingen, Federal Republic of Germany

The DNA polymerase α–primase complex from calf thymus was purified to near homogeneity by utilizing immobilized monoclonal antibodies as the principal purification step. From 1 kg thymus the procedure yielded 1–2 mg DNA polymerase α–primase complex. The complex sedimented at 9S and exhibited a Stokes radius of 6.0 nm. Sodium dodecyl sulfate polyacrylamide gel electrophoresis (SDS-PAGE) of the pure enzyme revealed bands at 148–180, and at 73, 59, and 48 kD in a relative stoichiometry of 1:1:3:3. As compared to the conventional preparation, the immunoaffinity-purified DNA polymerase α–primase complex displayed several features of a more intact enzyme. The K_m for binding to singly RNA-primed M13 DNA was 3 nM, and the K_i for binding to unprimed M13 DNA was 70 μM (nucleotide). The dNTP K_ms were between 0.6 and 0.9 μM. The DNA polymerase α–primase complex converted single-stranded M13 DNA into the double-stranded form within 10–30 minutes. With singly RNA-primed M13 DNA, the polymerase-primase exhibited an elongation rate of 26 nucleotides per second. Both potassium chloride and potassium acetate stimulated DNA synthesis two- to threefold at concentrations of 90–150 mM and 120–180 mM, respectively, when activated DNA served as a template-primer. Stimulation was 1.3- to 2-fold with 60–90 mM KCl and 60–120 mM potassium acetate, when primase-primed M13 replication was measured. The primase was extracted from the polymerase-primase and found to be associated with the 59- and the 48-kD polypeptides. Physical separation of the 48- and the 59-kD subunits demonstrated that only the 48-kD subunit was necessary for RNA primer formation. However, the 59-kD subunit stabilized the primase activity considerably.

The purification and characterization of DNA polymerase α, the main replicative entity in higher eukaryotes, has proven to be a difficult task. Although initial attempts to purify this enzyme date back nearly three decades (Bollum 1960), the subunit structure, the enzymatic features, and its association with accessory proteins have remained controversial. Recent advances in utilizing immobilized monoclonal antibodies for the purification of this enzyme clarified the picture considerably (Chang et al. 1984; Wahl et al. 1984; Wang et al. 1984; Holmes et al. 1986; Wong et al. 1986). In those preparations, DNA polymerase α typically consists of three to five subunits, sediments at 9S through sucrose gradients, and displays both DNA polymerase and DNA primase activities. Thus the structure and properties of the immunoaffinity-purified enzymes are similar to the 9S forms that have been isolated earlier by conventional column chromatography (Banks et al. 1979; Grosse and Krauss 1981, 1985; Masaki et al. 1982; Kaguni et al. 1983a).

In the present paper, we describe an immunoaffinity-purification protocol for the DNA polymerase α–primase complex from calf thymus that is based on the use of a commercially available monoclonal antibody. The polymerase-primase isolated in this way displayed many properties that come close to those that must exist for in vivo function, such as low K_ms for dNTPs and primers, a salt optimum at near physiological ionic strengths, and an elongation rate on single-stranded DNA approaching the in vivo rate of replicational fork migration. We also describe a method for the separation of the primase activity from the polymerase-primase complex. This allowed us to assign the catalytic site for RNA formation to the 48-kD subunit. The 59-kD subunit was mandatory for the stability of the DNA primase activity.

Experimental Procedures

Enzyme assays

DNA polymerase α and DNA primase activities were measured as described in our earlier publications (Grosse and Krauss 1981, 1984, 1985).

Immunoaffinity purification of DNA polymerase α and free DNA primase

An isotonic cytosolic extract was prepared from 1 kg calf thymus as described earlier (Schomburg and Grosse 1986). Batch concentration of pol α on phosphocellulose and subsequent chromatography on heparin-Sepharose were performed as described by Grosse and Krauss (1981). Immunoaffinity chromatography was performed on a 2-ml Sepharose 4B-column loaded with 8 mg BrCN-immobilized monoclonal antibody SJK287-38 (Tanaka et al. 1982). To obtain the intact DNA polymerase α–primase complex, the antibody column was eluted with 0.1 M K_3PO_4 (pH 13.2), 1 M KCl, 10% glycerol (Fig. 1A). To obtain the free DNA primase, the antibody column was eluted with 0.1 M K_2HPO_4 (pH 11.5), 1 M KCl, 10% glycerol (Fig. 1B, lane 1). After

397

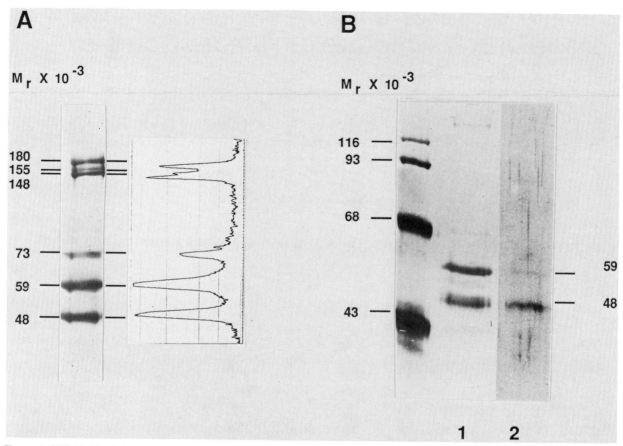

Figure 1 SDS-PAGE of the immunoaffinity-purified DNA polymerase α−primase complex. (*A*) Polypeptide structure of the pH 13.2 eluted DNA polymerase α−primase complex. (*B*) Polypeptide structure of the pH 11.5 eluted free DNA primase (lane *1*), and the DEAE-cellulose flow-through fraction of the free DNA primase (lane *2*).

elution, the fractions were adjusted to pH 7–8 by the addition of an appropriate amount of 0.5 M KH_2PO_4 and made 4 mM in dithiothreitol.

Physical separation of the 48- and the 59-kD subunits of the free DNA primase

Freshly eluted free DNA primase was dialyzed against 10 mM KH_2PO_4/K_2HPO_4 (pH 7.2), 10 mM $Na_2S_2O_5$, 4 mM dithiothreitol, 20% glycerol, and loaded on 100 μl DE-52 cellulose (Whatman), equilibrated with the same buffer. The flow-through was fractionated drop-wise (50 μl) into siliconized Eppendorf tubes. Primase-containing fractions were combined (Fig. 1B, lane 2) and used as soon as possible for enzymatic characterization. The half-life of DE-52-purified primase was about 60 minutes at 0°C.

Results

Physical structure and properties of the immunoaffinity-purified DNA polymerase α−primase complex

From the given protocol, 1–2 mg of nearly homogeneous polymerase-primase was obtained in a 15% yield from 1 kg calf thymus. The specific activity of pol α was 30,000–40,000 units/mg and the primase specific activity was 15,000–20,000 units/mg (Table 1). A typical enzyme preparation consisted of a cluster of α-subunits with M_rs of 180,000, 150,000, and 148,000 (α-subunit cluster) and three further subunits with M_rs of 73,000 (β-subunit), 59,000 (γ-subunit), and 48,000 (δ-subunit) (Fig. 1A). The relative intensity of the α-subunit cluster to the intensities of the three smaller subunits was roughly 1:1:3:3 (Fig. 1A). Upon zonal centrifugation through a sucrose gradient, pol α and DNA primase sedimented together at 9S in the presence of 0.5 M KCl. Part of the primase activity was separated from the complex under this condition (Fig. 2A). The separated primase cosedimented with polypeptides of M_r 59,000 and 48,000 (Fig. 2B). This result suggests that subunits that are present in a molar excess to the α-subunit cluster must be rather loosely associated to the whole complex. Similarly, gel filtration of the entire complex on a calibrated Sepharose 6B column revealed a Stokes radius of 60 Å. From these data one can calculate an M_r of 335,000 and a frictional ratio f/f_o of 1.31 for the native enzyme by following the method of Siegel and Monty (1966) and assuming a partial specific volume of 0.725 cm^3/g. The calculated M_r for the native enzyme complex is in a reasonable agreement with a 1:1:1:1

Table 1 Immunoaffinity Purification of the DNA Polymerase α–Primase Complex and Free DNA Primase from Calf Thymus

Fraction	Protein (mg)	Total activity (units)		Sp. act. (units/mg)		Yield (%)	
		pol-α	primase	pol-α	primase	pol-α	primase
Crude extract[a]	40,000	300,000	105,000	3.5	1	100	100
Phospho-cellulose	400	130,000	49,000	120	30	43	47
Heparin-Sepharose	80	90,000	35,000	500	400	30	37
MCAbC[b]:pH 11.5 eluate	0.06	360	3,600	1,500	24,000	0.1	3.3
MCAbC[b]:pH 13.2 eluate	1.6	46,000	15,000	29,000	15,000	15	14

[a]Data are based on the purification from 1 kg calf thymus.
[b]Monoclonal antibody column.

A

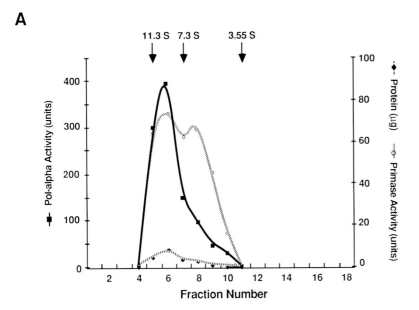

B

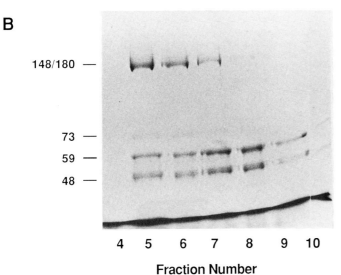

Figure 2 Preparative ultracentrifugation of the immunoaffinity-purified polymerase-primase. 100 μg of the pH 13.2 eluted polymerase-primase was sedimented at 4°C in a 5–20% linear sucrose gradient in the presence of 0.5 M KCl at 40,000 rpm for 16 hr in a Beckman SW56 rotor. (*A*) Aliquots of each fraction were assayed for protein (◆), polymerase (■), and primase (◇) activity. (*B*) SDS-PAGE of 100 μl of each fraction (with the exception of fraction 6, where only 30 μl were taken to avoid an overloading of the gel). Standard proteins, catalase (11.3S), lactate dehydrogenase (7.3S), and ovalbumin (3.55S) were analyzed on a separate gradient.

stoichiometry for the four subunits. The frictional ratio suggests a rather moderate elongated structure of the complex, comparable to serum albumin.

Physical structure and properties of the DNA primase separated from the immunoaffinity-purified DNA polymerase α–primase complex

Free DNA primase was separated from the entire complex by either zonal centrifugation as shown in Figure 2 or by treating the antibody-bound polymerase-primase with 0.1 M K_2HPO_4 (pH 11.5), 1 M KCl as described under Experimental Procedures. Both procedures yielded a DNA primase that consisted of two subunits with M_rs of 59,000 and 48,000 (Fig. 1B, lane 1). The specific activity was determined to be 30,000 units / mg. Free DNA primase sedimented through a sucrose gradient at the same position as DNA polymerase I from *E. coli*, i.e., 5.7S (data not shown). This indicates that the two smallest subunits form a rather tight 1 to 1 complex.

Immunoaffinity-purified DNA polymerase α and DNA primase display novel features

The immunoaffinity-purified DNA polymerase α is inhibited by 10 mM *N*-ethylmaleimide to 0.3% of its maximal activity. The K_i for aphidicolin, a competitive inhibitor for dCTP, was measured to be 0.6 μM. A 3′–5′ exonuclease, which characterizes DNA polymerase δ, was beyond the limit of detection (less than 10^{-7} dNMPs hydrolyzed per nucleotide incorporated). These features prove that we are really dealing with the α type of the eukaryotic enzyme. ATP, in concentrations of 0.1 to 5 mM, had no influence on the rate and extent of DNA synthesis on activated or double-stranded DNA (Table 2). On single-stranded DNA, ATP promoted priming. Priming was further stimulated by the addition of the other three rNTPs. Under these conditions, complex-bound primase and free primase formed RNA primers comprising 5–10 nucleotides when dNTPs were present and 5–10 and 15–25 nucleotides in the absence of dNTPs (Fig. 3). As observed with the conventionally purified polymerase-primase, 3–10 primers were formed upon replication of primase-initiated M13 DNA (data not shown).

Besides these well-known characteristics of polymerase-primase, the immunoaffinity-purified complex displayed several new properties characteristic for a more in vivo-like enzyme. Thus, self-primed in vitro replication of M13 (+) strand DNA was achievable with 10–30 minutes (Fig. 4). K_ms for dNTP binding were in the submicromolar range (Table 2), the K_m for binding to the 3′ end of singly RNA-primed M13 DNA was determined to be 3 mM, which is tenfold lower than that determined for the conventionally purified pol α. Moreover, unspecific binding to unprimed M13 DNA was fivefold lower for the immunoaffinity-purified enzyme as compared with the earlier preparation (Table 2). Perhaps most striking was the result that both pol α and primase activity were stimulated by salt. The salt optimum for pol α was determined to be at 90–150 mM KCl and 120–180 mM K-acetate, when activated DNA served as a template-primer. On measuring the self-primed

Table 2 Properties of the Immunoaffinity Purified DNA Polymerase α–Primase Complex

Template primer utilization[a]	(% of maximum)	
activated DNA	100	(100)[b]
activated DNA + 10 mM NEM	0.3	(0.2)
activated DNA + 0.1–5 mM ATP	100	
denatured calf thymus DNA	63	
poly(dA)·(dT)$_{10}$	41	(14)
alternating poly(dA-dT)	21	(16)
M13 single-stranded DNA	0.1	(0.1)
M13 single-stranded DNA + 1 mM ATP	15	
M13 single-stranded DNA + 1 mM ATP + 0.1 mM each of GTP, CTP, and UTP	25	(6.4)

Salt[c]	Activated DNA				Primase-printed M13 DNA			
	K-acetate		KCl		K-acetate		KCl	
(mM)	(% of maximum)				(% of maximum)			
0	25	(28)	25	(28)	46	(100)	70	(100)
30	48	(48)	44	(98)	70	(92)	86	(80)
60	61	(73)	63	(98)	89	(70)	97	(63)
90	76	(99)	96	(92)	100	(67)	100	(37)
120	96	(86)	96	(60)	84	(52)	72	(1)
150	98	(62)	84	(40)	42	(20)	18	(0)
180	85	(50)	42	(28)	1	(1)	0	(0)

Michaelis constants[d]	(μM)	
dATP	0.8	(4.2)
dGTP	0.6	(4.5)
dCTP	0.7	(6.7)
dTTP	0.9	(5.3)
aphidicolin (= K_i)	0.6	(3.2)
singly RNA-primed M13 DNA	0.003	(0.04)
unprimed M13 DNA (= K_i) (in μM nucleotides)	70	(12)
V_{max} on singly RNA-primed M13 DNA[e] (in nucleotides incorporated per second)	26	
processivity[f] (nucleotides incorporated per primer binding)	20	(20)

[a]The experiments were performed with 2.4 units of the pH 13.2 eluted enzyme in a 50 μl reaction containing 20 mM Tris-acetate (pH 7.3), 75 mM potassium acetate, 5 mM magnesium acetate, 1 mM dithiothreitol, 0.1 mM (each) of dNTPs, 10 cpm / pmol [α-^{32}P]dATP, and 0.1 mg/ml BSA. 0.2 mg/ml activated DNA, 0.1 mM (nucleotide) synthetic DNA, or 50 μM (nucleotide) M13(+) strand DNA served as templates. 1 unit pol α catalyzes the incorporation of 1 nmol dATP into acid-insoluble material in 1 hr at 37°C with activated DNA as a template primer.

[b]Data in parentheses were measured for the conventionally purified pol α–primase (Grosse and Krauss 1981).

[c]DNA synthesis was measured in 20 μl samples with 2 units pol α on either 0.2 mg/ml activated DNA or 50 μM (nucleotide) (+) strand M13 DNA. With the latter template, DNA priming was achieved by the addition of 1 mM ATP and 0.1 mM (each) GTP, CTP, and UTP.

[d]K_m's for dNTP utilization and the K_i for aphidicolin inhibition were determined with activated DNA. Singly RNA-primed M13 DNA was prepared as described by Grosse and Krauss (1984).

[e]Estimated by measuring the primer elongation at various incubation times. Primer lengths were determined by agarose gel electrophoresis under alkaline conditions.

[f]Determined by primer extension on poly(dT)·(rA)$_{10}$ as described by Hohn and Grosse (1987).

M13 DNA replication, salt optima were found to be at 60–90 mM KCl and 60–120 mM K-acetate (Table 2). The free primase displayed optimal activity at 50 mM K-acetate and half of the maximal activity at salt concentrations between 150 and 200 mM (data not shown). This contrasts to earlier findings on the conventionally purified polymerase-primase where primase activity was

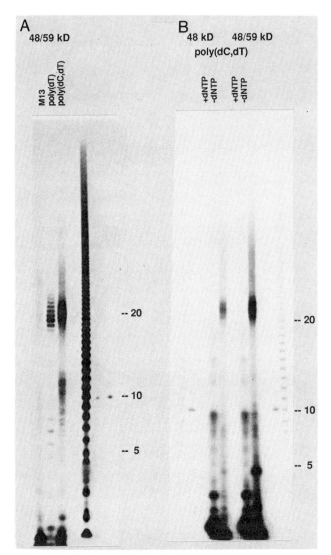

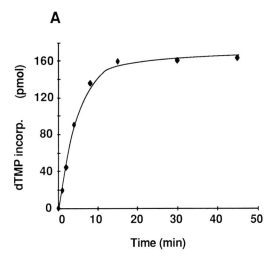

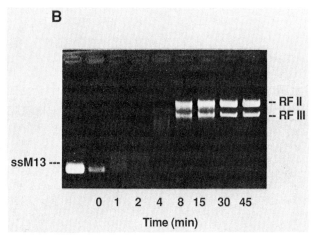

Figure 3 Primer formation by the pH 11.5 eluted free primase, and the 48-kD subunit of the free primase, essentially the same fraction as shown in Fig. 1B, lane 2. 100 μM of each of the templates were primed for 30 min with 100 units/ml of the free primase, or the 48-kD subunit at 37°C. 500 μM [α-³²P]ATP and/or 100 μM[α-³²P]GTP (10 Ci/mmol) served as the substrate. (A) RNA primer formation by the free heterodimeric DNA primase in the absence of dNTPs. Lane *1* shows RNA primers formed on single-stranded M13 DNA, lane *2* shows products on poly(dT), and lane *3* shows products on poly(dC,dT). (B) RNA primer formation by the isolated 48-kD subunit in the presence (lane *1*) or absence (lane *2*) of dNTPs. Lanes *3* and *4* show primers formed by the heterodimeric primase, the load fraction of DEAE-cellulose, from which the 48-kD subunit was separated.

Figure 4 Replication of single-stranded M13 DNA by the immunoaffinity-purified DNA polymerase α–primase complex. (A) M13mp8 (+) strand (50 μM) was replicated with 500 units/ml polymerase-primase in the presence of the four dNTPs and rNTPs. At the times indicated, samples were withdrawn and acid-precipitable radioactivity was determined. (B) Agarose gel electrophoresis of the replication products after various times of incubation.

inhibited at any salt concentration tested (Grosse and Krauss 1985).

Assignment of the polypeptide responsible for primase activity

The two subunits of the primase could be separated from each other by chromatography on DEAE-cellulose. Free primase bound to DEAE-cellulose under conditions of low ionic strengths (10 mM K$_i$PO$_4$ [pH 7.8], 10 mM Na$_2$S$_2$O$_5$). However, 5–10% of the total activity applied

to the column was reproducibly found in the flow-through fraction. The specific activity in the flow-through was about 40,000 units/mg when measured immediately after elution from the column. A genuine primase function of this fraction was demonstrated by product analysis using poly(dC, dT) as a template and ATP and GTP as substrates. Like the free primase of the loading fraction, the flow-through material could form products comprising 5–10 nucleotides in the presence of dNTPs and 5–10 and 15–25 nucleotides in the absence of dNTPs (Fig. 3B). Analysis of the flow-through activity by SDS-gel electrophoresis revealed one major band with a molecular mass of 48,000, contaminated by at most 5% of a band with an M_r 59,000 (Fig. 1B, lane 2). This suggests that only the 48,000 polypeptide is necessary for DNA primase function. Since the activity of the 48,000 polypeptide was extremely unstable, we assume that the 59,000 polypeptide is mandatory for the stabilization of the DNA primase activity.

Discussion

Immunoaffinity-purified DNA polymerase α–primase complex from calf thymus consists of four subunits with M_rs of 148,000, 155,000, and 180,000 (α-subunit cluster), 73,000 (β-subunit), 59,000 (γ-subunit), and 48,000 (δ-subunit). Functionally, the α-subunit cluster was attributed to the DNA polymerizing activity by several authors (for a recent review, see Fry and Loeb 1986). Our own antibody studies with anti-148-kD antibodies revealed cross-reactivities between the constituents of the α-subunit cluster and an inhibition of the DNA polymerizing activity (H.-P. Nasheuer and F. Grosse, unpubl.). On the other hand, the β, γ, and δ-subunit showed no cross-reactivity with antibodies produced to the 148-kD polypeptide. The function of the β-subunit is still obscure, since we have isolated preparations that completely lack this subunit but otherwise behave not differently as compared with the four-subunit enzyme complex (including the novel properties discussed below). Therefore, at least from a functional point of view, the β-subunit seems dispensable. Primase function could be attributed to the two smallest γ- and δ-subunits. This result is in accord with recent findings on a conventionally purified pol α from *Drosophila melanogaster* (Kaguni et al. 1983b) and another immunoaffinity-purified pol α from calf thymus (Holmes et al. 1986). In this work, the γ- and δ-subunits were separated from the polymerase-primase complex under mild conditions. The separated primase was shown to form a stable heterodimer and to be completely active. Thus, DNA synthesizing activity and primer formation activity are located on different subunits of the polymerase-primase. The active site for RNA priming was determined by separating the γ- from the δ-subunit. This study revealed that only the 48-kD subunit (δ-subunit) is responsible for RNA synthesis. The extreme lability of the free δ-subunit suggests, however, an activity stabilizing role for the 59-kD subunit. Although structurally related to conventional preparations, our immunoaffinity-purified polymerase-primase displayed several novel properties that suggest a more native state of the enzyme. Most strikingly, the immunoaffinity-purified polymerase-primase was stimulated by salt concentrations assumed to be present inside the cell. Furthermore, K_ms for primer binding and dNTP utilization were found to be five- to tenfold lower than those reported earlier. In vitro replication of primase-initiated (+) strand M13 DNA was accomplished within 10–30 minutes, which is at least threefold faster than hitherto known preparations. Although it is not known at the present what might be responsible for the novel properties displayed by the immunoaffinity-purified enzyme, we would like to speculate that the fastness of purification (1–2 days) and the high protein concentrations sustained during purification minimize the loosening of the quaternary structure and the loss of subunits. This might keep the enzyme complex in a more native state.

Acknowledgments

This work was supported in part by grant Gr-895/1-1 from the Deutsche Forschungsgemeinschaft.

References

Banks, G.R., J.A. Boezi, and I.R. Lehman. 1979. A high molecular weight DNA polymerase from *Drosophila melanogaster* embryos: Purification, structure, and partial characterization. *J. Biol. Chem.* **254:** 9886.

Bollum, F.J. 1960. Calf thymus polymerase. *J. Biol. Chem.* **235:** 2399.

Chang, L.M.S., E. Rafter, C. Augl, and F.J. Bollum. 1984. Purification of a DNA polymerase-DNA primase complex from calf thymus glands. *J. Biol. Chem.* **259:** 14679.

Fry, M. and L.A. Loeb. 1986. *Animal cell DNA polymerases.* CRC Press, Boca Raton, Florida.

Grosse, F. and G. Krauss. 1981. Purification of a 9 S DNA polymerase α species from calf thymus. *Biochemistry* **20:** 5470.

———. 1984. Replication of M13mp7 single-stranded DNA in vitro by the 9-S DNA polymerase α from calf thymus. *Eur. J. Biochem.* **141:** 109.

———. 1985. The primase activity of DNA polymerase α from calf thymus. *J. Biol. Chem.* **260:** 1881.

Hohn, K.-T. and F. Grosse. 1987. Processivity of the DNA polymerase α-primase complex from calf thymus. *Biochemistry* **26:** 2870.

Holmes, A.M., E. Cheriathundam, F.J. Bollum, and L.M.S. Chang. 1986. Immunological analysis of the polypeptide structure of calf thymus DNA polymerase-primase complex. *J. Biol. Chem.* **261:** 11924.

Kaguni, L.S., J.-M. Rossignol, R.C. Conaway, and I.R. Lehman. 1983a. Isolation of an intact DNA polymerase-primase from embryos of *Drosophila melanogaster. Proc. Natl. Acad. Sci.* **80:** 2221.

Kaguni, L.S., J.-M. Rossignol, R.C. Conaway, G.R. Banks, and I.R. Lehman. 1983b. Association of DNA primase with the β/γ subunits of DNA polymerase α from *Drosophila melanogaster* embryos. *J. Biol. Chem.* **258:** 9037.

Masaki, S., O. Koiwai, and S. Yoshida. 1982. 10 S DNA polymerase α of calf thymus shows a microheterogeneity in its large polypeptide component. *J. Biol. Chem.* **257:** 7172.

Schomburg, U. and F. Grosse. 1986. Purification and characterization of DNA topoisomerase II from calf thymus associated with polypeptides of 175 and 150 kDa. *Eur. J. Biochem.* **160:** 451.

Siegel, L.M. and K.J. Monty. 1966. Determination of molecular weights and frictional ratios of proteins in impure systems by use of gel filtration and density gradient centrifugation. Application to crude preparations of sulfite and hydroxylamine reductase. *Biochim. Biophys. Acta* **112:** 346.

Tanaka, S., S.-Z. Hu, T.S.-F. Wang, and D. Korn. 1982. Preparation and preliminary characterization of monoclonal antibodies against human DNA polymerase α. *J. Biol. Chem.* **257:** 8386.

Wahl, A.F., S.P. Kowalski, L.W. Harwell, E.M. Lord, and R.A. Bambara. 1984. Immunoaffinity purification and properties of a high molecular weight calf thymus DNA α-polymerase. *Biochemistry* **23:** 1895.

Wang, T.S.-F., S.-Z. Hu, and D. Korn. 1984. DNA primase from KB cells. *J. Biol. Chem.* **259:** 1854.

Wong, S.W., L.R. Paborski, P.A. Fisher, T.S.-F. Wang, and D. Korn. 1986. Structural and enzymological characterization of immunoaffinity-purified DNA polymerase α · DNA primase complex from KB cells. *J. Biol. Chem.* **261:** 7958.

Proposed Roles for DNA Polymerases α and δ at the Replication Fork

K.M. Downey, C.-K. Tan, D.M. Andrews, X. Li, and A.G. So

Departments of Medicine and Biochemistry and the Center for Blood Diseases, University of Miami School of Medicine, Miami, Florida 33101

DNA polymerases α and δ have been shown to be immunologically and functionally distinct enzyme species. Neutralizing monoclonal antibodies to KB cell DNA polymerase α inhibit calf thymus DNA polymerase α but not DNA polymerase δ. More importantly, neutralizing polyclonal antibody to DNA polymerase δ does not inhibit DNA polymerase α. A model of coordinate action of DNA polymerases α and δ at the replication fork is proposed, based on their functional properties. Consistent with a leading strand replicase, DNA polymerase δ is highly processive and capable of strand-displacement synthesis. Furthermore, DNA polymerase δ is regulated by an S-phase-specific protein, the proliferating cell nuclear antigen (PCNA/cyclin). Consistent with a lagging strand replicase, DNA polymerase α displays moderate processivity, is incapable of strand-displacement synthesis, and is not regulated by PCNA. In addition, the tightly associated primase activity of DNA polymerase α could perform the de novo priming necessary for Okazaki fragment synthesis on the lagging strand.

Four distinct forms of DNA polymerase (α, β, γ, and δ) have been described in mammalian tissues, based on their functional properties and subcellular locations (Fry and Loeb 1986). The results of numerous studies have suggested that DNA polymerase α is the sole DNA polymerase required for the replication of eukaryotic chromosomes (DePamphilis and Wasserman 1980; Fry and Loeb 1986; Huberman 1987). Although a replicative function for DNA polymerase α is well-established, the conclusions drawn from some of these studies must be reevaluated, since DNA polymerases δ and α have been shown to have similar sensitivities to inhibitors of DNA replication such as arabinosyl nucleotides and aphidicolin, and both polymerases are relatively resistant to dideoxynucleotides (Byrnes et al. 1976; Lee et al. 1981; Wahl et al. 1986; Lee and Toomey 1987). Thus, cellular systems studied with these inhibitors do not distinguish between the in vivo roles of DNA polymerases α and δ. However, in the presence of the nucleotide analogs BuPdGTP and BuAdATP, DNA polymerase α is over 100 times more sensitive to inhibition than is DNA polymerase δ (Byrnes 1985; Lee et al. 1985; Wahl et al. 1986; Lee and Toomey 1987). Recent studies utilizing BuPdGTP and BuAdATP in permeabilized cells (Dresler and Frattini 1986; Hammond et al. 1987), as well as studies on cellular extracts utilizing an SV40 in vitro replication system (Decker et al. 1987), have suggested that both DNA polymerases α and δ are required for DNA replication in mammalian cells.

DNA polymerase δ, as initially described in this laboratory, was distinguished from DNA polymerase α by the presence of a tightly associated 3′ to 5′ exonuclease activity, as well as other properties such as chromatographic behavior and template/primer specificities (Byrnes et al. 1976; Lee et al. 1980, 1984). The recent discovery of an auxiliary protein that allows DNA polymerase δ to utilize template/primers containing long stretches of single-stranded template, but which has no effect on DNA polymerase α (Tan et al. 1986), and the subsequent demonstration that the DNA polymerase δ auxiliary protein is identical to a cell-cycle-regulated protein, PCNA (Bravo et al. 1987; Prelich et al. 1987b), have added another dimension to the definition of DNA polymerase δ. This distinction is essential in light of recent reports describing the presence of exonuclease activity with certain forms of DNA polymerase α (Ottiger and Hubscher 1984; Skarnes et al. 1986; Cotterill et al. 1987).

In this report, we present data on the mechanism of regulation of DNA polymerase δ by the cell-cycle-regulated protein PCNA, also called cyclin, a protein synthesized during the S phase of the cell cycle (Bravo and Macdonald-Bravo 1985; Celis and Celis 1985; Kurki et al. 1986; Sadaie and Mathews 1986). Comparative functional and immunological evidence is presented that further establishes DNA polymerase δ as a unique enzymatic species. In addition, a model is proposed that exploits intrinsic properties of each enzyme for specific roles at the leading and lagging strands of the replication fork.

Materials and Methods

Fetal calf thymus was obtained from Bioresources. Radioactive nucleotides were obtained either from ICN or New England Nuclear. (dA)$_{800-1000}$ was obtained from Midland Certified Reagent Co., and (dT)$_{10}$ from Pharmacia. PvuI, AvaI, ClaI, AluI, pBR322 (RFI), M13mp19 (+) strand DNA, M13mp19 (RFI), and the M13 17-base primer were obtained from Bethesda Re-

403

search Laboratories. Terminal deoxynucleotidyl transferase was obtained from Collaborative Research Laboratories, and the Klenow fragment of *Escherichia coli* DNA polymerase I was obtained from United States Biochemical Corporation. Monoclonal antibodies against human DNA polymerase α, SJK 132-20 and SJK 287-38, and control myeloma IgG, P3X63Ag8(MOPC-21), were obtained from Pharmacia.

DNA polymerase δ was purified from fetal calf thymus through either step 6 or step 7 as described previously (Lee et al. 1984). DNA polymerase α was purified from fetal calf thymus essentially as described by Holmes et al. (1974).

DNA polymerase assays
Assays for DNA polymerase α, DNA polymerase δ, and the auxiliary protein with poly(dA)/oligo(dT) as template/primer were as described previously (Tan et al. 1986).

Neutralization assays
One unit of DNA polymerase α or δ was incubated with different amounts of IgG or sera in 10 mM Tris-HCl (pH 7.5), 0.1 M KCl, 1 mM EDTA, 250 μg/ml bovine serum albumin (BSA), 250 μg/ml soybean trypsin inhibitor, 0.5% Nonidet P-40, and 1 mM dithiothreitol (DTT) for 2 hours at 4°C. The preincubated mixtures were then assayed for DNA polymerase activity using poly(dA)/oligo(dT) (20:1) as template/primer. DNA polymerase δ activity was determined in the presence of excess auxiliary protein.

In vitro replication of primed, single-stranded M13 DNA
M13mp19 (+) strand DNA was annealed to the 17-base primer at a primer to template ratio of 2:1 in 10 mM Tris-HCl (pH 7.8), 10 mM $MgCl_2$, 30 mM NaCl. The reaction mixture contained in a final volume of 50 μl: 40 mM Bis-Tris buffer (pH 6.5), 40 μg/ml BSA, 10% glycerol, 50 μM each dATP, dGTP, dCTP, 10 μM [α-^{32}P]dTTP (7800 cpm/pmol), 4 mM $MgCl_2$, 160 ng primed M13 DNA, 1 mM DTT, and 1 unit of pol δ. Auxiliary protein, when present, was at 5 μg/ml. After incubation at 37°C for 30 minutes, the reaction was stopped by the addition of EDTA to 10 mM, carrier tRNA was added and, after incubation with 5 μg proteinase K, the DNA was extracted with phenol/chloroform and ethanol-precipitated. Samples were dissolved in 20 μl of Tris-HCl (pH 7.8), 0.1 mM EDTA, 5 mM NaCl, and aliquots were digested with *Ava*I and *Cla*I under the supplier's recommended conditions. Digests were electrophoresed on a 1.5% agarose gel in Tris-borate-EDTA buffer at 1 V/cm for 16 hours. The dried gel was autoradiographed at −70°C using Kodak XAR film and a Dupont Cronex intensifying screen.

Measurement of processivity
To ensure that product lengths reflected a single binding event per enzyme molecule, enzyme concentrations and incubation times were adjusted so that less than one mole of nucleotide was incorporated per mole of primer.

The reaction mixtures contained in a final volume of 50 μl: 40 mM HEPES buffer (pH 7.5), 5 mM $MgCl_2$, 10% glycerol, 40 μg/ml BSA, 1 mM DTT; 20 μM [α-^{32}P]dTTP (20 cpm/fmol), 0.23 mM (dA)$_{800-1000}$/(dT)$_{10}$ (80:1 in nucleotide, 1:1 in 3′ ends) and either DNA polymerase δ or DNA polymerase α. Aliquots (10 μl) were removed to measure incorporation, and the remainder of the sample was extracted once with phenol/chloroform, ethanol-precipitated, and electrophoresed on a 12% polyacrylamide-8 M urea gel (13 cm × 29 cm) at 150 V (constant voltage) overnight followed by autoradiography at −70°C.

Strand-displacement synthesis
Poly(dA)-tailed pBR322 was prepared according to Murakami et al. (1986). 15 μg of pBR322 (RFI) was linearized by incubation with 10 units of *Pvu*I for 4 hours at 37°C in a final volume of 25 μl under the supplier's recommended conditions. The linearized molecule was tailed with poly(dA) by incubation with 35 units of terminal transferase, 50 μM [^{3}H]dATP (200 cpm/pmol), 1 mM $CoCl_2$, 0.2 mM DTT, and 200 mM potassium cacodylate buffer (pH 7.2). The reaction was stopped after approximately 320 (dA) residues had been added per 3′ end. The DNA was phenol-extracted, ethanol-precipitated, and dissolved in 10 mM Tris-HCl (pH 7.8), 1 mM EDTA.

For strand-displacement synthesis, the reaction mixture contained in a final volume of 25 μl: 40 mM Bis-Tris buffer (pH 6.5), 4 mM $MgCl_2$, 80 μg/ml BSA, 10% glycerol, 100 μM each dGTP, dATP, dTTP, 4 μM [α-^{32}P]dCTP (20–40 cpm/fmol), 50 ng poly(dA)-tailed pBR322, 50 nM (dT)$_{12-18}$, 1 mM DTT, and 1.2 units of either DNA polymerase α or DNA polymerase δ. PCNA when present was 5 μg/ml. ATP when present was 2 mM. Incubation was at 37°C for 30 minutes.

Preparation of polyclonal antibody to DNA polymerase δ
DNA polymerase δ purified through step 6 (Lee et al. 1984) was further purified by phosphocellulose and DEAE-Sephadex A-25 chromatography before use as an antigen. Three BALB/c mice were each injected with 400 units of DNA polymerase δ in complete Freund's adjuvant. Booster injections of 200 units of DNA polymerase δ in incomplete Freund's adjuvant were given every 10 days. Serum from a responsive mouse was fractionated by ammonium sulfate, dialyzed extensively against 10 mM Tris-HCl (pH 7.5), 100 mM KCl, and 1 mM EDTA, and made to the original volume before use. Control sera were from mice injected only with Freund's adjuvant and processed as above.

Results

An auxiliary protein for DNA polymerase δ from calf thymus
We have recently purified a protein factor that is required by calf thymus DNA polymerase δ to utilize template/primers containing long stretches of single-stranded template (Tan et al. 1986). This auxiliary protein is specific for DNA polymerase δ; the activity of calf

thymus DNA polymerase α or the Klenow fragment of *E. coli* DNA polymerase I is not affected by the auxiliary protein, even at low enzyme concentrations (Table 1). The purified auxiliary protein has a subunit molecular weight of 37,000 and behaves on gel filtration as a dimer of 75,000 daltons. It is an acidic protein (pI = 4.5) and, in contrast to most protein factors that have been found to affect the template specificity of mammalian DNA polymerases, the 37-kD auxiliary protein does not bind to either single-stranded or double-stranded DNA. The auxiliary protein does increase the binding of DNA polymerase δ to DNA, suggesting that it interacts with the "core enzyme" in the presence of template/primer, forming a more stable polymerase-template/primer complex. No enzymatic activities were detectable with the purified auxiliary protein, e.g., DNA polymerase, primase, exonuclease, endonuclease, or ATPase.

The ability of DNA polymerase δ to replicate gapped, duplex DNA, e.g., poly(dA-dT) or activated calf thymus DNA, is only slightly affected by the presence of the auxiliary protein. However, it is required to replicate primed, single-stranded templates, e.g., poly(dA)/oligo(dT) (20:1), denatured calf thymus DNA, or primed, single-stranded phage DNA (Table 2).

The effect of the auxiliary protein on the ability of DNA polymerase δ to replicate singly primed M13mp19 (+) strand DNA is shown in Figure 1. The progress of the enzyme as it replicated the complementary strand was followed by assaying for the generation of restriction endonuclease cleavage sites using the enzymes *Ava*I and *Cla*I. Replicative form M13mp19 contains four cleavage sites for these enzymes, producing fragments of 422, 3297, 2898, and 636 bp. Thus, complete replication of the template in the presence of [α-³²P]dNTPs, followed by digestion with *Ava*I and *Cla*I, would produce four bands after agarose gel electrophoresis. As can be seen in this figure, DNA polymerase δ, in the presence of auxiliary protein, was able to synthesize

full-length products, as evidenced by the four fragments after restriction digest analysis. In contrast, in the absence of the auxiliary protein, none of the *Ava*I or *Cla*I restriction fragments was generated. Although the enzyme was able to sustain limited synthesis in the absence of the auxiliary protein, it was unable to extend the primer sufficiently to generate the second *Ava*I site, approximately 470 nucleotides downstream from the 3′ terminus of the primer.

Identity of the DNA polymerase δ auxiliary protein and PCNA

The evidence for the identity of the DNA polymerase δ auxiliary protein and PCNA is very strong. In collaboration with Stillman and his colleagues, we have demonstrated that the auxiliary protein for DNA polymerase δ is physically, antigenically, and functionally identical to

Table 2 Effect of the Auxiliary Protein on the Template Specificity of DNA Polymerase δ

Template/Primer	Incorporation (pmol dNMP/30 min)	
	polymerase alone	polymerase plus auxiliary protein
Poly(dA-dT), 2 mM MgCl₂	472	218
Poly(dA-dT), 6 mM MgCl₂	93	377
Poly(dA)/oligo (dT) (20/1)	2.8	1300
Activated calf thymus DNA	107	218
Denatured calf thymus DNA	1.3	106
Primed M13 DNA	1.3	20.2

The activity of 1 unit of DNA polymerase δ with the template/primers listed was determined in the presence and absence of 10.5 μg/ml auxiliary protein. Reaction mixtures were as described in Experimental Procedures for the poly(dA-dT) assay except: with poly(dA)/oligo(dT) (17 μg/ml) as template, 100 μM [³H]dTTP (40 cpm/pmol) was present; with either activated (15 μg/ml) or denatured (16 μg/ml) calf thymus DNA or primed M13 DNA (5.6 μg/ml) as template, 100 μM dATP, dGTP, and dCTP, and 40 μM [³H]dTTP (300 cpm/pmole) were present. (Reprinted, with permission, from Tan et al. 1986.)

Table 1 Enzyme Specificity of the Auxiliary Protein

Enzyme		Incorporation (pmol dNMP/30 min)	
		polymerase alone	polymerase plus auxiliary protein
DNA polymerase δ	(0.08 unit)	1	109
	(0.67 unit)	1.9	1070
DNA polymerase α-A	(0.08 unit)	16.6	20.9
	(0.64 unit)	174	183
DNA polymerase α-C	(0.09 unit)	13.9	15.0
	(0.72 unit)	346	345
DNA polymerase I-Klenow fragment			
	(0.0008 unit)	29.0	31.2
	(0.0063 unit)	250	256

DNA polymerase activity was assayed with poly(dA)/oligo(dT) (20/1) as template/primer as described in Experimental Procedures for the assay of auxiliary protein. Auxiliary protein, when present, was 10.5 μg/ml. One unit of DNA polymerase α or δ is defined as the incorporation of one nmol dNMP/hr with the assays described in Experimental Procedures. One unit of the Klenow fragment of DNA polymerase I is defined as the incorporation of 10 nmol dNMP/30 min with poly(dA-dT) as template/primer. (Reprinted, with permission, from Tan et al. 1986.)

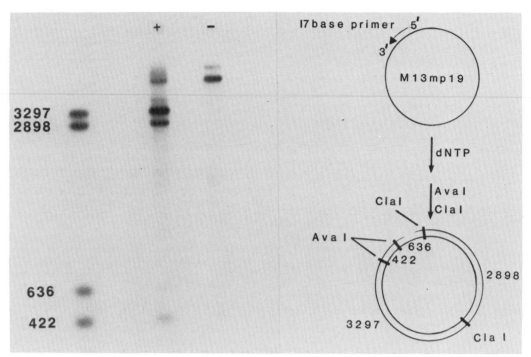

Figure 1 Effect of the auxiliary protein on the size of the products synthesized by DNA polymerase δ on primed M13 DNA. Reaction conditions and agarose gel electrophoresis are described in Materials and Methods. Size markers are an *Ava*I and *Cla*I digest of M13mp19 (RFI).

PCNA (Prelich et al. 1987b), a cell-cycle-regulated protein that has been shown to be required for efficient replication of plasmids containing the SV40 origin (Prelich et al. 1987a). Both proteins comigrate on SDS-polyacrylamide gel electrophoresis and both proteins are recognized by anti-PCNA autoantibodies. Significantly, calf thymus DNA polymerase δ auxiliary protein can substitute for human PCNA in SV40 replication in vitro and conversely, human PCNA can effectively substitute for the calf thymus auxiliary protein in markedly stimulating the activity and processivity of calf thymus DNA polymerase δ (Prelich et al. 1987b). The physical identity of PCNA/cyclin and the δ polymerase auxiliary protein has been independently confirmed by two-dimensional gel electrophoresis and partial amino acid sequencing, demonstrating 100% homology for the first ten amino acids (Bravo et al. 1987). Immunological cross-reactivity has also recently been demonstrated between PCNA and the auxiliary protein for DNA polymerase δ by immunoblotting using monoclonal and polyclonal antibodies to PCNA, as well as by neutralization of auxiliary protein activity by human autoantibodies to PCNA (Tan et al. 1987b).

Lack of immunological cross-reactivity between DNA polymerases α and δ

As shown in Figure 2, calf thymus DNA polymerase α is sensitive to inhibition by two neutralizing monoclonal antibodies to KB cell DNA polymerase α, SJK-132-20 and SJK 287-38 (Tanaka et al. 1982), whereas DNA

polymerase δ is resistant. Conversely, as shown in Figure 3, polyclonal antibody to calf thymus DNA polymerase δ neutralizes the activity of DNA polymerase δ but has no effect on the activity of DNA polymerase α. Furthermore, >98% of the activity of DNA polymerase δ was immunoprecipitated by 1 μl of antiserum, whereas DNA polymerase α activity was not immunoprecipitated by up to 20 μl of anti-DNA polymerase δ serum (data not shown). These results clearly demonstrate that these two DNA polymerases are immunologically distinct.

DNA polymerase δ is highly processive in the presence of PCNA

We have recently demonstrated that PCNA is essential for processive DNA synthesis by DNA polymerase δ (Prelich et al. 1987b). In the present studies we have compared the processivity of DNA polymerases α and δ on poly(dA)/oligo(dT) (80:1) as template/primer, and determined the effects of PCNA on the processivity of these polymerases. As shown in Figure 4, the processivity of DNA polymerase δ in the absence of PCNA is very low, less than 15 nucleotides being incorporated per enzyme binding event. However, the addition of PCNA markedly increased the processivity of DNA polymerase δ to 900, essentially the length of the template used. The processivity of DNA polymerase α was less than 100 nucleotides per enzyme binding event, and was not affected by PCNA, confirming the specificity of PCNA for DNA polymerase δ and not DNA polymerase α.

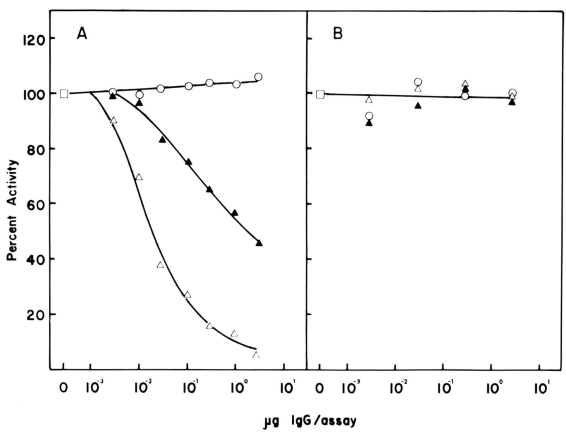

Figure 2 Effects of murine monoclonal antibodies to KB cell DNA polymerase α on DNA polymerase α (panel *A*) and DNA polymerase δ (panel *B*) from fetal calf thymus. Neutralization assays were performed as described in Materials and Methods. Without IgG (□), MOPC-21 (○), SJK 132-20 (▲), and SJK 287-38 (△).

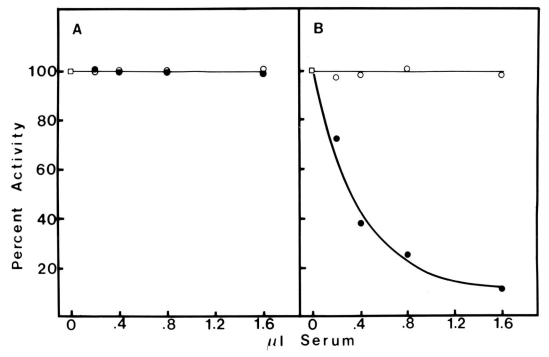

Figure 3 Effects of murine polyclonal antibody to calf thymus DNA polymerase δ on the homologous DNA polymerase α (panel *A*) and DNA polymerase δ (panel *B*). Neutralization assays were performed as described in Materials and Methods. Without serum (□), control serum (○), immune serum (●).

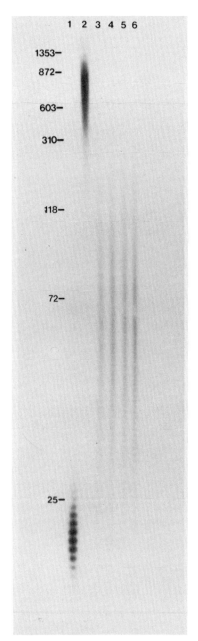

Figure 4 Processivity of DNA polymerases α and δ in the presence and absence of the auxiliary protein (PCNA). Reaction conditions and electrophoresis are described in Materials and Methods. (Lane *1*) DNA polymerase δ minus PCNA. (Lane *2*) DNA polymerase δ plus 130 ng PCNA. (Lane *3*) DNA polymerase α minus PCNA. (Lanes *4–6*) DNA polymerase α plus 65 ng, 130 ng, and 260 ng PCNA, respectively. Size markers are a *Hae*III digest of φ-X174.

DNA polymerase δ catalyzes strand-displacement synthesis

To further elucidate the roles of DNA polymerases α and δ in DNA replication, we have tested the abilities of both enzymes to catalyze strand-displacement synthesis, using poly(dA)-tailed pBR322 as a template. Strand-displacement synthesis was measured by following the incorporation of [α-^{32}P]dCTP in the presence of un-labeled dATP, dGTP, and dTTP, with oligo(dT) as primer. As can be seen in Figure 5, DNA polymerase δ in the presence of PCNA replicated approximately 8% of the input DNA, whereas DNA polymerase α was unable to catalyze strand-displacement synthesis on the poly(dA)-tailed pBR322. Addition of ATP did not stimulate displacement synthesis by either DNA polymerase α or δ, suggesting that DNA-dependent ATPase was not present in the enzyme preparations.

In a control experiment in which the ability of both DNA polymerases α and δ to incorporate [α-^{32}P]dTTP in the absence of the other three dNTPs was determined, it was found that both enzymes were able to incorporate dTMP on the oligo(dT)-primed poly(dA) tails and, as expected, DNA polymerase δ required PCNA but DNA polymerase α did not (data not shown). Thus, both DNA polymerases α and δ are able to replicate the single-stranded portion of the template, but only DNA polymerase δ can replicate the double-strand portion of the template. The inability of immunoaffinity-purified HeLa cell DNA polymerase α to carry out strand-displacement synthesis has recently been reported (Murakami et al. 1986).

Discussion

The present study demonstrates that DNA polymerase α and DNA polymerase δ are two separate and distinct enzymes, each having unique physical, immunological, and functional properties. In conjunction with the findings of previous studies, these two DNA polymerases can be distinguished from one another in the following ways: differences in chromatographic behavior, template/primer preferences, different sensitivities to the nucleotide analogs BuAdATP and BuPdGTP, differences in tightly associated enzymatic activities, i.e., primase for DNA polymerase α and 3'-5' exonuclease for DNA polymerase δ, lack of immunological cross-

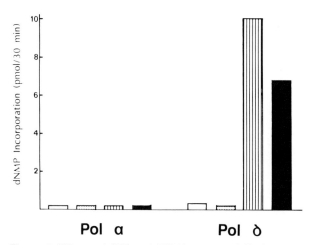

Figure 5 Effects of ATP and PCNA on strand-displacement synthesis by DNA polymerase α and DNA polymerase δ. Assay conditions were as described in Materials and Methods. (Open columns) no additions, (lined columns) plus PCNA, (dotted columns) plus ATP, (solid columns) plus PCNA and ATP.

reactivity, differing processivities, and differing ability to catalyze strand-displacement synthesis. Most importantly, PCNA, a cell-cycle-regulated protein, is a specific auxiliary protein for DNA polymerase δ, rendering the enzyme more holoenzyme-like.

The current study firmly establishes that DNA polymerase δ and DNA polymerase α are immunologically distinct, since polyclonal antibody that neutralizes DNA polymerase δ activity does not inhibit the activity of DNA polymerase α. Furthermore, this polyclonal antibody does not immunoprecipitate DNA polymerase α, but does precipitate DNA polymerase δ. Although a relationship between DNA polymerases α and δ cannot be excluded at this time, the lack of immunological cross-reactivity decreases that possibility. Based on the current findings, it is highly unlikely that the catalytic cores of the two enzymes are related.

The demonstration that the activity and processivity of DNA polymerase δ are regulated by an S-phase-specific protein (PCNA) strongly suggests a central role for DNA polymerase δ in cellular DNA replication. DNA polymerase δ is highly processive in the presence of PCNA, being able to copy a complete template, $(dA)_{800-1000}$, upon a single binding event. Taken together with the ability of DNA polymerase δ to carry out strand-displacement synthesis, DNA polymerase δ possesses the properties characteristic of a leading strand replicase at the replication fork, as depicted in Figure 6. On the other hand, we have determined that the processivity of DNA polymerase α is moderate, less than 100 nucleotides incorporated per binding event. Other studies have also reported processivity values of up to 100 nucleotides for DNA polymerase α (Hohn and Grosse 1987; Tan et al. 1987a). The moderate processivity of DNA polymerase α would be adequate to support synthesis on the lagging strand, where it would be advantageous for the polymerase to frequently dissociate. Furthermore, the tightly associated primase activity of DNA polymerase α

(Yoshida et al. 1983; Wang et al. 1984; Grosse and Krauss 1985) could perform the repeated de novo priming necessary for Okazaki fragment synthesis on the lagging strand (Fig. 6).

PCNA is synthesized during the S phase of the cell cycle (Bravo and Macdonald-Bravo 1985; Celis and Celis 1985; Kurki et al. 1986; Sadaie and Mathews 1986), and the induction of PCNA synthesis has been shown to correlate closely with the induction of DNA synthesis in cells treated with a variety of mitogenic agents, preceding DNA replication by a short interval (Bravo 1986). It has been observed in prokaryotes that the leading strand migrates ahead of the lagging strand by about the length of one nascent Okazaki fragment, suggesting that the controlling event in elongation of a replication fork is the commencement of leading strand synthesis (Kornberg 1980, 1982; Watson et al. 1987). Since the activity of DNA polymerase δ, but not DNA polymerase α, is regulated by PCNA, this further implicates DNA polymerase δ as a candidate for leading strand replicase.

In summary, we propose that DNA polymerase δ and DNA polymerase α possess the properties appropriate for roles at the leading and lagging strands of the replication fork, respectively.

Acknowledgments

This work was supported by research funds from the University of Miami School of Medicine. The excellent technical assistance of Carlos Castillo is gratefully acknowledged.

References

Bravo, R. 1986. Synthesis of the nuclear protein cyclin (PCNA) and its relationship with DNA replication. *Exp. Cell Res.* **163**: 287.

Bravo, R. and H. Macdonald-Bravo. 1985. Changes in the nuclear distribution of cyclin (PCNA) but not its synthesis on DNA replication. *EMBO J.* **4**: 655.

Bravo, R., R. Frank, P.A. Blundell, and H. Macdonald-Bravo. 1987. Cyclin/PCNA is the auxiliary protein of DNA polymerase δ. *Nature* **326**: 515.

Byrnes, J.J. 1985. Differential inhibitors of DNA polymerases α and δ. *Biochem. Biophys. Res. Commun.* **132**: 628.

Byrnes, J.J., K.M. Downey, V.L. Black, and A.G. So. 1976. A new mammalian DNA polymerase with 3′ to 5′ exonuclease activity: DNA polymerase δ. *Biochemistry* **15**: 2817.

Celis, J.E. and A. Celis. 1985. Cell cycle-dependent variations in distribution of nuclear protein cyclin (proliferating cell nuclear antigen) in cultured cells: Subdivision of S-phase. *Proc. Natl. Acad. Sci.* **82**: 3262.

Cotterill, S.M., M.E. Reyland, L.A. Loeb, and I.R. Lehman. 1987. A cryptic proofreading 3′ to 5′ exonuclease associated with the polymerase subunit of the DNA polymerase-primase from *Drosophila melanogaster*. *Proc. Natl. Acad. Sci.* **84**: 5635.

Decker, R.S., M. Yamaguchi, R. Possenti, M.K. Bradley, and M.L. DePamphilis. 1987. In vitro initiation of DNA replication in simian virus 40 chromosomes. *J. Biol. Chem.* **262**: 10863.

DePamphilis, M.L. and P.M. Wassarman. 1980. Replication of eukaryotic chromosomes: A close-up of the replication fork. *Annu. Rev. Biochem.* **49**: 627.

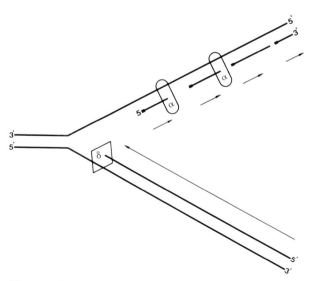

Figure 6 Schematic representation of the proposed roles of DNA polymerases δ and α in DNA replication.

Dresler, S.L. and M.G. Frattini. 1986. DNA replication and UV-induced repair synthesis in human fibroblasts are much less sensitive than DNA polymerase α to inhibition by butyl-phenyl-deoxyguanosine triphosphate. *Nucleic Acids Res.* **14:** 7093.

Fry, M. and L.A. Loeb. 1986. *Animal cell DNA polymerases.* CRC Press, Boca Raton, Florida.

Grosse, F. and G. Krauss. 1985. The primase activity of DNA polymerase α from calf thymus. *J. Biol. Chem.* **260:** 1881.

Hammond, R.A., J.J. Byrnes, and M.R. Miller. 1987. Identification of DNA polymerase δ in CV-1 cells: Studies implicating both DNA polymerase δ and DNA polymerase α in DNA replication. *Biochemistry* **26:** 6817.

Hohn, K.T. and F. Grosse. 1987. Processivity of the DNA polymerase α-primase complex from calf thymus. *Biochemistry* **26:** 2870.

Holmes, A.M., I.P. Hesslewood, and I.R. Johnson. 1974. The occurrence of multiple activities in the high-molecular-weight DNA polymerase fraction of mammalian tissues: A preliminary study of some of their properties. *Eur. J. Biochem.* **43:** 487.

Huberman, J.A. 1987. Eukaryotic DNA replication: A complex picture partially clarified. *Cell* **48:** 7.

Kornberg, A. 1980. *DNA replication.* W.H. Freeman, San Francisco.

————. 1982. Replication mechanisms and operations. In *Supplement to DNA replication,* p. s101. W.H. Freeman, San Francisco.

Kurki, P., M. Vanderlaan, F. Dolbeare, J. Gray, and E.M. Tan. 1986. Expression of proliferating cell nuclear antigen (PCNA/cyclin) during the cell cycle. *Exp. Cell Res.* **166:** 209.

Lee, M.Y.W.T. and N.L. Toomey. 1987. Human placental DNA polymerase delta: Identification of a 170-kilodalton polypeptide by activity staining and immunoblotting. *Biochemistry* **26:** 1076.

Lee, M.Y.W.T., N.L. Toomey, and G.E. Wright. 1985. Differential inhibition of human placental DNA polymerases δ and α by BuPdGTP and BuAdATP. *Nucleic Acids Res.* **13:** 8623.

Lee, M.Y.W.T., C.-K. Tan, K.M. Downey, and A.G. So. 1981. Structural and functional properties of calf thymus DNA polymerase δ. *Prog. Nucleic Acid. Res. Mol. Biol.* **26:** 82.

————. 1984. Further studies on calf thymus DNA polymerase delta purified to homogeneity by a new procedure. *Biochemistry* **23:** 1906.

Lee, M.Y.W.T., C.-K. Tan, A.G. So, and K.M. Downey. 1980. Purification of DNA polymerase δ from calf thymus: Partial characterization of physical properties. *Biochemistry* **19:** 2096.

Murakami, Y., C.R. Wobbe, L. Weissbach, F.B. Dean, and J. Hurwitz. 1986. Role of DNA polymerase α and DNA primase in simian virus 40 DNA replication *in vitro. Proc. Natl. Acad. Sci.* **83:** 2869.

Ottiger, H.-P. and U. Hubscher. 1984. Mammalian DNA polymerase alpha holoenzymes with possible functions at the leading and lagging strands of the replication fork. *Proc. Natl. Acad. Sci.* **81:** 3993.

Prelich, G., M. Kostura, D.R. Marshak, M.B. Mathews, and B. Stillman. 1987a. The cell cycle-regulated proliferating cell nuclear antigen is required for SV40 DNA replication *in vitro. Nature* **326:** 471.

Prelich, G., C.-K. Tan, M. Kostura, M.B. Mathews, A.G. So, K.M. Downey, and B. Stillman. 1987b. Functional identity of proliferating cell nuclear antigen and a DNA polymerase δ auxiliary protein. *Nature* **326:** 517.

Sadaie, M.R. and M.B. Mathews. 1986. Immunochemical and biochemical analysis of the proliferating cell nuclear antigen (PCNA) in HeLa cells. *Exp. Cell Res.* **163:** 423.

Skarnes, W., P. Bonin, and E. Baril. 1986. Exonuclease activity associated with a multiprotein form of HeLa cell DNA polymerase α. Purification and properties of the exonuclease. *J. Biol. Chem.* **261:** 6629.

Tan, C.-K., C. Castillo, A.G. So, and K.M. Downey. 1986. An auxiliary protein for DNA polymerase δ from fetal calf thymus. *J. Biol. Chem.* **261:** 12310.

Tan, C.-K., M.J. So, K.M. Downey, and A.G. So. 1987a. Apparent stimulation of calf thymus DNA polymerase α by ATP. *Nucleic Acids Res.* **15:** 2269.

Tan, C.-K., K. Sullivan, X. Li, E.M. Tan, K.M. Downey, and A.G. So. 1987b. Autoantibody to the proliferating cell nuclear antigen neutralizes the activity of the auxiliary protein for DNA polymerase δ. *Nucleic Acids Res.* **15:** 9299.

Tanaka, S., S.-Z. Hu, T.S.-F. Wang, and D. Korn. 1982. Preparation and preliminary characterization of monoclonal antibodies against human DNA polymerase α. *J. Biol. Chem.* **257:** 8386.

Wahl, A.F., J.J. Crute, R.D. Sabatino, J.B. Bodner, R.L. Marraccino, L.W. Harwell, E.M. Lord, and R.A. Bambara. 1986. Properties of two forms of DNA polymerase δ from calf thymus. *Biochemistry* **25:** 7821.

Wang, T.S.-F., S.-Z. Hu, and D. Korn. 1984. DNA primase from KB cells: Characterization of a primase activity tightly associated with immunoaffinity-purified DNA polymerase α. *J. Biol. Chem.* **259:** 1854.

Watson, J.D., N.H. Hopkins, J.W. Roberts, J.A. Steitz, and A.M. Weiner. 1987. The replication of DNA. In *Molecular biology of the gene,* 4th edition (ed. J.R. Gillen), vol. 1, p. 282. Benjamin/Cummings, Menlo Park, California.

Yoshida, S., R. Suzuki, S. Masaki, and O. Koiwai. 1983. DNA primase associated with 10S DNA polymerase α from calf thymus. *Biochim. Biophys. Acta* **741:** 348.

DNA Repair Synthesis in Permeabilized Human Fibroblasts Mediated by DNA Polymerase δ and Application for Purification of Xeroderma Pigmentosum Factors

C. Nishida and S. Linn

Department of Biochemistry, University of California, Berkeley, California 94720

If UV-irradiated cultured diploid human fibroblasts are permeabilized with Brij-58 then soluble material removed by centrifugation, conservative DNA repair synthesis can be restored by a soluble factor obtained from the supernate of similarly treated HeLa cells. Extensive purification of this factor has yielded a 10.2S, 220,000-dalton polypeptide with the DNA polymerase and 3′ → 5′ exonuclease of DNA polymerase δ (Nishida et al. 1988). Moreover, if monoclonal antibodies to DNA polymerase α, BuPdGTP, or BuAdATP are added to the reconstituted system, there is no significant inhibition. Thus, it appears that the major portion of UV-induced DNA repair synthesis is catalyzed by DNA polymerase δ, not α. When permeabilized xeroderma pigmentosum (XP) human diploid fibroblasts were utilized, DNA repair synthesis dependent on UV light could be restored by addition of T4 endonuclease V and DNA polymerase δ, but not by addition of either one alone. A positive response was also observed with XP-A and XP-E fibroblasts by the addition of DNA polymerase δ and crude fractions prepared from HeLa cells. This response has been exploited to partially purify a HeLa XP-A correcting factor.

Research into the process of UV-induced DNA repair in mammalian cells has been hampered by the lack of knowledge of the specific proteins and biochemical activities involved. To isolate mammalian DNA repair factors, we have developed an in vitro complementation assay utilizing permeabilized cultured human cells (Nishida et al. 1988). It became apparent, however, that a soluble DNA repair factor was diluted out during the permeabilization process, and we have recently detected this factor in soluble extracts from HeLa cells. Utilizing cytosol-depleted permeabilized normal human fibroblasts for a functional assay of its activity, we have purified this factor extensively and found it to be a 220,000-dalton polypeptide that copurifies with the 10.2S DNA polymerase and 3′ → 5′ exonuclease activities described for DNA polymerase δ (Nishida et al. 1988). This factor now allows us to exploit the permeabilized human fibroblasts for the identification of factors that are absent from DNA repair-defective cells.

Experimental Procedures

Materials

Brij-58 was obtained from McKesson Chemical (Los Angeles, CA). Poly(dA), (dT)$_{550}$ and (dT)$_{16}$ were obtained from Midland Certified Reagent Co. (Midland, TX). Monoclonal anti-DNA polymerase α IgG (SJK 132-20 and SJK 237-71) and the nonimmune control monoclonal IgG (P3) were purified as described by Tanaka et al. (1982). BuPdGTP and BuAdATP were generous gifts from Dr. G. Wright, University of Massachusetts Medical School. T4 endonuclease V (fraction VII) was

prepared as described previously (Evans and Linn 1984).

Cell culture

HeLa cells were grown in suspension in Joklik's modified Eagle's medium containing 5% calf serum supplemented with penicillin, streptomycin, and L-glutamine. The F65 (normal) human fibroblast strain was obtained from the Naval Biomedical Research Laboratory (Oakland, CA) and XP fibroblast strains GM2990 (complementation group A) and CRL1259 (complementation group E) were from the NIGMS Human Genetic Mutant Cell Repository (Camden, NJ) and the American Type Culture Collection (Rockville, MD), respectively. These cells were grown in a humidified 5% CO$_2$ incubator at 37°C. Subculturing of fibroblasts from 150 cm^2 tissue culture flasks to tissue culture dishes of 10-cm diameter followed trypsin treatment (0.05%) and suspension in Dulbecco's modified Eagle's (DME) medium containing 10% fetal bovine serum (FBS). Upon attaining a confluent state, cultures of F65 fibroblasts were maintained in DME medium containing 5% FBS. XP fibroblasts were grown and maintained in DME medium containing 20% FBS. Postconfluent cultures (i.e., cultures in a confluent state for at least 3 days but not exceeding 15 days) were utilized.

DNA repair assay

Postconfluent fibroblast cultures in tissue culture were washed twice with phosphate-buffered saline (PBS; 137 mM NaCl, 2.7 mM KCl, 6.46 mM Na$_2$HPO$_4$, 1.47 mM KH$_2$PO$_4$) and the liquid was drained off before the cells

411

were UV-irradiated or mock-irradiated. Irradiation was with a General Electric germicidal lamp G 15T8 (15 W) at an incident dose rate of 2.0 J/m^2/s and a dose of 40 J/m^2. One-half ml of 0.05% trypsin was added to each dish. After 5 minutes at 37°C, 2.5 ml PBS was added and the cells were transferred to a 50-ml polypropylene conical tube and pelleted in a clinical centrifuge at room temperature. The cells were resuspended at 0°C in permeabilization buffer (36 mM HEPES-KOH [pH 7.7], 270 mM sucrose, 0.9% [w/v] dextran [m.w. 500,000], 14.4 mM MgCl$_2$, 0.9 mM EGTA, 5 mM ATP, 1.8 mM dithiothreitol [DTT], 250 mM KCl, 0.05% [w/v], Brij-58) at a density of 6 × 10^6 cells/ml and incubated for 25 minutes at 0°C. Aliquots (130 μl) were layered onto 2.5 ml of buffer A (40 mM HEPES-KOH [pH 7.7], 300 mM sucrose, 1% [w/v] dextran [m.w. 500,000], 16 mM MgCl$_2$, 1 mM EGTA, 2 mM DTT) containing 250 mM KCl in 12 × 75 mm polypropylene tubes and centrifuged in a SS-34 rotor at 7500 rpm (6700g) for 20 minutes at 2°C in order to separate Brij-58 and other soluble molecules. The pellet was gently washed with 1 ml buffer A containing 5 mM ATP and resuspended in 20 μl of buffer B (buffer A plus 5 mM ATP, 100 μM each of dATP, dCTP, and dGTP, and 5 μM [^{3}H]dTTP, 30–50 × 10^3 cpm/pmol). Soluble sample (10 μl) was added to the cytosol-depleted permeabilized cell suspension, the tubes capped, and the reaction mixture incubated for 60 or 90 minutes at 30°C. The reaction was stopped by chilling and adding 1.9 ml of 1 M NaClO$_4$ and 60 μl of 10% (w/v) SDS, and the reaction mixture was extracted with 2 ml of phenol (saturated with 1 M NaClO$_4$ [pH 7.0])/chloroform (1:1). A portion of the upper phase (1.6 ml) was mixed with 2 ml of 0.1 M Na$_4$P$_2$O$_7$ followed by 5 ml of 10% (w/v) trichloroacetic acid. After 15 minutes on ice, solutions were filtered through Whatman GF/C filters presoaked for at least 1 hour in 0.1 M Na$_4$P$_2$O$_7$, then the filters were washed 10 times with 1 M HCl containing 0.1 M Na$_4$P$_2$O$_7$, once with 95% ethanol, and dried. Radioactivity was determined by liquid scintillation counting. One unit of DNA repair factor activity stimulates the incorporation of 1 pmol [^{3}H]dTMP per hour per 10^6 cytosol-depleted permeabilized fibroblasts at 30°C. Where indicated, XP fibroblasts were used in the standard DNA repair assay with 10 μl of 2X buffer B to increase the sample volume to 20μl.

Enzyme assays
DNA polymerase α activity was assayed with activated salmon sperm DNA as previously described (Linn et al. 1976), except that KCl was omitted and 50 mM Tris-HCl (pH 7.5), was used. DNA polymerase activity of pol δ was assayed using poly(dA) primed with (dT)$_{16}$ with an average interprimer distance of 150 nucleotides as described by Crute et al. (1986), except that ATP was omitted and the reaction was stopped by the addition of 0.2 ml 0.1 M Na$_4$P$_2$O$_7$ followed by 0.7 ml 10% (w/v) trichloroacetic acid. Samples were filtered through GF/C filters and radioactivity determined as described for the DNA repair assay. One unit catalyzes the incorporation of 1 nmol [^{3}H]dTMP per hour at 30°C. DNA poly-

merase δ nuclease activity was assayed as described by Lee et al. (1980) using [^{3}H](dT)$_{70}$ prepared as described by Crute et al. (1986) in a final reaction volume of 60 μl. One unit of nuclease catalyzes the release of 1 nmol dTMP from [^{3}H](dT)$_{70}$ per hour at 37°C.

Results

Identification and purification of the factor
Postconfluent normal diploid human fibroblasts were made permeable by exposure to Brij-58 by a modification of the procedure of Reinhard et al. (1979). Preliminary experiments showed that UV-irradiated cells treated with buffer containing 0.01% Brij-58 exhibited UV-dependent conservative DNA repair synthesis similar to that observed with unfractionated cells permeabilized by hypotonic treatment (Ciarrocchi and Linn 1978). DNA repair synthesis was not observed, however, when 0.05% Brij-58 and 250 mM KCl were utilized, but could be restored by addition of a DNA repair factor from soluble extracts of either normal human fibroblasts or HeLa cells. The DNA repair factor from HeLa soluble extract was purified 2000-fold as described in Table 1.

Properties of the repair factor
The repair factor could not be correlated with endonuclease activity on undamaged, UV-irradiated, or apurinic duplex or single-stranded DNAs; exonuclease activity on duplex or denatured *Escherichia coli* DNA; DNA-dependent or independent ATPase; native or UV-damage-specific DNA binding activity; DNA primase; and DNA polymerase α, β, or γ. However, a DNA polymerase activity with the synthetic template-primer poly(dA)·oligo(dT) did co-sediment exactly with repair activity at 10.2S (Fig. 1). This polymerase activity was resistant to inhibition by micromolar concentrations of the DNA polymerase-α-specific inhibitors, BuPdGTP and BuAdATP, and also to monoclonal antibody to KB cell DNA polymerase α. These properties are characteristic of DNA polymerase δ (Byrnes et al. 1976; Lee et al. 1985; Crute et al. 1986; Lee and Toomey 1987).

An additional characteristic of δ-polymerase, and one that is unique among the mammalian DNA polymerases,

Table 1 Purification of Soluble Repair Factor from HeLa Cells

Fraction	Total activity (units)	Specific activity (units/mg)
I. Soluble extract	2510	0.508
II. 30–50% (NH$_4$)$_2$SO$_4$ precipitate	1470	0.880
III. Heat-treatment (45°C, 12 min)	1210	0.725
IV. DEAE-Sephacel	526	1.23
V. Phosphocellulose	463	29.1
VI. Hydroxylapatite	372	116
VIa. Hydroxylapatite fraction 36	43.0	189
VIIa. Glycerol gradient ultracentrifugation	48.6	1000

The factor was purified as described by Nishida et al. (1988) from 6.2 × 10^{10} HeLa cells.

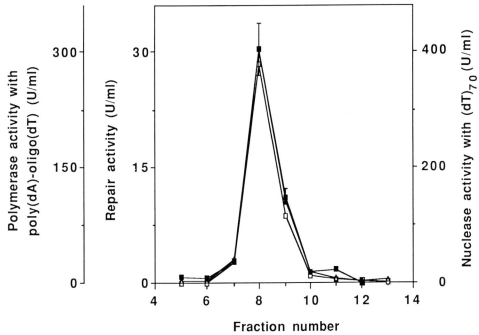

Figure 1 Co-sedimentation of repair factor with δ DNA polymerase and nuclease activities. (■) DNA repair activity; (□) DNA polymerase activity with poly(dA)-oligo(dT); (△) nuclease activity with [³H](dT)₇₀.

is the presence of an intrinsic 3′ → 5′ exonuclease (Byrnes et al. 1976). When nuclease activity with [³H](dT)₇₀ (a preferred substrate for the δ-exonuclease) was assayed, a sharp peak of 3′ → 5′ exonuclease activity was found also to co-sediment with the DNA repair activity (Fig. 1; Nishida et al. 1988). In addition, 5 mM AMP inhibited the initial rate of the exonuclease by 45%, in agreement with previously characterized δ-polymerases (Byrnes et al. 1977; Crute et al. 1986; Lee and Toomey 1987).

Finally, when the repair activity from the hydroxyl-apatite column (fraction VIa, Table 1) was sedimented through a glycerol gradient, it co-sedimented simultaneously with DNA polymerase δ and with a peptide that had a M_r of 220,000 daltons on an SDS polyacrylamide gel. This peptide was the only one detected in the peak fraction (Fig. 2). The sedimentation coefficient and gel band location are consistent with repair factor being a monomeric form of DNA polymerase δ with a molecular weight of approximately 220,000.

Effect of inhibitors of DNA polymerase α on the repair assay

Based on inhibitor studies with aphidicolin, DNA polymerase α has been assigned a major role in DNA replication and repair. However, since aphidicolin inhibits both δ- and α-polymerase (Goscin and Byrnes 1982), this interpretation must be reconsidered. Since DNA polymerase α may be present in the cytosol-depleted permeabilized cells, the question remained whether it too might play a role in UV-induced DNA repair synthe-

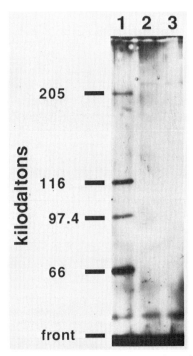

Figure 2 SDS-polyacrylamide gel electrophoresis of DNA polymerase δ/soluble repair factor. Tracks 2 and 3 were peak fractions from glycerol gradient sedimentation of fraction VIa (Table 1). Track 1 contained molecular weight markers (myosin, δ-galactosidase, phosphorylase b, and bovine serum albumin). The band present in all tracks corresponding to 54 kD derives from β-mercaptoethanol and was present when only SDS and β-mercaptoethanol were put into a well.

Table 2 Effect of Inhibitors of DNA Polymerase α on DNA Repair Activity

	Relative activity	
Inhibitor	repair	DNA pol α
None	1.00	1.00
10 μg P3 (nonimmune control) IgG	0.94	1.00
10 μg SJK 132-20 IgG	0.94	0.10
10 μg SJK 237-71 IgG	1.22	0.07
3.2 μM BuPdGTP	0.78	0.05
3.2 μM BuAdATP	0.86	0.04

sis. To explore this possibility, monoclonal anti-DNA polymerase α IgG, BuPdGTP, or BuAdATP was added with 0.86 unit of DNA polymerase δ to the standard DNA repair assay (Table 2). Levels of antibody that inhibited HeLa DNA polymerase α prepared by the method of Vishwanatha et al. (1986) by greater than 90% did not affect repair activity with respect to the nonimmune control IgG. In addition, concentrations of BuPdGTP and BuAdATP that inhibited DNA polymerase α by greater than 95%, but had no effect on DNA polymerase δ, affected repair activity only minimally, consistent with results reported for permeabilized human fibroblasts (Dresler and Frattini 1986). Taken together, these findings are most consistent with the involvement of DNA polymerase δ in UV-induced DNA repair synthesis, with DNA polymerase α serving a secondary role at best.

Studies with XP permeabilized fibroblasts and exogenous protein

The potential application of this DNA repair system is revealed by the response of cytosol-depleted, permeabilized DNA repair-defective xeroderma pigmentosum complementation group A (XP-A) cells to exogenous phage T4 endonuclease V. Permeable cells can take up the phage endonuclease, and the inability of XP cells to repair UV-induced DNA damage can be corrected by this treatment (Tanaka et al. 1975; Ciarrocchi and Linn 1978). However, when purified T4 endonuclease V (29 units) was added to cytosol-depleted permeabilized XP-A fibroblasts, no UV-dependent dTMP incorporation was observed unless HeLa DNA polymerase δ (0.85 unit) was also added (Table 3). This result not only reaffirms that δ-polymerase is required for repair DNA synthesis, but also suggests the application of this system to an in vitro complementation assay to purify from extracts of normal cells, DNA repair factors that are missing in repair-deficient cells.

Table 3 T4 Endonuclease V Activity with Cytosol-depleted Permeabilized XP-A Cells

	fmol [³H]dTMP incorporated per 10⁶ cells per hr following UV irradiation	
Additions	no irradiation	40 J/m²
None	10	11
T4 endo V	9	10
δ-pol	10	8
T4 endo V + δ-pol	10	174

In this manner, we have attempted to complement the DNA repair-deficiency in cytosol-depleted permeabilized XP fibroblasts with the addition of HeLa DNA polymerase δ together with HeLa soluble extract. UV-dependent DNA repair synthesis could be restored in this way for XP-A and for XP-E cells. In neither case was the DNA repair deficiency corrected by addition of DNA polymerase δ alone; thus, δ-polymerase does not appear to be either the XP-A or the XP-E correcting factor. The XP-A factor activity has been partially purified from HeLa soluble extract by ammonium sulfate fractionation at 25–45%, followed by stepwise elution from phosphocellulose at 150–300 mM potassium phosphate. After dialysis, this fraction yielded XP-A factor activity that was concentration-dependent (Fig. 3), demonstrating that the XP-A factor is the limiting component in the assay. Utilizing this assay, we are now trying to further purify and characterize this protein.

Discussion

A factor that is absolutely required for UV-induced DNA repair synthesis was purified from the soluble fraction of permeabilized HeLa cells. It sedimented through glycerol gradients and migrated through polyacrylamide gels at rates comparable to those for a polypeptide of 220,000 daltons, and it copurified with polymerase and exonuclease activities characteristic of DNA polymerase δ. The conclusion that DNA repair synthesis requires DNA polymerase δ is further supported by recent reports that suggest that DNA replication and repair may be at least partly dependent on DNA polymerase δ (Dresler and Frattini 1986, 1987; Dresler and Kimbro 1987; Decker et al. 1987; Prelich et al. 1987a,b). Moreover, data reported here, showing that potent and specific inhibitors of DNA polymerase α affect DNA repair activity at most only minimally, suggest that DNA polymerase α serves a role in UV-induced DNA repair synthesis in permeabilized human fibroblasts that is menial at best.

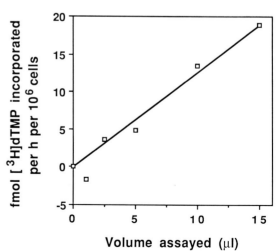

Figure 3 Concentration-dependence of XP-A factor activity.

It is not DNA polymerase activity per se that is required for DNA repair synthesis in the cytosol-depleted cells, because the function of δ-polymerase cannot be fulfilled by either DNA polymerase α or β or by DNA polymerase I large (Klenow) fragment (C. Nishida and S. Linn, unpubl). Of all the mammalian DNA polymerases, δ-polymerase alone possesses an intrinsic $3' \rightarrow 5'$ exonuclease, so that a possible role for δ-polymerase could be in the excision of damage from the $3'$ terminus so that a proper primer is formed.

The potential for an in vitro complementation assay to be able to identify mammalian DNA repair factors has engendered the development of a variety of systems utilizing isolated nuclei (Smith and Hanawalt 1978), cell-free extracts obtained by osmotic disruption (Ciarrocchi and Linn 1978) or sonication (Mortelmans et al. 1976), permeabilized cells (Roberts and Lieberman 1979; Dresler et al. 1982), or viable cells microinjected with cell extracts (de Jonge et al. 1983). To date none of these has been entirely successful. We have made preliminary observations of a positive response of XP cytosol-depleted permeabilized fibroblasts to exogenously supplied HeLa cell extract and purified δ-polymerase, and have begun purification of XP correcting factors.

Acknowledgments

We are indebted to Ms. Roberta Johnson for her invaluable help with tissue culture. This research was supported by grants DE-FG03-86ER60395 from the Department of Energy and GM-30415 from the National Institutes of Health, and training grant 732ES07075 to C.N.

References

Byrnes, J.J., K.M. Downey, V.L. Black, and A.G. So. 1976. A new mammalian DNA polymerase with 3' to 5' exonuclease activity: DNA polymerase δ. *Biochemistry* **15**: 2817.

Byrnes, J.J., K.M. Downey, B.G. Que, M.Y.W. Lee, V.L. Black, and A.G. So. 1977. Selective inhibition of the 3' to 5' exonuclease activity associated with DNA polymerases: A mechanism of mutagenesis. *Biochemistry* **16**: 3740.

Ciarrocchi, G. and S. Linn. 1978. A cell-free assay measuring repair DNA synthesis in human fibroblasts. *Proc. Natl. Acad. Sci.* **75**: 1887.

Crute, J.J., A.F. Wahl, and R.A. Bambara. 1986. Purification and characterization of two new high molecular weight forms of DNA polymerase δ. *Biochemistry* **25**: 26.

de Jonge, J.R., W. Vermeulen, B. Klein, and H.J. Hoeijmakers. 1983. Microinjection of human cell extracts corrects xeroderma pigmentosum defect. *EMBO J.* **2**: 637.

Decker, R.S., M. Yamaguchi, R. Possenti, M.K. Bradley, and M.L. DePamphilis. 1987. In vitro initiation of DNA replication in simian virus 40 chromosomes. *J. Biol. Chem.* **262**: 10863.

Dresler, S.L. and M.G. Frattini. 1986. DNA replication and UV-induced DNA repair synthesis in human fibroblasts are much less sensitive than DNA polymerase α to inhibition by butylphenyl-deoxyguanosine triphosphate. *Nucleic Acids Res.* **14**: 7093.

———. 1987. Inhibition of DNA replication, DNA repair synthesis, and DNA polymerases α and δ by butylphenyl deoxyguanosine triphosphate. *Fed. Proc.* **46**: 2208.

Dresler, S.L. and K.S. Kimbro. 1987. 2′, 3′-Dideoxythymidine 5′-triphosphate inhibition of DNA replication and ultraviolet-induced DNA repair synthesis in human cells: Evidence for involvement of DNA polymerase δ. *Biochemistry* **26**: 2664.

Dresler, S.L., J.D. Roberts, and M.W. Lieberman. 1982. Characterization of deoxyribonucleic acid repair synthesis in permeable human fibroblasts. *Biochemistry* **21**: 2557.

Evans, D.H. and S. Linn. 1984. Excision repair of pyrimidine dimers from SV40 minichromosomes in vitro. *J. Biol. Chem.* **259**: 10252.

Goscin, L.P. and J.J. Byrnes. 1982. DNA polymerase δ: One polypeptide, two activities. *Biochemistry* **21**: 2513.

Lee, M.Y.W.T. and N.L. Toomey. 1987. Human placental DNA polymerase δ: Identification of a 170-kilodalton polypeptide by activity staining and immunoblotting. *Biochemistry* **26**: 1076.

Lee, M.Y.W.T., N.L. Toomey, and G.E. Wright. 1985. Differential inhibition of human placental DNA polymerases δ and α by BuPdGTP and BuAdATP. *Nucleic Acids Res.* **13**: 8623.

Lee, M.Y.W.T., C.-K. Tan, A.G. So, and K.M. Downey. 1980. Purification of deoxyribonucleic acid polymerase δ from calf thymus: Partial characterization of physical properties. *Biochemistry* **19**: 2096.

Linn, S., M. Kairis, and R. Holliday. 1976. Decreased fidelity of DNA polymerase activity isolated from aging human fibroblasts. *Proc. Natl. Acad. Sci.* **73**: 2818.

Mortelmans, K., E.C. Friedberg, H. Slor, G. Thomas, and J.E. Cleaver. 1976. Defective thymine dimer excision by cell-free extracts of xeroderma pigmentosum cells. *Proc. Natl. Acad. Sci.* **73**: 2757.

Nishida, C., P. Reinhard, and S. Linn. 1988. DNA repair synthesis in human fibroblasts requires DNA polymerase δ. *J. Biol. Chem.* **263**: 501.

Prelich, G., M. Kostura, D.R. Marshak, M.B. Mathews, and B. Stillman. 1987a. The cell-cycle regulated proliferating cell nuclear antigen is required for SV40 DNA replication in vitro. *Nature* **326**: 471.

Prelich, G., C.-K. Tan, M. Kostura, M.B. Mathews, A.G. So, K.M. Downey, and B. Stillman. 1987b. Functional identity of proliferating cell nuclear antigen and a DNA polymerase-δ auxiliary protein. *Nature* **326**: 517.

Reinhard, P., P. Maillart, M. Schluchter, J.R. Gautschi, and R. Schindler. 1979. An assay system for factors involved in mammalian DNA replication. *Biochim. Biophys. Acta* **564**: 141.

Roberts, J.D. and M.W. Lieberman. 1979. Deoxyribonucleic acid repair synthesis in permeable human fibroblasts exposed to ultraviolet radiation and N-acetoxy-2-(acetylamino)-fluorene. *Biochemistry* **18**: 4499.

Smith, C.A. and P.C. Hanawalt. 1978. Phage T4 endonuclease V stimulates DNA repair replication in isolated nuclei from ultraviolet-irradiated human cells, including xeroderma pigmentosum fibroblasts. *Proc. Natl. Acad. Sci.* **75**: 2598.

Tanaka, K., M. Sekiguchi, and Y. Okada. 1975. Restoration of ultraviolet-induced unscheduled DNA synthesis of xeroderma pigmentosum cells by the concomitant treatment with bacteriophage T4 endonuclease V and HVJ (Sendai virus). *Proc. Natl. Acad. Sci.* **72**: 4071.

Tanaka, S., S.-Z. Hu, T.S.-F. Wang, and D. Korn. 1982. Preparation and preliminary characterization of monoclonal antibodies against human DNA polymerase α. *J. Biol. Chem.* **257**: 8386.

Vishwanatha, J.K., S.A. Coughlin, M. Wesolowski-Owen, and E.F. Baril. 1986. A multiprotein form of DNA polymerase α from HeLa cells: Resolution of its associated catalytic activities. *J. Biol. Chem.* **261**: 6619.

Molecular Cloning of Human DNA Polymerase β

L.M.S. Chang,* F.J. Bollum,* X.X. Xiu,* L.C. Cheung,* K. Huebner,[†] C.M. Croce,[†] B.K. Hecht,[‡] F. Hecht,[‡] and L.A. Cannizzaro,[‡]

*Department of Biochemistry, Uniformed Services University of the Health Sciences, Bethesda, Maryland 20814; [†]Wistar Institute of Anatomy and Biology, Philadelphia, Pennsylvania 19104; [‡]The Genetic Center, Southwest Biomedical Research Institute, Scottsdale, Arizona 85251

A cDNA fragment for human DNA polymerase β has been cloned by screening a human KM-3 cell cDNA library in λgt11 for expression of fused β-galactosidase/human DNA polymerase β proteins. Recombinants were detected with immunoaffinity-purified rabbit antibody to calf thymus DNA polymerase β. A single recombinant containing a 735-bp insert was isolated. The insert from this clone was used to isolate several additional clones by hybridization to several cDNA libraries. DNA sequencing of various cDNA clones produced overlapping sequences that could be merged into 1319 bp of human DNA polymerase β cDNA sequence. The merged sequence represents about 80% of the full-length DNA polymerase β cDNA, with an open reading frame starting at residue 2. The translated sequence contains 381 amino acids with a calculated molecular weight of 42,558. The DNA polymerase β DNA sequence has been localized to chromosome 8 by somatic cell hybrid analysis and sublocalized by in situ hybridization to the short arm of chromosome 8 in the region 8p11 → p12.

The low-molecular-weight, N-ethylmaleimide-resistant DNA polymerase β (Weissbach et al. 1975) of mammalian cells was first described in 1971 (Chang and Bollum 1971; Weissbach et al. 1971) and was purified to homogeneity in 1973 (Chang 1973a). Phylogenetic studies have shown that DNA polymerase β is most likely to be involved in DNA repair (Hübscher et al. 1979). A biological survey for DNA polymerase β indicated that the enzyme is present in sponges, the simplest of multicellular animal cells (Chang 1976). The enzyme has not been demonstrated in prokaryotes, free-living unicellular animal cells, or plants.

Antiserum to homogeneous calf thymus DNA polymerase β was produced in 1982 (Chang et al. 1982). Enzyme neutralization and immunoblot analyses have been interpreted as an indication that the enzyme protein is highly conserved through evolution both in molecular weight and in antigenic determinants. The molecular weight of DNA polymerase β in all species that contain it is around 45,000. Although the reaction properties and associated enzyme activities of the enzyme have been carefully analyzed (Chang 1973b; Wang et al. 1974), little is known about its physical and chemical properties because of the scarcity of pure enzyme. Isolation and characterization of a cDNA for DNA polymerase β provides an alternative approach for obtaining information about the structure of this important enzyme and the first step in producing recombinant enzyme. This communication describes our immunological procedure for verification of expression, sequence analysis of the DNA polymerase β cDNAs isolated from human cDNA libraries, and the chromosome sublocalization of the human DNA polymerase β cDNA.

Experimental Procedures

Materials

Poly(A)[+] mRNA from human lymphoblast cell line KM-3 and calf thymus glands and the λgt11 libraries containing human KM-3 cDNA were those described previously (Peterson et al. 1985). The human ALL cDNA λ 10 library (Wiginton et al. 1983) was generously provided by Dr. John J. Hutton, Children's Hospital, Cincinnati, Ohio. Sources of commercial enzymes, nucleotides, oligonucleotides, and immunological reagents were as described previously. Rabbit antiserum to calf thymus DNA polymerase β was as described previously (Chang et al. 1982). Human liver chromatin DNA polymerase β previously isolated from human liver chromatin (Chang 1974) was used as the test antigen. Other reagents were commercial grade.

Antibody screening of KM-3 library in λgt11

Affinity-purified antibody to human DNA polymerase β was obtained by adsorption of the rabbit antiserum onto a column containing homogeneous calf thymus DNA polymerase β covalently linked to controlled pore glass, and elution with 0.5 M NaCl in glycine-HCl buffer (pH 3.0) after washing with 0.5 M NaCl in 50 mM Tris-HCl buffer (pH 8.0). The affinity-purified rabbit anti-calf thymus DNA polymerase β was diluted to 2 μg per ml in 20% fetal calf serum containing 0.1 M NaCl in 50 mM Tris-HCl (pH 8.0) (TBS) for colony screening.

Recombinant phages were plated on *Escherichia coli* Y1090 and screened for antigen-producing clones as described by Young and Davis (1983) using a three-layer immuno-enzymatic detection system consisting of

417

affinity-purified rabbit anti-DNA polymerase β, IgG (immunoglobulin γ) of goat anti-rabbit IgG, followed by rabbit anti-horseradish peroxidase/horseradish peroxidase complex. The immune reaction was visualized on the nitrocellulose membrane using 0.5 mg per ml of 4-chloro-1-naphthol with 0.01% H_2O_2 in TBS as the peroxidase substrate. Plaque purification was carried out on the single positive recombinant phage obtained.

Screening of the human KM-3 and ALL cDNA libraries with nick-translated DNA probe

The insert from the recombinant λgt11 phage was obtained by *Eco*RI nuclease digestion and recloned into the *Eco*RI site of pUC-8 to give pB19. Phages in the λgt11 libraries were plated on *E. coli* Y1088, and in the λgt10 library were plated on *E. coli* C600 and screened for recombinants hybridizing to the nick-translated insert of pB19. Several additional positive recombinant phages were detected and plaque-purified. Analysis of the two recombinants with the largest inserts (1215 bp in λgt10 and 1190 bp in λgt11) are reported in this communication. The 1190-bp insert was obtained as two *Eco*RI fragments and recloned into the *Eco*RI site of pUC-8 to give pB26-1 and pB26-2. The 1215-bp insert was obtained by partial digestion with *Eco*RI nuclease and recloned into the *Pst*I site of pUC-8 to give pB159.

DNA sequencing

pB19 and pB26-1 were obtained in forward and reverse orientations in pUC-8. A series of deletion plasmids was generated for each isolate by cleaving the recombinant plasmids with *Bam*HI, digestion with *Pst*I, exonuclease III, and S1 nuclease, blunt-ended with the large fragment of *E. coli* DNA polymerase I, and finally ligated with bacteriophage T4 DNA ligase. Single-stranded templates for sequencing by the dideoxy chain termination method (Sanger et al. 1977) were made from plasmid DNA by cleavage with *Eco*RI followed by digestion with exonuclease III (Guo and Wu 1982). The 15-base M13 phage sequencing primer was used in the sequencing reaction. Deletion plasmids were generated from pB159 by cleaving with *Xma*I, filled in with the large fragment of *E. coli* polymerase I with α-S-dCTP and dGTP, digestion with *Sal*I, exonuclease III, and S1 nuclease, blunt-ended with the large fragment of *E. coli* DNA polymerase I, followed by ligation with bacteriophage T4 DNA ligase. Single-stranded DNA templates for sequencing were made from plasmid DNA by cleavage with *Hin*dIII followed by digestion with exonuclease III, and the 17-base M13 reverse sequencing primer was used in the sequencing reaction.

RNA blot hybridization analyses

Poly(A)$^+$ mRNAs (10 μg each from human KM-3 cells and calf thymus glands) were separated by electrophoresis on a 1.5% agarose gel containing 2.2 M formamide in 0.2 M sodium acetate and 5 mM EDTA, transferred to nitrocellulose, and probed for DNA polymerase β mRNA with nick-translated insert of pB19.

Production of mouse antibody to E. coli β-galactosidase-DNA polymerase β fused protein

Antiserum to *E. coli* β-galactosidase was produced in a New Zealand rabbit by immunization with commercial *E. coli* β-galactosidase. The titer of the immune serum used was sufficient to give a visible precipitin line on microdiffusion plates at 1/64 dilution. Immunoglobulin from 5 ml of this antiserum was covalently coupled onto a 1.5 ml protein-A-Sepharose with dimethylsuberimidate and the rabbit anti-β-galactosidase protein-A-Sepharose resin was used to isolate the fused protein expected to be present in the extract of recombinant phage-infected *E. coli*. Immunoreactive material present in recombinant λgt11 phage-infected and isopropyl-thiogalactoside-induced *E. coli* Y1088 cell extract was eluted from the antibody resin with 0.1 M acetic acid. Protein eluting from the anti-β-galactosidase resin was used to immunize BALB/c mice and the IgG from the immune mouse sera was isolated by adsorption onto and elution from protein-A-Sepharose.

Enzyme binding

0.75 μg of human liver DNA polymerase β in 5 mg per ml bovine serum albumin in TBS (15 μl) was incubated with various amounts of mouse anti-fused protein IgG diluted in 5 mg per ml bovine serum albumin in TBS (15 μl) for 12 hours at 4°C. 45 μl of a 33% suspension of protein-A-Sepharose in 0.2 M Tris-HCl (pH 8.7) was added to each incubation mixture. The suspensions were mixed for 2 hours at 4°C, and the protein-A-Sepharose was removed by centrifugation in an Eppendorf centrifuge. The supernatant solutions were assayed for DNA polymerase β activity as described previously (Harper and Saunders 1981). A parallel reaction containing pre-immune IgG at each concentration of immune IgG used was also set up. Results are expressed as percentage of control, which is the percentage of activity remaining in the immune IgG-treated supernatant fraction over the pre-immune IgG-treated level at each concentration of IgG used.

Immunoblots

Protein samples were separated by electrophoresis on a 10% polyacrylamide gel in the presence of sodium dodecyl sulfate as described by Laemmli (1970). After electrophoretic transfer to nitrocellulose filters (Towbin et al. 1979), immunoreactive materials were detected using a three-layer system consisting of mouse anti-fused protein IgG, rabbit anti-mouse IgG antiserum, and a horseradish peroxidase conjugate of goat anti-rabbit IgG. The immunological reaction was detected using 4-chloro-1-naphthol/H_2O_2 as the peroxidase substrate.

In situ hybridization

Metaphase chromosome preparations were obtained by culturing peripheral blood lymphocytes from a normal male subject, and in situ hybridization was performed using a modification of the standard protocol (Harper and Saunders 1981; Cannizzaro and Emanuel 1984).

Results

Antibody screening of the KM-3 cDNA libraries

Affinity-purified rabbit antibody to calf thymus DNA polymerase β was used to screen the human cDNA libraries in expression vector λgt11. One recombinant phage producing immunoreactive material was isolated from a library with an original size of 20,000 recombinants (Peterson et al. 1985). The insert in this recombinant phage is 735 bp. Using this insert as a DNA probe to rescreen the same library produced no other positive recombinants.

After recloning this 735 bp in sequencing plasmid pUC-8 (pB19), DNA sequence analysis showed that the insert is flanked by an EcoRI site on one end and a stretch of 20 A residues on the other end. The cloned cDNA sequence therefore represents the 3′ terminus of the mRNA and the carboxyl terminus of the protein.

RNA blot hybridization analyses

DNA polymerase β mRNA from chick embryos has been shown previously to be about 1800 nucleotides long (Yamaguchi et al. 1983). Preliminary analysis of DNA polymerase β mRNA from human and calf thymus cells by in vitro translation from total poly(A)$^+$ mRNA separated on denaturing sucrose gradients and immunoprecipitation of translated products indicated that the mRNA sediments at 16S. If the cloned 735-bp cDNA represents DNA polymerase β sequence, we would expect that it would hybridize to mRNAs from human and cow within the size range of 1600–1800 nucleotides.

When total poly(A)$^+$ mRNA from human KM-3 cells and calf thymus glands was analyzed by blot hybridization after electrophoresis in agarose gel under denaturing conditions and probed with nick-translated pB19, the results in Figure 1 were obtained. One major band of hybridizable material at about 1600 nucleotides is seen for both human and bovine samples. These results show that the cloned 735-bp fragment detects an mRNA of a size consistent with that expected for DNA polymerase β mRNA.

Relationship of the fused protein produced by the recombinant phage and human DNA polymerase β

Even though the recombinant phage was isolated using an immunoaffinity-purified antibody to homogeneous calf thymus DNA polymerase β, independent confirmation of the relationship of recombinant protein and DNA polymerase β is essential to avoid the possibility that a minor contaminant of DNA polymerase β preparations has been cloned. Since amino acid sequence for human DNA polymerase β was not available, an alternative method was required to establish the identity of the cloned sequence.

To demonstrate that the fused protein contains epitopes related to DNA polymerase β, we purified the fused protein produced by the recombinant λgt11 phage using an antibody column to E. coli β-galactosidase and used this fused protein to generate a mouse antibody. When the mouse anti-fused protein was used

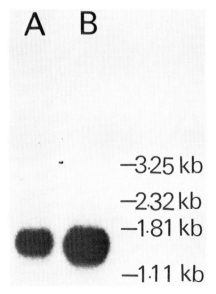

Figure 1 Blot hybridization of human KM-3 and calf thymus RNA with cloned DNA polymerase β cDNA. (Lane A) Autoradiogram of calf thymus mRNA hybridizing to nick-translated pB19; (lane B) hybridization of KM-3 mRNA. Size markers used were restriction enzyme (BglI and HincII) fragments of pBR322 DNA.

in an enzyme binding assay with human DNA polymerase β, activity was removed from solution, as seen in the results presented in Figure 2. This experiment demonstrates that mouse antibody to the recombinant protein binds human enzyme and the antigen/antibody complex can be removed by protein-A-Sepharose.

The reactivity of the mouse antibody to the fused protein with DNA polymerase β is demonstrated directly by testing relevant proteins in an immunoblot procedure

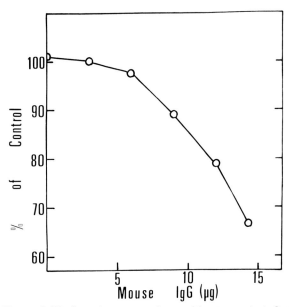

Figure 2 Binding of mouse anti-recombinant protein IgG to human liver chromatin DNA polymerase β. Immunological and enzyme reactions were carried out as described in Experimental Procedures.

(Fig. 3). Because of the small amount of the mouse antibody obtained, affinity purification was not carried out. This antibody reacts nonspecifically with several irrelevant proteins in uninfected *lac⁻ E. coli* extract (Fig. 3, lane A). An immunoreactive band at a higher molecular weight than *E. coli* β-galactosidase (representing the fused protein) was detected in the crude extract of recombinant phage-infected cells (Fig. 3, lane B). The mouse antibody reacts with purified *E. coli* β-galactosidase as expected (Fig. 3, lane C) and also reacts with purified human DNA polymerase β (Fig. 3, lane D).

Since the mouse antibody was produced against an *E. coli* protein purified on an anti-*E. coli* protein column, there is no trivial reason that this antibody should react specifically with any human protein. The fact that the mouse antibody reacts with human DNA polymerase β proves that the recombinant protein contains human DNA polymerase β amino acid sequence and thus that the recombinant phage contains DNA polymerase β cDNA sequence.

Isolation of longer cDNA sequences for human DNA polymerase β

The insert from pB19 was used as a nick-translated probe to screen other human cDNA libraries. Several positive recombinant phages were isolated and plaque-purified for each library screened. The longest sequences found are in a recombinant phage from the

human ALL cDNA library that contained a 1215-bp insert, and a recombinant phage from the human KM-3 cDNA library that contained a 1190-bp insert. The 1190-bp insert was cleaved with *Eco*RI and recloned as two fragments of 590 bp and 600 bp into the *Eco*RI site of pUC-8 to give pB26-1 and pB26-2, respectively. The 600-bp insert hybridizes to the insert of pB19 and has the *Eco*RI site at the 5′ end but is 135 nucleotides shorter at the 3′ end of the mRNA. When the recombinant phage DNA containing the 1215-bp insert was cleaved with *Eco*RI nuclease, two fragments of 675 bp and 540 bp were obtained, with the 675-bp fragment hybridizing to the insert in pB19. These 1215 bp were removed from the λgt 10 vector by partial digestion with *Eco*RI and recloned into the *Pst*I site of pUC-8 to give pB159. The relationships between the isolates of DNA polymerase β cDNA described are presented graphically in Figure 4.

DNA sequences of cloned human DNA polymerase β cDNAs

Complete DNA sequence analysis of pB19 showed an *Eco*RI site on one end and a stretch of 20 A residues on the other end. The AATAAA polyadenylation sequence is found in the 3′ nontranslated regions of eukaryotic mRNA (Proudfoot and Brownlee 1976) and is located about 20 nucleotides upstream of the poly(rA) tail in this 735-bp fragment. Computer translation of this DNA sequence showed open reading frames in all three phases with a minimum size of 150 amino acids from the *Eco*RI site. The 735-bp insert in pB19 therefore represents the 3′ terminus of the mRNA and the carboxyl terminus of the protein. Complete sequence analyses of the inserts in pB159 showed a 635-bp sequence identical to that present in pB19 downstream from the *Eco*RI site, and a 540-bp sequence identical to that present in pB26-1 upstream of the *Eco*RI site. Merging the sequences of the inserts in pB19, pB159, and pB26-1 resulted in a 1319-bp cDNA sequence for the human DNA polymerase β cDNA (Fig. 5).

Computer translation of this 1319-bp cDNA shows an open reading frame starting from residue 2 and ending with a TGA codon at residues 1141–1144. The translated polypeptide contains 381 amino acids with a calculated molecular weight of 42,558. The first ATG codon in this 1319-nucleotide sequence is located at residues 188-190. If initiation of translation starts at this codon,

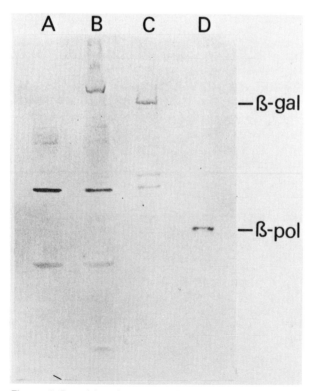

Figure 3 Reactivity of mouse anti-recombinant protein with human liver chromatin DNA polymerase β. (Lane *A*) Lysate of Y1090 cells; (lane *B*) lysate of recombinant phage-infected *E. coli* (Y1090) cells; (lane *C*) 2 μg of *E. coli* β-galactosidase; and (lane *D*) 2 μg of purified DNA polymerase β.

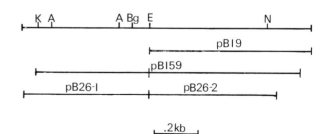

Figure 4 Schematic diagram of cDNAs coding for human DNA polymerase β. (N) *Nci*I, (E) *Eco*RI, (Bg) *Bgl*II, (A) *Ava*II, and (K) *Kpn*I.

```
1                                        31                                              61
G AAC CAT TGT TCC GCC GGT CGC GCC GGA GCT GGG TTG CTC CGG CTC CCG TCT CCA AGT CCT
  Asn His Cys Ser Ala Gly Arg Ala Gly Ala Gly Leu Leu Arg Leu Pro Ser Pro Ser Pro
                                         91                                            121
  GGT ACC TCC TTC AAG CTG GGA GAG GGC TCT AGG TCC CTG GTT CTG AAC ACT CTG GGG TTC
  Gly Thr Ser Phe Lys Leu Gly Glu Gly Ser Arg Ser Leu Val Leu Asn Thr Leu Gly Phe
                                        151                                            181
  TCG GGT GCA GGC CGC CAT GAG CAA ACG GAA GGC GCC GCA GAG ACT CTC AAC GGG GGA ATC
  Ser Gly Ala Gly Arg His Glu Gln Thr Glu Gly Ala Ala Glu Thr Leu Asn Gly Gly Ile
                                        211                                            241
  ACC GAC ATG CTC ACA GAA CTC GCA AAC TTT GAG AAG AAC GTG AGC CAA GCT ATC CAC AAG
  Thr Asp Met Leu Thr Glu Leu Ala Asn Phe Glu Lys Asn Val Ser Gln Ala Ile His Lys
                                        271                                            301
  TAC AAT GCT TAC AGA AAA GCA GCA TCT GTT ATA GCA AAA TAC CCA CAC AAA ATA AAG AGT
  Tyr Asn Ala Tyr Arg Lys Ala Ala Ser Val Ile Ala Lys Tyr Pro His Lys Ile Lys Ser
                                        331                                            361
  GGA GCT GAA GCT AAG AAA TTG CCT GGA GTA GGA ACA AAA ATT GCT GAA AAG ATT GAT GAG
  Gly Ala Glu Ala Lys Lys Leu Pro Gly Val Gly Thr Lys Ile Ala Glu Lys Ile Asp Glu
                                        391                                            421
  TTT TTA GCA ACT GGA AAA TTA CGT AAA CTG GAA AAG ATT CGG CAG GAT GAT ACG AGT TCA
  Phe Leu Ala Thr Gly Lys Leu Arg Lys Leu Glu Lys Ile Arg Gln Asp Asp Thr Ser Ser
                                        451                                            481
  TCC ATC AAT TTC CTG ACT CGA GTT AGT GGC ATT GGT CCA TCT GCT GCA AGG AAG TTT GTA
  Ser Ile Asn Phe Leu Thr Arg Val Ser Gly Ile Gly Pro Ser Ala Ala Arg Lys Phe Val
                                        511                                            541
  GAT GAA GGA ATT AAA ACA CTA GAA GAT CTC AGA AAA AAT GAA GAT AAA TTG AAC CAT CAT
  Asp Glu Gly Ile Lys Thr Leu Glu Asp Leu Arg Lys Asn Glu Asp Lys Leu Asn His His
                                        571                                            601
  CAG CGA ATT GGG CTG AAA TAT TTT GGG GCC TTT GAA AAA AGA ATT CCT CGT GAA GAG ATG
  Gln Arg Ile Gly Leu Lys Tyr Phe Gly Ala Phe Glu Lys Arg Ile Pro Arg Glu Glu Met
                                        631                                            661
  TTA CAA ATG CAA GAT ATT GTA CTA AAT GAA GTT AAA AAA GTG GAT TCT GAA TAC ATT GCT
  Leu Gln Met Gln Asp Ile Val Leu Asn Glu Val Lys Lys Val Asp Ser Glu Tyr Ile Ala
                                        691                                            721
  ACA GTC TGT GGC AGT TTC AGA AGA GGT GCA GAG TCC AGT GGT GAC ATG GAT GTT CTC CTG
  Thr Val Cys Gly Ser Phe Arg Arg Gly Ala Glu Ser Ser Gly Asp Met Asp Val Leu Leu
                                        751                                            781
  ACC CAT CCC AGC TTC ACT TCA GAA TCA ACC AAA CAG CCA AAA CTG TTA CAT CAG GTT GTG
  Thr His Pro Ser Phe Thr Ser Glu Ser Thr Lys Gln Pro Lys Leu Leu His Gln Val Val
                                        811                                            841
  GAG CAG TTA CAA AAG GTT CAT TTT ATC ACA GAT ACC CTG TCA AAG GGT GAG ACA AAG TTC
  Glu Gln Leu Gln Lys Val His Phe Ile Thr Asp Thr Leu Ser Lys Gly Glu Thr Lys Phe
                                        871                                            901
  ATG GGT GTT TGC CAG CTT CCC AGT AAA AAT GAT GAA AAA GAA TAT CCA CAC AGA AGA ATT
  Met Gly Val Cys Gln Leu Pro Ser Lys Asn Asp Glu Lys Glu Tyr Pro His Arg Arg Ile
                                        931                                            961
  GAT ATC AGG TTG ATA CCC AAA GAT CAG TAT TAC TGT GGT GTT CTC TAT TTC ACT GGG AGT
  Asp Ile Arg Leu Ile Pro Lys Asp Gln Tyr Tyr Cys Gly Val Leu Tyr Phe Thr Gly Ser
                                        991                                           1021
  GAT ATT TTC AAT AAG AAT ATG AGG GCT CAT GCC CTA GAA AAG GGT TTC ACA ATC AAT GAG
  Asp Ile Phe Asn Lys Asn Met Arg Ala His Ala Leu Glu Lys Gly Phe Thr Ile Asn Glu
                                       1051                                           1081
  TAC ACC ATC CGT CCC TTG GGA GTC ACT GGA GTT GCA GGA GAA CCC CTG CCA GTG GAT AGT
  Tyr Thr Ile Arg Pro Leu Gly Val Thr Gly Val Ala Gly Glu Pro Leu Pro Val Asp Ser
                                       1111                                           1141
  GAA AAA GAC ATC TTT GAT TAC ATC CAG TGG AAA TAC CGG GAA CCC AAG GAC CGG AGC GAA
  Glu Lys Asp Ile Phe Asp Tyr Ile Gln Trp Lys Tyr Arg Glu Pro Lys Asp Arg Ser Glu
                                       1171                                           1201
  TGA GGC CTG TAT CCT CCC TGG CAG ACA CAA CCC AAT AGG AGT CTT AAT TTA TTT CTT AAC
                                       1231                                           1261
  CTT TGC TAT GTA AGG GTC TTT GGT GTT TTT AAA TGA TTG TTT CTT CTT CAT GCT TTT GCT
                                       1291
  TGC AAT GTA GTC AAT AAA ACC TCA TGT ACT ATT ATT GGA AAA AAA AAA AAA AAA AAA A
```

Figure 5 DNA and translated amino acid sequences for cloned human DNA polymerase β cDNA. The first codon for methionine and the termination codon are underlined.

then a protein of 319 amino acids would be produced having a calculated molecular weight of about 36,000. This molecular weight is considerably less than the molecular weight for human DNA polymerase β measured by us and by others (Wang et al. 1974; Chang et al. 1982). Since the mRNA for DNA polymerase β is estimated to be 1600 nucleotides, we conclude that we still lack the 5' terminal noncoding sequences for the mRNA and nucleotides coding for 10–20 amino acids at the amino terminus of the protein.

Chromosome sublocalization of cDNA for human DNA polymerase β

Somatic cell hybridization studies showed that human DNA polymerase β gene mapped to chromosome 8 (Matsukage et al. 1986; Cannizzaro et al. 1988). Sub-localization of the gene on the short arm of chromosome 8 was obtained by in situ hybridization studies using the pB159 probe. A total of 249 metaphases were analyzed and 706 grains were counted. The histogram of the localization of grains to all chromosomes is shown in Figure 6. Since 10.3% of the grains were localized to the p region of chromosome 8, we conclude that the human A polymerase β gene maps to chromosome sub-region 8p11 → p12.

Discussion

DNA polymerase β is unusual among eukaryotic DNA polymerases by virtue of its constitutive presence in the nucleus of a wide spectrum of multicellular species throughout the animal kingdom (Chang 1976). A high degreee of conservation of molecular structure (Chang et al. 1982) may be indicative of an essential biological function or at least an unperturbed vestige of some early evolutionary event related to DNA metabolism. Biochemical and immunological methods have fostered the detection and development of interest in this family of proteins, but the paucity of expression makes traditional isolation and study of molecular structure a rather intensive physical exercise.

We have isolated recombinant phages containing 80% of human DNA polymerase β cDNA sequence as a first major step in resolving this problem. Translation of the cDNA sequences determined for DNA polymerase β shows an open reading frame for 381 amino acids starting from residue 2, suggesting that the cloned sequence still lacks the 5′ terminal sequence of the mRNA. If translation of this mRNA initiates at the first ATG codon, present at residues 188–190, then a protein containing 319 amino acids with a molecular weight of only about 36,000 would be produced. Since in vitro translation of human and bovine mRNAs (L.M.S. Chang, unpubl.), as well as extensive immunoblot studies (Chang et al. 1982), detect peptides of 45,000 daltons, we believe that our cDNA still lacks 10-20 amino acids at the amino terminus of the protein and the 5′-terminal leader sequences for the mRNA.

Zmudzka et al. (1986) and SenGupta et al. (1986) reported the isolation of full cDNA sequence for DNA polymerase β from a rat brain and human teratocarcinoma cell libraries. Translation of these cDNAs produces proteins of 318 amino acids (about 36,000 daltons). The amino acid sequences of the human enzyme and rat enzyme show 95% homology. A more recent report by Matsukage et al. (1987) extended the 5′-coding sequence of rat DNA polymerase β cDNA by 17 amino acids using sequences found in genomic DNA. Comparison of the coding sequence of rat DNA polymerase β (Matsukage et al. 1987) and the human DNA polymerase β showed 95% homology from amino acid residue 9 in the rat sequence and amino acid 54 in the human sequence. Significant homology was not found either in translated amino acid or nucleotide sequence at the 5′ end of the cDNAs from human and rat.

Since the 5′ sequence from rat cDNA was obtained from exons in genomic DNA, possible explanations for the observed discrepancy include DNA polymorphism as well as true differences in 5′-nucleotide sequences in rat cDNA and human DNA. The differences in rat cDNA sequences reported by Matsukage et al. (1987) and Zmudzka et al. (1986) has not been explained. Clarification on the amino-terminal amino acid sequence of mammalian DNA polymerase β awaits experimental data on the enzyme protein. At the present time there is no evidence that the complete cDNA sequence for DNA polymerase β has been determined. Since amino-terminal amino acid sequences and upstream leader sequences are of considerable importance in investigation of protein regulation and distribution, we believe that much more research is required.

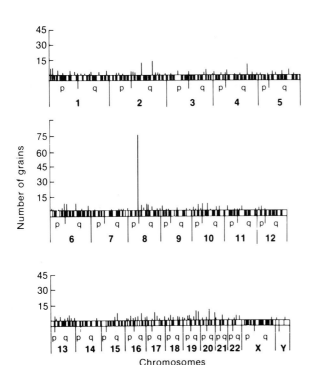

Figure 6 Localization of the human DNA polymerase β gene to 8p11 → p12 by chromosomal in situ hybridization.

Acknowledgments

This research was supported by grant CA-23365 from the National Cancer Institute, Department of Health and Human Services. The authors wish to thank R.C. Peterson, S.P. White, and C.M. Hong for DNA sequence analysis. The opinions or assertions contained herein are the private ones of the authors and are not to be construed as official or reflecting the views of the Department of Defense or the Uniformed Services University of the Health Sciences.

References

Cannizzaro, L.A. and B.S. Emanuel. 1984. An improved method for G-banding chromosomes after in situ hybridization. *Cytogenet. Cell Genet.* **38:** 308.

Cannizzaro, L.A., F. Bollum, K. Huebner, C.M. Croce, L.C. Cheung, X. Xu, B.K. Hecht, F. Hecht, and L.M.S. Chang. 1988. Molecular cloning and chromosome sublocalization to 8p11→p12 of a cDNA for human DNA polymerase-β. *Cytogenet. Cell Genet.* (in press).

Chang, L.M.S. 1973a. Low molecular weight DNA polymerase from calf thymus chromatin. I. Preparation of homogeneous enzyme. *J. Biol. Chem.* **248:** 3789.

———. 1973b. Low molecular weight DNA polymerase from calf thymus chromatin. II. Initiation and fidelity of homopolymer replication. *J. Biol. Chem.* **248:** 6983.

———. 1974. Replication of initiated polyriboadenylaic acid by mammalian low molecular weight DNA polymerase. *J. Biol. Chem.* **249:** 7441.

———. 1976. Phylogeny of DNA polymerase-β. *Science* **191:** 1183.

Chang, L.M.S. and F.J. Bollum. 1971. Low molecular weight DNA polymerase in mammalian cells. *J. Biol. Chem.* **246:** 5835.

Chang, L.M.S., P. Plevani, and F.J. Bollum. 1982. Evolutionary conservation of DNA polymerase-β structure. *Proc. Natl. Acad. Sci.* **79:** 758.

Guo, L.H. and R. Wu. 1982. New rapid methods for DNA sequencing based on exonuclease III digestion followed by repair synthesis. *Nucleic Acids Res.* **10:** 2065.

Harper, M.E. and G.F. Saunders. 1981. Localization of single copy DNA sequences on G-banded human chromosomes by in situ hybridization. *Chromosoma* **83:** 431.

Hübscher, U., C.C. Kuenzle, W. Limacher, P. Scherrer, and S. Spadari. 1979. Functions of DNA polymerase α, β, and γ in neurons during development. *Cold Spring Harbor Symp. Quant. Biol.* **43:** 626.

Laemmli, U.K. 1970. Cleavage of structural proteins during the assembly of the head of bacteriophage T4. *Nature* **227:** 680.

Matsukage, A., K. Nishikawa, T. Ooi, Y. Seto, and M. Yamaguchi. 1987. Homology between mammalian DNA polymerase-β and terminal deoxynucleotidyl transferase. *J. Biol. Chem.* **262:** 8960.

Matsukage, A., M. Yamaguchi, K.R. Utsumi, Y. Hayashi, R.

Ueda, and M.C. Yoshida. 1986. Assignment of the gene for human DNA polymerase-β (POLB) to chromosome 8. *Jpn. J. Cancer Res. (Gann)* **77:** 330.

Peterson, R.C., L.C. Cheung, R.J. Mattaliano, S.P. White, L.M.S. Chang, and F.J. Bollum. 1985. Expression of human terminal deoxynucleotidyl transferase in *E. coli. J. Biol. Chem.* **260:** 10495.

Proudfoot, N.J. and G.G. Brownlee. 1976. 3′ Non-coding region sequences in eukaryotic messenger RNA. *Nature* **263:** 211.

Sanger, F., S. Nicklen, and A.R. Coulson. 1977. DNA sequencing with chain terminating inhibitors. *Proc. Natl. Acad. Sci.* **74:** 5463.

SenGupta, D.N., B.Z. Zmudzka, P. Kumar, F. Cobianchi, J. Skowronski, and S.H. Wilson. 1986. Sequence of human DNA polymerase-β obtained through cDNA cloning. *Biochem. Biophys. Res. Commun.* **136:** 341.

Towbin, H., T. Staehlin, and J. Gordon. 1979. Electrophoretic transfer of proteins from polyacrylamide gel to nitrocellulose sheets: Procedure and some application. *Proc. Natl. Acad. Sci.* **76:** 4350.

Wang, T.S.F., W.D. Sedwick, and D. Korn. 1974. Nuclear DNA polymerase: Purification and properties of the homogeneous enzyme from human KB cells. *J. Biol. Chem.* **249:** 841.

Weissbach, A., A. Schlabach, B. Friedlander, and A. Bolden. 1971. DNA polymerase from human cells. *Nat. New Biol.* **231:** 167.

Weissbach, A., D. Baltimore, F.J. Bollum, R. Gallo, and D. Korn. 1975. Nomenclature of eukaryotic DNA polymerases. *Science* **190:** 401.

Wiginton, D.A., G.S. Adrian, R.L. Friedman, D.P. Suttle, and J.J. Hutton. 1983. Cloning of cDNA sequences of human adenosine deaminase. *Proc. Natl. Acad. Sci.* **80:** 7481.

Yamaguchi, M., T. Takahashi, K. Yasuda, Y. Shimura, and A. Matsukage. 1983. Characterization of messenger-RNA from chick embryo DNA polymerase-β and its translation product *in vitro. Eur. J. Biochem.* **133:** 277.

Young, R. and R.W. Davis. 1983. Efficient isolation of genes by using antibody probes. *Proc. Natl. Acad. Sci.* **80:** 1194.

Zmudzka, B.Z., D. SenGupta, A. Matsukage, F. Cobianti, P. Kumar, and S.H. Wilson. 1986. Structure of rat DNA polymerase-β revealed by partial amino acid sequencing and cDNA cloning. *Proc. Natl. Acad. Sci.* **83:** 5106.

Structural and Catalytic Features of the Mitochondrial DNA Polymerase from *Drosophila melanogaster* Embryos

L.S. Kaguni, C.M. Wernette, M.C. Conway, and P. Yang-Cashman

Department of Biochemistry, Michigan State University, East Lansing, Michigan 48824

Drosophila DNA polymerase γ (Pol γ) has been purified 2500-fold from embryonic mitochondria. The near-homogeneous enzyme has a sedimentation coefficient of 7.6S, a native molecular weight of 160,000, and comprises two polypeptides of 125,000 and 35,000 daltons. Our results indicate that the enzyme is a heterodimer and allow assignment of the DNA polymerization function to the larger of the two polypeptides.

Unlike DNA polymerization by the replicative α polymerase, that catalyzed by γ polymerase is efficient on single-stranded as compared to double-stranded DNA templates. Although analysis of nascent DNA strands during the course of DNA synthesis reveals a pattern of site-specific pausing characteristic of eukaryotic DNA polymerases, Pol γ is capable of polymerizing through sites of stable secondary structure to replicate fully singly primed φX174 DNA.

The *Drosophila* mitochondrial DNA (mtDNA) polymerase replicates single-stranded DNA with a high degree of accuracy: The fidelity of DNA synthesis by Pol γ is comparable to that of *Escherichia coli* DNA polymerase III. In consideration of the high rate of evolution and ribosubstitution in mtDNA, the high fidelity of DNA synthesis exhibited by Pol γ is remarkable.

Although the mtDNA of animal cells generally represents < 1% of the total cellular DNA, its replication properties have been studied extensively in vivo, and mtDNA replication origins are among the most thoroughly characterized initiation regions thus far isolated from eukaryotes. mtDNAs from numerous sources have similar structural and replication properties (Clayton 1982). Because the mode of mtDNA replication in vivo is well understood, and sequences containing mtDNA replication origins are available, mitochondria provide us with a model system for study of replication in vitro. In general, less is known about *Drosophila* or insect mtDNA replication in comparison with mammalian systems, but the available data suggest similar enzymatic requirements. *Drosophila* mitochondrial genomes have sizes ranging from 15.7–19.5 kilobase pairs, differing from one another and from mammalian genomes almost exclusively in the relative size of a single region known as the A + T region (Wolstenholme et al. 1979). *Drosophila* mtDNA contains the same gene complement as the mouse, human, and bovine mtDNAs, but exhibits a novel gene order (Clary et al. 1982; de Bruijn 1983).

DNA replication proceeds unidirectionally on all mtDNAs examined to date (Clayton 1982). However, the direction of leading DNA strand synthesis in *Drosophila* is opposite (relative to the rRNA genes) to that observed in mouse and human mtDNA (Goddard and Wolstenholme 1978, 1980). Furthermore, although leading and lagging DNA strand synthesis initiates at two distinct sites separated by a distance of ~70% of the genome in mammalian mtDNAs (Clayton 1982), most data indicate that both DNA strand initiation sites in *Drosophila*

lie in the A + T region (Goddard and Wolstenholme 1978, 1980; Wolstenholme and Clary 1985). Nevertheless, the enzymatic mechanisms functioning to replicate *Drosophila* and mammalian mtDNAs are likely not different, as the mode of lagging DNA strand synthesis would require ~95% replication of the leading strand prior to lagging DNA strand initiation in *Drosophila*, relative to ~70% in mammalian DNAs: That is, replication of all mtDNAs likely occurs by a highly asymmetric mechanism in which leading DNA strand synthesis is largely complete before lagging DNA strand synthesis initiates.

The asymmetric mode of DNA replication in mitochondria presents unique requirements for DNA polymerization. After initiation of mtDNA replication, the duplex circular mtDNA template must be unwound at or in advance of the replication fork as in chromosomal DNA replication. On the other hand, at the time of lagging DNA strand initiation the template is predominantly single-stranded. The major nuclear DNA polymerase (Pol α) functions very inefficiently on predominantly single-stranded DNAs as compared to duplex DNAs (Kaguni et al. 1984). Furthermore, its processivity in nucleotide polymerization is low (≤15 nucleotides, Villani et al. 1981). Thus, the major replicative DNA polymerase would perhaps not meet the requirements for mtDNA synthesis.

Although the mode of unidirectional asynchronous synthesis suggests the possibility of continuous DNA synthesis on both strands, experimental evidence to eliminate semidiscontinuous or discontinuous mechanisms for mtDNA replication is lacking. In fact, the presence of up to 0.1% ribosubstitutions distributed through-

425

out the genome (Brennicke and Clayton 1981) might signify incomplete removal of RNA primers formed during Okazaki fragment initiation on one or both DNA strands, as could be envisioned if RNA primer removal proceeds less efficiently than nascent DNA strand ligation. If, however, the high rate of ribosubstitution observed in mtDNA results from infidelity of DNA polymerization and subsequent lack of DNA repair, mechanistic analysis of the mitochondrial DNA polymerase should clearly distinguish it from the high fidelity replicative DNA polymerase α.

To address these issues and to begin to define the biochemical and genetic requirements for mtDNA replication in *Drosophila*, we have directed our efforts at the isolation and mechanistic and structural analysis of the mtDNA polymerase.

Experimental Procedures

Nucleotides and nucleic acids

Unlabeled deoxy-, dideoxy-, and ribonucleoside triphosphates were purchased from P-L Biochemicals. [^{3}H]dNTPs, [^{32}P]dNTPs, and [^{32}P]ATP were from ICN and New England Nuclear, respectively. Calf thymus DNA (highly polymerized type I) was purchased from Sigma and was activated by partial digestion with DNase I (Boehringer-Mannheim). Poly(dA)$_{700}$·p(dT)$_{10}$ was purchased from P-L Biochemicals and contains adenine and thymine in a molar ratio of 20:1, respectively, such that the average single-stranded DNA region between primers is 200 nucleotides.

φX174*am*3 DNA was prepared essentially as described (Kunkel and Loeb 1979). A synthetic oligodeoxynucleotide homologous to the sequence extending from position 778 to 764 in φX174 DNA (Sanger et al. 1978) was prepared in an Applied Biosystems Model 477 oligonucleotide synthesizer and annealed at a 6:1 molar ratio of primer to homologous φX174 DNA. The primer terminus is 177 nucleotides upstream of the *am*3 mutation, which is located at position 587.

Multi-primed M13 DNA was prepared by a modification of the method of Matson et al. (1980), using an M13 recombinant DNA (10,907 nucleotides). This template-primer contains an average of six primer fragments per M13 single-stranded DNA molecule.

Enzymes

Drosophila DNA polymerase α (fraction VI, 5.2×10^4 units/mg; Kaguni et al. 1983) and γ (fraction VI, 2.7×10^4 units/mg; Wernette and Kaguni 1986) were prepared as described. *E. coli* DNA polymerase I (lot 41/2101) and its Klenow fragment (lot 29) were purchased from Amersham and New England Biolabs, respectively; units were as defined by the manufacturers. *E. coli* DNA polymerase III holoenzyme (fraction V, 2×10^5 units/mg; McHenry and Kornberg 1977), and single-stranded DNA binding protein (SSB) (fraction III, 4×10^4 units/mg; Weiner et al. 1975) were kindly provided by J. Kaguni of this department.

DNA polymerase γ assay

Reaction mixtures (0.05 ml) contained 50 mM Tris-HCl (pH 8.5), 5 mM MgCl$_2$, 20 mM dithiothreitol, 110–200 mM KCl, 400 μg/ml bovine serum albumin (BSA), 60 μM each dATP, dCTP, and dGTP, 30 μM [^{3}H]dTTP (500–2000 cpm/pmol), saturating levels of DNA template-primer, and enzyme, unless otherwise indicated. The saturating concentration for the DNA template-primers examined and the optimal concentration of KCl used were: 180 μM DNase-I-activated calf thymus DNA at 200 mM KCl, 180 μM poly(dA)·p(dT)$_{10}$ at 120 mM KCl, 48 μM singly primed φX174 DNA at 120 mM KCl, and 48 μM multiprimed M13 DNA at 110 mM KCl. Incubation was for 10 minutes at 30°C unless otherwise indicated.

Gel electrophoresis and protein transfers

Proteins in SDS-polyacrylamide gels were stained in situ with silver (Giulian et al. 1983). Alternatively, the proteins were transferred electrophoretically from the polyacrylamide gel to nitrocellulose paper and then stained with iodine-starch (Kumar et al. 1985).

Fidelity of DNA synthesis

DNA synthesis reactions were as described for the standard DNA polymerase assay with the following modifications. The DNA template-primer was singly primed φX174*am*3 DNA (235 pmol as nucleotide); the reaction volume was 0.1 ml; and [^{3}H]dTTP was present at 3000 cpm/pmol. In the unbiased nucleotide pool determinations, dATP, dCTP, dTTP, and dGTP were present at 40 μM each. In the biased nucleotide pool determinations, the biased deoxynucleoside triphosphates were present at 1000 and 10 μM each, and the remaining two at 40 μM each. Incubation was for 40 minutes with 0.72 unit of DNA polymerase γ, 4.6 units of DNA polymerase α, or 3.0 units of DNA polymerase III holoenzyme in the presence of 1.0 μg of SSB.

Spheroplasts of *E. coli* C600 (CR34) were prepared and assay of progeny phage was performed as described by Kunkel and Loeb (1979), using *E. coli* CR and *E. coli* C as permissive and nonpermissive hosts, respectively.

Results and Discussion

Purification

The early embryo is an excellent source of chromosomal replication enzymes from *Drosophila*: DNA polymerase α (Banks et al. 1979), DNA topoisomerase II (Shelton et al. 1983), RNase H (DiFrancesco and Lehman 1985), and DNA ligase (Rabin et al. 1986) are very abundant and have been purified to near-homogeneity. We sought to determine the appropriate developmental stage for the purification of mitochondrial enzymes. Before doing so, we developed a differential assay for Pol γ and then a suitable enzyme fraction for conducting a developmental survey. Because the replicative polymerase (Pol α) is generally 100-fold more abundant than the mitochondrial enzyme, a differential assay is absolutely required. We found that the DNA polymerase activity extractable from partially purified mitochondria is stimulated by high salt (~200 mM KCl), whereas Pol α is highly sensitive to salt, exhibiting < 10% of its optimal activity at 200 mM KCl. Even at 10% of optimal activity, Pol α would likely be tenfold more abundant than Pol γ in a whole embryo homogenate. Consequently, we developed a method for purification of mitochondria based on multiple differential centrifugation steps.

Next, we examined various mitochondrial extraction conditions and found a 200-fold dependence on detergent (2% sodium cholate) and high salt (0.3 M NaCl) relative to extraction in low ionic strength buffer alone. In addition, in the absence of detergent, the yield of DNA polymerase activity was 20-fold less than in its presence. A survey of six developmental stages of *Drosophila* from early embryo to adult fly was conducted to determine the most abundant source of the mitochondrial enzyme. Embryos yielded 16–180-fold greater activity than organisms harvested at other developmental stages. Correspondingly, the specific activity of Pol γ was 5–30-fold greater in embryos relative to more highly developed *Drosophila*.

Thus, employing the differential assay for enzyme activity and detergent-and-salt-extracted mitochondria from embryos, we devised a purification scheme that has resulted in a near-homogeneous enzyme purified 2500-fold with a yield of 3% (Wernette and Kaguni 1986). The procedure involves four chromatographic steps and a glycerol gradient sedimentation (Table 1). After chromatography on phosphocellulose and ammonium sulfate fractionation, the enzyme is chromatographed on single-stranded DNA cellulose. At this point and thereafter, large losses of activity due to adsorption to surfaces required the addition of detergent (0.015% Triton X-100) to all buffer and the silanizing of all surfaces. This problem in purification indicated that the enzyme has substantial hydrophobic character. The enzyme is further chromatographed on octyl Sepharose and Cibacron blue agarose, and then sedimented in a 10–30% glycerol gradient. The procedure yields 10 μg of near-homogeneous enzyme from 200 g of embryos.

Physical properties

Homogeneity

Electrophoresis of the fraction VI enzyme in an SDS-polyacrylamide gel revealed two major polypeptides of 125,000 and 35,000 daltons (Fig. 1). Densitometric scanning after transfer of the polypeptides to nitrocellulose paper and staining with iodine-starch or after staining in situ with silver indicated that the relative abundance of the two polypeptides by the two staining methods was 1:1 and 1:0.9, respectively. Furthermore, when the fraction VI enzyme was chromatographed on Sephacryl S-200 prior to electrophoresis, the electrophoretic pattern was unchanged and the stoichiometry of the two polypeptides remained 1:1.

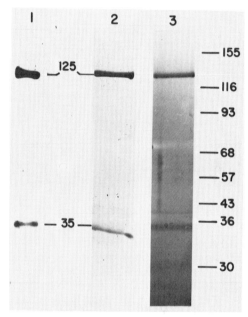

Figure 1 SDS-polyacrylamide gel electrophoresis of *D. melanogaster* DNA polymerase γ. Fraction VI, prior to (68 units, lane *1*; 25 units, lane *2*) and after (11 units, lane *3*) chromatography on Sephacryl S-200, was denatured and electrophoresed in a 5–15% linear gradient SDS-polyacrylamide slab gel. Protein was detected by iodine-starch (lane *1*) or silver (lanes *2* and *3*) staining as described in Experimental Procedures. Marker proteins electrophoresed in adjacent lanes and indicated by their molecular weights ($\times 10^{-3}$) were: *E. coli* RNA polymerase β subunit, *E. coli* β-galactosidase, rabbit muscle glycogen phosphorylase *b*, BSA, rabbit muscle pyruvate kinase, *E. coli* alkaline phosphatase, *E. coli* RNA polymerase α subunit, and bovine carbonic anhydrase. (Reprinted, with permission, from Wernette and Kaguni 1986.)

Table 1 Purification of DNA Polymerase γ from *D. melanogaster* Embryos

Fraction	Volume (ml)	Protein (mg)	Activity (units)	Specific activity (units/mg)	Yield (%)
I. Mitochondrial extract[a]	254	813	8458	10.4	100
II. Phosphocellulose and ammonium sulfate	3.0	10.2	2205	216	26.1
III. DNA-cellulose	31	0.6	1180	1,967	14.0
IV. Octyl-Sepharose	2.8	0.29	608	2,097	7.2
V. Cibacron blue-agarose	1.3	0.10	516	5,160	6.1
VI. Glycerol gradient	2.7	0.01	269	26,900	3.2

[a]Fraction I was prepared from 200 g of embryos.

Stokes radius

The Stokes radius was determined by Sephacryl S-200 gel filtration in the presence of 0.2 M $(NH_4)_2SO_4$. DNA polymerase γ (fraction VI) had an observed Stokes radius of 51 Å (two determinations, Fig. 2A).

Sedimentation coefficient

Glycerol gradient sedimentation of the enzyme (fraction V) in the presence of 0.2 M $(NH_4)_2SO_4$ yielded a single peak of DNA polymerase activity with a sedimentation coefficient of 7.6S (Fig. 2B). Values of 7.5–7.7S were obtained in four determinations on three preparations.

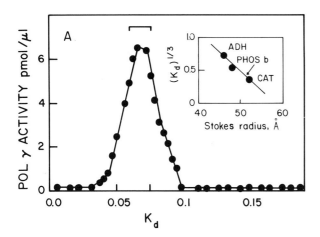

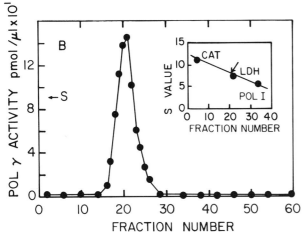

Figure 2 (*A*) Gel filtration of *Drosophila* DNA polymerase γ. Pol γ (fraction VI, 19 units) was chromatographed on Sephacryl S-200; the yield was 58%. Fractions containing the peak of activity were pooled as indicated by the bracket and analyzed by SDS-polyacrylamide gel electrophoresis (Fig. 1, lane 3). The protein markers indicated were yeast alcohol dehydrogenase (ADH, 46 Å), rabbit muscle phosphorylase *b* (PHOS b, 48 Å), and bovine liver catalase (CAT, 52 Å). (*B*) Glycerol gradient sedimentation of *Drosophila* DNA polymerase γ. Pol γ (fraction V) was sedimented in a 10–30% glycerol gradient; the yield was 52%. Protein markers run in parallel gradients were: bovine liver catalase (CAT, 11.3S), rabbit muscle L-lactate dehydrogenase (LDH, 7.3S), and *E. coli* DNA polymerase I (POL I, 5.5S). (Reprinted, with permission, from Wernette and Kaguni 1986.)

Molecular mass

The native molecular mass of the mtDNA polymerase was estimated by combining the sedimentation coefficient with the Stokes radius to yield a calculated value of approximately 160,000 daltons. Thus, the data indicate that the *Drosophila* DNA polymerase γ is most likely a heterodimer.

Catalytic properties

Preliminary characterization

We examined the effects of the chain terminator dideoxy TTP (ddTTP) and the sulfhydryl group blocking agent *N*-ethylmaleimide (NEM) on catalysis by the mitochondrial enzyme. Whereas *Drosophila* Pol α is insensitive to ddTTP but sensitive to NEM (Kaguni et al. 1983), Pol γ was inhibited by both. At the same time, Pol β is inhibited by ddTTP but not by NEM (Sakaguchi and Boyd 1985).

Template-primer utilization

Preliminary template utilization studies indicated that the *Drosophila* mtDNA polymerase catalyzes efficient DNA synthesis on single-stranded as compared to double-stranded DNA templates (Wernette and Kaguni 1986). To further evaluate this finding, the reaction conditions with each of four template-primers were optimized with regard to KCl concentration, and the kinetic parameters of DNA polymerization were determined (C.M. Wernette et al., in prep.).

DNA synthesis proceeded linearly for 60 minutes at 30°C on all template-primers and to the greatest extent on poly(dA)·oligo(dT) (Fig. 3). Notably, *Drosophila* mtDNA genomes are 74–80% A + T (Fauron and Wolstenholme 1976). Enzyme activity was about twofold less at all time points on DNase-I-activated calf thymus DNA, but the specificity constants (k_{cat}/K_m) were nearly equal for the natural as compared to the synthetic double-stranded DNA substrate (Table 2). Furthermore,

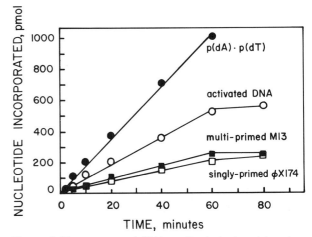

Figure 3 Time course of DNA synthesis in template-primer excess. DNA polymerase γ (fraction VI, 1.26 units) was assayed on poly(dA)$_{700}$·oligo(dT)$_{10}$ (180 μM), DNase-I-activated calf thymus DNA (180 μM), multiprimed M13 DNA (48 μM), and singly-primed φX174 DNA (48 μM). (Adapted from C.M. Wernette et al., in prep.)

Table 2 Kinetic Parameters of Template-Primer Utilization by DNA Polymerase γ

Template-primer	KCl optimum (mM)	K_m (μM)	k_{cat} (nt inc. s^{-1} enzyme molecule^{-1})	Specificity constant (k_{cat}/K_m)
Poly(dA) · p(dT)	120	30.3 ± 6.8	6.75 ± 0.81	0.22
Activated calf thymus DNA	200	12.5 ± 3.0	3.08 ± 0.32	0.25
Multiprimed M13 DNA	110	0.57 ± 0.17	2.41 ± 0.21	4.23
Singly primed φX174 DNA	120	1.06 ± 0.27	1.66 ± 0.81	1.57

Pol γ (fraction VI) was assayed under standard conditions, except that the template-primer concentration was varied, and the optimal KCl concentration for each template-primer was used. Incubation was for 5 min at 30°C.

Pol γ activity on activated DNA was approximately twofold greater than that observed on the two natural single-stranded DNAs for which the enzyme exhibited a markedly higher affinity (lower K_m values) and, as a result, the greatest substrate specificity. Whereas DNA polymerization on singly-primed φX174 DNA by γ polymerase is approximately 50% relative to that on activated calf thymus DNA, it is dramatically higher than that observed with the replicative α polymerase, which exhibits only a 3–8% relative efficiency (Kaguni et al. 1984 and this paper).

Taken together, the data suggest that the template features of nucleotide composition (or DNA sequence specificity), single-strandedness, and primer density influence catalysis by DNA polymerase γ. To evaluate independently the effects of nucleotide composition and single-strandedness, a series of poly(dA)$_{5000}$ · oligo-(dT)$_{15}$ template-primers was prepared at varying molar ratios of A:T such that the average single-stranded DNA region between primers ranged from 150 to 3000 nucleotides. The optimal rate of DNA synthesis by both *Drosophila* DNA polymerase γ and α was observed on poly(dA) · (dT) with an average interprimer distance of 750 nucleotides (Fig. 4). Surprisingly, the values varied only twofold over the entire range from largely double-stranded to predominantly single-stranded DNAs. How-

ever, whereas the extent of DNA synthesis by Pol α on the optimal poly(dA) · (dT) substrate was only 20% of that on DNase I-activated calf thymus DNA, Pol γ exhibited a 200% relative efficiency. At the same time, the relative efficiency of Pol γ on poly(dA) · (dT) (200:1) was 185% relative to singly primed φX174 DNA, which has a comparable primer to single-stranded DNA ratio. Thus, although Pol γ is able to copy efficiently both single- and double-stranded natural DNAs, the enzyme prefers the homopolymer poly(dA) independent of primer density. These catalytic features indicate that the *Drosophila* mtDNA polymerase suits the unique requirements for DNA polymerization in vivo that result from the highly asymmetric mode of mtDNA replication.

Stimulatory and stability factors

Role of DNA, dNTPs, and ATP
Drosophila DNA polymerase γ retains ~60% of its catalytic activity upon preincubation for 40 minutes at 30°C under standard assay conditions in the absence of DNA and dNTPs. To assess the potential stabilizing and/or stimulatory roles of various factors, we examined their effects under conditions of preincubation at 37°C prior to assay at 30°C. In the absence of DNA and dNTPs, Pol γ exhibited 35% residual activity after 2 minutes, and only 0.2% activity after 20 minutes of preincubation at 37°C (Fig. 5A). The addition of dNTPs to the preincubation mixture yielded only a small increase in enzyme stability. However, DNA provided a 200-fold increase in enzyme stability such that 49% of the catalytic activity was retained after 20 minutes of preincubation at 37°C. Because the DNA polymerase likely binds the template-primer prior to nucleotide binding, it is perhaps significant that dNTPs provide a 1.2–2.0-fold stabilization over DNA alone at times exceeding 20 minutes of preincubation. In evaluating further the effect of DNA on the thermal stability of Pol γ, we found that at 40 minutes of preincubation the enzyme retained 100% activity at 30°C, 73% at 34°C, and 19% at 37°C, but was completely inactivated by preincubation at 42°C (Fig. 5B).

Although ATP is not a substrate for Pol γ, we investigated its potential stabilizing and stimulatory effects in part because the ATP concentration in mitochondria is high. Further, Burgers and Kornberg (1982) have demonstrated that ATP activates *E. coli* DNA polymerase III holoenzyme via the formation of a reactive initiation

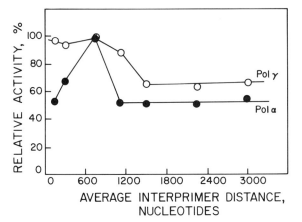

Figure 4 DNA synthesis on poly(dA) · oligo(dT) template-primers of varying primer densities. DNA polymerase γ (fraction VI, 0.03–0.12 units) and DNA polymerase α (fraction VI, 0.08–0.24 units) were assayed under standard conditions on poly(dA)$_{5000}$ (70 μM) to which was annealed (dT)$_{15}$ at A:T ratios ranging from 10:1 to 200:1 to yield single-stranded DNA regions of 150–3000.

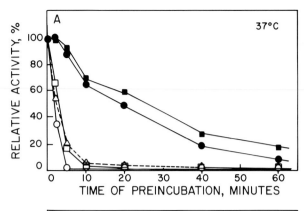

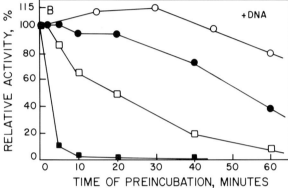

Figure 5 (*A*) Thermal stability of DNA polymerase γ. DNA polymerase γ (fraction VI, 0.12 unit) was assayed under standard conditions on DNase-I-activated calf thymus DNA for 20 min at 30°C, except that a preincubation at 37°C was performed in assay buffer lacking DNA and dNTPs with the following additions: (O–O) none; (●–●) + DNA; (□–□) + dNTPs; (■–■) + dNTPs, DNA; (△–△) + ATP. (*B*) DNA polymerase γ was assayed as indicated above except that the DNase-I-activated calf thymus DNA was included in the preincubation buffer, and preincubation was performed at the following temperatures: (O–O) 30°C; (●–●) 34°C; (□–□) 37°C; (■–■) 42°C.

complex, and Wierowski et al. (1983) have shown that ATP both stimulates and stabilizes calf thymus DNA polymerase α. Our data indicate that ATP (1 mM) does not increase the thermal stability of Pol γ (Fig. 5A). Furthermore, ATP does not stimulate DNA polymerase activity under standard assay conditions on a variety of template-primers when it is included in the reaction mixture at levels ranging from 0.05 to 5 mM.

Stimulation by E. coli *SSB*
Pol γ is able to replicate completely a single-stranded DNA template with substantial secondary structure (C.M. Wernette et al., in prep.). However, the enzyme exhibits site-specific pausing during in vitro DNA synthesis, indicating that the rate of DNA synthesis is greater in copying the template strand between pause sites than it is in polymerizing through these regions. When *E. coli* single-stranded DNA binding protein was included in the reaction mixture to coat the φX174 or M13 viral DNA, the rate of DNA synthesis by the mtDNA polymerase increased 1.4–6-fold, depending on the enzyme-to-template ratio. The effect of SSB is greatest under

conditions of moderate substrate excess. These data imply that a mtDNA binding protein might function in an analogous role during replication of the mtDNA genome. On the other hand, the formation of stable secondary structures in mtDNA might perhaps be minimal as a result of its high A + T content.

Fidelity of nucleotide polymerization

Kinetic parameters
Wolstenholme and Clary (1985) have suggested that in *Drosophila* mtDNAs there is a continuous selection for A + T nucleotides at all sites where it is compatible with function, and that differences in deoxyribonucleotide pools may perhaps account for the high mutation rate. We have examined the possibility that the mtDNA polymerase may have a greater affinity for dATP and dTTP as substrates by two methods. First, we determined the K_m for each of the four dNTPs and found that they are all very similar, ranging from 0.43 μM for dCTP to 0.84 μM for dATP (Table 3). Second, we examined the K_i for the homologous dideoxy analog for each dNTP. The data confirm the sensitivity of Pol γ to ddNTPs and demonstrate that the K_i values for all four ddNTPs are similar. This indicates that the mtDNA polymerase has no preference for dATP or dTTP, as would be expected of an enzyme that binds and reads the template strand before nucleotide selection.

Ribosubstitution
The animal mtDNA genome contains up to 0.1% ribosubstitutions (Clayton 1982). Except for those ribonucleotides remaining at the origins of replication (Martens and Clayton 1979), the remainder could result from misincorporation during DNA synthesis (Brennicke and Clayton 1981). The mtDNA polymerase from *Drosophila* embryos does not misincorporate ATP (which is present at a much higher concentration than GTP, UTP, and CTP in mitochondria) during in vitro DNA synthesis. First, incorporation of radiolabeled ATP of very high specific activity was not detected under conditions where DNA synthesis on calf thymus DNA was measured in the absence of dATP (Table 4). Second, the K_i for ATP as an inhibitor of dATP incorporation by Pol γ was 2.1 mM, in striking contrast to the K_m for dATP of 0.84 μM and the K_i for ddATP of 1.64 μM.

Table 3 Kinetic Parameters of Deoxynucleotide Utilization by DNA Polymerase γ

dNTP	K_m	Dideoxy analog	K_i
dTTP	0.53	ddTTP	3.51
dCTP	0.43	ddCTP	2.42
dATP	0.84	ddATP	1.64
dGTP	0.70	ddGTP	0.98

Pol γ (fraction VI) was assayed under standard conditions on DNase I-activated calf thymus DNA, except that the deoxynucleotide concentration was varied. Incubation was for 10 min at 30°C.

Table 4 Lack of Ribosubstitution by DNA Polymerase γ

Method of analysis	[dATP] (μM)	[ATP] (μM)	Incorporation/ inhibition
Direct measurement of ATP incorporation ([^{32}P]ATP 9×10^6 cpm/pmol)	0	0.16–2.8	<1 ATP/10^4 dNTPs
Inhibition of dATP incorporation by ATP	1–17	0–3000	$K_i = 2100$ μM

Pol γ (fraction VI) was assayed under standard conditions on DNase-I-activated calf thymus DNA, except that the dATP concentration was varied and ATP was added as indicated. Assays were performed in triplicate.

Another explanation for the high frequency of ribosubstitution in mtDNA may relate to incomplete removal of RNA primers resulting from Okazaki fragment synthesis during replication. Because both of the two DNA strands of mtDNA are alkali-labile at multiple sites, this would imply discontinuous DNA synthesis of both DNA strands. Alternatively, the presence of ribonucleotides could result from lack of repair of DNA damage.

Misincorporation of dNTPs

The overall fidelity of DNA replication in vivo is determined by two processes. The first is DNA replication per se and the second is postreplicational repair. In prokaryotes, the DNA polymerase itself controls fidelity in two respects. The first is base selection and incorporation, which involves reading of the template by the enzyme, choosing of the correct nucleotide, and incorporation of that nucleotide. The second is the editing out of misincorporated nucleotides by the 3′→5′ exonuclease function of the DNA polymerase. Inasmuch as DNA repair processes are absent or at least very limited in mitochondria, the burden of assured fidelity must fall on the DNA polymerase. Because mtDNA evolves at a five- to ten-fold greater rate than single copy genomic DNA (Dawid 1972; Brown et al. 1979), it is not clear whether DNA polymerization, lack of repair, or an increase in the rate of fixation of mutations is a major component in mitochondrial evolution.

To examine the fidelity of DNA synthesis by DNA polymerase γ, we have utilized the φX174 SS→RF system of Weymouth and Loeb (1978) to measure the reversion of the φX174*am*3 mutation to wild type and pseudo-wild type as a result of nucleotide misincorporation during DNA synthesis in vitro. The possible results of this assay are affected by three factors. If misincorpo-

ration results in insertion of an amino acid other than the wild-type amino acid, then progeny phage will be produced only if the pseudo-protein is functional. To obtain a particular final product, the DNA polymerase must be capable of tolerating the formation of the corresponding mispair. Third, by biasing the nucleotide pools, the DNA polymerase may be encouraged to misinsert nucleotides.

Reactions were performed with both unbiased and biased deoxynucleotide pools. Parallel experiments were carried out with *D. melanogaster* DNA polymerase α, and *E. coli* DNA polymerase III holoenzyme in the presence of SSB. The average number of nucleotides polymerized by the three enzymes on each primer terminus was more than fivefold greater than the distance from the primer terminus to the *am*3 mutation that lies 177 nucleotides downstream. The extent of DNA synthesis was unaffected by the various dNTP pool bias conditions.

In the unbiased pool determinations, all three enzymes exhibited high-fidelity DNA synthesis, such that reversion frequencies were ≤ twofold higher than the in vivo background resulting from transfection of uncopied DNA into *E. coli* (Table 5). All three enzymes were capable of forming an A:A mispair as a result of an A > T bias to yield pseudo-wild-type phage. The effect of the bias was 40–100-fold. This indicates that the enzyme responsible for fixing the deoxynucleotide pool concentrations (ribonucleotide reductase) is an important contributor to fidelity of DNA replication in vivo. Inasmuch as the mtDNA genome is 60–80% A + T, this seems an even more important consideration. Notably, Wolstenholme and Clary (1985) have found that A→T transversions in *Drosophila* mtDNAs are more than twice as frequent as would be predicted based on

Table 5 Reversion Frequency of φX174*am*3 DNA Synthesized In Vitro

Reaction condition	DNA polymerase γ	DNA polymerase α	DNA polymerase III + SSB
Unbiased pool	1.8×10^{-6}	2.6×10^{-6}	1.9×10^{-6}
A > T	1.4×10^{-4} (78)[a]	1.1×10^{-4} (42)	1.9×10^{-4} (100)
G > A	2.1×10^{-6} (1.2)	4.1×10^{-6} (1.6)	1.4×10^{-5} (7.4)
G > C	1.9×10^{-6} (1.1)	3.1×10^{-6} (1.2)	8.3×10^{-7} (0.4)
C > T	8.1×10^{-6} (4.5)	5.8×10^{-7} (0.2)	5.8×10^{-7} (0.3)

The reversion frequency of uncopied DNA was 1.0×10^{-6}. In the unbiased pool determinations, the concentration of all four dNTPs was 40 μM. In the biased pool determinations, the concentrations of the indicated nucleotides were 1000 and 10 μM, respectively.

[a]Numbers in parentheses represent biased/unbiased values.

nucleotide composition values alone, and account for 86% of transversions and 44% of all third base changes in a 5000-nucleotide sequence comparison between *D. melanogaster* and *D. yakuba* mtDNA.

In pool bias experiments where the concentrations of other pairs of nucleotides were altered, no large increase in the number of revertants was observed with any of the DNA polymerases. Thus, the accuracy of polymerization on single-stranded DNA in vitro by the near-homogeneous mtDNA polymerase is nearly identical to that of the replicative α polymerase (Kaguni et al. 1984) from the same source—*D. melanogaster* embryos. Furthermore, the fidelity of these eukaryotic DNA polymerases is remarkably similar to that of *E. coli* DNA polymerase III holoenzyme (Fersht 1979), even though the subunit structures, reaction requirements, kinetics, and processivities of the three enzymes differ greatly.

In summary, we conclude that the mtDNA polymerase from *D. melanogaster* embryos is both effective and accurate in the synthesis of DNA.

Acknowledgments

We are grateful to Richard Newcomb and Brad Davis for technical assistance. This work was supported by grant GM-34042 from the National Institutes of Health and by a Junior Faculty Research Award JFRA-144 to L.S.K. from the American Cancer Society.

References

Banks, G.R., J.A. Boezi, and I.R. Lehman. 1979. A high molecular weight DNA polymerase from *Drosophila melanogaster* embryos: Purification, structure, and partial characterization. *J. Biol. Chem.* **254:** 9886.

Brennicke, A. and D.A. Clayton. 1981. Nucleotide assignment of alkali-sensitive sites in mouse mitochondrial DNA. *J. Biol. Chem.* **256:** 10613.

Brown, W.M., M. George, Jr., and A.C. Wilson. 1979. Rapid evolution of animal mitochondrial DNA. *Proc. Natl. Acad. Sci.* **76:** 1967.

Burgers, P.M.J. and A. Kornberg. 1982. ATP activation of DNA polymerase III holoenzyme from *Escherichia coli*. II. Initiation complex: Stoichiometry and reactivity. *J. Biol. Chem.* **257:** 11474.

Clary, D.O., J.M. Goddard, S.C. Martin, C.M.-R. Fauron, and D.R. Wolstenholme. 1982. *Drosophila* mitochondrial DNA: A novel gene order. *Nucleic Acids Res.* **10:** 6619.

Clayton, D.A. 1982. Replication of animal mitochondrial DNA. *Cell* **28:** 693.

Dawid, I.B. 1972. Evolution of mitochondrial DNA sequences in *Xenopus*. *Dev. Biol.* **29:** 139.

de Bruijn, M.H.L. 1983. *Drosophila melanogaster* mitochondrial DNA: A novel organization and genetic code. *Nature* **304:** 234.

DiFrancesco, R.A. and I.R. Lehman. 1985. Interaction of ribonuclease H from *Drosophila melanogaster* embryos with DNA polymerase-primase. *J. Biol. Chem.* **260:** 14764.

Fauron, C.M.-R. and D.R. Wolstenholme. 1976. Structural heterogeneity of mitochondrial DNA molecules within the genus *Drosophila*. *Proc. Natl. Acad. Sci.* **73:** 3623.

Fersht, A.R. 1979. Fidelity of replication of phage φX174 DNA by DNA polymerase III holoenzyme: Spontaneous mutation by misincorporation. *Proc. Natl. Acad. Sci.* **76:** 4946.

Giulian, G.G., R.L. Moss, and M. Greaser. 1983. Improved methodology for analysis and quantitation of proteins on one-dimensional silver-stained slab gels. *Anal. Biochem.* **129:** 277.

Goddard, J.M. and D.R. Wolstenholme. 1978. Origin and direction of replication in mitochondrial DNA molecules from *Drosophila melanogaster*. *Proc. Natl. Acad. Sci.* **75:** 3886.

———. 1980. Origin and direction of replication in mitochondrial DNA molecules from the genus *Drosophila*. *Nucleic Acids Res.* **8:** 741.

Kaguni, L.S., R.A. DiFrancesco, and I.R. Lehman. 1984. The DNA polymerase-primase from *Drosophila melanogaster* embryos: Rate and fidelity of polymerization on single-stranded DNA templates. *J. Biol. Chem.* **259:** 9314.

Kaguni, L.S., J.-M. Rossignol, R.C. Conaway, and I.R. Lehman. 1983. Isolation of an intact DNA polymerase-primase from embryos of *Drosophila melanogaster*. *Proc. Natl. Acad. Sci.* **80:** 2221.

Kumar, B.V., M.V. Lakshmi, and J.P. Atkinson. 1985. Fast and efficient method for detection and estimation of proteins. *Biochem. Biophys. Res. Commun.* **131:** 883.

Kunkel, T.A. and L.A. Loeb. 1979. On the fidelity of DNA replication: Effect of divalent metal ion activators and deoxyribonucleoside triphosphate pools on in vitro mutagenesis. *J. Biol. Chem.* **254:** 5718.

Martens, P.A. and D.A. Clayton. 1979. Mechanism of mitochondrial DNA replication in mouse L-cells: Localization and sequence of the light strand origin of replication. *J. Mol. Biol.* **135:** 327.

Matson, S.W., P.J. Fay, and R.A. Bambara. 1980. Mechanism of inhibition of the avian myeloblastosis virus deoxyribonucleic acid polymerase by adriamycin. *Biochemistry* **19:** 2089.

McHenry, C. and A. Kornberg. 1977. DNA polymerase III holoenzyme of *Escherichia coli*: Purification and resolution into subunits. *J. Biol. Chem.* **252:** 6478.

Rabin, B.A., R.S. Hawley, and J.W. Chase. 1986. DNA ligase from *Drosophila melanogaster* embryos: Purification and physical characterization. *J. Biol. Chem.* **261:** 10637.

Sakaguchi, K. and J.B. Boyd. 1985. Purification and characterization of a DNA polymerase β from *Drosophila*. *J. Biol. Chem.* **260:** 10406.

Sanger, F., A.R. Coulson, T. Friedmann, G.N. Air, B.G. Barrell, N.L. Brown, J.C. Fiddes, C.A. Hutchison III, P.M. Slocome, and M. Smith. 1978. Nucleotide sequence of bacteriophage φX174. *J. Mol. Biol.* **125:** 225.

Shelton, E.R., N. Osheroff, and D.L. Brutlag. 1983. DNA topoisomerase II from *Drosophila melanogaster*: Purification and physical characterization. *J. Biol. Chem.* **258:** 9530.

Villani, G., P.J. Fay, R.A. Bambara, and I.R. Lehman. 1981. Elongation of RNA-primed DNA templates by DNA polymerase α from *Drosophila melanogaster* embryos. *J. Biol. Chem.* **256:** 8202.

Weiner, J.H., L.L. Bertsch, and A. Kornberg. 1975. The deoxyribonucleic acid unwinding protein of *Escherichia coli*: Properties and functions in replication. *J. Biol. Chem.* **250:** 1972.

Wernette, C.M. and L.S. Kaguni. 1986. A mitochondrial DNA polymerase from embryos of *Drosophila melanogaster*: Purification, subunit structure, and partial characterization. *J. Biol. Chem.* **261:** 14764.

Weymouth, L.A. and L.A. Loeb. 1978. Mutagenesis during in vitro DNA synthesis. *Proc. Natl. Acad. Sci.* **75:** 1924.

Wierowski, J.V., K.G. Lawton, J.W. Hockensmith, and R.A. Bambara. 1983. Stimulation of calf thymus DNA α-polymerase by ATP. *J. Biol. Chem.* **258:** 6250.

Wolstenholme, D.R. and D.O. Clary. 1985. Sequence evolution of *Drosophila* mitochondrial DNA. *Genetics* **109:** 725.

Wolstenholme, D.R., J.M. Goddard, and C.M.-R. Fauron. 1979. Structure and replication of mitochondrial DNA from the genus *Drosophila*. In *Extrachromosomal DNA* (ed. D. Cummings et al.), p. 409. Academic Press, New York.

Centromere Structure and Function in Budding and Fission Yeasts

J. Carbon, H. Amstutz, L. Clarke, S. Cumberledge, B. Fishel, and R. Ng
Department of Biological Sciences, University of California, Santa Barbara, California 93106

In the budding yeast, *Saccharomyces cerevisiae*, the functional centromere is specified by a 130–150-bp DNA sequence (*CEN*) that serves as a specific binding site for kinetochore proteins. The *CEN* region is free of repetitive DNA sequences, and the kinetochore contains only 250 bp of DNA. Point mutations within a highly conserved 25-bp sequence (element III) can inactivate the centromere. Specific binding proteins that interact with this site can be detected in cell extracts; these proteins do not bind to *CEN* DNA fragments that contain a single inactivating point mutation. In contrast, the centromeric DNA in fission yeast (*Schizosaccharomyces pombe*) is relatively large (at least 35 kb) and contains several classes of moderately repetitive DNA sequences. In the centromere region of chromosome II, these sub-repeats are symmetrically organized into a 35-kb palindromic arrangement. This entire region is not transcribed and thus is heterochromatic in character. Apparently, the larger and more highly condensed chromosomes in fission yeast require a region of specialized DNA sequences to form a relatively large differentiated kinetochore.

The centromere region of a eukaryotic chromosome provides a discrete structure (termed a kinetochore) to which the spindle fibers attach to ensure proper segregation of the replicated chromosomes during both mitotic and meiotic cell divisions. In addition, the centromere holds the replicated sister chromatids together during the first meiotic division, and mediates their separation during the subsequent second meiotic division. Chromosomes of higher eukaryotes often contain a relatively large and complex kinetochore. This structure consists of chromatin loops that are tightly packed into a trilaminar arrangement containing a million or more base pairs of heterochromatic DNA (Ris and Witt 1981). The sequences in this region are highly repetitive and are not transcribed; their exact role in centromere function is yet to be established (Singer 1982).

The extreme complexity of centromeric DNA in higher eukaryotes has stimulated research on chromosome segregation in unicellular yeasts; in particular, the budding yeast, *S. cerevisiae*, and the fission yeast, *S. pombe* (for review, see Clarke and Carbon 1985). In these organisms, the chromosomes are relatively small (about 2 orders of magnitude smaller than those in animal cells), and it was anticipated that the kinetochore structures would be correspondingly much simpler and easier to analyze using standard molecular genetic techniques. In fact, the functional centromere regions in chromosomes of the budding yeast consist of only about 250 bp of DNA folded into a specific chromatin conformation, completely lacking highly repetitive sequences (Clarke and Carbon 1985). More recently, it has been shown that the larger and more highly condensed chromosomes in *S. pombe* contain several classes of repeated DNA sequences in the centromere

regions, implying that the kinetochore structure is more complex than what has been observed in *S. cerevisiae* (Clarke et al. 1986; Nakaseko et al. 1986). In this paper, we have summarized some of our recent findings in the comparative analysis of centromere structure-function in these two organisms.

Experimental Procedures

Standard procedures
Experimental details regarding bacterial and yeast strains, growth media, bacterial and yeast transformations, and genomic and plasmid DNA isolations can be found in recent papers from our laboratory (Clarke and Carbon 1983; Clarke et al. 1986; Cumberledge and Carbon 1987; Ng and Carbon 1987). Restriction enzymes, T4 DNA ligase, and DNA polymerase were from New England Biolabs and were used according to the vendor's instructions.

Mutational analysis of S. cerevisiae CEN3
Mutationally altered centromeres were assayed for mitotic function by replacing wild-type *CEN3* sequences in yeast chromosome III and measuring chromosome III loss (nondisjunction) as described in Clarke and Carbon (1983) and Carbon and Clarke (1984). Meiotic function was assayed by following the segregation pattern of *CEN3-ARS* plasmids using standard yeast tetrad analysis (Clarke and Carbon 1980; Cumberledge and Carbon 1987). Details of the construction and nucleotide sequences of mutations in *CEN3* elements I and II can be found in Cumberledge and Carbon (1987). The construction of mutations in *CEN3* element III is described in Ng et al. (1986a) and Ng and Carbon (1987).

433

Centromere binding protein assays
Yeast cell extracts were prepared from the protease-deficient strain JHRY20-2c according to the procedure of Newman et al. (1985), with modifications as described in Ng and Carbon (1987). Homogenization of spheroplasts was carried out in a hypotonic buffer in a Dounce homogenizer, and the extract was adjusted to a final salt concentration of 1.0 M KCl to solubilize chromatin proteins. To remove nonspecific DNA binding proteins, the final extract was passed through a heparin-agarose (Bio-rad, Richmond, CA) column pre-equilibrated with buffer A (Ng and Carbon 1987). The binding reaction was carried out by incubating at 15°C for 20 minutes 1 ng of labeled restriction fragment plus yeast extract in 25 μl of buffer containing 10 mM HEPES K$^+$ (pH 8.0), 6 mM MgCl$_2$, 150 mM KCl, 2 mM KPO$_4$ (pH 8.0), 0.5 mM dithiothreitol (DTT), 15 μg/ml tRNA, and 0.5 μg λ DNA predigested with HaeIII. The binding mixture was electrophoresed on a 4% polyacrylamide gel and autoradiographed. Additional details are given in Ng and Carbon (1987).

Results

Centromeres in the budding yeast, *S. cerevisiae*

General properties
The key observation in this field is that a circular or linear plasmid containing an intact centromeric DNA sequence (*CEN*) plus a DNA replicator (*ARS*) (and telomeres, in the case of linear molecules) segregates as an aneuploid chromosome when introduced into yeast cells by transformation (Clarke and Carbon 1980; Murray and Szostak 1983). The *CEN* minichromosome is relatively stably maintained in single copy during mitotic cell divisions, and plasmid genetic markers segregate 2 + :2 − through meiosis. The replicated sister chromatids segregate together in the first division, held together at the centromere, and then separate normally in the second meiotic division. The genetic information necessary to carry out this process is contained entirely within a 130–150-bp DNA segment whose consensus sequence, derived from analysis of the centromeres from ten yeast chromosomes (for review, see Clarke and Carbon 1985), is shown in Figure 1. This sequence consists of three parts, a 78–86-bp high-AT (> 90% AT) region (element II) flanked on one side by the highly conserved sequence PuTCACPuTG (element I) and on the other by the consensus sequence TGTTT(T/A)TG.TTTCCGAAA....AAA (element III). The latter sequence contains some bilateral symmetry centered about the C at position 14 (designated by arrows in Fig. 1). Several lines of evidence (see below, and Hegemann

et al. 1986; McGrew et al. 1986; Ng et al. 1986a; Ng and Carbon 1987) indicate that element III is a protein binding site and is absolutely required for proper centromere function.

When chromatin structure in the centromere region is probed by mapping nuclease-sensitive sites, the consensus sequence shown in Figure 1 can be shown to be contained within a 250-bp region that is protected from nuclease cleavage, but which is flanked on both sides by hypersensitive cleavage sites (Bloom and Carbon 1982). No repetitive DNA sequences occur near the *S. cerevisiae* centromeres, and the flanking transcribed genes occur within a few hundred bp on each side of the *CEN* consensus sequence (Yeh et al. 1986). Thus, kinetochores in the budding yeast are thought to contain no more than about 250 bp of DNA.

Mutational analysis of CEN *structure-function*
Several laboratories have carried out in vitro mutagenesis studies on *S. cerevisiae* centromeric DNA (Clarke and Carbon 1985; Hegemann et al. 1986; Ng et al. 1986a; Cumberledge and Carbon 1987; Gaudet and Fitzgerald-Hayes 1987; Ng and Carbon 1987). The structurally altered centromeres are tested for in vivo function either on autonomously replicating plasmids or by direct replacement of the corresponding wild-type DNA sequences in the yeast genome and subsequent analysis of the mitotic and meiotic segregation behavior of the altered yeast chromosome (Clarke and Carbon 1983). The latter method makes use of DNA fragment-mediated transformation (transplacement; Rothstein 1983) to replace the wild-type *CEN* sequence in the yeast genome.

The essential findings from our in vitro mutagenesis studies are summarized in Figures 2 and 3. Deletion of sequence element I has a minor effect on mitotic segregation of the parent chromosome; the mitotic nondisjunction frequency, normally about 10^{-5} in yeast, is somewhat increased to 10^{-4} in the absence of element I (mutation 303-17, Fig. 2; Cumberledge and Carbon 1987). However, meiotic function is quite aberrant in the element I mutant, in that the replicated sister chromatids segregate randomly in the first division, probably due to precocious chromatid separation. Deletion of 48 bp of the high-AT element II region (mutation 303-7) has a much greater effect on mitotic centromere function, but the wild-type activity is nearly restored by replacement of the deleted sequences with a 49-bp DNA segment containing an essentially random 100% AT sequence derived from yeast mitochondrial DNA (mutation 303-2). Apparently, the exact nucleotide sequence of the element II region is relatively unimportant; the critical factors are the length and the AT content. For example,

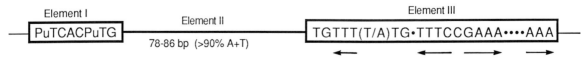

Figure 1 Consensus sequence of functional centromeric DNA in *S. cerevisiae*. The arrows indicate the region of bilateral symmetry found in element III. (Pu = purine).

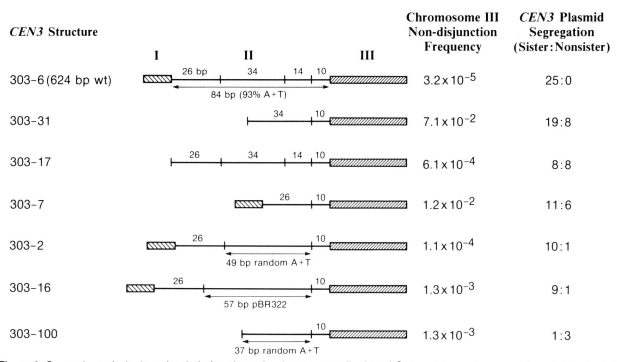

CEN3 Structure				Chromosome III Non-disjunction Frequency	CEN3 Plasmid Segregation (Sister:Nonsister)
	I	II	III		
303-6 (624 bp wt)	(26 bp, 34, 14, 10) 84 bp (93% A+T)			3.2×10^{-5}	25:0
303-31	(34, 10)			7.1×10^{-2}	19:8
303-17	(26, 34, 14, 10)			6.1×10^{-4}	8:8
303-7	(26, 10)			1.2×10^{-2}	11:6
303-2	(26, 10) 49 bp random A+T			1.1×10^{-4}	10:1
303-16	(26, 10) 57 bp pBR322			1.3×10^{-3}	9:1
303-100	(10) 37 bp random A+T			1.3×10^{-3}	1:3

Figure 2 Comparison of mitotic and meiotic functions of various structurally altered *S. cerevisiae* centromeres (*CEN3*). The shaded bars indicate sequence elements I and III (see Fig. 1 for sequences). Cleavage sites within element II for the restriction endonuclease *Aha*III are indicated by the vertical lines. Fragment lengths are in bp. Nucleotide sequences of these *CEN3* constructions, assays for mitotic loss of chromosome III, and meiotic segregation of the *CEN3* plasmids, as well as other details are described in Cumberledge and Carbon (1987). (Reprinted, with permission, from Cumberledge and Carbon 1987).

Centromere Substitution	Insert Size (bp)	Element III Sequence	Chromosome III Non-Disjunction per Cell Division	Orientation of CEN3 Insert
JC303-4	624	TGTATTTGATTTCCGAAAGTTAAAA	1.1×10^{-5}	Normal
JC303-14	289	•••	0.7×10^{-5}	Normal
JC303-12	289	•••	2.8×10^{-5}	Reverse
RN2010	305	TGTATTTGATTTCC**A**AAAGTTAAAA	1.7×10^{-1}	Reverse
RN2011	305	TGTATTTGATTTCC**C**AAAGTTAAAA	3.0×10^{-1}	Reverse
RN2012	305	TGTATTT**A**ATTTCCGAAAGTTAAAA	1.0×10^{-5}	Normal
RN2006	305	TGTATTTGATTTCCGAAAGTTAAAA AAGA**TCT** (*Bgl*II)	1.9×10^{-5}	Reverse
RN2001	139	TGTATTTGATTTCCGAAAGTTAAAA AAGA**TC** – – –	0.7×10^{-4}	Normal
RN20	624	TGTATTTGATTTCCGAAAGTTAA**CA** (*Hpa*I)	3.3×10^{-4}	Normal
RN13	305	•••	0.9×10^{-4}	Normal
RN14	305	•••	2.7×10^{-4}	Reverse
RN1E	179	TGTATTTGATTTCCGAAAGTT**CATC** – – – – – – – –	2.5×10^{-2}	Normal
RN1A	174	TGTATTTGATTTCCGA**CCACTT** – – – – – – – – – – –	ND	Normal
RN1B	173	TGTATTTGATTTCCG**CCACTT** – – – – – – – – – – –	ND	Normal

Figure 3 Effect on mitotic centromere function of mutations in *S. cerevisiae CEN3* sequence element III. Structural alterations are indicated in bold print. Newly created restriction sites are indicated underneath the sequence alterations. Dashed lines indicate deletions that extend into the centromere from the right. In all cases, the structures of *CEN3* elements I and II are wild type. Details are given in Experimental Procedures and in Ng et al. (1986a) and Ng and Carbon (1987).

CEN mutation 303-16 (Fig. 2), in which a 57-bp segment of pBR322 DNA (44% AT) is substituted for the same 48 bp of element II, results in a 30-fold increase in the nondisjunction frequency of the altered chromosome. All of the changes in element II that we have investigated also result in some random segregation during the first meiotic division, as evidenced by the increased frequency of tetratype distribution of the mutationally altered *CEN* plasmid with respect to authentic centromere markers (Fig. 2; Cumberledge and Carbon 1987).

Sequence element III (Figs. 1 and 3) is critical for proper centromere function. Single point mutations in the element III sequence can completely inactivate the centromere (McGrew et al. 1986; Ng et al. 1986a; Ng and Carbon 1987; see Fig. 3). The CCG sequence located at the center of bilateral symmetry appears to be especially important, since a change in any of these three nucleotides inactivates the centromere (McGrew et al. 1986; Fig. 3). Here the exact sequence appears to be important since inversion of a base pair, i.e., a G to C change (mutation RN2011), is inactivating. Deletions extending from the centromere distal direction only 4 bp into the consensus element III sequence also inactivate the centromere (mutation RN1E; Fig. 3). These results, in conjunction with protein binding studies summarized below, indicate that element III is a key protein binding site in the *S. cerevisiae* centromere.

Centromere binding proteins
Cell-free yeast extracts, prepared in 1 M NaCl to solubilize chromatin components, contain proteins that bind specifically to wild-type double-stranded *CEN* DNA fragments, but not to mutationally inactivated *CEN* DNAs (Ng and Carbon 1987; Fig. 4). This binding depends on a structurally intact element III sequence, since double-stranded DNAs containing a single G to C substitution in III (Fig. 3, mutation RN2011) do not bind (Fig. 4). The binding can be demonstrated using either an exonuclease III protection assay (Ng et al. 1986b; Ng and Carbon 1987) or a DNA fragment mobility shift assay (Fig. 4). Binding reactions were carried out using labeled 305-bp *Bam*HI fragments containing either wild-type *CEN3* (Fig. 4, lanes A–D) or mutation RN2011 (lanes E–G). Several distinct labeled bands with retarded mobilities are seen in the presence of extract; however, the two low mobility bands seen near the top of the gel when wild-type *CEN3* DNA fragments are assayed are completely absent when similar fragments containing the mutationally inactivated *CEN3* are used. Similar results are obtained using the *CEN3* mutation RN2010. Competition assays confirm the above results (Ng and Carbon 1987); unlabeled wild-type *CEN* sequences compete for the binding regardless of their chromosome of origin, whereas functionally inactive *CEN* sequences mutationally altered in element III do not compete. In addition, synthetic double-stranded oligodeoxyribonucleotides 34 bp in length containing only the wild-type element III sequence compete out the observed mobility shifts, confirming that the element III

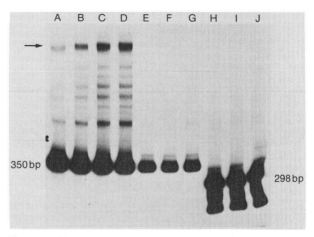

Figure 4 Use of a fragment mobility shift assay to detect centromere DNA-protein binding. Binding reactions (Experimental Procedures) were carried out on a ^{32}P-labeled 305-bp *Eco*RI-*Bam*HI restriction fragment containing either wild-type *CEN3* (lanes A–D; 3, 6, 9, and 12 μg extract protein) or *CEN3* mutant RN2011 (Fig. 3) (lanes E–G; 3, 6, and 9 μg extract protein). As control, a labeled restriction fragment from pBR322 was employed (lanes H–J; 3, 6, and 9 μg extract protein). See Experimental Procedures and Ng and Carbon (1987) for details.

region is critical in forming the *CEN*-specific chromatin complex. The binding reaction requires Mg^{++} at an optimum concentration of 6 mM, is greatly stimulated by 150 mM KCl or NaCl, and does not require ATP or GTP. The binding activity is inactivated by heating to 90°C, is sensitive to proteinase K treatment, and is not inactivated by various RNases. Efforts to purify the centromere binding protein(s) have been greatly hampered by the extremely low quantity of these proteins in chromatin extracts. Various genetic methods (e.g., Tschumper and Carbon 1987) will need to be employed to increase the quantity and facilitate the identification of these kinetochore components.

Centromeres in the fission yeast, *S. pombe*
Cells of the unicellular yeast, *S. pombe*, divide by a fission mechanism very similar to that seen in most eukaryotic species. *S. pombe* cells contain three chromosomes that are relatively highly condensed during the mitotic cell cycle and are easily visualized (Robinow 1977). On the average, these three chromosomes are about six times larger than the seventeen *S. cerevisiae* chromosomes, since the genome sizes are roughly equivalent in the two organisms. Centromeric DNA in fission yeast has been investigated by the molecular cloning of various centromere-linked genes and chromosome walking in the direction of the centromeres (Clarke et al. 1986; Nakaseko et al. 1986). The centromere-linked genes, *lys1* and *cyh1* on chromosome I and *tps13* and *ran1* on chromosome II, were cloned by complementation of genomic mutations at these loci. On chromosome II, directionality of the DNA physical map with respect to the genetic map was determined by integrating a *S. cerevisiae LEU2* gene at

various locations surrounding *tps13* by site-directed integration and subsequently measuring meiotic recombination frequencies to map the integrated marker with respect to the centromere and *tps13* (Clarke et al. 1986; Nakaseko et al. 1986). These measurements reveal a pronounced drop in meiotic recombination frequencies near the centromere; the ratio of physical to genetic map distance at the centromere becomes several-fold higher than the normal value of about 8 kb/cm. This phenomenon appears to be quite similar to the recombination suppression commonly observed in the centromere regions of higher eukaryotic chromosomes (Charlesworth et al. 1986).

Chromosome walking in the direction of the centromere on both chromosomes I and II reveals the presence of at least three classes of moderately repetitive DNA sequences, designated B, K, and L. (Clarke et al. 1986; Fishel et al. 1988). In similar studies, Nakaseko et al. (1986, 1987) have characterized repetitive sequences, designated yn, dg, and dh, in the *S. pombe* centromere regions. Sequence K is 6.4 kb in length and occurs either as isolated single copies or in head-to-tail tandem arrays of three or more copies (Figs. 5 and 6). Various cloned DNA segments identified in *S. pombe* genomic libraries by hybridization to a K repeat probe are shown in Fig. 5. The complete K repeat unit (6.4 kb) is defined by the inserts containing several tandemly arranged copies of the repeat. Repeat dg, a 3.8-kb sequence characterized by Nakaseko et al. (1986), appears to be a portion of the 6.4-kb repeat, at least in the *S. pombe* strain that we use (972h⁻). Similarly, dh (4 kb) (Nakaseko et al. 1987) contains portions of K and

L from a region where these repeats occur in a tandem arrangement. Sequence repeats B, K, and L occur *only* in the centromere regions of the three *S. pombe* chromosomes. This was established by demonstrating that these repeats occur only on three large *Sal*I genomic restriction fragments (120, 90, and 50 kb) that are derived from the three centromere regions (Fishel et al. 1988). Site-directed integration of a plasmid containing the *S. cerevisiae LEU2* gene into K repeats can occur at each of the centromeres, as determined by genetic mapping of the integrated marker with respect to known centromere-linked markers. Each integration event can be correlated with an alteration of mobility of one of the three *Sal*I fragments that contain the K sequence. These experiments establish that the 120-, 90-, and 50-kb *Sal*I genomic DNA fragments contain the centromere regions from chromosomes III, II, and I, respectively.

In the centromere region of chromosome II, repeats B, K, and L are arranged into a large palindromic sequence that measures at least 17 kb on each arm of the repeat (Fig. 6). This 35-kb sequence can be visualized in the electron microscope (EM) as a large hairpin or snap-back structure, after melting the purified 90-kb *Sal*I restriction fragment that contains the *CEN2* region and allowing the DNA to reassociate for a short time at high dilution (Fishel et al. 1988). The EM reveals a 1–2-kb unpaired loop in the center of the large inverted repeat. Northern analysis indicates that none of the sequences making up this 35-kb palindromic region are transcribed. The exact structural arrangement of the repetitive sequences at the centromeres of chromo-

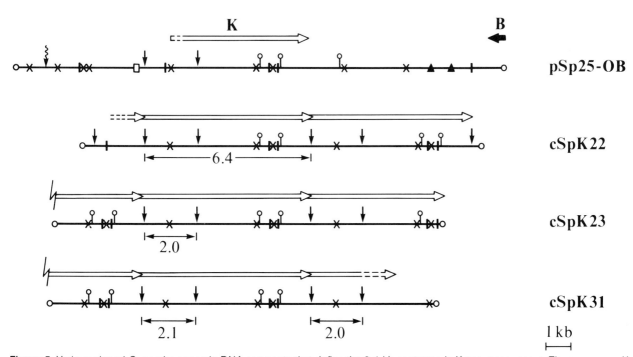

Figure 5 Various cloned *S. pombe* genomic DNA segments that define the 6.4-kb centromeric K sequence repeat. The consensus K repeat is indicated by the open arrows. Restriction sites are *Eco*RI (I), *Hin*dIII (×), *Bam*HI (▲), *Bgl*II (ǒ), *Kpn*I (↓), *Sal*I (□), *Bst*EII (ζ), and selected *Sau*3A (○) sites. (Reprinted, with permission, Clarke et al. 1986.)

SpCEN2 REGION

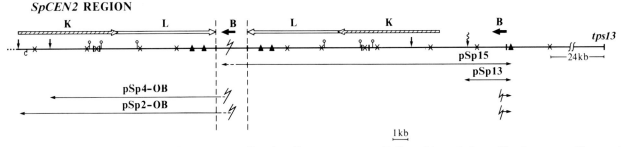

Figure 6 Physical map of the *S. pombe* centromere II region. Sequence repeats B, K, and L are indicated by the arrows. The exact length of the central *Eco*RI fragment within the inverted repeat is unknown, since sequences extending across the center of the palindrome are structurally unstable in *E. coli*. Various cloned sequences are indicated by the horizontal arrows below the map. Restriction sites are as in Fig. 5, plus *Cla*I (C).

somes I and III is still unknown, although hybridization studies using a unique DNA segment from cosmid cSpK31 indicate that a linear tandem array of K repeats occurs in the chromosome III centromere region (H. Amstutz et al., unpubl.). Apparently all three classes of repeats occur at each of the three centromeres, but perhaps not in the same relative structural arrangement.

The exact role of these moderately repetitive sequences in centromere function has not yet been established. Chromosome nondisjunction is known to cause haploidization of diploids in fission yeast, since aneuploids are extremely unstable (Gutz et al. 1974). However, integration of multiple copies of a plasmid containing *LEU2* into the centromeric K repeats or integration of an intact K repeat on a chromosome arm has no effect on the stability of *S. pombe* diploids and thus does not impair normal centromere function. None of the cloned DNA segments that contain repeats B, K, or L convert an autonomously replicating circular plasmid in *S. pombe* into a functional minichromosome, although an intact DNA segment containing all of the repeats in the normal in vivo configuration has not yet been tested in *S. pombe* as a synthetic linear minichromosome containing functional telomeres.

Discussion

It now appears that centromeric DNAs in budding and fission yeasts are quite different. In the budding yeast, *S. cerevisiae*, the functional centromere is specified by a relatively short (130–150 bp) DNA sequence that is complexed with one or more kinetochore proteins (plus histones?) and folded into a specific chromatin conformation that includes about 250 bp of DNA. This small kinetochore neither includes nor is surrounded by repetitive sequence elements, and the flanking genes occur within a few hundred bp on either side. In contrast, the centromere regions in the three *S. pombe* chromosomes include relatively long regions of moderately repetitive DNA sequences, which are arranged (at least in the case of chromosome II) into a bilaterally symmetrical structure measuring over 35 kb in length (Fig. 6). At this point, it is unknown whether the *S. pombe* centromeres contain sequences analogous to the element I-II-III sequences characteristic of the *S.*

cerevisiae centromeres. It is doubtful that the identical sequence arrangement occurs in the fission yeast centromeres, however, since no segment of DNA from the *S. pombe* centromere regions has been found to display centromere function when introduced into budding yeast on circular plasmid vectors. In addition, the budding yeast centromeres do not function in *S. pombe* on circular plasmid vectors, although *S. cerevisiae CEN3* does serve as an efficient DNA replicator (*ARS*) in *S. pombe* (J. Carbon, unpubl.).

The exact DNA sequences required for centromere function in *S. pombe* are still unknown. Although we know that repeats B, K, and L occur only in the three centromere regions in fission yeast, the biological function of these sequences is still unclear. Since disruption of a K repeat at any of the centromeres has no effect on mitotic or meiotic centromere function, the exact structural integrity of the region containing the repeats is unnecessary for proper chromosome segregation. At this point, the association of the moderately repetitive sequences with centromere function is purely circumstantial, based entirely on their centromeric location in the genome. As in the previous *CEN* studies in budding yeast (Clarke and Carbon 1980), identification of the DNA sequences necessary for centromere function in fission yeast will depend on the construction of autonomously replicating minichromosomes that segregate properly as aneuploid chromosomes in *S. pombe*. This should be possible, since Niwa et al. (1986) have shown that linear deletion derivatives of chromosome III, produced by γ-irradiation of an unstable strain disomic for chromosome III, are relatively stable mitotically and segregate properly through meiosis. These minichromosomes do contain the centromeric repeated sequences; however, the relatively large size (300-500 kb) of those described to date has precluded an exact analysis of centromere structure-function.

The *S. pombe* centromeric DNA sequence repeats possess many of the properties of heterochromatic repetitive sequences found in the centromeric regions of higher eukaryotic chromosomes (Singer 1982). For example, the B, K, and L repeats are not transcribed, a property typical of constitutive heterochromatin. In addition, sequence analysis of portions of the K and L repeat (Clarke et al. 1986; Nakaseko et al. 1986, 1987) reveals the presence of several classes of smaller internal repeats, such as PyACCAPy, and the absence of any lengthy translational reading frames, although long regions containing highly repetitive sequences were not found. Repeats K and L are also quite similar to the moderately repetitive sequence elements found in the telomere regions of *S. cerevisiae* chromosomes (Chan and Tye 1983). The *S. pombe* repeat K is similar in size to a 6.7-kb telomeric repeat (termed Y) that is often found adjacent to a more variable repeat (X). However, K repeat probes do not hybridize to total genomic DNA isolated from *S. cerevisiae*.

The most obvious function to suggest for the *S. pombe* centromeric sequence repeats would be to specify a chromatin conformation that would differentiate the kinetochore from the highly condensed chromosome arms. At *CEN2*, the 1–2-kb sequence occurring at the center of bilateral symmetry (Fig. 6) could contain the actual spindle fiber attachment site, and the repeated sequences might serve to maintain a specific chromatin conformation by binding to kinetochore-specific proteins. Thus, the kinetochore in fission yeast (about 35 kb) could be over 100 times larger than the 250-bp region observed in *S. cerevisiae*. It is unclear, however, what aspects of cell division and chromosome segregation would lead to this large difference in kinetochore size between the two organisms. In this regard, however, the *S. pombe* centromeres appear to be more similar to those commonly observed in other eukaryotes, but of an intermediate complexity that promises to be more amenable to molecular and functional analysis.

Acknowledgments

This research was supported by grants from the National Institutes of Health (CA-11034 and GM-33783) and by postdoctoral fellowships from the American Cancer Society, California Division (to R.N.), the National Institutes of Health (to B.F.), and the Swiss National Foundation (to H.A.). Expert technical assistance was provided by Mary Baum.

References

Bloom, K.S. and J. Carbon. 1982. Yeast centromere DNA is in a unique and highly ordered structure in chromosomes and small circular minichromosomes. *Cell* **29**: 305.

Carbon, J. and L. Clarke. 1984. Structural and functional analysis of a yeast centromere (*CEN3*). *J. Cell Sci.* (suppl.) **1**: 43.

Chan, C.S.M. and B.-K. Tye. 1983. Organization of DNA sequences and replication origins at yeast telomers. *Cell* **33**: 563.

Charlesworth, B., C.H. Langley, and W. Stephan. 1986. The evolution of restricted recombination and the accumulation of repeated DNA sequences. *Genetics* **112**: 947.

Clarke, L. and J. Carbon. 1980. Isolation of a yeast centromere and construction of functional small circular chromosomes. *Nature* **287**: 504.

———. 1983. Genomic substitutions of centromeres in *Saccharomyces cerevisiae*. *Nature* **305**: 23.

———. 1985. The structure and function of yeast centromeres. *Annu. Rev. Genet.* **19**: 29.

Clarke, L., H. Amstutz, B. Fishel, and J. Carbon. 1986. Analysis of centromeric DNA in the fission yeast *Schizosaccharomyces pombe*. *Proc. Natl. Acad. Sci.* **83**: 8253.

Cumberledge, S. and J. Carbon. 1987. Mutational analysis of meiotic and mitotic centromere function in *Saccharomyces cerevisiae*. *Genetics* **117**: 203.

Fishel, B., H. Amstutz, M. Baum, J. Carbon, and L. Clarke. 1988. Structural organization and functional analysis of centromeric DNA in the fission yeast *Schizosaccharomyces pombe*. *Mol. Cell. Biol.* **8**: 754.

Gaudet, A. and M. Fitzgerald-Hayes. 1987. Alterations in the adenine-plus-thymine-rich region of *CEN3* affect centromere function in *Saccharomyces cerevisiae*. *Mol. Cell. Biol.* **7**: 68.

Gutz, H., H. Heslot, U. Leupold, and N. Loprieno. 1974. *Schizosaccharomyces pombe*. In *Handbook of genetics* (ed. R.D. King), vol. 1, p. 395. Plenum Press, New York.

Hegemann, J.H., R.D. Pridmore, R. Schneider, and P. Philippsen. 1986. Mutations in the right boundary of *Saccharomyces cerevisiae* centromere 6 lead to nonfunctional or partially functional centromeres. *Mol. Gen. Genet.* **205**: 305.

McGrew, J., B. Diehl, and M. Fitzgerald-Hayes. 1986. Single base-pair mutations in centromere element III cause aberrant chromosome segregation in *Saccharomyces cerevisiae*. *Mol. Cell. Biol.* **6**: 530.

Murray, A.W. and J.W. Szostak. 1983. Construction of artificial chromosomes in yeast. *Nature* **305**: 189.

Nakaseko, Y., N. Kinoshita, and M. Yanagida. 1987. A novel sequence common to the centromere regions of *Schizosaccharomyces pombe* chromosomes. *Nucleic Acids Res.* **15**: 4705.

Nakaseko, Y., Y. Adachi, S. Funahashi, O. Niwa, and M. Yanagida. 1986. Chromosome walking shows a highly homologous repetitive sequence present in all the centromere regions of fission yeast. *EMBO J.* **5**: 1011.

Newman, A.J., R.-J. Lin, S.-C. Cheng, and J. Abelson. 1985. Molecular consequences of specific intron mutations on yeast mRNA splicing *in vivo* and *in vitro*. *Cell* **42**: 335.

Ng, R. and J. Carbon. 1987. Mutational and in vitro protein binding studies on centromere DNA from *Saccharomyces cerevisiae*. *Mol. Cell. Biol.* **7**: 4522.

Ng, R., S. Cumberledge, and J. Carbon. 1986a. Structure and function of centromeres. In *Yeast cell biology* (ed. J. Hicks), p. 25. A.R. Liss, New York.

Ng, R., J. Ness, and J. Carbon. 1986b. Structural studies on centromeres in the yeast, *Saccharomyces cerevisiae*. In *Extrachromosomal elements in lower eukaryotes* (ed. R. Wickner et al.), p. 479. Plenum Press, New York.

Niwa, O., T. Matsumoto, and M. Yanagida. 1986. Construction of a minichromosome by deletion and its mitotic and meiotic behavior in fission yeast. *Mol. Gen. Genet.* **203**: 397.

Ris, H. and P.L. Witt. 1981. Structure of the mammalian kinetochore. *Chromosoma* **82**: 153.

Robinow, E.F. 1977. The number of chromosomes in *Schizosaccharomyces pombe*: Light microscopy of stained preparations. *Genetics* **87**: 491.

Rothstein, R.J. 1983. One step gene disruption in yeast. *Methods Enzymol.* **101**: 202.

Singer, M. 1982. Highly repeated sequences in mammalian genomes. *Int. Rev. Cytol.* **76**: 67.

Tschumper, G. and J. Carbon. 1987. *Saccharomyces cerevisiae* mutants that tolerate centromere plasmids at high copy number. *Proc. Natl. Acad. Sci.* **84**: 7203.

Yeh, E., J. Carbon, and K. Bloom. 1986. Tightly centromere-linked gene (*SP015*) essential for meiosis in the yeast *Saccharomyces cerevisiae*. *Mol. Cell. Biol.* **6**: 158.

Isolation and Cloning of Conditionally Lethal Chromosome Transmission Fidelity Genes in *Saccharomyces cerevisiae*

F. Spencer, C. Connelly, S. Lee, and P. Hieter

Department of Molecular Biology and Genetics, Johns Hopkins University School of Medicine, Baltimore, Maryland 21205

We have begun the collection and analysis of mutant strains that exhibit decreased fidelity of chromosome transmission in mitosis using a visual assay to monitor the inheritance of an artificially generated nonessential marker chromosome. Of 136 independent haploid mutant strains recovered, six are completely deficient for growth at 37°C. Complementation analysis demonstrates that this subset represents five different chromosome transmission fidelity (*ctf*) genes: *ctf12* through *ctf16*. Four of the original isolates could be analyzed for meiotic cosegregation of the sectoring and temperature-sensitive phenotypes. All four showed cosegregation, suggesting that single mutations are responsible for both the selected (sectoring) and unselected (temperature sensitivity) phenotypes. Authentic yeast chromosome III is affected by the presence of the *ctf* mutations, as shown by the rate of appearance of mating-competent diploids in *ctf/ctf* mutant backgrounds. None of the temperature-sensitive strains shows a classic cell division cycle (*cdc*) arrest phenotype, although three of them do appear to arrest preferentially in the large budded stage of the cell cycle. For three complementation groups, genomic DNA complementing the temperature sensitivity has been obtained and the chromosomal origin of each clone has been determined.

The correct segregation of sister chromatids to the two daughter cells of a mitotic division occurs with a high degree of fidelity, requiring the faithful execution of a large number of complex processes. These include complete replication of chromosomal DNA, maintenance of structural elements required in *cis* for chromosome organization and movement, and the correct assembly and function in *trans* of the mitotic apparatus. Mutational analysis of chromosome transmission allows the identification of gene products involved without requiring prior knowledge of or assumptions about the physical properties of the molecules of interest. One approach to the isolation of mutants exhibiting chromosome transmission defects has been the subsequent screening of collections of mutants originally isolated on the basis of their conditional lethality. For example, the *cdc* mutants in *S. cerevisiae* (Hartwell et al. 1970; Hartwell 1978) have been a rich source of cell-cycle-specific genes that are required for mitotic chromosome transmission (Wood and Hartwell 1982). This has been directly demonstrated in a subset of nuclear division pathway *cdc* genes that alter chromosome loss and recombination rates in mitosis (Hartwell and Smith 1985). A similar approach has been taken in *Drosophila melanogaster* (Smith et al. 1985), where a large collection of random temperature-sensitive lethal mutations were secondarily screened at a semipermissive temperature for defective mitotic chromosome behavior, yielding a small subset of mutants for study.

Until recently, the genetic analysis of chromosome transmission in *S. cerevisiae* has been limited to the study of *cdc* mutants. However, it is expected that many genes important to the processes necessary for mitotic chromosome transmission may not mutate to give a Cdc⁻ phenotype and thus would not have been identified in these early screens (Pringle and Hartwell 1981). Several alternative approaches have recently been undertaken, including the use of reverse genetic techniques to study topoisomerase II (DiNardo et al. 1984; Goto and Wang 1984; Holm et al. 1985) and DNA polymerase I (Budd and Campbell 1987), the isolation of cold-sensitive *cdc* mutations and second-site revertants of these (Moir et al. 1982; Moir and Botstein 1982; Thomas and Botstein 1986), the study of mutants conditionally functional for the maintenance of circular minichromosomes (Maine et al. 1984; Sinha et al. 1986), identification of genomic sequences with chromosome instability phenotypes associated with overexpression (Meeks-Wagner and Hartwell 1986; Meeks-Wagner et al. 1986), and analysis of tubulin mutants (Neff et al. 1983; Thomas et al. 1985; Schatz et al. 1986a,b).

We have applied a different strategy for isolation and characterization of mutations that disrupt various aspects of the chromosome cycle in yeast. Since chromosome segregation is essential for growth, mutations that destroy this process are expected to be lethal. However, mutations that cause a sublethal decrease in the fidelity of chromosome transmission should be directly identifiable. These are expected to include null mutations in genes that are important but not essential to the process, and leaky mutations in genes essential for chromo-

441

some transmission. In the present screen, the mutagenesis strategies of the Cdc screens in yeast and the mitotic mutant screen in *Drosophila* are reversed: Mutants are identified first by an increase in the frequency of mistakes in chromosome transmission, and secondarily screened for temperature conditional lethality. We have named mutants recovered in the primary screen *ctf* mutants, in reference to their phenotype. The subset of temperature-sensitive mutations are presumably hypomorphic alleles of genes required for viability. Initial characterization of this small subset is presented.

Methods

Yeast strains and media

Table 1 lists the genotypes of strains employed in this work. With the exception of the mating testers YPH315 and YPH316, all YPH yeast strains used are isogenic derivatives of S288C (derived from YNN217, original source M. Carlson). The additional auxotrophic markers trp1Δ1 and his3Δ200 were introduced (Hieter et al. 1985) by one-step gene replacement (Rothstein 1983), as was the leu2Δ1 allele (M. Saltarelli, unpubl.), a 0.6-kb *Eco*RI to *Cla*I deletion of the 5′ coding region of the *LEU2* gene. All Ctf mutant strains mentioned are derived from these isogenic YPH strains. DBY1385 and 237.1A were obtained from the Botstein lab collection, and 4528-091 and 4528-282 were obtained from the Hartwell lab collection. YM189 is a strain from M. Snyder derived from SD1-4 (DiNardo et al. 1984) by one cross with a strain isogenic to YPH98. Media recipes from Sherman et al. (1986) were utilized, with the exception of the concentration of supplemental adenine, which was added at a low concentration (6 μg/ml) to enhance the development of red pigment by *ade2-101* cells. All yeasts were cultured at 25°C unless otherwise stated.

Construction of marker chromosome fragments

Stably inherited, large, linear, nonessential marker chromosomes were generated in vivo by a recently developed transformation method (Fig. 1) using vectors pYCF1 and pYCF2 (P. Hieter et al., in prep.). The plasmid pYCF2 is a YRP14/*CEN4* derivative (Hieter et al. 1985) in which the *Bgl*II site in the *CEN4* sequence has been destroyed, and the 346-bp *Hind*III-*Bam*HI pBR322 fragment is replaced by the 1.5-kb *Hind*III-*Bgl*II fragment (Y′a) and 1-kb *Bgl*II-*Bam*HI fragment (Y′b) from the telomere-adjacent sequence Y′ (Chan and Tye 1983) in head-to-head orientation as shown. The 1-kb *Bgl*II-*Bam*HI Y′b fragment was replaced with a 2-kb *Bgl*II fragment from RAD2 such that the centromere-distal end of the *RAD2* sequence is at the free end of the *Bgl*II linearized plasmid, as diagramed in C. The plasmid pYCF1 is a YRP14 derivative (Hieter et al. 1985) similarly modified by addition of the head-to-head Y′ sequences as described for pYCF1. The 1-kb *Bgl*II-*Bam*HI Y′b fragment was replaced with a 7-kb *Bgl*II-*Bam*HI fragment from *CEN3* (Clark and Carbon 1980). YPH98 and YPH102 made competent for DNA-mediated transformation (Ito et al. 1983) were exposed to 3 μg of linearized plasmid DNA and grown on supplemented minimal medium lacking uracil. Ura⁺ transformants were picked and streaked on YPD (rich) medium to observe the behavior of the newly introduced *SUP11* marker. Approximately 50% of all transformants exhibited stable inheritance of this marker and the electrophoretic karyotypes of these strains were determined by orthogonal-field-alternation-gel-electrophoresis (OFAGE) (Carle and Olson 1984, 1985). Greater than 90% of the karyotypes revealed the presence of a new chromosome band, and individual strains were picked for mutagenesis. The chromosomal origin of the newly generated chromosome fragment (CF) in each case was

Table 1 Genotypes of Strains Used

Strain designations	Genotype
YPH98	MAT*a* ura3-52 lys2-801 ade2-101 trp1Δ1 leu2Δ1
YPH102	MATα ura3-52 lys2-801 ade2-101 his3Δ200 leu2Δ1
YPH277	MAT*a* ura3-52 lys2-801 ade2-101 trp1Δ1 leu2Δ1 + CF 1.1 (7:RAD2d) URA3⁺ SUP11
YPH278	MATα ura3-52 lys2-801 ade2-101 his3Δ200 leu2Δ1 + CF 5.1 (3:CEN3L) URA3⁺ SUP11
YPH279	MATα/MAT*a* ura3-52/ura3-52 lys2-801/lys2-801 ade2-101/ade2-101 HIS⁺/his3Δ200 trp1Δ1/TRP⁺ leu2Δ1/leu2Δ1 + CF 1.1 (7:RAD2d) URA3⁺ SUP11
YPH280	MATα/MAT*a* ura3-52/ura3-52 lys2-801/lys2-801 ade2-101/ade2-101 HIS⁺/his3Δ200 trp1Δ1/TRP⁺ leu2Δ1/leu2Δ1 + CF 5.1 (3:CEN3L) URA3⁺ SUP11
YPH315	MAT*a* his1
YPH316	MATα his1
DBY1385	MATα ura3-52 ade2ochre tub2-104
237.1A	MAT*a* ura3-52 ade2ochre his3Δ200 leu2-3,112 tub1-1
4528-091	MATα ade2 ade3 his7 leu2 can1 sap3 cdc9-1
4522-282	MAT*a* ura1 ade2 ade3 his7 leu2 can1 sap3 cdc28-1
YM189	MAT*a* ura3-52 lys2-801 leu2-3,112 trp1 top2-1

All mutant strains generated in this study and all diploids or triploids produced by mating are derived from these, as described in the text.

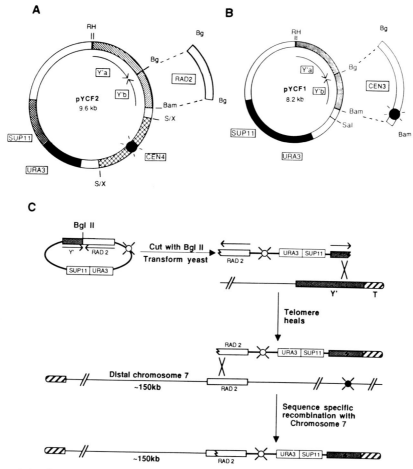

Figure 1 Construction of the *SUP11*-marked chromosome fragments (CF). The plasmids used in transformation to produce the marker CFs are shown in panels *A* and *B*. Panel *C* illustrates the proposed events leading to the generation of the CF 1.1 (in YPH277) on transformation with linearized plasmid from panel *A*. In the transformation to generate CF 5.1 (in YPH278), the *CEN3* sequence functions in place of the *RAD2* unique sequence and *CEN4*, serving as the targeting unique sequence and the functional centromere for the chromosome fragment.

confirmed by probe hybridization to nitrocellulose filters of the OFAGE gels (data not shown). The pYCF2/*RAD2* construct yields a chromosome fragment with the *URA3* $^+$ and *SUP11* markers on the short arm and chromosome VII sequences distal to *RAD2* on the long arm (CF1.1[7:RAD2d]). The pYCF1/*CEN3* construct yields a chromosome fragment with an equivalent *URA3* $^+$ *SUP11* short arm and a long arm composed of the entire left arm of chromosome III (CF5.1 [3:CEN3L]). Each of these chromosome fragments is approximately 150 kb in length.

EMS mutagenesis
Haploid strains YPH277, YPH278, YPH362, and YPH363 were mutagenized with ethylmethane sulfonate (EMS). (Strains YPH362 and YPH363 are CF[7:RAD2d]-bearing transformants of YPH98 and YPH102, respectively. The CF they carry differs from CF1.1 in the orientation of the *SUP11* marker. Because they did not give rise to temperature-sensitive mutants, they will not be discussed further here.) The conditions chosen for EMS treatment yielded ⩾80% viability and a

10–50-fold increase over the spontaneous rate of mutation to canavanine resistance.

Haploid strains were grown overnight to near saturation in YPD. Approximately 10^8 cells were washed in distilled water, resuspended in 1 ml of 100 mM potassium phosphate (pH 8.0), and incubated in the presence of 1.5–3 μl EMS (Sigma) for 1 hour at room temperature. After three 1-ml washes in 5% sodium thiosulfate, the cells were resuspended in 1 ml of YPD and aliquots plated on supplemented minimal medium at a density of 200 cells/plate. The cells in YPD suspension were used in multiple platings for up to 3 weeks after treatment with mutagen. Aliquots taken before and after EMS treatment were plated on YPD to determine viability. Approximately 10^6 cells were spread on plates containing supplemented complete minimal medium minus arginine (Sherman et al. 1986) with 60 μg/ml canavanine added to determine the frequency of resistant cells obtained after EMS treatment; a control tube with no added EMS carried in parallel through the mutagenesis protocol gave the spontaneous frequency (approximately 1–6 × 10^{-6}).

Assays for conditional lethality
Assays for conditional lethal secondary phenotypes possessed by the *ctf* haploid mutant strains were carried out as follows. Mutant strains were grown to saturation in supplemented minimal medium at 25°C. Logarithmic dilution series were prepared in minimal medium (100 μl total volume) in microtiter wells, and transferred to test plates using a prong device. The resulting series of patches contained from 10^6 to 10^2 cells. Temperature conditional growth (at 37°C or 11°C) was determined by incubating the test plates at the desired temperature (for 3 days or 21 days, respectively) and comparing the growth on test plates to controls cultured at 25°C for 5 days. Temperature conditional lethality was scored as tight (no growth even in the most concentrated patch of cells) or leaky (some growth but less than wild type). Benomyl (Dupont) sensitivity was assayed by addition of concentrated stock (10 mg/ml in DMSO) to YPD plates at a final concentration of 0, 1, 5, 10, or 15 μg/ml. All Benomyl tests were cultured at 25°C for 4 to 5 days before scoring. Each test included the isogenic parent strains (YPH277 and YPH278), as well as a strain harboring a well-characterized mutation conferring sensitivity to the treatment applied. For growth at 37°C, the control strain was YM189; for growth at 11°C, the control was DBY1385; for growth in the presence of Benomyl, the control was 237.1A.

Genetic crosses
Heterozygous diploids (*CTF$^+$/ctf*) were obtained in two different crosses. In one, a single colony exhibiting a sectoring phenotype was picked and patched together on YPD with the appropriate red strain of opposite mating type (YPH98 or YPH102). Diploids were selected on the basis of His$^+$ and Trp$^+$ prototrophy. The reciprocal cross was also performed: A pool of 6–10 red segregants from a sectoring strain was mated with the appropriate CF-bearing strain of opposite mating type (YPH277 or YPH278) and diploids selected as above. To ascertain whether the genetic determinants for temperature sensitivity and for sectoring cosegregate in meiosis, diploids from either cross were sporulated (Sherman et al. 1986), four-spored tetrads dissected on rich medium, and genotype of the strains derived from the haploid spores determined.

Diploid selection in other matings also depended on His$^+$ and Trp$^+$ prototrophy. The complementation tests performed among the temperature-sensitive ctf mutants utilized haploid strains from the once-backcrossed spores where possible as well as the original isolate strains. Homozygous diploids (*ctf/ctf*) for use in the fluctuation analysis of *MAT* genotype were obtained by crossing appropriate pairs of haploid strains from once-outcrossed spores.

Fluctuation analysis of mater occurrence in diploid strains
Each homozygous mutant diploid strain was plated at low density (about 100 cells/plate) and incubated at 25°C until the average colony diameter indicated a colony size of approximately 50,000 cells. Eight individual test colonies in logarithmic growth were removed from the plate on agar plugs with sterile pasteur pipettes and resuspended in 100 μl YPD. One μl of each test colony was plated on rich medium for viable cell count. The total number of diploid cells in each colony competent to mate with *MATa* haploid testers was determined separately from the number competent to mate with *MATα* haploids. Aliquots (40 μl each) were mixed with a tenfold excess of YPH315 or YPH316 in log phase (OD_{600} = 1.0–5.0) in a final volume of 140 μl YPD. The mixture of haploid and diploid cells were pelleted together in a short centrifugation, incubated without shaking at 25°C for 4–6 hours, and plated on minimal medium with no supplements to select for triploids. (Under these conditions, the mating efficiency observed for *MATa* and *MATα* haploid yeast is between 30 and 50%.) After incubation at 25°C for 4 days, triploid colonies were counted, multiplied by 2.5 to represent the entire colony picked, and rate of formation of diploid maters per cell division was calculated using the method of the median (Lea and Coulson 1949).

The measured rate under the protocol chosen may deviate from the true rate depending on the mating efficiency achieved in each experiment, as well as the degree of phenotypic lag and leakiness for mating type locus alteration and mating. The method also assumes that cells of all chromosome III constitutions are of approximately equal fitness. The degree to which these potential deviations affect the assay as performed is unknown. Each experiment included a wild-type diploid genotype in an attempt to control for these systematic errors, and the ratio of diploid mater formation in mutant backgrounds versus wild-type backgrounds is presented. The rates of diploid mater formation calculated for wild-type backgrounds was comparable to published measurements for mitotic missegregation of markers on chromosomes V and VII (Hartwell et al. 1982; Hartwell and Smith 1985). Data obtained from fluctuation analysis in six independent experiments indicate that diploids competent to mate with the *MATa* tester strain arose at a rate of 2.8×10^{-5} with standard deviation 1.2×10^{-5}. Similarly, diploids competent to mate with the *MATα* tester arose at a rate of 2.2×10^{-5} with standard deviation 1.4×10^{-5}.

Clone isolation and chromosome assignment
All sectoring strains generated in this mutagenesis contain a nonreverting deletion in the *LEU2* gene. To obtain yeast genomic sequences that complement ctf mutations, a genomic library (F. Spencer, unpubl.) was constructed in a *LEU2/CEN4/ARS1* shuttle vector (pSB32, J. Trueheart, unpubl.). The temperature-sensitive haploid yeast strains were made competent (Ito et al. 1983), exposed to 3 μg library DNA and plated on supplemented minimal medium without leucine. An aliquot grown at 25°C measured the transformation efficiency; the remainder incubated at 37°C gave rise only to Ts$^+$ colonies. Plasmids complementing the temperature sensitivity were rescued from yeast in HB101 as described

previously (Davis et al. 1980). Gel-purified genomic restriction fragments were radiolabeled (Feinberg and Vogelstein 1983) and used to probe an OFAGE electrophoretic karyotype of *S. cerevisiae* blotted to nitrocellulose. The hybridization and wash were performed using standard conditions (Maniatis et al. 1982). The electrophoretic karyotype of the yeast strain used (C. Connelly and P. Hieter, in prep.) provides unambiguous hybridization signals for all chromosomes except chromosome 12, which does not enter the gel under the conditions used in OFAGE.

Terminal arrest morphology

Haploid strains were grown at 22°C in YPD liquid suspension to a density of $1-6.5 \times 10^6$ cells per ml. Aliquots were shifted to 37°C and similarly incubated in liquid suspension for up to 20 hours. Four to five hours after shift, an aliquot was removed, 5 μl samples were scored immediately for bud morphology, and the remainder of the cells were fixed in 70% ethanol at room temperature for further analysis. Data obtained before and after fixation were equivalent, as were data obtained 8 hours post-shift. At several time points after shift to 37°C, measurement of the OD_{600} was taken of cultures incubated at the nonpermissive temperature. These demonstrated that all six temperature-sensitive strains had arrested within two cell cycles at 37°C and that growth had ceased within 4 hours. Strains 4528-091 and 4522-282 served as positive controls: Both exhibited > 90% homogeneity 4 hours after shift.

Results and Discussion

Identification of ctf^ts mutant strains

The strategy utilized in the mutagenesis protocol presented takes advantage of a colony color assay for chromosome stability in *S. cerevisiae* (Hieter et al. 1985). This assay is built on the observation that colonies of wild-type *S. cerevisiae* are white, whereas mutants blocked in late steps of adenine biosynthesis (*ade2* or *ade1*) accumulate a red pigment (Roman 1957). Thus, the mitotic behavior of a marker chromosome that carries an ochre-suppressing allele of tyrosyl tRNA (*SUP11*) can be monitored visually in an *ade2-*ochre background. Stably inherited nonessential chromosomes carrying the *SUP11* marker were constructed using an in vivo chromosome fragmentation method (P. Hieter et al., in prep.) diagrammed in Figure 1. In this method, a circular CEN plasmid is opened at a unique restriction site to generate a linear molecule with telomere-adjacent Y' DNA (Chan and Tye 1983) on one free end and a unique sequence of choice from the yeast genome on the other. When the telomere-adjacent sequence and the unique sequence are present in the orientations shown, interaction between the plasmid free end sequences and yeast genomic sites results in the formation of the molecule diagrammed. This molecule can be visualized as a new band a ethidium bromide staining material in the electrophoretic karyotype of the transformant, and we call the new band a chromosome

fragment (CF). Resultant haploid transformants are disomic for all sequences distal to the unique sequence chosen. CFs are produced in about 50% of the transformants, the other class apparently resulting from recircularization of the linearized plasmid. The two outcomes can be easily distinguished by the relative stability of the *SUP11* marker in the absence of selection: The unstable transformants are found to contain a circular CEN plasmid, whereas the stable transformants have acquired a CF.

To generate haploid strains of opposite mating type with nonoverlapping CFs (and therefore nonoverlapping partial disomies), YPH98 and YPH102 were transformed with linearized forms of the plasmids shown in Figure 1. Ura+ transformants from each were restreaked on rich medium for identification of strains that stably maintained the *SUP11* marker. The presence and structure of each CF thus produced was verified by Southern analysis of chromosome bands separated by OFAGE (data not shown). Electrophoretic karyotypes and genotypes of the relevant parent strains used for mutagenesis are shown in Figure 2.

Both of the CFs generated are approximately 150 kb in length (representing about 1% of the genome), and appear to be maintained with mitotic stability about tenfold below that possessed by authentic yeast chromosomes (J. Shero, unpubl.). Strains carrying these CFs produce colonies with no or very rare red sectors when plated on nonselective media (see Fig. 3A). The CF is ideally suited to serve as a marker for chromosome loss: Its structure does not include homology to the yeast genome between the plasmid-derived CEN sequence and the *URA3+ SUP11* marker region on the short arm. Thus the frequency of marker loss by mitotic recombination should be small, requiring interaction between 1 kb of either marker gene and the corresponding genomic homologous sites. This is directly supported by the observation that 16 independently derived red segregants from CF-containing strains show no evidence for *SUP11* loss by gene conversion or by chromosome rearrangement. The red segregant derivatives (*SUP11−*) were all Ura−, show no chromosome fragment band in the OFAGE karyotype, no change in the sizes of the remaining genomic chromosomes, and no hybridization to CF-specific pBR322 sequences from the long arm. Thus, loss of *URA3+* and *SUP11* markers is predominantly associated with loss of the CF in wild-type strains.

Because the goal of the mutagenesis was to isolate mutations that result in constitutive missegregation of chromosomes, we chose a light mutagenesis strategy that we hoped would minimize the probability of inducing multiple mutations within the same nucleus. The CF-bearing haploid yeast strains were exposed to EMS and plated nonselectively on supplemented minimal medium to obtain single colonies. The plates were incubated at 25°C for 5−7 days, after which the colonies founded by the mutagenized cells were visually screened for the presence of multiple red sectors. A total of approximately 600,000 colonies screened gave rise to 136 strains,

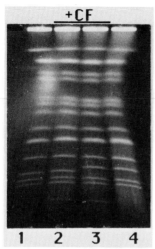

1 MATα ura3 ade2 leu2 his3 TRP1⁺

2 MATα ura3 ade2 leu2 his3 TRP1⁺
   + CF 5.1 (3:CEN3L) URA3⁺ SUP11

3 MAT**a** ura3 ade2 leu2 HIS3⁺ trp1
   + CF1.1 (7:RAD2d) URA3⁺ SUP11

4 MAT**a** ura3 ade2 leu2 HIS3⁺ trp1

Figure 2 Genotypes and electrophoretic karyotypes of parent strains used in the mutagenesis. Shown are (*1*) YPH102; (*2*) YPH278, the CF-containing strain derived from YPH102; (*3*) YPH277, the CF-containing strain derived from YPH98; (*4*) YPH98.

which reproducibly transmitted their sectoring phenotypes upon restreaking for colony purification. Figure 3 illustrates the stable transmission of the marker chromosomes in a wild-type background and the range of sectoring phenotypes obtained in most of the mutant strains collected. A few mutant strains recovered (about

4%) develop unusual colony color phenotypes: Two examples will be described below.

The entire collection of 136 haploid strains was assayed for temperature-sensitive conditional lethality. A logarithmic dilution series for each strain was prepared in microtiter wells and transferred to YPD medium by

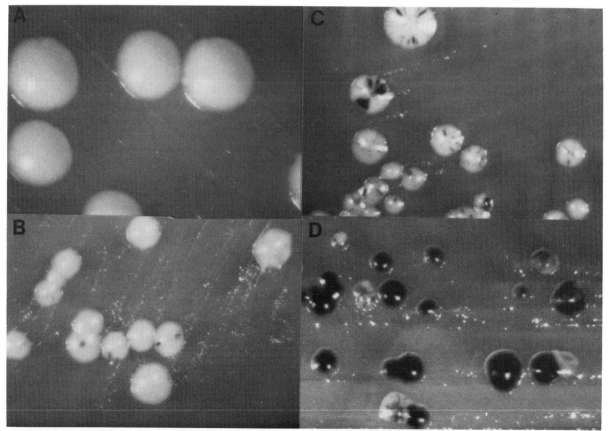

Figure 3 Colony sectoring phenotypes of strains with *SUP11*-marked CFs. Stable mitotic transmission of a chromosome fragment in wild-type background is shown (*A*), as well as examples of rare sectoring (*B*), moderately sectoring (*C*), and frequently sectoring (*D*) mutant phenotypes obtained in this mutagenesis.

use of a prong device, such that the resulting patches on the YPD plates contained from 10^2 (most dilute) to 10^6 (most concentrated) cells. These were scored for growth after incubation for 3 days at 37°C. Seven strains (Table 2) were completely deficient for growth even at the highest concentration tested. One of these has since lost its sectoring phenotype by reversion or suppression and will not be discussed further. An additional 12 mutant strains exhibited leaky but significant temperature sensitivity. These strains have not been characterized and will not be discussed further.

Genetic characteristics of the six temperature-sensitive haploid strains

The parental origin and sectoring phenotypes of the six characterized temperature-sensitive strains are listed in Table 2. Four of the mutant strains have sectoring phenotypes similar to the major classes obtained in the primary screen (see examples in Fig. 3). Two strains (s42 and s124) have unusual phenotypes. Mutant strain s42 is heterogeneous both in colony size and sectoring characteristic. Approximately 90% of the colonies are of normal size (comparable to the parent strain) and show variable rare sectoring that overlaps the wild-type phenotype, and 10% are small (one-quarter diameter) and produce frequent red sectors. The large, rarely sectoring colonies stably transmit their rare sectoring phenotype on restreaking; the small frequently sectoring colonies regenerate 90% large moderately sectoring colonies on restreaking. Mutant strain s124 is like s42 in phenotype, except the colonies of normal size develop a nonsectoring phenotype indistinguishable from wild type.

The mutations obtained in the six temperature-sensitive haploid strains were tested for dominant or recessive character by scoring ctf/CTF^+ diploid colonies for sectoring phenotype and temperature sensitivity. All six mutations are recessive by both criteria. The heterozygous diploids were produced as shown in Figure 4. A single sectoring colony was mixed with a patch of cells from the appropriate red strain of opposite mating type (YPH98 or YPH102) and His$^+$ Trp$^+$ diploids were select-

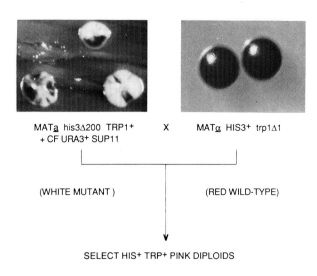

MAT**a** his3Δ200 TRP1$^+$ X   MATα HIS3$^+$ trp1Δ1
+ CF URA3$^+$ SUP11

(WHITE MUTANT)   (RED WILD-TYPE)

SELECT HIS$^+$ TRP$^+$ PINK DIPLOIDS

MUTANT PHENOTYPE (SECTORED) = DOMINANT
WILD-TYPE PHENOTYPE (NONSECTORED) = RECESSIVE

Figure 4 Genetic test for dominance or recessiveness.

ed. The marker chromosome stability was ascertained by visual inspection of approximately 50 diploid colonies grown in the absence of selection for the marker chromosome; none showed a mutant sectoring phenotype equivalent to the original haploid phenotype. The mutation in strain s30 was incompletely recessive, exhibiting slight but detectably increased sectoring relative to the controls. All other heterozygous diploids were indistinguishable from CTF^+/CTF^+ diploids (YPH279 or YPH280). The temperature sensitivity of the diploid strains was tested in streaks grown at 37°C for 3 days; all heterozygous diploids were viable at the nonpermissive temperature.

We have been able to demonstrate that the lesion responsible for the sectoring phenotype exhibits close genetic linkage to the temperature sensitivity in four of the six strains (Table 3). Heterozygous ctf/CTF^+ diploids were sporulated and tetrads dissected. All spores were tested for ability to grow at 37°C, and all four-spored tetrads exhibited 2:2 segregation for the temperature sensitivity. In general, two of the spores possessed a marker chromosome that allowed the sectoring phenotype to be visualized. If the lethality and sectoring are due to the same mutation, all spores with marker chromosomes that survive at 37°C should sector at wild-type levels, and all spores with marker chromosomes that fail to survive should show a mutant sectoring phenotype.

The temperature conditional phenotype in s8, s18, s30, and s122 clearly cosegregates with the sectoring mutation present. If the scoreable spores are analyzed as a random sample, a maximum genetic distance expected (with 95% confidence) between the determinants of the sectoring and temperature-sensitive phenotypes can be calculated as $1 - (0.05)^{1/x}$, where x is the sample size in which no recombinants are seen. For analysis of s30 (16 observations made), this equa-

Table 2 Origin and Phenotypic Properties of the Temperature-sensitive Sectoring Strains

Mutant isolate	Parent strain	Sectoring characteristics	Other properties
s8	YPH278	moderate	
s18	YPH278	frequent	
s30	YPH278	moderate	
s42	YPH278	heterogeneous[a]	
s103	YPH277	moderate	sectoring lost[b]
s122	YPH277	moderate	growth deficient at 11°C
s124	YPH277	heterogeneous[a]	Benomyl supersensitive

[a]Mutant strains s42 and s124 are heterogeneous in colony size and sectoring phenotype as described in the text.

[b]Mutant strain s103 lost its sectoring phenotype (without loss of its temperature sensitivity) early in analysis, presumably due to reversion or suppression. This strain has not been further characterized.

Table 3 Meiotic Cosegregation of Temperature Conditional Lethality and Sectoring Phenotypes

Cross[a]	Number of tetrads analyzed[b]	Cosegregation of *ts* lethality and sectoring[c]
s8 (CF⁻) × YPH277	9	18/18
s18 (CF⁻) × YPH277	8	16/16
s30 (CF⁻) × YPH277	4	8/8
s30 (CF⁺) × YPH98	10	20/20
s42 (CF⁻) × YPH277	6	10/12[d]
s122 (CF⁻) × YPH278	11	22/22
s124 (CF⁻) × YPH278	0	n.d.[e]
s124 (CF⁺) × YPH98	0	n.d.[e]

[a]To generate diploids with a single CF, red segregants lacking a chromosome fragment (CF⁻) of the mutant strain were crossed with appropriate wild-type haploids containing a CF, or sectoring (CF⁺) mutant colonies were crossed with appropriate wild-type haploids lacking a CF.

[b]This analysis includes tetrads with four viable spores. Spores from partially viable tetrads exhibited segregation patterns consistent with those shown.

[c]Shown as (spores that are unable to grow at 37°C and sector at 25°C + spores that are able to grow at 37°C and do not sector at 25°C)/total number of CF-bearing spores.

[d]Both spores showing separation of the two phenotypes are temperature sensitive and nonsectoring. Therefore, this apparent separation of phenotypes may indicate the presence of two separate genetic lesions, or may be due to the frequent reversion of the sectoring phenotype observed in strain s42. A larger sample will be required to resolve this issue.

[e]Not determined. s124 produced no tetrads of four viable spores in the cross with YF5.1 (n = 28 tetrads), and only one completely viable tetrad with aberrant segregation of recessive markers in the cross with YPH98 (n = 40 tetrads).

tion predicts a maximum genetic distance of 17 map units. In yeast, one map unit corresponds to approximately 2.6 kb of genomic DNA (Mortimer and Schild 1985). Thus, if separate mutations are responsible for the two phenotypes, they are located within approximately 45 kb of one another. Thus, the genetic data suggest that the two phenotypes result from the same mutation.

For the mutant strain s42, apparent failure of the sectoring and temperature-sensitive phenotypes to cosegregate was seen in two of the twelve spores analyzed. Whether this is due to the complexity of the sectoring phenotype or to segregation of separate mutations is not yet clear. The two spores in which the phenotypes are apparently separated are each temperature sensitive and nonsectoring, which may simply be due to the frequent reversion of the sectoring phenotype seen in the original haploid isolate. Analysis of a larger sample may resolve this issue. The mutant composition of strain s124 has not been approachable by meiotic analysis to date due to the remarkably low spore viability (46%) obtained upon dissection of four-spored tetrads.

The observed meiotic cosegregation of multiple phenotypes is important in at least two respects. The genetic linkage strongly suggests that the phenotypes are not due to separate mutations in the genome. In addition, meiosis allows separation of the primary ef-

fects of the mutation studied from the effects of specific aneuploidies that may have been clonally fixed during colony purification. If the experimental inaccessibility of strains s42 and s124 is due to complex genomic composition, subsequent rounds of meiotic analysis may yield more tractable derivatives.

Because the *SUP11*-marked CF was present during the mutagenesis, the recovery of mutations in *cis* on the marker chromosome is theoretically possible. The recessive character and cosegregating temperature sensitivity of this subset clearly suggests that the mutations are in *trans*-acting genetic loci. Function in *trans* was directly demonstrated by introduction of a nonmutagenized CF into the mutant background. This was accomplished in the haploid spores generated by the crosses listed in Table 3, and in all cases (except s124, which was not testable) a *trans* effect of the sectoring mutations was observed.

The six temperature-sensitive strains were crossed inter se and tested for complementation of their temperature sensitivity. All but one heteroallelic diploid combination was proficient for growth at 37°C. The exceptional diploid combination, s8/s18, failed to grow at 37°C and, furthermore, exhibited a sectoring phenotype at 25°C. Thus, the six strains represent five complementation groups, and have been designated *ctf12* through *ctf16* (Table 4).

Authentic yeast chromosomes are affected by ctf temperature-sensitive mutations

In wild-type populations of yeast, mating-competent diploids arise rarely, due to hemi- or homozygosis of the mating type locus. The change in *MAT* genotype may arise in a number of ways: due to loss of one chromosome III homolog, due to mitotic recombination on chromosome III proximal to *MAT*, or due to gene conversion between mating type loci. The frequency of diploid maters in a population can be easily ascertained by a quantitative mating assay (Dutcher and Hartwell 1982), followed by direct selection for the resultant triploids. To ascertain whether the mutations isolated on the basis of the *SUP11*-marked CF in haploids also affect the behavior of authentic yeast chromosomes, we measured

Table 4 Complementation Analysis of Temperature Conditional Lethality

ctf allele	Original isolate	Complementation matrix				
		s8	s18	s30	s42	s122
ctf12-8	s8					
ctf12-18	s18	−				
ctf13-30	s30	+	+			
ctf14-42	s42	+	+	+		
ctf15-122	s122	+	+	+	+	
ctf16-124	s124	+	+	+	+	+

Original isolates of mutant strains or appropriate derivatives were crossed inter se to test complementation of temperature sensitivities and sectoring phenotypes. The mutations identified by the five complementation groups in this analysis have been named as shown.

rates of occurrence of rare diploid maters in clonal populations of homozygous mutant *ctf/ctf* diploid yeast.

Individual diploid colonies in log phase were picked, resuspended in liquid, and aliquotted to assay for the number of cells hemi- or homozygous for *MAT* by quantitative mating, as well as to ascertain the number of viable cells present. The rate of diploid mater occurrence for each genotype was calculated using the method of the median of Lea and Coulson (1949). For all allelic combinations tested, the ratio of mater occurrence in mutant diploids to mater occurrence in wild-type diploids was greater than 1 (Table 5), demonstrating that authentic yeast chromosomes experience enhanced rates of chromosome loss or mitotic recombination in the *ctf/ctf* mutant backgrounds. Because the mutant strains were originally identified due to loss of the marker CF, the mechanism for mater occurrence in most genotypes is probably chromosome loss rather than mitotic recombination.

Although the assay performed was quantitative mating, the results must be interpreted qualitatively. If the mutant strains are constitutively defective in chromosome transmission, then the sectoring diploids tested are likely to be heterogeneous in chromosome number per nucleus and continuously evolving. The number of third chromosome homologs present will clearly affect the outcome, as may indirect effects of aneuploidy for other chromosomes. In this context, the quantitative mating assay has been repeated for some diploid genotypes (particularly those with low loss rate ratios), and qualitatively comparable results were obtained.

The observation of an alteration in the fidelity of mitotic transmission for an authentic yeast chromosome is important. It addresses and discounts the possibility that the sectoring seen in mutant colonies is due simply to artifactual effects, such as differential growth advantage possessed by pigment-containing over pigmentless cells, or *sup*[+] over *SUP11* cells within a colony. These results directly support the initial supposition that mutant strains picked for CF-sectoring phenotype are defective in chromosome transmission fidelity.

Other secondary phenotypes exhibited by *ctf* temperature-sensitive mutant strains

The original isolate *ctf* strains have also been tested for a number of other secondary conditional lethal phenotypes, including inability to grow at 11°C and inability to grow in the presence of Benomyl (a benzimidazole drug). These tests were carried out on logarithmic dilution series transferred to the test plate by a prong device, as for the assay for temperature sensitivity described above. Other secondary phenotypes found in the temperature-sensitive strains are listed in Table 2.

The mutant strain containing the *ctf15-122* genetic lesion that is associated with deficiency for growth at 37°C also fails to grow at 11°C. Four-spored tetrads from *ctf15-122/CTF*[+] heterozygotes exhibit 2:2 segregation for this phenotypic trait. Surprisingly, the cold sensitivity cosegregates with the temperature-sensitive phenotype (100% cosegregation in 10 four-spored tetrads), and by extension with the red sectoring phenotype (Table 3). It is likely that a single genetic lesion is responsible for these diverse traits. None of the other temperature-sensitive strains fail to grow at 11°C.

Although the cellular targets of the benzimidazole drugs have not been characterized at the biochemical level, these drugs are observed to bind fungal tubulin in vitro (Davidse and Flach 1977) and have proven to be useful probes of microtubule function in *S. cerevisiae* (Thomas et al. 1985; Schatz et al. 1986b; Huffaker et al. 1987). Recently, Benomyl has been used in a mutant screen to select a drug-sensitive subset of chromosome instability (*cin*) mutants (M.A. Hoyt et al., unpubl.). The strain containing *ctf16-124* failed to grow in the presence of Benomyl at a low concentration (10 μg/ml) that does not inhibit the growth of *CTF*[+] strains YPH277 and YPH278. To date it is not known whether the temperature conditional, red sectoring, and Benomyl supersensitive phenotypes in strain s124 are due to a single lesion or mutations in multiple loci.

Cellular morphology at ts arrest

The terminal morphology produced by temperature-sensitive *ctf* strains was determined by shifting log phase cultures to the nonpermissive temperature and analyzing the cell cycle distribution at lethality (Fig. 5). None of the six temperature-sensitive strains shows a classic *cdc* phenotype on arrest. However, three of them (*ctf12-8*, *ctf-14-42*, and *ctf16-124*) exhibit a marked shift in distribution at the nonpermissive temperature; on the order of 55–70% of the cells arrest with large buds. This is not a *cdc* phenotype as defined at >80% morphological homogeneity (Hartwell et al. 1970) but does show a preferential arrest during M phase. Recently, a similar preferential arrest at the nonpermissive temperature has been described for *ndc1-1*, a cold-sensitive allele of a gene required for chromosome separation in mitosis (Thomas and Botstein 1986).

Further work in progress addresses the question of nuclear and spindle morphology under permissive and nonpermissive conditions. Preliminary analysis of *ctf12-8* reveals nuclear location at arrest near the neck in the predominant class of large-budded cells, with either one or two chromatin masses, and the presence of a uniformly short spindle. Thus the predominant class of

Table 5 Chromosome III Loss or MAT Homozygosis in *ctf/ctf* Diploids

Diploid genotype	Rate ratio mutant/wild type	
	x *MATa* tester	x *MATα* tester
ctf12-8/ctf12-8	87	144
ctf12-18/ctf12-18	136	173
ctf13-30/ctf13-30	27	29
ctf14-42/ctf14-42	6.7	4.8

In cases where the observed ratio is low, repetition of the same experiment yields similarly small ratios, all greater than 1 (data not shown). The consistency seen in multiple determinations strongly suggests that even a small measured increase in chromosome III alteration is significant.

Relevant Genotype	Temperature (°C)	# cells scored	Bud Morphology (%)			
			none	small	medium	large
CTF⁺(YPH278)	22	152	37	17	32	14
	37	224	42	33	14	11
ctf12-8	22	119	30	35	25	10
	37	209	14	17	12	**57**
ctf12-18	22	123	41	26	14	19
	37	170	36	15	8	41
ctf13-30	22	175	17	39	20	24
	37	231	16	24	14	46
ctf14-42	22	146	23	34	29	14
	37	193	13	6	12	**69**
CTF⁺(YPH277)	22	99	40	12	44	4
	37	200	25	31	33	11
ctf15-122	22	140	33	20	28	19
	37	127	36.5	10	36.5	17
ctf16-124	22	115	35	27	26	12
	37	110	14	13	13	**60**

Figure 5 Cell cycle distribution at terminal arrest. Bud morphology classes were arbitrarily assigned as *none* (no bud visible), *small* (bud ≤ 25% mother cell volume), *medium* (bud between 25 and 75% mother cell volume), and *large* (bud ≥ mother cell volume) as estimated by eye. Observation of > 50% accumulation in a morphology category is emphasized in bold numbers.

cells appears to arrest during the process of chromosome separation. This is most typical of a defect in medial nuclear division (Pringle and Hartwell 1981).

Chromosomal location of CTF⁺ DNA segments
Chromosome stability mutations obtained in a new mutagenesis may be alleles of a number of previously identified genes. Exhaustive complementation analysis between all new isolates and preexisting mutants would be a prohibitively arduous procedure and is not necessary, given the rapidity with which genes can be cloned by complementation in yeast. Possession of the cloned gene allows rapid determination of the chromosomal

location by hybridization to yeast chromosomes. Knowledge of the genomic location of a mutation immediately disqualifies genes present on the other 15 chromosomes and greatly narrows the number of relevant genes to be tested.

DNA segments complementing the genetic lesions responsible for temperature sensitivity in strains containing *ctf12-8*, *ctf12-18*, *ctf13-30*, and *ctf14-42* were obtained by transforming haploid mutant cells with a genomic library and directly selecting transformants able to grow at the nonpermissive temperature. The library (F. Spencer, unpubl.) contains 10–12-kb fragments of yeast genomic DNA cloned into a pBR322-

based *LEU2/CEN4/ARS1* shuttle vector. The plasmid-rescued transformants were distinguished from revertants by demonstrating that the ability to grow at 37°C was conferred by the library plasmid: Leu⁻ segregants obtained in the absence of plasmid selection lose the ability to grow at the nonpermissive temperature. In addition, the library plasmids were cloned back into *Escherichia coli* and subsequently shown to confer wild-type growth at 37°C when reintroduced into mutant haploids. In addition, the cloned DNAs rescuing the temperature sensitivity in *ctf12-8*, *ctf12-18*, and *ctf13-30* also fully complement the sectoring phenotypes. (Because of the frequent phenotypic reversion of the sectoring phenotype in the strain carrying *ctf14-42*, we have been unable as yet to unambiguously demonstrate rescue of the chromosome transmission defect by the cloned DNA.) In theory, the cloned DNA may carry the wild-type copy of the *ctf* lesion, or less likely, an extragenic suppressor of the temperature-sensitive and sectoring phenotypes. These two alternatives can be clearly distinguished using standard genetic techniques.

Chromosomal origin of restriction fragments from the complementing genomic segments was determined by hybridization to yeast chromosomal DNA bands separated by OFAGE and blotted to nitrocellulose (Fig. 6). The yeast strain karyotype is one in which all chromosomal doublets have been separated (P. Hieter et al., unpubl.), thus a hybridization signal unambiguously assigns cloned DNA to a single chromosome, with the exception of chromosome 12, which does not enter the gel under the OFAGE conditions used. Genomic DNA obtained separately for *ctf12-8* and *ctf12-18* complementation hybridize to the same chromosomal DNA band (chromosome 4), consistent with their allelism.

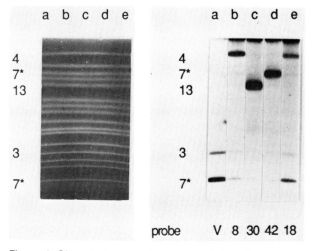

Figure 6 Chromosomal location of cloned DNA that complements ctfᵗˢ mutations. The left panel is a photograph of a preparative scale OFAGE of a yeast strain in which all chromosomal doublets have been separated. This gel was blotted to nitrocellulose, cut into strips (a–e), and hybridized with the probes indicated (V = vector sequences alone; 8 = genomic DNA from the clone complementing s8 defects, etc.). The chromosomal identity of hybridizing bands is shown.

Genomic DNA complementing *ctf13-30* maps to chromosome 13, and DNA that rescues the temperature sensitivity in the strains containing *ctf14-42* is derived from chromosome 7.

Conclusions

The goal of this work was to isolate conditionally functional mutations in genes essential for viability that play an important role in the process of chromosome transmission in mitosis. The mutagenesis rationale was to obtain mutant strains that lose a marker chromosome at elevated rates in a visual screen, and secondarily identify those also exhibiting temperature sensitivity for growth. On the order of 5% of the *ctf* mutations isolated by the visual screen appear to be associated with temperature-sensitive conditional lethality. This proportion can be improved in the future, as 22% of the non-temperature-sensitive mutations isolated belong to a single complementation group (F. Spencer and C. Connelly, unpubl.). A similar mutagenesis in a strain containing an extra wild-type copy of this predominant mutant will eliminate reisolation of this class.

Early genetic and phenotypic characterization of the six temperature-sensitive strains has been encouraging. They represent five different complementation groups. In all four of the strains where meiotic segregation of the conditional lethality and sectoring can be clearly followed, these phenotypes are observed to be closely linked. Four of the complementation groups (those testable) affect stability of the *SUP11*-marked chromosome fragments in *trans*. Three complementation groups have been tested for behavior of authentic yeast chromosomes by quantitative analysis of diploid mater occurrence, and all show increased levels of loss of or mitotic recombination on chromosome III. Other unselected secondary phenotypes found among the six strains include cold sensitivity (one strain), supersensitivity to Benomyl (one strain), and terminal arrest phenotypes with preferential arrest in large bud (three strains). Complementing yeast DNA has been obtained by transformation with a genomic library, and the location of this DNA in the genome determined by hybridization to chromosomal DNA separated by OFAGE (for three complementation groups). Knowledge of the genomic location will allow efficient complementation analysis among new and previously isolated mutations, and the cloned DNA sequences will provide tools for addressing structure and function of the gene products.

We expect that mutations isolated in this way will include lesions in genes that function in a broad spectrum of processes necessary to the chromosome cycle. Some may be required in chromosome metabolism (for example, replication of the DNA or condensation and decondensation of chromosomes), whereas others may be necessary for spindle function (segregation of sister chromatids to the poles or separation of the poles themselves). Detailed phenotypic analysis, information about the structure of the gene product, and further mutagenesis of cloned genes will provide opportunities to learn about the requirements for proper chromosome transmission in the mitotic cell cycle.

Acknowledgments

We thank J. Boeke, W. Merz, and T. Dunn for critical reading of the manuscript; G. Rozanski, J. Shero, S. Gerring, and R. Sikorski for stimulating and helpful discussions; and David Utzschneider for excellent technical assistance. This work was supported by National Institutes of Health grant 5P01CA-16519-13 and by Pew Scholars grant 86-909GHE to P.H. and by a Monsanto fellowship in molecular genetics to F.S.

References

Budd, M. and J.L. Campbell. 1987. Temperature-sensitive mutations in the yeast DNA polymerase I gene. *Proc. Natl. Acad. Sci.* **84:** 2838.

Carle, G. and M. Olson. 1984. Separation of chromosomal DNA molecules from yeast by orthogonal-field-alternation gel electrophoresis. *Nucleic Acids Res.* **12:** 5647.

———. 1985. An electrophoretic karyotype for yeast. *Proc. Natl. Acad. Sci.* **82:** 3756.

Chan, C. and B.-K. Tye. 1983. Organization of DNA sequences and replication origins at yeast telomeres. *Cell* **33:** 563.

Clark, L. and J. Carbon. 1980. Isolation of a yeast centromere and construction of functional small circular chromosomes. *Nature* **287:** 504.

Davidse, L.C. and W. Flach. 1977. Differential binding of methyl benzimidazole-2-yl-carbamate to fungal tubulin as a mechanism of resistance to this antimitotic agent in mutant strains of *Aspergillus nidulans. J. Cell Biol.* **72:** 174.

Davis, R.W., M. Thomas, J. Cameron, T.P. St. John, S. Scherer, and R.A. Padgett. 1980. Rapid DNA isolations for enzymatic and hybridization analysis. *Methods Enzymol.* **65:** 404.

DiNardo, S., K. Voelkel, and R. Sternglanz. 1984. DNA topoisomerase II mutant of *Saccharomyces cerevisiae*: Topoisomerase II is required for segregation of daughter molecules at the termination of DNA replication. *Proc. Natl. Acad. Sci.* **81:** 2616.

Dutcher, S. and L. Hartwell. 1982. The role of *S. cerevisiae* cell division cycle genes in nuclear fusion. *Genetics* **100:** 175.

Feinberg, A. and B. Vogelstein. 1983. A technique for radiolabelling DNA restriction fragments to high specific activity. *Anal. Biochem.* **132:** 6.

Goto, T. and J.C. Wang. 1984. Yeast DNA topoisomerase II is encoded by a single-copy, essential gene. *Cell* **36:** 1073.

Hartwell, L.H. 1978. Cell division from a genetic perspective. *J. Cell. Biol.* **77:** 627.

Hartwell, L.H. and D. Smith. 1985. Altered fidelity of mitotic chromosome transmission in cell cycle mutants of *S. cerevisiae. Genetics* **110:** 381.

Hartwell, L.H., J. Culotti, and B. Reid. 1970. Genetic control of the cell-division cycle in yeast. I. Detection of mutants. *Proc. Natl. Acad. Sci.* **66:** 352.

Hartwell, L.H., S. Dutcher, J. Wood, and B. Garvik. 1982. The fidelity of mitotic chromosome reproduction in *S. cerevisiae. Recent Adv. Yeast Mol. Biol.* **1:** 28.

Hieter, P., C. Mann, M. Snyder, and R. Davis. 1985. Mitotic stability of yeast chromosomes: A colony color assay that measures nondisjunction and chromosome loss. *Cell* **40:** 381.

Holm, C., T. Goto, J.C. Wang, and D. Botstein. 1985. DNA topoisomerase II is required at the time of mitosis in yeast. *Cell* **41:** 553.

Huffaker, T.C., M.A. Hoyt, and D. Botstein. 1987. Genetic analysis of the cytoskeleton of yeast. *Annu. Rev. Genet.* **21:** 259.

Ito, H., Y. Fukuda, K. Murata, and A. Kimura. 1983. Transformation of intact cells treated with alkali cations. *J. Bacteriol.* **153:** 163.

Lea, D.E. and C.A. Coulson. 1949. The distribution of numbers of mutants in bacterial populations. *J. Genet.* **49:** 264.

Maine, G.T., P. Sinha, and B.-K. Tye. 1984. Mutants of *S. cerevisiae* defective in the maintenance of minichromosomes. *Genetics* **106:** 365.

Maniatis, T., E.F. Fritsch, and J. Sambrook. 1982. *Molecular cloning: A laboratory manual.* Cold Spring Harbor Laboratory, Cold Spring Harbor, New York.

Meeks-Wagner, D. and L.H. Hartwell. 1986. Normal stoichiometry of histone dimer sets is necessary for high fidelity of mitotic chromosome transmission. *Cell* **44:** 43.

Meeks-Wagner, D., J.S. Wood, B. Garvik, and L.H. Hartwell. 1986. Isolation of two genes that affect mitotic chromosome transmission in *S. cerevisiae. Cell* **44:** 53.

Moir, D. and D. Botstein. 1982. Determination of the order of gene function in the yeast nuclear division pathway using *cs* and *ts* mutants. *Genetics* **100:** 565.

Moir, D., S.E. Stewart, B.C. Osmond, and D. Botstein. 1982. Cold-sensitive cell-division-cycle mutants of yeast: Isolation, properties, and pseudoreversion studies. *Genetics* **100:** 547.

Mortimer, R.K. and D. Schild. 1985. Genetic map of *Saccharomyces cerevisiae*. edition 9. *Microbiol. Rev.* **49:** 181.

Neff, N.F., J.H. Thomas, P. Grisafi, and D. Botstein. 1983. Isolation of the beta-tubulin gene from yeast and demonstration of its essential function in vivo. *Cell* **33:** 211.

Pringle, J. and L. Hartwell. 1981. The *Saccharomyces cerevisiae* cell cycle. In *The molecular biology of the yeast* Saccharomyces: *Life cycle and inheritance* (ed. J. Strathern et al.), p. 97. Cold Spring Harbor Laboratory, Cold Spring Harbor, New York.

Roman, H. 1957. Studies of gene mutations in *Saccharomyces cerevisiae. Cold Spring Harbor Symp. Quant. Biol.* **21:** 175.

Rothstein, R. 1983. One-step gene disruption in yeast. *Methods Enzymol.* **101:** 202.

Schatz, P.J., F. Solomon, and D. Botstein. 1986a. Genetically essential and nonessential alpha-tubulin genes specify functionally interchangeable proteins. *Mol. Cell. Biol.* **6:** 3722.

Schatz, P.J., L. Pillus, P. Grisafi, F. Solomon, and D. Botstein. 1986b. Two functional alpha-tubulin genes of the yeast *Saccharomyces cerevisiae* encode divergent proteins. *Mol. Cell. Biol.* **6:** 3711.

Sherman, F., G.R. Fink, and J.B. Hicks. 1986. *Methods in yeast genetics: Course manual.* Cold Spring Harbor Laboratory, Cold Spring Harbor, New York.

Sinha, P., V. Chang, and B.-K. Tye. 1986. A mutant that affects the function of autonomously replicating sequences in yeast. *J. Mol. Biol.* **192:** 805.

Smith, D., B. Baker, and M. Gatti. 1985. Mutations in genes encoding essential mitotic functions in *Drosophila melanogaster. Genetics* **110:** 647.

Thomas, J.H. and D. Botstein. 1986. A gene required for the separation of chromosomes on the spindle apparatus of yeast. *Cell* **44:** 65.

Thomas, J.H., N.F. Neff, and D. Botstein. 1985. Isolation and characterization of mutations in the beta-tubulin gene of *Saccharomyces cerevisiae. Genetics* **112:** 715.

Wood, J.S. and L.H. Hartwell. 1982. A dependent pathway of gene functions leading to chromosome segregation in *Saccharomyces cerevisiae. J. Cell Biol.* **94:** 718.

Structure, Synthesis, and Regulation of Telomeres

E. Henderson, D. Larson, W. Melton, J. Shampay, E. Spangler, C. Greider, T. Ryan, and E. Blackburn

Department of Molecular Biology, University of California, Berkeley, California 94720

Telomeres maintain chromosome integrity by stabilizing the linear chromosomal DNA and enabling complete replication of its ends. Telomeres of several eukaryotes consist of variable numbers of tandemly repeated GC-rich simple DNA sequences. We earlier reported an activity in *Tetrahymena* extracts that synthesizes tandem repeats of the *Tetrahymena* telomeric sequence, TTGGGG, onto primers of telomere sequence, without any apparent template (Greider and Blackburn 1985).

Lengthening of telomeres by addition of telomeric repeats occurred in vivo in *Tetrahymena*. Telomere length varied with the physiological and developmental state of the cells. This variation was attributable to variation of the length of the duplex portion of the CCCCAA:TTGGGG repeats. The properties of this duplex were analyzed using enzymatic and physical probes of DNA duplex structure. Duplex repeated CCCCAA:TTGGGG in nontorsionally stressed form had unusual structural properties, which may play a role in telomere recognition and/or length regulation.

Telomeres, the ends of eukaryotic chromosomes, are specialized structures whose nature first became evident from cytological studies (for review, see Blackburn and Szostak 1984). More recently, molecular studies have shown that telomeres consist of essential DNA sequences (for reviews, see Blackburn 1984; Blackburn and Szostak 1984) associated with specific proteins in a nonnucleosomal structure (Blackburn and Chiou 1981; Gottschling and Cech 1984; Budarf and Blackburn 1986; Gottschling and Zakian 1986). The role of telomeres is to stabilize the ends of chromosomes; this stabilization is thought to have two, possibly related, aspects: completion of the replication of the ends of the linear chromosomal DNA molecule and protection of the chromosomal ends from degradation and recombination.

The sequences and structure of telomeres have been informative about their role in chromosome stabilization. In the evolutionarily diverse eukaryotes whose telomere structure has been examined, telomeres consist of GC-rich, simple, tandemly repeated sequences (Blackburn 1984). In many organisms, telomere length varies, both in the population of telomeres at any given instant (Blackburn and Gall 1978; Shampay and Blackburn 1988) and in response to growth conditions, developmental state, or genetic background (Larson et al. 1987, and references therein). It was proposed that such variation reflected the ability of telomeres to be both elongated and shortened in the course of their normal maintenance in cells, and that telomeres were in fact dynamic structures (Shampay et al. 1984). Evidence for elongation of telomeres in vivo by de novo addition of telomeric repeated DNA sequences came from observations that the telomeres of ciliated protozoa, when introduced into yeast, were lengthened by the apparently non-templated addition of yeast telomeric sequences (Szostak and

Blackburn 1982; Pluta et al. 1984; Shampay et al. 1984). Telomere elongation by non-templated de novo addition of telomeric repeats has been demonstrated in vitro. A telomere terminal transferase (telomerase) activity has been identified in cell-free extracts of *Tetrahymena* (Greider and Blackburn 1985). Characterization and extensive purification of this activity has shown that it is a ribonucleoprotein enzyme (Greider and Blackburn 1987). This activity requires a primer for synthesis of GGGGTT repeats. The primer can be an oligonucleotide consisting of a few repeats of any of the known G-rich telomeric sequences. However, oligonucleotides with non-telomeric sequences or with sequences of the telomeric C-rich strand or fully duplex telomeric oligonucleotides are inactive as primers. This specificity suggested that the G-rich telomeric sequences are capable of assuming a secondary structure that is recognized by the telomere terminal transferase (Greider and Blackburn 1987). Direct evidence for such a structure has been found (Henderson et al. 1987).

In all organisms analyzed, there is a single-stranded overhang of the G-rich strand at the extreme end of the telomere. In the case of the hypotrichous ciliates, this was shown by direct sequence analysis. The TTTTGGGG strand forms a 16- or 14-base overhang (Klobutcher et al. 1981). In *Tetrahymena*, at least some molecules have recessed TTGGGG strands (Blackburn and Gall 1978; Blackburn et al. 1983). However, recent work has shown that in at least a subset of the population of molecules purified from growing cells, the TTGGGG repeat strand, like the G-rich strand of hypotrich telomeres, also has a 12-base overhang (E. Henderson and E. Blackburn, in prep.). Similar overhangs have been demonstrated in telomeres purified from the acellular slime mold *Didymium* (E. Henderson and E. Blackburn, in prep.). Thus, it appears that the telomeres

453

from diverse organisms share similar structures at their extreme ends, with respect to the common presence of a 3' overhang of the G-rich strand. It is this structure that is apparently recognized in vitro by the telomere terminal transferase enzyme. The common structure of the telomeric end and the proposed role of the telomere terminal transferase activity in telomere replication are diagrammed in Figure 1.

Although the ability of telomeres to be elongated may rely on recognition of the extreme terminus, the duplex portion of the telomere located internally from its terminus has been shown to be packaged in chromatin in a specialized non-nucleosomal complex (Blackburn and Chiou 1981; Gottschling and Cech 1984; Budarf and Blackburn 1986). In two species, sequence-specific binding proteins have been identified that bind to these telomeric sequences (Berman et al. 1986; Gottschling and Zakian 1986). Analysis of the duplex poly d(CCCCAA)·d(TTGGGG) of Tetrahymena telomeres has shown that this duplex is hypersensitive to S1 nuclease cleavage along its entire length in supercoiled plasmids (Budarf and Blackburn 1987).

The overall length regulation of telomeres in vivo may involve specific interactions with this inner portion of telomeres. To investigate this question, we undertook further studies of the length regulation and structure of telomeres.

Materials and Methods

Tetrahymena strains and culture
Tetrahymena thermophila strains were maintained and cultured as described previously (Larson et al. 1987).

Telomere replication and length regulation

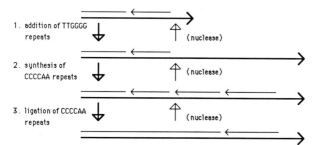

1. addition of TTGGGG repeats (nuclease)
2. synthesis of CCCCAA repeats (nuclease)
3. ligation of CCCCAA repeats (nuclease)

Figure 1 Structure of telomeres and proposed model for telomere replication. One terminal region of a chromosomal or nuclear linear DNA molecule is shown, with the molecular end at the right. The thin line represents the C-rich repeat strand and the thicker line the G-rich repeat strand. Horizontal arrowheads indicate 5' to 3' orientation of each strand. In this model (Shampay et al. 1984), (1) telomere terminal transferase (Greider and Blackburn 1985) extends the G-rich strand by adding G-rich telomeric repeats by non-templated synthesis. (2) The complementary C-rich strand is synthesized by discontinuous DNA synthesis by DNA primase-polymerase, using the extended G-rich strand as template. (3) The inner breaks are ligated, but incomplete ligation of the most terminal breaks leaves distally located breaks in the C-rich repeat strand. Shortening of telomeres (upward thin arrows) may involve specific or nonspecific nuclease(s) and/or the failure of DNA replication to completely replicate the ends of the linear DNA molecule.

End labeling of rDNA
The 3' ends of the GGGGTT repeat strands of the palindromic rDNA molecule of Tetrahymena were ^{32}P-labeled using dideoxy-ATP (Amersham) and the reaction conditions for terminal tranferase given by the nucleotide manufacturer, except that reactions were done at 22°C. The 5' ends of the CCCCAA repeat strand were ^{32}P-end-labeled using the exchange reaction of T4 polynucleotide kinase. The end-labeled rDNA was then restricted with DraI, and the terminal fragment run on a 5% polyacrylamide urea sequencing gel.

Construction of plasmids containing telomere sequences
Poly d(CCCCAA)·d(TTGGGG) sequences from the palindromic rDNA of Tetrahymena were cloned into the BamHI site of pBR322 (Budarf and Blackburn 1987). The poly d(CCCCAA)·d(TTGGGG) sequence was cut away from the vector with BamHI, and digested with BAL-31 to remove non-telomeric sequences from the end of the insert (Budarf and Blackburn 1987). The BAL-31-treated poly d(CCCCAA)·d(TTGGGG) fragments were ligated to BamHI linkers and then inserted into the BamHI site of pUC118 to produce a collection of plasmids containing poly d(CCCCAA)·d(TTGGGG) stretches ranging from 70 to 220 bp in length. The sequences of these plasmid inserts were determined by modifications of the Sanger dideoxy chain termination method. Reverse transcriptase was used to carry out the primer extension reactions for sequencing. Efficient copying of the CCCCAA strand required a threefold decreased ratio of ddGTP to dGTP compared with standard conditions.

Synthetic DNA oligonucleotides
DNA oligonucleotides were synthesized on an Applied Biosystems DNA Synthesizer. After deblocking, the reaction products were fractionated by denaturing polyacrylamide gel electrophoresis. The eluted oligonucleotides were purified over a Sep-Pak C18 column (Waters).

Primer extension reactions on rDNA or plasmids
Native rDNA (~0.03 pmoles ends) was allowed to hybridize with 0.1–0.5 pmoles of d(CCCCAA)₄, previously 5' end-labeled, by incubation at 22°C for 10–20 minutes. Ligations of the primer were carried out in 20 μl by addition of 50 units of T4 DNA ligase and incubation under standard conditions for 1 hour at 22°C, then overnight at 4°C. Primer extension reactions were initiated by addition of 5 units of Klenow fragment of DNA polymerase I (IBI) or 5 units of complete DNA polymerase I enzyme (IBI) and 25–50 μM unlabeled dNTPs as specified in the figure legends. Reactions were allowed to proceed for 30–60 minutes at 22°C. The labeled reaction products were fractionated on a 6% or 8% polyacrylamide sequencing gel.

Helical repeat measurement by the band-shift method
pUC118 plasmids containing poly d(CCCCAA)·
d(TTGGGG) inserts of various lengths (determined by
DNA sequence analysis) were incubated overnight at
0°C with 50 units of rat liver or yeast DNA topoisomerase I (generously provided by N. Cozzarelli) per 20 μg
of plasmid DNA, in 20 mM Tris-HCl (pH 7.6), 200 mM
KCl, and 5 μg/ml BSA to produce plasmids that were
positively supercoiled at room temperature and low salt,
conditions under which the helical repeat was measured
(Wang 1979). The extent of topoisomerase reaction was
checked by fractionation of topoisomers by chloroquine
(2.5 μg/ml) agarose gel electrophoresis. The helical
repeat was first determined using positively supercoiled
topoisomers. Topoisomers differing by small numbers of
nucleotides of the CCCCAA·TTGGGG repeat stretch,
but otherwise identical, were compared initially. Plasmids with 122, 121, and 117 bp of CCCCAA·
TTGGGG repeat inserts were compared in pairwise
combinations. Comparison of plasmids with greater
length differences was done using plasmids with
CCCCAA·AGGGG repeat insert lengths of 74,79,78,
and 125 bp. Differences in mobility associated with
molecular-weight differences were corrected by nor-
malizing the distances migrated for nicked circles of
various plasmids as described (Wang 1979). The helical
repeat was calculated by the method of Wang (1979).

Results

Telomere length variation

To analyze telomere length variation, the overall length
of telomeres was measured in *Tetrahymena* and yeast
cells under different physiological conditions. The vegetative macronucleus of *Tetrahymena* has 10^4–10^5 telomeres on the multiple copy linear subchromosomal macronuclear DNA molecules that comprise the macronuclear genome. All these telomeres consist of a block of
terminal poly d(CCCCAA)·d(TTGGGG) repeats. The
length of these telomeres was measured in cells under-
going vegetative cell divisions under exponential growth
conditions. DNA was prepared from cells every 10–50
cell generations, digested with a restriction enzyme,
Southern blotted, and probed with telomere-specific
probes (Larson et al. 1987). The results of a typical
experiment are shown in Figure 2. The hybridization
probe was the terminal region of the linear amplified
macronuclear rDNA molecules of *Tetrahymena*. Figure 2
shows that the terminal restriction fragment, which is a
characteristically broad band, steadily increased in
length during prolonged vegetative growth. The same
results were found using a hybridization probe specific
for another macronuclear DNA telomeric region and
when poly d(CCCCAA)·d(TTGGGG) was used as the
hybridization probe. Thus, all telomeric fragments increased in length during log phase vegetative fissions.
These results were seen in all strains of *Tetrahymena*
tested (Larson et al. 1987).

Shortening of *Tetrahymena* telomeres took place
under two kinds of circumstances. After many hundreds

Number of Generations

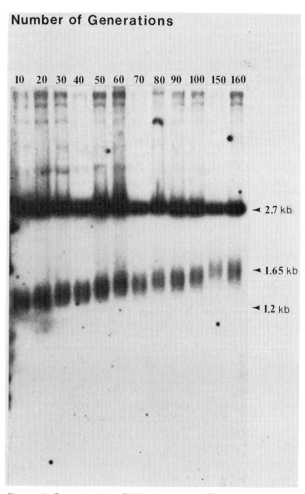

Figure 2 Growth of the rDNA telomeres of *Tetrahymena* during
prolonged vegetative cell divisions. Total cellular DNA was
isolated from cells vegetatively propagated under exponential
growth conditions for the numbers of generations indicated.
The DNA was digested with *Bam*HI and *Pst*I, and after agarose
gel electrophoresis and Southern blotting, probed with a plasmid (pTre1) containing the terminal *Bam*HI fragment of B strain
rDNA (Larson et al. 1987). The 2.7-kb fragment is an internal
fragment, and the 1.2–1.65-kb fragment the telomeric fragment
of the rDNA.

of continuous vegetative divisions in log phase growth
conditions, the telomeres were seen to shorten at variable times. Alternatively, if the cells containing long
telomeres following log phase vegetative divisions were
then maintained for prolonged periods (several days) in
stationary phase in stock tube cultures, the telomeres of
the population of cells were all found to shorten. The
time at which the population of telomeres shortened
varied from one stock tube to another in duplicate
experiments. However, as with the log phase growth
experiments, the entire population of telomeres was
shortened in concert (Larson et al. 1987).

Similar experiments were carried out with the yeast
Saccharomyces cerevisiae. In contrast to the results
seen with the *Tetrahymena* macronuclear telomeres, the
telomeres of yeast chromosomes stayed constant in
length throughout prolonged vegetative divisions under

exponential growth conditions. However, when the yeast cells were maintained in stationary phase, their telomeres were increased in length relative to their length in log phase conditions (J. Shampay et al., unpubl.).

Molecular basis of telomere length variation

To test whether the observed growth of telomeric restriction fragments in continuously dividing cultures of *Tetrahymena* resulted from addition of poly d(CCCCAA)·d(TTGGGG) sequences to the existing telomeric repeats, we compared the extent of BAL-31 nuclease digestion required to progressively remove the repeats from long and short telomeres. Genomic DNAs from cultures of cells with short or long telomeres were treated with BAL-31 for times ranging from 0 to 10 minutes. The BAL-31-treated samples were subsequently digested with both *Bam*HI and *Pst*I, Southern blotted, and the extent of BAL-31 digestion measured by hybridization with poly d(CCCCAA)·d(TTGGGG) probe or the terminal restriction fragment of the rDNA used in Figure 2. This rDNA terminal fragment hybrid-

izes with an internal fragment as well as the telomeric fragment, providing a control for endonucleolytic degradation of the DNA. The results of this experiment are shown in Figure 3. The poly d(CCCCAA)·d(TTGGGG) homologous bands steadily decreased in size with increasing time of digestion with BAL-31, until all of the telomeric repeats were removed and the hybridization signal was lost. The size and intensity of the internal rDNA fragment did not change (Fig. 3, lower panel). The poly d(CCCCAA)·d(TTGGGG) homology of long telomeres was more resistant to extensive digestion with BAL-31 than that of short telomeres. At the point just before the poly d(CCCCAA)·d(TTGGGG) hybridizing signal was lost, the hybridizing fragments were the same size for both the long and short telomeres. Thus the 8-minute "long telomere" time point and the 3-minute "short telomere" time point appear identical. This was the case for non-rDNA as well as rDNA telomeres, as shown by the fainter CCCCAA repeat-hybridizing bands. These results demonstrate that telomere elongation in dividing *Tetrahymena* cultures is due to the addition of sequences to the telomeric repeats.

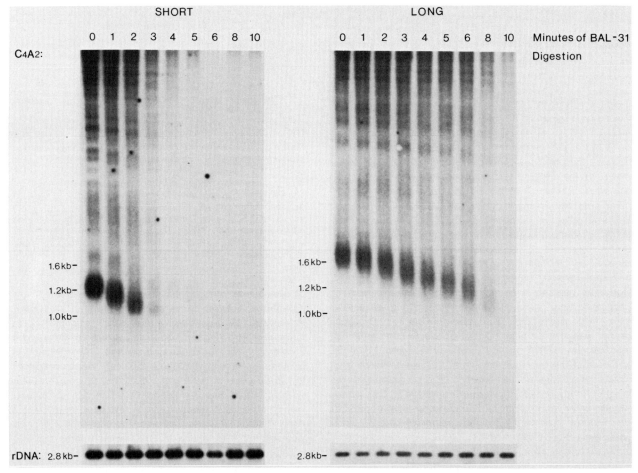

Figure 3 BAL-31 digestion of long and short telomeres. Samples of total cellular DNA from cultures with short (10 generations) or long (150 generations) telomeres were treated with BAL-31 nuclease for times ranging from 0 to 10 min. Samples were then digested with *Bam*HI and *Pst*I and analyzed by Southern blotting. Autoradiograms of filters hybridized with a CCCCAA·TTGGGG repeat-specific probe are shown on top. Small panels below show parts of duplicate filters hybridized with the pTre1 rDNA probe. The non-telomeric fragment detected with this probe is unaffected by BAL-31 treatment.

To analyze further the molecular structures of the long and short telomeres, the lengths of each strand of the telomeres were measured. rDNA with long or short telomeres was ^{32}P-end-labeled on the 5′ ends by polynucleotide kinase to label the CCCCAA repeat strand, or ^{32}P-end-labeled on the 3′ ends with dideoxy-ATP by terminal transferase to label the TTGGGG repeat strand. The end-labeled rDNAs were then digested with *Dra*I, which cuts the rDNA ∼ 100 nucleotides in from the poly d(CCCCAA)·d(TTGGGG). The end-labeled terminal restriction fragments were heterogeneous in length (Blackburn and Gall 1978; Larson et al. 1987). They were then fractionated on a denaturing polyacrylamide DNA sequencing gel. As shown in Figure 4, both strands of both the short and long telomeres consisted of multiple discrete bands. Comparison with DNA markers showed that, for both the short and long telomeres, these bands formed a regular series, each separated from the next by six bases. These results provide evidence that telomere lengthening is the result of the addition of CCCCAA·TTGGGG repeats. For both the long and the short telomeres, the distribution of lengths was very similar for both strands. This is most clearly seen in Figure 4 for the short telomeres, for which the resolution on the sequencing gels is better. This suggests that both long and short telomeres are duplex structures almost all the way out to their ends, since the length distribution of the CCCCAA strands in the population of telomeres is very similar to that of the complementary TTGGGG repeat strands. Furthermore, the fact that each strand consists of a series of bands differing by six bases suggests that the processes defining the ends of the telomeres act in a sequence-specific fashion. Thus, even though telomeres show overall length heterogeneity, on both strands the position of the termini within the hexanucleotide repeat unit is fixed.

Duplex poly d(CCCCAA)·d(TTGGGG) has unusual properties in linear form

We analyzed the structure of duplex CCCCAA·TTGGGG repeats using enzymatic and physical methods. It was shown previously that the duplex form of the telomeric sequence of *Tetrahymena* is hypersensitive to digestion with S1 nuclease (Budarf and Blackburn 1987). Because the torsional state of telomeres in vivo is not known, we examined some properties of this duplex in linear form. Two sources of poly d(CCCCAA)·d(TTGGGG) were chosen for study: the natural telomeres of the ciliate *Tetrahymena* and a stretch of this telomeric sequence cloned in a circular plasmid vector. First, the sensitivity of the rDNA and non-rDNA telomeres to digestion with the nuclease BAL-31 was tested. Whole genomic DNA was prepared from *Tetrahymena* macronuclei and digested with BAL-31 nuclease. The rate of digestion was measured as the BAL-31 digestion proceeded from the molecular ends toward the interior of the molecules, and was plotted in Figure 5 for three different macronuclear DNA telomeric regions. The telomere-associated sequences adjoining

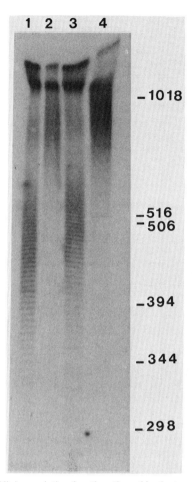

Figure 4 High-resolution fractionation of both strands of rDNA telomeres. The rDNA was isolated from *T. thermophila* cells that had undergone 10 (lanes *1* and *3*) or 165 (lanes *2* and *4*) cell divisions under exponential growth conditions (Larson et al. 1987). The rDNA was ^{32}P-end-labeled at the 5′ end of the CCCCAA strand (lanes *1* and *2*) or the 3′ end of the TTGGGG strand (lanes *3* and *4*) and digested with *Dra*I to release the telomeric restriction fragment. The radiolabeled digestion products were fractionated on a 5% polyacrylamide denaturing DNA sequencing gel. The mean size of the long telomeres has increased by ∼300 bp. Lengths (in nucleotides) of DNA marker restriction fragments are indicated on the right.

the terminal poly d(CCCCAA)·d(TTGGGG) repeats are all highly AT-rich (Spangler et al. 1988). As the BAL-31 enzyme proceeded inward from the GC-rich poly d(CCCCAA)·d(TTGGGG) telomeric repeats and into the AT-rich adjoining sequences, the rate of digestion slowed. This is surprising, given the extreme AT richness of these adjoining sequences. A similar analysis of the telomeres of yeast (Shampay et al. 1984) showed the same relatively rapid rate of digestion as BAL-31 proceeded through the telomeric repeats of this organism (inset in Fig. 5). In control experiments, cloned telomeric repeats from *Tetrahymena* and yeast showed similar rates of BAL-31 digestion to native *Tetrahymena* and yeast telomeres (data not shown).

Further evidence for an unusual structure of the duplex region of telomeres of *Tetrahymena* came from ex-

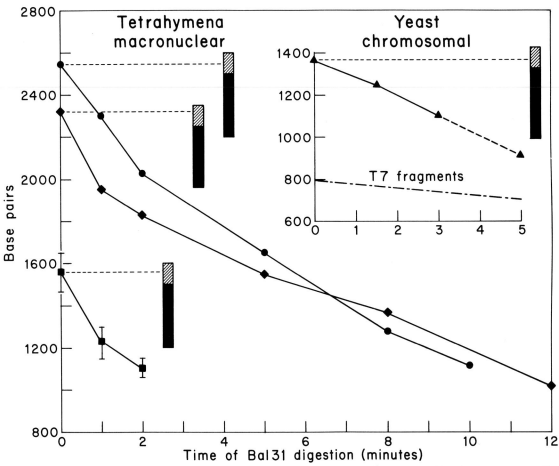

Figure 5 Rates of BAL-31 digestion through telomeric repeats. Total cellular DNA from either *Tetrahymena* or yeast (*inset*) was digested with BAL-31 nuclease for the times shown. After restriction digestion, Southern blotting, and probing with appropriate telomere-specific probes, the sizes of the telomeric restriction fragments were measured and are shown plotted as a function of time of BAL-31 treatment. Vertical solid bars indicate the terminal CCCCAA · TTGGGG (*Tetrahymena*) or $C_{1-3}A.TG_{1-3}$ (yeast) repeats for each telomere probed. The hatched portion of the bar indicates the terminal length heterogeneity. The dashed line shows the rate of digestion of bacteriophage T7 restriction fragments by BAL-31 in the yeast telomere experiment (Shampay et al. 1984).

periments in which the ability of the Klenow fragment of DNA polymerase I from *Escherichia coli* to strand-invade the duplex and carry out primer extension was measured. As discussed above, the rDNA telomeres of *Tetrahymena* have overhanging 3' terminal extensions of the TTGGGG strand. First, this overhang was found to be available for hybridization by an added synthetic DNA oligonucleotide of the sequence (CCCCAA)$_4$. This was shown by hybridizing (CCCCAA)$_4$, ^{32}P-labeled at the 5' end, with purified native rDNA and ligating it to the rDNA with T4 DNA ligase. The radiolabeled oligonucleotide became ligated not only to itself but also to the rDNA C-rich strand (Fig. 6a). This requires a single-stranded portion of the G-rich strand and the precise 3' to 5' alignment of the primer and native rDNA C-rich strand. Although several oligonucleotides became ligated to each other, only one was ligated to the rDNA, as demonstrated by complete loss of the ^{32}P label from the terminal *Dra*I fragment by calf intestinal phosphatase treatment (Fig. 6a, lanes 1 and 4).

When the [32]P 5' end-labeled DNA oligonucleotide (AACCCC)$_4$ was subjected to the same procedure, it

was much less efficiently ligated to the native rDNA C-rich strand, although it ligated to itself as efficiently as (CCCCAA)$_4$ in the same experiment (data not shown). These results showed that the TTGGGG strand at the rDNA terminus forms an overhang to which (CCCCAA)$_4$ can hybridize. The specificity of the ligation for (CCCCAA)$_4$ as opposed to (AACCCC)$_4$ showed that the underhanging CCCCAA repeat strand of the rDNA molecule ends at a specific residue, consistent with the results above and previous observations (Katzen et al. 1981).

Primer extension experiments were next done to determine whether *E. coli* DNA polymerase I or the Klenow fragment of this enzyme was able to utilize this hybridized (CCCCAA)$_4$ oligonucleotide as a primer for extension on the native rDNA molecule, by synthesis of CCCCAA repeats. As shown previously (Blackburn and Gall 1978) and in Figure 1, such CCCCAA synthesis would involve synthesis in the direction toward the interior of the template rDNA molecule. However, the Klenow fragment of DNA polymerase I lacks the 3' to 5' exonuclease activity necessary for nick-translation on a

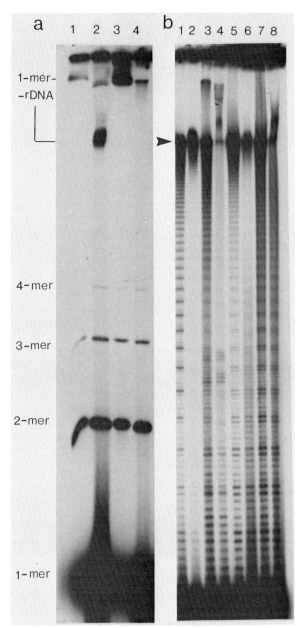

Figure 6 Primer extension through duplex telomeric repeats. (a) Ligation of (CCCCAA)₄ to native rDNA telomeres. After ligation, aliquots were digested with *Dra*I (lanes *1* and *2*) and calf intestinal phosphatase (lanes *1* and *4*). Ligation products of the ³²P-labeled (CCCCAA)₄ oligonucleotide are indicated on the left. (b) Primer extension reactions. 5′ end-labeled (CCCCAA)₄ was added to native rDNA unpretreated (lanes *5–8*), or pretreated with dideoxy TTP and Klenow fragment (lanes *1–4*), under nondenaturing conditions and allowed to hybridize to the native telomere. This labeled oligonucleotide was then extended by addition of unlabeled dNTPs and Klenow fragment (lanes *1, 3, 5,* and *7*) or whole (lanes *2, 4, 6,* and *8*) DNA polymerase I from *E. coli.*; (lanes *1, 2, 5,* and *6*) dCTP +dATP; (lanes *3,4,7, and 8*) all 4 dNTPs. Arrowhead indicates pausing of the polymerases at the inner boundary of the CCCCAA·TTGGGG repeats.

double-stranded template such as the rDNA. Figure 6b shows that both forms of *E. coli* DNA polymerase efficiently utilized the (CCCCAA)₄ primer and extended it on

the native rDNA template through the entire length (~400 bp) of CCCCAA repeats. The reaction required dCTP and dATP, as expected, and was not seen when only dGTP and dTTP were present. Interestingly, in the presence of all four dNTPs, although the primer extension reaction proceeded through the CCCCAA repeats with either the Klenow or the complete form of DNA polymerase I (Fig. 6b), extension proceeded beyond the CCCCAA repeats and into the inner adjoining sequences only with the complete DNA polymerase and not the Klenow fragment. The results suggest that the duplex CCCCAA·TTGGGG region has a structure that allows Klenow fragment to strand-displace the CCCCAA strand from the template TTGGGG strand as CCCCAA repeat synthesis proceeds. This ability for apparent strand displacement does not extend to the adjoining inner sequence, even though this adjoining sequence is very AT-rich. A further striking result of the experiment shown in Figure 6b was that both forms of the polymerase showed marked pausing or chain termination at the inner end of the CCCCAA stretch, even in the presence of all four dNTPs (arrowhead in Fig. 6b), again suggesting a change in the nature of the DNA duplex at the inner boundary of the telomeric repeats.

To test whether the results of the primer extension experiments were attributable to some special property of rDNA telomeres such as minor bases, although none have been found in these regions of the rDNA (P.M.M. Rae and E.H. Blackburn, unpubl.), the same primer extension experiments were carried out on duplex poly d(CCCCAA)·d(TTGGGG) cloned into the bacterial vector pUC118. The plasmid containing the repeats was linearized by restriction digestion at various points on both sides of the CCCCAA·TTGGGG repeats and used as the template under the same conditions as in the native rDNA primer extension experiments described above. Remarkably, even though the plasmid template was a duplex, both the synthetic oligonucleotides (CCCCAA)₄ and (TTGGGG)₄ were able to prime the synthesis of repeats by the Klenow fragment of DNA polymerase I as well as by complete DNA polymerase I (data not shown). In contrast, a synthetic oligonucleotide consisting of a short sequence of pUC118 vector DNA was unable to prime synthesis of an extended DNA strand in the vector portion of the linearized plasmid under these conditions. Thus the poly d(CCCCAA)·d(TTGGGGG) was susceptible to strand invasion by complementary oligonucleotides. These results also show that the ability of Klenow fragment to extend a primer by synthesis of CCCCAA or TTGGGG repeats on a duplex template is attributable to properties of the sequence poly d(CCCCAA)·d(TTGGGG) itself, and not to any special properties peculiar to this sequence in rDNA purified from *Tetrahymena* cells.

Base pairs per helical turn in duplex poly d(CCCCAA)·d(TTGGGG)

The use of the enzymes BAL-31 and the Klenow fragment of DNA polymerase I as probes to examine the structure of the duplex telomeric sequence of *Tetrahy-*

mena suggested that this sequence assumes an unusual structure. To examine this structure, the band-shift method of Wang (1979) was used to determine the number of base pairs per helical turn of this sequence. Conditions were chosen to allow the sequence to be examined in a state as close to linear as possible; that is, conditions of minimal torsional stress. B-DNA has a helical repeat of 10.4 bp per helical turn. Duplex poly dG·dC and poly dA·dT have helical repeats of 10.7 and 10.1, respectively, in solution (Peck and Wang 1981). A series of plasmids containing different numbers of CCCCAA·TTGGGG repeats was constructed and the number of nucleotides in the repeats confirmed by DNA sequence analysis. The DNAs were first treated with topoisomerase I at 0°C and then subjected to band-shift analysis at room temperature by the method of Wang (1979). The DNA under these conditions had a superhelical density range of 0 to +0.02. From these experiments (data not shown), the helical repeat was calculated to be 10.5 ±1 bp per helical turn. Thus the CCCCAA·TTGGGG repeats at low superhelical densities had the helical repeat expected for B-DNA.

Discussion

The results described here, together with those published elsewhere (Larson et al. 1987, and references therein), show that telomeres of *Tetrahymena*, yeast, and trypanosomes are dynamic, capable of variation in length. The dynamic nature of telomeres is reflected in their structure. Telomeres have variable numbers of simple repeated sequences at their ends. All available data support a model for telomere metabolism involving de novo addition of repeats to pre-existing telomeres by a non-templated mechanism (Shampay et al. 1984; Greider and Blackburn 1985), this lengthening being counterbalanced by shortening. The net length of telomeres depends on the physiological conditions of the cells. The model shown in Figure 1 predicts that the length regulation is accomplished by regulating the net rates of addition or loss of telomeric repeats.

Although the mechanism of telomere shortening is not known, there is evidence from in vivo studies of *Tetrahymena* telomeres that in cells in stationary phase, telomeres can be shortened in the absence of DNA replication (Larson et al. 1987). Such shortening would most likely involve activity of as yet unidentified nuclease(s). However, in dividing cells, it is also possible that telomere length regulation involves balancing rates of addition of repeats with the rate of shortening caused by incomplete semiconservative DNA replication of the chromosomal ends. A model has been proposed, based on just these two processes, that is sufficient to explain the observed dynamic properties and length variability of the telomeres of vegetatively growing yeast (Shampay and Blackburn 1988).

The results presented here show that the telomeres of *Tetrahymena* vary in length because of variation in the number of duplex CCCCAA·TTGGGG repeats, rather than the length of single-strand overhangs of either

strand. The six-base periodicities seen in Figure 3 and the specificity of ligation of (CCCCAA)₄ to native rDNA suggest a precise nucleotide arrangement at the 5' and 3' ends of the rDNA telomere. The implications of these findings for telomere end structure will be discussed in more detail elsewhere (E. Henderson et al., in prep.).

Because telomere length regulation affects the length of the duplex portion of telomeres, this region may require special recognition in vivo. The experiments described here suggest that the duplex region of telomeric repeats, in linear form, has special properties that make it susceptible to an unusually rapid rate of digestion by the combined exonuclease and single-stranded endonuclease activities of BAL-31 nuclease. Similar rapid BAL-31 digestion has been reported previously for the telomeric regions of the hemoflagellate *Trypanosoma brucei*, although in this case an unidentified minor base was suggested as playing a role in the sensitivity (Raibaud et al. 1983). Our results with duplex CCCCAA·TTGGGG repeats cloned in plasmids show that the unusual properties of this duplex sequence seen with enzymatic methods of probing DNA structure are not attributable to anything other than the unmodified duplex sequence itself.

Our results also show that the property of CCCCAA·TTGGGG repeat duplex that makes it susceptible to strand displacement by Klenow fragment as well as rapid digestion by BAL-31 is not the result of a helical repeat very different from that expected for B-DNA. This conclusion is reinforced by the results of other physical studies on linear duplex poly d(CCCCAA)·d(TTGGGG). It was shown previously that this sequence in linear form showed no unusual melting or circular dichroism properties, and no evidence for a bent helix in polyacrylamide gel assays (Budarf and Blackburn 1987). It will be of interest to determine whether telomeric repeated sequences are excluded from nucleosomes because of these structural properties, and whether these structural features play a role in telomere function in vivo.

Acknowledgments

This work was supported by National Institutes of Health grant GM-26259 to E.H.B.

References

Berman, J., C.Y. Tachibana, and B.-K. Tye. 1986. Identification of a telomeric-binding activity from yeast. *Proc. Natl. Acad. Sci.* **83**: 3713.

Blackburn, E.H. 1984. Telomeres: Do the ends justify the means? *Cell* **37**: 7.

Blackburn, E.H. and S.-S. Chiou. 1981. Non-nucleosomal packaging of a tandemly repeated DNA sequence at termini of extrachromosomal DNA coding for rRNA in *Tetrahymena*. *Proc. Natl. Acad. Sci.* **78**: 2263.

Blackburn, E.H. and J. Gall. 1978. A tandemly repeated sequence at the termini of the extrachromosomal ribosomal RNA genes in *Tetrahymena*. *J. Mol. Biol.* **120**: 33.

Blackburn, E.H. and J.W. Szostak. 1984. The molecular structure of centromeres and telomeres. *Annu. Rev. Biochem.* **53**: 163.

Blackburn, E.H., M.L. Budarf, P.B. Challoner, J.M. Cherry, E.A. Howard, A. Katzen, W.-C. Pan, and T. Ryan. 1983. DNA termini in ciliate macronuclei. *Cold Spring Harbor Symp. Quant. Biol.* **47**: 1195.

Budarf, M. and E.H. Blackburn. 1986. Chromatin structure of the telomeric region and 3′-nontranscribed spacer of *Tetrahymena* ribosomal RNA genes. *J. Biol. Chem.* **261**: 363.

———. 1987. S1 nuclease sensitivity of double stranded telomeric DNA sequences. *Nucleic Acids Res.* **15**: 6273.

Gottschling, D.E. and T.R. Cech. 1984. Chromatin structure of the molecular ends of *Oxytricha* macronuclear DNA: Phased nucleosomes and a telomeric complex. *Cell* **38**: 501.

Gottschling, D.E. and V.A. Zakian. 1986. Telomere proteins: Specific recognition and protection of the natural termini of *Oxytricha* macronuclear DNA. *Cell* **47**: 195.

Greider, C.W. and E.H. Blackburn. 1985. Identification of a specific telomere terminal transferase activity in *Tetrahymena* extracts. *Cell* **43**: 405.

———. 1987. The telomere terminal transferase of *Tetrahymena* is a ribonucleoprotein with two kinds of primer specificity. *Cell* **51**: 887.

Henderson, E., C.C. Hardin, S.K. Wolk, I. Tinoco, and E.H. Blackburn. 1987. Telomeric DNA oligonucleotides form novel intramolecular structures containing guanine · guanine base pairs. *Cell* **51**: 899.

Katzen, A.L., G.M. Cann, and E.H. Blackburn. 1981. Sequence-specific fragmentation of macronuclear DNA in a holotrichous ciliate. *Cell* **24**: 313.

Klobutcher, L.A., M.T. Swanton, P. Donini, and D.M. Prescott.

1981. All gene-sized DNA molecules in four species of hypotrichs have the same terminal sequence and an unusual 3′ terminus. *Proc. Natl. Acad. Sci.* **78**: 3015.

Larson, D.D., E.A. Spangler, and E.H. Blackburn. 1987. Dynamics of telomere length variation in *Tetrahymena thermophila*. *Cell* **50**: 477.

Peck, L.J. and J.C. Wang. 1981. Sequence dependence of the helical repeat of DNA in solution. *Nature* **292**: 375.

Pluta, A.F., G.M. Dani, B.B. Spear, and V. Zakian. 1984. Elaboration of telomeres in yeast: Recognition and modification of termini from *Oxytricha* macronuclear DNA. *Proc. Natl. Acad. Sci.* **81**: 1475.

Raibaud, A., C. Gaillard, S. Longacre, U. Hibner, G. Buck, G. Bernardi, and H. Eisen. 1983. Genomic environment of variant surface antigen genes of *Trypanosoma equiperdum*. *Proc. Natl. Acad. Sci.* **80**: 4306.

Shampay, J. and E.H. Blackburn. 1988. Generation of telomere length heterogeneity *S. cerevisiae*. *Proc. Natl. Acad. Sci.* (in press).

Shampay, J., J.W. Szostak, and E.H. Blackburn. 1984. DNA sequences of telomeres maintained in yeast. *Nature* **310**: 154.

Spangler, E., T. Ryan, and E.H. Blackburn. 1988. Developmentally regulated telomere addition in *Tetrahymena thermophila*. *Nucleic Acids Res.* (in press).

Szostak, J.W. and E.H. Blackburn. 1982. Cloning yeast telomeres on linear plasmid vectors. *Cell* **29**: 254.

Wang, J.C. 1979. Helical repeat of DNA in solution. *Proc. Natl. Acad. Sci.* **76**: 200.

Mouse ARS Elements and ARS-binding Proteins

F. Grummt, A. Holst, F. Müller, M. Wegner, S. Schwender, H. Luksza, G. Zastrow, and A. Klavinius

Institut für Biochemie, Universität Würzburg, D-8700, Würzburg, Germany

We have isolated 21 autonomously replicating sequences from chromosomal mouse DNA (muARS) that allow autonomous replication of plasmids in homologous mouse cells. Free plasmids in mouse cells were demonstrated by hybridization with a specific plasmid probe, by electron microscopic visualization of circular DNA, by recovering plasmids using *E. coli* transformation, and by mitotic instability. Replication of plasmids in mouse cells was shown by *Mbo*I sensitivity, 5-bromodeoxyuridine (BrdU) substitution, and copy number determination. Fluorescence-activated cell sorter (FACS) analysis revealed plasmid replication only during S phase. Sequence analysis of 12 muARS elements revealed a conserved element ($CTC_T^A GAGA_{CC}^{GG} AA$) in five muARSs. We have identified from nuclear extracts an activity that binds specifically to four muARS elements. This activity is sensitive to phenol and proteinase K and is heat (10′, 100°C) and acid (1% TCA) resistant. DNase I footprinting allows the resolution of 47-bp-long AT-rich protected sequences in two muARS elements interacting with the muARS-binding protein.

The ability of an extrachromosomal DNA molecule to replicate autonomously is an indication that it contains sequences recognized as an initiation site for DNA replication. Such autonomously replicating DNA molecules can be propagated by selecting for the expression of a linked marker. This approach has been utilized to select for autonomously replicating sequences in mouse cells (Holst et al. 1988). The rationale of this screening for murine ARS elements is based on the observation that plasmids containing a thymidine kinase gene with an inefficient, truncated promoter (McKnight et al. 1984) were unable to transform mouse Ltk⁻ cells to the tk⁺ phenotype, since apparently only subthreshold levels of thymidine kinase were generated in transfected cells (Wigler et al. 1977; Wilkie et al. 1979). However, recombinant transfection vectors containing functionally active ARS elements could replicate and amplify in transfected mouse cells and hence compensate the inefficient tk gene promoter by a positive gene dosage effect. Applying this assay, 21 murine ARS elements were isolated and characterized.

If these murine ARS elements are origins of replication, then, by analogy to the prokaryotic and viral replication systems, we anticipate that the mouse cell has initiator proteins that will recognize and interact with a specific nucleotide sequence at the ARSs. This belief prompted us to search for ARS-specific DNA-binding proteins in nuclear extracts from mouse cells. Here we report the identification of such an activity.

Materials and Methods

Materials

Enzymes and nucleotides were from Boehringer, Mannheim GmbH; radioactive compounds were from Amersham.

In vivo replication assay

Transfection of mouse L cells, propagation of transformed Ltk⁺ clones, and the analysis of the cellular DNA were carried out as described previously (Holst et al. 1988).

Protein-DNA binding assay

muARS-NTS-1 3′-labeled with ^{32}P by Klenow polymerase was used as binding substrate in this reaction, either in full length or digested to the 141-bp 5′ and 253-bp 3′ subfragments. Nuclear non-histone protein fractions from Ehrlich ascites tumor cells were prepared according to Dignam et al. (1983). The ARS DNA–protein-binding reaction included 0.2–0.5 ng ARS DNA fragment, 1 μg *Hpa*II-digested pUC18 DNA, 80 μM of each dXTP, 10 μg yeast tRNA, 10 mM Tris-HCl (pH 7.5), 1 mM EDTA, 80 mM NaCl, 10 mM β-mercaptoethanol, 4% glycerol, 0.1% Triton X-100, and 0.5–2 μg protein extract. Incubation was at 30°C for 10 minutes, followed by loading the reaction mixtures on a 4% polyacrylamide gel. Electrophoresis was in 0.5 × TEB (45 mM Tris base, 55 mM borate, 1.25 mM EDTA, pH 8.3) at 120 V for 3 hours.

DNase I footprinting

The nucleotide sequence in muARS-NTS-1 and -2 protected from DNase I digestion by the muARS DNA-binding protein was determined by the footprinting technique of Galas and Schmitz (1978). muARS-1, the DNA used for footprint analysis of the upper strand, was obtained as a 387-bp fragment from a pUC plasmid by digestion with *Bam*HI and *Eco*RI, which was labeled at the 5′ *Eco*RI site. For footprint analysis of the lower strand, a 146-bp *Eco*RI–*Dra*I fragment was labeled at the 5′ *Dra*I site.

463

Results and Discussion

Isolation of 21 mouse ARS elements

Two different approaches were chosen to detect putative origins of replication in chromosomal mouse DNA and to characterize them as ARS elements: (1) a shotgun experiment with 480 random genomic DNA fragments, and (2) an aimed search in the nontranscribed spacer (NTS) region of mouse rDNA cistrons. In the shotgun experiment, 19 distinct ARS-element-containing DNA fragments out of 480 approximately 1-kb-long fragments were scored (muARS1-19). In the second set of experiments two further ARSs (muARS-NTS-1 and -2) were found approximately 4.1 and 4.6 kb, respectively, upstream of the transcription initiation site of the rDNA cistrons. These 21 elements were isolated, some of them subcloned, and 11 ARSs sequenced.

Intracellular status and in vivo replication of muARS-containing plasmids

Functional analysis of these ARS elements using the transfection assay revealed that plasmids bearing such ARS elements exist and replicate as episomal circular DNA in transformed mouse L cells. The extrachromosomal circular nature of the ARS-containing transfection vectors was demonstrated (1) by identical electrophoretic mobility in agarose gels of reference *E. coli* plasmid DNA and DNA isolated from transfected mouse cell lines; (2) by electron microscopic visualization of supercoiled and relaxed circular DNA molecules in low-molecular-weight DNA fractions from transformed mouse cells, the contour length of the circles corresponding to the size of the original vector DNA used for transfection; (3) by transformation of bacteria with DNA isolated according to Hirt (1967) from transformed mouse cell lines; (4) by the high segregation rate of the tk⁺ phenotype if selective pressure was relieved in transformed mouse cell lines; (5) by Southern analysis of total genomic DNA from transformed mouse L cells with nick-translated plasmid DNA that revealed exclusively signals for plasmid DNA bands if pretreated with noncutting, once-, or twice-cutting restriction endonucleases.

In vivo replication of transforming plasmid DNA was demonstrated (1) by BrdU substitution generating the heavy/light form of replicating plasmid DNA in mouse cells within 24 hours and the heavy/heavy conformation within 48 hours upon BrdU application to transformed mouse L cells; (2) by acquiring *Mbo*I sensitivity as well as *Dpn*I resistance; (3) by a high copy number of plasmids (several hundred) in transformed mouse Ltk⁺ cells. Plasmid replication occurs exclusively during S phase of the cell division cycle, as demonstrated by FACS separation of BrdU-substituted transformed mouse cell population.

Sequence analysis of muARS elements

Of 21 isolated muARS fragments, 11 were sequenced, according to Sanger et al. (1980), four of them after subcloning. Five of the ARSs contain a dodecameric sequence with a high degree of similarity (consensus: 5'-CTC$_T^A$GAGA$_{CC}^{GG}$AA). This sequence was also found in a

human ARS element not described here. The 219-bp-long muARS-9 was subcloned, resulting in a 174-bp fragment lacking this CTC...consensus box and a 45-bp subfragment containing it. The ARS activity was lost in the large subfragment, whereas the remaining small 45-bp subfragment containing the muARS box was as active as total 218-bp muARS-9 element. Insertion of four of the 45-bp subfragments of muARS-9 in a tandem array into the ARS screening vector ptk resulted in an increase of the transfection rate of mouse Ltk⁻ cells by 1 order of magnitude. muARS-5 contains a sequence with a high degree of similarity to the DNA-binding site of the transcription/replication initiation factor NFIII. Two similar NFIII-binding sites were also found in a human ARS element (data not shown). Some of the muARS elements, especially muARS-NTS-1 and -2 and muARS 3 and 4, contain long AT-rich regions. In muARS-NTS-1 and -2, an AT-rich sequence interacts site-specifically with a DNA-binding protein of homologous mouse cells.

Identification of a murine protein activity that binds to muARS elements

In our search for an ARS DNA-binding protein, gel retardation of DNA-protein complexes on polyacrylamide gels was used to assay a nuclear extract from mouse Ehrlich ascites tumor cells prepared according to Dignam et al. (1983) for DNA-binding protein(s) interacting preferentially and site-specifically with muARS elements. ³²P-labeled muARS-NTS-1 containing DNA fragments were used either in total length or split into two subfragments containing the 5' first third and the 3' two-thirds, respectively. As shown in Figure 1, the mobility of the total muARS-NTS-1 DNA fragment, as well as the mobility of the subfragment comprising the first third of it, was retarded in electrophoresis on poly-

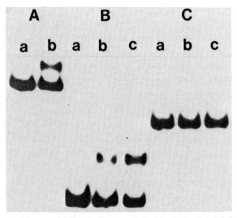

Figure 1 Mouse ARS-binding protein binds to the 5' first third of the muARS-NTS-1 sequence. (*A*) A 391-bp DNA fragment containing the total 372-bp sequence of muARS-NTS-1 was incubated either without (*a*) or with (*b*) 0.4 μg mouse nuclear extract (pretreated 10 min at 65°C). (*B*) A 139-bp DNA fragment containing the 5' first 123 bp of muARS-NTS-1 was incubated without (*a*), with 0.4 μg (*b*), or with 1 μg (*c*) nuclear extract. (*C*) A 252-bp DNA fragment containing the 3' two-thirds (249 bp) of muARS-NTS-1 was incubated without (*a*), with 0.4 μg (*b*), or with 1 μg (*c*) nuclear extract.

acrylamide gels, whereas the subfragment comprising the 3′ two-thirds of this ARS element remained unaffected. The amount of DNA that was shifted to a new position in the gel appeared to be proportional to the amount of protein added. Pretreatment of the nuclear extract with phenol and proteinase K destroyed the complex-forming activity. However, this activity was resistant against heating (10′, 100°C) and remained soluble and active in 1% trichloroacetic acid.

Further experiments revealed that three muARS elements (muARS 3 + 4, muARS-NTS-2) compete efficiently with the NTS-1 element for complex formation with this DNA binding protein. Also, similar gel shifts were observed if labeled fragments containing these three ARSs were preincubated with mouse nuclear extracts.

muARS DNA-binding proteins bind specific nucleotide sequences

To define the binding sites on the nucleotide level, DNase I protection experiments were performed with both muARS-NTS-1 and -2. The fragments containing these ARSs were differentially 5′-end-labeled and subjected to limited DNase I cleavage after preincubation with mouse nuclear extracts in the absence or presence of various specific and unspecific competitor DNA fragments. Figure 2, lanes 1–30, shows such an experiment carried out with muARS-NTS-1. It clearly demonstrates protection of a distinct sequence (bar) in the presence of extract protein that is efficiently competed in the presence of an increasing amount of unlabeled DNA fragments of muARS-NTS-1, of muARS-3, -4, and NTS-2, but not by muARS-1, poly d(AT), poly d(IC) or HpaII-digested pUC18 DNA. The alignment of the resistant sites of both muARS-NTS-1 and -2 is given in Figure 3. Both binding sites are 47 bp in length and reside within AT-rich regions of these elements. In the case of muARS-NTS-2, two 50–60-bp-long AT-rich sequences are found, only one of which interacts with the mouse ARS-binding protein. One distinct feature of the binding sites is that they are palindromic, whereas the nonbinding AT-rich element in muARS-NTS-2 is of nonpalindromic nature. It remains to be demonstrated whether

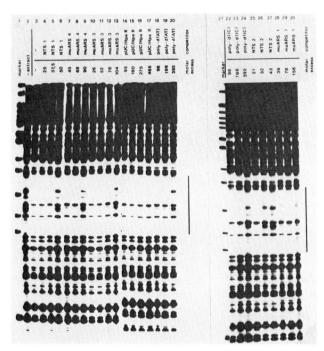

Figure 2 DNase I footprinting of muARS-NTS-1 element. A 391-bp EcoRI-BamHI fragment containing muARS-NTS-1 was generated by digestion of pUC18-muARS-NTS-1. The fragments used for footprinting were selectively 5′-labeled at the EcoRI site. Incubation with 3 μg mouse nuclear extract (pretreated by heating for 10 min at 65°C) was carried out for 10 min at 20°C before DNase I-digestion. Diverse competitor DNAs of a size comparable to that of the muARS-NTS-1 fragment were added in molar excesses as shown above each lane. The dark bar indicates the approximate regions protected by the ARS-binding protein, the sequences of which are shown in Fig. 3.

the potentiality to form cruciforms is an essential feature of the recognition site of this murine ARS-binding protein.

Acknowledgments

This work was supported by the Deutsche Forschungsgemeinschaft (SFB 165).

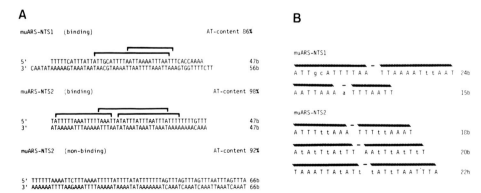

Figure 3 Sites of DNase I protection. (A) Shown are the AT-rich sequences of muARS-NTS-1 and muARS-NTS-2, two of them interacting with the ARS-binding protein. The brackets above the sequences indicate the position of palindromes. The detailed structures of the palindromes are depicted in B.

References

Dignam, J.D., R.M. Lebowitz, and R.G. Roeder. 1983. Accurate transcription initiation by RNA polymerase II in a soluble extract from isolated mammalian nuclei. *Nucleic Acids Res.* **2:** 1475.

Galas, D. and A. Schmitz. 1978. DNase footprinting: A simple method for the detection of protein-DNA binding specificity. *Nucleic Acids Res.* **5:** 3157.

Hirt, B. 1967. Selective extraction of polyoma DNA from infected mouse cell cultures. *J. Mol. Biol.* **26:** 365.

Holst, A., F. Müller, G. Zastrow, H. Zentgraf, S. Schwender, E. Dinkl, and F. Grummt. 1988. Murine genomic DNA sequences replicating autonomously in mouse L cells. *Cell* **52:** (in press).

McKnight, S.L., R.C. Kingsbury, A. Spence, and M. Smith. 1984. The distal transcription signals of the herpesvirus tk gene share a common hexanucleotide control sequence. *Cell* **37:** 253.

Sanger, F., A.R. Coulson, B.G. Barrell, A.J.H. Smith, and B.A. Roe. 1980. Cloning in single-stranded bacteriophage as an aid to rapid DNA sequencing. *J. Mol. Biol.* **143:** 161.

Wigler, M., S. Silverstein, L.-S. Lee, A. Pellicer, Y. Cheng, and R. Axel. 1977. Transfer of purified herpes virus thymidine kinase gene to cultured mouse cells. *Cell* **11:** 223.

Wilkie, N.M., J.B. Clements, W. Boll, N. Mantei, D. Lonsdale, and C. Weissmann. 1979. Hybrid plasmids containing an active thymidine kinase gene of Herpes simplex virus I. *Nucleic Acids Res.* **7:** 859.

Episomal Persistence of a Plasmid Containing Human c-*myc* DNA

C. McWhinney and M. Leffak

Department of Biochemistry, Wright State University, Dayton, Ohio 45435

To test the ability of the 5′ region of the human c-*myc* locus to promote episomal plasmid replication in eukaryotic nuclei, a 2.4-kb *Hind*III-*Xho*I fragment spanning the c-*myc* promoter domain and transcription initiation sites was cloned in a selectable vector and transfected into HeLa cells. The resulting pNeo.Myc2.4 construct has been maintained as an extrachromosomal element for more than 200 cell generations under G418 selection. Removal of the selective pressure results in less than 5% plasmid loss per generation. The pNeo.Myc2.4 monomer has been recovered in supercoiled and relaxed forms, and has generated both oligomeric and miniplasmid variants in vivo. Chromosomally integrated copies of the plasmid have not been detected in the culture.

Eukaryotic chromosomes are organized into multiple domains of replication, or replicons, whose size, number, and temporal order of activity vary in a cell-specific and developmentally regulated manner (Edenberg and Huberman 1975; Hand 1978). Chromosome replication is thought to initiate with the binding of cellular factors to chromosomal sites from which replication proceeds bidirectionally; these sites have been termed replication origins. The proposal that discrete replication origin sequences exist in the chromosomes of higher eukaryotes has gained support from the observation that specific DNA sequences function as replication origins in polyomavirus, SV40, and bovine papillomavirus; viruses that are packaged in a nucleosome structure similar to that of the host chromosome and that utilize host cell enzymes for replication (Fareed et al. 1972; Griffin et al. 1974; Tooze 1980; Waldeck et al. 1984). Experiments localizing the initiation sites for over-replication of the *Drosophila* chorion genes (Spradling and Mahowald 1981; deCicco and Spradling 1984) and the amplified dihydrofolate reductase genes in methotrexate-resistant hamster cells (Heintz et al. 1983; Montoya-Zavala and Hamlin 1985; Burhans et al. 1986) are consistent with this model.

Based on data suggesting that yeast chromosomal replication origins can promote the autonomous replication of plasmid DNAs in yeast cells (Struhl et al. 1979; Stinchcomb et al. 1980), several groups have investigated the ability of mammalian DNA sequences to act as autonomously replicating elements (ARSs). Recently, Carroll et al. (1987) have detected the formation of a large episome in PALA-selected hamster cells that replicates semiconservatively from an origin within the *CAD* gene region. Chromosomal sequences cloned from the extruded nascent DNA strands of replicating monkey cells have been reported to support autonomous plasmid replication in CV-1 and HeLa cells (Frappier and Zannis-Hadjopoulos 1985), and a cloned 2.5-kb mouse DNA fragment that hybridizes to a portion of the SV40 replication origin palindrome has been shown to display ARS activity in mouse and human cells (Ariga et al. 1987).

In the course of experiments designed to analyze the direction of replication through transcriptionally active and inactive genes, the region 5′ to the human c-*myc* proto-oncogene was implicated as a potential chromosomal replication origin (M. Leffak and D. James, in prep.). The c-*myc* gene is a homolog of the transforming gene of the avian acute leukemia virus MC-29 (Duesberg et al. 1977). Expression of c-*myc* is related to the growth state of normal cells (Kelly et al. 1983; Campisi et al. 1984), and c-*myc* mRNA levels are elevated in several forms of neoplasia (Collins and Groudine 1982; Westin et al. 1982; Dalla-Favera et al. 1983). Amplification of the c-*myc* gene with a concomitant increase in c-*myc* mRNA is observed in a variety of human tumor cell lines (Collins and Groudine 1982; Westin et al. 1982; Dalla-Favera et al. 1983), and chromosomal translocations involving the 5′ flanking DNA of c-*myc* are commonly associated with Burkitt's lymphomas (Taub et al. 1982; Klein and Klein 1985). To test whether the c-*myc* 5′ flanking DNA could serve as an ARS element, a 2.4-kb *Hind*III-*Xho*I fragment flanking the c-*myc* gene was cloned in the selectable plasmid vector pdMMTneo(302-3) to yield the plasmid pNeo.Myc2.4. This plasmid was transfected into HeLa cells and has been maintained under G418 selection as an episomal element for more than 200 cell generations. During this time, pNeo.Myc2.4 has generated both oligomeric and miniplasmid forms that retain c-*myc* sequences; however, chromosomally integrated forms of the plasmid have not been observed.

Results

The 2.4-kb region bounded by the *Hind*III site 5′ to c-*myc* exon I and the *Xho*I site within c-*myc* exon I (Fig. 1) contains the transcriptional promoters for this gene. In nuclei, three domains of altered chromatin structure hypersensitive to digestion by DNase I are detected in

CANCER CELLS 6 / *Eukaryotic DNA Replication.* © 1988 by Cold Spring Harbor Laboratory 0-87969-308-8/88 $1.00

A

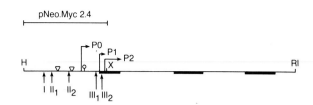

B

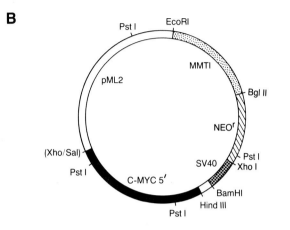

pNeo. Myc 2.4

Figure 1 Maps of c-*myc* DNA. (*A*) The human chromosomal c-*myc* locus. The map is based on the data of Siebenlist et al. (1984) and Bentley and Groudine (1986). (Solid boxes) c-*myc* exons; (H) *Hind*III; (RI) *Eco*RI; (X) *Xho*I. (P0, P1, P2) c-*myc* promoters; (I, II₁, II₂, III₁, III₂) DNase I hypersensitive sites; (▽) NFI recognition sites; (○) BPV PMS1 homology. The 2.4-kb *Hind*III-*Xho*I fragment insert of pNeo.Myc2.4 is indicated. (*B*) The pNeo.Myc2.4 plasmid. *Eco*RI cleaves at a pair of sites flanking a duplication of the 29-bp *Eco*RI-*Hind*III fragment of pML2. Clockwise from the *Eco*RI sites: (stippled bar) mouse metallothionein I promoter region; (hatched bar) TN5 neomycin phosphotransferase gene; (checkered bar) SV40 early region transcriptional processing signals; (open bar) pBR322 DNA; (solid bar) c-*myc* DNA; (open bar) pML2 DNA (a pBR322 derivative lacking replication ''poison'' sequences) (Lusky and Botchan 1981).

this region (Siebenlist et al. 1984). This DNA fragment also contains a binding site for HeLa cell nuclear factor I (NFI; Gronostajski et al. 1985; Rosenfeld and Kelly 1986), and sequences homologous to the plasmid maintenance sequence of bovine papillomavirus (BPV; Lusky and Botchan 1984) and to a murine ARS sequence (Ariga et al. 1987). Bidirectional transcription initiating within the 5′ flanking DNA of the c-*myc* gene has been reported (Bentley and Groudine 1986) which, based on the results of Seidman et al. (1979), would predict the existence of a chromosomal origin of replication in this region. Using the technique of run-off replication (James and Leffak 1986), our preliminary experiments suggested the presence of a barrier to the progression of replication forks immediately 5′ to c-*myc* exon I (M. Leffak and D. James, in prep.). To determine whether the 2.4-kb *Hind*III-*Xho*I fragment of c-*myc* DNA displayed ARS activity, this sequence was cloned in the

vector pdMMTneo(302-3) (Law et al. 1983), which contains the bacterial neomycin phosphotransferase gene driven by the mouse metallothionein I transcriptional promoter. This construct, pNeo.Myc2.4 (Fig. 1), was transfected into HeLa cells, and selection with the antibiotic G418 was applied (Colbere-Garapin et al. 1981).

The input plasmid contained primarily supercoiled monomer and oligomer forms (Fig. 2, lane 1). Total DNA isolated 12 hours after transfection showed that monomer DNA had been converted largely to the relaxed form; however, by 48 hours a relative increase in the amount of supercoiled monomer was observed (Fig. 2, lanes 2 and 3). Plasmid DNA isolated by Hirt extraction (1967) and CsCl-ethidium bromide gradient centrifugation 290 days (approximately 150–200 cell generations) after transfection displayed a complex mixture of monomeric and oligomeric forms, as well as the presence of a miniplasmid (Fig. 2, lane 4). Oligomeric forms of the plasmid are found in both the supernatant and pellet of Hirt preparations (see below). Relaxation of the plasmid DNA with topoisomerase II implicates the bands migrating near the 2.0-kb and 4.4-kb markers as supercoiled and relaxed forms, respectively, of the miniplasmid. Supercoiled pNeo.Myc.2.4 monomer is also observed, migrating near the 6.6-kb marker (Fig. 2, lane 5). (Non-supercoiled DNAs present in the sample prior to topoisomerase II treatment represent contamination due to the broad fractionation of the gradient necessary to ensure recovery of plasmid DNA present at levels not detectable by ethidium bromide staining.) On these gels the electrophoretic resolution of the oligomers is not sufficient to distinguish between supercoiled and relaxed forms (see below).

To date, the mixed HeLa culture containing pNeo.Myc2.4 has been maintained under G418 selection for more than 200–250 cell generations, and more

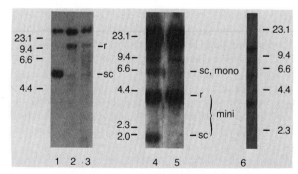

Figure 2 Blot hybridization of plasmid DNAs. The *Bgl*II-*Bam*HI fragment of pNeo.Myc2.4 (neoʳ probe) was hybridized to the following DNA preparations: (lane *1*) input pNeo.Myc2.4 DNA; (lane *2*) total cellular DNA recovered 12 hr after transfection; (lane *3*) total cellular DNA recovered 48 hr after transfection; (lane *4*) Hirt supernatant DNA recovered 290 days after transfecton; (lane *5*) Hirt supernatant DNA recovered 290 days after transfection and treated with topoisomerase II; (lane *6*) *Eco*RI-digested oligomer plasmid DNA. Sizes are shown in kilobase pairs. (r) Relaxed; (sc) supercoiled; (mono) monomer pNeo.Myc2.4; (mini) miniplasmid.

than 1000 times the mass of plasmid originally transfected has been recovered. Moreover, subcultures of the transfected HeLa cells grown in the absence of G418 showed less than 5% loss of the pNeo.Myc2.4 plasmid per generation, and in vivo recombinant miniplasmids that have lost their neomycin resistance (*neo*[r]) sequences but retained c-myc DNA are stably maintained in the culture, arguing that drug selection is not essential for persistence of the plasmid. In contrast, HeLa cells transfected with the parent vector and selected for G418 resistance did not retain the pdMMTneo(302-3) plasmid as an extrachromosomal element beyond 21 days, consistent with a previous report (Law et al. 1983).

Extrachromosomal pNeo.Myc2.4 is not generated by continuous excision of chromosomally integrated plasmid. A preparation enriched for chromosomal DNA was isolated approximately 125 cell generations after transfection by two cycles of CsCl-ethidium bromide centrifugation, and hybridized to a *neo*[r] gene probe (the BglII-BamHI fragment of pNeo.Myc2.4) and to a c-myc probe (the PstI-PstI fragment internal to the c-myc sequences of pNeo.Myc2.4; Fig. 3). As expected, the c-myc probe detects hybridizable DNA, presumably the germ-line c-myc sequences, at approximately single-copy intensity (Fig. 3A); however, virtually no hybridization to the *neo*[r] probe is seen, even on overexposure of the film (Fig. 3B). The ability to remove plasmid oligomers from the chromosomal DNA fraction by CsCl-ethidium bromide centrifugation also argues that the pNeo.Myc2.4 oligomers persist in supercoiled form.

The time-dependent increase in the level of high-molecular-weight pNeo.Myc2.4 forms is reminiscent of the accumulation of oligomeric viral genomes seen in cells infected with SV40 (Martin et al. 1976; Goff and Berg 1977; Weaver et al. 1985). To analyze the structure of the high-molecular-weight plasmids, a DNA preparation enriched for oligomers by CsCl-ethidium bromide centrifugation of a Hirt pellet preparation (Martin et al. 1976) was digested with EcoRI, which cuts at two adjacent sites in the 9.1-kb pNeo.Myc2.4 DNA. The major EcoRI digestion products are two DNA fragments of approximately 3.8 kb and 14.0 kb (Fig. 2, lane 6), suggesting that the oligomers are predominantly head-to-head, tail-to-tail concatemers. The oligomers are also resistant to disaggregation by topoisomerase II (Fig. 2, lane 5), consistent with a concatemeric, rather than an interlocking ring, structure.

Discussion

The plasmid pNeo.Myc2.4, containing the 5' region of the human c-myc locus, has been shown to persist as an extrachromosomal element in HeLa cells. Hybridization intensity comparisons with known amounts of c-myc DNA indicate that the c-myc sequences are present on average at roughly 10–50 copies per cell. In the absence of detectable chromosomally integrated copies of the plasmid, the long-term retention and amplification of pNeo.Myc2.4 demonstrate that it is able to replicate autonomously. The inability of the parental vector to be retained in nonintegrated form suggests that the c-myc sequences contain a site for the initiation of DNA replication or are able to induce such a site in the plasmid.

Within 48 hours after transfection, a substantial proportion of the pNeo.Myc2.4 plasmid is recoverable in supercoiled form, suggesting the acquisition of nucleosomal packaging, as reported for other transfected DNAs (Reeves et al. 1985). The time-dependent appearance of pNeo.Myc2.4 oligomer and deletion derivatives demonstrates that the plasmid is a substrate for cellular recombination enzymes in this form. By analogy to viral systems (Martin et al. 1976; Goff and Berg 1977), the formation of pNeo.Myc2.4 oligomers also provides evidence for the autonomous replication of the plasmid.

In SV40 and polyoma there is a clustering of DNA sequences that regulate transcription and replication, and these processes are integrated during the life cycle of these viruses (Fried and Prives 1986). Although less well defined, a relationship between the replication and transcription of eukaryotic chromosomal genes has also been suggested by several laboratories (Smithies 1982; Calza et al. 1984; Goldman et al. 1984; Giunta et al. 1986; James and Leffak 1986); as such, the proximity of a putative chromosomal replication origin near the transcriptional control elements of the c-myc gene raises the speculation that not only may elevated c-myc mRNA levels in human tumors be due to gene amplification, but that c-myc amplification may be the result of an event that acts to enhance c-myc transcription.

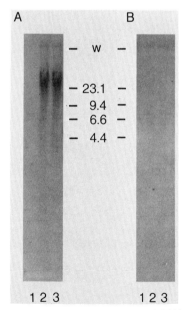

Figure 3 Blot hybridization of chromosomal DNAs. A single filter was hybridized to a c-myc gene probe (*A*), and to the *neo*[r] probe (*B*) (see text). (Lanes *1*) internal hybridization control (1 pg plasmid DNA); (lanes *2* and *3*) duplicate samples of chromosomal DNA. Sizes are in kilobase pairs; (w) sample wells.

Materials and Methods

Transfection of plasmid pNeo.Myc2.4

A 12.5-kb *Eco*RI fragment containing the human c-*myc* gene was generously provided as a λ bacteriophage clone by P. Leder (Siebenlist et al. 1984). The 8-kb *Hind*III/*Eco*RI c myc fragment was subcloned in pBR322 and the 2.7-kb subfragment extending from the vector *Bam*HI site to the *Xho*I site in exon I of the c-*myc* gene cloned between the *Bam*HI and *Sal*I sites in the vector pdMMTneo(302-3) (kindly provided by P. Howley.) Two μg of pNeo.Myc2.4 and 30 μg of carrier salmon sperm DNA were transfected into HeLa cells (Wigler et al. 1978). After an incubation of 4 hours, the transfection medium was replaced by fresh medium and the cells incubated for an additional 24 hours. The antibiotic G418 was applied at 500 μg/ml and the cells maintained under selection.

Isolation of plasmid pNeo.Myc2.4 DNA from HeLa cells

Low-molecular-weight DNA was extracted by the method of Hirt (1967). Plasmid DNA was purified from cleared bacterial cell lysates or from Hirt supernatant or pellet DNA by centrifugation on CsCl-ethidium bromide gradients. DNA was subjected to electrophoresis on 0.8% agarose gels and transferred to nitrocellulose or Nytran (Schleicher and Schuell) filters (Southern 1975). Filters were hybridized as recommended by the supplier to probes labeled with [α-^{32}P]dCTP (James and Leffak 1984). Hybridization was performed in 50% formamide at 42°C, with final stringency washes at 65°C in 0.1X SSC (15 mM NaCl, 1.5 mM sodium citrate [pH 7.4]), 0.1% SDS. Filters were exposed to Kodak XR-5 film at −80°C with Dupont Cronex LP intensifying screens.

Acknowledgment

This work was supported by a grant from the National Institutes of Health to M.L.

References

Ariga, H., T. Itani, and S.M. Iguchi-Ariga. 1987. Autonomous replicating sequences from mouse cells which can replicate in mouse cells in vivo and in vitro. *Mol. Cell. Biol.* **7**: 1.

Bentley, D.L. and M. Groudine. 1986. A block to elongation is largely responsible for decreased transcription of c-*myc* in differentiated HL60 cells. *Nature* **321**: 782.

Burhans, W.C., J.E. Selegue, and N.H. Heintz. 1986. Isolation of the origin of replication associated with the amplified Chinese hamster dihydrofolate reductase domain. *Proc. Natl. Acad. Sci.* **83**: 7790.

Calza, R.E., L.A. Eckhardt, T. DelGiudice, and C.L. Schildkraut. 1984. Changes in gene position are accompanied by a change in time of replication. *Cell* **36**: 689.

Campisi, J., H. Gray, A.B. Pardee, G.E. Dean, and G.E. Sonenshine. 1984. Cell-cycle control of c-*myc* but not c-*ras* expression is lost following chemical transformation. *Cell* **36**: 241.

Carroll, S.M., P. Gaudray, M.L. DeRose, J.F. Emery, J.F. Meinkoth, E. Nakkim, M. Subler, D.D. Von Hoff, and G.M. Wahl. 1987. Characterization of an episome produced in hamster cells that amplify a transfected CAD gene at high frequency: Functional evidence for a mammalian replication origin. *Mol. Cell. Biol.* **7**: 1740.

Colbere-Garapin, F. Hordoniceanu, P. Kourilsky, and A.C. Garapin. 1981. A new dominant hybrid selective marker for higher eukaryotic cells. *J. Mol. Biol.* **150**: 1.

Collins, S. and M. Groudine. 1982. Amplification of endogenous *myc*-related DNA sequences in a human myeloid leukaemia cell line. *Nature* **298**: 679.

Dalla-Favera, R., S. Martinotti, R. Gallo, J. Erikson, and C.M. Croce. 1983. Translocation and rearrangement of the c-*myc* oncogene locus in human undifferentiated B-cell lymphomas. *Science* **219**: 963.

deCicco, D.V. and A.C. Spradling. 1984. Localization of a *cis*-acting element responsible for the developmentally regulated amplification of *Drosophila* chorion genes. *Cell* **38**: 45.

Duesberg, P., K. Bister, and P.K. Vogt. 1977. The RNA of avian acute leukemia virus MC29. *Proc. Natl. Acad. Sci.* **74**: 4320.

Edenberg, H.J. and J.A. Huberman. 1975. Eukaryotic chromosome replication. *Annu. Rev. Genet.* **9**: 245.

Fareed, G.C., C.F. Garon, and N.P. Salzman. 1972. Origin and direction of simian virus 40 replication. *J. Virol.* **10**: 484.

Frappier, L. and M. Zannis-Hadjopoulos. 1985. Cloning of nascent monkey DNA synthesized early in the cell cycle. *Mol. Cell. Biol.* **5**: 721.

Fried, M. and C. Prives. 1986. The molecular biology of simian virus 40 and polyomavirus. *Cancer Cells* **4**: 1.

Giunta, D.R., J.Y. Tso, S. Narayanswami, B. Hamkalo, and L.J. Korn. 1986. Early replication and expression of oocyte-type 5SRNA genes in a *Xenopus* somatic cell line carrying a translocation. *Proc. Natl. Acad. Sci.* **83**: 5150.

Goff, S.P. and P. Berg. 1977. Structure and formation of circular dimers of simian virus 40 DNA. *J. Virol.* **24**: 295.

Goldman, M.A., G.P. Holmquist, M.C. Gray, L.A. Caston, and A. Nag. 1984. Replication timing of genes and middle repetitive sequences. *Science* **224**: 686.

Griffin, B., M. Fried, and A. Cowie. 1974. Polyoma DNA: A physical map. *Proc. Natl. Acad. Sci.* **71**: 2077.

Gronostajski, R.M., S. Adhya, K. Nagata, R.A. Guggenheimer, and J. Hurwitz. 1985. Site-specific DNA binding of nuclear factor 1: Analysis of cellular binding sites. *Mol. Cell. Biol.* **5**: 964.

Hand, R. 1978. Eucaryotic DNA: Organization of the genome for replication. *Cell* **15**: 317.

Heintz, N.H., J.D. Milbrandt, K.S. Griesen, and J.L. Hamlin. 1983. Cloning of the initiation region of a mammalian chromosomal replicon. *Nature* **302**: 439.

Hirt, B. 1967. Selective extraction of polyoma DNA from infected mouse cell cultures. *J. Mol. Biol.* **26**: 265.

James, C.D. and M. Leffak. 1984. Replacement synthesis labeling of recombinant DNA molecules using the *E. coli* exonuclease III/DNA polymerase enzyme pair. *Anal. Biochem.* **141**: 33.

———. 1986. Polarity of DNA replication through the avian alpha-globin locus. *Mol. Cell. Biol.* **6**: 976.

Kelly, K., B.H. Cochran, C.D. Stiles, and P. Leder. 1983. Cell-specific regulation of the c-*myc* gene by lymphocyte mitogens and platelet-derived growth factor. *Cell* **35**: 603.

Klein, G. and E. Klein. 1985. Evolution of tumours and the impact of molecular oncology. *Nature* **315**: 190.

Law, M.F., J.C. Byrne, and P.M. Howley. 1983. A stable bovine papillomavirus hybrid plasmid that expresses a dominant selective trait. *Mol. Cell. Biol.* **3**: 2110.

Lusky, M. and M. Botchan. 1981. Inhibition of SV40 replication in simian cells by specific pBR322 DNA sequences. *Nature* **293**: 79.

———. 1986. Transient replication of bovine papillomavirus type 1 plasmids: *cis* and *trans* requirements. *Proc. Natl. Acad. Sci.* **83**: 3609.

Martin, M.A., P.M. Howley, J.C. Byrne, and C.F. Garon. 1976. Characterization of supercoiled oligomeric SV40 DNA molecules in productively infected cells. *Virology* **71**: 28.

Montoya-Zavala, M. and J.L. Hamlin. 1985. Similar 150 kilobase DNA sequences are amplified in independently derived methotrexate-resistant Chinese hamster cells. *Mol. Cell. Biol.* **51**: 619.

Reeves, R., C.M. Gorman, and B. Howard. 1985. Minichromosome assembly of non-integrated plasmid DNA transfected into mammalian cells. *Nucleic Acids Res.* **13:** 3599.

Rosenfeld, P.J. and T.J. Kelly. 1986. Purification of nuclear factor I by DNA recognition site affinity chromatography. *J. Biol. Chem.* **261:** 1398.

Seidman, M.M., A.J. Levine, and H. Weintraub. 1979. The asymmetric segregation of parental nucleosomes during chromosome replication. *Cell* **18:** 439.

Siebenlist, U., L. Hennighausen, J. Battey, and P. Leder. 1984. Chromatin structure and protein binding in the putative regulatory region of the c-*myc* gene in Burkitt lymphoma. *Cell* **37:** 381.

Smithies, O. 1982. The control of globin and other eukaryotic genes. *J. Cell. Physiol.* (suppl.) **1:** 137.

Southern, E.M. 1975. Detection of specific sequences among DNA fragments separated by gel electrophoresis. *J. Mol. Biol.* **98:** 503.

Spradling, A.C. and A.P. Mahowald. 1981. A chromosome inversion alters the pattern of specific DNA replication in *Drosophila* follicle cells. *Cell* **27:** 203.

Stinchcomb, D.T., M. Thomas, J. Kelly, E. Selker, and R.W. Davis. 1980. Eukaryotic DNA segments capable of autonomous replication in yeast. *Proc. Natl. Acad. Sci.* **77:** 4559.

Struhl, K., D.T. Stinchcomb, S. Sherer, and R.W. Davis. 1979. High-frequency transformation of yeast: Autonomous replica-tion of hybrid DNA molecules. *Proc. Natl. Acad. Sci.* **76:** 1035.

Taub, R., L. Kirsch, C. Morton, C. Lenoir, D. Swan, S. Tronick, S. Aaronson, and P. Leder. 1982. Translocation of the c-*myc* gene into the immunoglobulin heavy chain locus in human Burkitt lymphoma and mouse plasmacytoma cells. *Proc. Natl. Acad. Sci.* **79:** 7837.

Tooze, J. 1980. *Molecular biology of tumor viruses*, 2nd edition: *DNA tumor viruses.* Cold Spring Harbor Laboratory, Cold Spring Harbor, New York.

Waldeck, W., F. Rosl, and H. Zentgraf. 1984. Origin of replication in episomal bovine papillomavirus type 1 DNA isolated from transformed cells. *EMBO J.* **3:** 2173.

Weaver, D.T., S.C. Fields-Berry, and M.L. DePamphilis. 1985. The termination region for SV40 DNA replication directs the mode of separation for the two sibling molecules. *Cell* **41:** 565.

Westin, E.H., F. Wong-Staal, E.P. Gelmann, R. Dalla-Favera, T. Papas, J.A. Lautenberger, A. Eva, E.P. Reddy, S.R. Tronick, S.A. Aaronson, and R.C. Gallo. 1982. Expression of cellular homologues of retroviral *onc* genes in human hematopoietic cells. *Proc. Natl. Acad. Sci.* **79:** 2490.

Wigler, M., A. Pellicer, S. Silverstein, and R. Axel. 1978. Transfer of purified herpes virus thymidine kinase gene to cultured mouse cells. *Cell* **14:** 725.

DNA Sequences Required for Unwinding Prokaryotic and Eukaryotic Replication Origins

R.M. Umek, M.J. Eddy, and D. Kowalski
Molecular and Cellular Biology Department, Roswell Park Memorial Institute, Buffalo, New York 14263

We have developed an assay to detect the unwinding of replication origins on supercoiled DNA molecules. The assay uses a single-strand-specific endonuclease, P1 nuclease or mung bean nuclease, to detect DNA unwinding. We have reported previously the detection of preferential unwinding in the origins of replication of the phage PM2 genome and the yeast 2-μm plasmid. Here, we report that our previous findings can be generalized to chromosomally derived origins from *Escherichia coli* (*oriC*) and *Saccharomyces cerevisiae* (H4 *ARS*). In *oriC*, a derivative containing a 16-bp deletion in the unwound sequence is replication negative and shows no DNA unwinding in our assay. In the H4 *ARS*, a series of external deletion derivatives have been prepared and their replication phenotypes characterized (Bouton and Smith 1986). We find that the ease of unwinding a DNA sequence in the *ARS* correlates with the ability to replicate. The data suggest that a readily unwound DNA sequence is a conserved component of origins of replication.

Studies of the DNA sequences that serve as origins of replication have focused on the specific nucleotide sequences required (Kearsey 1984; Oka et al. 1984). The use of limited- or single-base substitutions has generated a model of origin organization that includes essential protein recognition sequences separated by essential and "nonessential" spacer sequences (Oka et al. 1984; for review, see Campbell 1986). However, in addition to protein recognition, DNA unwinding is an obvious requirement for the initiation of replication. We have developed an assay to study the DNA unwinding properties of sequences present on supercoiled molecules. We have reported previously that the origins of replication of the bacteriophage PM2 and the 2-μm plasmid unwind in preference to all other sequences in their genomes (Sheflin and Kowalski 1984; Umek and Kowalski 1987). In the present study, we show that our previous findings can be generalized to chromosomally derived origins from *E. coli* and *S. cerevisiae*. We have identified the DNA sequences most susceptible to unwinding in the prokaryotic and eukaryotic origins. The sequences lie within the minimal required region and adjacent to the protein recognition sequences of the origins. We find a direct correlation between the ability of these replication origins to unwind in vitro and their ability to facilitate the initiation of DNA replication in vivo.

Materials and Methods

Enzymes

P1 nuclease prepared according to Fujimoto et al. (1974) was from Yamasa Shoyu Co. Ltd., Choshi, Japan. Mung bean nuclease was isolated and purified to homogeneity as described by Kowalski et al. (1976). Enzymes from commercial suppliers were as follows: restriction enzymes and T4 DNA ligase (New England Biolabs), calf intestinal phosphatase (CAP) (Boehringer Mannheim), polynucleotide kinase (P-L Biochemicals).

DNA

All plasmids were grown in *E. coli* HB101 cells in L-broth. DNA was obtained from cells lysed by boiling in the presence of lysosyme (Holmes and Quigley 1981) and purified by two rounds of equilibrium centrifugation in cesium chloride density gradients containing ethidium bromide (Radloff et al. 1967).

Positional specificity of P1 nuclease and mung bean nuclease nicks

P1 nuclease and mung bean nuclease reactions contained 10 mM Tris-HCl (*oriC*, pH 7.0; H4 *ARS*, pH 7.5), 1.0–1.6 μg plasmid DNA, and 1 mM EDTA in a volume of 16 μl. After preincubation for 15 minutes at 37°C, 5 ng of P1 nuclease or 0.08 units (in 4 μl; units detailed in Kowalski et al. 1976) of mung bean nuclease were added and the reactions incubated at 37°C for 30 minutes or 1 hour, respectively. The reactions were stopped by phenol/chloroform extraction and ethanol-precipitated. The samples were restricted with *Pvu*II, dephosphorylated with CAP, and ^{32}P 5′ end-labeled (Maniatis et al. 1982). Radiolabeled restriction fragments of known length were prepared in a similar fashion to serve as mobility markers. After sample concentration by ethanol precipitation, equivalent counts of various samples were denatured with glyoxal (McMaster and Carmichael 1977). The glyoxal-denatured samples were electrophoresed through 1.2% agarose gels (20 cm) at 30 volts for 18.0 hours at room temperature. The gels were then dried onto Whatman 3MM paper and autoradiographed.

473

Results

A DNA sequence in *oriC* required for P1-nuclease-detectable unwinding and the initiation of replication

We used the single-strand-specific endonuclease P1 nuclease to probe for unwinding in the *E. coli* origin of replication (*oriC*) present on a supercoiled plasmid. A diagram of the plasmid, pGS81, is shown in Figure 1A. The 530-bp *oriC* fragment contains the 245-bp minimal origin sequence and is substituted for the small *Pst*I-*Eco*RI fragment of pBR322. Supercoiled pGS81 was incubated with P1 nuclease in conditions that result in the conversion of greater than 95% of the molecules to the nicked circular form with one nick per molecule (Kowalski 1984). The nicks are localized by agarose gel electrophoretic separation of molecules, linearized, and 5' ³²P end-labeled at the unique *Pvu*II site in the plasmid and permanently denatured with glyoxal (McMaster and Carmichael 1977). The number of bp in the sub-unit-length bands indicates the distance, in bp, from the *Pvu*II site to the nuclease-introduced nick. Each sub-unit-length band is site and strand specific. Band pairs whose combined length is equal to the total length of the plasmid are generated as a result of P1 nuclease cleavage on the top and bottom strands. Unit-length fragments (4144 bp) are generated from the strand not cleaved by P1 nuclease. Restriction fragments of known size were also end-labeled and denatured to serve as size markers. Additional unique restriction sites were used to confirm the assignment of the nuclease nicks (not shown). Lane 2 in Figure 1B shows two band pairs, indicative of nuclease recognition of two unwound regions in supercoiled pGS81. The sites map to the *oriC* insert (2.2- and 2.0-kb bands) and a previously characterized site in the pBR322 vector (3.0- and 1.2-kb bands) (Sheflin and Kowalski 1985). The equal intensities of the members of the band pairs indicate similar frequency of cleavage on the two strands of the unwound structure. Similar results are obtained when pGS81 is probed with the single-strand-specific endonuclease mung bean nuclease (not shown).

Lane 1 of Figure 1B shows that the hypersensitive sites are not detected in a pGS81 sample that was linearized at the *Pvu*II site prior to incubation with P1 nuclease. Thus, detectable unwinding at *oriC* is strictly dependent on DNA supercoiling. High-resolution mapping of the P1-nuclease cleavages in *oriC* reveals that a 42-bp AT-rich sequence that spans nucleotides 21–62 is cleaved (see below) (Sugimoto et al. 1979). The region lies at the left-hand boundary of the minimal *oriC* (Hirota et al. 1981). This AT-rich sequence contains two *Bgl*II sites at positions 22 and 37. We obtained a plasmid that has a 16-bp deletion between the two *Bgl*II sites. The resulting plasmid, pUA82, was probed for unwinding using P1 nuclease, and the nicked DNA was analyzed as described above. Lane 3 of Figure 1B shows that cleavage of pUA82 occurs exclusively at the vector site and not in the truncated *oriC*. The loss of nuclease-detectable unwinding is accompanied by the

A.

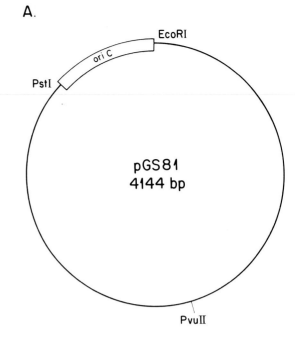

B

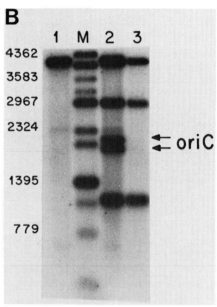

Figure 1 P1 nuclease assay for DNA unwinding in *E. coli oriC*. (*A*) Map of the *oriC*-containing plasmid pGS81. A 530-bp fragment (open line) containing the 245-bp minimal *oriC* has been cloned into pBR322 (solid line) such that it substitutes the small *Pst*I-*Eco*RI fragment of the vector. The positions of the *Pst*I and *Eco*RI sites are indicated as well as the *Pvu*II site used to map the nuclease hypersensitive sites. (*B*) Analysis of unwinding in Ori⁺ and Ori⁻ plasmids. Supercoiled pGS81 (lane *2*) and the 16-bp deletion derivative pUA82 (lane *3*) were incubated with P1 nuclease. The nicked molecules were purified, restricted with *Pvu*II and 5'-end-labeled at the restriction site. The products were denatured with glyoxal and electrophoresed through a 1.2 agarose gel. The 2.2- and 2.0-kb bands are the result of nuclease cleavage in the *oriC* insert, and the 3.0- and 1.2-kb bands are the result of nuclease cleavage at the vector site. Lane *1* shows the results obtained when the pGS81 plasmid is linearized prior to incubation with P1 nuclease. Lane *M* shows mobility markers whose sizes are reported in bp to the right of the autoradiogram.

loss of the ability to initiate DNA replication at the truncated origin (Hirota et al. 1981).

Deletions in a DNA sequence in a yeast origin lead to reductions in both nuclease-detectable unwinding and replication efficiency

The DNA sequence requirements of the origin of replication cloned from the copy 1 histone H4 gene locus of *S. cerevisiae* have been extensively examined (Bouton and Smith 1986). The results present a paradox of sequence requirements for the region flanking the suspected protein recognition (core) sequence of the origin. Deletion mutations indicate that the flanking region is required for *ARS* function, whereas linker-scanning mutations fail to detect a specific nucleotide sequence requirement. Similar to other well-studied *ARS*s, the flanking region within the H4 *ARS* is AT-rich (Broach et al. 1983; Bouton and Smith 1986). Our finding of an easily unwound, AT-rich DNA sequence in the 2-μm origin of replication (Umek and Kowalski 1987) suggested that the flanking region might facilitate unwinding of the H4 *ARS*. Figure 2A is a diagram of the deletion series plasmids used to establish the flanking sequence requirement of the H4 *ARS*. The origin derivatives are substituted for the small *Eco*RI-*Hin*dIII fragment of the YIp5 vector. The vector includes pBR322 sequences and the *URA3* gene, a selectable marker in yeast. Successive deletions result in a reduction in the amount of AT-rich origin DNA remaining, whereas the adjacent vector sequence is constant. The plasmid pAB4 (not shown) contains the wild-type sequence, a 375-bp *Sau*3A fragment, cloned into the unique *Bam*HI site of the vector. Panel B of Figure 2 shows the cleavage products obtained when supercoiled pAB4 is incubated with P1 nuclease (P) or mung bean nuclease (M). Both single-strand-specific probes detect preferential unwinding in the yeast origin of replication (cleavage products of 3.0 and 2.8 kb). The minor products of 4.6 and 1.2 kb are the result of nuclease cleavage in the pBR322 vector site, which is the same as the vector site detected in the pGS81 and pUA82 plasmids (above). The unwound region encompasses 206 bp from coordinates 42 to 247 (not shown).

The autoradiogram in Figure 2C shows the nuclease cleavage products of certain deletion derivatives of the H4 *ARS*. Plasmids containing the derivatives were incubated with mung bean nuclease and the nicks mapped as described above. The identity and replication phenotype of the derivatives are indicated above each lane. Replication-positive derivatives are able to transform a *ura3* yeast strain to *URA*⁺ at high frequency, indicative of autonomous replication of the plasmid (Bouton and Smith 1986). The rL55 derivative transforms at intermediate frequency and grows slowly in liquid media, characteristic of plasmids containing a weak origin of replication (Kearsey 1984). The number of bp remaining in the region flanking the core sequence in the derivatives is indicated below each lane. Mung bean nuclease cleavage of the origin sequences in the deletion derivatives yields bands of 3.3 and 2.4 kb. In

the rL35 derivative, the frequency of nuclease cleavage in the *ARS* compared to the vector site (4.5 and 1.2 kb bands) is similar to the wild-type plasmid, pAB4 (panel B). Further deletions into the H4 *ARS* sequence progressively reduce the frequency of nuclease cleavage in the *ARS* relative to the vector site. The effect of the deletions on the frequency of nuclease cleavage is most clearly seen in the densitometric analysis presented in panel D of Figure 2. Each scan from left to right corresponds to the bottom-to-top orientation of the sub-unit-length bands in one lane of the autoradiogram in Figure 2C. The results graphically show that the gradual substitution of origin DNA by vector DNA results in a gradual reduction in the frequency of nuclease cleavage in the remaining origin sequence (two central peaks). In supercoiled DNA, unwinding occurs at the sequence requiring the least free energy to unwind and reduces the likelihood of unwinding at a second site in the molecule (Benham 1981). The gradual shift from preferential unwinding of the origin to preferential unwinding of the vector site reflects the increase in energy required to unwind the origin. The direct correlation between the increase in the energy required to unwind the origin and the reduction in replication efficiency strongly suggests that the AT-rich region influences replication efficiency by determining the energy required to unwind the region during the initiation of DNA replication.

Similarities in the sequence organization of *E. coli* and *S. cerevisiae* replication origins

The sequence organization of the chromosomally derived origins studied here shows striking similarity in the location of the unwound, AT-rich region relative to the known or suspected protein recognition sequences of the origins. Figure 3 shows the location of the unwound region detected by the nucleases (bracketed). The unwound region in *oriC* lies at the left-hand boundary of the minimal origin (bp 20) and adjacent to the leftmost *dnaA* binding site (underlined) (Fuller et al. 1984). *dnaA* serves as the initiator protein by recognizing specific sequences in *oriC* and directing the initiation of DNA replication to that region (for review, see Zyskind and Smith 1986). The initiator protein involved in specific initiation from yeast origins has not been identified, but it is thought to recognize the core sequence common among *ARS* (underlined) (for review, see Campbell 1986). Similar to *oriC*, the unwound region lies predominantly unidirectionally from the recognition sequence. The 2-μm plasmid origin exhibits a similar arrangement (Umek and Kowalski 1987). The similarities between bacterial and yeast origins may indicate a conserved role for the sequence organization of origins of DNA replication.

Discussion

The results presented here show that the DNA-unwinding properties of chromosomally derived origins of replication can be studied through the use of single-strand-specific endonucleases. Nuclease P1 (Fig. 1B) and

A

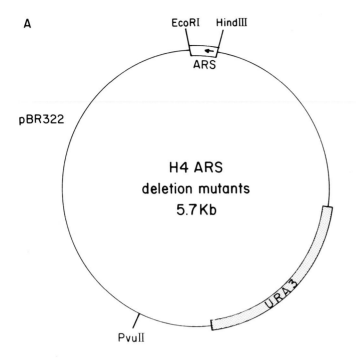

B

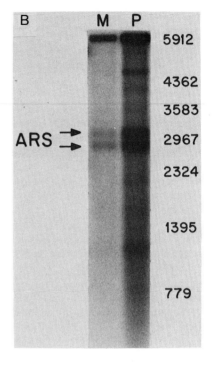

C

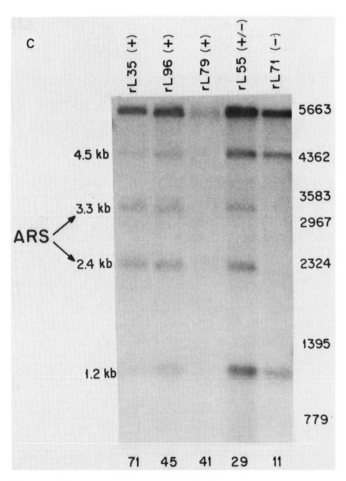

D

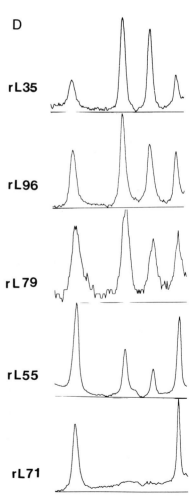

Figure 2 (*See facing page for legend.*)

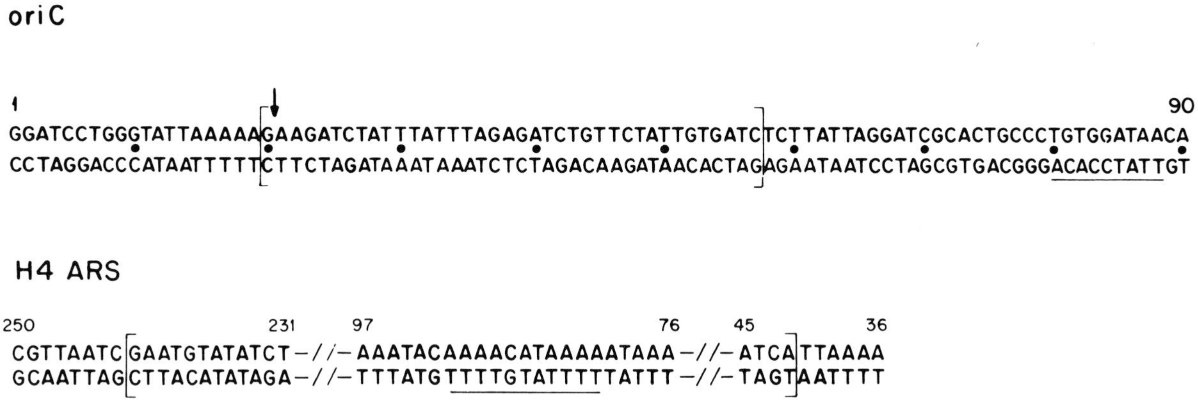

oriC

```
1                              ↓                                                              90
GGATCCTGGGTATTAAAAA GAAGATCTATTTATTTAGAGATCTGTTCTATTGTGATC TCTTATTAGGATCGCACTGCCCTGTGGATAACA
CCTAGGACCCATAATTTTT CTTCTAGATAAATAAATCTCTAGACAAGATAACACTAG AGAATAATCCTAGCGTGACGGGACACCTATTGT
```

H4 ARS

```
250              231     97                          76       45         36
CGTTAATC GAATGTATATCT –//– AAATACAAAACATAAAAATAAA –//– ATCA TTAAAA
GCAATTAG CTTACATATAGA –//– TTTATGTTTTGTATTTTTATTT –//– TAGT AATTTT
```

Figure 3 Similarities in the DNA sequence organization of chromosomal replication origins of *E. coli* and *S. cerevisiae*. The unwound regions detected by the single-strand-specific nuclease probes are bracketed for both *oriC* (*E. coli*) and the H4 *ARS* (*S. cerevisiae*). The unwound regions lie adjacent to the leftmost *dnaA* binding site (underlined) in *oriC* and predominantly 3' of T-rich strand of the suspected protein recognition (core) sequence (underlined) of the H4 *ARS*.

mung bean nuclease (M.J. Eddy and D. Kowalski) both direct DNA unwinding in the same AT-rich sequence of *oriC*. The unwinding, along with the ability to initiate DNA replication, is abolished by a 16-bp deletion within the sequence. Similar results are obtained with a yeast origin of replication. Sequential deletions into the H4 *ARS* reduce unwinding and replication efficiency. We believe that our assay reflects a fundamental thermodynamic property of origins of replication, that is, the energy requirement for unwinding. The assay presupposes only that DNA must unwind to initiate replication and that this process requires energy, independent of the actual source in vivo. We postulate that the replication-deficient origins described in this study cannot be unwound by the energy contained in their respective initiation complexes.

Our results suggest that a readily unwound DNA sequence is a component of replication origins, in addition to the previously identified protein recognition sequences. In the origins studied, the readily unwound region lies adjacent to the known or suspected protein recognition sequences of the regions. The unwound sequence of *oriC* is highly conserved in six bacterial origins, although the region tolerates single-base substi-

tutions, insertions, and deletions (Zyskind et al. 1983). The unwound region of the yeast origin shows less sequence conservation, even among *S. cerevisiae ARS* elements. However, all *ARSs* are very AT-rich (> 75%) (Broach et al. 1983; Bouton and Smith 1986). Similar to the bacterial origins, the yeast AT-rich sequence that flanks the core sequence tolerates substitutions, insertions, and deletions (Kearsey 1984; Bouton and Smith 1986). We have found that 10-bp GC-rich substitutions throughout the minimal H4 *ARS* do not alter the unwinding properties of the region (R.M. Umek and D. Kowalski). The ability of the flanking, AT-rich sequences of prokaryotic and eukaryotic origins to tolerate small base changes has led to the suggestion that these sequences are nonessential and act as "spacer" regions between required protein recognition sequences (Asada et al. 1982; Oka et al. 1984; Campbell 1986). Our results show that these DNA sequences are required to facilitate unwinding of the origins in vitro. We believe they play a similar role in vivo during the initiation of DNA replication. These DNA sequences tolerate limited base substitutions not because they are nonessential but instead because the substitutions do not significantly alter the unwinding properties of the region.

Figure 2 Sequential deletions into the yeast H4 *ARS* reduce DNA unwinding and replication efficiency. (*A*) Map of the YIp5 vector containing the H4 *ARS* deletion derivatives. The YIp5 vector contains pBR322 sequences (solid line) as well as a selectable marker, the *URA3* gene (shaded). The derivatives are inserted into the YIp5 vector such that they substitute the small *Eco*RI-*Hin*dIII fragment of the pBR322 sequence. The deletions are generated at the left-hand end of the insert, 3' to the T-rich strand of the core sequence (arrow). The positions of the *Eco*RI and *Hin*dIII sites are shown along with the position of the *Pvu*II site used to map the nuclease hypersensitive sites. The plasmid pAB4 has a 375-bp *Sau*3A fragment containing the H4 *ARS* inserted at the *Bam*HI site. (*B*) Autoradiogram of the cleavage products of single-strand-specific nuclease probes of supercoiled pAB4. Supercoiled pAB4 was nicked with nuclease P1 (P) or mung bean nuclease (M) and the nicks mapped as described above. Cleavage products of 3.0 and 2.8 kb are indicative of nuclease cleavage in the *ARS*. (*C*) Analysis of unwinding at Ori⁺ and Ori⁻ derivatives of the H4 *ARS*. Supercoiled plasmids containing H4 *ARS* derivatives were incubated with mung bean nuclease. The 3.3- and 2.4-kb bands are the result of nuclease cleavage at the origin. The identity and replication phenotypes of the derivatives are indicated above each lane. The derivatives from left to right correspond to increasing deletions into the yeast origin. The number of bp remaining adjacent to the core sequence is indicated below each lane. (*D*) Densitometric analysis of the autoradiogram in *B*. The sub-unit-length bands of each lane of the autoradiogram in *B* were scanned and normalized for the intensity of the strongest peak in the lane. The two central peaks correspond to the products of nuclease cleavage in the yeast origin and the two peripheral peaks correspond to the products of cleavage at the vector site.

Acknowledgments

We thank Dr. Ben Munson for providing the *oriC*-containing plasmids. We are grateful to Drs. Amy Bouton and M. Mitchell Smith for providing the H4 *ARS* derivatives. Finally, we thank Michelle Fisher for excellent technical assistance. This research was supported by a grant (GM-30614) from the National Institutes of Health. R.U. is the recipient of a Buffalo Foundation Award.

References

Asada, K., K. Sugimoto, A. Oka, M. Takanami, and Y. Hirota. 1982. Structure of replication origin region of the *Escherichia coli* K-12 chromosome: The presence of spacer sequences in the *ori* region carrying information for autonomous replication. *Nucleic Acids Res.* **10:** 3745.

Benham, C.J. 1981. Theoretical analysis of competitive conformational transitions in torsionally stressed DNA. *J. Mol. Biol.* **150:** 43.

Bouton, A.H. and M.M. Smith. 1986. Fine-structure analysis of the DNA sequence requirements for autonomous replication of *Saccharomyces cerevisiae. Mol. Cell. Biol.* **6:** 2354.

Broach, J.R., Y.-Y. Li, J. Feldman, M. Jayaram, K.A. Nasymth, and J.B. Hicks. 1983. Localization and sequence analysis of yeast origins of DNA replication. *Cold Spring Harbor Symp. Quant. Biol.* **47:** 1165.

Campbell, J.L. 1986. Eukaryotic DNA replication. *Annu. Rev. Biochem.* **55:** 733.

Fujimoto, M., A. Kuninaka, and H. Yoshino. 1974. Purification of a nuclease from *Penicillium citrinium. Agric. Biol. Chem.* **38:** 777.

Fuller, R.S., B.E. Funnell, and A. Kornberg. 1984. The dnaA protein complex with the *E. coli* chromosomal replication origin (*oriC*) and other DNA sites. *Cell* **38:** 889.

Hirota, Y., A. Oka, K. Sugimoto, K. Asada, H. Sasaki, and M. Takanami. 1981. *Escherichia coli* origin of replication: Structural organization of the region essential for autonomous replication and the recognition frame model. *ICN-UCLA Symp. Mol. Cell. Biol.* **22:** 1.

Holmes, D.S. and M. Quigley. 1981. A rapid boiling method for the preparation of bacterial plasmids. *Anal. Biochem.* **114:** 193.

Kearsey, S. 1984. Structural requirements for the function of a yeast chromosomal replicator. *Cell* **37:** 299.

Kowalski, D. 1984. Changes in site specificity of single-strand specific endonuclease on supercoiled PM2 DNA with temperature and ionic environment. *Nucleic Acids Res.* **12:** 7071.

Kowalski, D., W.D. Kroeker, and M. Laskowski, Sr. 1976. Mung bean nuclease I: Physical, chemical and catalytic properties. *Biochemistry* **15:** 4457.

Maniatis, T., E.F. Fritsch, and J. Sambrook. 1982. *Molecular cloning: A laboratory manual.* Cold Spring Harbor Laboratory, Cold Spring Harbor, New York.

McMaster, G.K. and G.G. Carmichael. 1977. Analysis of single- and double-stranded nucleic acids on polyacrylamide and agarose gels by using glyoxal and acridine orange. *Proc. Natl. Acad. Sci.* **74:** 4835.

Oka, A., H. Sasaki, K. Sugimoto, and M. Takanami. 1984. Sequence organization of the replication origin of the *Escherichia coli* K-12 chromosome. *J. Mol. Biol.* **176:** 443.

Radloff, R., W. Bauer, and J. Vinograd. 1967. A dye-buoyant-density method for the detection and isolation of closed circular duplex DNA: The closed circular DNA of HeLa cells. *Proc. Natl. Acad. Sci.* **57:** 1514.

Sheflin, L.G. and D. Kowalski. 1984. Mung bean nuclease cleavage of a dA + dT sequence or an inverted repeat sequence in supercoiled PM2 DNA depends on ionic environment. *Nucleic Acids Res.* **12:** 7087.

———. 1985. Altered DNA conformations detected by mung bean nuclease occur in promoter and terminator regions of supercoiled pBR322 DNA. *Nucleic Acids Res.* **13:** 6137.

Sugimoto, K., A. Oka, H. Sugisaki, M. Takanami, A. Nishimura, Y. Yasuda, and Y. Hirota. 1979. Nucleotide sequence of the *Escherichia coli* K-12 replication origin. *Proc. Natl. Acad. Sci.* **76:** 575.

Umek, R.M. and D. Kowalski. 1987. Yeast regulatory sequences preferentially adopt a non-B conformation in supercoiled DNA. *Nucleic Acids Res.* **15:** 4467.

Zyskind, J.W. and D.W. Smith. 1986. The bacterial origin of replication *oriC. Cell* **46:** 489.

Zyskind, J.W., J.M. Cleary, W.S.A. Brusilow, N.E. Harding, and D.W. Smith. 1983. Chromosomal replication origin from the marine bacterium *Vibrio harveyi* functions in *Escherichia coli*: *oriC* consensus sequence. *Proc. Natl. Acad. Sci.* **80:** 1164.

DNA Replication Promotes Assembly of Spaced Chromatin In Vitro

G. Almouzni and M. Méchali

Institut Jacques Monod, 75251 Paris Cédex 05, France

Xenopus egg extracts reproduce the events occurring at the replicative fork during chromosomal DNA replication. With single-stranded circular DNA added to these extracts, more than 95% of the template DNA is converted to a supercoiled double-stranded DNA molecule, with a rate of synthesis comparable to the fastest rates of chromosomal DNA synthesis in early embryogenesis. This synthesis is tightly coupled to chromatin assembly of the newly replicated DNA, as shown by supercoiling and micrococcal nuclease digestion. With double-stranded DNA, supercoiling subsequent to chromatin assembly requires DNA topoisomerase I and is not dependent on ATP. However, ATP increases the stability and promotes physiological spacing of the assembled chromatin. Chromatin assembly coupled to DNA replication occurs with a faster rate than in the absence of DNA replication, indicating that replicating DNA contains structural features that facilitate nucleosome assembly. When histones are first removed, complementary strand synthesis is then uncoupled from chromatin assembly. Although the DNA thus produced is found in a relaxed state, such uncoupling affects neither the priming reaction nor the rate of DNA synthesis.

Chromatin assembly and DNA replication are cellular events that are coupled during S phase in eukaryotes. Thus, the DNA synthetic process is temporally coordinated with the assembly of nucleosomes on the newly replicated DNA, close to the replication fork. Although the subunit structure of the nucleosomes is now well understood (for review, see Kornberg 1977; McGhee and Felsenfeld 1980; Eissenberg et al. 1985), it is still not clear how assembly occurs during replication nor how chromatin structure can be modified for modulating gene expression. The assembly of histones on replicating DNA remains controversial. Both conservative (Tsanev and Russev 1974; Seale 1976, 1978; Weintraub 1976; Leffak et al. 1977; Worcel et al. 1978; Seidman et al. 1979; Roufa and Marchionni 1982; Leffak 1984) and distributive mechanisms (Jackson et al. 1975; Cremisi et al. 1978; Jackson and Chalkley 1981a,b; Fowler et al. 1982; Pospelov et al. 1982; Russev and Hancock 1982; Annunziato and Seale 1984; Cusick et al. 1984) have obtained experimental support. Such studies have often been hampered by the lack of in vitro experimental systems that produce a physiological spaced chromatin on replicating DNA. For most of the chromatin assembly systems originally developed (Laskey et al. 1977; Nelson et al. 1979; Stein et al. 1979; Glikin et al. 1984), assembly does not occur as replication proceeds. Recently an in vitro replication system using papovavirus DNA molecules (Ariga and Sugano 1983; Li and Kelly 1984; Stillman and Gluzman 1985; Wobbe et al. 1985) has been shown to support chromatin assembly (Stillman 1986). Such a system is entirely dependent on the presence of SV40 T antigen as well as the viral replication origin, and about 15% of the exogenous template DNA is replicated (Stillman and Gluzman 1985).

We describe here a cell-free system derived from *Xenopus* eggs that reproduce the events occurring at the replicative fork with respect to both DNA synthesis and chromatin assembly, with an efficiency above 95%.

Experimental Procedures

Preparation of the egg extract

Unfertilized eggs were obtained from *Xenopus laevis* frogs by injection of chorionic gonadotropin (Pregnyl, Organon). The extracts were prepared by a modification of a method described by Lohka and Masui (1983). The dejellied eggs were washed and packed in centrifuge tubes. Excess medium was removed, leaving only the interstitial buffer between the cells. The eggs were then crushed directly by centrifugation (12,000g for 30 min) and the supernatant collected. The supernatant was then recentrifuged at 40,000 rpm for 60 minutes in a Beckman 50Ti rotor. The extract was stored in small aliquots at $-80°C$. In these conditions one μl of extract corresponds to one egg (the detailed procedure will be described elsewhere).

Preparation of DNA

DNA from bacteriophage M13mp18 was prepared from phages purified by CsCl buoyant density centrifugation. We prepared ^{32}P-labeled double-stranded form I M13 DNA by growing infected cells in low-phosphate medium inoculated with 100 μCi/ml ^{32}P-orthophosphate (Amersham). Plasmid pUC18 DNA and double-stranded form I M13 DNA were prepared as described in Maniatis et al. (1982). pUC18 DNA was ^{32}P-labeled at the *Bam*HI site and circularized as described by Razvi et al. (1983).

479

DNA synthesis and chromatin assembly reaction
Unless specified, our standard reaction mixtures contained 15 μg DNA per ml of egg extract supplemented with 3 mM ATP, 5 mM $MgCl_2$, and 10–15 μCi/ml [^{32}P]dATP. At various times after incubation at 22°C, aliquots were taken and either transferred to Whatman GF/C filters and processed for the counting of acid-insoluble material as described previously (Méchali and Harland 1982), or processed for digestion by micrococcal nuclease (P.L. Biochemicals). The dATP pool of the extract was determined in steady-state conditions by isotope dilution during the replication reaction (Méchali and Harland 1982) and was found to vary between 50 and 60 μM, depending on the extract.

Digestion by micrococcal nuclease
Unless otherwise specified, chromatin assembly reactions were digested by micrococcal nuclease (150 u/μg assembled DNA) after addition of 3 mM $CaCl_2$. Aliquots were taken during digestion, made up to 30 mM EDTA, 0.5% SDS, and treated as described above, either for gel electrophoresis (Maniatis et al. 1982) or for counting of acid-insoluble material.

Results

DNA replication accelerates chromatin assembly
Xenopus eggs have been successfully used to study DNA replication in eukaryotes both in vivo (Harland and Laskey 1980; Méchali et al. 1983; Méchali and Kearsey 1984) and in vitro (Méchali and Harland 1982; Blow and Laskey 1986). Cell extracts have been prepared from high-speed centrifugation of total eggs in conditions of minimal dilution, thus maintaining the in vivo concentration of cell components (Experimental Procedures).

Complementary strand synthesis occurs with an unusual efficiency on single-stranded circular DNA templates added to the extract. RNA primers of 10 nucleotides are synthesized by a DNA primase activity, and DNA polymerase α elongates the nascent DNA chains in an ATP-dependent reaction (Méchali and Harland 1982; Méchali et al. 1983). Figure 1A shows the reaction products observed after deproteinization. Overexposition of the autoradiogram reveals that after a 5-minute lag, replication gives rise to molecules immediately supercoiled (form I) as soon as 20 minutes after incubation, and no topoisomer intermediate is detected. Some nicked molecules (form II) are present and may arise from unligated products. Linear single-stranded parental molecules are also replicated and converted to double-stranded linear molecules (form III). The rate of DNA synthesis in vitro is comparable to the fastest rate of DNA replication in the early embryo. Thus up to 20 ng of DNA can be replicated and supercoiled in 1 hour by one egg equivalent (1 μl of extract). This activity is stable for months at −80°C.

The production of supercoiled DNA implies the formation of DNA–protein complexes as found in chromatin. Micrococcal nuclease digestion of the reaction products (Fig. 1B) confirms that nucleosomes were assembled

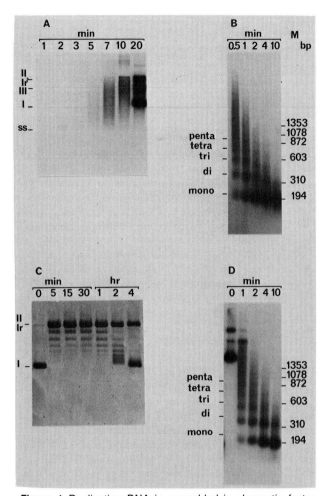

Figure 1 Replicating DNA is assembled in chromatin faster than nonreplicating DNA. The reaction mixtures contained 15 μg DNA per ml of egg extract supplemented with 3 mM ATP, 5 mM $MgCl_2$. The supercoiling kinetics are shown with single-stranded M13 DNA with [^{32}P]dATP (10–15 μCi/ml) (*A*), or with double-stranded form I PUC18 DNA (*C*). Aliquots were taken at the indicated times and processed for 1% agarose gel electrophoresis. The micrococcal nuclease digestion patterns presented were obtained with single-stranded M13 DNA after 3 hr incubation with [^{32}P]dATP (10–15 μCi/ml) (*B*) or with ^{32}P-labeled double-stranded form I PUC18 DNA after an overnight incubation. (*D*) Aliquots were taken at the indicated times during digestion and processed for 1.5% agarose gel electrophoresis as described in Experimental Procedures. (I, Ir, II, III, SS) Position of double-stranded DNA forms I, I relaxed, II, III, and ϕX*Hae*III digest used as molecular weight markers.

on the replicated molecules with the expected spacing of 200 bp.

When double-stranded circular DNA is incubated in such extracts, no replication is detected (Méchali and Harland 1982). However, chromatin assembly occurs on such molecules. The DNA is first rapidly relaxed and then progressively becomes supercoiled in a 4-hour reaction (Fig. 1C). The supercoiling reaction is coincident with chromatin assembly as shown by micrococcal nuclease digestion of the reaction products (Fig. 1D). A characteristic repeating pattern is observed with nucleosomes spaced every 180–200 bp in different experiments, in agreement with results reported previously (Laskey et al. 1977). Thus, micrococcal nuclease digestion did not reveal differences between chromatin assembly that is either coupled to DNA replication or uncoupled from replication. However, the kinetics of the reactions differ in two ways. First, the progressive accumulation of discrete topoisomers during assembly on double-stranded DNA (Fig. 1C) is not observed during chromatin assembly coupled to single-stranded DNA replication (Fig. 1A). Second, supercoiled DNA is detected as soon as 20 minutes after replication (Fig. 1A), whereas 2–4 hours are required to obtain form I molecules from relaxed double-stranded DNA (Fig. 1C). These two observations suggest that DNA replication promotes chromatin assembly in vitro.

The rate of replication is not affected by uncoupling DNA synthesis from chromatin assembly

Histones and other chromatin proteins were titrated by preincubating the extract with an excess of double-stranded DNA. Preliminary experiments indicated that 150 μg/ml double-stranded DNA was sufficient to achieve nearly complete titration, in agreement with a histone pool of 140 ng/egg (Woodland and Adamson 1977). Preincubation was for 2 hours before DNA replication was initiated on the M13 single-stranded DNA template. Figure 2 shows that titration of chromatin proteins dramatically prevents the supercoiling of replicated molecules. However, the rate and extent of reaction were not affected, as shown in Table 1. A similar result was observed with up to 600 μg/ml competitor double-stranded DNA with 10 μg/ml single-stranded DNA. We conclude from these experiments that the replication complexes on single-stranded DNA templates are stable and that double-stranded DNA does not compete for replication proteins in the extracts. Moreover, the same major chromatin proteins are likely to be involved in assembly on double-stranded DNA and replicating DNA.

Involvement of ATP and topoisomerase activity in chromatin assembly coupled or uncoupled to DNA replication

When double-stranded form I DNA is incubated in the extract, chromatin assembly occurs via relaxation and

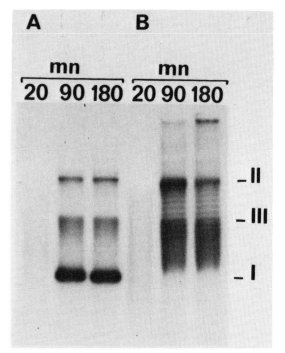

Figure 2 Preincubation of the extract with double-stranded DNA prevents the supercoiling of the newly replicated DNA. Double-stranded M13 DNA (150 μg/ml) was preincubated for 2 hr at 22°C with 27 μl of egg extract supplemented with 3 mM ATP, 5 mM $MgCl_2$ in a total volume of 30 μl. M13 single-stranded DNA (10 μg/ml) was then added with 10 μCi/ml [^{32}P]dATP. Aliquots were withdrawn at the times indicated and processed both for analysis on agarose gel electrophoresis, and for counting acid-insoluble material. (A) Control experiment, no addition of double-stranded DNA; (B) preincubated with double-stranded DNA. (I, II, III) Positions of M13 double-stranded DNA forms I, II, and III.

supercoiling of the template DNA (Fig. 1C). The first step of the reaction, relaxation, has been attributed to topoisomerase I. The second step, supercoiling, was coincident with the assembly of nucleosomes on DNA with a topoisomerase activity allowing the absorption of the constraints generated by chromatin assembly. Thus, after deproteinization, topoisomers with an increasing number of negative supercoils are observed as assembly proceeds (Laskey et al. 1977). Neither ATP, nor Mg^{++} or small dialyzable molecules were necessary for DNA supercoiling. The overall reaction occurs directly in a dialysis bag with an extract already extensively dialyzed (Fig. 3), or with a dialyzed extract containing apyrase, an enzyme that specifically degrades ATP (Cande 1982). This result is not consistent with a specific involvement of DNA topoisomerase II, which is dependent on ATP. Moreover, the kinetics of relaxation is slower (compare Fig. 3 with Fig. 1C), in accordance with the stimulating effect of Mg^{++} on *Xenopus* topoisomerase I (Attardi et al. 1981). Drug inhibition studies as well as the use of topoisomers of unique linking number indicated that DNA topoisomerase I was acting dominantly in both relaxation and the supercoiling subsequent to assembly (G. Almouzni and M. Méchali, in prep.). The novobiocin inhibition of the reaction re-

Table 1 Preincubation of the Extract with Double-stranded DNA Does Not Alter DNA Replication

	μg DNA synthesized/ml extract		
	20 min	90 min	180 min
Control	2.5	11.4	10.9
Titrated	3.0	15.0	16.0

Quantities of DNA synthesized at the times indicated are given for the experiment presented in Figure 2. (Control) Preincubation with no addition. (Titrated) Preincubation with 150 μg/ml double-stranded M13 DNA added to the extract.

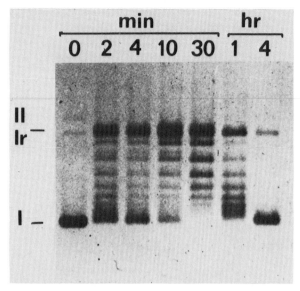

Figure 3 ATP and Mg^{++} are not required for the supercoiling reaction on double-stranded DNA. The extract was dialyzed 24 hr at 4°C against extract buffer containing 1 mM phenylmethyl-sulfonyl fluoride and 1 μM pepstatin in Sartorius collodion bags, as described by Méchali and Harland (1982), then pUC18 DNA (15 μg/ml) was added directly into dialysis bag. Aliquots were withdrawn at the indicated times and processed for agarose gel electrophoresis. (I, Ir, II) Position of PUC18 DNA form I, I relaxed, and II.

ported by Glikin et al. (1984) was only observed at high concentrations of the drug (1.5 mg/ml) and was probably due to the precipitation of histones and other chromatin proteins (Cotten et al. 1986; Sealy et al. 1986). Although ATP and Mg^{++} are not necessary for the supercoiling reaction on double-stranded DNA, the addition of these components has a marked effect on chromatin spacing and stability (G. Almouzni and M. Méchali, in prep.).

The replication reaction with single-stranded DNA is totally ATP-dependent both for priming reaction and elongation (Méchali and Harland 1982; Méchali et al. 1983). In addition, ATP is also necessary for the spacing of nucleosomes on the replicated DNA. Thus, if the endogenous ATP pool of the extract (estimated to be 1.5–2 mM) is sufficient for replication and assembly, a further addition of this cofactor (3 mM) has a positive effect on the spacing of the assembled replicated chromatin. The same positive effect is registered by adding an ATP regenerating system in the extract (Méchali and Harland 1982). Neither camptothecin, a topoisomerase I inhibitor, nor VP16, a topoisomerase II inhibitor, affects the replication rate or the supercoiling of the replicated molecule. No requirement for to-poisomerase activity is necessary when single-stranded DNA is replicated, since no constraints arise during this process as opposed to double-stranded DNA that is subjected to torsions upstream of the replication fork.

Complementary strand synthesis and chromatin assembly are coincident

M13 single-stranded DNA was incubated in the extract supplemented with [^{32}P]dATP, and the kinetics of

chromatin assembly were analyzed during complementary strand synthesis. Replication was followed by acid precipitation of the reaction products, and chromatin assembly was assayed by micrococcal nuclease digestion to mononucleosomes. Maximum protection from digestion was 73%, a value that corresponds to 100% assembly (146 bp protected for a unit nucleosome length of 200 bp).

Figure 4A shows that chromatin assembly proceeds coincidentally with DNA replication. Both processes exhibit a kinetic lag after addition of the template and are nearly completed by 1-hour incubation. The protection from micrococcal nuclease indeed corresponds to the formation of nucleosomes, as shown in Figure 4B. Nucleosomes can be clearly observed as early as 20 minutes after incubation. Then, as replication progresses, protection from micrococcal nuclease increases, and spaced chromatin can be detected after 40 minutes of incubation. This observation suggests a rapid spacing of nucleosomes after their assembly during replication. In contrast, assembly on double-stranded DNA form I, in the absence of DNA replication, is a slower process (Fig. 4A, closed circles), as was observed with the supercoiling reaction (Fig. 1C).

Discussion

The cell-free system described here allows studies of chromatin assembly coupled to DNA replication with an unusual efficiency. Nucleosome formation occurs with kinetics identical to DNA replication and the only limiting step in the formation of nucleosomes is the complementary DNA strand synthesis. ATP is necessary at all steps of this reaction from the RNA priming of DNA synthesis to the stability and correct spacing of the assembled chromatin. Chromatin assembly also occurs on double-stranded DNA in the absence of replication. This process takes 2–4 hours before completion, and requires topoisomerase I to relax the topological constraints generated as the assembly proceeds. ATP is not necessary for supercoiling subsequent to nucleosome assembly on double-stranded DNA but has a strong positive effect on the spacing and the stability of chromatin.

Upon removal of chromatin proteins by preincubation of the extract with an excess of double-stranded DNA, DNA replication on single-stranded DNA is uncoupled from chromatin assembly, and the replicated product is found in a relaxed state. However, neither the RNA priming nor the rate of synthesis is affected with concentrations of competitor DNA up to 60-fold higher than the concentration of the single-stranded DNA template. This result indicates that the replication proteins have a strong affinity for single-stranded DNA as opposed to double-stranded DNA. The opposite histones previously trapped on double-stranded DNA do not dissociate during single-stranded DNA replication.

The in vitro system described here permits assembly of physiologically spaced chromatin equivalent to 3300 diploid nuclei in 1 hour by one egg equivalent of extract. This is the only nonviral system that reconstitutes chromatin assembly during complementary strand syn-

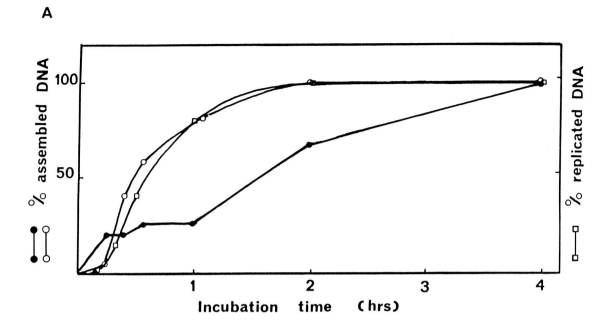

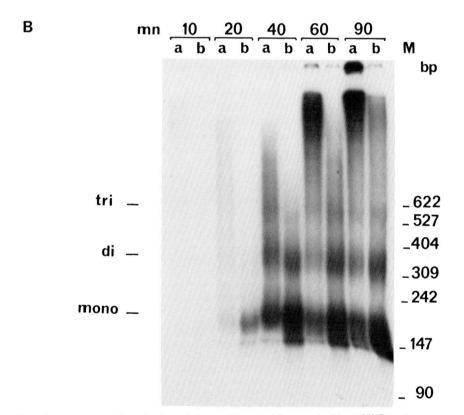

Figure 4 Complementary strand synthesis and chromatin assembly are coincident. (*A*) Reactions were as described in Experimental Procedures with 15 μg/ml DNA in the extract supplemented with 3 mM ATP and 5 mM MgCl$_2$. Aliquots were taken at the indicated times and were processed both for acid-insoluble radioactivity and for 10-min digestion by micrococcal nuclease (300 U/μg DNA) after addition of 3 mM CaCl$_2$. A portion of the digestion reaction was used to verify complete digestion to the mononucleosomal form, and the remainder was processed for acid-insoluble radioactivity determination. (□—□) % of the single-stranded M13 DNA replicated in the extract added with [^{32}P]dATP (10–15 μCi). (○—○) % assembly during complementary strand synthesis in the previous reaction (protection of 73% of the replicated DNA corresponds to 100% assembly). (●—●) % assembly of ^{32}P-labeled double-stranded M13 DNA. (*B*) Aliquots from a parallel replication reaction were taken at the indicated times and digested by micrococcal nuclease (300 U/μg DNA) for 1 mn (*a*) and 2 mn (*b*). After deproteinization, the samples were analyzed on a 4% acrylamide gel. Markers were from a pBR322-*Hpa*II digest.

thesis and should be valuable to analyze the importance of DNA replication in establishing the chromatin of transcribed or nontranscribed genes.

Acknowledgments

We are indebted to Peter Brooks for critical reading of this manuscript and to Martine Robin for help in typing. This work was supported by a Centre National de la Recherche Scientifique grant ATP-960097 and by the Association pour la Recherche sur le Cancer.

References

Annunziato, A.T. and R.L. Seale. 1984. Presence of nucleosomes within regularly cleaved fragments of newly replicated chromatin. *Nucleic Acids Res.* **12:** 61.

Ariga, H. and S. Sugano. 1983. Initiation of SV40 DNA replication in vitro. *J. Virol.* **48:** 481.

Attardi, D.G., A. De Paolis, and G.P. Tocchini-Valentini. 1981. Purification and characterization of *Xenopus laevis* type I topoisomerase. *J. Biol. Chem.* **256:** 3654.

Blow, J.J. and R.A. Laskey. 1986. Initiation of DNA replication in nuclei and purified DNA by a cell-free extract from *Xenopus* eggs. *Cell* **47:** 577.

Cande, W.Z. 1982. Nucleotide requirements for anaphase chromosome movement in permeabilized mitotic cells: Anaphase B but not anaphase A requires ATP. *Cell* **28:** 15.

Cotten, M., D. Bresnahan, S. Thompson, L. Sealy, and R. Chalkley. 1986. Novobiocin precipitates histones at concentration normally used to inhibit eukaryotic type I topoisomerase. *Nucleic Acids Res.* **14:** 3671.

Cremisi, C., A. Chestier, and M. Yaniv. 1978. Assembly of SV40 and polyoma minichromosomes during replication. *Cold Spring Harbor Symp. Quant. Biol.* **42:** 409.

Cusick, C.E., M.L. De Pamphilis, and P.M. Wassarman. 1984. Dispersive segregation of nucleosomes during replication of simian virus 40 chromosomes. *J. Mol. Biol.* **178:** 249.

Eissenberg, J.C., I.L. Cartwright, G.H. Thomas, and S.C.R. Elgin. 1985. Selected topics in chromatin structure. *Annu. Rev. Genet.* **19:** 485.

Fowler, E., R. Farb, and S. El-Saidy. 1982. Distribution of the core histones H2A, H2B, H3 and H4 during cell replication. *Nucleic Acids Res.* **10:** 735.

Glikin, G.C., I. Ruberti, and A. Worcel. 1984. Chromatin assembly in *Xenopus* oocytes: In vitro studies. *Cell* **37:** 33.

Harland, R.M. and R.A. Laskey. 1980. Regulated replication of DNA microinjected into eggs of *X. laevis. Cell* **21:** 761.

Jackson, V. and R. Chalkley. 1981. A new method for the isolation of replicative chromatin: Selective deposition of histone on both new and old DNA. *Cell* **23:** 121.

———. 1981. A reevaluation of new histone deposition on replicating chromatin. *J. Biol. Chem.* **256:** 5095.

Jackson, V., D. Granner, and R. Chalkley. 1975. Deposition of histone onto the replicating chromosome: Newly synthesized histone is not found near the replication fork. *Proc. Natl. Acad. Sci.* **73:** 2266.

Kornberg, R.D. 1977. Structure of chromatin. *Annu. Rev. Biochem.* **46:** 931.

Laskey, R.A., A.D. Mills, and N.R. Morris. 1977. Assembly of SV40 chromatin in a cell-free system from *Xenopus* eggs. *Cell* **10:** 237.

Leffak, I.M. 1984. Conservative segregation of nucleosome core histones. *Nature* **307:** 82.

Leffak, I.M., R. Grainger, and H. Weintraub. 1977. Conserva-

tive assembly and segregation of nucleosomal histones. *Cell* **12:** 837.

Li, J.J. and T.J. Kelly, Jr. 1984. Simian virus 40 DNA replication in vitro. *Proc. Natl. Acad. Sci.* **81:** 6973.

Lohka, M.J. and Y. Masui. 1983. Formation in vitro of sperm pronuclei and mitotic chromosomes induced by amphibian ooplasmic contents. *Science* **280:** 719.

Maniatis, T., E.F. Fritsch, and J. Sambrook. 1982. *Molecular cloning: A laboratory manual.* Cold Spring Harbor Laboratory, Cold Spring Harbor, New York.

McGhee, T.D. and G. Felsenfeld. 1980. Nucleosome structure. *Annu. Rev. Biochem.* **49:** 1115.

Méchali, M. and R. Harland. 1982. DNA synthesis in a cell-free system from *Xenopus* eggs: Priming and elongation on single-stranded DNA in vitro. *Cell* **30:** 93.

Méchali, M. and S. Kearsey. 1984. Lack of specific sequence requirement for DNA replication in *Xenopus* eggs compared with high sequence specificity in yeast. *Cell* **38:** 55.

Méchali, M., R. Harland, and R. Laskey. 1983. *Xenopus* eggs as a model-system for DNA replication in eukaryotes. *UCLA Symp. Mol. Cell. Biol.* **10:** 563.

Nelson, T., T.S. Hsieh, and D. Brutlag. 1979. Extracts of *Drosophila* embryos mediate chromatin assembly in vitro. *Proc. Natl. Acad. Sci.* **76:** 5510.

Pospelov, V., G. Russev, L. Vassilev, and R. Tsanev. 1982. Nucleosomes segregation in chromatin replicated in the presence of cycloheximide. *J. Mol. Biol.* **156:** 79.

Razvi, F., G. Gargiulo, and A. Worcel. 1983. A simple procedure for parallel sequence analysis on both strands of 5′ labeled DNA. *Gene* **23:** 175.

Roufa, D.J. and M.A. Marchionni. 1982. Nucleosome segregation at a defined mammalian chromosomal site. *Proc. Natl. Acad. Sci.* **79:** 1810.

Russev, G. and R. Hancock. 1982. Assembly of new histones into nucleosomes and their distribution in replicating chromatin. *Proc. Natl. Acad. Sci.* **79:** 3143.

Seale, R.L. 1976. Studies on the mode of segregation of histones Nu bodies in HeLa cells. *Cell* **9:** 423.

———. 1978. Nucleosomes associated with newly replicated DNA have an altered conformation. *Proc. Natl. Acad. Sci.* **75:** 2717.

Sealy, L., M. Cotten, and R. Chalkley. 1986. Novobiocin inhibits passive chromatin assembly in vitro. *EMBO J.* **5:** 3305.

Seidman, M.M., A.J. Levine, and H. Weintraub. 1979. The asymmetric segregation of parental nucleosomes during chromosome replication. *Cell* **18:** 439.

Stein, A., J.P. Whitlock, Jr., and M. Bina. 1979. Acidic polypeptides can assemble both histones and chromatin in vitro at physiological ionic strength. *Proc. Natl. Acad. Sci.* **76:** 5000.

Stillman, B.W. 1986. Chromatin assembly during SV40 DNA replication in vitro. *Cell* **45:** 555.

Stillman, B.W. and Y. Gluzman. 1985. Replication and supercoiling of simian virus 40 DNA in cell extracts from human cells. *Mol. Cell. Biol.* **5:** 2051.

Tsanev, R. and G. Russev. 1974. Distribution of newly synthesized histones during DNA replication. *Eur. J. Biochem.* **43:** 257.

Weintraub, H. 1976. Cooperative alignment of Nu bodies during chromosome replication in the presence of cycloheximide. *Cell* **9:** 419.

Wobbe, C.R., F. Dean, L. Weissbach, and J. Hurwitz. 1985. In vitro replication of duplex circular DNA containing the simian virus DNA origin site. *Proc. Natl. Acad. Sci.* **82:** 5710.

Woodland, H.R. and E.D. Adamson. 1977. The synthesis and storage of histones during the oogenesis of *Xenopus laevis. Dev. Biol.* **57:** 118.

Worcel, A., S. Han, and M.L. Wong. 1978. Assembly of newly replicated chromatin. *Cell* **15:** 969.

Author Index

Subject Index

Actin, 188
Adeno-associated virus type 2, 101–104
   rep gene, 101–104
Adenovirus, 61–85, 101–104, 236
   DNA-binding protein (DBP), 61–62
   DNA replication, 61–75
   E1A protein, 193, 291
   E1B protein, 36, 39, 193
   precursor terminal protein (pTP), 61–62, 71, 73
   type 2, 61–85
   type 4, 61–85
α-amanitin, 173
Amplification, 183–188, 305–333
Amylase, 339
Aphidicolin, 110, 317, 320–321, 329, 347, 381, 400, 403
Asymmetric dimer model, 37
Autonomously replicating sequences (ARS), 227, 229–243, 331, 347–357, 434, 463–466, 473–478
   binding factors, 235–242, 347–357, 463–471
   binding factors I and II, 235–242
Auxiliary protein for DNA polymerase δ. *See* Proliferating cell nuclear antigen

Bacculovirus, 97
Bacteriophage λ, 25–34, 49, 113, 120–121, 131, 149, 236, 348
   O protein, 25–26, 29–31, 113, 131, 149, 348, 355
   P protein, 25–26, 29–31, 131, 149
Bacteriophage Mu, gene B protein, 39
Bacteriophage T4, 1–10, 49
   dda gene, 8
   DNA ligase, 458
   endonuclease V, 414
   gene 32, 1–10, 49
   gene 41, 1–10, 49
   gene 43, 1–10
   gene 44, 1–10
   gene 45, 1–10
   gene 61, 1–10
   gene 62, 1–10
   endonuclease VII, 89
Bacteriophage T7, 11–18
   gene 2.5, 16
   gene 3, 81
   gene 4, 8, 11–18
   gene 5, 11–18

Benomyl, 444–452
β-like globin genes, 335–340
Bovine papilloma virus (BPV), 191–196, 339, 467–468
BuAdATP, 403, 412, 414
BuPdGTP, 347, 403, 412, 414
Butylphenylguanine, 381

Cairns form, 28–29, 227, 230
Camptothecin, 482
Catenanes, 230
Catenated dimer(s), 29
Cell cycle, 191–196, 240, 289–295, 317–323, 347–357
   G_0, 162, 283, 289
   G_1, 162, 185, 193, 256–257, 259, 262, 268–269, 272–273, 275, 277, 284
   G_2, 193, 259–263, 273, 279, 286
   M, 245, 259–263, 284, 286
   S, 185, 188, 193, 230, 245, 265–268, 274, 277, 279, 284, 286, 289–295, 300–301, 303
Centromeres, 433–452
   binding proteins, 433–452
Chromatin assembly, 479–484
Chromosome
   nondisjunction, 438
   segregation, 433–452
   transmission, 441–452
Complementation, 44
Concanavalin A, 283
Concatemeric junction, 87–94
Concatemers, 87–94
Control of cell division, 251–257
Cruciform, 77–85, 89
Cyclin. *See* Proliferating cell nuclear antigen

D loop, 207–212
Decatenation, 279
Dependovirus, 103
Dihydrofolate reductase, 95, 183, 292, 317–333, 335, 467
Dividin, 289–295
DMS footprinting, 127, 129
DNA bending, 123, 127, 235–242
DNA helicase, 345, 348
   bacteriophage T4 gene 41, 1–11, 15, 26
   SV40 large T antigen, 105–157
DNA ligase, 114–115, 121, 345, 394, 426

DNA polymerase I. *See Escherichia coli* DNA polymerase I
DNA polymerase III. *See Escherichia coli* DNA polymerase III
DNA polymerase α–primase, 8, 96–97, 110, 113, 115, 120–121, 123, 133–135, 137, 140, 149, 153–162, 173–174, 177–180, 186, 188, 193, 203, 291–292, 299, 341–357, 359–403, 412, 415, 425, 429–430
   accessory proteins, 373–384, 393–396
DNA polymerase β, 412, 415, 417–423
   antibodies, 417–423
   cDNA, 417–423
   mRNA, 417–423
DNA polymerase δ, 8, 140, 146, 149, 157, 178, 291–292, 299, 347, 370, 381, 391, 403–415
DNA polymerase γ, 412, 425–432
DNA repair synthesis, 411–415
DNase I footprinting, 9, 126, 129, 173, 208, 235–242, 347–357, 463–466
DNase I hypersensitivity, 338
Double-stranded DNA-binding protein, 49
Drosophila melanogaster
   chorion genes, 305–315, 467
   DNA polymerase α–primase, 367–371, 373, 400
   DNA polymerase γ, 425–432
dUTPase, 53
Dyad symmetry, 198, 203

Elutriation, 193, 259–263, 283, 337, 350
Endoribonuclease, 207–212
Enhancer, 170
   SV40, 61–62, 68, 124, 165–174, 198
   polyomavirus, 165–174
Epstein-Barr virus, 197–204
Epitope, 154–157
Epstein-Barr virus (EBV), 197–204, 216
   nuclear antigen (EBNA-1), 197–204
   oriP, 197–204
Erythropoiesis, 280–283
Escherichia coli
   CAP protein, 238
   dnaA, 19–22, 131, 149, 156, 240, 348, 475